UNDERSTANDING HUMAN SEXUALITY

FOURTH CANADIAN EDITION

Janet Shibley Hyde
University of Wisconsin-Madison

John D. DeLamater
University of Wisconsin-Madison

E. Sandra Byers
University of New Brunswick

McGraw-Hill Ryerson

Toronto   Montréal   Boston   Burr Ridge, IL   Dubuque, IA   Madison, WI   New York
San Francisco   St. Louis   Bangkok   Bogotá   Caracas   Kuala Lumpur   Lisbon   London
Madrid   Mexico City   Milan   New Delhi   Santiago   Seoul   Singapore   Sydney   Taipei

The McGraw-Hill Companies

McGraw-Hill Ryerson

UNDERSTANDING HUMAN SEXUALITY
FOURTH CANADIAN EDITION

ISBN-13: 978-0-07-076410-1
ISBN-10: 0-07-076410-7

2 3 4 5 6 7 8 9 10 CPI 0 9

Printed and bound in the United States.

Vice-President and Editor-in-Chief: Joanna Cotton
Publisher: Cara Yarzab
Marketing Manager: Michele Peach
Senior Developmental Editor: Denise Foote
Supervising Editor: Kara Stahl
Editorial Associate: Marina Seguin
Photo/Permission Research: My Editor Inc.
Copy Editor: Valerie Adams
Production Coordinator: Sheryl MacAdam
Cover Design: Brett J. Miller, BJM Graphic Design & Communications
Interior Design: Brett J. Miller, BJM Graphic Design & Communications
Cover Image Credit: © Masterfile
Page Layout: Tom Dart, Kim Hutchinson, Arleane Ralph and Cara Scime/First Folio Resource Group, Inc.
Printer: Courier Companies Inc.

Library and Archives Canada Cataloguing in Publication

Hyde, Janet Shibley
    Understanding human sexuality / Janet Shibley Hyde, John D. DeLamater, E. Sandra Byers. — 4th Canadian ed.

Includes bibliographical references and index.
ISBN 978-0-07-076410-1

1. Sex—Textbooks. I. DeLamater, John D. II. Byers, E. Sandra, 1951– III. Title.
HQ12.H92 2009   306.7   C2008-907152-2

AUTHOR BIOGRAPHIES

Janet Shibley Hyde, the Helen Thompson Woolley Professor of Psychology and Women's Studies at the University of Wisconsin–Madison, received her education at Oberlin College and the University of California, Berkeley. She has taught a course in Human Sexuality since 1974, first at Bowling Green State University, then at Denison University, and now at the University of Wisconsin. Her research interests are in gender differences and gender development in childhood and adolescence. Author of the textbook *Half the Human Experience: The Psychology of Women*, she is a past president of the Society for the Scientific Study of Sexuality and is a Fellow of the American Psychological Association and the American Association for the Advancement of Science. She has received many other honours, including an award for excellence in teaching at Bowling Green State University, the Chancellor's Award for teaching at the University of Wisconsin, and the Kinsey Award from the Society for the Scientific Study of Sexuality for her contributions to sex research. In 2000–01 she served as one of the three scientific editors for U.S. Surgeon General David Satcher's report, *Promoting Sexual Health and Responsible Sexual Behavior*. She is married to John DeLamater.

John D. DeLamater, Professor of Sociology at the University of Wisconsin–Madison, received his education at the University of California, Santa Barbara and the University of Michigan. He created the Human Sexuality course at the University of Wisconsin in 1975 and has since taught it regularly. His current research and writing are focused on the effects of life-course transitions on sexuality. He has published papers on the effects of having a child, of dual-career couples, and of divorce, and is studying the effects of menopause and later-life transitions on sexual attitudes and behaviour. He is the co-author of the textbook *Social Psychology*. He is a Fellow of the Society for the Scientific Study of Sexuality and the 2002 recipient of the Kinsey Award from the Society for Career Contributions to Sex Research. He has received awards for excellence in teaching from the Department of Sociology and Interfraternity Council-Panhellenic Association, and is a Fellow and past Chair of the Teaching Academy at the University of Wisconsin. He regularly teaches a seminar for graduate students on teaching undergraduate courses. He is married to Janet Hyde.

E. Sandra Byers is a Professor and Chair of the Department of Psychology at the University of New Brunswick. She was honoured by UNB with a University Research Scholar Award in 2008. Dr. Byers grew up in Montreal and received her university education at the University of Rochester and West Virginia University. She created the human sexuality course at the University of New Brunswick in 1979 and has taught it annually since then. She is the author or co-author of more than 95 journal articles and book chapters, and has supervised the thesis research of 41 students. Much (but not all) of her research has been in the areas of sexual satisfaction, sexual communication, sexual violence, and attitudes toward sexual health education. She also has a private practice in clinical psychology specializing in the treatment of sexual problems and concerns, and regularly teaches a graduate seminar on sex therapy. She is a past president of the Canadian Sex Research Forum, a fellow of the Canadian Psychological Association and the Society for the Scientific Study of Sexuality, a member of the Advisory Board of the Sex Information and Education Council of Canada, an editorial board member of two sexuality journals, and the founding director of the Muriel McQueen Fergusson Centre for Family Violence Research. Dr. Byers has given more than 140 invited addresses and workshops, and has been interviewed about sexual issues by numerous radio and television stations, magazines, and newspapers. As a sexuality educator, researcher, and therapist in Canada, Dr. Byers is uniquely placed to provide a Canadian perspective on human sexuality. She has been married to Dr. Larry Heinlein, who is also a psychologist, for 35 years, and has two daughters, Krista and Alyssa. To learn more about Dr. Byers and her research, you can visit her website at www.unbf.ca/arts/psychology/faculty/s-byers.html.

CONTENTS IN BRIEF

CONTENTS

CHAPTER 11   SEXUALITY AND THE LIFE CYCLE: ADULTHOOD   328

CHAPTER 20   ETHICS, RELIGION, AND SEXUALITY
See the Online Learning Centre at www.mcgrawhill.ca/olc/hyde

REFERENCES   R2

GLOSSARY   *See the Online Learning Centre at www.mcgrawhill.ca/olc/hyde*

ACKNOWLEDGEMENTS   A2

INDEX   I1

PREFACE

Our goal in creating the Fourth Canadian Edition of *Understanding Human Sexuality* was to maintain the best features of the highly regarded American textbook while providing a truly Canadian focus. Over the past two decades, *Understanding Human Sexuality* has been widely recognized for its comprehensive and multidisciplinary coverage of a broad range of topics, its commitment to excellent scholarship, and its appeal and accessibility to students. The Fourth Canadian Edition retains these strengths while incorporating the latest information about a range of sexual topics including Internet issues related to sexuality, adolescent sexual behaviour, transgender individuals, the causes and treatment of sexual disorders, and legal decisions related to the rights of gays and lesbians.

WHAT IS UNIQUE ABOUT THE FOURTH CANADIAN EDITION OF *UNDERSTANDING HUMAN SEXUALITY*?

A COMMITMENT TO CANADIAN CONTENT

First and foremost is the Canadian content. There are many ways in which sexuality in Canada is different from sexuality in the United States—whether it's rates of breast-feeding, teenage pregnancy, and STIs; attitude towards same-sex relationships; or laws regulating sexuality. These differences are reflected throughout the text—every chapter has significant Canadian content. Thus, students are provided with information that is relevant to their own lives, their own experiences, and their own communities. In keeping with the substantial amount of excellent sexuality research being conducted in Canada, the textbook also highlights Canadian sexuality research and researchers. Professors who reviewed the Fourth Canadian Edition were extremely positive about the inclusion of Canadian content, enthusiastically praising both the *extent* and *relevance* of Canadian information compared to other texts available.

A FOCUS ON DIVERSITY AND AN INCLUSIVE APPROACH

Second, in the Fourth Canadian Edition we have paid special attention to making the text more inclusive. In keeping with the diversity within Canadian society, we use inclusive language that respects diversity and does not assume any particular lifestyle or life choices. Thus, for example, we use "partner" rather than "spouse," and language that applies equally to gay, lesbian, bisexual, and heterosexual students. We have also highlighted sexuality in Canadian ethnocultural communities, including the Chinese, South Asian, Caribbean, and First Nations communities, as well as regional differences, such as between Canadians living in Quebec and those living in other provinces.

CANADIAN LEGAL INFORMATION IN EVERY CHAPTER

Third, students will find discussion of Canadian laws and Canadian legal issues in each chapter. This includes laws related to same-sex relationships, sexual assault, child sexual abuse, contraception and abortion, pornography, and prostitution, among others. We have provided a complete list of the sexually related statutes in the Criminal Code of Canada, as well as a history of the evolution of some of these statutes.

RELEVANT, ENGAGING IN FOCUS BOXES

Fourth, we highlight research and issues of particular interest to Canadian students in each chapter's In Focus boxes. The Fourth Canadian Edition features 16 new In Focus boxes that highlight the lived experiences of individual Canadians and can serve as a stimulus to classroom discussion. These In Focus boxes put a personal face on many of the topics that are covered in the textbook, including arranged marriage, teenage pregnancy, first sexual experiences, being bisexual, and being a gay Anglican priest.

PLAN OF THE BOOK

First and foremost, we have kept in mind that students *want* to learn about sexuality and that our job as writers is to help them learn. We have covered topics completely, with as clear a presentation as possible, and have made a special effort to use language that will enlighten rather than intimidate. In the selection and preparation of illustrations for the book, our goal has always been to convey as much information as possible, simply and clearly.

The book assumes no prior university or college courses in biology, psychology, or sociology. It is designed as an introduction following the four major objectives of our own courses in human sexuality:

1. To provide practical information needed for everyday living and to deal with problems in sexual functioning.
2. To help students appreciate the fabulous diversity of human sexuality along many dimensions, including age, sexual orientation and identity, ethnicity within Canada, and culture around the world.
3. To help students feel more comfortable with thinking and talking about sex, both to minimize their own personal anxiety about a tension-causing topic and to help them become responsible decision-makers in an important aspect of their lives.
4. To familiarize students with methods used in research on sexuality, and particularly with problems inherent in some of these methods, so that they can read research reports critically and intelligently.

Our own courses are surveys, designed to provide students with a broad range of information about sexuality. Reflecting that approach, this book is intended to be complete and balanced in its coverage. For instructors who lack the time or resources to cover the entire book, or for those who prefer to rearrange the order of topics, we have written all the chapters to be fairly independent of one another.

The background of the Hyde, DeLamater, and Byers team is quite compatible with this interdisciplinary approach. Janet Hyde's original graduate training was in psychology, with specialties in behaviour genetics and statistics; later her interests expanded to include psychology of women and gender roles. As a result, her expertise is in the biological and psychological viewpoints. John DeLamater's graduate training was in psychology and sociology, so his expertise includes sociological and cultural viewpoints. Sandra Byers's graduate training was in clinical psychology. She adds the clinical and Canadian perspectives. The team's goal has been to cover all aspects of sexuality with integrity.

Certainly, some aspects of sexuality are very serious. Nonetheless, it is our belief that, in modern North American culture, we are in danger of taking some aspects of sexuality far too seriously. We may not be serious about it in the same way as were our Victorian ancestors, but we are serious nonetheless—serious about whether we are using the best and most up-to-date sexual techniques, serious about whether our partners are having as many orgasms as possible, and so on. To counteract this tendency, we have tried to use a light touch, with occasional bits of humour, in this book. We hope this will help us all keep things in perspective.

One thing we are serious about is the quality of research. The quality of sex research is highly variable, to put it mildly. Journalists think they are sex researchers if they have interviewed 10 people and written a book about it! We see other sexuality textbooks that cite an article from the local newspaper with equal authority as a refereed journal article from *The New England Journal of Medicine* or *The Journal of Sex Research*—and readers have to do a lot of detective work to find out what the real source is for a statement. We believe that it is our responsibility as textbook authors to sift through available studies and *not* cite all of them, but rather present those that are of the best quality. We are pleased to observe that the quality of sex research improves every decade. In this edition we were able to prune out many studies of lesser quality and rely much more on recent studies that are of excellent quality, in terms of sampling, research design, and measurements.

WHAT'S NEW IN THE FOURTH CANADIAN EDITION?

Building on the first three editions, this new edition provides Canadian data wherever reliable figures are available, features Canadian research and researchers, describes sexuality in the major Canadian ethnocultural communities, highlights issues important to Canadian students, and ensures inclusive language and visuals appear throughout. Some of the major content changes and additions to the Fourth Canadian Edition are as follows:

CHAPTER 1   SEXUALITY IN PERSPECTIVE
- New section on sexual health and sexual rights.
- Data on mass media thoroughly updated.
- Added In Focus Box on the experiences of a gay Anglican priest.

CHAPTER 2   THEORETICAL PERSPECTIVES ON SEXUALITY
- Clarified evolutionary perspectives.
- Clarified issue of sexual orientation versus sexual behaviour in In Focus 2.1.
- Updated In Focus 2.2, including new offence of voyeurism.

CHAPTER 3   SEX RESEARCH
- Clarified stratified random sampling.
- Added discussion of critical discourse analysis.
- Added information on the benefits of qualitative research.
- Added a number of new sex researchers in Canada to In Focus 3.2.
- Added In Focus box on the career of Dr. William Fisher.

CHAPTER 4   SEXUAL ANATOMY
- New section added on genital self-image, which discusses piercings and genital surgery—including hymen reattachment.
- Added information on diameter of fallopian tubes.
- Data from the latest international Demographic and Health Surveys on Female Genital Cutting (FGC) added to the In Focus box on FGC.

- Updated information on circumcision rates in Canada and research on circumcision and HIV infection, including halted clinical trials in Kenya and Uganda.
- Added information on the new vaccine against human papillomavirus (HPV) infection and cervical cancer.
- Added In Focus box on Lance Armstrong's battle with testicular cancer.

CHAPTER 5　SEX HORMONES, SEXUAL DIFFERENTIATION, AND MENSTRUATION

- Discussion of menstrual cycle streamlined.
- Added an In Focus box with the latest research on environmental pollutants that affect the endocrine system and the behaviour of humans and other species.
- New terminology for intersex—disorders of sex development—included.
- Updated Table 5.2 on ages of menarche and other aspects of pubertal development.

CHAPTER 6　CONCEPTION, PREGNANCY, AND CHILDBIRTH

- Expanded discussion of surrogacy, including for gay couples, and of IVF for lesbian couples.
- Added section on midwives, including training and reasons why some women prefer midwives.
- Added discussion of reasons for breast-feeding difficulties.
- Introduced the "pregnancy as silent struggle" perspective, which argues that mother and fetus are in continuing struggle for adequate nourishment and nutrients.
- Updated statistics and discussion of Caesarean section deliveries and vaginal birth after Caesarean (VBAC).
- Updated coverage of postpartum depression.
- Updated coverage of infertility and new reproductive technologies.
- Updated birth weights with new Canadian data, including information on variations in birth weight by ethnicity.
- Added In Focus box on giving birth under the care of a midwife.

CHAPTER 7　CONTRACEPTION AND ABORTION

- Added new In Focus Box on Henry Morgentaler.
- Updated discussion of contraceptives currently available in Canada (including Seasonale).
- Mentioned using male condoms as dental dams.
- Provided updates on contraceptive use and availability in Canada, including what to do when a pill is missed.
- Provided the latest in developments on male contraception.

CHAPTER 8　SEXUALLY TRANSMITTED INFECTIONS

- Explained why the term STI is preferred over STD.
- Added scientific advances regarding genes that confer resistance to HIV infection.
- Updated WHO recommendation for circumcision to reduce HIV infection.
- Mentioned importance of screening men for chlamydia.
- Added discussion of the rapid HIV test available in Canada.
- Added the latest research on HPV, including high-risk and low-risk types, as well as the HPV vaccine.
- New content on the latest developments in microbicides.
- Added definition and discussion of cumulative risk.
- Added a new In Focus box on coping with herpes.

CHAPTER 9   SEXUAL RESPONSE

- In keeping with contemporary trends to modify Masters and Johnson's four-stage model, dropped the distinction between the excitement phase and the plateau phase.
- Updated discussion on pheromones, including discussion of cranial nerve zero.
- Elaborated on research on difference between ejaculation and sensation of orgasm.
- In Focus 9.2 updated with work by Whipple.
- Expanded section on sex toys.
- New discussion of two-person cybersex.
- Clarified that sodomy is a legal term.
- Incorporated material on techniques of arousal that was previously covered in other chapters.
- Incorporated the latest research on the brain, spinal cord, and sex, including MRI studies.
- Substantially updated discussion of pheromones, with new research on humans and other primates.
- Added In Focus box on one man's experience with chemical castration as a treatment for prostate cancer.

CHAPTER 10   SEXUALITY AND THE LIFE CYCLE: CHILDHOOD AND ADOLESCENCE

- Added more information on developing gender awareness and sexual orientation awareness.
- Added more discussion of same-sex attraction and disclosure, including parents' reactions.
- Added detailed coverage of report of APA Task Force Report on the Sexualization of Girls.
- Updated statistics on childhood and adolescent sexual experience throughout.
- Updated In Focus box on mass media; added new content analyses on sex in the media.
- Added an In Focus box in which youth describe their first sexual experience.
- Added an In Focus box describing an Aboriginal woman's experience as a teenage mother.

CHAPTER 11   SEXUALITY AND THE LIFE CYCLE: ADULTHOOD

- Added new research on patterns in couples' level of sexual desire/lust.
- Added new research on polyamory.
- Updated research on sexuality in later life including older women's sexual relationships after remarriage.
- Added new research on extradyadic sexual activity.
- Defined barebacking and added research on gay men's reasons for unprotected sex.
- Updated statistics to reflect the 2006 Canadian Census.

CHAPTER 12   ATTRACTION, LOVE, AND COMMUNICATION

- New discussion of the use of scientific theories by Internet matching services.
- Expanded discussion of the theory of evolutionary roots of attraction and mating processes.
- Added new data on homophily in Canada.
- Added sexual orientation as a basis for attraction.
- Incorporated material on sexual communication previously covered in another chapter.
- Added an In Focus box on a couple's experience of their arranged marriage.
- Added material on the combination of Sternberg's three components.
- Added an In Focus box on a disabled woman's experience of her sexuality.

CHAPTER 13   GENDER AND SEXUALITY

- Research on the media and gender socialization thoroughly updated.
- New research on MRI scans of brains before and during the gender reassignment process.

- New research on thermal imaging technology for assessing genital arousal
- The latest on controversies about the treatment of Gender Identity Disorder discussed.
- New genetic study of transsexuals added.
- Added discussion of gynephilic and androphilic transgender individuals.
- Added Chivers and Bailey's research on category-specific sexual arousal.

CHAPTER 14   SEXUAL ORIENTATION AND IDENTITY: GAY, LESBIAN, BI, OR STRAIGHT?

- Renamed chapter to include identity.
- Added new research on the genetics of sexual orientation.
- Added new research on differences between gay men and lesbians.
- Increased Canadian content in the text.
- Added statistics on same-sex relationships from the 2006 Canadian Census.
- Discussed multiple forms of prejudice.
- Enhanced discussion of asexuality.
- Added an In Focus Box on a woman's experience of being bisexual.

CHAPTER 15   VARIATIONS IN SEXUAL BEHAVIOUR

- Added discussion of Bancroft and colleagues' high-arousal, low-inhibition perspective on variations.
- Updated Canadian laws with respect to voyeurism.
- Updated information on BDSM.
- Elaborated on range of atypical sexual behaviour in the introductory paragraph.
- Elaborated on the work by Kleinplatz and Moser regarding the controversy over whether paraphilias should be included in the *DSM-IV*.
- Elaborated on the complexity of whom to treat.
- Integrated sections on prevention and treatment.
- Added an In Focus box describing the experiences of a BDSM practitioner and advocate.

CHAPTER 16   SEXUAL COERCION

- Added reason why women do not report sexual assault to the police.
- Added data on risk of sexual assault for women with disabilities.
- Discussed connection between use of child pornography and child molestation.
- Enhanced discussion of comprehensive treatment of sex offenders.
- Highlighted controversy about the Sex Offender Registry.
- Added discussion of sexual harassment of gays and lesbians.
- Enhanced description of effects of child sexual abuse on adult sexual functioning.
- Added worldwide child sexual abuse statistics.

CHAPTER 17   SEX FOR SALE

- Added coverage of live sex shows.
- Added new data from Kinsey Institute survey of users of pornography.
- Added Canadian research on sex workers.
- Added discussion of pornography aimed at gay and lesbian audiences.
- Added research on the connection between child pornography and pedophilia.
- Updated information on child pornography offences in the Criminal Code of Canada.
- Added an In Focus box describing the experiences of sex workers in the Maritimes.

CHAPTER 18   SEXUAL DISORDERS AND SEX THERAPY

- The New View of Women's Sexual Problems (Tiefer, Basson) integrated throughout (e.g., the concept of "responsive desire" added in the section on desire disorders).
- Added new In Focus Box on a case of low sexual desire, which illustrates an application of the New View.

- The concept of sexual health, introduced in Chapter 1, is revisited in the section on practical advice for preventing sexual disorders.
- Mentioned prevalence of SSRIs and the percentage of people on them who experience a sexual disorder.
- Expanded on situational sexual disorders.

CHAPTER 19   SEXUALITY EDUCATION

- Completely rewritten discussion of sex education curricula and research on effectiveness.
- Added section on education around sexual orientation issues, and incorporated issue of homonegativity into discussion of teacher training.
- Expanded on education to combat homonegativity.

CHAPTER 20   ETHICS, RELIGION, AND SEXUALITY

- Discussion of Buddhism expanded to include a new discussion of Tantric Buddhism.
- Section on religious positions on homosexuality updated and reorganized into rejectionist, love-the-sinner-but-hate-the-sin, and full acceptance.
- Statements by religions updated and Web sites provided when available.
- Section on Judaism updated.
- Mentioned debate in Anglican Church.
- Qualified Greek acceptance of pederasty.
- Condensed discussion of Christianity.

SUPERIOR SERVICE

Service takes on a whole new meaning with McGraw-Hill Ryerson and *Understanding Human Sexuality*. More than just bringing you the textbook, we have consistently raised the bar in terms of innovation and educational research. These investments in learning and the educational community have helped us to understand the needs of students and educators across the country and allowed us to foster the growth of truly innovative, integrated learning.

INTEGRATED LEARNING

Your Integrated Learning Sales Specialist is a McGraw-Hill Ryerson representative who has the experience, product knowledge, training, and support to help you assess and integrate any of our products, technology, and services into your course for optimum teaching and learning performance. Whether it's using our test bank software, helping your students improve their grades, or putting your entire course online, your *i*Learning Sales Specialist is there to help you do it. Contact your local *i*Learning Sales Specialist today to learn how to maximize all of McGraw-Hill Ryerson's resources!

*i*LEARNING SERVICES PROGRAM

McGraw-Hill Ryerson offers a unique *i*Services package designed for Canadian faculty. Our mission is to equip providers of higher education with superior tools and resources required for excellence in teaching. For additional information visit **www.mcgrawhill.ca/ highereducation/iservices**.

TEACHING, LEARNING, & TECHNOLOGY CONFERENCE SERIES

The educational environment has changed tremendously in recent years, and McGraw-Hill Ryerson continues to be committed to helping you acquire the skills you need to succeed in this new milieu. Our innovative Teaching, Learning, & Technology Conference Series brings faculty together from across Canada with 3M Teaching Excellence award winners to share teaching and learning best practices in a collaborative and stimulating environment. Pre-conference workshops on general topics such as teaching large classes and technology integration are also offered. We will also work with you at your own institution to customize workshops that best suit the needs of your faculty.

COURSESMART

CourseSmart brings together thousands of textbooks across hundreds of courses in an eTextbook format providing unique benefits to students and faculty. By purchasing an eTextbook, students can save up to 50 percent off the cost of a print textbook, reduce their impact on the environment, and gain access to powerful Web tools for learning, including full text search, notes and highlighting, and e-mail tools for sharing notes between classmates. For faculty, CourseSmart provides instant access to review and compare textbooks and course materials in their discipline area without the time, cost, and environmental impact of mailing print examination copies. For further details, contact your *i*Learning Sales Specialist or go to **www.coursesmart.com**.

SUPPLEMENTS

A complete, integrated supplements package supports students and instructors to help them meet their learning and teaching challenges.

FOR INSTRUCTORS

Instructor's Online Learning Centre

The Online Learning Centre (**www.mcgrawhill.ca/olc/hyde**) includes password-protected instructor supplements, fully adapted to accord with the Fourth Canadian Edition:

- An **Instructor's Manual** that provides ideas for lectures, class discussions, and class activities.
- A **Computerized Test Bank** that contains more than 1500 questions that vary in type and are keyed to the appropriate page number in the textbook.
- **Microsoft® PowerPoint® slides** to accompany each chapter.

The site also offers SexSource Online featuring high-quality educational clips plus post-viewing questions, animations that demonstrate biological processes, and polls to measure students' behaviour and attitudes toward sexuality.

eInstruction's Classroom Performance System (CPS)

CPS is a student response system using wireless connectivity. It gives instructors and students immediate feedback from the entire class. The response pads are remotes that are easy to use and engage students. **CPS** helps to increase student preparation, interactivity, and active learning; allows you to administer quizzes, tests, and immediate grading; and facilitates evaluation of classroom attendance and activity.

CPS-ready content is available for use with Hyde/DeLamater/Byers, *Understanding Human Sexuality*. Please contact your *i*Learning Sales Specialist for more information on how you can integrate CPS into your psychology classroom.

Content cartridges are available for the course management systems **WebCT** and **Blackboard**. These platforms provide instructors with user-friendly, flexible teaching tools. Please contact your local McGraw-Hill Ryerson *i*Learning Sales Specialist for details.

Annual Editions—Human Sexuality

This McGraw-Hill publication offers articles on topics related to the latest research and thinking in human sexuality from more than 300 public press sources. These editions are updated annually and contain helpful features such as a topic guide, an annotated table of contents, unit overviews, and a topical index. An Instructor's Guide containing testing materials is also available.

Taking Sides: Clashing Views on Controversial Issues in Human Sexuality

This debate-style reader carefully examines issues with pro and con essays representing the arguments of leading scholars and commentators. An instructor's guide with testing materials is also available.

FOR STUDENTS

Online Learning Centre

The Online Learning Centre (**www.mcgrawhill.ca/olc/hyde**) provides chapter quizzes and review questions, interactive exercises, searchable glossary, and other study tools. The password-protected portion of the site provides students with access to SexSource Online videos that illustrate core concepts in human sexuality.

ACKNOWLEDGEMENTS

I am extremely fortunate to have been able to call on a wide network of Canadian scholars in preparing the Canadian editions of *Understanding Human Sexuality*. Many of my colleagues and friends have been as generous with their time and expertise as I prepared this Fourth Edition as they were for the previous editions. I appreciate their contributions enormously. I am also appreciative that so many people were willing to provide me with copies of their scholarly work—their work is cited throughout this book. I have also benefited from the students in my classes. They keep me up to date on what university students are thinking and wondering about sexuality; a number of them also provided specific suggestions for improvements to the textbook.

I am extremely indebted to the current and former member of my sexuality research group at the University of New Brunswick who provided input for all three editions. Thank you especially to Shannon Archibald, Marvin Claybourn, Jacqueline Cohen, Lyndsay Foster, Cindy Letts, Christie Little, Sheila MacNeil, Sarah McAulay, Lorna Scott, Krystelle Shaughnessy, Deanne Simms, Jennifer Thurlow, and Angela Weaver. Jacqueline Cohen's contributions regarding transgender issues and discussion of sexual orientation were fabulous. I am indebted to the various people who helped me identify the individuals whose life experiences are highlighted in the many new In Focus boxes. These individuals often wrote or edited these stories themselves. This includes Freda Burdett, Jacqueline Cohen, Lyndsay Foster, Gayle MacDonald, Krystelle Shaughnessy, Cory Silverberg, and Kris Wells. I am particularly grateful to the people (all Canadians) who agreed to share their own experiences in these In Focus boxes, including Cheryl Dobinson, William Fisher, Trevor Jacques, Trish McCourt, Kim McKay-McNab, Fran Odette, Faizal Suhukhan, Ayesha Suhukhan, and Richard Wassersung, as well as the people who chose to remain anonymous.

I am also enormously grateful to Susan Voyer, who has served as my research assistant for both the Second and Third Canadian Editions. She was not only relentless in tracking down information, regardless of how obscure, but also proactive in bringing new developments and new sources to my attention. Her organizational skills are without equal. I relied heavily on her wise advice. This book would be noticeably poorer without her contributions.

The Fourth Canadian Edition of *Understanding Human Sexuality* has benefited from the careful reviews and valuable feedback of the following instructors:

Lori Anne Brotto, *University of British Columbia*
Meredith Chivers, *University of Western Ontario*
Shaniff Esmail, *University of Alberta*
Corey Isaacs, *University of Western Ontario*
Nicki Monahan, *George Brown College*
Dawn More, *Algonquin College*
Eleonore Northam, *Seneca College*
Caroline Pukall, *Queens University*
David Reagan, *Camosun College*
Melike Schalomon, *Grant MacEwan College*
Monika Stelzl, *St. Thomas University*
Ronald Stevenson, *Simon Fraser University*
Noreen Stuckless, *York University*
Bruce Tallon, *Niagara College*
Harald Taukulis, *University of New Brunswick*
Claire Vanston, *University College of the Fraser Valley*

I also owe many thanks to the editors and staff at McGraw-Hill Ryerson whose friendly and encouraging support through every step of the process made my job so much easier: Cara Yarzab, Publisher; Denise Foote, Senior Developmental Editor; Kara Stahl, Supervising Editor; Sheryl MacAdam, Production Coordinator; Valerie Adams, Copy Editor; and Heather Cameron, My Editor Inc., Photo Researcher.

Finally, I could not have written this book without the enthusiastic support of my family. The love and gratitude I feel toward my husband Larry and our daughters Krista and Alyssa are immeasurable.

E. Sandra Byers

STUDENT'S GUIDE TO UNDERSTANDING HUMAN SEXUALITY

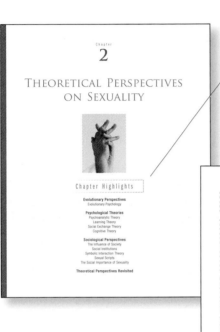

CHAPTER HIGHLIGHTS

A brief outline at the beginning of each chapter provides a preview of topics to help students prepare for reading and studying.

KEY TERMS

Each Key Term is defined and placed in the margin of the page where the term is introduced. In addition, all Key Terms are included in the online Glossary.

IN FOCUS BOXES

In Focus boxes in each chapter offer more in-depth information about a particular topic or research study mentioned in the chapter. Many of the boxes deal with multicultural and multiethnic perspectives, and explore cultures around the world, as well as in Canada.

END-OF-CHAPTER STUDY AND REVIEW TOOLS

Chapter Summaries; Questions for Thought, Discussion and Debate; and *Suggestions for Further Reading* are found at the end of each chapter.

Chapter

1

SEXUALITY IN PERSPECTIVE

Chapter Highlights

Sex and Gender

**The History of Understanding Sexuality:
Religion and Science**
    Religion
    Science

The Media

Cross-Cultural Perspectives on Sexuality
    Variations in Sexual Techniques
    Masturbation
    Premarital and Extramarital Sex
    Sex with Same-Sex Partners
    Standards of Attractiveness
    Regional and Cultural Variation in Sexuality
    The Significance of Cross-Cultural Studies

Cross-Species Perspectives on Sexuality
    Masturbation
    Same-Sex Sexual Behaviour
    In What Ways Are Humans Unique?
    The Non-sexual Uses of Sexual Behaviour

The Sexual Health Perspective

YOU'RE SO BEAUTIFUL," HE WHISPERED. "I WANT A PICTURE OF YOU JUST LIKE THIS WITH YOUR FACE FLUSHED AND YOUR LIPS WET AND SHINY." . . . HE TORE OPEN A FOIL PACKET HE'D RETRIEVED FROM HIS POCKET. MESMERIZED, SHE WATCHED HIM SHEATH HIMSELF, AMAZED AT HOW HARD HE WAS. SHE REACHED OUT TO TOUCH HIM, BUT HE MOVED BACK, MADE SURE SHE WAS READY, AND THEN SLID NEATLY INSIDE HER, SO DEEPLY SHE GASPED. SHE CONTRACTED HER MUSCLES AROUND HIM, AND HE CLOSED HIS EYES AND GROANED, THE SOUND SO PRIMAL, IT MADE HER SKIN TINGLE.*

HUMAN SEXUAL BEHAVIOR IS A DIVERSE PHENOMENON. IT OCCURS IN DIFFERENT PHYSICAL LOCATIONS AND SOCIAL CONTEXTS, CONSISTS OF A WIDE RANGE OF SPECIFIC ACTIVITIES, AND IS PERCEIVED DIFFERENTLY BY DIFFERENT PEOPLE. AN INDIVIDUAL ENGAGES IN SEXUAL ACTIVITY ON THE BASIS OF A COMPLEX SET OF MOTIVATIONS AND ORGANIZES THAT ACTIVITY ON THE BASIS OF NUMEROUS EXTERNAL FACTORS AND INFLUENCES. THUS, IT IS UNLIKELY THAT THE TOOLS AND CONCEPTS FROM ANY SINGLE SCIENTIFIC DISCIPLINE WILL SUFFICE TO ANSWER ALL OR EVEN MOST OF THE QUESTIONS ONE MIGHT ASK ABOUT SEXUAL BEHAVIOR.†

HAVING CHILDREN AND HEALTHY FAMILIES ARE IMPORTANT GOALS TO MOST CANADIANS, BUT SOME PEOPLE CANNOT REACH THOSE GOALS WITHOUT HELP. IF THERE ARE TECHNOLOGIES THAT CAN BE USED TO HELP, A CARING SOCIETY SHOULD PROVIDE THESE. BUT THERE ARE MISUSES AND HARMS, AS WELL AS BENEFITS, THAT MAY COME FROM USE OF THE TECHNOLOGIES—HARMS TO BOTH INDIVIDUALS AND SOCIETY.‡

Strikingly different though they may seem, all of the above quotations are talking about the same thing—sex. The first quotation is from a romance novel. It is intended to stimulate the reader's fantasies and arousal. The second is from a scholarly book about sex. It aims to stimulate the brain but not the genitals. The third is from a Royal Commission on treatment of infertility. It points out the complexity of many sexual issues. From reading these brief excerpts, we can quickly see that the topic of sexuality is diverse, complex, and fascinating.

Why study sex? Most people are curious about sex, particularly because exchanging sexual information is somewhat taboo in our culture, so curiosity motivates us to study sex. Sex is an important force in many people's lives, so there are practical reasons for wanting to learn about it. Finally, most of us at various times experience problems with our sexual functioning or wish that we could function better, and we hope that learning more about sex will help us. This book is designed to address all of these needs. So let's consider various perspectives on sexuality—the effects of religion, science, the media, and culture on our understanding of

*Debbi Rawlins. (2003). *Anything goes*. New York: Harlequin Blaze.
†Laumann et al. (1994).
‡Royal Commission on New Reproductive Technologies. (1993). *Proceed with care: Final report of the Royal Commission on New Reproductive Technologies*. Ottawa: Minister of Government Services Canada.

sexuality as well as a sexual health perspective. These perspectives make it clear that the study of sexuality is not confined to one discipline, but rather is multidisciplinary. However, first we must draw an important distinction between sex and gender.

SEX AND GENDER

Sometimes the word "sex" is used ambiguously. In some cases it refers to being male or female, and sometimes it refers to sexual behaviour or reproduction. In most cases, of course, the meaning is clear from the context. If you are filling out a job application form and one item says "Sex," you don't write, "I like it" or "As often as possible." It is clear that your prospective employer wants to know whether you are a male or a female. In other cases, though, the meaning may be ambiguous. For example, when a book has the title *Sex and Temperament in Three Primitive Societies*, what is it about? Is it about the sexual practices of primitive people and whether having sex frequently gives them pleasant temperaments? Or is it about the kinds of personalities that males and females are expected to have in those societies? Not only does this use of "sex" create ambiguities, but it also clouds our thinking about some important issues.

Gender: The state of being male or female.

To remove—or at least reduce—this ambiguity, the term "sex" will be used in this book in contexts referring to sexual anatomy and sexual behaviour, and the term gender will be used to refer to the state of being male or female.

This is a book about sex, not gender; it is about sexual behaviour and the biological, psychological, and social forces that influence it. Of course, although we are arguing that sex and gender are conceptually different, we would not try to argue that they are totally independent of each other. Certainly, gender roles—the ways in which males and females are expected to behave—exert a powerful influence on the way people behave sexually, and so one chapter will be devoted to gender roles and their effects on sexuality.

How should we define "sex," aside from saying that it is different from "gender"? A biologist might define sexual behaviour as "any behavior that increases the likelihood of gametic union [union of sperm and egg]" (Bermant & Davidson, 1974). This definition emphasizes the reproductive function of sex. However, particularly in the last few decades, medical advances such as the birth control pill have been developed that allow us to separate reproduction from sex. Most Canadians now have sex not only for procreation but also for pleasure and intimacy.[1]

The noted sex researcher Alfred Kinsey defined "sex" as behaviour that leads to orgasm. Although this definition has some merits (it does not imply that sex must be associated with reproduction), it also presents some problems. If one person has intercourse with another person but does not have an orgasm, was that not sexual behaviour for her or him? If an individual has an orgasm through oral–genital stimulation, is that sex? Indeed, researchers in New Brunswick have shown that undergraduate students have a very narrow definition of the term "sex." Whereas almost everybody thought that penile–vaginal intercourse constituted having sex, only 23 percent of participants thought that oral sex resulting in orgasm would be defined as sex (Randall & Byers, 2003).

Sexual behaviour: Behaviour that produces arousal and increases the chance of orgasm.

To try to avoid some of these problems, sexual behaviour will be defined in this book as *behaviour that produces arousal and increases the chance of orgasm.*[2]

---

[1]Actually, even in former times sex was not always associated with reproduction. For example, a man in 1850 might have fathered 10 children; using a very conservative estimate that he engaged in sexual intercourse 1500 times during his adult life (once a week for the 30 years from age 20 to age 50), one concludes that only 10 in 1500 of those acts, or fewer than 1 percent, resulted in reproduction.

[2]This definition, though an improvement over some, still has its problems. For example, consider a woman who feels no arousal at all during intercourse. According to the definition, intercourse would not be sexual behaviour for her. However, intercourse would generally be something we would want to classify as sexual behaviour. It should be clear that defining "sexual behaviour" is difficult.

The History of Understanding Sexuality: Religion and Science

RELIGION

Religion is a source of values and ethics regarding sexuality and, as such, is a powerful influence on the sexual attitudes and behaviour of many individuals. The moral code for each religion is unique—each religion has different views on what is right and what is wrong with respect to sexuality. Throughout most of recorded history, at least until about 100 years ago, religion (and rumour) provided most of the information that people had about sexuality, and in some cultures it still does. Here are a few historical examples of how different religions understood sexuality.

The ancient Greeks openly acknowledged both heterosexuality and homosexuality in their society and explained the existence of the two in a myth in which the original humans were double creatures with twice the normal number of limbs and organs; some were double males, some were double females, and some were half male and half female (LeVay, 1996). The gods, fearing the power of these creatures, split them in half, and forever after each one continued to search for its missing half. Heterosexuals were thought to have resulted from the splitting of the half male, half female; male homosexuals, from the splitting of the double male; and female homosexuals, from the splitting of the double female. It was through this mythology that the ancient Greeks understood sexual orientation and sexual desire.

Fifteenth-century Christians believed that "wet dreams" (nocturnal emissions) resulted from intercourse with tiny spiritual creatures called *incubi* and *succubi*, a notion put forth in a papal bull (an official document) of 1484 and a companion book, the *Malleus Maleficarum* ("witch's hammer"). The *Malleus* became the official manual of the Inquisition, in which people, particularly women, were tried as witches. Wet dreams, sexual dysfunction, and sexual lust were seen to be caused by witchcraft (Hergenhahn, 2001).

Over the centuries, Muslims have believed that sexual intercourse is one of the finest pleasures of life, reflecting the teachings of the great prophet Muhammad. Sexuality is regarded primarily as a source of pleasure and only secondarily as a means of reproduction, although the way the laws of the Koran are carried out has varied considerably across the Muslim world (Boonstra, 2001; Ilkkaracan, 2001).

People of different religions hold different understandings of human sexuality, and these religious views often have a profound impact. The influence of religion on Canadians is particularly apparent in the discussion of homosexuality and abortion. For example, conservative Christians often use their interpretation of the Bible, an interpretation that is not shared by other Christian denominations, to justify their opposition to homosexuals, same-sex sexual behaviour, and same-sex marriage. Other Canadians feel that these arguments have more to do with anti-gay prejudice and homophobia than religion. A detailed discussion of religion and sexuality is provided in Chapter 20 on the Online Learning Centre (also see In Focus 1.1).

SCIENCE

It was against this background of religious understandings of sexuality that the scientific study of sex began in the nineteenth century; although, of course, religious notions continue to influence our ideas about sexuality. In addition, the groundwork for an understanding of the biological aspects of sexuality had already been laid by the research of physicians and biologists. The Dutch microscopist Anton van Leeuwenhoek (1632–1723) had discovered sperm swimming in human semen. In 1875 Oskar Hertwig (1849–1922) first observed the actual fertilization of the egg by the sperm in sea urchins, although the ovum in humans was not directly observed until the twentieth century.

In Focus 1.1

Paul: The Story of a Gay Anglican Priest

Paul was born in 1950, the second of two children, to upper-middle-class parents in Nova Scotia. His parents stressed the importance of education, and there was no question that Paul would go to university, something his parents had not done. Paul described his parents as old fashioned—more like parents were in the 1930s than like parents in the 1950s.

By the age of five, Paul realized two things about how he was different than other children. First, he wasn't interested in typical childhood activities, such as sports. Second, he was interested in boys, not girls. As a result, he was a loner and turned to reading, art, music, and painting. It also became very important to Paul to receive the approval of adults. Growing up, Paul's parents attended the Anglican Church every week, but religion was not emphasized in his home. Nonetheless, Paul was drawn to religion, especially the ritual, music, and artistic form that were part of it.

Paul's parents never talked to him about sex. Indeed, he never heard his father mention anything sexual. He did hear his mother whisper and giggle about sexual issues with her friends. This made him realize that his parents couldn't handle sexuality issues. Sexuality also was never mentioned by anyone connected with the Anglican Church, although Paul got the impression that "it was seen as an unpleasantness." He played sex games such as "You show me yours and I'll show you mine" with other boys, but had no interest in playing these games with girls. He did not have bad feelings about his sexual orientation but sensed that this was something he should definitely not discuss with either his parents or his priest. The fact that he could not be open about his sexual orientation made him feel increasingly lonely as a teenager.

Paul's first sexual experimentation occurred in university. These were "no strings attached, conveniently available" partners. He found the opportunity to express his sexuality fulfilling. He fell in love three times but says he "got hurt every time." When he was 37, he became engaged to a woman who had been kind to him when he was ill and wanted to marry him even though she knew that he was gay. In the end, he realized that he was confusing kindness with love and that he could never be faithful to her, so he called the engagement off.

At first Paul fought the idea of entering the ministry. However, in his 20s he realized that "he had no choice" but to study for the priesthood. According to Paul, his sexuality went underground as a result because he was aware that being gay was not something the Anglican Church would tolerate. When he was ordained as a priest at age 26, he resigned himself to the realization that he would never have the opportunity to live in a loving long-term relationship with another man. At the time, he felt that he could accept this because he had "married the church." Nonetheless, he continued to have unattached sex.

Paul feels that, because he was not heterosexually married, the Church hierarchy assumed he was gay. However, they were careful to "never ask the question so that they would not have to deal with the answer." Nonetheless, he feels that his career in the church was clearly impeded by his sexual orientation. For example, in contrast to married priests, he was not given the opportunity to move to other diocese to take on new challenges or to assume positions of leadership. He believes that the people in his parish also assumed he was gay. He heard reports of criticism of his sexual orientation by some of his parishioners, but these complaints did not go anywhere because there was never proof that he was gay. Nonetheless, the secrecy and lack of acceptance took their toll on Paul, and he became an alcoholic. Paul also knew other gay priests, including a gay bishop who was a good friend and lover, who also were forced to hide their sexual orientation. Nonetheless, Paul never waivered in his commitment to his religion.

According to Paul, the official policy of the Anglican Church of Canada with respect to sexual orientation is that "heterosexual sex may be exercised within the confines of heterosexual marriage. Homosexuals must be celibate. Human rights do not enter the issue." However, Paul feels that the actual reception that non-heterosexual church members get depends on whom they talk to. Whereas some clergy are open and welcoming to people of all sexual orientations, others appear to be "waging a vendetta against anyone who is not heterosexual."

Paul retired from the church at the age of 44 due to illness, although he remains a priest. Since that time, he has been more open about his sexuality. He has taken on the task of promoting the rights of non-heterosexuals within the church, trying to make the church more inclusive. This was something he did not feel he could do when he was a parish priest. He would like the church to provide a safe environment in which people find spiritual sustenance and give support to one another without fear or reprisal.

Source: Based on an interview by Sandra Byers.

(a)   *(b)*

Figure 1.1 Two important early sex researchers. *(a)* Sigmund Freud. *(b)* Henry Havelock Ellis.

A major advance in the scientific understanding of the psychological aspects of human sexuality came with the work of the Viennese physician Sigmund Freud (1856–1939), founder of psychiatry and psychoanalysis. His ideas will be discussed in detail in Chapter 2.

It is important to recognize the cultural context in which Freud and the other early sex researchers crafted their research and writing. They began their work in the Victorian era, the late 1800s, both in North America and Europe. Norms about sexuality were extraordinarily rigid and oppressive (see Figure 1.2). Historian Peter Gay characterized this repressive aspect of Victorian cultural norms as

> . . . a devious and insincere world in which middle-class husbands slaked their lust by keeping mistresses, frequenting prostitutes, or molesting children, while their wives, timid, dutiful, obedient, were sexually anesthetic and poured all their capacity for love into their housekeeping and their child-rearing. (Gay, 1984, p. 6)

Yet at the same time the actual sexual behaviour of Victorians was sometimes in violation of societal norms and expectations. Dr. Clelia Mosher was a physician who conducted a sex survey of Victorian women in the United States over a period of 30 years. Although the sample was small (47 women) and non-random, her results provide an alternative description of female sexuality during this period. For example, despite the Victorian stereotype that women felt no sexual desire, 80 percent of women who answered the question said that they felt a desire for sexual intercourse. Similarly, 72 percent of women indicated that they experienced orgasm. One woman commented that sex had been unpleasant for her for years because of her "slow reaction" but "orgasm [occurs] if time is taken." In his history of sexuality in the Victorian era, Gay (1984) documented the story of Mabel Loomis Todd, who, though married, carried on a lengthy affair with Austin Dickinson, a community leader in Amherst, Massachusetts. Many people actually knew about the "secret" affair, yet Mrs. Loomis did not become an outcast. Another demonstration of a discrepancy between social norms and behaviour occurred in a somewhat earlier era. Many fur traders married Aboriginal women—at least until white women began to arrive—knowing that this would not be acceptable in Europe (Kinsman, 1996).

An equally great—though not so well-known—early contributor to the scientific study of sex was Henry Havelock Ellis (1859–1939). A physician in Victorian England, he compiled a vast collection of information on sexuality—including medical and anthropological findings, as well as case histories—which was published in a series of volumes entitled *Studies in the*

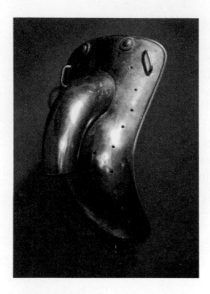

Figure 1.2 The Victorian era, from which Freud and Ellis emerged, was characterized by extreme sexual repression. Here is an apparatus that was sold to prevent onanism (masturbation).

Psychology of Sex beginning in 1896. Havelock Ellis was a remarkably objective and tolerant scholar, particularly for his era. He believed that women, like men, are sexual creatures. A sexual reformer, he believed that sexual deviations from the norm are often harmless, and he urged society to accept them. In his desire to collect information about human sexuality rather than to make judgments about it, he can be considered the forerunner of modern sex research (for his autobiography, see Ellis, 1939; numerous biographies exist).

Another important figure in nineteenth-century sex research was the German psychiatrist Richard von Krafft-Ebing (1840–1902) (Oosterhuis, 2000). His special interest was "pathological" sexuality. He managed to collect more than 200 case histories of pathological individuals, which appeared in his book entitled *Psychopathia Sexualis.* His work tended to be neither objective nor tolerant. Nonetheless, it has had a lasting impact. He coined the concepts of sadism, masochism, and pedophilia. The terms "heterosexuality" and "homosexuality" entered the English language in the 1892 translation of his book (Oosterhuis, 2000). One of his case histories is presented in Chapter 15.

One other early contributor to the scientific understanding of sexuality deserves mention, the German Magnus Hirschfeld (1868–1935). He founded the first sex research institute and administered the first large-scale sex survey, obtaining data from 10 000 people on a 130-item questionnaire. Unfortunately, most of the information he amassed was destroyed by Nazi hoodlums. Hirschfeld also established the first journal devoted to the study of sexuality, established a marriage counselling service, worked for legal reforms, and gave advice on contraception and sex problems. His special interest, however, was homosexuality. He made important contributions as a pioneer sex researcher (Bullough, 1994).

In the twentieth century, major breakthroughs in the scientific understanding of sex came with the massive surveys of human sexual behaviour in the United States conducted by Alfred Kinsey and his colleagues in the 1940s and with Masters and Johnson's investigations of sexual disorders and the physiology of sexual response. These studies changed how people thought about sex and also led to more open public discussion of sexuality (Connell & Hunt, 2006). At about the same time that the Kinsey research was being conducted, some anthropologists—most notably Margaret Mead and Bronislaw Malinowski—were beginning to collect data on sexual behaviour in other cultures. The 1990s saw a significant increase in research on sexuality in close relationships (Christopher & Sprecher, 2000).

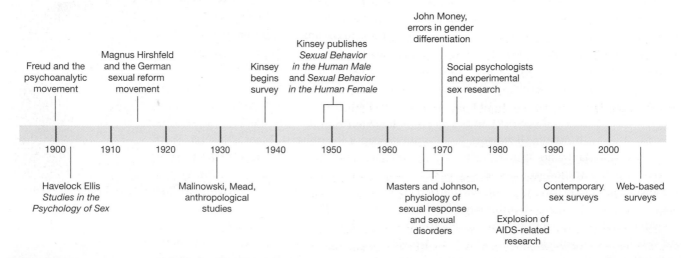

Figure 1.3 The history of scientific research on sex.

There has never been a major national survey of the sexual behaviour of Canadians. However, Statistics Canada has included some questions about sexuality in a number of national surveys, such as the Canada Community Health Survey, the National Population Health Survey, the General Social Survey, and the National Longitudinal Survey of Children and Youth. Canadian researchers have also conducted a large number of smaller investigations that have provided important information on a rich array of sexual topics (see In Focus 3.2 on page 67 for a description of the work of some of these researchers).

The scientific study of sexuality has not emerged as a separate, unified academic discipline like biology or psychology or sociology, although some researchers do call themselves sexologists. Rather, it tends to be interdisciplinary—a joint effort by biologists, psychologists, sociologists, anthropologists, and physicians (see Figure 1.3). This approach to understanding sexuality gives us a better view of humans in all their sexual complexity.

THE MEDIA

In terms of potency of influence, the mass media in North America today may play the same role that religion did in previous centuries. Canadians are influenced both by Canadian programs and, perhaps more so, by American prime-time television. Across a typical week in 2005, 35 percent of programs showed some sexual behaviour—ranging from kissing to intercourse—up from 23 percent in 1998 (Kunkel et al., 2005). In a study of sex on the soaps, the most frequent sexual activity was heterosexual intercourse between unmarried persons (Greenberg & Busselle, 1996)—although this pattern is far from what occurs in the real world, where marital sex is most frequent. References to safer sex—for prevention of both sexually transmitted infections and pregnancy—are rare. Only 2 percent of sexual scenes portray any sexual precautions (Kunkel et al., 2005). Nonetheless, references to safer sex are increasing (Kaiser Family Foundation, 2003). Many Canadians (47 percent) think there is too much sexually explicit programming on prime-time TV (*Maclean's*/Global Poll, 2000).

In short, the average Canadian's views about sexuality are likely to be much more influenced by the mass media than by scientific findings. Communications theorists believe that the media can have three types of influence (Brown, 2002). The first, called cultivation, refers to the notion that people begin to think that what they see on television and in other media really represents the mainstream of what happens in our culture (Gerbner et al., 2002). For example, university students who watch the soaps are more likely than non-viewing students to overestimate the incidence of divorce. The second influence is agenda-setting. News reporters select what to report and what to ignore and, within the stories they report, what to emphasize. For example, in 1998 the U.S. media chose to highlight the sexual dalliances of President Bill Clinton, suggesting to the public that these matters were important. In contrast, the Canadian media have rarely focused on the sexual activities of Canadian politicians. The media in many ways tell us what the agenda is to which we should pay attention. The third influence is social learning, a theory we will take up in detail in Chapter 2. The contention here is that characters on television, in the movies, or in romance novels may serve as models whom we imitate, perhaps without even realizing it. Research has found, for example, that teens who watch more sexy television engage in first intercourse earlier than do other teens (Brown, 2002).

The *Internet* is the newest, and perhaps most powerful, mass media influence. Computer and Internet use is spreading more rapidly than any previous technology, and it is estimated that by 2010 most North American homes with children will have Internet access (Brown,

Cultivation: In communications theory, the view that exposure to the mass media makes people think that what they see there represents the mainstream of what really occurs.

Agenda-setting: In communications theory, the idea that the media define what is important and what is not by which stories they cover.

Social learning: In communications theory, the idea that the media provide role models whom we imitate.

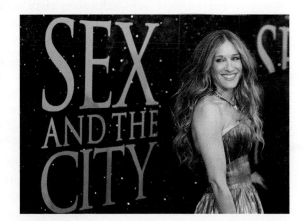

Figure 1.4 The explicit sexual content of the cable TV series *Sex and the City* didn't prevent its star Sarah Jessica Parker from winning a Golden Globe award for her performance in the show. The series also spawned a recent film.

2002). In 2005, 68 percent of Canadian adults were online, for personal non-business reasons (Statistics Canada, 2006); use of Facebook and MySpace and viewing videos on YouTube are especially common among youth. As we will discuss in later chapters, the Internet has the potential for both positive and negative effects on sexual health. A number of sites, such as that for the Society of Obstetricians and Gynaecologists of Canada (see http://sexualityandu.ca), provide excellent information about sexuality and promote sexual health. At the same time, a well-sampled study of youth between the ages of 10 and 17 who use the Internet regularly indicated that approximately 20 percent had received at least one sexual solicitation or approach over the Internet in the last year, and 3 percent had received an aggressive sexual solicitation, in which the initiator asked to meet the recipient somewhere or sent him or her money or gifts (Finkelhor et al., 2000).

In the chapters that follow, we will examine the content of the media on numerous sexual issues and we will consider what the effects of exposure to this media content might have on viewers.

Let us now consider the perspectives on sexuality that are provided by scientific observations of humans in a wide variety of societies.

CROSS-CULTURAL PERSPECTIVES ON SEXUALITY

Culture: Traditional ideas and values passed down from generation to generation within a group and transmitted to members of the group by symbols (such as language).

Humans are a cultural species (Heine & Norenzayan, 2006). Although some other species are capable of learning from others, humans are unique in the way that cultural learning accumulates over time. What do anthropologists mean by the term "culture"? Generally, **culture** refers to traditional (that is, passed down from generation to generation) ideas and values transmitted to members of the group by symbols (such as language). These ideas and values then serve as the basis for patterns of behaviour observed in the group (Frayser, 2004; Kroeber & Kluckhohn, 1963).

Figure 1.5 Margaret Mead, an anthropologist who contributed much to the early cross-cultural study of sexuality.

Ethnocentrism: The tendency to regard one's own ethnic group and culture as superior to others and to believe that its customs and way of life are the standards by which other cultures should be judged.

Ethnocentrism tends to influence people's understanding of human sexual behaviour. Most of us have had experience with sexuality in only one culture—Canada, for example—and we tend to view our sexual behaviour as the only pattern in existence, and certainly as the only "natural" pattern. But anthropologists have discovered that there are wide variations in sexual behaviour and attitudes from one culture to the next. There are even significant differences between Canada and the United States. For example, Canadians tend to have more permissive attitudes toward sexuality than Americans. In 2005, 80 percent of Canadians, compared to 64 percent of Americans, approved of premarital sex. Similarly, 60 percent of Canadians, but only 38 percent of Americans, approved of same-sex relationships (Bibby, 2006). Considering variations across cultures should help us to put our own sexual behaviour in perspective.

Incest taboo: A regulation prohibiting sexual interaction between close blood relatives, such as brother and sister or father and daughter.

The major generalization that emerges from cross-cultural studies is that all societies regulate sexual behaviour in some way, though the exact regulations vary greatly from one culture to the next (DeLamater, 1987). Apparently, no society has seen fit to leave sexuality totally unregulated, perhaps fearful that social disruption would result. As an example, **incest taboos** are nearly universal: Sex is regulated in that intercourse between blood relatives is prohibited (Gregersen, 1996). Most societies also condemn forced sexual relations such as rape.

Beyond this generalization, though, regulations vary greatly from one society to the next, and sexual behaviour and attitudes vary correspondingly (see In Focus 1.2). In fact, a recent comparison of data from 59 countries concluded that there are currently large differences in patterns of sexual behaviour from one region of the world to another (Wellings et al., 2006). Let's look at the ways in which various societies treat some key areas of human sexual behaviour.

VARIATIONS IN SEXUAL TECHNIQUES

Kissing is one of the most common sexual techniques in our culture. It is also very common in most other societies (Gregersen, 1996). There are a few societies, though, in which kissing is unknown. For example, when the Thonga of Africa first saw Europeans kissing, they laughed and said, "Look at them; they eat each other's saliva and dirt." There is also some variation in techniques of kissing. For example, among the Kwakiutl of British Columbia and the Trobriand Islanders, kissing consisted of sucking the lips and tongue of the partner, permitting saliva to flow from one mouth to the other.

Cunnilingus (mouth stimulation of the female genitals) is fairly common in our society, and it occurs in a few other societies as well, especially in the South Pacific. A particularly interesting variation is reported on the island of Ponape; the man places a fish in the woman's vulva and then gradually licks it out prior to coitus.

Inflicting pain on the partner is also a part of the sexual technique in some societies. The Apinaye woman of the Brazilian highlands may bite off bits of her partner's eyebrows, noisily spitting them aside. Ponapean men usually tug at the woman's eyebrows, occasionally yanking out tufts of hair. People of various societies bite their partners to the point of drawing blood and leaving scars; most commonly men and women mutually inflict pain on each other (Frayser, 1985).

The frequency of intercourse for married couples varies considerably from one culture to the next. The lowest frequency seems to be among the Irish natives of Inis Beag, discussed in In Focus 1.2, who engage in intercourse perhaps only once or twice a month; however, the anthropologists who studied them were unable to determine exactly how often couples did have sex because so much secrecy surrounds the act. At the opposite extreme, the Mangaians, also described in In Focus 1.2, have intercourse several times a night, at least among the young. The Santals of southern Asia engage in sexual intercourse as often as five times per day every day early in marriage (Gregersen, 1996). Surveys of Canadian sexuality in the 1990s indicated that our frequency of intercourse was then about in the middle compared with other societies (e.g., *Maclean's*/CBC Poll, 1999).

Very few societies encourage people to engage in sexual intercourse at particular times (Frayser, 1985). Instead, most groups have restrictions that forbid intercourse at certain times or in certain situations. For example, almost every society has a postpartum sex taboo—that is, a prohibition on sexual intercourse for a period of time after a woman has given birth, with the taboo lasting from a few days to more than a year (Gregersen, 1996).

MASTURBATION

Attitudes toward masturbation, or sexual self-stimulation of the genitals, vary widely across cultures. Some societies tolerate and some encourage masturbation during childhood and adolescence, whereas others condemn the practice at any age. Almost all human societies express some disapproval of adult masturbation, ranging from mild ridicule to severe punishment (Gregersen, 1996). Yet at least some adults in all societies appear to practise it.

Female masturbation certainly occurs in other societies. The African Azande woman uses a phallus made of a wooden root; however, if her husband catches her masturbating, he may beat her severely. The following is a description of the Lesu of the South Pacific, one of the few societies that express no disapproval of adult female masturbation:

A woman will masturbate if she is sexually excited and there is no man to satisfy her. A couple may be having intercourse in the same house, or near enough for her to see them, and she

Masturbation:
Self-stimulation of the genitals to produce sexual arousal.

IN FOCUS 1.2

How Much Can Behaviours Vary? Sexuality in Three Societies

Inis Beag

Inis Beag is a small island off the coast of Ireland. It is probably one of the most naïve and sexually repressive societies in the world.

The people of Inis Beag seem to have no knowledge of a number of sexual activities, such as French kissing, mouth stimulation of the breast, or hand stimulation of the partner's penis, much less oral sex or homosexuality. Sex education is virtually non-existent; parents do not seem to be able to bring themselves to discuss such embarrassing matters with their children, and they simply trust that, after marriage, nature will take its course.

Menstruation and menopause are sources of fear for the island women because they have no idea of their physiological significance. It is commonly believed that menopause can produce insanity; in order to ward off this condition, some women have retired from life in their mid-40s, and a few have confined themselves to bed until death years later.

The men believe that intercourse is hard on one's health. They will desist from sex the night before they are to do a job that takes great energy. They do not approach women sexually during menstruation or for months after childbirth; a woman is considered dangerous to the male at these times.

The islanders abhor nudity. Only babies are allowed to bathe while nude. Adults wash only the parts of their bodies that extend beyond their clothing—face, neck, lower arms, hands, lower legs, and feet. The fear of nudity has even cost lives. Sailors who never learned to swim because it involved wearing scanty clothing have drowned when their ships have sunk.

Premarital sex is essentially unknown. In marital sex, foreplay is generally limited to kissing and rough fondling of the buttocks. The husband invariably initiates the activity. The male-on-top is the only position used, and both partners keep their underwear on during the activity. The man has an orgasm quickly and falls asleep immediately. Female orgasm either is believed not to exist or is considered deviant.

Mangaia

In distinct contrast to Inis Beag is Mangaia, an island in the South Pacific. For the Mangaians, sex—for pleasure and for procreation—is a principal interest.

The Mangaian boy first hears of masturbation when he is about seven, and he may begin to masturbate at age eight or nine. At around age 13 he undergoes the superincision ritual (in which a slit is made on the top of the penis, along its entire length). This ritual initiates him into manhood; more important, however, the expert who performs the superincision gives him sexual instruction. He shows the boy how to perform oral sex, how to kiss and suck breasts, and how to bring his partner to

may thus become aroused. She then sits down and bends her right leg so that her heel presses against her genitalia. Even young girls of about six years may do this quite casually as they sit on the ground. The women and men talk about it freely, and there is no shame attached to it. It is a customary position for women to take, and they learn it in childhood. They never use their hands for manipulation. (Powdermaker, 1933, pp. 276–277)

PREMARITAL AND EXTRAMARITAL SEX[3]

Societies differ considerably in their rules regarding premarital sex (Frayser, 1985). At one extreme are the Marquesans of eastern Polynesia. Both boys and girls in that culture have participated in a wide range of sexual experiences before puberty. Their first experience

[3]Although marriage as an institution is found in most, if not all, cultures, some people never marry or marry late in life. Some people choose not to marry; others are in same-sex relationships and cannot marry legally, as many countries do not permit same-sex marriages. For these individuals the terms "premarital sex" and "extramarital sex" do not have much meaning. For example, is a 50-year-old person who has never been married engaging in premarital sex? Is a person who is having sex outside a common-law relationship engaging in extramarital sex? Nonetheless, the pervasiveness of marriage as an institution (for example, 90 to 95 percent of Canadians marry) makes it meaningful to discuss cultural rules regarding premarital and extramarital sex.

orgasm several times before he has his own. About two weeks after the operation, the boy has intercourse with an experienced woman, which removes the scab from the superincision. She provides him with practice in various acts and positions and trains him to hold back until he can have simultaneous orgasms with his partner.

After this, the Mangaian boy actively seeks out girls, or they seek him out; soon he has coitus every night. The girl, who has received sexual instruction from an older woman, expects demonstration of the boy's virility as proof of his desire for her. What is valued is the ability of the male to continue vigorously the in-and-out action of coitus over long periods of time while the female moves her hips "like a washing machine." Nothing is despised more than a "dead" partner who does not move. A good man is expected to continue his actions for 15 to 30 minutes or more.

Between the ages of 13 and 20, the average "nice" girl will have three or four successive boyfriends; the average boy may have ten or more girlfriends. Mangaian parents encourage their daughters to have sexual experiences with several men. They want them to find marriage partners who are congenial.

At around age 18, the Mangaians typically have sex most nights of the week, with about three orgasms per night. By about age 48, they have sex two or three times per week, with one orgasm each time.

All women in Mangaia apparently learn to have orgasms. Bringing his partner to orgasm is one of the man's chief sources of sexual pleasure.

Mehinaku

Between Inis Beag, where there is little sex and plenty of anxiety, and Mangaia, where there is plenty of sex and little anxiety, is Mehinaku, where there is plenty of sex and plenty of anxiety.

In the central Brazilian village of Mehinaku, sex is believed to be very fascinating and the culture is highly eroticized. There is an openness with children about sex, and children can easily list the names of their parents' extramarital lovers, who are typically many. The men have a very high libido, leading them to compete with each other for women's sexual favours by bringing small gifts such as fish.

On the other hand, the culture is very gender-segregated. There is a men's house and if a woman enters it and sees what she is forbidden to see, she is taken to the woods and gang raped, in a culture that is otherwise very non-violent. Mehinaku women are believed to have a much weaker sex drive than men, and there seems to be no recognition of female orgasm. Women's menstruation is believed to be dangerous.

The dreams and mythic stories told by the people testify to their sexual anxieties—for example, those in myths who engage in extramarital sex typically die in fantastic ways. In reality, the people continue with a great deal of sexual activity while feeling intense ambivalence and anxiety about it.

Sources: Messenger, 1993, in Suggs & Miracle, 1971; Marshall & Suggs, 1985; Gregor, 1985.

with intercourse occurs with a heterosexual partner who is 30 to 40 years old. Mothers are proud if their daughters have many lovers. Only later does marriage occur. In contrast are the Egyptians of Siwa. In this culture a girl's clitoris is removed at age seven or eight in order to decrease her potential for sexual excitement and intercourse. Premarital intercourse is believed to bring shame on the family. Marriage usually occurs around the age of 12 or 13, shortening the premarital period and any temptations it might contain.

These two cultures are fairly typical of their regions. According to one study, 90 percent of Pacific Island societies permit premarital sex, as do 88 percent of African and 82 percent of Eurasian societies; however, 73 percent of Mediterranean societies prohibit premarital sex (Frayser, 1985).

Extramarital sex is more complex and conflicted for most cultures. Extramarital sex ranks second only to incest as the most strictly prohibited type of sexual contact. One study found that it was forbidden for one or both partners in 74 percent of the cultures surveyed (Frayser, 1985). Even when extramarital sex is permitted, it is subjected to regulations; the most common pattern of restriction is to allow extramarital sex for husbands but not wives.

SEX WITH SAME-SEX PARTNERS

A wide range of attitudes toward same-sex sexual expression exists in various cultures (Murray, 2000). At one extreme are societies that strongly disapprove of same-sex sexual behaviour for people of any age. In contrast, some societies tolerate the behaviour for children but disapprove of it in adults. Still other societies actively encourage all their male members to engage in some same-sex sexual behaviour, usually in conjunction with puberty rites (Herdt, 1984). A few societies have a formalized role for the adult gay man that gives him status and dignity.

While there is wide variation in attitudes toward homosexuality and in same-sex sexual activity, three general rules do seem to emerge (Ford & Beach, 1951; Murray, 2000; Whitam, 1983): (1) No matter how a particular society views homosexuality, the behaviour always occurs in at least some individuals—that is, same-sex sexuality is found universally in all societies; (2) males are more likely to engage in same-sex sexual activity than females; and (3) same-sex sexual activity is never the predominant form of sexual behaviour for adults in any of the societies studied.

In Canada and other Western nations, we hold an unquestioned assumption that people have a sexual identity, whether gay, lesbian, bisexual, or heterosexual. Yet sexual identity as an unvarying, lifelong characteristic of the self is unknown or rare in some cultures, such as Indonesia (Stevenson, 1995). In those cultures, the self and individualism, so prominent in Canadian culture, are downplayed. Instead, a person is defined in relation to others and behaviour is seen as much more the product of the situation than of lifelong personality traits. In such a culture, having a "gay identity" just doesn't make sense. Sexual orientation is discussed in detail in Chapter 14.

STANDARDS OF ATTRACTIVENESS

In all human societies physical characteristics are important in determining whom one chooses as a sex partner. What is considered attractive varies considerably, though. For example, the region of the body that is judged for attractiveness varies from one culture to the next. For some peoples, the shape and colour of the eyes are especially significant. For others, the

(a)

(b)

Figure 1.6 Cross-cultural differences, cross-cultural similarities. *(a)* Woman of West Africa. *(b)* Miss Canada 2008, Samantha Tajik. The custom of female adornment is found in most cultures, although the exact definition of beauty varies from culture to culture.

shape of the ears is most important. Some societies go directly to the heart of the matter and judge attractiveness by the appearance of the external genitals. In a few societies, elongated labia majora (the pads of fat on either side of the vaginal opening in women) are considered sexually attractive, and it is common practice for a woman to pull on hers in order to make them longer. Among the Nawa women of Africa, elongated labia majora are considered a mark of beauty and are quite prominent.

Our society's standards are in the minority in one way: In most cultures, a plump woman is considered more attractive than a thin one. In Canada and other Western nations today, the ideal for women, particularly as portrayed in the media, is unrealistically and unhealthily thin.

One standard does seem to be a general rule: A poor complexion is considered unattractive in the majority of human societies. Research on sexual attraction is discussed in detail in Chapter 12.

REGIONAL AND CULTURAL VARIATION IN SEXUALITY

The discussion so far may have seemed to imply that there is one uniform standard of sexual behaviour in Canada and that all Canadians behave alike sexually. In fact, though, the Canadian population is composed of many cultural and ethnic groups. There are both differences and similarities among these groups in sexual behaviour. Some of these subcultural variations can be classified as social-class differences and some as ethnic differences. Here we discuss variations in sexual behaviour and attitudes between French-speaking and English-speaking Canadians of European descent. We also examine sexual behaviour and attitudes among Aboriginal Canadians, and in six of the largest ethnocultural communities in Canada.

SOCIAL CLASS AND SEX

Table 1.1 shows data on some social-class variations in sexuality. There was little difference in the percentage of respondents who had engaged in sexual intercourse ever or in the past 12 months based on social class—most respondents in all social classes had done so. However, respondents from the lower social classes were more likely to have first engaged in intercourse when they were 15 years old or younger and to have had one or more sexually transmitted infections. There also are some differences in sexual behaviour across social classes. A study conducted in Montreal using a francophone sample found that manual workers engaged in both sexual intercourse and oral–genital sex more frequently than respondents with office and professional jobs (Sampson et al., 1991, 1993).

Table 1.1 Social-Class Variations in Sexual Behaviour in Canada			
	Low and Low-Middle Income	Middle Income	Upper-Middle and High Incomes
Percentage who have ever had intercourse			
Men	87%	91%	94%
Women	93%	92%	94%
Percentage who had intercourse in the last 12 months			
Men	90%	92%	94%
Women	78%	88%	92%
Percentage who had first sexual intercourse before age 16			
Men	31%	23%	19%
Women	23%	16%	12%
Percentage who had at least one sexually transmitted infection			
Men	4%	1%	1%
Women	3%	2%	2%

Source: Adapted from Statistics Canada *National Population Health Survey,* 1996–1997, http://www.lib.unb.ca/gddm/data/NPHS.html#nps96. Percentages are based only on members of the sample who responded to the question.

REGIONAL DIFFERENCES IN SEXUALITY

A number of surveys have examined whether there are regional differences in sexual behaviour and attitudes from province to province. These results are based on self-report and typically are conducted in English or French. Therefore, they may not be totally accurate. For example, respondents may not remember their behaviour accurately, or may give the answer that they think is more socially acceptable (see Chapter 3 for a discussion of possible biases in self-report data). The results of various surveys do not show consistent differences from one province to another, with one exception: Francophones in Quebec often are more liberal in their attitudes and behaviour than Canadians in other provinces. In Focus 1.3 discusses the differences between Quebec and the rest of Canada in more depth.

COMPARING CANADA AND THE UNITED STATES

The United States is our closest neighbour. Yet, when it comes to sexual attitudes and behaviour, Canada and the United States are quite different. Some of these differences are depicted in Table 1.2. In general, Canadians are more liberal than Americans are. For example, we are more accepting of premarital sex, abortion, homosexuality, same-sex marriage, and even extramarital sex. Canadians also have lower rates of adolescent pregnancy and sexually transmitted infections and higher rates of breast-feeding than Americans.

Table 1.2 Percentage of Canadians and Americans Who Approve of Various Issues		
	Canada	*United States*
Premarital sex	80%	60%
Legal abortion upon demand	43%	27%
Homosexual relations	60%	38%
Same-sex marriage	48%	39%
Extramarital sex	14%	7%

Source: Bibby, R.W. (2006). *The Boomer Factor: What Canada's most famous generation is leaving behind* (pp. 28, 176). Toronto: Bastian Books.

ABORIGINAL PEOPLES AND SEXUALITY

Before contact with Europeans, most First Nations populations were considered sexually permissive by European standards. For example, among First Nations peoples, women were encouraged to take the initiative, and premarital and extramarital sex were acceptable. In many cultures, gay men, lesbians, and people who assumed cross-gender roles were respected and admired (McCormick, 1993). Sex was considered a magical spiritual gift to humans designed to bring pleasure—a gift that should be used only with respect for others and for ourselves (Newhouse, 1998).

Depictions of Aboriginal peoples in the popular media over the last century have portrayed them as noble savages who are both exotic and erotic (Bird, 1999). Aboriginal males have been shown nearly naked, emphasizing well-developed, masculine bodies. In romance novels of the 1990s, they became cultural icons for vanishing standards of masculinity—handsome and virile, yet tender and vulnerable and magnificent lovers for white women (Van Lent, 1996). Aboriginal women, although less visible in the popular media, are stereotyped as princesses or squaws (Bird, 1999). The princess is noble, beautiful, and erotic. The Disney animated film *Pocahontas* features such a voluptuous princess. The stereotypical squaw, in contrast, is unattractive, uninteresting, and ignored.

Today, the sexual behaviour and attitudes of most Aboriginal communities have been influenced by the Judeo-Christian tradition, abusive experiences in residential schools, whether they live on or off the reserve, and the poor economic and crowded social conditions

IN FOCUS 1.3

Is Quebec a Sexually Distinct Society?

Prior to the 1950s, the attitudes of Quebec franco-phones on sexual issues were very conservative. For example, talking about sex, except in the context of reproduction, was seen as taboo. However, starting at the end of the 1950s Quebec began a period of rapid social change sometimes called the "Quiet Revolution," which included liberalization of attitudes and behaviour. The revolution in sexual attitudes and behaviour began in the 1970s (Gemme & Badeau, 1997). Today, partly due to a decline in the influence of the Roman Catholic Church, *les Québécois(e)* tend to be tolerant of different forms of sexual expression. Just how different are Quebecers from Canadians in other parts of Canada?

Table 1.3 compares Quebecers to Canadians as a whole on a number of attitudes and behaviours related to sexuality. The data for Quebec include not only franco-phones, but also anglophones and allophones (people whose first language is neither English nor French) living in Quebec; these groups differ in many ways from *les Québécois(e)*. These data show that Quebecers are more liberal in their attitudes; for example, they are more accepting of teenagers engaging in sexual activity and they are more likely to favour same-sex marriage. The 2002 *Maclean's* Poll showed that the highest percentage of Canadians who reported having an active sex life were in Quebec; in past polls, Newfoundlanders were the most likely to report having an active sex life.

A higher percentage of Quebecers live in common-law relationships; a smaller percentage live in marital relationships. However, there are no differences between Quebecers and other Canadians in attitudes toward equal rights for gays and lesbians or in their likelihood to fantasize about a person of the same sex. In terms of sexual health indicators, Quebec women are less likely to breast-feed compared to the national average but so are women in the Atlantic provinces; the teenage pregnancy rate in Quebec is below the national average but so are the rates in the Atlantic provinces; and Quebec has a lower rate of chlamydia, a common sexually transmitted infection, than the national average, but so do Ontario and the Atlantic provinces. This suggests that Quebecers are not distinct from the rest of Canada in their likelihood of engaging in safer sex.

The only academic Department of Sexology in Canada is in Quebec, at l'Université du Québec à Montréal (UQAM). In other Canadian universities, human sexuality is studied through departments such as psychology, sociology, family studies, or education. The Sexology Department at UQAM is interdisciplinary and students can earn either a Bachelor of Sexology or a Masters of Sexology specializing in counselling or research.

So is Quebec a sexually distinct society? In terms of attitudes, the answer clearly appears to be yes. However, in terms of behaviour, the answer is less clear.

Table 1.3 Comparison of Sexuality in Quebec to Sexuality in Canada Overall

	Quebec	Canada
Parents who agree that teens should be allowed to spend the night together in their home with their sex partner	41%	13%
Parents who agree that it's appropriate for 16-year-olds to have sex outside of marriage	35%	6%
In favour of same-sex marriage	51%	43%
Think homosexuals should have the same rights as heterosexuals	77%	74%
Fantasized about having sex with a person of the same sex	5%	7%
Active sex life	76%	62%
Couples living in common-law relationships	30%	14%

Sources: NLSCY, Statistics Canada; *Maclean's*, 2000, 2002; Leger Marketing, 2004.

in which many live. Unfortunately, there have been few studies of sexual behaviour within Aboriginal communities or of the influence of Aboriginal culture on sexual behaviour. This is important because a study of Aboriginal people living on-reserve in Ontario found that cultural variables, such as the traditions of learning through the telling of stories by elders, had an important influence on sexual behaviour. For example, in many communities AIDS was seen as a gay white man's disease. As a result, safer sex behaviours such as consistent condom use are rare (Myers et al., 1994, 1999). However, data from the Canadian Community Health Survey indicate that Aboriginal youth were as likely as non-Aboriginal youth to have used a condom the last time they had intercourse (Rotermann, 2005).

ETHNOCULTURAL COMMUNITIES IN CANADA AND SEXUALITY

Changing patterns of immigration to Canada in recent years have resulted in a Canadian population that is becoming more and more ethnically diverse. According to the 2001 Census, 18 percent of Canadians were not born in Canada. There have been few studies of sexual behaviour in Canadian ethnocultural communities. However, a federally funded study, *Ethnocultural Communities Facing AIDS*, which focused on preventing HIV and AIDS in the communities with large recent immigration, examined selected aspects of sexual behaviour and attitudes in six ethnic communities. Participants were from the Chinese, South Asian, Horn of Africa, English-speaking Caribbean, North African Muslim, and Latin American communities.[4] The researchers made sure that the sample was representative of the community in terms of age and how long respondents had lived in Canada. The study used both focus groups (a research procedure in which participants discuss their answers to the research questions in small groups) and questionnaires (Cappon et al., 1996; Manson Singer et al., 1996).

The sexual behaviour of individuals from ethnic minorities is influenced both by the culture of their country of origin as well as by the process of adapting to Canada's majority culture. The study found that in many ways sexual attitudes and behaviour in these Canadian communities resemble attitudes and behaviour in the countries of origin. Generally, men and women are seen as having distinct roles, with men expected to be the head of the family and women expected to be the caregivers. Sex is not talked about in the family, even between husbands and wives. Women are expected to be passive, inexperienced, and to fulfill men's sexual needs, whereas men are expected to be sexually active and experienced. Women have little power in sexual relationships to refuse sex or to insist on condom use. In many of these communities it is expected that men, but not women, will have extramarital affairs or use prostitutes. Homosexuality is often considered abnormal and shameful. Thus, most gay men and lesbians keep their same-sex relationships or feelings secret.

Expectations regarding adolescent dating and sexual behaviour in these ethnocultural communities are different from those in the dominant Canadian culture. In general, virginity at marriage is highly valued in women but is not expected of men. In the South Asian communities, girls may not be allowed to date. On the other hand, young people do not always conform to these expectations and are adopting some aspects of the dominant culture after learning about them from friends and the media. This often creates conflict between youth and their more traditional parents. For example, Chinese youth, including girls, are becoming increasingly likely to engage in sexual activity. However, a Vancouver study found that both male and female Asian university students are more conservative and less experienced than are non-Asians in their

---

[4]Communities in Vancouver (Chinese and South Asian), Toronto (English-speaking Caribbean and Horn of Africa), and Montreal (North African Muslim and Latin American) were studied. The Chinese participants came from Hong Kong, Taiwan, and the People's Republic of China. Most of the participants from the South Asian communities were from India and Pakistan. The English-speaking Caribbean participants were from all of the English-speaking Caribbean islands and Guyana. Participants from the Horn of Africa came largely from Ethiopia, Eritrea, and Somalia. The North African Muslim participants came mostly from North Africa and the Middle East. The Latin American participants came primarily from Peru, Chile, Guatemala, and El Salvador.

(a)

(b)

Figure 1.7 The sexuality of members of different ethnic groups is profoundly shaped by their cultures. *(a)* This advertisement for a Montreal conference on childhood sexuality included a drawing of two children that showed their genitals. Consistent with cultural attitudes, the French-language newspaper in Montreal published the drawing at the left. The children's genitals are not shown in the advertisements run by the English-language newspaper in Toronto (right). *(b)* There is strong emphasis on the traditional family among Asian Canadians.

sexual behaviour. Notably, half as many Asian students (36 percent) as non-Asian students (66 percent) had engaged in sexual intercourse (Meston et al., 1996). Research in British Columbia has also shown that the attitudes of Asian Canadians become more liberal as they become more acculturated (Brotto et al., 2005, 2007; Meston et al., 1998).

Of course, there are also many ways in which the behaviour and attitudes of members of one ethnocultural community are different from those of other communities. For example, single South Asian men were more likely than single men from Latin America or the English-speaking Caribbean to report having had more than one sexual partner in the previous year. In contrast, married South Asian men were the least likely to report having had more than one partner in the previous year (Maticka-Tyndale et al., 1996).

THE SIGNIFICANCE OF CROSS-CULTURAL STUDIES

What relevance do cross-cultural data have to an understanding of human sexuality? They are important for two basic reasons. First, they give us a notion of the enormous variation that exists in human sexual behaviour, and they help us put our own standards and behaviour in perspective. Second, these studies provide impressive evidence concerning the importance of culture and learning in the shaping of our sexual behaviour; they show us that human sexual behaviour is not completely determined by biology or drives or instincts. For example, a woman of Inis Beag and a woman of Mangaia presumably have vaginas that are similarly constructed and clitorises that are approximately the same size and have the same nerve supply. But the woman of Inis Beag never has an orgasm, and all Mangaian women orgasm.[5] Why? Their cultures are different, and they and their partners learned different things about sex as they were growing up. Culture is a major determinant of human sexual behaviour.

The point of studying sexuality in different cultures is *not* to teach ourselves that there are a lot of exotic people out there doing exotic things. Rather, the point is to remind ourselves that each group has its own culture, and this culture has a profound influence on the sexual expression of the women and men who grow up in it. We will return with more examples in many of the chapters that follow.

---

[5]We like to use the word "orgasm" not only as a noun but also as a verb. The reason is that alternative expressions, such as "to *achieve* orgasm" and "to *reach* orgasm," reflect the tendency of Canadians to make sex an achievement situation (an idea to be discussed further in Chapter 9). To avoid this, we use "to have an orgasm" or "to orgasm,"

CROSS-SPECIES PERSPECTIVES ON SEXUALITY

Humans are just one of many animal species, and all of them display sexual behaviour. To put our own sexual behaviour in evolutionary perspective, it is helpful to explore the similarities and differences between our own sexuality and that of other species. (See Chapter 2 for a discussion of evolutionary perspectives). There is one other reason for this particular discussion. Some people classify sexual behaviours as "natural" or "unnatural," depending on whether other species do or do not exhibit those behaviours. Sometimes, though, the data are twisted to suit the purposes of the person making the argument, and so there is a need for a less biased view. Let's see exactly what some other species do!

MASTURBATION

Humans are definitely not the only species that masturbates. Masturbation is found among many species of mammals, particularly among the primates (monkeys and apes). Male monkeys and apes in zoos can be observed masturbating, often to the horror of the proper folk who have come to see them. At one time it was thought that this behaviour might be the result of the unnatural living conditions of zoos. However, observations of free-living primates indicate that they, too, masturbate. Techniques include hand stimulation of the genitals or rubbing the genitals against an object. In terms of technique, monkeys and non-human apes have one advantage over humans: their bodies are so flexible that they can perform mouth–genital sex on themselves. A unique form of male masturbation is found among red deer; during the rutting season they move the tips of their antlers through low-growing vegetation, producing erection and ejaculation (Beach, 1976).

Female masturbation is also found among many species besides our own. The prize for the most inventive technique probably should go to the female porcupine. She holds one end of a stick in her paws and walks around while straddling the stick; as the stick bumps against the ground, it vibrates against her genitals (Ford & Beach, 1951). Human females are apparently not the only ones to enjoy vibrators.

(a)

(b)

Figure 1.8 The sexual behaviour of animals. *(a)* Females have various ways of expressing choice. Here a female Barbary macaque presents her sexual swelling to a male. He seems to be interested. (Photograph by Frans deWaal.) *(b)* Same-gender sexuality in animals: Two male giraffes "necking." They rub necks and become aroused. (Photograph by Stephen G. Maka.)

SAME-SEX SEXUAL BEHAVIOUR

Same-sex behaviour is found in many species besides our own (Bagemihl, 1999; Vasey, 2002; Wallen & Parsons, 1997). Indeed, observations of other species indicate that our basic mammalian heritage is bisexual, composed of both heterosexual and homosexual elements (Bagemihl, 1999).

Males of many species will mount other males, and anal intercourse has been observed in some male primates (Wallen & Parsons, 1997). Among domestic sheep, 9 percent of adult males strongly prefer other males as sex partners (Ellis, 1996; Roselli et al., 2002). In a number of primate species, including bonobos and Japanese macaques, females mount other females and derive sexual rewards from these behaviours (Vasey et al., 2006; Vasey & Duckworth, 2006).

IN WHAT WAYS ARE HUMANS UNIQUE?

Are humans in any way unique in their sexual behaviour? The general trend, as we move from lower species such as fish or rodents to higher species like primates, is for sexual behaviour to be more hormonally (instinctively) controlled among the lower species and to be controlled more by the brain (and therefore by learning and social content) in the higher species (Wallen, 2001). However, environmental influences are much more important in shaping primate—especially human—sexual behaviour than they are in shaping the sexual behaviour of other species.

Nonetheless, research has shown that in addition to instinctual or hard-wired preferences (such as the preference of males for sexually receptive females), learning affects the sexual preferences of a number of different species. For example, Quebec psychologist James Pfaus and his colleagues have shown in laboratory experiments that male rats can be conditioned (see Chapter 3 for an explanation of classical conditioning) to prefer female rats with a particular neutral odour, such as almond or lemon extract, to unscented females by first pairing the neutral odour with ejaculation (Kippin et al., 1998; Pfaus et al., 2003). They have found similar results in female rats.

An illustration of this fact is provided by studies of the adult sexual behaviour of animals raised in deprived environments. If mice are reared in isolation, their adult sexual behaviour will nonetheless be normal (Scott, 1964). But if rhesus monkeys are reared in isolation, their adult sexual behaviour is severely disturbed, to the point that they may be incapable of reproducing (Harlow et al., 1963). Thus, environmental experiences are crucial in shaping the sexual behaviour of higher species, particularly humans; for us, sexual behaviour is a lot more than just "doin' what comes naturally."

Female sexuality provides a particularly good illustration of the shift in hormonal control from lower to higher species. Throughout most of the animal kingdom, female sexual behaviour is strongly controlled by hormones. In virtually all mammals, females do not engage in sexual behaviour at all except when they are in "heat" (estrus), which is a particular hormonal state. In contrast, human females are capable of engaging in sexual behaviour—and actually do engage in it—during any phase of their hormonal (menstrual) cycle. Thus, the sexual behaviour of the human female is not nearly as much under hormonal control as that of females of other species.

Traditionally, it was thought that female orgasm is unique to humans and does not exist in other species. Then some studies found evidence of orgasm in macaques (monkeys), as indicated by the same physiological responses indicative of orgasm in human females—specifically, increased heart rate and uterine contractions—in stump-tailed macaques as a result of female same-sex sexual activity, and perhaps for heterosexual activity as well (Burton, 1970; Goldfoot et al., 1980; Zumpe & Michael, 1968). Thus, humans can no longer claim to have a corner on the female orgasm market. This fact has interesting implications for understanding the evolution of sexuality. Perhaps the higher species, in which the females are not driven to sexual activity by their hormones, have the pleasure of orgasm as an incentive.

In summary, then, there is little in human sexuality that is completely unique to humans, except for elaborate, complex cultural influences. In other respects, we are on a continuum with other species.

THE NON-SEXUAL USES OF SEXUAL BEHAVIOUR

Two male baboons are locked in combat. One begins to emerge as the victor. The other "presents" (the "female" sexual posture, in which the rump is directed toward the other and is elevated somewhat).

Two male monkeys are members of the same troop. Long ago they established which one is dominant and which is subordinate. The dominant one mounts (the "male" sexual behaviour) the subordinate one.

These are examples of animals sometimes using sexual behaviour for non-sexual purposes (Small, 1993; Wallen & Zehr, 2004). Commonly, such behaviour signals the end of a fight, as in the first example. The loser indicates his surrender by presenting, and the winner signals victory by mounting. Sexual behaviours can also symbolize an animal's rank in a dominance hierarchy. Dominant animals mount subordinate ones. As another example, male squirrel monkeys sometimes use an exhibitionist display of their erect penis as part of an aggressive display against another male in a phenomenon called *phallic aggression* (Wickler, 1973).

The bonobo, an ape that is perhaps our closest genetic relative, is a particularly interesting example of the use of sexual behaviour for non-sexual purposes (de Waal, 1995). Bonobos live in female-centred, egalitarian groups and use sex for peacemaking in situations that might lead to aggression among other animals, such as situations involving food or jealousy. Since sex is a key part of their social life, bonobos engage in a wide range of sexual behaviours (including oral sex, massage of another's genitals, and intense tongue-kissing) with a wide range of partners, both same sex and opposite sex. The female is sexually attractive and sexually active during most of her cycle, rather than for just a few days around estrus.

All this is perfectly obvious when we observe it in monkeys. But do humans ever use sexual behaviour for non-sexual purposes? Consider the rapist, who uses sex as an expression of aggression against and power over a woman or another man (Holmstrom & Burgess, 1980). Another example is the exhibitionist, who uses such a display of his erect penis to shock and frighten women, much as the male squirrel monkey uses such a display to shock and frighten his opponent. Humans also use sex for economic purposes; the best examples are male and female prostitutes.

There are also less extreme examples. Consider the couple who have a fight and then make love to signal an end to the hostilities.[6] Or consider the person who goes to bed with an influential—though unattractive—politician because this gives him or her a vicarious sense of power.

You can probably think of other examples of the non-sexual use of sexual behaviour. Humans, just like members of other species, can use sex for a variety of non-sexual purposes.

THE SEXUAL HEALTH PERSPECTIVE

Sexual health: A state of physical, emotional, mental, and social well-being related to sexuality.

Sexual health is an important new concept as well as a social and political movement that is gaining momentum worldwide. Although many discussions of sexual health are actually about sexual diseases such as HIV infection, sexual health is a much broader concept that

---

[6]It has been our observation, particularly for couples in therapy, that this practice may not mean the same thing to men and women. To men it can mean that everything is fine again, but women can be left feeling dissatisfied and not at all convinced that the issues are resolved. Thus, this situation can be a source of miscommunication in heterosexual couples.

involves a vision of positive sexual health (Edwards & Coleman, 2004; Parker et al., 2004). The World Health Organization (WHO) definition, adopted in 2002, is as follows:

> Sexual health is a state of physical, emotional, mental and social well-being in relation to sexuality; it is not merely the absence of disease, dysfunction or infirmity. Sexual health requires a positive and respectful approach to sexuality and sexual relationships, as well as the possibility of having pleasurable and safe sexual experiences, free of coercion, discrimination and violence. For sexual health to be attained and maintained, the sexual rights of all persons must be respected, protected and fulfilled.

Notice that this definition includes not only sexual physical health, but also sexual mental health and positive sexual relationships. Therefore, public health efforts to prevent HIV or chlamydia infection, programs to enhance romantic relationships, and activism to end discrimination and violence against gays and lesbians, all fall under the umbrella of sexual health. Notice also that the definition includes both negative and positive rights. Negative rights are freedoms "from"—for example, freedom from sexual violence. Positive rights are freedoms "to"—for example, the freedom to experience sexual pleasure or the freedom to express one's sexuality with same-sex partners.

Using a similar framework, Health Canada (1999) proposed several principles to guide protection and promotion of the sexual health of Canadians, including:

1. All individuals are sexual beings throughout their lives.
2. Individual autonomy and responsibility should guide all aspects of decision-making.
3. The greatest benefits will be achieved by emphasizing promotion of sexual and reproductive health and prevention of problems.
4. Access to sexual and reproductive health programs and services should be equitable, responsive to diversity, and not limited because of discrimination based on gender, race, ethnicity, marital status, sexual orientation, religion, culture, language, socioeconomic status, disability, or geographic location.

With the growth of the sexual health movement, the concept of **sexual rights** has also come to centre stage and, in fact, the term is used in the WHO definition and Health Canada guidelines just mentioned. The idea here is that all human beings have certain basic, inalienable rights regarding sexuality, just as equality is guaranteed in the Canadian Constitution. The question, then, is: What are our basic sexual rights? The principles are new and evolving, but they generally include elements such as a right to reproductive self-determination and freedom from sexual violence, as well as the right to sexual self-expression (providing, of course, that it doesn't interfere with someone else's sexual rights) (Sandfort & Ehrhardt, 2004). According to the WHO, they also include the right to access reproductive health care service, receive sex education, consent or not consent to marriage, and experience a satisfying, safe and pleasurable sex life. Unfortunately, in many parts of the world people, particularly women, do not have these rights. For example, women may be forced to marry, have no recourse if they experience sexual assault, be expected to tolerate their husband having sex with sex workers even when it puts them at risk for disease, and receive little or no sex education. In order to assure that human beings and societies develop healthy sexuality, these sexual rights must be recognized promoted, respected, and defended by all societies through all means. Sexual health is the result of an environment that recognizes, respects, and exercises these sexual rights.

The concepts of sexual health and sexual rights provide yet another broad and thought-provoking perspective on sexuality.

Sexual rights: Basic, inalienable rights regarding sexuality, both positive and negative, such as rights to reproductive self-determination and sexual self-expression and freedom from sexual abuse and violence.

SUMMARY

"Sexual activity" is activity that produces arousal and increases the chance of orgasm. "Sex" (sexual behaviour and anatomy) is distinct from "gender" (being male or female).

Throughout most of human history, religion was the main source of information concerning sexuality. In the late 1800s and early 1900s, important contributions to the scientific understanding of sex were made by Sigmund Freud, Havelock Ellis, Richard von Krafft-Ebing, and Magnus Hirschfeld. These early researchers emerged from the Victorian era, in which sexual norms were highly rigid—although many people's actual behaviour violated these norms. By the 1990s, major, well-conducted sex surveys were available. Today, the mass media are a powerful influence on most North American and European people's understanding of sexuality.

Studies of various human cultures around the world provide evidence of the enormous variations in human sexual behaviour. For example, the frequency of intercourse may vary from once a week in some cultures to three or four times a night in others. All societies regulate sexual behaviour in some way. Attitudes regarding premarital and extramarital sex, masturbation, same-sex sexual behaviour, and gender roles vary considerably from one culture to the next. The great variations provide evidence of the importance of learning in shaping sexual behaviour.

Within Canada, sexual behaviour varies with one's social class and ethnic group. For example, French-speaking Canadians in Quebec are more permissive in their sexual attitudes and behaviour than are English-speaking Canadians. Canada's ethnocultural communities with large recent immigration are characterized by traditional gender roles and restrictions on female sexuality, but not on male sexuality. Asian cultures tend to be conservative about sexuality for both males and females.

Studies of sexual behaviour in various animal species show that masturbation, mouth–genital stimulation, and same-gender sexual behaviour are by no means limited to humans. They also illustrate how sexual behaviour may be used for a variety of non-sexual purposes, such as expressing dominance.

A new international movement is focusing on sexual health and principles of sexual rights.

QUESTIONS FOR THOUGHT, DISCUSSION, AND DEBATE

1. In the wide spectrum of sexual practices in different cultures, from the conservatism of Inis Beag to the permissiveness of Mangaia, where would you place Canada today? Are we permissive, restrictive, or somewhere in between? Why?

2. Research indicates that masturbation, mouth–genital stimulation, and same-sex sexual activity are present in other species besides humans. What is the significance of that finding?

3. Sally is a newspaper reporter in Captown, the provincial capital. She learns, through a trusted friend, that the highly popular premier, George Smith, has been having a long-term affair with a local woman lawyer, despite the fact that each of them is apparently happily married. Should Sally break the news in an article? In terms of communications theories, what effects might she expect her article to have on the public's attitudes about sexuality?

4. How does premarital sexual behaviour in Canada compare with premarital sex in Mangaia and Inis Beag (see In Focus 1.2 on page 12)? Which of these three cultures do you think is best for adolescents to grow up in? Why? In which of those three cultures do you think adults are likely to have the most positive feelings about their sexuality? Why?

SUGGESTIONS FOR FURTHER READING

Bagemihl, Bruce. (1999). *Biological exuberance: Animal homosexuality and natural diversity.* New York: St. Martin's. The author documents the blindness of scientists to the homosexual behaviour they observed and at the same time catalogues the extensiveness of homosexual behaviours in hundreds of species.

Bullough, Vern L. (1994). *Science in the bedroom: A history of sex research.* New York: Basic Books. Bullough is one of the most knowledgeable historians of sexuality, and this book provides fascinating details about sex research from the ancient Greeks to Hirschfeld, Ellis, and Freud and brings us up to the 1990s.

Greenberg, Bradley S., Brown, Jane D., & Buerkel-Rothfuss, Nancy L. (Eds.). (1993). *Media, sex, and the adolescent.* This is a marvellous collection of articles on the sexual content of the media to which adolescents are exposed and tells how they respond.

Gregersen, Edgar. (1996). *The world of human sexuality.* New York: Irvington. Gregersen, an anthropologist, has compiled a vast amount of information about sexuality in cultures around the world. The book also is a treasure trove of fascinating illustrations.

Zuk, Marlene. (2002). *Sexual selections: What we can and can't learn about sex from animals.* Berkeley: University of California Press. Zuk, a biologist, carefully analyzes what can be inferred from studies of the sexual behaviour of animals.

For review questions, web resources, and other learning and study tools, visit the *Understanding Human Sexuality* Online Learning Centre at www.mcgrawhill.ca/olc/hyde.

THEORETICAL PERSPECTIVES ON SEXUALITY

Chapter Highlights

ONE OF THE DISCOVERIES OF PSYCHOANALYSIS CONSISTS IN THE ASSERTION THAT IMPULSES, WHICH CAN ONLY BE DESCRIBED AS SEXUAL IN BOTH THE NARROWER AND THE WIDER SENSE, PLAY A PECULIARLY LARGE PART, NEVER BEFORE SUFFICIENTLY APPRECIATED, IN THE CAUSATION OF NERVOUS AND MENTAL DISORDERS. NAY, MORE, THAT THESE SEXUAL IMPULSES HAVE CONTRIBUTED INVALUABLY TO THE HIGHEST CULTURAL, ARTISTIC, AND SOCIAL ACHIEVEMENTS OF THE HUMAN MIND.*

FROM AN EVOLUTIONARY PERSPECTIVE, NO SINGLE DECISION IS MORE IMPORTANT THAN THE CHOICE OF A MATE. THAT SINGLE FORK IN THE ROAD DETERMINES ONE'S ULTIMATE REPRODUCTIVE FATE.†

Imagine, for a moment, that you are sitting in a bedroom watching two people making love. Imagine, too, that sitting with you in the room, thinking your same thoughts, are Sigmund Freud (creator of psychoanalytic theory), E. O. Wilson (a leading sociobiologist), Albert Bandura (a prominent social learning theorist), and John Gagnon (a proponent of script theory). The scene you are imagining may evoke arousal and nothing more in you, but your imaginary companions would have a rich set of additional thoughts as they viewed the scene through the specially coloured lenses of their own theoretical perspectives. Freud might be marvelling at how the biological sex drive, the *libido*, expresses itself so strongly and directly in this couple. Wilson, the sociobiologist, would be thinking how mating behaviour in humans is similar to such behaviour in other species of animals, and how it is clearly the product of evolutionary selection for behaviours that lead to successful reproduction. Bandura might be thinking how sexual arousal and orgasm act as powerful positive reinforcers that will lead the couple to repeat the act frequently, and how they are imitating a technique of neck nibbling that they saw in an X-rated film last week. Finally, Gagnon's thoughts might be about the social scripting of sexuality; this couple begins with kissing, moves on to stroking and fondling, and finishes up with intercourse, following a script written by society.

Some of the major theories in the social sciences have had many—and different—things to say about sexuality, and it is these theories that we consider in this chapter. Theories provide us with answers to the question "why?" We often wonder why others do or do not engage in particular sexual behaviours and relationships. We sometimes ask the "why" question about our own sexuality. Creative minds have developed theories to answer such questions. Given the diversity of human sexuality, we need a range of theories to understand it.

EVOLUTIONARY PERSPECTIVES

Evolutionary perspectives use principles from evolutionary biology to explain why certain patterns of social behaviour and psychological mechanisms have evolved in animals, including humans (Barash, 1982; Buss, 1991). The idea that some behaviours are a result of evolution is called sociobiology. Sexual behaviour, of course, is a form of social behaviour, so sociobiologists, often based on observation of other species, argue that certain sexual behaviours evolved because they gave our ancestors an evolutionary advantage. Before we proceed,

Sociobiology: The application of evolutionary biology to understanding the social behaviour of animals, including humans.

*Sigmund Freud. (1924). *A general introduction to psychoanalysis*. New York: Permabooks, 1953 (Boni & Liveright edition, 1924), pp. 26–27.

†David Buss. (2000). *The dangerous passion: Why jealousy is as necessary as love and sex*. New York: Free Press, p. 10.

Evolution: A theory that all living things have acquired their present forms through gradual changes in their genetic endowment over successive generations.

Natural selection: A process in nature resulting in greater rates of survival of those plants and animals that are adapted to their environment.

we should note that in terms of evolution, what counts is producing lots of healthy, viable offspring who will carry on one's genes. Evolution occurs via natural selection, the process by which the individuals who are best adapted to their environment are more likely to survive, reproduce, and pass on their genes to the next generation.

How do humans choose mates? One major criterion is the physical attractiveness of the person (see Chapter 12). The sociobiologist argues that many of the characteristics we evaluate in judging attractiveness—for example, physique and complexion—are indicative of the health and vigour of the individual. These in turn are probably related to the person's reproductive potential; the unhealthy are less likely to produce many vigorous offspring. Natural selection would favour individuals preferring mates who would have maximum reproductive success. Thus, perhaps our concern with physical attractiveness is a product of evolution and natural selection. (See Barash, 1982, for an extended discussion of this point and the ones that follow.) We choose an attractive, healthy mate who will help us produce many offspring. Can you guess why it is that the sociobiologist thinks most men are attracted to women with large breasts?

From this viewpoint, dating, going steady, getting engaged, and similar customs are much like the courtship rituals of other species (see Figure 2.1). For example, many falcons and eagles have a flying courtship in which objects are exchanged between the pair in midair. The sociobiologist views this courtship as an opportunity for each member of the prospective couple to assess the other's fitness. For example, any lack of speed or coordination would be apparent during the airborne acrobatics. Perhaps that is exactly what we are doing in our human courtship rituals. The expenditure of money by men on dates indicates their ability to support a family. Dancing permits the assessment of physical prowess, and so on.

Sociobiologists can also explain why the nuclear family structure of a man, a woman, and their offspring is found in every society. Once a man and a woman mate, there are several obstacles to reproductive success; two being infant vulnerability and maternal death. Infant

(a)   *(b)*

Figure 2.1 *(a)* The courtship rituals of great egrets. *(b)* Dancing is a human dating custom. According to sociobiologists, human customs of dating and becoming engaged are biologically produced and serve the same functions as courtship rituals in other species: they allow potential mates to assess each other's fitness.

vulnerability is greatly reduced if the mother provides continuing physical care, including breast-feeding. It is further reduced if the father provides resources and security from attack for mother and infant. Two mechanisms that facilitate these conditions are a *pair-bond* between mother and father, and *attachment* between infant and parent (Miller & Fishkin, 1997). Thus, an offspring's chances of survival are greatly increased if the parents bond emotionally (i.e., love each other) and if the parents have a propensity for attachment. Further, an emotional bond might lead to more frequent sexual interaction; the pleasurable consequences of sex in turn will strengthen the bond. Research with small mammals, including mice and voles, demonstrates the advantages of biparental care of offspring and the critical role of bonding (Morell, 1998).

According to this theory, parents are most interested in the survival and reproductive success of their genetic offspring. *Parental investment* refers to the behaviour and resources invested in offspring to achieve this end. Due to the high rates of divorce and remarriage in Canada, many men have both biological children and stepchildren. This situation leads to the prediction that men will tend to invest more in their genetic children than in their stepchildren. Do research results support this prediction? Fathers have been found to invest the most money in the genetic children of their current union and the least money in stepchildren from a past relationship, as would be predicted from parental investment theory. However, they spend an equal amount on their genetic children and the stepchildren of their current relationship, perhaps to cement the pair-bond with their current partner (Anderson et al., 2001).

In addition to natural selection, Darwin also proposed a mechanism that is not as much a household word, **sexual selection** (Gangestad & Thornhill, 1997). Sexual selection is selection that results from differences in traits affecting access to mates. It consists of two processes: (1) competition among members of one gender (usually males) for mating access to members of the other gender; and (2) preferential choice by members of one gender (usually females) for certain members of the other gender. In other words, in many, though not all, species, males compete among themselves for the right to mate with females; and females, for their part, prefer certain males and mate with them while refusing to mate with other males.[1] Researchers are currently testing with humans some of the predictions that come from the theory of sexual selection. For example, the theory predicts that men should compete with each other in ways that involve displaying material resources that should be attractive to women, and men should engage in these displays more than women do (Buss, 1988). Examples might be giving impressive gifts to potential mates, flashy showing off of possessions (e.g., cars, stereos), or displaying personality characteristics that are likely to lead to the acquisition of resources (e.g., ambition). Research shows that men engage in these behaviours significantly more than women do, and that both men and women believe these tactics are effective (Buss, 1988).

Many criticisms of sociobiology have been made. Some critics object to the biological determinism that it implies. Sociobiology also has been criticized for resting on an outmoded version of evolutionary theory that modern biologists consider naïve (Gould, 1987). For example, sociobiology has focused mainly on the individual's struggle for survival and efforts to reproduce; modern biologists focus on more complex issues such as the survival of the group and the species. Further, sociobiologists assume that the central function of sex is reproduction; this may have been true in our evolutionary past, but probably is not true today. Given the emphasis in the theory on reproduction, its proponents have a difficult time explaining homosexuality. Finally, recent research does not support some of the evidence that is widely cited in support of the theory. Singh (1993) reported that the winners of the Miss America contest and *Playboy*'s centrefold models have consistently had a waist-to-hip ratio of 0.7, arguing that this reflects a universal standard related to reproductive fitness. A closer look at the data shows that the average is not 0.7 but 0.66. The average for Miss America winners steadily declined from 0.78 in 1921 to 0.64 in 1986, contradicting the claim that a preference for a ratio of 0.7 was hard-wired by evolution thousands of years ago (Freese & Meland, 2002).

Sexual selection: Selection that results from differences in traits affecting access to mates.

---

[1]Sociobiologists use this mechanism to explain gender differences.

EVOLUTIONARY PSYCHOLOGY

Evolutionary psychology: The study of psychological mechanisms that have been shaped by natural selection.

A somewhat different approach is taken by evolutionary psychology, which focuses on how natural selection has shaped psychological mechanisms and processes (that is, the mind) rather than on how it has shaped sexual behaviour directly (Buss, 1991). If behaviours evolved in response to selection pressures, it is plausible to argue that cognitive or emotional structures evolved in the same way. Thus, a man who accurately judged whether a woman was healthy and fertile would be more successful in reproducing. If his offspring exhibited the same ability to judge accurately, they in turn would have a competitive advantage.

One line of research has concentrated on *sexual strategies* (Buss & Schmitt, 1993). According to this theory, females and males face different adaptive problems in short-term, or casual, mating and in long-term mating and reproduction. These differences lead to different strategies, or behaviours designed to solve these problems. In short-term mating, a female may choose a partner who offers her immediate resources, such as food or money. In long-term mating, a female may choose a partner who appears able and willing to provide resources for the indefinite future. A male may choose a sexually available female for a short-term liaison, but avoid such females when looking for a long-term mate.

Based on research with college students, Buss (1994) argued that men generally relax their standards when seeking a short-term partner, for example, requiring of them less education, honesty, and emotional stability; relaxing one's standards is assumed to make it more likely that one will find a mate. Women's preferences change less than men's do when looking for a short-term mate, and they are more likely to seek someone who has resources and is generous with them.

Buss (1994) and others have reported research data that support a number of specific predictions based on this theory. However, research using the same measures with both men and women, and controlling for confounding effects, has found that men and women are very similar in their mating preferences. Both prefer long-term mating strategies and few or no short-term partners (Pederson, Miller, Putcha-Bhagavatula, & Young, 2002). Another criticism of evolutionary psychology is that some of the characteristics we observe that are assumed to have some adaptive significance may be simply "design flaws" or side effects of other adaptations (de Waal, 2002).

PSYCHOLOGICAL THEORIES

Four of the major theories in psychology are relevant to sexuality: psychoanalytic theory, learning theory, social exchange theory, and cognitive theory.

PSYCHOANALYTIC THEORY

Psychoanalytic theory: A psychological theory originated by Sigmund Freud; it contains a basic assumption that part of human personality is unconscious.

Sigmund Freud's psychoanalytic theory has been one of the most influential of all psychological theories. Because Freud saw sex as one of the key forces in human life, his theory gives full treatment to human sexuality.

Libido (lih-BEE-doh): In psychoanalytic theory, the term for the sex energy or sex drive.

Freud termed the sex drive or sex energy libido, which he saw as one of the two major forces motivating human behaviour (the other being *thanatos*, or the death instinct).

ID, EGO, AND SUPEREGO

Id: According to Freud, the part of the personality containing the libido.

Freud described the human personality as being divided into three major parts: the id, the ego, and the superego. The id is the basic part of personality and is present at birth. It is the reservoir of psychic energy (including libido). Basically it operates on the *pleasure principle*.

Ego: According to Freud, the part of the personality that helps the person have realistic, rational interactions.

While the id operates only on the pleasure principle and can thus be pretty irrational, the ego operates on the *reality principle* and tries to keep the id in line. The ego functions to make the person have realistic, rational interactions with others.

Finally, the superego is the conscience. It contains the values and ideals of society that we learn, and it operates on *idealism*. Thus, its aim is to inhibit the impulses of the id and to persuade the ego to strive for moral goals rather than realistic ones.[2]

To illustrate the operation of these three components of the personality in a sexual situation, consider the case of the CEO of a corporation who is at a meeting of the board of directors; the meeting is also attended by her gorgeous, muscular, hot colleague. She looks at him, and her id says, "He's a real hottie. I want to throw him on the table and make love to him immediately. Let's do it!" The ego intervenes and says, "We can't do it now because the other members of the board are also here. Let's wait until 5 P.M., when they're all gone, and then do it." The superego says, "I shouldn't make love to this hot guy at all because I'm a married woman." What actually happens? It depends on the relative strengths of this woman's id, ego, and superego.

The id, ego, and superego develop sequentially. The id contains the set of instincts present at birth. The ego develops a few years later, as the child learns how to interact realistically with his or her environment and the people in it. The superego develops last, as the child learns moral values.

Erogenous Zones

Freud saw the libido as being focused in various regions of the body known as erogenous zones. An erogenous zone is a part of the skin or mucous membrane that is extremely sensitive to stimulation; touching it in certain ways produces feelings of pleasure. The lips and mouth are one such erogenous zone, the genitals a second, and the rectum and anus a third.

Stages of Psychosexual Development

Freud believed that the child passes through a series of stages of development. In each of these stages a different erogenous zone is the focus of pleasure.

According to Freud, the first stage, lasting from birth to about one year of age, is the *oral stage*. The child's chief pleasure is derived from sucking and otherwise stimulating the lips and mouth. Anyone who has observed children of this age knows how they delight in putting anything they can into their mouths. The second stage, which occurs during approximately the second year of life, is the *anal stage*. During this stage, the child's interest is focused on elimination.

The third stage of development, lasting from age three to perhaps age five or six, is the *phallic stage*. Boys' and girls' interest is focused on the genital area—the boy on his phallus (penis) and the girl on her clitoris—and they derive great pleasure from masturbating.[3] Perhaps the most important occurrence in this stage according to Freud is the development of the Oedipus complex, which derives its name from the Greek story of Oedipus, who killed his father and married his mother. In the male Oedipus complex, the boy loves his mother and desires her sexually. He hates his father, whom he sees as a rival for the mother's affection. The boy's hostility toward his father grows, but eventually he comes to fear that his father will retaliate by castrating him—cutting off his prized penis. Thus, the boy feels *castration anxiety*. Eventually, the castration anxiety becomes so great that he stops desiring his mother and shifts to identifying with his father, taking on the father's gender role and acquiring the characteristics expected of males by society. Freud considered the Oedipus complex and its resolution to be one of the key factors in human personality development.

---

[2]Fans of the television show *The Simpsons* might have noticed that Homer seems to be ruled primarily by his id and the pleasure principle, Lisa by her superego, and Marge by her ego and the reality principle.

[3]Masturbation to orgasm is physiologically possible at this age, although males are not capable of ejaculation until they reach puberty (see Chapter 5).

Superego: According to Freud, the part of the personality containing the conscience.

Erogenous (eh-RAH-jen-us) zones: Areas of the body that are particularly sensitive to sexual stimulation.

Oedipus (EH-di-pus) complex: According to Freud, the sexual attraction of a little boy for his mother.

Female Oedipus complex: According to Freud, the sexual attraction of a little girl for her father. Sometimes called the Electra complex.

The female Oedipus complex (sometimes called the Electra complex, although not by Freud) is similar to the male Oedipus complex, beginning with the girl's love for her mother and her focus on her clitoris. The little girl realizes, perhaps after observing her father or her brother, that she has no penis. She feels envious and cheated, and she suffers from *penis envy*, wishing that she too had a wonderful wand as well as the privileges that go along with being male. Thus, she shifts her desire for her mother onto her father, forming the female Oedipus complex. The girl resolves penis envy by identifying with her mother and switching her erogenous zone from her clitoris to her vagina in order to have a baby, a son, as a substitute for a penis. Unlike the boy, the girl is not driven by castration anxiety to resolve her Oedipus complex. Thus the girl's resolution of the Oedipus complex is not so complete as the boy's, and Freud wrote that for the rest of her life her superego is not as developed as men's.

Freud said that following the resolution of the Oedipus complex, children pass into a prolonged stage known as *latency*, which lasts until adolescence. During this stage, the sexual impulses are repressed or are in a quiescent state, and so nothing much happens sexually. The postulation of this stage is one of the weaker parts of Freudian theory, because it is clear from the data of modern sex researchers that children do continue to engage in behaviour with sexual components during this period (see Chapter 10).

With puberty, sexual urges reawaken, and the child moves into the *genital stage*. During this stage, sexual urges become more specifically genital, and the oral, anal, and genital urges all fuse together to promote the biological function of reproduction.

According to Freud, people do not always mature from one stage to the next as they should. A person might remain permanently fixated, for example, at the oral stage; symptoms of such a situation would include incessant cigarette smoking or fingernail biting, which gratify oral urges. Most adults have at least traces of earlier stages remaining in their personalities.

EVALUATION OF PSYCHOANALYTIC THEORY

From a scientific point of view, one of the major problems with psychoanalytic theory is that most of its concepts cannot be evaluated scientifically to see whether they are accurate. Freud postulated that many of the most important forces in personality are unconscious, and thus cannot be studied using the scientific techniques common to the twentieth century. Recent advances in our ability to image brain activity—for example, with high-powered magnetic resonance imagery—have opened the possibility of testing Freud's ideas. He believed that dreams provide a window into the person's id, and that during sleep the activity of the ego and superego are reduced. Research in the developing area of *neuropsychoanalysis* suggests that it is activity in the prefrontal area of the brain that constrains the sometimes bizarre imagery that is generated by the limbic and postcortical regions. During rapid eye movement (REM) sleep, there is a reduction of activity in the former (the ego?) and vivid and bizarre dreams are at times associated with activity in the latter (the id?) (Solms, 1997).

Another criticism is that Freud derived his data almost exclusively from his work with patients who sought therapy from him. Thus, his theory may provide a view not so much of the human personality as of *disturbances* in the human personality.

Feminists also have been critical of Freudian theory as a male-centred theory that may cause harm to women (Lerman, 1986). They object to Freud's assumption that, because they do not have a penis, women are biologically inferior to men. One could just as easily argue that men have a powerful envy of women's reproductive capacity, which is just what psychoanalyst Karen Horney (1926/1973) did when she coined the concept of *womb envy*, although this notion is equally open to criticism. They also criticize the distinction Freud made between *vaginal orgasm* (obtained through heterosexual intercourse with the penis stimulating the vagina) and clitoral orgasm (obtained through *clitoral stimulation*) in women. Research by Masters and Johnson (reviewed in Chapter 9) has shown that there is little or no physiological difference between orgasms resulting from clitoral stimulation and those resulting from heterosexual intercourse. Further, Freud's assertion that vaginal orgasm is more mature is not supported by findings that most adult women orgasm as a result of clitoral stimulation.

Nonetheless, Freud did make some important contributions to our understanding of human behaviour. He managed to rise above the sexually repressive Victorian era of which he was a member and teach that the libido is an important part of personality (although he may have overestimated its importance). His recognition that humans pass through stages in their psychological development was a great contribution. Perhaps most important from the perspective of this text, Freud took sex out of the closet, brought it to the attention of the general public, and suggested that we could talk about it and that it was an appropriate topic for scientific research.

Of course, psychoanalytic theory has evolved since Freud did his writing. Most contemporary psychoanalysts feel that Freud overemphasized the biological determinants of behaviour and instincts and that he gave insufficient recognition to the importance of environment and learning. For example, Erikson (1950), an influential theorist in developmental psychology, described how development continues throughout life rather than ending around age five. Most recent psychoanalytic theories, some of which are called object-relations theories, also describe relationships with other people, particularly the child's relationship with his or her primary caretaker (usually his or her mother or father), as crucial to development, although they have not totally abandoned Freud's view that sexuality is important to development. In particular, the type of attachment relationship children have to their mothers and fathers in infancy and childhood may have a profound effect on their romantic relationships in adulthood (see Chapter 12 for more about the attachment theory of love).

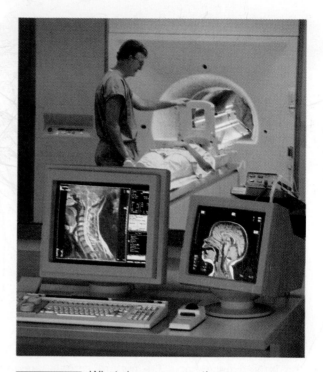

Figure 2.2 What does a magnetic resonance imaging machine have to do with psychoanalytic theory? The answer is that by studying patterns in brain waves, we can test some of Freud's ideas about the relationship between the id and the ego.

LEARNING THEORY

Although psychoanalytic and sociobiological theories are based on the notion that much of human sexual behaviour is biologically controlled, it is also quite apparent that much of it is learned. Some of the best evidence for this point comes from studies of sexual behaviour across different human societies, which were considered in Chapter 1. Here the various principles of modern learning theory will be reviewed, because they can help us understand our own sexuality (for a more detailed discussion, see Hogben & Byrne, 1998).

CLASSICAL CONDITIONING

Classical conditioning is a concept usually associated with the work of the Russian scientist Ivan Pavlov (1849–1936). Think of the following situations: You salivate in response to the sight or smell of food, you blink in response to someone poking a finger in your eye, or you experience sexual arousal in response to stroking the inner part of your thigh. In all these cases, an unconditioned stimulus (US; for example, appealing food) automatically, reflexively elicits an unconditioned response (UR; for example, salivation). The process of learning that occurs in classical conditioning takes place when a new stimulus, the conditioned stimulus (CS; for example, the sound of a bell) repeatedly is paired with the original unconditioned stimulus (food). After this happens many times, the conditioned stimulus (ringing bell) can eventually be presented without the unconditioned stimulus (food) and will evoke the original response, now called the conditioned response (CR; salivation).

As an example, suppose that Nadia's first serious boyfriend in high school always wears Erotik cologne when they go out. As they advance in their sexual intimacy, they have many

Classical conditioning: The learning process in which a previously neutral stimulus (conditioned stimulus) is repeatedly paired with an unconditioned stimulus that reflexively elicits an unconditioned response. Eventually, the conditioned stimulus itself will evoke the response.

IN FOCUS 2.1

Ritualized Same-Sex Sexual Activity in a Non-Western Society

Melanesia is an area of the southwest Pacific that includes the islands of New Guinea and Fiji as well as many others. Anthropologists' research on same-sex sexual behaviour in those cultures provides great insight into the ways in which sexual behaviours are the products of the scripts of a culture as well as of social learning theory. This research is rooted in sociological and anthropological theory. As such, the analysis focuses on the norms of the society and the symbolic meaning that is attached to sexual behaviours.

Among Melanesians, same-sex sexual behaviour has a very different symbolic meaning from the one it has in Western culture. It is viewed as natural, normal, and indeed necessary. The culture actually prescribes the behaviour, in contrast to Western cultures, in which it is forbidden or proscribed. Among Melanesians, age organizes the same-sex sexual behaviour. It is not to occur among two men of the same age. Instead, it occurs between an adolescent and a preadolescent, or between an adult man and a pubertal boy. The older partner is always the inserter for the acts of anal intercourse, the younger partner is the insertee.

Ritualized same-sex sexual behaviour serves several social purposes in these cultures. It is viewed as a means by which a boy at puberty is incorporated into the adult society of men. It is also thought to encourage a boy's growth, so that it helps to "finish off" his growth in puberty. In these societies, semen is viewed as a scarce and valuable commodity. Therefore, the same-sex sexual behaviours are viewed as helpful and honourable, a means of passing on strength to younger men and boys. As one anthropologist observed:

> Semen is also necessary for young boys to attain full growth to manhood. . . . They need a boost, as it were. When a boy is eleven or twelve years old, he is engaged for several months in homosexual intercourse with a healthy older man chosen by his father. (This is always an in-law or unrelated person, since the same notions of incestuous relations apply to little boys as to marriageable women.) Men point to the rapid growth of adolescent youths, the appearance of peach fuzz beards, and so on, as the favorable results of this child-rearing practice. (Schieffelin, 1976, p. 124)

In all cases, these men are expected later to marry and father children. These observations defy the commonly held, although not necessarily accurate, view in

---

pleasant times in the back seat of the car, where he strokes her thighs and other sexually responsive parts of her body and she feels highly aroused, always with the aroma of Erotik in her nostrils. One day she enters an elevator full of strangers in a department store, and someone is wearing Erotik. Nadia instantly feels sexually aroused, although she is not engaged in any sexual activity. From the point of view of classical conditioning, this makes perfect sense, although Nadia may wonder why she is feeling so aroused in the elevator. The thigh-stroking and sexy touching were the US. Her arousal was the UR. The aroma of the cologne, the CS, was repeatedly paired with the US. Eventually, the aroma by itself evoked arousal, the CR.

Classical conditioning of sexual arousal has been demonstrated in an experiment using male students at Queen's University as participants (Lalumière & Quinsey, 1998). Participants were first shown 20 slides of partially clothed women; a slide rated as 5 on a scale of sexual attractiveness ranging from 1 to 10 was selected as the target slide. Ten participants were shown the target slide, followed by a 40-second segment of a sexually explicit videotape, for 11 trials; men in the control group saw only the target slide for 11 trials. Arousal was measured by a penile strain gauge, which measures the extent of engorgement or erection of the penis (see Chapter 13). Each man then rated the 20 original slides again. In the experimental group, the target slide was associated with an increase in arousal as measured by the strain gauge; in the control group, men were less aroused by the target slide following the repeated exposure. Subsequent research has also demonstrated classical conditioning of sexual arousal in

Western societies that one's sexual orientation is a permanent characteristic throughout life. This points out the contrast between sexual identity and sexual behaviour. The sexual behaviours are ones that we would surely term "homosexual," yet these cultures are so structured that the boys and men who engage in same-sex sexual behaviours do not form a homosexual identity. Indeed, the very concepts of having a "heterosexual identity" or "homosexual identity" are not present in these cultures.

Can social learning theory also explain these patterns of sexual behaviour? It can, according to the analysis of John and Janice Baldwin. First, positive conditioning in the direction of heterosexuality occurs early in life. The boy spends the first seven to ten years of his life with his family. He has a close, warm relationship with his mother. In essence, he has been conditioned to positive feelings about women.

Second, observational learning occurs. In those same first seven to ten years, the boy observes closely the heterosexual relationship between two adults, his mother and father. This observational learning can be used a decade later when it is time for him to marry and form a heterosexual relationship.

Third, the boy is provided with much cognitive structuring, a notion present in social learning theory as well as cognitive psychology. He is instructed that a boy must pass through a series of stages to become

a strong, masculine man. This includes first becoming the receptive partner to fellatio, then being the inserting partner to fellatio, marrying, defending himself from his wife's first menstruation (girls are usually married before puberty and undergo no homosexual stage of development), and then fathering a child by her. Essentially, he is given all the cognitive structures necessary to convince him that it is perfectly natural, indeed desirable, to engage in sex with men for ten years and then switch to women. Finally, there is some aversive conditioning to the homosexual behaviour that leads it to be not particularly erotic. The boy performs fellatio for the first time after several days of initiation, when he is exhausted. The activities are staged so that the boy feels fearful about it. He must do it in darkness with an older boy who may be an enemy, and he is required to do it with many males in succession. In essence, unpleasantness or punishment is associated with some of the homosexual behaviour.

Ritualized same-sex sexual behaviours are declining as these cultures are colonized by Westerners. It is fortunate that anthropologists were able to make their observations over the last several decades to document these interesting and meaningful practices before they disappear.

Sources: Baldwin & Baldwin, 1989; Herdt, 1982, 1984.

women (Hoffman, Jannsen, & Turner, 2004).

Classical conditioning is useful in explaining a number of phenomena in sexuality. One example is fetishes, explained in Chapter 15.

OPERANT CONDITIONING

Operant conditioning, a concept that is often associated with the psychologist B. F. Skinner, refers to the following process. A person performs a particular behaviour (the operant). That behaviour may be followed by either a reward (positive reinforcement) or a punishment. If a reward follows, the person will be likely to repeat the behaviour again in the future; if a punishment follows, the person will be less likely to repeat the behaviour. Thus, if a behaviour is repeatedly rewarded, it may become very frequent, and if it is repeatedly punished, it may become very infrequent or even be eliminated.

Some rewards are considered to be primary reinforcers; that is, there is something intrinsically rewarding about them. Food is one such primary reinforcer; sex is another. Male rats, for example, can be trained to learn a maze if they find a willing sex partner at the end of it. Thus, sexual behaviour plays dual roles in learning theory: It can itself be a positive reinforcer, but it can also be the behaviour that is rewarded or punished.

Simple principles of operant conditioning can help explain some aspects of sex (McGuire et al., 1965). For example, if a woman repeatedly experiences pain when she has intercourse

Operant (OP-ur-unt) conditioning: The process of changing the frequency of a behaviour (the operant) by following it with positive reinforcement (which will make the behaviour more frequent in the future) or punishment (which should make the behaviour less frequent in the future).

(perhaps because she has a vaginal infection), she will probably want to have sex infrequently or not at all. In operant conditioning terms, sexual intercourse has repeatedly been associated with a punishment (pain), and so the behaviour becomes less frequent.

Another principle of operant conditioning that is useful in understanding sexual behaviour holds that consequences, whether reinforcement or punishment, are most effective in shaping behaviour when they occur immediately after the behaviour. The longer they are delayed after the behaviour has occurred, the less effective they become. As an example, consider a young man who has had gonorrhea three times yet continues to have unprotected sexual intercourse. The pain associated with gonorrhea is certainly punishing, so why does he persist in having sex without a condom? The delay principle suggests the following explanation. Each time he engages in unprotected intercourse, he finds it highly rewarding; this immediate reward maintains the behaviour; the punishment, gonorrhea, does not occur until several days later and so is not effective in eliminating that behaviour.

A third principle that has emerged in operant conditioning studies is that, compared with rewards, punishments are not very effective in shaping behaviour. Often, as in the case of the child who is punished for taking an illicit cookie, punishments do not eliminate a behaviour but rather teach the person to be sneaky and engage in it without being caught. As an example, some parents, as many commonly did in earlier times in our culture, punish children for masturbating; yet most of those children continue to masturbate, perhaps learning instead to do it under circumstances (such as in a bathroom with the door locked) in which they are not likely to be caught.

One important difference between psychoanalytic theory and learning theory should be noticed. Psychoanalytic theorists believe that the determinants of human sexual behaviour occur in early childhood, particularly during the Oedipal complex period. Learning theorists, in contrast, believe that sexual behaviour can be learned and changed at any time in one's lifespan—in childhood, in adolescence, in young adulthood, or later. When we try to understand what causes certain sexual behaviours and how to treat people with sex problems, this distinction between the theories will have important implications.

Behaviour Modification

Behaviour modification:
A set of operant conditioning techniques used to modify human behaviour.

Behaviour modification involves a set of techniques, based on principles of classical or operant conditioning, that are used to change (or modify) human behaviour. In particular, these methods can be used to modify problematic sexual behaviours—that is, sexual disorders such as orgasm problems (see Chapter 18) or compulsive sexual behaviour (see Chapter 15). Behaviour modification methods differ from more traditional methods of psychotherapy such as psychoanalysis in that the behavioural therapist considers only the problem behaviour and how to modify it using learning-theory principles; the therapist does not worry about an in-depth analysis of the person's personality to see, for example, what unconscious forces might be motivating the behaviour. Most often treatment programs combine behaviour modification techniques with cognitive therapy approaches—called cognitive behaviour therapy.

Social Learning

Social learning theory (Bandura, 1977; Bandura & Walters, 1963) is a somewhat more complex form of learning theory. It is based on principles of operant conditioning, but it also recognizes two other processes at work: *imitation* and *identification*. These two processes are useful in explaining the development of gender identity, or one's sense of maleness or femaleness. For example, it seems that a little girl acquires many characteristics of the female role by identifying with her mother and imitating her, as when she plays at dressing up after observing her mother getting ready to go to a party. Also, various forms of sexuality may be learned through imitation. In high school, for example, the sexiest girl in the senior class may find that other girls are imitating her behaviours and the way she dresses. Or a boy might see a movie in which the hero's technique seems to "turn women on"; then he tries to use this technique with his own dates. The latter example points to the importance of mass media as a source of images of sexuality that young people imitate and personalities that they identify with.

Once a behaviour is learned, the likelihood of its being performed depends on its consequences. The young man who imitates actor Brad Pitt's romantic technique may not succeed in arousing his companion. If the behaviour is not reinforced, he will stop performing it. If it is reinforced, he will repeat it. Successful experiences with an activity over time create a sense of competence or self-efficacy at performing the activity (Bandura, 1982). If a woman feels efficacious at using the female condom, she will expend more effort (going to the drugstore to buy one) and will show greater persistence in the face of difficulty (continuing to adjust it until it fits properly) than she did before. The concept of self-efficacy has been widely used in designing health intervention programs such as those that encourage individuals to use condoms to prevent transmission of sexually transmitted infections and HIV (e.g., DeLamater, Wagstaff, & Havens, 2000). These programs provide opportunities for participants to practise the behaviours that are being promoted and be successful.

Figure 2.3 According to social learning theory, children learn about sex and gender in part by imitation. These children may be imitating their parents or a scene they have watched on TV.

Self-efficacy: A sense of competence at performing an activity.

SOCIAL EXCHANGE THEORY

An important process based on the principle of reinforcement is social exchange. Social exchange theory (Cook, 1987) has emerged out of social learning theory and uses the concept of reinforcement to explain satisfaction, stability, and change in relationships among people. It is also useful in explaining *sexuality* in close relationships (Byers & Wang, 2004). The theory assumes that we have freedom of choice and often face choices among alternative actions. Every action provides some rewards and entails certain costs. There are many kinds of rewards (money, goods, services, sexual gratification, approval by others) and costs (time, effort, money, embarrassment, emotional distance). The theory states that we are *hedonistic*; that we try to maximize rewards and minimize costs when we act. Thus, we choose actions that produce a favourable balance of rewards to costs or profits (profits equalling rewards minus costs), and avoid actions that produce poor profits.

Social exchange theory: A theory that assumes people will choose actions that maximize rewards and minimize costs.

As its name indicates, social exchange theory views social relationships primarily as exchanges of goods and services among persons. People participate in relationships only if they find that the relationships provide profitable outcomes. An individual judges the attractiveness of a relationship by comparing the profits it provides against both the profits he or she thinks should be received in the relationship as well as to the profits available in alternative relationships. The level of expected outcomes is called the *comparison level*; the level of outcomes in the best alternative relationship is called the *comparison level for alternatives* (Byers & Wang, 2004). These ideas have been applied to personal relationships. Studies of heterosexual couples in long-term relationships have found that the concepts of rewards and costs can explain whether people stay in a relationship (Rusbult, 1983; Rusbult, Johnson, & Morrow, 1986). Individuals are more likely to stay in when the partner is physically and personally attractive, when the relationship does not entail undue costs (such as high monetary commitments, broken promises, or arguments), and when romantic relationships with attractive others are not available. In other words, they are more likely to stay in a relationship when its rewards are high, its costs are low, and the comparison level for alternatives is low.

Social exchange theory also predicts the conditions under which people try to change their relationships. A central concept is *equity* or *equality* (Walster [Hatfield], Walster, & Berscheid, 1978). A state of equity exists when participants in a relationship believe that the rewards they receive from it are proportional to the costs they bear. Equality exists when both partners experience the same balance of rewards to costs (profit). If a person feels that the allocation of rewards and costs is inequitable or unequal, then the relationship is unstable. People find inequity unpleasant and may feel cheated or angry. As we will see in Chapter 12, a married person experiencing inequity may engage in extradyadic sex as a result.

Social exchange theory has also been used to explain various other aspects of sexuality in close relationships such as partner selection, sexual frequency, and sexual satisfaction (for a review, see Byers & Wang, 2004). For example, one of this book's authors, New Brunswick psychologist Sandra Byers, and her colleagues have shown that, in both dating and long-term relationships, sexual satisfaction is highest the more sexual rewards exceed sexual costs (i.e., profit is high), sexual rewards and costs compare favourably to expectations, and sexual rewards and costs between partners are equal (Byers et al., 1998; Byers & MacNeil, 2006; Lawrance & Byers, 1995).

Social exchange theories have been criticized for applying the ideas of rewards and costs to romantic relationships. Some people believe that love is not and should not be about what one can get out of a relationship (i.e., its rewards). A related criticism is that social exchange theories downplay other motivations. Because of the emphasis on rewards and costs, such theories cannot explain, for example, selfless behaviours such as altruism and martyrdom.

COGNITIVE THEORY

In the 1980s and 1990s, a "cognitive revolution" swept through psychology. In contrast to the older behaviourist tradition (which insisted that psychologists should study only behaviours that could be directly observed), cognitive psychologists believe that it is very important to study people's cognitions—that is, the way people perceive and think.

COGNITION AND SEXUALITY

Cognitive psychology can readily explain some aspects of human sexuality (Walen & Roth, 1987). A basic assumption is that what we think influences what we feel. If we think happy, positive thoughts, we will tend to feel better than if we think negative ones. Therapists using a cognitive approach believe that psychological distress is often a result of unpleasant thoughts that do not reflect reality and include misconceptions, distortions, exaggerations of problems, and unreasonably negative evaluations of events.

To the cognitive psychologist, how we perceive and evaluate a sexual event makes all the difference in the world (Walen & Roth, 1987). For example, suppose that a man engaged in sexual activity with his partner does not get an erection. Starting from that basic event, his thoughts might take one of two directions. In the first, he thinks that it is quite common for a man in his age group (fifties) not to get an erection every time he has sex; this has happened to him a few times before, once every two or three months, and it's nothing to worry about. At any rate, the oral sex was fun, and his partner had an orgasm from that, so all in all it was a nice enough encounter. In the second possibility, he began the sexual activity thinking that he had to have an erection, had to have intercourse, and had to have an orgasm. When he didn't get an erection, he mentally labelled it *impotence* and worried that he would never again have an erection. He thought of the whole episode as a frustrating disaster because he never had an orgasm. Who do you think would be more likely to experience sexual problems the next time he has sex?

As cognitive psychologists point out, our perception, labelling, and evaluation of events are crucial. In one case, the man perceived a slight problem, labelled it a temporary erection problem, and evaluated his sexual experience as pretty good. In the other case, the man perceived a serious problem, labelled it impotence, and evaluated the experience as horrible.

We shall see cognitive psychology several times again in this book, as theorists use it to understand the cycle of sexual arousal (see Chapter 9), the causes of some sexual variations such as fetishes (see Chapter 15), and the causes and treatment of sexual disorders (see Chapter 18).

Before we leave cognitive psychology, however, we will look at one cognitive theory, schema theory, that has been used especially to understand issues of sex and gender.

GENDER SCHEMA THEORY

Psychologist Sandra Bem (1981, 1993) has proposed a schema theory to explain gender-role development and the impact of gender on people's daily lives and thinking. "Schema" is a term taken from cognitive psychology. A schema is a general knowledge framework that a person has about a particular topic. A schema organizes and guides perception; it helps us remember, but it sometimes also distorts our memory, especially if the information is inconsistent with our schema. Thus, for example, you might have a "hockey game schema," the set of ideas you have about what elements should be present at the game (two teams, spectators, stands, etc.) and what kinds of activities should occur (opening face-off, occasional goal, penalties, power plays, etc.).

It is Bem's contention that all of us possess a *gender schema*—a cognitive structure comprised of the set of attributes (behaviours, personality, appearance) that we associate with males and females. Children not only learn about appropriate roles for men and women, they also learn that the distinctions between men and women and between masculine and feminine are extremely important ways to understand reality. Thus our gender schema, according to Bem, predisposes us to process information on the basis of gender. That is, we tend to think of things as gender-related and to want to dichotomize them on the basis of gender. A good example is the case of the infant whose gender isn't clear when we meet him or her. We eagerly seek out the information or feel awkward if we don't, because we seem to need to know the baby's gender in order to continue to process information about it.

Bem (1981) has done a number of experiments that provide evidence for her theory, and there are confirming experiments by other researchers as well, although the evidence is not always completely consistent (Ruble & Stangor, 1986). In one of the most interesting of these experiments, five- and six-year-old children were shown pictures of males or females performing activities that were either stereotype-consistent activities (such as a girl baking cookies) or stereotype-inconsistent (such as girls boxing) at that time (Martin & Halverson, 1983). One week later the children were tested for their recall of the pictures. The results indicated that the children distorted information by changing the gender of people in the stereotype-inconsistent pictures, while not making such changes for the stereotype-consistent pictures. That is, children tended to remember a picture of girls boxing as having been a picture of boys boxing. These results are just what would be predicted by gender schema theory. The schema helps us remember schema-consistent (stereotype-consistent) information well, but it distorts our memory of information that is inconsistent with the schema (stereotype-inconsistent).

One of the interesting implications of gender schema theory is that stereotypes—whether they are about males and females, or heterosexuals and homosexuals, or other groups—may be very slow to change. The reason is that our schemas tend to filter out stereotype-inconsistent (that is, schema-inconsistent) information so that we don't even remember it.

Schema (SKEE-muh): A general knowledge framework that a person has about a particular topic.

SOCIOLOGICAL PERSPECTIVES

Sociologists are most interested in the ways in which society or culture shapes human sexuality. (For a detailed articulation of the sociological perspective, see DeLamater, 1987; the arguments that follow are taken from that source.)

Sociologists approach the study of sexuality with three basic assumptions: (1) Every society regulates the sexuality of its members. (For a discussion of the reasons why, see Horrocks, 1997.) (2) Basic institutions of society (such as religion and the family) affect the rules governing sexuality in that society. (3) The appropriateness or inappropriateness of a particular sexual behaviour depends on the culture in which it occurs.

Figure 2.4 Families today are no longer defined by traditional stereotypes. Here, a lesbian couple enjoy the playground with their son.

THE INFLUENCE OF SOCIETY

Sociologists view societal influences on human sexuality as occurring on several levels, including the macro-level or society as a whole and the subcultural level, at which one's social class or ethnic group may have an impact on one's sexuality. Our discussion in this section emphasizes the macro-level of influence.

SOCIAL INSTITUTIONS

According to the sociological perspective, at the macro-level our sexuality is influenced by powerful social institutions, including religion, the family, the economy, medicine, and the law. Each major institution supports a sexual ideology, or discourse, about sexual activity. This ideology influences the beliefs and behaviours of those affiliated with the institution.

RELIGION

Historically, the Judeo-Christian religious tradition has been a powerful shaper of sexual norms in Western culture. A detailed discussion of that religious tradition and its teachings on sexuality is provided in Chapter 19. Suffice it to say here that the Christian religion (but not the Jewish religion) has contained within it a tradition of asceticism, in which abstinence from sexual pleasures—especially by certain persons such as monks and priests—is seen as virtuous. The tradition, at least until recently, has also been oriented toward procreation—that is, a belief that sexuality is legitimate only within traditional heterosexual marriage and only with the goal of having children, a *procreational ideology*. This view has created within our culture a set of norms, or standards for behaviour, that say, for example, that premarital sex, extramarital sex, and homosexual sex are wrong. The procreational ideology is one argument that some people use for asserting that marriage is exclusively for a man and a woman, since only a heterosexual couple can procreate without intervention. Many of these norms are changing, so that today many Canadians do not subscribe to some of these views. Further, many Canadians come from non-Christian traditions such as Judaism, Islam, Hinduism, Buddhism, or humanism that have their own views about sexuality. These traditions are also described in Chapter 20 on the Online Learning Centre.

THE ECONOMY

The nature and structure of the economy is another macro-level influence on sexuality. Before the industrial revolution, most work was done in the family unit in the home or farm. This kind of togetherness permitted rather strict surveillance of family members' sexuality and thus strict norms could be enforced. However, with the industrial revolution, people—most frequently men—spent many hours per day at work away from the home. Thus they were under less surveillance, and scripts such as extramarital affairs and same-sex sexual activity could be acted out more often.

Today we see evidence of the extent to which economic conditions can affect sexuality. For example, the average monthly wage is very low in Russia. As a result, few people can afford to use condoms and the rate of sexually transmitted infections is very high. Economic conditions have also led to a major increase in the number of prostitutes. It is difficult to support a family on the salary earned in most jobs, including professional jobs. In contrast, a Russian prostitute may earn the equivalent of the average monthly salary in just a few hours. As a result, many Russian prostitutes are highly educated and choose prostitution for financial reasons. Many Russians see prostitution as a viable way of earning a living (Byers & Slattery, 1997).

In a capitalist economy such as Canada, goods and services become commodities that can be sold for a price (an exchange). Not surprisingly, this includes sexual images and sexual gratification, giving rise to the sale of sexually explicit materials in stores and on the Internet, and commercial sex work. The increasing globalization of the economy has led to the development of sex tourism, in which affluent men and women travel to other cultures, such as Thailand, to purchase sexual gratification from "exotic" (e.g., Asian) sex workers (see Chapter 18).

THE FAMILY

The family is a third institution influencing sexuality. As we noted earlier, before the industrial revolution the family was an important economic unit, producing the goods necessary for survival. As that function waned after the industrial revolution, there was increased emphasis on the quality of interpersonal relationships in the family. At the same time, love was increasingly seen as an important reason for marriage. Thus, a triple linkage between love, marriage, and sex was formed. Ironically, the linkage eventually became a direct one between love and sex so that, by the 1970s, some people were arguing that sex outside of marriage, if in the context of a loving relationship, was permissible, as was same-sex sexual activity, again if the relationship was a loving one. This is the *relational ideology*.

The family exerts a particularly important force on sexuality through its *socialization* of children. That is, parents socialize their children—teach them appropriate norms for behaviour—in many areas, including sexuality. Others, of course, such as the peer group, also have important socializing influences.

MEDICINE

The institution of medicine has become a major influence on our sexuality over the last 100 years. Physicians tell us what is healthy and what is unhealthy. In the late 1800s, physicians warned that masturbation could cause various pathologies. Today sex therapists tell us that sexual expression is natural and healthy and sometimes even "prescribe" masturbation as a treatment. Another example is provided by childbirth; until the end of the nineteenth century, most babies were born at home, with an experienced woman (a midwife) providing assistance to the labouring woman. Today the vast majority of births occur in hospitals and birthing facilities, with medical personnel in charge. We tend to have great confidence in medical advice, so the pronouncements of the medical establishment, based on a *therapeutic ideology*, have an enormous impact on sexuality.

The increasing influence of medicine on sexuality has not been taken lying down. The domination of contemporary theory and research by the biomedical model is referred to as the medicalization of sexuality (Tiefer, 2004). Medicalization has two components: certain behaviours or conditions are defined in terms of health and illness, and problematic experiences or practices are given medical treatment. The medicalization of male sexuality is being hastened by the development of drugs to treat erectile dysfunction, and many physicians and pharmaceutical companies are seeking to medicalize female sexual dysfunction by finding a pill that will "cure" them. In contrast, the sexual health perceptive described in Chapter 1 is geared toward enhancing health and preventing illness; it takes a biopsychosocial perspective, acknowledging the interaction of biological, psychological and social factors on sexual health.

Medicalization of sexuality: The process by which certain sexual behaviours or conditions are defined in terms of health and illness, and problematic experiences or practices are given medical treatment.

THE LAW

The legal system is another institution influencing sexuality at the macro-level. From a sociological perspective, the law influences people's sexual behaviour in a number of ways. First, laws help to determine norms. Generally, we think that what is legal is right and what is illegal is wrong. In Canada, only the federal government has the right to pass criminal laws, and all sexual offences are contained in the Criminal Code of Canada and apply to all Canadians regardless of the province or territory in which they live (Roach, 2000). Provincial and municipal

Figure 2.5 In 1969, under Prime Minister Pierre Elliott Trudeau, Parliament decriminalized consensual sexual behaviour between two adults in private, including providing birth control information and engaging in anal or oral sex.

governments have the right to enact regulatory offences, such as zoning bylaws and licensing requirements, to help them govern matters within their jurisdiction, as long as these regulations do not stray into the criminal area. In contrast, in the United States and Australia, states have the right to enact criminal laws, resulting in significant differences in sexual offences from one state to another.

A major change to Canadian criminal law occurred in 1969 when, under Prime Minister Pierre Elliott Trudeau, the House of Commons passed an omnibus bill that introduced sweeping changes to the Criminal Code of Canada. This bill removed provisions that had made consensual sexual behaviours between adults done in private illegal, such as use of contraception, oral sex, and anal sex. These changes may have reflected the fact that laws that go against prevailing social or subcultural norms are often ignored, and most Canadians agreed with Trudeau when he said, "The state has no business in the bedrooms of the nation." In contrast, although arrests for criminal sexual conduct are rare in the United States, in many states oral intercourse, anal intercourse ("sodomy"), sex with someone who is legally married to someone else (adultery), cohabitation, sex between two unmarried persons ("fornication"), and sexual contact between two persons of the same gender are crimes (Posner, 1992). Thus, every day millions of Americans engage in sexual behaviours that are illegal.

Second, laws are the basis for the mechanisms of social control. They may specify punishments for certain acts and thus discourage people from engaging in them. It seems obvious that people ought to be free from sexual assault and coercion, and that children should not be exploited and, indeed, the Criminal Code of Canada has a number of laws prohibiting sexual assault of adults and children (see In Focus 2.2 on page 44). However, sex laws also have been designed to control other behaviours that are more open to debate. For example, historically one rationale for laws against adultery or desertion of a spouse was that these laws would preserve the family as the principal unit of the social order. A current example is the law prohibiting nudity in a public place. One wonders how many people would prefer to be nude at the beach if they did not fear arrest and the possible embarrassing publicity such as having their names in the paper as the result of an arrest.

Third, the law reflects the interests of the powerful, dominant groups within a society. In part, the law functions to confirm the superiority of the ideologies of these dominant groups although the arguments in favour of these laws often centre on the protection of society's morals. The concern for public morality results in laws against non-procreative sex, for reasons outlined in Chapter 19. Thus, there have been laws against same-sex sexual activity, bestiality, and contraception. In fact, same-sex couples have had to challenge the law that restricted marriage to the union of one man and one woman province by province to establish their legal right to marry (see Chapter 14). Consider also the Mormons in Canada and the United States. In the past, their religion approved of polygyny (a man having several wives). Mormons did not become the dominant group in North America. Rather, the Judeo-Christian tradition was the ideology of the dominant group and that tradition takes a dim view of polygyny. Accordingly, polygyny is illegal in both Canada and the United States. However, there is a breakaway sect of the Mormon Church, called the Fundamentalist Church of Jesus Christ of Latter Day Saints, located in Bountiful, British Columbia. This sect of about 1000 people practises polygyny. They have not been prosecuted in Canada, in part because the B.C.

government has received legal opinions that the group could likely successfully argue the law making polygyny illegal violates their Constitutional right to freedom of religion. However, polygyny may violate women's right to equality, particularly if they are pressured or forced into polygynist marriages (Department of Justice, 2007). In 2007, the American leader of the sect, Warren Jeffs, was convicted by a U.S. court of being an accomplice to rape for forcing a 14-year-old girl to marry her 19-year-old cousin. However, this was not a polygynist marriage. Canadian immigrants from some African cultures that practise polygyny cannot do so in Canada because it is illegal. Nonetheless, in keeping with ethnocultural norms, many of these men have multiple relationships although they are married to only one woman, and this is accepted in their community (Maticka-Tyndale et al., 1996).

It can also be argued that another principal source of sex laws is sexism, which is deeply rooted in Western culture. Men have historically held the power and made the laws. One scholar has suggested that the history of the regulation of sexual activity could as well be called the history of the double standard (Parker, 1983). In fact, women were considered "not persons in matters of rights and privileges" under Canadian law prior to 1929. The Supreme Court of Canada had ruled that the word "persons" in the British North America Act of 1867 referred only to men. On October 18, 1929, this decision was overturned by the Judicial Committee of the Privy Council of Britain, the highest court of appeal, which ruled that the word "persons" included both men and women. It is probably not coincidental that the movement for sex-law reform has gone hand in hand with the movement for the equality of women.

The Canadian Charter of Rights and Freedoms guarantees freedom of conscience and religion as well as equality. Therefore, criminal law cannot be based on the religious views and practices of one specific religion or be used to enforce morality per se (Roach, 2000). To the extent that today's laws are derived from the Judeo-Christian (or any other) religious tradition, they violate this principle. Increasingly, statutes in the Criminal Code that reflected specific moral values have been eliminated or rewritten, in part as the result of Supreme Court of Canada decisions based on Charter rights. For example, the Supreme Court found that statutes on abortion and those that did not extend the same benefits to same-sex couples as to heterosexual couples violated the equality guarantees in the Charter. Nonetheless, some experts argue that certain laws, such as those pertaining to prostitution and obscenity, stem from a particular moral view or ideology.

In summary, then, the sociological perspective focuses on how society or culture shapes and controls our sexual expression, at levels from institutions such as religion and the law to the interpersonal level of socialization by family and peers.

SYMBOLIC INTERACTION THEORY

An important sociological theory is symbolic interaction theory (Charon, 1995; Stryker, 1987). Its premise is that human nature and the social order are products of symbolic communication among people. A person's behaviour is constructed through his or her interactions with others. People can communicate successfully with one another only to the extent that they ascribe similar meanings to objects and people. An object's meaning for a person depends not on the properties of the object but on what the person might do with it; an object takes on meaning only in relation to a person's plans. Thus, the theory views people as proactive and goal-seeking. Achieving most goals requires the cooperation of others. This is especially true of many forms of sexual expression. For example, suppose a woman invites a person she is dating to her apartment; what meaning does this invitation have? Does she want to prolong the conversation or engage in intimate sexual activity? The woman and her partner will have to achieve an agreement about the purpose of the visit before joint activity is possible. In terms of the theory, they have to develop a *definition of the situation*. Thus, to fit their actions together and achieve agreement, people interacting with each other must continually reaffirm old meanings or negotiate new ones.

Symbolic interaction theory: A theory that proposes human nature and the social order are products of communication among people.

IN FOCUS 2.2

What Are the Sexual Offences in the Criminal Code of Canada in 2009?

Offence	Description	Sentence
Sexual assault	Sexual assault involving minor or no physical injuries to the victim	10 years
Sexual assault with a weapon or threats	Sexual assault with a weapon, threats, or causing bodily harm, use of restricted or prohibited firearm, or use of any firearm if the offence involves a criminal organization	14 years
Aggravated sexual assault	Sexual assault resulting in wounding, maiming, or disfiguring or endangering the life of the victim, use of restricted or prohibited firearm, or use of any firearm if the offence involves a criminal organization	Life
Sexual interference	Direct or indirect touching (for a sexual purpose) of a person under the age of 16 using a part of the body or an object	10 years
Invitation to sexual touching	Inviting, counselling, or inciting a person under the age of 16 to touch (for a sexual purpose) the body of any person directly or indirectly with a part of the body or with an object	10 years
Sexual exploitation	Sexual interference or invitation to sexual touching by a person in a position of trust or authority toward a young person aged 16 to 18 with whom the young person is in a position of dependency or toward a person with a disability.	10 years
Parent or guardian procuring, permitting sexual activity, or corrupting children	A parent or guardian or other person enticing or forcing a person under 18 to engage in an act prohibited under the Code or permitting them to engage in such an act on their premises	5 years
Corrupting children	Engaging in adultery or sexual immorality in the home of a child rendering the home unfit for the child	2 years
Luring a child	Using a computer to facilitate the commission of a sexual offence against a child under 16 years	10 years
Incest	When an individual has sexual intercourse with a person that has a known defined blood relationship with them	14 years
Anal intercourse	Anal intercourse between two people if either is under 18 or if more than two people take part or are present or if engaged in in a public place	10 years

Central to social interaction is the process of *role-taking*, in which an individual imagines how he or she looks from the other person's viewpoint. By viewing the self and potential actions from the perspective of the other person, we are often able to anticipate what behaviour will enable us to achieve our goal. One consequence of role-taking is self-control; we see ourselves from the viewpoint of others and so strive to meet their standards. In the process, we exercise control over our behaviour.

This perspective emphasizes the importance of symbolic communication (see Chapter 10). It alerts us to the mutual effort required to arrive at a definition of the situation. Criticisms of this theory include the fact that it emphasizes rational, conscious thought, whereas in the realm of sexuality, emotions are very important in many interactions. Also, this perspec-

Offence	Description	Sentence
Bestiality	Having sex with an animal, compelling someone to have sex with an animal, or having sex with an animal in the presence of a child	10 years
Voyeurism	Surreptitiously observing or making a visual recording of a person in a private place who is nude or engaging in sexual activity. Also anyone who distributes such visual recordings.	5 years
Communicating for the purpose of engaging in prostitution	Communicating with another person in public to buy or sell sexual services	6 months and/or $2000
Bawdy-house offences	Keeping, transporting a person to, or occupying a place used for prostitution or indecent acts	2 years
Procuring	Procuring or enticing or forcing another person to engage in prostitution or living on the income of another person's prostitution activities. Also purchasing the sexual services of someone under 18	10 years
Corrupting morals	Making, publishing, or distributing any obscene written matter, photograph, videotape, etc.	2 years
Child pornography	Possessing, making, or distributing any material that shows a person under 18 or who is depicted as being under 18 engaging in sexual activity or shows their genitals for a sexual purpose unless the material has artistic merit or an educational, scientific, or medical purpose	5–10 years
Immoral theatrical performance	Taking part in or presenting an immoral, indecent, or obscene performance or entertainment	2 years
Mailing obscene matter	Mailing anything that is obscene, indecent, immoral, or scurrilous	2 years
Indecent acts/exposure	Committing an indecent act in a public place or exposing genitals to a person under the age of 16	6 months and/or $2000
Nudity	Being nude in a public place or in public view on private property	6 months and/or $2000

Source: Martin, J. C. (2009). *Martin's annual criminal code 2009.* Aurora, Ontario: Canada Law Book Inc. http://69.17.141.139/martins_online.

tive portrays humans as *other-directed individuals,* concerned primarily with meeting other people's standards. A third criticism is that we don't always consciously role-take and communicate in an effort to achieve agreement. Sometimes we rely on past experience and habit. Situations such as these are the province of script theory.

SEXUAL SCRIPTS

The outcome of these social influences, according to symbolic interaction theories, is that each of us learns the meanings of various behaviours through our interactions with others (Plummer, 1975). We also learn a set of *sexual scripts* (Gagnon, 1990; Gagnon & Simon, 1973). The idea is that sexual behaviour is a result of extensive prior learning that teaches us sexual etiquette and how to interpret specific situations. According to this concept, we have all learned an elaborate script that tells us the who, what, when, where, and why of sexual behaviour. For example, the "who" part of the dominant Canadian script tells us that sex should occur with someone of the other gender, of approximately our own age, of our own race, and so on. Even the sequence of sexual activity is scripted. *Scripts*, then, are plans that people carry around in their heads for what they are doing and what they are going to do; they are also devices for helping people remember what they have done in the past (Gagnon, 1977, p. 6).

How can we study these scripts? How can we find out if there are widely shared beliefs about how one should behave in a specific situation? One way is to ask people to describe what one should do in such a situation. Researchers asked male and female college students to make a list of the things that a man or woman would typically do on a first date (Rose & Frieze, 1993). The hypothetical script written by many of the participants included a core sequence of acts: dress, pick up, get to know, evaluate, eat, make out, and go home. This is the first-date script. This script is also influenced by contemporary views of gender roles. Males were portrayed as proactive, taking the initiative: pick up the female, pay for the date, attempt to make out, and ask for another date. Females were portrayed as reactive: be picked up, be treated, accept or reject the male's attempt to make out, and accept or reject the invitation to another date. The widely shared nature of this script enables relative strangers to interact smoothly on their first date.

One study attempted to identify the sequence of sexual behaviours that is scripted for male–female relationships in our culture (Jemail & Geer, 1977). People were given 25 sentences, each describing an event in a heterosexual interaction. They were asked to rearrange the sentences in a sequence that was "most sexually arousing" and then to do it again to indicate what was "the most likely to occur." There was a high degree of agreement among the participants about what the sequence should be. There was also high agreement between males and females. The standard sequence was kissing, hand stimulation of the breasts, hand stimulation of the genitals, mouth–genital stimulation, intercourse, and orgasm. Does this sound familiar? Interestingly, not only is this the sequence in a sexual encounter, it is also the sequence that occurs as a couple progresses in a relationship. These results suggest that there are culturally defined sequences of behaviours that we all have learned, much as the notion of a "script" suggests.

Can you imagine a young man, on the first date, attempting oral stimulation of the young lady's genitals before he has kissed her? The idea seems amazing, and perhaps humorous or shocking. Why? Because the young man has performed Act IV before Act I.

While the first-date script provides guidelines, each couple will enact that script in a unique way. Where they go, what they talk about, what they eat or drink will reflect the desires and expectations of each, and the course of the interaction. Each couple creates their own first date, which may be memorable and become a story they tell their grandchildren, or a disaster that becomes their only date with that person.

Scripts also tell us the meaning we should attach to a particular sexual event (Gagnon, 1990). Television programs and films frequently suggest but do not show sexual activity between people. How do we make sense out of these implicit portrayals? A study of how women interpret such scenes in films found that they utilize scripts. If the film showed a couple engaging in two actions that are part of the accepted script for sexual intercourse (e.g., kissing and undressing each other) and then faded out, viewers inferred that intercourse had occurred (Meischke, 1995).

Figure 2.6 According to some people's sexual scripts, a man taking a woman to dinner is one scene of the first act in a sexual script that features intercourse as the finale.

THE SOCIAL IMPORTANCE OF SEXUALITY

Ira Reiss (1986) has proposed a sociological theory of human sexuality. Borrowing from script theory, he defines sexuality as "erotic and genital responses produced by the cultural scripts of a society" (p. 37). As he points out, a sociological theory, because it focuses on societal influences on sexuality, must be able to account for both cross-cultural variations in sexuality as well as cross-cultural universals in sexuality.

One cross-cultural universal is that all societies believe that sexuality is important. Even in cultures that are sexually repressive, sexuality is still accorded great importance as something that is dangerous and must be controlled. Why is sexuality considered so important? Many theorists have claimed that it is the link of sexuality to making babies, which is undeniably important for any society. Reiss argues against this notion, however. His explanation for the universal importance of sexuality points to two components: (1) sexuality is associated with great physical pleasure, and (2) sexual interactions are associated with great personal self-disclosure, involving not only disclosure of one's body, but in an intimate interaction, of one's thoughts and feelings as well. Humans seem to find intrinsic value in the physical pleasures of sex and in the psychic satisfaction of the self-disclosures associated with sex. Societies consider this important because they are key elements of social bonding. Recall our discussion of the importance of the pair bond to the welfare of children; the pair bond is the foundation of social structure.

Figure 2.7 According to Reiss's sociological theory, sex is important to us because it is associated with great physical pleasure and self-disclosure.

According to Reiss, sexuality is linked to the structures of any society in three areas: the kinship system, the power structure, and the ideology of the society.

First, because sexuality is the source of reproduction, it is always linked to *kinship*, and all societies seek to maintain social order through stable kinship systems. This linkage is the explanation for sexual jealousy, which is universal cross-culturally although it exists in varied forms. Jealousy is a way of setting boundaries on a relationship that is considered very important, essential enough so that it should not be breached. Marriage is typically such a relationship, and jealousy in marriage about extramarital affairs exists in all human societies. Kin define what relationships are and are not acceptable and enforce the resulting rules. Furthermore, all societies have structured ways of dealing with such jealousy. Even in societies that practise polygyny, rituals develop to minimize jealousy among the wives—for example, the husband must sleep one night with one wife, the next with another, and so on, and has violated norms if he spends two nights with the same wife. Reiss argues, therefore, that no society will be able to eliminate sexual jealousy because jealousy is a statement of the value or importance that kinship groups and individuals attach to a particular relationship such as marriage.

Second, sexuality is always linked to the *power structure* of a society. Reiss defines power as the ability to influence others and achieve one's objectives even if there is opposition from the other person. Powerful groups in any society generally seek to control the sexuality of the less powerful. Males are more powerful than females in most societies, so sexuality becomes linked to gender roles and males exercise control over female sexuality. Cross-cultural research shows, interestingly, that the closer females are in power to males in a society, the more sexual freedom women have; in societies in which women have little power, their sexuality is greatly restricted.

Third, sexuality is closely linked to the *ideologies* of a culture. Reiss defines "ideology" as fundamental assumptions about human nature. Societies define carefully what sexual practices are normal and abnormal, and which are right and wrong. Some cultures define homosexuality as abnormal, whereas others define it as normal—but the point is that all cultures define it one way or the other. Similarly, some cultures take a permissive attitude toward premarital sex both for males and females, some are permissive for males but not for females, and some are permissive for neither. A culture's ideologies define what is right and wrong sexually.

In summary, Reiss's sociological theory of sexuality argues that societies regard sexuality as important because it is associated with physical pleasure and with self-disclosure. Sexuality is tightly woven into the fabric of any society because of its links to the kinship system, to power structures, and to the ideologies of the society.

THEORETICAL PERSPECTIVES REVISITED

We started this chapter by showing how differently various theorists might view the same behaviour. Does this mean that only one of these theories is correct? No it doesn't. Rather, there is at least some truth in all of these theories. One theory might apply best in a particular situation. Another theory might play a role at a particular time in a person's life but not at another stage. Yet another theory might be best for developing treatments to help people deal with their sexual problems. Human sexual development and behaviour is complex, and there is no one theory that explains it all. As a result, we will refer to each of these theories at different places in this textbook—that is, where they provide the best explanations for people's sexual behaviour.

SUMMARY

Theories provide explanations for sexual phenomena. Sociobiologists view human sexual behaviours as the product of natural selection in evolution, and thus view these behavioural patterns as being genetically controlled. Contemporary evolutionary theorists view behaviour as the result of an interaction between evolved mechanisms and environmental influence.

Among the psychological theories, Freud's psychoanalytic theory views the sex energy, or libido, as a major influence on personality and behaviour. Freud introduced the concepts of erogenous zones and psychosexual stages of development. Learning theory emphasizes how sexual behaviour is learned and modified through reinforcements and punishments according to principles of operant conditioning. Behaviour modification techniques—therapies based on learning theory—are used in treating sexual variations and sexual disorders. Social learning theory adds the concepts of imitation, identification, and self-efficacy to learning theory. Social exchange theory highlights the role of rewards and costs in relationships. Cognitive psychologists focus on people's thoughts and perceptions—whether positive or negative—and how these influence sexuality.

Sociologists study the ways in which society influences our sexual expression. At the macrolevel of analysis, sociologists investigate the ways in which institutions such as religion, the economy, the family, medicine, and the law influence sexuality. Symbolic interaction theory draws attention to processes of communication and interaction. Sexual scripts provide us with guidelines for behaviour in many situations. Reiss's sociological theory argues that all societies regard sexuality as important because it is associated with great physical pleasure and self-disclosure.

QUESTIONS FOR THOUGHT, DISCUSSION, AND DEBATE

1. Compare and contrast how a sociobiologist, a psychoanalyst, and a sociologist would explain why people engage in premarital intercourse.

2. Of the theories described in this chapter, which do you think provides the most insight into human sexuality? Why?

3. You are visiting your married sister and her family for the holidays. Her six-year-old asks you a question: "Why do mommies stay home with kids?" Drawing on the knowledge you gained from Chapter 2, how would you answer this question? Which ideas about parental investment, social learning, or social norms and scripts would you use to explain why, in most cultures, women perform the child-rearing activities?

4. From a sociologist's point of view, how have social institutions controlled female sexuality?

5. Could script theory explain the pattern of homosexual and heterosexual behaviour of Melanesian males described in In Focus 2.1 (page 34)? Explain your answer.

6. Find out more about a recent decision by the Supreme Court of Canada with respect to a sex law. Do you agree or disagree with the decision? To what extent does the decision reflect current Canadian social norms?

7. In Chapter 1, we identified a number of differences in the sexual behaviour of various ethnocultural communities in Canada. Which of the theories discussed in Chapter 2 can most easily explain these differences? Pick one specific difference and construct an explanation for it using that theory. How well does the theory help you to understand cultural differences in sexuality?

SUGGESTIONS FOR FURTHER READING

Baker, Robin. (1996). *Sperm wars: The science of sex*. Toronto: HarperCollins. Baker uses a series of vignettes describing sexual interactions to illustrate the many ways evolutionary mechanisms may influence our selection of mates, frequency of intercourse, success and failure to conceive, and infidelity.

Buss, David M. (1994). *The evolution of desire: Strategies of human mating*. New York: Basic Books. A detailed presentation of sexual strategy theory and data that are consistent with the theory.

Freud, Sigmund. (1943). *A general introduction to psychoanalysis*. Garden City, NY: Garden City Publishing. (Original in German, 1917.) Good for the reader who wants a basic introduction to Freud. For a good one-chapter summary, see Hall, C. S., and Lindzey, G. (1970). *Theories of personality* (2nd ed.). New York: Wiley.

Gagnon, John H., and Simon, William. (1987). The sexual scripting of oral–genital contacts. *Archives of Sexual Behavior*, 16, 1–26. An interesting discussion and application of script theory.

For review questions, web resources, and other learning and study tools, visit the *Understanding Human Sexuality* Online Learning Centre at www.mcgrawhill.ca/olc/hyde.

SEX RESEARCH

Chapter Highlights

WHAT IS RESEARCH, BUT A BLIND DATE WITH KNOWLEDGE.

—WILLIAM HENRY

This chapter is about sex research: how it is done, and how to evaluate it. It also describes some of the major sexuality studies. Why do we need sex research? What are its goals? Don't we already know everything we need to know about human sexuality? Isn't common sense sufficient?

The reality is there are still many things we do not know about human sexuality. People often have opinions and views about these issues and believe that their opinions are based on fact. Yet, too often they are based on misinformation, and sometimes even stereotypes or prejudice. Research is important because it creates accurate knowledge. Research puts beliefs, opinions, and theories to the systematic test.

There are a number of goals of sex research. First, it can be geared toward creating basic knowledge and understanding. For example, we might want to know what percentage of 15-year-olds have engaged in sexual activity, how often long-term couples have sex, or how effective the male condom is in preventing sexually transmitted infections. Second, research can be directed toward enhancing our understanding in order to influence sexual behaviour. For example, we might want to identify risk factors for individuals who might commit a sexual offence in order to prevent child sexual abuse; we might want to determine factors that affect sexual satisfaction in long-term relationships in order to help couples maintain satisfying sexual relationships; or, we might want to find out whether prepared childbirth techniques are effective in reducing anxiety and discomfort during labour and delivery. How can we provide effective prevention or intervention programs without this kind of knowledge on which to base these programs? Third, research can be geared toward public policy. For example, sexual health education is often a very controversial topic. An important question is whether individuals opposed to comprehensive sexual health education represent a majority of parents or a vocal minority of parents. Research can answer this question, thus allowing governments and school boards to take the wishes of the majority of parents into account when designing their sexual health education curriculum. Similarly, research can inform laws and regulations on a variety of issues, including access to emergency contraception, new reproductive technologies, pornography, and sex work.

Throughout this book, we describe the results of research that has attempted to answer these types of questions. In this chapter, we examine some questions related to sex research in general. How do sex researchers do it? How valid are their conclusions?

There are many different types of sex research, but basically the techniques vary in terms of the following: (1) whether they rely on people's self-reports of their sexual behaviour or whether the scientist observes the sexual behaviour directly; (2) whether large numbers of people are studied (surveys) or whether a small number or just a single individual is studied (in laboratory studies, qualitative research, or case studies); (3) whether the studies are conducted in the laboratory or in the field; and (4) whether sexual behaviour is studied simply as it occurs naturally or whether some attempt is made to manipulate it experimentally.

Examples of studies using all these techniques will be considered and evaluated later in this chapter. First, some issues in sex research will be discussed.

It is important to understand the techniques of sex research and their strengths as well as their limitations. This knowledge will help you evaluate the studies that are cited as evidence for various conclusions in later chapters and will also help you decide how willing you are to accept these conclusions. Perhaps more important, this knowledge will help you evaluate future sex research. Much sex research has been conducted already, but much more will be

Population: A group of people a researcher wants to study and make inferences about.

Sample: A part of a population.

Probability sampling: A method of sampling in research in which each member of the population has a known probability of being included in the sample.

Random sampling: An excellent method of sampling in research, in which each member of the population has an equal chance of being included in the sample.

Stratified random sampling: A method of sampling in which the population is divided into groups and then random sampling occurs in each group.

Problem of refusal or non-response: The problem that some people will refuse to participate in a sex survey, thus making it difficult to have a random sample.

Volunteer bias: A bias in the results of sex surveys that arises when some people refuse to participate, so that those who are in the sample are volunteers who may in some ways differ from those who refuse to participate.

done in the future. The information in this chapter should help you understand and evaluate sex research that appears 10 or 20 years from now. Moreover, the mass media often report poor-quality research as enthusiastically as high-quality research. You should be equipped to tell the difference.

ISSUES IN SEX RESEARCH
SAMPLING

One of the first steps in conducting sex research is to identify the appropriate population of people to be studied. Does the population in question consist of all adult human beings, all adults in Canada, all adolescents in Saskatchewan, all people guilty of sex crimes, or all married couples who engage in swinging? Generally, of course, the scientist is unable to get data for all the people in the population, and so a sample is taken.

At this point, things begin to get sticky. If the sample is a representative sample of the population in question and if it is a reasonably large sample, then results obtained from it can safely be generalized to the population that was originally identified. One way of obtaining a representative sample is by using probability sampling. The simplest form of probability sampling is random sampling. That is, if a researcher has really randomly selected 1 out of every 50 adolescents in Canada, then the results obtained from that sample are probably true of all adolescents in Canada. Another technique that is sometimes used to get such a sample is stratified random sampling.[1] But if the sample consists only of adolescents with certain characteristics—for example, only those whose parents agree to let them participate in sex research—then the results obtained from that sample may not be true of all adolescents. Sampling has been a serious problem in sex research.

Typically, sampling proceeds in three phases: the population is identified, a method for obtaining a sample is adopted, and the people in the sample are contacted and asked to participate. What is perhaps the thorniest problem occurs in the last phase: getting the people identified for the sample to participate. If any of the people refuse to participate, then the great probability sample is ruined. This is called the problem of refusal (or non-response). As a result, the researcher is essentially studying volunteers; that is, people who agree to be in the research. The outcomes of the research may therefore contain distortions, called volunteer bias. In casually conducted research such as the Hite report (Hite, 1976, 1981), the response rate was only 3 percent, making it impossible to reach any conclusions about the population based on the sample. The problem of refusal in sex research is difficult, since there is no ethical way of forcing people to participate when they do not want to.

The problem of volunteer bias would not be so great if those who refused to participate were identical in their sexual behaviour to those who participated. But it is likely that those who refuse to participate differ in some ways from those who agree to, and that means the sample is biased. Evidence suggests that volunteers who participate in sex research hold

[1]A detailed discussion of stratified random sampling is beyond the scope of this book. For a good description of this method as applied to sex research, see Cochran et al. (1953). In brief, with a random sample, each individual in the population has an equal probability of being chosen. With a stratified random sample, the researchers can set a higher probability of inclusion for certain groups, a technique called oversampling. For example, if we had funds to interview 1000 people in Canada, a random sample would yield only about 30 Aboriginal individuals and 30 Chinese-Canadian individuals because each group constitutes about 3 percent of the Canadian population. We might not feel confident reaching conclusions about Aboriginal individuals or Chinese Canadians based on only 30 people, so we could decide to use stratified random sampling and give each of these groups a higher probability of inclusion compared with whites. If we tripled the probability of including these ethnocultural minority groups, the resulting sample of 1000 would include 90 Aboriginal individuals, 90 Chinese Canadians, 82 individuals from other visible ethnocultural minorities (e.g., South Asian, black) and 738 Canadians from non–visible-minority groups. Although these minority samples are still small, we would feel more confident about making conclusions about each group. We could do even more oversampling of Aboriginal individuals or of other ethnocultural groups that constitute even smaller percentages of the Canadian population to increase our confidence in our conclusions.

more permissive attitudes about sexuality and are more sexually experienced than those who don't; for example, they masturbate more frequently and have had more sexual partners (Bogaert, 1996; Morokoff, 1986; Strassberg & Lowe, 1995; Wiederman et al., 1994). In addition, women are less likely to volunteer for some but not all types of sex research than men are (Senn & Desmarais, 2001; Wiederman et al., 1994), so that female samples are even more highly selected than male samples. In sum, volunteer bias is potentially a serious problem when we try to reach conclusions based on sex research.

Table 3.1 shows how different the results of sex surveys can be, depending on how carefully the sampling is done (Greeley, 1994). The table shows results from two American surveys. The Janus report (Janus & Janus, 1993) used sampling methods so haphazard that the researchers ended up with what some call a "convenience sample." It included volunteers who came to sex therapists' offices and friends recruited by the original volunteers. In contrast, the General Social Survey conducted in 1993 by the University of Chicago obtained a probability sample. Notice that a considerably higher level of sexual activity is reported by the convenience sample in the Janus report, compared with the probability sample. This difference is especially pronounced among older adults. Convenience samples simply do not give us a very good picture of what is going on in the general population.

Table 3.1	The Percentage of People Reporting Having Sex at Least Once a Week: Comparing a Convenience Sample with a Probability Sample			
	Men		Women	
Age	Convenience Sample (Janus Report)	Probability Sample (General Social Survey)	Convenience Sample (Janus Report)	Probability Sample (General Social Survey)
18–26	72%	57%	68%	58%
27–38	83	69	78	61
39–50	83	56	68	49
51–64	81	43	65	25
Over 65	69	17	74	6

Source: A. M. Greeley (1994), The Janus Report, *Contemporary Sociology, 23,* 221–223. Reprinted by permission of the American Sociological Association and Andrew M. Greeley.

RELIABILITY OF SELF-REPORTS OF SEXUAL BEHAVIOUR

Most sex researchers have not directly observed the sexual behaviour of their research participants. Instead, most have relied on respondents' self-reports of their sexual practices. The question is: How accurately do people report their own sexual behaviour? Inaccuracies may occur in several ways.

PURPOSEFUL DISTORTION

If you were an interviewer in a sex research project and a 90-year-old man said that he and his wife made love twice a day, would you believe him, or would you suspect that he might be exaggerating slightly? If a 35-year-old woman told you that she had never masturbated, would you believe her, or would you suspect that she had masturbated but was unwilling to admit it?

Respondents in sex research may, for one reason or another, engage in **purposeful distortion**, intentionally giving self-reports that are distortions of reality. These distortions may be in either of two directions. People may exaggerate their sexual activity (a tendency toward *enlargement*), or they may minimize their sexual activity or hide the fact that they have done certain things (*concealment*). Participants will often distort responses in the direction that they believe will be seen as more acceptable by the researcher, called **social desirability**. For example, an individual in a long-term relationship who believes that he or she engages in sexual activity

Purposeful distortion: Purposely giving false information in a survey.

Social desirability: The tendency to distort answers to a survey in the direction perceived to be more acceptable.

Figure 3.1   The reliability of self-reports of sexual behaviour: If you were interviewing this man in a sex survey and he said that he had never masturbated, would you believe him, or would you think that he was concealing a taboo behaviour?

with his or her partner much less often and masturbates much more often than other people do may exaggerate his or her sexual frequency but minimize his or her masturbation frequency. Participants are often not aware that social desirability is affecting their answers.

Distortion is a basic problem when using self-reports. To minimize distortion, participants must be impressed with the fact that because the study will be used for scientific purposes, their reports must be as accurate as possible. They must also be assured that their responses will be completely anonymous. If they are not anonymous, people would be likely to hide behaviours that they do not want other people to know about or that embarrass them such as an extramarital affair or a history of sex with animals.

But even if all respondents were very truthful and tried to give as accurate information as possible, three factors might still cause their self-reports to be inaccurate: memory, difficulties with estimates, and interpreting the question in a different way than the researcher intended.

MEMORY

Some of the questions asked in sex surveys require respondents to recall what their sexual behaviour was like many years before. For example, some of the data we have on sexual behaviour in childhood comes from the Kinsey study, in which adults were asked about their childhood sexual behaviour. This might involve asking a 50-year-old man to remember at what age he began masturbating and how frequently he masturbated when he was 16 years old. It might be difficult to remember such facts accurately. The alternative is to ask people about their current sexual behaviour, although getting data like these from children raises serious ethical and practical problems.

DIFFICULTIES WITH ESTIMATES

One of the questions sex researchers have asked is: How long, on the average, do you spend in precoital foreplay? If you were asked this question, how accurate a response do you think you could give? It is rather difficult to estimate time to begin with, and it is even more difficult to do so when engaged in an absorbing activity. For example, New Brunswick researchers found that, on average, men estimated the duration of foreplay as 13.4 minutes, which was significantly longer than the 11.3 minutes estimated by their female partners, suggesting that the men or the women or both were not accurate in the estimates of the duration of foreplay (Miller & Byers, 2004). The men and women both estimated the duration of intercourse at between seven and eight minutes, however. The point is that in some sex surveys people are asked to give estimates of things that they probably cannot estimate very accurately. This may be another source of inaccuracy in self-report data.

INTERPRETING THE QUESTION

One of the questions that sex researchers often ask is: How many sexual partners have you had? This question assumes that participants all give the same meaning to the term sexual partner as the research intended. Yet, research in New Brunswick has shown that university students do not agree in their definitions of sexual terms including the terms *having sex, sexual partner,* and *abstinence* (Randall & Byers, 2003; Byers, Henderson, & Hobson, in press). For example, about two-thirds of students would include a person they engaged in oral sex with a sexual partner, but one third would not. Thus, estimates participants provide about the number of sexual partners will be affected not only by the accuracy of their memory, but also by how they define sexual partner.

EVIDENCE ON THE RELIABILITY OF SELF-REPORTS

Scientists have developed several methods for assessing how reliable or accurate people's reports are (Catania et al., 1995). One is the method of test–retest reliability, in which the respondent is asked a series of questions and then is asked the same set of questions after a period of time has passed, for example, a week or a month. The correlation[2] between answers at the two times (test and retest) measures the reliability of responses. If people answer identically both times, the correlation would be 1.0, meaning perfect reliability. If there were absolutely no relationship between what they said the first time and what they said the second time, the correlation would be 0, meaning that the responses are not at all reliable.

In one study, urban African-American and Latina girls between the ages of 12 and 14 were interviewed about their sexual experiences and then were interviewed again three weeks later (Hearn et al., 2003). The test–retest reliability was .84 for the age at which they had their first crush and .95 for the age at which they first touched a penis, which indicates excellent reliability. Other research generally indicates that respondents give their best estimates about short, recent time intervals (Catania et al., 1990a).

Another method for assessing reliability involves obtaining independent reports from two different people who share sexual activity, such as husbands and wives. One study found that on a simple item such as whether a couple had engaged in intercourse in the last month, there was 93 percent agreement. Agreement on the number of times they had had intercourse in the last month, something that requires more difficult estimation, was .80, which is lower but still good (Hyde et al., 1996). Similarly, researchers in Quebec asked partners to indicate the behaviours that had occurred during lovemaking. The partners agreed 87 percent of the time on average, which is a high level of agreement (Ochs & Binik, 1999).

WEB-BASED SURVEYS

The possibility of having surveys administered on websites has opened a whole new era in sex research. Compared with other methods for administering surveys, Web-based surveys have many advantages, but also some disadvantages (Bowen, 2005; Gosling et al., 2004; Kraut et al., 2004; Mustanski, 2001; Ochs et al., 2002).

Test–retest reliability: A method for testing whether self-reports are reliable or accurate; participants are interviewed (or given a questionnaire) and then interviewed a second time some time later to determine whether their answers are the same both times.

---

[2]The statistical concept of correlation is discussed later in this chapter.

Web-based sex surveys can recruit much larger samples than can traditional interview or questionnaire studies. For example, one Web survey of gays, lesbians, and bisexuals yielded 2800 completed surveys in just two months (Mustanski, 2001). In addition, Web surveys can potentially produce broader samples than traditional survey methods can. For example, if you were conducting a survey on students' sexuality using traditional methods, you would probably sample students at your own college or university. If, instead, you administered the questionnaire on the Web, you could sample students from colleges and universities across Canada and, indeed, around the world. These new methods open up exciting possibilities for cross-cultural research.

Web-based surveys have particular advantages for studying special populations defined by their sexual behaviour, particularly if the behaviour is taboo. For example, traditional studies of gays and lesbians have used methods such as recruiting the sample through gay activist organizations and gay bars. These methods have been criticized because they omit from the sample closeted gays and those who do not actively participate in organizations or go to bars. Closeted gays have equal access to Web-based surveys and can answer them in a highly anonymous way, respecting their own decision to remain closeted. Therefore, Web methods can access this population that had previously been studied very little and can yield a much wider sample of gays and lesbians. Web methods can also locate stigmatized sexual minorities, such as those involved in sadomasochism, bondage, and discipline, by recruiting participants through virtual communities and websites specialized for that particular sexual group.

Web-based surveys, then, have substantial strengths on the issue of sampling. Nonetheless, they still rely on self-reports, which as we saw earlier can be inaccurate to some degree.

Web-based surveys have the ability to eliminate extraneous influences on responding (discussed in the next section). For example, the gender or ethnicity of the interviewer may influence an individual's responses, but these factors are eliminated in a Web-administered questionnaire.

Do all these substantial advantages come with any disadvantages? Some bias is introduced because not everyone has Internet access. Access grows every day, but Internet users still, on average, have incomes above the national average. Internet samples are nonetheless considerably more diverse than the university-student samples used in much research. The researcher lacks control of the environment in which the respondent completes the survey—something that can be controlled in personal interviews but cannot in mailed-out questionnaires. One can imagine, for example, a group of students living in residence filling out a Web sex survey together and having fun faking the answers. Individuals might respond multiple times or might actually try to sabotage or skew the results to show a particular outcome. Internal checks can be built into the sequence of questions that can detect faked patterns of answers, and methods have been devised to detect repeat responders. Nonetheless, these issues continue to be a concern.

On balance, Web-based surveys offer substantial advantages over traditional survey methods. Researchers will have to continue to monitor and control potential problems such as repeat responders.

INTERVIEWS VERSUS QUESTIONNAIRES

In the large-scale sex surveys, three methods of collecting data have been used: the face-to-face interview, the phone interview, and the written questionnaire. Each of these methods has some advantages when compared with the others (Catania et al., 1995).

The advantage of the interview method, particularly the face-to-face interview, is that the interviewer can establish rapport with the respondent and try to convince that person of the research's worth and of the necessity for being honest. An interviewer can also vary the sequence of questions depending on the person's response. For example, if a person mentioned having engaged in same-sex sexual activity, he or she would be asked a series of questions about the experience; those questions would be omitted if the person reported having had no same-sex experiences. It is hard to get this kind of flexibility in a printed questionnaire. Finally, interviews can be administered to persons who cannot read or write. However, it is possible that respondents would be more honest in answering a questionnaire because they are more anonymous.

What do the data say about which method works best for sex research? Several researchers have compared the results obtained through use of two different methods. For example, in one study, the rate of reporting rape was nearly double (11 percent) in a face-to-face interview compared with a telephone interview (6 percent) (Koss et al., 1994, p. 174). This finding seems to indicate that interviewers can establish rapport and trust better in person than over the telephone. In a study assessing risky sexual behaviour among gay men, both face-to-face interviews and written questionnaires were administered to all respondents (Siegel et al., 1994). Riskier behaviours were more likely to be reported on the questionnaire than in the interview. People evidently feel a bit freer to report particularly sensitive information on the more private written questionnaire than to an interviewer. Many experts in sex research recommend that a face-to-face interview to build rapport be combined with a written questionnaire administered during the interview to tap particularly sensitive information (Laumann et al., 1994; Siegel et al., 1994).

A recent innovation is the computer-assisted self-interview method (CASI), which can be combined with an audio component so that the respondent not only reads but also hears the questions. This method offers the privacy of the written questionnaire while accommodating poor readers. The computer can be programmed to follow varying sequences of questions depending on respondents' answers, just as a human interviewer does. In a survey among 15-year-old boys, 16 percent reported in a personal interview that they had engaged in vaginal intercourse, but 25 percent said they had done so when CASI was used (Mosher et al., 2005). Although these findings suggest that CASI produces more honest responses, it is also possible that the some boys exaggerated their sexual history on the computer.

Computer-assisted self-interview method (CASI): A method of data collection in which the respondent fills out questionnaires on a computer. Headphones and a soundtrack reading the questions can be added for young children or poor readers.

SELF-REPORTS VERSUS DIRECT OBSERVATIONS

As we noted earlier, one of the major ways of classifying techniques of sex research is by whether the scientist relied on people's self-reports of their behaviour or observed the sexual behaviour directly.

The problems of self-reports have just been discussed. In a word, self-reports may be inaccurate. Direct observations—such as those done by Masters and Johnson in their work on the physiology of sexual response—have a major advantage over self-reports in that they are accurate. No purposeful distortion or inaccurate memory can intervene. On the other hand, direct observations have their own set of problems. They are expensive and time-consuming, with the result that generally only a rather small sample is studied. Furthermore, obtaining a representative sample of the population is even more difficult than in survey research. While some people are reticent about completing a questionnaire concerning their sexual behaviour, even more would be unwilling to come to a laboratory where their sexual behaviour would be observed by a scientist or where they would be hooked up to recording instruments while they engaged in sex. Thus, results obtained from the unusual group of volunteers who would be willing to do this might not be generalizable to the rest of the population. One study showed that volunteers for a laboratory study of male sexual arousal felt less guilty, were less sexually fearful, and were more sexually experienced than non-volunteers (Farkas et al., 1978; for similar results with females, see Wolchik et al., 1983).

Direct observations of sexual behaviour in the laboratory, such as those made by Masters and Johnson, involve one other problem: Is sexual behaviour in the laboratory the same as sexual behaviour in the privacy of one's own bedroom? For example, might sexual response in the laboratory be somewhat inhibited?

EXTRANEOUS FACTORS

Various extraneous factors such as the gender, race, or age of the interviewer, may influence the outcome of sex research. Questionnaires do not get around these problems, since such simple factors as the wording of a question may influence the results. In one study, respondents were given either standard or supportive wording of some items (Catania et al., 1995). For the question about extramarital sex, the standard wording was as follows:

> At any time while you were married during the past 10 years, did you have sex with someone other than your (husband/wife)?

The supportive wording was as follows:

> Many people feel that being sexually faithful to a spouse is important, and some do not. However, even those who think being faithful is important have found themselves in situations where they ended up having sex with someone other than their (husband/wife). At any time while you were married during the past 10 years, did you have sex with someone other than your (husband/wife)?

The supportive wording significantly increased reports of extramarital sex from 12 percent with the standard wording to 16 percent with the supportive wording if the interviewer was of the same gender as the respondent; the wording made no difference when the interviewer and respondent were of different genders. Sex researchers must be careful to control these extraneous factors so that they influence the results as little as possible.

ETHICAL ISSUES

There is always a possibility of ethical problems involved in doing research. Ethical problems are particularly difficult in sex research, because people are more likely to feel that their privacy has been invaded when you ask them about sex than when you ask them to name their favourite political candidate or memorize a list of words. All research conducted at Canadian universities must conform to a policy established by the federal government that sets standards for conducting ethical research involving human participants (Medical Research Council of Canada, 1998). The cardinal ethical principle is respect for human dignity: above all, researchers need to keep this in mind when they are establishing the goals and the procedures of their research. The principle of respect for human dignity leads to several other ethical principles, including respect for free and informed consent and protection from harm.

FREE AND INFORMED CONSENT

Free and informed consent: An ethical principle in research, in which people have a right to be informed, before participating, of what they will be asked to do in the research.

According to the principle of free and informed consent, participants have a right to be told, before they participate, what the purpose of the research is and what they will be asked to do. They can choose not to participate or not to continue. An investigator may not coerce people to be in a study, and it is the scientist's responsibility to see to it that all participants understand exactly what they are agreeing to do. In the case of children who may be too young to give truly informed consent, consent is usually given by the parents.

The principle of informed consent was adopted by scientific organizations in the 1970s. It was violated in some of the earlier sex studies, as will be discussed later in this chapter.

PROTECTION FROM HARM

Investigators should minimize the amount of physical and psychological stress to people in their research. Thus, for example, if an investigator must shock participants during a study, there should be a good reason for doing this. Questioning people about their sexual behaviour may be psychologically stressful to them and might conceivably harm them in some way, so sex researchers must be careful to minimize the stress involved in their procedure.

The principle of respect for privacy and confidentiality of response, for example, by making sure that responses are anonymous, is important to ensure that participants will not suffer afterward for their participation in research.

JUSTICE

The principle of justice in research ethics holds that the risks of participating in research and benefits of the results of the research should be distributed fairly across groups in society. For example, early testing of the birth control pill was done on poor women in Puerto Rico, not on wealthy women in Vancouver. The risks were not distributed fairly, and a particular group bore a disproportionate burden. As a second example, research on the potential benefits of taking Aspirin for preventing heart attacks was conducted with an all-male sample. Whether this effect worked for women as well remained unknown. Thus, the benefits of the research did not extend fairly to everyone. Researchers have an obligation to make sure that they conduct their research in a way that benefits as wide a range of persons as possible.

BALANCING HARMS AND BENEFITS

Considering the possible dangers involved in sex research, is it ethical to do such research? Officials in universities and government agencies sponsoring sex research must answer this question for every proposed sex research study. In doing so, they must do a **harms–benefits analysis**. That is, the stress to research participants should be minimized as much as possible, but some stresses will remain; they are the harms. The question then becomes: Will the benefits that result from the research be greater than the harm? That is, will the participants benefit in some way from being in the study, and will science and society in general benefit from the knowledge resulting from the study? Do these benefits outweigh the potential harms? If they do, the research is justifiable; otherwise, it is not.

As an example, Masters and Johnson considered these issues carefully and concluded that their research participants benefited from being in their research; they collected data from former participants that confirm this belief. Thus, a harms–benefits analysis would suggest that their research was ethical, even though their participants might have been temporarily stressed by it. Even in a study as ethically questionable as Laud Humphreys's study of the tearoom trade (discussed later in this chapter), the potential harms to the participants should be weighed against the benefits that accrue to society from being informed about this aspect of sexual behaviour.

Harms–benefits analysis: An approach to analyzing the ethics of a research study, based on weighing the harms of the research (such as stress to subjects) against the benefits of the research (gaining knowledge about human sexuality).

SOME STATISTICAL CONCEPTS

Before you can understand reports of sex research, you must understand some basic statistical concepts.

AVERAGE

Suppose we get data from a sample of common-law couples on how many times per week they have sexual intercourse. How can we summarize the data? One way to do this is to compute some average value; this will tell us how often, on the average, these people have intercourse. In sex research, the number that is usually calculated is either the mean or the median, although the mode is sometimes used; all of these give us an indication of approximately where the average value for that group of people is. The **mean** is calculated by adding up all the scores and dividing by the number of people. The **median** is the score that splits the sample in half, with half the respondents scoring below that number and half scoring above it. The **mode** is the score with the greatest number of responses. People whose thoughts, feelings and behaviour are close to the average for their group might be said to be typical of that group.

Mean: The average of respondents' scores calculated by adding the scores and dividing by the number of people.

Median: The middle score.

Mode: The most frequent score.

VARIABILITY

In addition to having an indication of the average for the sample of respondents, it is also interesting to know how much variability there is from one respondent to the next in the numbers reported. That is, it is one thing to say that the average common-law couple in a sample had intercourse three times per week, with a range in the sample from two to four times per week, and it is quite another thing to say that the average was three times per week, with a range from zero to 15 times per week. In both cases the mean is the same, but in the first there is little variability, and in the second there is a great deal of variability. These two alternatives are shown graphically in Figure 3.2. There is great variability in virtually all sexual behaviour.

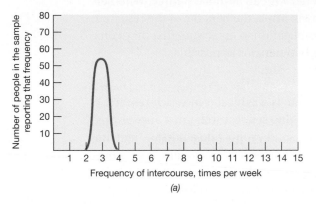
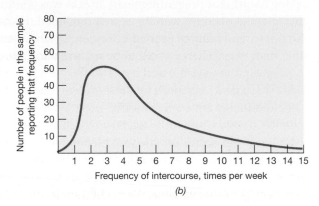

Figure 3.2 Two hypothetical graphs of the frequency of intercourse for common-law couples in a sample. In both, the average frequency is about three times per week, but in *(a)* there is little variability (almost everyone has a frequency between two and four times per week), whereas in *(b)* there is great variability (the frequency ranges from zero to 15 or more times per week). The graph for most sexual behaviour looks like *(b)*, with great variability.

AVERAGE VERSUS NORMAL

It is interesting and informative to report the average frequency of a particular sexual behaviour, but this also introduces the danger that people will confuse "average" with "normal." That is, there is a tendency, when reading a statistic like "The average person has intercourse twice per week," to think of one's own sexual behaviour, compare it with that average, and then conclude that one is abnormal if one differs much from the average. If you read that statistic and your frequency of intercourse is only once a week, you may begin to worry that you are undersexed or that you are not getting as much as you should. If you are having intercourse seven times per week, you might begin worrying that you are oversexed. Such conclusions are a mistake, first because they can make you miserable and second because there is so much variability in sexual behaviour that any behaviour (or frequency or length of time) within a wide range is perfectly normal. Don't confuse average with normal.

INCIDENCE VERSUS FREQUENCY

Incidence: The percentage of people giving a particular response.

Frequency: How often a person does something.

In sex statistics, the terms "incidence" and "frequency" are often used. **Incidence** refers to the percentage of people who have engaged in a certain behaviour. **Frequency** refers to how often people do something. Thus, we might say that the incidence of masturbation among males is 92 percent (meaning that 92 percent of all males masturbate at least once in their lives), whereas the average frequency of masturbation among males between the ages of 16 and 20 is about once per week.

A closely related concept is that of cumulative incidence. If we consider a sexual behaviour according to the age at which each person in the sample first engaged in it, the *cumulative incidence* refers to the percentage of people who have engaged in that behaviour before a certain age. Thus, the cumulative incidence of masturbation in males might be 10 percent by age 11, 25 percent by age 12, 80 percent by age 15, and 95 percent by age 20. Graphs of cumulative incidence always begin in the lower left-hand corner and move toward the upper right-hand corner. An example of a cumulative-incidence curve is shown in Figure 3.3.

CORRELATION

The term "correlation" is used by laypeople in contexts such as the following: "There seems to be a correlation here between how warm the days are and how fast the corn is growing." But

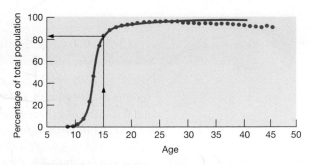

Figure 3.3 A cumulative-incidence curve for masturbation in males. From the graph, you can read off the percentage of males who report having masturbated by a given age. For example, about 82 percent have masturbated to orgasm by age 15.

what do statisticians mean by the term "correlation"? A **correlation** is a number that measures the relationship between two variables. A correlation can be positive or negative. A positive correlation occurs when there is a positive relationship between the two variables; that is, people who have high scores on one variable tend to have high scores on the other variable, and low scores go with low scores. A negative correlation occurs when there is an opposite relationship between the two variables; that is, people with high scores on one variable tend to have low scores on the other variable. We might want to know, for example, whether there is a correlation between the number of years a couple has been together and the frequency with which they have sexual intercourse. In this case we might expect that there would be a negative correlation, and that is just what researchers have found. That is, the *greater* the number of years together, the *lower* the frequency of intercourse. As another example, we might want to know whether there is a correlation between people's sexual attitudes and their sexual behaviour, specifically whether people who hold more permissive attitudes about premarital sex have more premarital partners. In this case we expect a positive correlation in the sense that the people who score high on the measure of permissive attitudes are expected to have more partners and that people who score low on the measure of permissiveness are expected to have fewer partners.

Correlation: A number that measures the relationship between two variables.

Correlations range between +1.0 and −1.0. A correlation of +1.0 indicates a perfect positive relationship between two variables, meaning that the person in the sample who scores highest on one variable also has the highest score on the other variable, the person with the second highest score on the first variable also has the second highest score on the other variable, and so on. A correlation of 0 indicates no relationship between the two variables. Knowing a person's score on one variable tells us nothing about whether the person will have a high or low score on the other variable. Positive correlations between 0 and +1.0—for example, +.62—say that the relationship is positive but not a perfect relationship.

As discussed earlier in this chapter, we use correlations to assess test–retest reliability. Suppose we administer a questionnaire to a sample of adults. One of the questions asks, "How many times did you masturbate to orgasm during the month of September?" We ask this question of the sample on October 1 and again on October 8. If each person in the sample gives us exactly the same answer on October 1 and on October 8, the correlation between the two variables (the number given on October 1 and the number given on October 8) would be +1.0 and the test–retest reliability would be a perfect +1.0. Test–retest reliabilities for questions about sex typically range between +.60 and +.90, indicating that people's answers on the two occasions are not identical but are very similar.

IN FOCUS 3.1

What Is the Legacy of Alfred C. Kinsey?

Alfred C. Kinsey was born in 1894 in New Jersey, the first child of uneducated parents. In high school he did not date, and a classmate recalled that he was "the shyest guy around girls you could think of."

His father was determined that Kinsey become a mechanical engineer. From 1912 to 1914 he tried studying mechanical engineering at Stevens Institute, but he showed little talent for it. At one point he was close to failing physics, but a compromise was reached with the professor, who agreed to pass him if he would not attempt any advanced work in the field! In 1914 Kinsey made his break and enrolled at Bowdoin College to pursue his real love: biology. Because this went against his father's wishes, Kinsey was put on his own financially.

In 1916 he began graduate work at Harvard. There he developed an interest in insects, specializing in gall wasps. While still a graduate student, he wrote a definitive book on the edible plants of eastern North America.

In 1920 he went to Bloomington, Indiana, to take a job as assistant professor of zoology at Indiana University. That fall he met Clara McMillen, whom he married six months later. They soon had four children.

With his intense curiosity and driving ambition, Kinsey quickly gained academic success. He published a high school biology text in 1926, which received enthusiastic reviews. By 1936 he had published two major books on gall wasps; they established his reputation as a leading authority in the field and contributed not only to knowledge of gall wasps but also to genetic theory.

Kinsey came to the study of human sexual behaviour as a biologist. His shift to the study of sex began in 1938, when Indiana University began a "marriage" course; Kinsey chaired the faculty committee teaching it. When confronted with teaching the course, he became aware of the appalling lack of information on human sexual behaviour. Thus, his research resulted in part from his realization of the need of people, especially young people, for sex information. In 1939 he made his first field trip to collect sex histories in Chicago. His lifetime goal was to collect 100 000 sex histories.

His work culminated in the publication of the Kinsey reports in 1948 (*Sexual Behavior in the Human Male*)

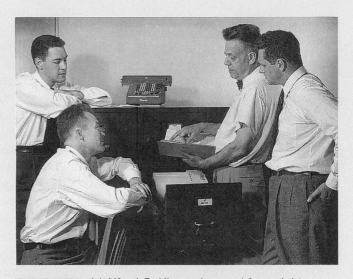

Figure 3.4 *(a)* Alfred C. Kinsey (second from right, holding the folder), with colleagues Martin, Gebhard, and Pomeroy.

THE MAJOR SEX SURVEYS

In the major sex surveys, the data were collected from a large sample of people by means of questionnaires or interviews. The best known of these studies is the one done by Alfred Kinsey, so we will consider it first. His data were collected in the late 1930s and 1940s in the United States, and thus the results are now largely of historical interest. However, Kinsey documented his methods with extraordinary care, so his research is a good example to study for both the good and the bad points of surveys.

THE KINSEY REPORT

THE SAMPLE

Kinsey (see In Focus 3.1) and his colleagues interviewed a total of 5300 men and 5940 women between 1938 and 1949 in the United States.

and 1953 (*Sexual Behavior in the Human Female*). While the scientific community generally received them as a landmark contribution, they also provoked hate mail.

In 1947 Kinsey founded the Institute for Sex Research (known popularly as the Kinsey Institute) at Indiana University. It was financed by a grant from the Rockefeller Foundation and, later, by book royalties. But in the 1950s United States Senator Joseph McCarthy, the communist baiter, was in power. He made a particularly vicious attack on the Institute and its research, claiming that its effect was to weaken American morality and thus make the nation more susceptible to a communist takeover. Under his pressure, the Rockefeller Foundation terminated its support.

Kinsey's health began to fail, partly as a result of the heavy workload he set for himself, and partly because he saw financial support for the research collapsing. He died in 1956 at the age of 62 of heart failure while honouring a lecture engagement when his doctor had ordered him to convalesce.

By 1957 McCarthy had been discredited and the grant funds returned. The Kinsey Institute was then headed by Paul Gebhard, an anthropologist who had been a member of the staff for many years. The Institute continues to do research today; it also houses a large library on sex and an archival collection including countless works of sexual art.

In a highly publicized, tell-all biography of Kinsey, James Jones (1997) argued that, although Kinsey's public self was a heterosexual married man, he was homosexual (more accurately, bisexual) and practised masochism. According to Jones, this discredits Kinsey's research.

Figure 3.4 *(b)* Liam Neeson plays Kinsey in the 2004 movie *Kinsey*.

Jones's logic is poor, though, because one can evaluate the quality of the research methods independent of one's views about Kinsey's personal sex life. Moreover, Kinsey's sexual experimenting may have contributed to the innovativeness of his research.

Sources: Bancroft, 2004; Christensen, 1971; Gathorne-Hardy, 2000; Gebhard, 1976; Jones, 1997.

Initially, Kinsey was not much concerned with sampling issues. His goal was simply to collect sex histories from as wide a variety of people as possible. He later became more concerned with sampling issues and developed a technique called *100 percent sampling*. In this method he contacted a group, obtained its cooperation, and then got every one of its members to give a history. Once the cooperation of a group had been secured, peer pressure ensured that all members would participate. Unfortunately, although he was successful in getting a complete sample from such groups, the groups themselves were by no means chosen randomly. Thus, among the groups from which 100 percent samples were obtained were two sororities, nine fraternities, and 13 professional groups.

In the 1953 volume on females, Kinsey said that he and his colleagues had deliberately chosen not to use probability sampling methods because of the problems of non-response. This is a legitimate point. But as a result, we have almost no information on how adequate the sample was. One might say that the sampling was haphazard but not random. Generally, the following kinds of people were overrepresented in the sample: university students, young people, well-educated people, Protestants, people living in cities, and people living in Indiana and the Northeast United States. Underrepresented groups included manual labourers, less well-educated people, older people, Roman Catholics, Jews, members of racial minorities, and people living in rural areas.

THE INTERVIEWS

Although scientists generally regard Kinsey's sampling methods with some dismay, his face-to-face interviewing techniques are highly regarded. More than 50 percent of the interviews were done by Kinsey himself and the rest by his associates, whom he trained carefully. The interviewers made every attempt to establish rapport with the people they spoke to, and they treated all reports matter-of-factly. They were also skillful at phrasing questions in language that was easily understood. Questions were worded so as to encourage people to report anything they had done. For example, rather than asking "Have you ever masturbated?" the interviewers asked "At what age did you begin masturbating?" They also developed a number of methods for cross-checking a person's report so that false information would be detected. Wardell Pomeroy recounted an example:

> Kinsey illustrated this point with the case of an older Negro male who at first was wary and evasive in his answers. From the fact that he listed a number of minor jobs when asked about his occupation and seemed reluctant to go into any of them [Kinsey] deduced that he might have been active in the underworld, so he began to follow up by asking the man whether he had ever been married. He denied it, at which Kinsey resorted to the vernacular and inquired if he had ever "lived common law." The man admitted he had, and that it had first happened when he was 14.
>
> "How old was the woman?" [Kinsey] asked.
>
> "Thirty-five," he admitted, smiling.
>
> Kinsey showed no surprise. "She was a hustler, wasn't she?" he said flatly.
>
> At this the subject's eyes opened wide. Then he smiled in a friendly way for the first time, and said, "Well, sir, since you appear to know something about these things, I'll tell you straight."
>
> After that, [Kinsey] got an extraordinary record of this man's history as a pimp. . . . (Pomeroy, 1972, pp. 115–116)

Kinsey took strict precautions to ensure that responses were anonymous and that they remained anonymous. The data were stored on IBM cards, but using a code that had been memorized by only a few people directly involved in the project and which was never written down. The research team had even made contingency plans for destroying the data in the event that the police tried to demand access to the records for prosecuting people.

Put simply, the interviewing techniques were probably very successful in minimizing purposeful distortion. However, other problems of self-report remained: the problems of memory and of the inability to estimate some of the numbers requested.

HOW ACCURATE WERE THE KINSEY STATISTICS?

When all is said and done, how accurate were the statistics presented by Kinsey? The American Statistical Association appointed a blue-ribbon panel to evaluate the Kinsey reports (Cochran et al., 1953; for other evaluations, see Terman, 1948; Wallin, 1949). While the panel members generally felt that the interview techniques had been excellent, they were dismayed by Kinsey's failure to use probability sampling and concluded, somewhat pessimistically:

> In the absence of a probability-sample benchmark, the present results must be regarded as subject to systematic errors of unknown magnitude due to selective sampling (via volunteering and the like). (Cochran et al., 1953, p. 711)

However, they also felt that this was a nearly insoluble problem for sex research; even if a probability sample were used, refusals would still create serious problems.

The statisticians who evaluated Kinsey's methods felt that one aspect of his findings might have been particularly subject to error: the generally high levels of sexual activity, and particularly the high incidence of homosexual behaviour. These conclusions might, they felt, have been seriously influenced by sampling problems, particularly Kinsey's tendency to seek out persons with unusual sexual practices.

In sum, it is impossible to say how accurate the Kinsey statistics are; some may be very accurate and some may contain serious errors. Probably the single most doubtful figure is the high incidence of homosexuality.

SEXUAL BEHAVIOUR IN THE UNITED STATES

U.S. researchers identified a need to conduct a large-scale, national survey of sexuality using probability sampling methods to determine what Americans' patterns of sexual behaviour are today. Such a study appeared in 1994. The research team was headed by Edward Laumann, a distinguished sociologist at the University of Chicago, and was conducted by the National Opinion Research Center, one of the best-respected survey organizations in the United States. The survey was called the National Health and Social Life Survey; to keep things simple, we will call this study the NHSLS (Laumann et al., 1994; Michael et al., 1994).

The research method involved a probability sampling of households in the United States. This excluded less than 3 percent of Americans but did exclude people living in institutions (e.g., prisons, university dormitories) and the homeless. People were eligible if they were adults between the ages of 18 and 59.

The researchers obtained an impressive 79 percent cooperation rate. Apparently, the great majority of people are willing to respond to a carefully conducted sex survey. The response rate is particularly impressive in view of the fact that today even surveys of more neutral topics such as political opinions generally have a response rate of only about 75 percent.

The data were obtained in face-to-face interviews supplemented by brief written questionnaires, which were handed to the respondents for particularly sensitive topics (such as masturbation) and sealed in a "privacy envelope" when they had been completed. The researchers chose the face-to-face interview because they felt that it would yield a higher response rate than a written questionnaire alone, and it allowed the researchers to ask more complex, detailed sequences of questions than would have been possible with just a written questionnaire or a telephone interview.

Laumann's team was careful to obtain the respondents' informed consent. About a week before an interviewer went to a household, a letter was sent explaining that the purpose of the survey was to help "doctors, teachers, and counselors better understand and prevent the spread of diseases like AIDS and better understand the nature and extent of harmful and of healthy sexual behavior in our country" (Laumann et al., 1994, p. 55). The purpose was therefore clearly and honestly described to participants before their consent was requested. In order to protect confidentiality, all identifying information about the respondent was destroyed after the interview. Each respondent was paid US$35 for the interview, which lasted, on the average, 90 minutes.

The NHSLS is the best sex survey of the general population of the United States available today, and its findings will be referred to in many chapters in this book. The researchers made outstanding efforts to use the best sampling methods and interview techniques. Nonetheless, no doubt some respondents engaged in concealment and perhaps also in enlargement, because self-reports were used. The skill of the interviewers and their ability to build rapport is crucial in overcoming such problems. The researchers reported training the interviewers extensively, but nonetheless the extent of concealment, or *underreporting*, remains unknown.

Ironically, the most controversial statistic in the study was the same as in Kinsey's research—the incidence of homosexuality. In Kinsey's case, people thought the numbers were too high. In the case of the NHSLS, some people thought they were too low. We will return to this issue in Chapter 14.

SEXUAL BEHAVIOUR IN FRANCE AND BRITAIN

Again stimulated by a need for far better information about sexual behaviour in order to deal with the AIDS crisis, a team of French researchers, called the ACSF Investigators, conducted a major French sex survey (ACSF Investigators, 1992). The data were collected in 1991 and 1992. These researchers chose the method of telephone interviews, preceded by a letter notifying potential respondents that they had been identified for the representative sample. The response rate was 76.5 percent. The result was a sample of 20 055 adults ranging in age from 18 to 69.

The results indicate, for example, that 13 percent of French men, compared with 6 percent of French women, had multiple sex partners (two or more) in the past 12 months and therefore were at higher risk of HIV infection.

Anne Johnson and her colleagues conducted surveys in Britain in 1990–1991 and again in 1999–2001 (Johnson et al., 1992, 2001). The more recent survey used computer-assisted interviews. It yielded data for 11 161 men and women aged 16 to 44. The response rate was 63 percent. The researchers found that the average number of opposite-sex sexual partners in the previous five years was 3.8 for men and 2.4 for women; 2.6 percent of both men and women reported a same-sex partner; both rates were higher than were found in the 1990 survey. However, they also found increases in consistent condom use, particularly for men with multiple partners in the past year.

Figure 3.5 Research conducted among racial and ethnic minority groups must be culturally sensitive. Ideally, for example, interviewers should be of the same cultural background as research participants.

SEXUAL BEHAVIOUR IN CANADA

Although Canadians have often used the large-scale American surveys to draw conclusions about the situation in Canada, Canadians differ from Americans in ways that are likely to affect sexual behaviour, such as family patterns, laws, attitudes, and health (Barrett et al., 1997). Thus, it is impossible to be certain of the extent to which these data reflect the sexual behaviour of Canadians. Unfortunately, there have been no large-scale Canadian sexuality surveys, with the exception of a few questions contained in the National Population Health Survey and other general surveys. This makes it difficult to develop a clear picture of the sexual behaviour of adult Canadians. In contrast, as just described, the United States, England, and France have all conducted this kind of large-scale survey in recent years. Many of the statistics in the French and British surveys match quite closely those from the United States. Thus, it is likely that a Canadian survey would also have similar, but not identical, findings. There are, however, many active sex researchers in Canada (see In Focus 3.2). These researchers have conducted surveys of selected groups, such as university students, teenagers, First Nations peoples, sex trade workers, people living with chronic illnesses, or gay and bisexual men, some of which are described in this chapter.

THE CANADA YOUTH, SEXUAL HEALTH, AND HIV/AIDS STUDY

Researchers from four Canadian universities—Queen's, Acadia, Laval, and the University of Alberta—conducted a study on youth sexuality and sexual health called the Canada Youth, Sexual Health, and HIV/AIDS Study, or CYSHHAS for short (Boyce et al., 2003). It examined a number of factors thought to influence adolescent sexual knowledge, attitudes, and behaviour.

IN FOCUS 3.2

Where Can I Go in Canada to Become a Sex Researcher?

There are many active sex researchers in Canada, and their numbers are growing. Most are in academic departments within specific disciplines such as psychology, sociology, family studies, or medicine. Most supervise students. The only Department of Sexology located in Canada operates in French at l'Université du Québec à Montréal. Although it is impossible to name all Canadian sex researchers, here are some of the most active researchers (from east to west).

Psychologist Lisa Price studies sexual coercion and risky sexual behaviour among adolescents at Acadia University. At the University of New Brunswick, psychologist Sandra Byers is particularly well known for her research on sexual interactions in close relationships, including sexual satisfaction, sexual dysfunction, and sexual coercion, and Lucia O'Sullivan is an expert in adolescent sexual health.

In Quebec, psychologist Francine Lavoie of Laval University studies high school students' sexually coercive experiences. Joseph Levy and Joanne Otis at the Département de sexologie, l'Université du Québec à Montréal, have been active in assessing the sexual behaviour of Quebecers. In the same department, Martine Hébert investigates child sexual abuse, and psychologist Sophie Bergeron studies women's sexual pain disorders. At McGill University, psychologists Yitzchak Binik studies sexual pain in women, and Bärbel Knäuper investigates how individuals make sexual health–related judgments. At Concordia University, sociologist Frances Shaver is a leading researcher on sex work, and James Pfaus studies the neurochemical and molecular events underlying sexual behaviour.

A number of Ontario universities have active sex research programs. Researchers at the Social Program Evaluation Group at Queen's University in Kingston have published extensively on adolescent sexual behaviour. Also at Queen's, psychologists William Marshall and Vernon Quinsey have an international reputation for their work on the assessment and treatment of sex offenders, and Caroline Pukall does research related to sexual pain and its effects on sexual and marital functioning. At the University of Ottawa, psychiatrist Paul Federoff studies the treatment of sex offenders; psychologist Elke Reissing investigates sexual pain disorders as well as sexual adjustment following treatment for cancer. At the Centre for Addiction and Mental Health, Clarke Division, in Toronto, psychologists Ken Zucker and Ray Blanchard are well known for their work on gender identity disorders

in children and adults, Harold Barbaree and Michael Seto do research related to sexual offenders, and Meredith Chivers studies sexual psychophysiology. Ted Myers at the University of Toronto does research related to HIV.

Psychologist Anthony Bogaert at Brock University is well known for his work on the origins of sexual orientation. Psychologist Terry Humphreys at Trent University does research related to human sexuality and social psychology. At the University of Waterloo, psychologist B. J. Rye studies HIV/AIDS and attitudes toward sexual minorities, and Christine Purdon examines the role of anxiety in sexual functioning. At the University of Guelph, Robin Milhausen does research related to sexual arousal and sexual health. William Fisher of the Department of Psychology at the University of Western Ontario has an international reputation for his work on the prevention of teen pregnancy, STIs, and HIV infection. At the University of Windsor, sociologist Eleanor Maticka-Tyndale is well known for her qualitative and multimethod research on risk behaviour related to pregnancy and STI/HIV infection, and sociologist Barry Adam does research on HIV and same-sex relationships.

Psychologist Melanie Morrison at the University of Saskatchewan studies prejudice and discrimination toward sexual minorities. At the University of Alberta, Maryanne Doherty studies sexual health education and risky sexual health behaviours. Martin Lalumière at the University of Lethbridge does research on sexual aggression, and Paul Vasey studies sexuality and gender from a biocognitive perspective.

At the University of British Columbia, physician Rosemary Basson conducts research on sexual dysfunction, physician Stacy Elliott does research on sexuality and disability, psychologist Lori Brotto studies women's sexual health, psychologist Judith Daniluk is well known for her research on infertility, and psychologist Boris Gorzalka conducts psychophysiological sex research. Sociologist Aaron Devor at the University of Victoria has made important contributions in his work on conceptualization of gender dysphoria.

Canadian sex researchers publish their findings in both national and international journals. There is one Canadian journal committed to the dissemination of sex research: the quarterly *Canadian Journal of Human Sexuality*. Many belong to the Canadian Sex Research Forum (www.csrf.ca), the only national association for sex researchers, as well as to international sexological organizations.

Many of these questions were also used in the Canada Youth and AIDS Study conducted in 1987 by Alan King and his colleagues (King et al., 1988), allowing comparisons between the two studies. Because the CYSHHAS focused on sexual health, it is not a comprehensive survey of adolescent sexual behaviour and attitudes.

The researchers collected data in all 10 provinces as well as in the Yukon and Northwest Territories. They surveyed 11 074 youth in grades 7, 9, and 11. However, in order to be acceptable to school administrations, the grade 7 version included only one question about sexual experiences. The study was conducted in both French and English. The researchers used excellent sampling methods. They designed their sampling procedure so that the data would be representative of Canada as a whole and they also would have enough participants that they could present the findings separately for each province. However, some selected schools refused to participate. This resulted in a sample that was not equally representative of the whole country and was too small to analyze by province or territory. There also were some problems related to potential volunteer bias. For example, 18 percent of students either failed to return their signed permission slip or had parents who refused to give them permission to participate, and 5 percent of the students refused to participate. The students who did participate may differ in some important ways from those who did not.

The researchers found that many youth had begun engaging in sexual intercourse by age 14. For example, 23 percent of boys and 19 percent of girls in grade 9 and 40 percent of boys and 46 percent of girls in grade 11 reported having engaged in sexual intercourse at least once. These percentages are similar to, and if anything somewhat lower than, those obtained in the Canada Youth and AIDS Study in 1987, indicating that the percentage of students engaging in sexual intercourse does not appear to be increasing. However, the students who are engaging in sexual intercourse reported doing so more frequently than did students in 1987. Although 78 percent of the boys and 68 percent of the girls said that they had used a condom at last intercourse, between 5 and 10 percent had not used any form of birth control. Further, students who participated in 2002 were less accurate in their sexual knowledge than were the students who participated in 1987. Although this study assessed both anglophone and francophone youth, the researchers did not assess ethnicity. Thus, we do not know how cultural background affects the sexual attitudes and behaviours of Canadian youth.

MAGAZINE SURVEYS

Many large-scale sex surveys have been conducted through magazines. Often the survey is printed in one issue of the magazine and readers are asked to respond. The result can be a huge sample—perhaps 20 000 people—which sounds impressive. But are these magazine surveys really all they claim to be?

Sampling is just plain out of control with magazine surveys. The survey is distributed just to readers of the magazine, and different magazines have different clienteles. No one magazine reaches a representative sample of Canadians. If the survey appeared in *Chatelaine*, it would go to certain kinds of women; if it were in *Canadian Living*, it would go to others. It would be risky to assume that women who read *Chatelaine* have the same sexual patterns as those who read *Canadian Living*. To make matters worse, the response rate is unknown. We can't know how many people saw the survey and did not fill it out, compared with the number who did. The response rate could be something like 3 percent. One does not, therefore, even have a random sample of readers of that magazine.

As an example, let's consider a survey that was reported in the August 2000 issue of *Cosmopolitan* (Gilbert, 2000). The headline on the cover announces "Our Biggest Sex Survey Ever, Thousands of Guys Reveal What Sends Them Over the Edge (Their Answers Will Shock You)." The description of the method in the articles says that *Cosmo* polled 60 000 "loose-lipped men and women." That's a much larger sample than the NHSLS—but, in sex surveys as in some other aspects of sexuality, bigger is not always better. How did *Cosmo* distribute the surveys? If they were printed in a previous issue, which seems like a good guess, how can we know the response rate? And how did so many men receive the survey, given that *Cosmo* is a magazine carefully aimed at a female audience? Among the respondents, how many were married? Single? What about their ethnic backgrounds? How old were they? Of course, these details are probably not the sort of thing that *Cosmo* thinks will entertain its readers. Nonetheless, the editors could have printed the information in a small box at the end of the article. More importantly, these details are crucial in understanding whether one can take the survey's claims seriously.

One question asked what a guy thinks of a girl who has sex on a first date. Of the men who were polled, 44 percent said they were happy when a women went with her desires and wouldn't think negatively about her, as long as she was comfortable with her decision. From this, can we conclude that 44 percent of American men don't think ill of a woman who goes to bed with them on a first date? This conclusion would require a leap of logic that is too big for safety. *Cosmo* wasn't even close to having a random sample in this survey.

For all these reasons, it would not be legitimate to infer that these statistics characterize North American women in general. We could continue with more examples of magazine surveys, but the general conclusion should be clear by now. Although they may appear impressive because of their large number of respondents, magazine sex surveys actually are poor in quality because the sample generally is seriously biased.

STUDIES OF SPECIAL POPULATIONS

In addition to the large-scale surveys of Americans and of Canadian youth discussed earlier, many studies of special populations have been done. Two examples are given here: the Maticka-Tyndale study of exotic dancers and a survey of First Nations peoples in Ontario.

EXOTIC DANCERS

Eleanor Maticka-Tyndale and her colleagues conducted a study of exotic dancers working at strip clubs in Southern Ontario (Lewis & Maticka-Tyndale, 1998; Maticka-Tyndale et al., 1999). Their goal was to determine whether the dancers' activities, both inside and outside the club, put them at risk for STIs, including HIV infection. They interviewed 30 female exotic dancers who had been dancing from one to 22 years. The researchers used a qualitative methodology rather than the quantitative methodology used in the other research described in this chapter. In **qualitative research**, the researchers try to make sense of experiences in terms of the meanings that people give to them (Denzin & Lincoln, 1994). Thus, qualitative researchers emphasize the participant's point of view and represent this point of view by providing quotations from participants rather than by giving statistics.

It is difficult to recruit a representative sample of sex workers because of the stigma attached to the work and because sex workers are often distrustful of researchers (Benoit et al., 2005). Therefore, the researchers used a procedure called *non-probability purposive sampling* to maximize the diversity in the small sample. They wanted to make sure that the conclusions drawn from the research would reflect all the situations in which dancers find themselves. Participants were identified by key informants, by research assistants who had worked as dancers themselves, and by dancers who participated in the study, a technique called *snowballing*. Thus, as with all qualitative research, this was not a random or representative sample and thus we cannot draw conclusions about frequencies and prevalences. Nonetheless, it provides an in-depth understanding of the world of exotic dancers.

Participants responded to an informal set of open-ended questions that allowed them to freely express themselves. The interviews were analyzed to identify themes that emerged

Qualitative research: Research, usually involving interviews, in which the researchers try to make sense of the meanings that people give to their experiences.

IN FOCUS 3.3

Confessions of a Scientist: The Career of Dr. William Fisher

Dr. William Fisher is a professor in the Department of Psychology and the Department of Obstetrics and Gynaecology at the University of Western Ontario. He received his Ph.D. in Social Psychology from Purdue University in 1978. He is world-renowned for the Information–Motivation–Behavioural Skills model, his conceptualization of the factors that drive sexual and reproductive health behaviour, and for his work on HIV/AIDS prevention and on the effects of pornography on men's and women's behaviour. Dr. Fisher's work is described throughout this book (see Chapters 7, 10, and 17). He has received a National Health Scientist Award from Health Canada, the Hellmuth Award for Achievement in Science from the University of Western Ontario, and he is a Fellow of the Society for the Scientific Study of Sexuality. Below he reflects, with humour, on how he came to be a sexuality researcher.

Coming out of the chaos, commitment, and politics of the Vietnam- and Civil Rights-era in the 1960s, I resolved, naïvely, to try to understand and improve the human condition, a delusional state from which I have yet to recover. Accordingly, I applied for admission to a graduate school that featured stellar researchers in the areas of human attraction and human aggression—which seemed to me at the time to be the issues we need to understand if we are to have any chance to survive as a species. Astoundingly, Donn Byrne, one of the world's premier scientists in the area of love and attraction, accepted me for graduate study. He had just shifted his research focus from interpersonal attraction to sexual behaviour—a natural progression, in retrospect, and we were off to the races.

As a graduate student I conducted research on the effects of pornography (what else?), and two things caught my eye immediately. First, I found that men and women who viewed pornography and who were most revolted by it showed large increases in their sexual activity levels in the days following exposure. (As an aside, the study was published in both the *Journal of Personality and Social Psychology* and in *Screw* magazine. Fortunately, the publication in *Screw* magazine did not turn out to be a career ender—no prospective employer ever admitted to having seen it). Second, I found that men and women who responded to pornography with the most pronounced negative emotions also, and puzzlingly, had the most children. At first it was difficult to understand why—and indeed how—this happened. Then we realized that erotophobic persons—that is, people who are emotionally negative to sex—have a really tough time doing just about everything you need to do to not have children. That is, they find it hard to learn about contraception, talk with a partner about it, acquire it from a physician or a pharmacy, and use it consistently.

That was my start, and since graduate school, building

from the sex workers' responses. There were two different types of dancers. Women begin dancing primarily for the money, with the view that it will be temporary. Goal-oriented dancers continue to treat dancing as a temporary job and usually do not use alcohol or drugs or engage in sexual activity as part of the job. College and university students are one group of goal-oriented dancers. Dancing is attractive to them because it pays well and can fit into their class schedule. Some women shift from viewing dancing as a temporary job to viewing it as a career. These career dancers are usually part of the strip club culture, are often heavy drinkers, and may be involved in drug use. They may have sex with customers as part of the dancing or on dates with the men they meet while dancing at the clubs.

The researchers faced a number of difficulties that are common in this type of research. First, it was difficult to recruit participants. Dancers do not have much interest in participating in research and are suspicious of researchers. Second, as there is a stigma associated with exotic dancing, the researchers had to take extra steps to ensure that participants could not be identified. However, by using a qualitative methodology, they provided insights into the experiences of women who work as exotic dancers from their own points of view that can be difficult to get from quantitative methods such as questionnaires.

on this observation, I have worked toward development of a theory of the basic psychological factors that drive human sexual behaviour. My research has been aimed at improving people's sexual and reproductive health by applying this theory in areas as diverse as adolescent pregnancy prevention, HIV prevention, and reproductive health care seeking. I have been fortunate to do this work in settings as varied and challenging as inner-city high schools in the United States, South African AIDS treatment centres, and Israeli–Palestinian HIV containment programs. I've been at this work for years. I've published 150 papers in this area, and I feel like I've barely begun.

Why I Do What I Do

I do what I do because I believe that the development and application of psychological theory in the area of sexual and reproductive health is important for the human condition. I do what I do because I enjoy creating conceptual models that can with power and precision be used to predict and promote human sexual and reproductive health outcomes. I do what I do because my work has had the unintended but often enjoyable effect of inflaming both the political right (see my work on contraceptive behaviour and how to promote it) and the political left (see my work on pornography and failure to find that it has negative effects), so I know I must be doing something right.

Figure 3.6 Dr. William Fisher is a well-known psychologist and sex researcher.

Proudest Achievements

Catching the occasional fish. Not really. My proudest achievements involve my resolute insistence on following my data, regardless of their political correctness or incorrectness, and insisting on maintaining fundamental human values and principles, regardless of my data.

ONTARIO FIRST NATIONS AIDS AND HEALTHY LIFESTYLE SURVEY

The Ontario First Nations AIDS and Healthy Lifestyle Survey was conducted by Ted Myers and his colleagues (1993) at the Division of Community Health at the University of Toronto in collaboration with the First Nations Steering Committee. The goal of the study was to assess knowledge, attitudes, and behaviours related to HIV infection among First Nations peoples in Ontario. All decisions were made by consensus between the academic researchers and the Steering Committee in order to take the unique concerns of communities into account. The researchers used random selection to obtain a representative sample. They selected equal numbers of men and women as well as equal numbers within each of four age groups (Myers et al., 1993).

The data were collected using face-to-face interviews as well as an answer booklet for highly personal questions. All interviewers were hired from participating communities, spoke the appropriate First Nations language, and participated in two days of training. For questions about sexual behaviour, respondents were given a choice of using technical terms or slang terms. Most communities took steps to promote the study. The researchers found that many participants had engaged in high-risk sexual behaviours. For example, 40 percent of the men and 18 percent of the women reported two or more sexual partners in the past year. Sixty percent of respondents did not consistently use a condom when engaging in vaginal or anal intercourse.

The methodology used in this study demonstrates a number of issues that need to be kept in mind in doing research with different cultural groups (Ford & Norris, 1991). First, respondents should be interviewed by an interviewer of the same gender and ethnic background as themselves. This practice is important for building rapport and establishing trust during the interview, both of which are critical in obtaining honest answers. Language is another important issue in constructing interviews. Many people, including those from the majority Canadian culture, do not know scientific terms for sexual concepts. Interviewers therefore have to be ready with a supply of slang terms so that they can switch to these if a respondent does not understand a question. This problem becomes more complex when interviewing people whose first language is not English. In keeping with these recommendations, Myers and his colleagues used interviewers from the communities involved in the study, allowed interviewers to translate the question into the appropriate First Nations language as they conducted the interview, if required, and trained them in both technical and slang terms.

This research also demonstrates another important principle—representatives of the target communities participated in the design and management of the study. This has two advantages. First, it allows the communities to have input into the research design and methodology to ensure that the research takes the unique concerns of each community into account. Second, minority-group members are more likely to agree to participate in research if they know that representatives of their communities were involved in designing the study.

In conclusion, doing sex research with people from diverse ethnocultural communities in Canada requires more than just administering the same old surveys to samples of people from these groups. It requires revisions to methodology that are culturally sensitive to issues such as the ethnicity of the interviewer, the language used in the interview, and the special sensitivity of some groups regarding some topics.

MEDIA CONTENT ANALYSIS

To this point we have focused on methods used to analyze people's responses. Yet we also have recognized the profound impact of the mass media on Canadians' sexuality. To be able to understand this impact, we need to be able to analyze the media. As an example, let's suppose that your friend Rachel says that it is deeply disturbing that women are shown in nothing but traditional roles on prime-time TV, and this situation hasn't improved a bit over the years. Your other friend Monique disagrees, saying that there may still be some traditional images of women, but there are many examples of women in non-traditional roles such as doctors, and the media's portrayals of women have changed a lot over the years. How can you decide who is right? Arguing won't settle the debate. However, you could use a technique called content analysis to analyze how the media portray women today and how they have portrayed women in the past (Reinharz, 1992; Weber, 1990).

Content analysis: A set of procedures used to make valid inferences about text.

Content analysis refers to a set of procedures used to make valid inferences about text. The "text" might be romance novels, advice columns in *Chatelaine* magazine, lyrics from rap music, movies, or prime-time television programs. As it turns out, many of the same methodological issues discussed earlier also come into play with content analysis. Here, we have used a recently published study on depictions of sex and rape in popular films to exemplify these issues (Bufkin & Eschholz, 2000).

Sampling is one such issue. The first thing the researchers conducting this study needed to do was define the population. Were they interested in all films or particular types of films? Next, they needed to define the time period of interest: films released in the current year, the past five years, the past ten years, and so on. Finally, they needed to decide whether to analyze all films that met these criteria or a subsample of these films, and whether to analyze the entire film or selected parts of the film. The researchers decided to include the 50 top-grossing films in the United States in 1996 in their sample.

The next step is to create a coding scheme. First, the researchers needed to define the recording unit—was it the film, the scene, particular behaviours, or specific statements? The authors chose to use two units of analysis: the movie and the sex scene. Next, perhaps more importantly, they needed to define coding categories. Creating the coding scheme involves defining the basic content categories, the presence or absence of which will be recorded; the coding categories used depend on the research questions. In this instance, the researchers categorized sex scenes as heterosexual or homosexual and consensual or rape. They had to define what observable behaviours count as "sex"; they used a broad definition of sex including not only depictions of sexual activities but also sexual intercourse that was implied; for example, when characters were shown in bed after sexual intercourse. There were other categories used for categorizing rape scenes, including the type of rape and whether the offender was punished for the crime.

Figure 3.7 Precise methods have been developed for analyzing the content of the media.

Researchers doing content analysis must demonstrate that their data are reliable and not biased. Usually, a measure called intercoder or interrater reliability is used. Two or more trained individuals independently code all or some of the text in the sample. This is done to ensure that the coding is accurate and the coder is not either overreporting (e.g., recording scenes as rape when they did not actually include rape) or underreporting (e.g., failing to record scenes that include forced intercourse as rape scenes). To give a measure of the interrater reliability, the researcher computes a correlation or percentage agreement between the two coders' results. In this study, the interrater reliability for the occurrence of rape was a correlation of 0.98. This is very high, since if the coders agreed exactly the correlation would be 1.0.

Intercoder or interrater reliability: In content analysis, the correlation or percentage of agreement between two coders independently rating the same texts.

Content analysis is a powerful scientific technique that allows us to know how the media portray sexuality. For example, in this study researchers found that—contrary to common perceptions that most movies contain sex—60 percent of the movies in this sample did not show a single sex scene. They found a total of 30 sex scenes, of which five were rapes.

A related topic to content analysis is *critical discourse analysis*, which analyzes written texts for their underlying meaning. One such study examined how HIV/AIDS was portrayed in the 20 highest-circulating Canadian magazines in 1991, 1996, and 2001 (Clarke, 2006). The results showed that these stories were still characterized by heterosexism and homonegativity, although more subtly than in the past.

LABORATORY STUDIES USING DIRECT OBSERVATIONS OF SEXUAL BEHAVIOUR

The numerous problems associated with using self-reports of sexual behaviour in scientific research have been discussed. The major alternative to using self-reports is to make direct observations of sexual behaviour in the laboratory. These direct observations overcome the major problems of self-reports: purposeful distortion, inaccurate memory, and inability of people to estimate correctly or describe certain aspects of their behaviour. The pioneering example of this approach is Masters and Johnson's work on the physiology of sexual response.

MASTERS AND JOHNSON: THE PHYSIOLOGY OF SEXUAL RESPONSE

William Masters began his research on the physiology of sexual response in 1954. No one had ever studied human sexual behaviour in the laboratory before, so he had to develop all the necessary research techniques from scratch. He began by interviewing 188 female prostitutes, as well as 27 male prostitutes working for a homosexual clientele. They gave him important preliminary data in which they "described many methods for elevating and controlling sexual tensions and demonstrated innumerable variations in stimulative techniques," some of which were useful in the later program of therapy for sexual disorders.

Meanwhile, Masters began setting up his laboratory and equipping it with the necessary instruments: an electrocardiograph to measure changes in heart rate over the sexual cycle, an electromyograph to measure muscular contractions in the body during sexual response, and a pH meter to measure the acidity of the vagina during the various stages of sexual response.

SAMPLING

Masters made a major breakthrough when he decided that it should be possible to recruit normal participants from the general population and have them engage in sexual behaviour in the laboratory, where their behaviour and physiological responses could be carefully observed and measured. This approach had never been used before, as even the daring Kinsey had settled for people's verbal reports of their behaviour.

Masters let it be known in the medical school and university community that he needed volunteers for laboratory studies of human sexual response. Some people volunteered because of their belief in the importance of the research. Some, of course, came out of curiosity or because they were exhibitionists; they were weeded out in the initial interviews. Participants were paid for their hours in the laboratory, as is typical in medical research, so many medical students and graduate students participated because it was a way to earn money.

Initially, all prospective participants were given detailed interviews by Masters and his colleague Virginia Johnson. People who had histories of emotional problems or who seemed uncomfortable with the topic of sex either failed to come back after this interview or were eliminated even if they were willing to proceed. Participants were also assured that the anonymity and confidentiality of their participation would be protected carefully. In all, 382 women and 312 men participated in the laboratory studies reported in *Human Sexual Response* (Masters & Johnson, 1966). The men ranged in age from 21 to 89, while the women ranged from 18 to 78. A total of 276 married couples participated, as well as 106 women and 36 men who were unmarried. The unmarried persons were helpful mainly in the studies that did not require sexual intercourse, as, for example, studies of the ejaculatory mechanism in males and of the effects of sexual arousal on the positioning of the diaphragm in the vagina.

Certainly, the group of people Masters and Johnson studied were not a random sample of the population of the United States. In fact, one might imagine that people who would agree to participate in such research would be rather unusual. The data indicate that they were more educated than the general population, and the sample was mostly white, with only a few ethnic minority persons participating. Paying the participants probably helped broaden the sample since it attracted some people who simply needed the money. The sample omitted two notable types of people: those who were not sexually experienced or did not respond to sexual stimulation and those who were unwilling to have their sexual behaviour studied in the laboratory. Therefore, the results Masters and Johnson obtained might not generalize to such people.

Just exactly how critical is this sampling problem to the validity of the research? Masters and Johnson were not particularly concerned about it because they assumed that the processes they were studying are normative; that is, they work in essentially the same way in all people. This assumption is commonly made in medical research. For example, a researcher who is studying the digestive process does not worry that the sample is composed of all medical students, since the assumption is that digestion works the same way in all human beings. If this assumption is also true for the physiology of sexual response, then all people respond similarly, and it does not matter that the sample is not random. Whether this assumption is correct remains to be seen (see Chapter 9 for further critiques). The sampling problem, however, does mean that Masters and Johnson could not make statistical conclusions on the basis of their research; for example, they could not say that X percent of all women have multiple orgasms. Any percentages would be specific to their sample and could not be generalized to the rest of the population.

In defence of their sampling techniques, even if they had identified an initial probability sample they would still almost surely have had a very high refusal rate, probably higher than in survey research, and the probability sample would have been ruined. At present, this seems to be an unsolvable problem in this type of research.

DATA COLLECTION TECHNIQUES

After they were accepted for the project, participants proceeded to the laboratory phase of the study. First, they had a "practice session," in which they engaged in sexual activity in the laboratory in complete privacy, with no data being recorded and no researchers present. The purpose of this was to allow the participants to become comfortable with engaging in sexual behaviour in a laboratory setting.

The physical responses of the participants were then recorded during sexual intercourse, masturbation, and "artificial coition." Masters and Johnson made an important technical advance with the development of the artificial coition technique. In it, a female participant stimulates herself with an artificial penis constructed of clear plastic; it is powered by an electric motor, and the woman can adjust the depth and frequency of the thrust. There is a light and a recording apparatus inside the artificial penis, so the changes occurring inside the vagina can be photographed.

Measures such as these avoid the problems of distortion that are possible with self-reports. They also answer much different questions. That is, it would be impossible from such measures to tell whether the person had engaged in same-sex sexual activity or how frequently he or she masturbated. Instead, they ascertain how the body responds to sexual stimulation, with a kind of accuracy and detail that would be impossible to obtain through self-reports.

One final potential problem also deserves mention. It has to do with the problems of laboratory studies: That is, do people respond the same sexually in the laboratory as they do in the privacy of their own homes?

ETHICAL CONSIDERATIONS

Masters and Johnson were attentive to ethical principles. They were careful to use informed consent. Potential participants were given detailed explanations of the kinds of things they would be required to do in the research and were given ample opportunity at all stages to withdraw from the research if they so desired. Furthermore, Masters and Johnson eliminated people who appeared too anxious or distressed during the preliminary interviews.

It is also possible that participating in the research itself might have been harmful in some way to some people. Masters and Johnson were particularly concerned with the long-term effects of participating in the research. Accordingly, they made follow-up contacts with the participants at five-year intervals. In no case did a participant report developing a sexual disorder. In fact, many of the couples reported specific ways in which participating in the research enriched their marriages. Thus, the available data seem to indicate that such research does not harm the participants and may in some ways benefit them, not to mention the benefit to society that results from gaining information in such an important area.

In sum, direct observations of sexual behaviour of the type done by Masters and Johnson have some distinct advantages but also some disadvantages compared with survey-type research. Their research avoids the problems of self-reports and is capable of answering much more detailed physiological questions than self-reports could. But the research is costly and time-consuming, making large samples impractical; furthermore, a high refusal rate is probably inevitable, so probability samples are impossible to obtain.

Participant-Observer Studies

Participant-observer technique: A research method in which the scientist becomes part of the community to be studied and makes observations from inside the community.

A research method used by anthropologists and sociologists is the participant-observer technique. In this type of research, the scientist tries to become a part of the community to be studied, and she or he makes observations from inside the community. In the study of sexual behaviour, the researcher thus may be able to get direct observations of sexual behaviour combined with interview data.

Examples of this type of research are studies of sexual behaviour in other cultures, such as those done in Mangaia, Mehinaku, and Inis Beag, which were discussed in Chapter 1. Two other examples are Laud Humphreys's study of the tearoom trade and Charles Moser's study of S/M (sadomasochistic) parties.

HUMPHREYS: THE TEAROOM TRADE

Sociologist Laud Humphreys (1970) conducted a participant-observer study of impersonal sex between men in public places. Briefly, Humphreys acted as a lookout while men engaged in sex acts in public restrooms ("tearooms"); his job was to sound a warning if police or other intruders approached. This permitted Humphreys to make direct observations of the sexual behaviour. He also got the licence-plate numbers of the men involved, traced them, and later interviewed them in their homes under the pretext of conducting a routine survey.

Humphreys obtained a wealth of information from the study, but in so doing he violated several ethical principles of behavioural research. He had no informed consent from his subjects; they were never even aware of the fact that they were participants in research, much less of the nature of the research. Thus, this study was quite controversial.

S/M PARTIES

Sex researcher Charles Moser observed S/M (sadomasochistic) interactions in semi-public settings in the United States, attending more than 200 S/M parties (Moser, 1998). Parties are typically highly scripted. The person who gives the party may advertise it widely (e.g., on the Internet) or may issue personal invitations to only a very selected list. The parties may have a particular theme, such as female dominant/male submissive only or women only. The party might be held at a person's home or in a rented space.

Each party has a particular set of rules, which vary from one party to another, and guests may be required to sign a written agreement to follow the rules. Issues covered in these rules include who may talk to whom (can a submissive be spoken to?), who may play with whom, who may have sex with whom, prohibited S/M or sexual behaviours, what constitutes safer sex, not blocking equipment by sitting on it, and so on. Drunkenness is never acceptable; some parties allow wine or beer, but others ban all alcohol.

Some individuals plan to have a first "date" at a party. Parties clearly have the function of ensuring safety for participants, since others are always present if an interaction goes too far. Potential partners negotiate what kind of interaction they desire—for example, pain versus humiliation.

Perhaps most interesting is the fact that coitus and genitally focused activity designed to produce orgasm are very rare at these parties. The participants describe the S/M experience as highly sexual, but orgasm typically is not the goal.

Moser did not report that he obtained informed consent from the people he observed. However, their behaviour was public, leading to a relaxation of human subjects regulations. In his report, he was careful not to divulge any identifying information about individuals.

EXPERIMENTAL SEX RESEARCH

All the studies discussed so far have had one thing in common: they were all studies of people's sexual behaviour as it occurs naturally, conducted by means of either self-reports or direct observations. Such reports are correlational studies; that is, at best the data they obtain can tell us that certain factors are related. They cannot tell us, however, what causes various aspects of sexual behaviour.

For instance, suppose we conduct a survey and find that women who masturbated to orgasm before marriage are more likely to have a high consistency of orgasm in marriage than women who did not. From this it would be tempting to conclude that practice in masturbating causes women to have more orgasms in heterosexual sex. Unfortunately, this is not a legitimate conclusion to draw from the data, since many other factors might also explain the results. For example, it could be that some women have a higher sex drive than others, which causes them to masturbate and also have orgasms in heterosexual sex. Therefore, the most we can conclude is that masturbation experience is related to (or correlated with) orgasm consistency in marital sex.

An alternative method that does allow researchers to determine the causes of various aspects of behaviour is the experiment. According to its technical definition, in an experiment one factor must be manipulated while all other factors are held constant. Thus, any differences among the groups of people who received different treatments on that one factor can be said to be caused by that factor. For obvious reasons, most experimental research is conducted in the laboratory.

As an example of an experiment, let us consider a study that investigated whether being interviewed face-to-face causes children to underreport their sexual experiences (Romer et al., 1997). The participants were approximately 400 low-income children between the ages of 9 and 15. Some were assigned to a face-to-face interview with an experienced adult interviewer of their own gender. Others were assigned to be interviewed by a "talking computer," which had the same questions programmed into it. The questions appeared on the screen and, simultaneously, came through headphones for those who were not good readers. Presumably in the talking computer condition, the child feels more of a sense of privacy and anonymity and therefore responds more truthfully.

Among 13-year-old boys interviewed by the talking computer, 76 percent said they had "had sex," compared with only 50 percent of the boys in the face-to-face interview. Forty-eight percent of 13-year-old girls interviewed by computer said they had had sex, compared with 25 percent of those interviewed by a human. The children clearly reported more sexual activity to the computer than to a human interviewer.

In the language of experimental design, the *independent variable* (manipulated variable) was the type of interview (computer or human interviewer). The *dependent variable* (the measured variable) was whether they reported that they had had sex (there were a number of other dependent variables as well, but a discussion of them would take us too far afield).

The results indicated that those interviewed by humans reported significantly less sexual activity than those interviewed by computer. Because the research design was experimental,

> **Correlational study:** A study in which the researcher does not manipulate variables but rather studies naturally occurring relationships (correlations) among variables.

> **Experiment:** A type of research study in which one variable (the independent variable) is manipulated by the experimenter while all other factors are held constant; the researcher can then study the effects of the independent variable on some measured variable (the dependent variable); the researcher is permitted to make causal inferences about the effects of the independent variable on the dependent variable.

Figure 3.8 An innovation in surveys of children is the use of "talking computers" to ask questions, with the child entering her answers using the mouse or the keyboard.

we can make causal inferences. We can say confidently that the type of interview had an effect on children's answers. We might also say that a face-to-face interview causes children to underreport their activity. That statement is a bit shakier than the previous one, because it assumes that the answers given to the talking computer were "true." It is possible that children overreported or exaggerated in responding to the computer and that their answers to the human interviewer were accurate.

Experimental sex research permits us to make much more powerful statements about the causes of various kinds of sexual phenomena. As for disadvantages, much of the experimental sex research, including the study described here, still relies on self-reports. Experimental sex research is time-consuming and costly, and it can generally be done only on small samples of participants. Sometimes in their efforts to control all variables except the independent variable, researchers control too much. Finally, experiments cannot address some of the most interesting, but most complex, questions in the field of sexual behaviour, such as what factors cause people to develop a heterosexual, homosexual, or bisexual orientation.

SUMMARY

Knowledge of the major methods that have been used in sex research and of the problems and merits associated with each is necessary for understanding and evaluating sex research. Sex research can use quantitative or qualitative methods.

Ideally, quantitative sex research should employ probability sampling techniques.

Large-scale surveys of sexual behaviour generally rely on people's self-reports, which may be inaccurate because of purposeful distortion, problems of memory, or an inability to estimate some of the information requested. Direct observations of sexual behaviour avoid these problems, but they lead to an even more restricted sample. They also answer questions that are somewhat different from those answered by surveys. Web-based surveys offer new opportunities for sex research.

In all behavioural research, the ethical principles of informed consent, protection from harm, and justice must be observed, although historically some sex researchers did not do this.

The following statistical terms were introduced: average, mean, median, mode, variability, incidence, frequency, and correlation.

No major national sex surveys have been conducted in Canada. However, there are two large-scale U.S. surveys of sexual behaviour: Kinsey's interview study and the recent NHSLS, which was based on probability sampling. The Canada Youth, Sexual Health, and HIV/AIDS Study assessed adolescent sexuality across Canada. It is difficult to draw any general conclusions from large magazine surveys because the samples are so restricted.

Canadian studies of special populations include a qualitative study of exotic dancers by Maticka-Tyndale and a survey of First Nations peoples headed by Myers.

In media content analysis, researchers use systematic coding categories to analyze what is represented in the media, such as on television, in romance novels, or in magazine ads.

In participant-observer studies, the scientist becomes a part of the community to be studied, and uses a combination of direct observations and interviewing. Examples are studies of sexual behaviour in other cultures, Humphreys's study of the tearoom trade, and Moser's study of S/M parties.

In experimental sex research, the goal is to discover what factors cause or influence various aspects of sexual behaviour. The researcher manipulates an independent variable and measures a dependent variable.

QUESTIONS FOR THOUGHT, DISCUSSION, AND DEBATE

1. Find a recent sex survey in a magazine. Evaluate the quality of the study, using concepts you have learned in this chapter.

2. Of the research techniques in this chapter—surveys, laboratory studies using direct observations, media content analysis, participant-observer studies, experiments—which do you think is best for learning about human sexuality? Why?

3. You want to conduct a survey, using face-to-face interviews, to determine whether there are differences between Asian-Canadian and white-Canadian teenagers ages 15 to 19 in their sexual behaviour and attitudes. In what ways would you tailor the research methods to make them culturally sensitive?

4. Imagine that you have been hired by your college or university to produce a report on the patterns of sexual behaviour of the students there, with the goal of helping the administration plan better in areas such as health services and counselling. You are given a generous budget for data collection. How would you go about collecting the data you would need to produce a truly excellent report?

SUGGESTIONS FOR FURTHER READING

Matsumoto, David. (1994). *Cultural influences on research methods and statistics.* Pacific Grove, CA: Brooks/Cole. This concise book, written for undergraduates, explains principles of cross-cultural research and how one should modify research methods depending on the culture being studied.

Michael, Robert T., Gagnon, John H., Laumann, Edward O., & Kolata, Gina. (1994). *Sex in America: A definitive survey.* Boston: Little, Brown.

This book reports the results of the NHSLS, and is written for the general public.

Wiederman, Michael W. (2001). *Understanding sexuality research.* Belmont, CA: Wadsworth. This slim volume, written for undergraduates, takes up where the present chapter leaves off and offers an excellent analysis of methodological issues in sex research, with interesting examples.

For review questions, web resources, and other learning and study tools, visit the *Understanding Human Sexuality* Online Learning Centre at www.mcgrawhill.ca/olc/hyde.

Chapter

4

SEXUAL ANATOMY

Chapter Highlights

> MEN AND WOMEN, ALL IN ALL, BEHAVE JUST LIKE OUR BASIC SEXUAL ELE-
> MENTS. IF YOU WATCH SINGLE MEN ON A WEEKEND NIGHT THEY REALLY ACT
> VERY MUCH LIKE SPERM—ALL DISORGANIZED, BUMPING INTO THEIR FRIENDS,
> SWIMMING IN THE WRONG DIRECTION.
>
> "I WAS FIRST."
>
> "LET ME THROUGH."
>
> "YOU'RE ON MY TAIL."
>
> "THAT'S MY SPOT."
>
> WE'RE LIKE THE THREE BILLION STOOGES.
>
> BUT THE EGG IS VERY COOL: "WELL, WHO'S IT GOING TO BE? I CAN DIVIDE.
> I CAN WAIT A MONTH. I'M NOT SWIMMING ANYWHERE."*

The women's health movement has emphasized that women need to know more about their bodies. Actually, that is a good principle for everyone to follow, and is consistent with the sexual health perspective described in Chapter 1. The current trend is away from the elitist view that only a select group of people—physicians—should understand the functioning of the body and toward the view that everyone needs more information about his or her own body. The purpose of this chapter is to provide basic information about the structure and functions of the parts of the body that are involved in sexuality and reproduction. In this way, you will be in a better position to identify myths and misinformation about breast and genital size and shape so prevalent in the media that they might lead you to have poor genital self-image. Some readers may anticipate that this will be a boring exercise. Everyone, after all, knows what a penis is and what a vagina is. But even today, we find some bright college and university students who think a woman's urine passes out through her vagina. And how many of you know what the epididymis and the seminiferous tubules are? Even if you know, keep reading. You may find out a few interesting things that you were not aware of.

GENITAL SELF-IMAGE

You may have heard of body image (how we feel about our bodies), but have you thought about how people feel about their genitals? Genital self-image can be defined as our attitudes and feelings about our genitals. Research has shown that although on average the genital self-image of most people is positive, some people see their own genitals quite negatively (Berman et al., 2003; Morrison et al., 2006). People's feelings about their genitals may be affected by whether they perceive their genitals to fit with general cultural norms about genitals (too big, too small), their sexual experiences (e.g., child sexual abuse), and by medical conditions (such as genital surgery). For example, an Alberta study found that men who viewed pornography on the Internet had more negative feelings about their genitals (Morrison et al., 2006). This may be because they came to see their penises as "too small" after viewing the very large penises of men on the Internet. Some people with poor genital body image are choosing to undergo genital cosmetic surgery. For example, vaginal enhancement

Genital self-image: Our attitudes and feelings towards our genitals.

---

*Jerry Seinfeld. (1993). *SeinLanguage*. New York: Bantam Books, p. 17.

surgery is the fastest-growing trend in cosmetic surgery (Laliberté, 2006). Women choose to have this surgery because they believe that it will make their vulva more beautiful and erotic. Vaginal enhancement surgery includes vaginoplasty (tightening of the vagina), hoodectomy (removing the clitoral hood), labia minora reduction, labia majora remodelling, and pubis tuck (removing excess skin above the pubic area to elevate the pubis). Most popular among the patients of one Toronto plastic surgeon and costing thousands of dollars is the "Toronto Trim," which involves reduction of the labia and clitoral hood (Laliberté, 2006). Similarly, some Canadian men are undergoing penis enlargement surgery because they believe (often incorrectly) that their partners would be more satisfied if they had a larger penis. Such surgery results in cosmetic penis enlargement, not actual penis enlargement.

Although not specifically related to poor genital self-image, some people seek to enhance the appearance of their genitals and sexual pleasure by getting a genital piercing.

FEMALE SEXUAL ORGANS

The female sexual organs can be classified into two categories: the *external organs* and the *internal organs*.

EXTERNAL ORGANS

Vulva (VULL-vuh):
The collective term for the external genitals of the female.

The external genitals of the female consist of the clitoris, the mons pubis, the inner lips, the outer lips, and the vaginal opening (see Figure 4.1). Collectively, they are known as the vulva ("crotch"; other terms such as "cunt" and "pussy" may refer either to the vulva or to the vagina, and some ethnic groups use "cock" for the vulva—slang, alas, is not so precise as scientific language).[1] "Vulva" is a wonderful term but, unfortunately, it tends to be underused—the term, that is. The appearance of the vulva varies greatly from one woman to another (see Figure 4.2).

THE CLITORIS

Clitoris (KLIT-or-is):
A small, highly sensitive sexual organ in the female, found in front of the vaginal entrance.

The clitoris is a sensitive organ that is exceptionally important in female sexual response (Figure 4.3). It consists of the tip, a knob of tissue situated externally in front of the vaginal opening and the urethral opening; a shaft consisting of two corpora cavernosa (spongy bodies similar to those in the male's penis) that extends perhaps an inch into the body; and two crura, longer spongy bodies that lie deep in the body and run from the tip of the clitoris to either side of the vagina, under the major lips (Clemente, 1987). Some refer to the entire structure as having a "wishbone" shape. Close to the crura are the vestibular bulbs, which will be discussed in the section on internal organs.

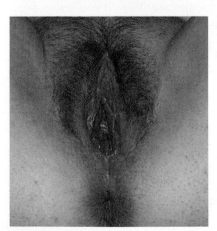

Figure 4.1 The vulva: The external genitals of the female.

As discussed in Chapter 5, female sexual organs and male sexual organs develop from similar tissue before birth; thus we can speak of the organs of one gender as being *homologous* (in the sense of developing from the same source) to the organs of the other gender. The female's clitoris is homologous to the male's penis; that is, both develop from the same embryonic tissue. The clitoris and the penis are similar in several ways. They both have corpora cavernosa, they vary in size from one person to the next, and they are erectile because their internal structures contains corpora cavernosa that fill with blood. The corpora cavernosa and the mech-

---

[1] For a discussion of slang terms for female and male genitals, see Braun and Kitzinger (2001).

anism of erection will be considered in more detail in the discussion of the male sexual organs. The clitoris has a rich supply of nerve endings, making it very sensitive to stroking. Most women find it to be more sensitive to erotic stimulation than any other part of the body.

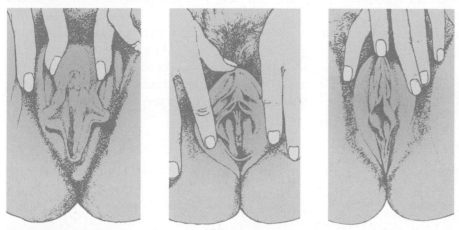

Figure 4.2 The shape of the vulva varies widely from one woman to the next.

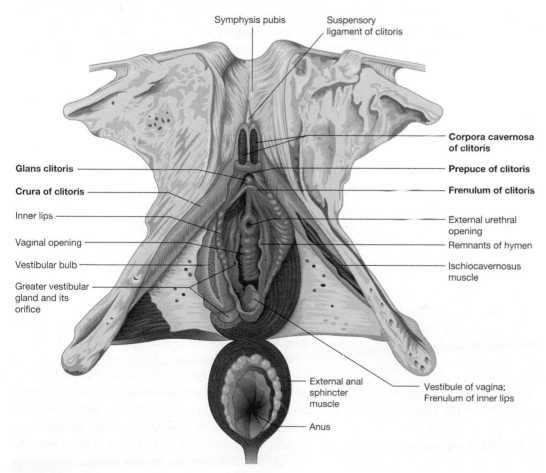

Symphysis pubis

Suspensory ligament of clitoris

Corpora cavernosa of clitoris

Glans clitoris

Prepuce of clitoris

Crura of clitoris

Frenulum of clitoris

Inner lips

External urethral opening

Vaginal opening

Remnants of hymen

Vestibular bulb

Ischiocavernosus muscle

Greater vestibular gland and its orifice

External anal sphincter muscle

Vestibule of vagina; Frenulum of inner lips

Anus

Figure 4.3 Structure of the clitoris.

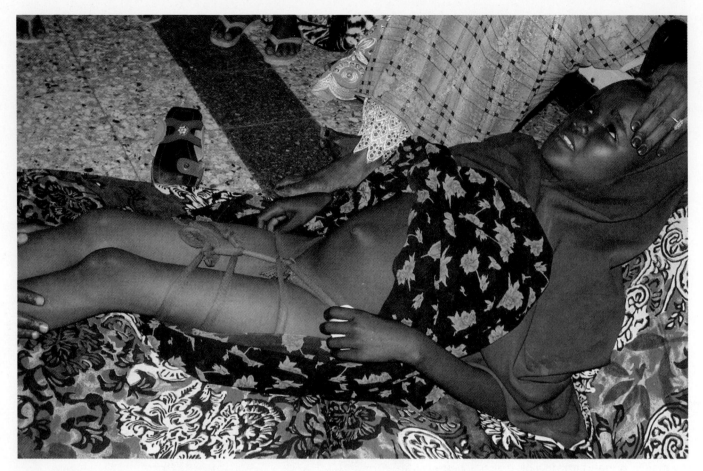

Figure 4.4 Twenty-five African nations practise some form of ritualized genital cutting of young girls as an initiation into womanhood. Clitoridectomy is also practised in Muslim countries outside Africa, and was practised in North America during the Victorian era (see In Focus 4.1 on page 86).

The clitoris is unique in that it is the only part of the sexual anatomy with no known reproductive function. All the other sexual organs serve sexual and reproductive functions. For example, not only is the vagina used for sexual intercourse, but it also receives the sperm and serves as the passageway through which the baby travels during childbirth. The penis not only produces sexual arousal and pleasure but also is responsible for ejaculation and impregnation. The clitoris clearly has an important function in producing sexual arousal. Unlike the other sexual organs, however, it appears to have no direct function in reproduction.

THE MONS

Mons pubis (PYOO-bis): The fatty pad of tissue under the pubic hair.

Other parts of the vulva are the mons pubis, the inner lips, and the outer lips. The **mons pubis** (also called the *mons* or the *mons veneris,* for "mountain of Venus") is the rounded, fatty pad of tissue, covered with pubic hair, at the front of the body. It lies on top of the pubic bones.

THE LABIA

Outer lips: Rounded pads of fatty tissue lying on either side of the vaginal entrance.

Inner lips: Thin folds of skin lying on either side of the vaginal entrance.

The **outer lips** (or *labia majora,* for "major lips") are rounded pads of fatty tissue lying along both sides of the vaginal opening; they are covered with pubic hair. The **inner lips** (or *labia minora,* for "minor lips") are two hairless folds of skin lying between the outer lips and running right along the edge of the vaginal opening. Sometimes they are folded over, concealing the vaginal opening until they are spread apart. The inner lips extend forward and come together in front, forming the clitoral hood. The inner and outer lips are well supplied with nerve endings and thus are also important in sexual stimulation and arousal.

A pair of small glands, the Bartholin glands, lie just inside the inner lips (refer to Figure 4.1 on page 82). Their function is unknown, and they are of interest only because they sometimes become infected.[2]

A few more landmarks should be noted (see Figure 4.1). The place where the inner lips come together behind the vaginal opening is called the *fourchette*. The area of skin between the vaginal opening and the anus is called the perineum. The vaginal opening itself is sometimes called the introitus. Notice also that the urinary opening lies about midway between the clitoris and the vaginal opening. Thus urine does not pass out through the clitoris (as might be expected from analogy with the male) or through the vagina, but instead through a separate pathway, the *urethra,* with a separate opening.

THE VULVAR VESTIBULE

The area enclosed by the inner lips is called the vestibule ("entranceway"). It contains the openings to the vagina and the urethra. This area is highly sensitive to pleasurable stimulation because it is well-supplied with nerve endings. However, some women develop vulvar vestibulitis, in which the vestibule gets extremely sensitive and red such that any touch of the area around the vaginal opening elicits moderate to severe pain. For women with vulvar vestibulitis, pain can result from genital touching during sexual activity and vaginal penetration, but also from biking, exercise, tight clothing, and tampon insertion.

SELF-KNOWLEDGE

One important difference between the male sex organs and the female sex organs—and a difference that has some important psychological consequences—is that the female's external genitals are much less visible than the male's. A male can view his external genitals directly either by looking down at them or by looking into a mirror while naked. Either of these two strategies for the female, however, will result at best in a view of the mons. The clitoris, the inner and outer lips, and the vaginal opening remain hidden. Indeed, many adult women have never taken a direct look at their own vulva. This obstacle can be overcome by the simple method of using a mirror. The genitals can be viewed either by putting a mirror on the floor and sitting in front of it or by standing up and putting one foot on the edge of a chair, bed, or something similar and holding the mirror up near the genitals (see Figure 4.5). We recommend that all women use a mirror to identify on their own bodies all the parts shown in Figure 4.1.

Figure 4.5 Body education: The mirror exercise lets women see their own genitals. (Photograph by Hazel Hankin Photography.)

Bartholin glands: Two tiny glands located on either side of the vaginal entrance.

Perineum (pair-ih-NEE-um): The skin between the vaginal entrance and the anus.

Introitus: Another word for the vaginal entrance.

Vestibule: Area of the vulva enclosed by the inner lips.

[2]And there is a limerick about them:
> There was a young man from Calcutta
> Who was heard in his beard to mutter,
> "If her Bartholin glands
> Don't respond to my hands,
> I'm afraid I shall have to use butter."

Actually, there is a biological fallacy in the limerick. Can you spot it? If not, see Chapter 9.

IN FOCUS 4.1

What Is Female Genital Cutting?

Today a worldwide sexual health controversy rages over female genital cutting (FGC, also known as female genital mutilation). FGC is practised in 25 African nations as well as in several countries in the Middle East and among Muslim populations in Indonesia and Malaysia. The United Nations estimates that it affects between 100 and 140 million women and girls worldwide. Typically, girls are subjected to the procedure between the ages of four and ten, although sometimes it is done during infancy. Often the procedure is performed by a village woman, with no anaesthetic and under unsanitary conditions. However, it increasingly is being performed by trained health personnel. If these practices seem remote to many North Americans, it is important to recognize that immigrant women from these countries now reside in North America. Moreover, some of these practices were performed in Britain and North America in the 1800s, during the Victorian era, to cure various "female weaknesses" such as masturbation and "nervousness." Currently, increasing numbers of Canadian women are opting for "vaginal enhancement surgery" because they believe that their vulva is more beautiful and erotic that way. Although not as extreme as FGC, the message about female genitals is similar: Women need to undergo surgical procedures such as labiaplasty (reduction of the inner or outer lips) to make the appearance of their labia more acceptable and avoid embarrassment.

FGC is practised in several forms, depending on the customs of the particular culture. The mildest form, called sunna, refers to the removal of just the clitoral hood (prepuce), not the clitoris; it is the only procedure that could legitimately be called "female circumcision," analogous to male circumcision. In its mildest form, it may involve only making a slit in the prepuce, not removing it. A second form of FGC is excision (sometimes known as clitoridectomy), which refers to complete removal of the clitoris and perhaps some of the inner lips. The most extreme form is infibulation or pharaonic circumcision (named for the pharaohs of Egypt, under whose reign the practice is said to have originated thou-

sands of years ago). It involves the removal of the clitoris, all of the inner lips, and part of the outer lips; the raw edges of the outer lips are then stitched together to cover the urethral opening and the vaginal entrance, with only a small opening left for the passage of urine and menstrual fluid.

Infibulation poses severe health problems for women. Hemorrhaging may occur, leading to shock and even to bleeding to death. Because of the unsanitary conditions present during the procedure, tetanus and other infections are risks. Because the same instrument may be used on many girls, HIV and hepatitis B can be transmitted. A common problem is that the pain of the wound is so severe and the stitching so tight that the girl avoids urinating or cannot urinate properly, leading to urinary infections and other complications. A tightly infibulated woman can only urinate drop by drop, and her menstrual period may take 10 days and be extremely painful. Women who have undergone FGC are also at higher risk of infection such as herpes and bacterial vaginosis.

The sexual and reproductive health consequences are no less severe. Infibulation is an effective method for ensuring virginity until marriage, but on the wedding night the man must force an opening through stitching and scar tissue. This is painful and may take days; a midwife may be called to cut open the tissue. Some men report wounds to the penis as a result of attempts at intercourse with wives who have had FGC. Infibulation drastically affects women's sexual pleasure. For example, orgasm would be only a remote possibility for a woman whose clitoris has been removed. Infibulated women have a substantial risk of complications during childbirth. The scar must always be cut open to permit delivery and, if done too late, the baby may die.

A recent study surveyed 432 Somali women who had given birth in Canada within the previous five years (Chalmers & Omer-Hashi, 2000). Almost all (96 percent) had experienced FGC before coming to Canada, often having eagerly anticipated the procedure. Most of these women had been five or six years old at the time of the procedure, which was done most often by a traditional birth attendant or a midwife using a razor blade. Thorns were often used to hold the labia in place, and the girls legs were bound together to suture the incision. On average the women had had to have the operation repeated more than three times because the procedure did not heal well. Most had experienced serious health consequences and reported that they did not enjoy sex. Nonetheless, almost half said they would want their daughters to have the procedure. Most (70 percent) said they would prefer to be left open if they were to deliver a baby again. Most (88 percent) reported hurtful comments and insensitivity about their pain from health care professionals during their pregnancy and delivery.

If these procedures are so harmful, why do they persist? Why do girls submit to them, and even ask for them, and why do their parents permit or even encourage it? The answer lies in the complex and powerful interplay of culture and gender. Being infibulated indicates not only virginity but also a woman's loyalty to and identification with her culture and its traditions, a particularly sensitive issue for people long dominated by European colonizers. A woman who is not infibulated is not marriageable in these cultures in which marriage is the only acceptable way of life for an adult woman. When those are the rules of the game, it is less surprising that girls submit or even want to be circumcised and that their parents require them to do it. Particular communities may also hold certain beliefs that make these procedures seem necessary. For example, in some areas there is a belief that the clitoris contains poison and can harm men during sexual intercourse and kill children during birth. Some Muslims mistakenly believe that it is required by their faith, although it is not mentioned in the Koran. In practice, FGC is only loosely associated with Islam. In Mali, for example, 92 percent of Muslim women have had FGC, but so have 76 percent of Christian women (Yoder et al., 2004).

Infibulation raises a dilemma for Canadians. As a multicultural country, we generally encourage the approach of "cultural relativism," an openness to and appreciation of the customs of other cultures. FGC is definitely a custom of other cultures. If we apply standards of cultural relativism, we should say, "Great, if that's what people from those cultures want." However, the World Health Organization, as well as many of the organizations that regulate the practice of medicine in Canada, has condemned the practice of FGC. Both the parents who arrange FGC and the person who performs it may be charged with assault under Canadian law. Recent immigrants to Canada from Somalia and other areas of Africa may feel torn between loyalty to their native cultures and the realities of Canadian law in deciding about FGC for their daughters. In addition, many immigrant women from these areas who have been subjected to FGC before arriving in Canada may have physicians who are not knowledgeable about FGC. While physicians may cut open an infibulated woman to permit childbirth, they are not allowed to reconstruct the infibulation following childbirth, regardless of the wishes of the woman.

On a more hopeful note, a grassroots movement of women has sprung up in a number of African nations, including Kenya, Gambia, Sudan, Somalia, and Nigeria, that is dedicated to eliminating these practices. In 2003, member states of the African Union signed the Maputo Protocol, which prohibits FGC; however, the protocol has not yet been ratified by the 15 countries required for it to come into effect. Furthermore, to put matters into perspective, only about 15 percent of cultures that practise FGC do the severe form, infibulation. The remaining cultures practise the milder forms ranging from a slit in the prepuce to clitoridectomy. Although far more cultures practise male genital modification (such as circumcision, supercision, and subcision) than practise FGC, these procedures do not cause either the considerable daily discomfort or the health risks associated with FGC.

Sources: Almroth et al., 2001; Chalmers & Omer-Hashi, 2000; Council on Scientific Affairs, 1995; Gregersen, 1996; Gruenbaum, 2000; Horowitz & Jackson, 1997; Kiragu, 1995; Laliberté, 2006; Lightfoot-Klein, 1993; Leonard, 2000; Morrison et al., 2001; Schroeder, 1994; Toubia, 1994, 1995; Williams & Sobieszyczyk, 1997.

The Hymen

The **hymen** ("cherry," "maidenhead") is a thin membrane which, if present, partially covers the vaginal opening. The hymen may be one of a number of different types (see Figure 4.6), although it generally has some openings in it; otherwise the menstrual flow would not be able to pass out.[3] For many women the hymen is broken or stretched at the time of first intercourse as the penis moves into the vagina. This may cause bleeding and possibly some pain. Typically, though, it is an untraumatic occurrence and goes unnoticed in the excitement of the moment. For a woman who is very concerned about her hymen and what will happen to it at first coitus, there are two possible approaches. A physician can cut the hymen neatly so that it will not tear at the time of first intercourse, or the woman herself can stretch it by repeatedly inserting a finger into the vagina and pressing on it.

The hymen, and its destruction at first intercourse, has captured the interest of people in many cultures. In Europe during the Middle Ages, the lord might claim the right to deflower a peasant bride on her wedding night before passing her on to her husband (the practice is called *droit du seigneur* in French for "right of the lord," and *jus primae noctis* in Latin for "law of the first night"). The hymen has been taken as evidence of virginity. Thus bleeding on the wedding night was proof that the bride had been delivered intact to the groom; the parading of the bloody bed sheets on the wedding night, a custom of the Kurds of the Middle East, is one ritual based on this belief.

Such practices rest on the assumption that a woman without a hymen is not a virgin. However, we now know that this is not true. Some girls are simply born without a hymen, and others may tear it in active sports such as horseback riding. Unfortunately, this means that in cultures that prize female virginity, some women have been humiliated unjustly for their lack of a hymen.

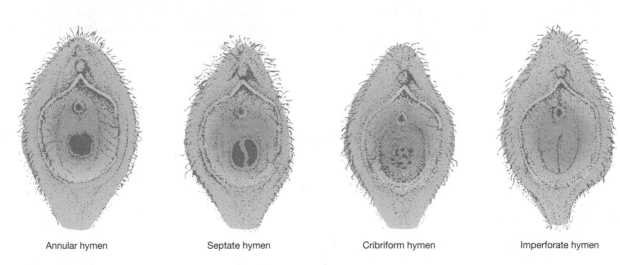

Annular hymen   Septate hymen   Cribriform hymen   Imperforate hymen

Figure 4.6   There are several types of hymens.

---

[3]The rare condition in which the hymen is a tough tissue with no opening is called *imperforate hymen* and can be corrected with fairly simple surgery.

INTERNAL ORGANS

The internal sex organs of the female consist of the vagina, the vestibular bulbs, the Skene's glands, the uterus, a pair of ovaries, and a pair of fallopian tubes (see Figure 4.7).

THE VAGINA

The **vagina** is the tube-shaped organ into which the penis is inserted during coitus; it also receives the ejaculate. Because it is the passageway through which a baby travels during birth, it is sometimes also called the *birth canal*. In the resting or unaroused state, the vagina is about 8 to 10 centimetres (3 to 4 inches) long and tilts slightly backward from the bottom to the top. At the bottom it ends in the vaginal opening, or *introitus*. At the top it connects with the cervix

Vagina (vuh-JINE-uh): The tube-shaped organ in the female into which the penis is inserted during coitus and through which a baby passes during birth.

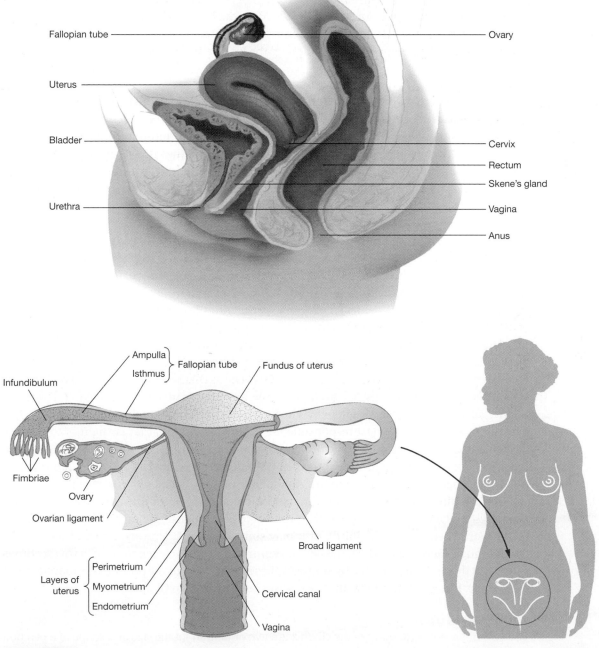

Figure 4.7   Internal sexual and reproductive organs of the female from a side view (top) and a front view.

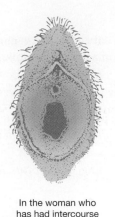
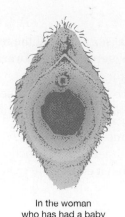

Virginal   In the woman who   In the woman
                            has had intercourse   who has had a baby

Figure 4.8 Appearance of the vulva of a woman who is a virgin (see Figure 4.6 for other appearances); a woman who has had intercourse but has not had a baby (nulliparous); and a woman who has had a baby (parous).

(the lower part of the uterus). It is a very flexible organ that works somewhat like a balloon. In the resting state its walls lie against each other like the sides of an uninflated balloon; during arousal it expands like an inflated balloon, allowing space to accommodate the penis.

The walls of the vagina have three layers. The inner layer, the *vaginal mucosa,* is a mucous membrane similar to the inner lining of the mouth. The middle layer is muscular, and the outer layer forms a covering. The walls of the vagina are extremely elastic and are capable of expanding to the extent necessary during intercourse and childbirth, although with age they become thinner and less flexible.

The nerve supply of the vagina is mostly to the lower one-third, near the introitus. That part is sensitive to erotic stimulation. The inner two-thirds of the vagina contains almost no nerve endings and is therefore relatively insensitive except to feelings of deep pressure. Some women have a spot on the front wall of the vagina that is more sensitive than the rest of the vagina, but even it is not nearly so sensitive as the inner lips, outer lips, or clitoris (Schultz et al., 1989). This spot is referred to by some as the G-spot (see Chapter 9).

The number of slang terms for the vagina (e.g., "beaver," "cunt") and the frequency of their usage testify to its power of fascination across the ages. One concern has been with size: whether some vaginas are too small or too large. As noted earlier, though, the vagina is highly elastic and expandable. Thus, at least in principle, any penis can fit into any vagina. The penis is, after all, not nearly so large as a baby's head, which manages to fit through the vagina. The part of the vagina that is most responsible for a man's sensation, that is "tight," "too tight," or "too loose," is the introitus. One of the things that can stretch the introitus is childbirth; indeed, there is a considerable difference in the appearance of the vulva of a woman who has never had a baby *(nulliparous)* and the vulva of a woman who has *(parous)* (see Figure 4.8).

Surrounding the vagina, the urethra, and the anus is a set of muscles called the *pelvic floor muscles.* One of these muscles, the pubococcygeus muscle, is particularly important. It may be stretched during childbirth, or it may simply be weak. However, it can be strengthened through exercises in which the woman contracts the muscle ten times in a row six times a day, and this is recommended by sex therapists as well as by many popular sex manuals and magazines. Details of how to do these exercises are provided in Chapter 18.

THE VESTIBULAR BULBS

The vestibular bulbs (or bulbs of the clitoris) are two organs about the size and shape of a pea pod (refer to Figure 4.3 on page 83). They lie on either side of the vaginal wall, near the entrance, under the inner lips (O'Connell et al., 2005a). They are erectile tissue and lie close to the crura of the clitoris.

Pubococcygeus muscle (pyoo-bo-cox-ih-GEE-us): A muscle around the vaginal entrance.

Vestibular bulbs: Erectile tissue running under the inner lips and Skene's gland.

THE SKENE'S GLAND, OR FEMALE PROSTATE

The Skene's gland, or female prostate (also called the paraurethral gland), lies between the wall of the urethra and the wall of the vagina (Zaviačič et al., 2000). Its ducts empty into the urethra, but it can be felt on the front wall of the vagina. Although controversial in the past, the evidence indicates that it secretes fluid that is biochemically similar to male prostate fluid. Many women find it to be a region of special erotic sensitivity on the wall of the vagina. The size of the female prostate varies considerably from one woman to the next, as does the amount of its secretions. Some women experience no secretion, whereas others have an actual ejaculation when they orgasm. This is the organ dubbed the G-spot, which is responsible for female ejaculation, discussed in Chapter 9.

Skene's gland: The female prostate. Also called the paraurethral gland.

THE UTERUS

The uterus (womb) is about the size and shape of an upside-down pear. It is usually tilted forward and is held in place by ligaments. The narrow lower third, called the *cervix*, opens into the vagina. The top is the *fundus,* the main part the *body*. The entrance to the uterus through the cervix is very narrow, about the diameter of a drinking straw, and is called the *os* (or cervical canal). The major function of the uterus is to hold and nourish a developing fetus.

Uterus (YOO-tur-us): The organ in the female in which the fetus develops.

The uterus, like the vagina, consists of three layers. The inner layer, or *endometrium,* is richly supplied with glands and blood vessels. Its state varies according to the age of the woman and the phase of the menstrual cycle. It is the endometrium that is sloughed off at menstruation and creates the menstrual discharge. The middle layer, the *myometrium,* is muscular. The muscles are very strong, creating the powerful contractions of labour and orgasm, and also highly elastic, capable of stretching to accommodate a nine-month-old fetus. The outer layer—the *perimetrium*—forms the external cover of the uterus.

THE FALLOPIAN TUBES

Extending out from the sides of the upper end of the uterus are the fallopian tubes, also called the *oviducts* ("egg ducts") or *uterine tubes* (refer to Figure 4.7 on page 89). The fallopian tubes are extremely narrow (0.2 to 0.5 mm) and are lined with hairlike projections called *cilia*. The fallopian tubes are the pathway by which the egg travels toward the uterus and the sperm reach the egg. Fertilization of the egg typically occurs in the infundibulum, the section of the tube closest to the ovary; the fertilized egg then travels the rest of the way through the tube to the uterus. The infundibulum curves around toward the ovary; at its end are numerous fingerlike projections called *fimbriae,* which extend toward the ovary.

Fallopian (fuh-LOW-pee-un) tubes: The tubes extending from the uterus to the ovaries; also called the oviducts.

THE OVARIES

The ovaries are two organs about the size and shape of unshelled almonds; they lie on either side of the uterus. The ovaries have two important functions; they produce eggs (ova), and they manufacture the sex hormones *estrogen* and *progesterone.*

Ovaries: Two organs in the female that produce eggs and sex hormones.

Each ovary contains numerous follicles. A *follicle* is a capsule that surrounds an egg (not to be confused with hair follicles, which are quite different). A female is born with an estimated 1 million immature eggs (Federman, 2006). Beginning at puberty, one or several of the follicles mature during each menstrual cycle. When the egg has matured, the follicle bursts open and releases the egg. The ovaries do not actually connect directly to the fallopian tubes. Rather, the egg is released into the body cavity and reaches the tube by moving toward the fimbriae. If the egg does not reach the tube, it may be fertilized outside the tube, resulting in an abdominal pregnancy (see the discussion of ectopic pregnancy in Chapter 6). There have also been cases recorded of women who, although they were missing one ovary and the opposite fallopian tube, nonetheless became pregnant. Apparently, in such cases the egg migrates to the tube on the opposite side.

THE BREASTS

Although they are secondary sex characteristics and not actually sex organs, the *breasts* deserve discussion here because of their erotic and reproductive significance. The breast consists of about 15 or 20 clusters of *mammary glands,* each with a separate opening to the nipple, and of fatty and fibrous tissue that surrounds the clusters of glands (see Figure 4.9). The nipple, into which the milk ducts open, is at the tip of the breast. It is richly supplied with nerve endings and therefore very important in erotic stimulation for many women. The nipple consists of smooth muscle fibres; when they contract, the nipple becomes erect. The darker area surrounding the nipple is called the *areola.*

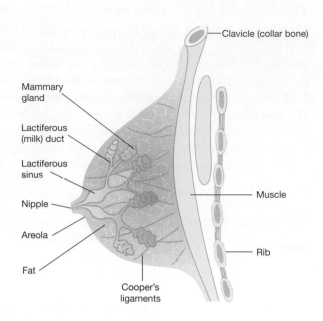

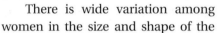

Figure 4.9   The internal structure of the breast.

There is wide variation among women in the size and shape of the breasts. One thing is fairly consistent, though: many women are not satisfied with the size of their breasts. Many women think they are either too small or too large. It is well to remember that there are the same number of nerve endings in small breasts as in large breasts. It follows that small breasts are actually more erotically sensitive per square centimetre than are large ones.

Breasts may take on enormous psychological meaning; they can be a symbol of femininity or a means of attracting men. Ours is a very breast-oriented culture. Many Canadian men develop a powerful interest in, and attraction to, women's breasts. The social definition of beauty is a compelling force; many women strive to meet the ideal and a few overadapt, going too far in their striving (Mazur, 1986). Breast augmentation surgery has increased steadily, while other women undergo breast reduction surgery, in both cases to meet a socially defined standard of beauty.[4] Breast reduction is also done for medical reasons—for example, to reduce back pain.

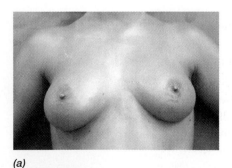
(a)

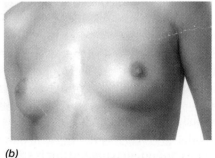
(b)

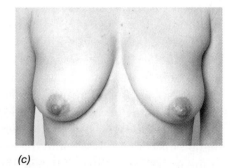
(c)

Figure 4.10   Breasts come in many sizes and shapes.

[4]We can see this trend on the reality makeover television shows. For example, in the third season of *Extreme Makeover,* all of the women featured in the first ten episodes received surgery to their breasts, in most cases breast enlargement.

MALE SEXUAL ORGANS

Externally, the most noticeable parts of the male sexual anatomy are the penis and the scrotum, or scrotal sac, which contains the testes (see Figure 4.11).

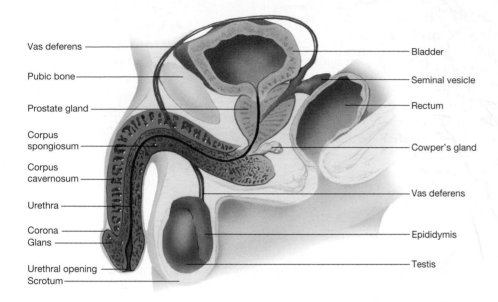

Vas deferens —
Pubic bone —
Prostate gland —
Corpus spongiosum —
Corpus cavernosum —
Urethra —
Corona —
Glans —
Urethral opening —
Scrotum —

— Bladder
— Seminal vesicle
— Rectum
— Cowper's gland
— Vas deferens
— Epididymis
— Testis

Figure 4.11 The male sexual and reproductive organs from a side view.

EXTERNAL ORGANS

THE PENIS

The **penis** (phallus, "prick," "cock," "johnson," and many other slang terms too numerous to list) serves important functions in sexual pleasure, reproduction, and elimination of body wastes by urination. It is a tubular organ with an end or tip called the *glans*. The opening at the end of the glans is the *meatus*, or *urethral opening*, through which urine and semen pass. The main part of the penis is called the *shaft*. The raised ridge at the edge of the glans is called the *corona* ("crown"), or *coronal ridge*. While the entire penis is sensitive to sexual stimulation, the corona and the rest of the glans are the most sexually excitable regions of the male anatomy.

Internally, the penis contains three long cylinders of spongy tissue running parallel to the *urethra*, which is the pathway through which semen and urine pass. The two spongy bodies lying on top are called the **corpora cavernosa**, and the single one lying on the bottom of the penis is called the **corpus spongiosum** (the urethra runs through the middle of it). During erection, the corpus spongiosum can be seen as a raised column on the lower side of the penis. As the names suggest, these bodies are tissues filled with many spaces and cavities, much like a sponge. They are richly supplied with blood vessels and nerves. In the flaccid (unaroused, not erect) state, they contain little blood. *Erection*, or *tumescence*, occurs when they become filled with blood (engorged) and expand, making the penis stiff.[5]

Penis: The male external sexual organ, which functions both in sexual activity and in urination.

Corpora cavernosa: Spongy bodies running the length of the top of the penis.

Corpus spongiosum: A spongy body running the length of the underside of the penis.

[5]Normally, after stopping psychological and physical stimulation or orgasms, the man loses his erection (see Chapter 9). *Priapism* is a painful and potentially harmful medical condition in which the erect penis does not return to its flaccid state within about four hours despite stopping stimulation.

Contrary to popular belief, the penis does not contain a muscle, and no muscle is involved in erection. Erection is purely a vascular phenomenon; that is, it results entirely from blood flow. It is also commonly believed that the penis of the human male contains a bone. This is not true either, although in some other species—for example, dogs—the penis does contain a bone, which aids in intromission (insertion of the penis into the vagina). In human males, however, there is none.

Foreskin: A layer of skin covering the glans or tip of the penis in an uncircumcised male; also called the prepuce.

The skin of the penis usually is hairless and is arranged in loose folds, permitting expansion during erection. The foreskin, or *prepuce,* is an additional layer of skin that forms a sheathlike covering over the glans; it may be present or absent in the adult male, depending on whether he has been circumcised (see Figure 4.12). Under the foreskin are small glands (Tyson's glands) that produce a substance called *smegma,* which is cheesy in texture. The foreskin is easily retractable,[6] and its retraction is extremely important for proper hygiene. If it is not pulled back and the glans washed thoroughly, the smegma may accumulate, producing a very unpleasant smell.

Circumcision: Surgical removal of the foreskin of the penis.

Circumcision refers to the surgical cutting away or removal of the foreskin. Circumcision is practised in many parts of the world and, when parents so choose, is done to boys in Canada within a few days after birth.

Circumcision may be done for cultural and religious reasons. Circumcision has been a part of Jewish religious practice for thousands of years. It symbolizes the covenant between God and the Jewish people and is done on the eighth day after birth, according to scriptural teaching (Genesis 17:9–27). Circumcision is also common in Muslim cultures. In some cultures circumcision is done at puberty as an initiation ritual, or *rite de passage.* The ability of the young boy to stand the pain may be seen as a proof of manhood.

In the 1980s, an anti-circumcision movement began gaining momentum in North America. Its proponents argue that circumcision does not have any health benefits and does entail some health risk as well as psychological trauma. According to this view, circumcision is nothing more than cruel mutilation. (For a statement of this anti-circumcision position, see Wallerstein, 1980.) In 1996, the Canadian Pediatric Society reviewed the literature and reached the conclusion that there are no valid medical indications for circumcision of newborn boys. Reflecting current advice from Canadian physicians, the controversy

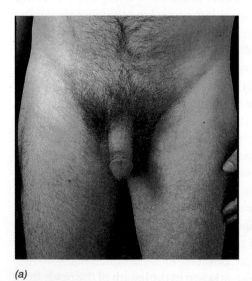 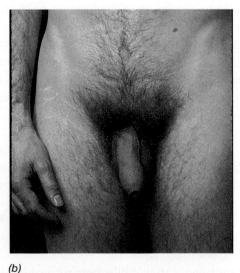

(a)   *(b)*

Figure 4.12 *(a)* A circumcised penis and *(b)* an uncircumcised penis, showing the foreskin.

---

[6]In a rare condition, the foreskin is so tight that it cannot be pulled back; this condition is called *phimosis* and requires correction by circumcision.

about circumcision, and the fact that circumcision is not usually covered by provincial health insurance plans, the rate of infant circumcision in Canada has been decreasing. Currently, less than 10 percent of infant boys are circumcised, although the rate varies considerably from province to province.

New evidence has accumulated, however, that there are potential medical benefits and advantages to circumcision, as well as potential risks. As a result, the Canadian Pediatric Society is currently reviewing its recommendation against circumcision. The new evidence indicates, for example, that uncircumcised male babies are 11 times more likely to get urinary tract infections than are circumcised babies, although the risk of urinary tract infections is low (Wiswell et al., 1987). There is also growing evidence that uncircumcised men have a higher risk of infection with HIV, the AIDS virus (Quinn et al., 2000; Szabo, 2000). It is thought that the inner surface of the foreskin is particularly susceptible to HIV and other viruses. In a study of different geographic and ethnic groups in Africa, some of which practise circumcision and some of which do not, it was found that HIV infection rates were very low among groups that practise circumcision and high among those that do not (Moses et al., 1990). In a five-nation study including Spain, Colombia, Brazil, Thailand, and the Philippines, circumcised men showed lower rates of HPV infection (Catellsagué et al., 2002). HPV is the virus that causes genital warts and predisposes women to cervical cancer. In this same study, the monogamous women partners of the circumcised men had lower rates of cervical cancer. In Kenya and Uganda, adult men who wanted to be circumcised were randomly assigned to either be circumcised immediately or in two years (Roehr, 2007). The circumcised men had half the rate of infection compared to the men waiting to be circumcised. Therefore, the trial was halted early over ethical concerns about withholding circumcision from those who wanted it.

Other arguments have focused on whether the circumcised or the uncircumcised man receives more pleasure from sexual intercourse. In fact, researchers in Quebec found no differences in how sensitive the penis of circumcised and uncircumcised men were to touch (Payne et al., 2007).

Other forms of male genital cutting are done throughout the world. In fact, male genital cutting is done in more cultures than is female genital cutting (Gregersen, 1996). A common form across most of Polynesia is supercision (also known as *superincision*), which involves making a slit on the length of the foreskin on the top, with the foreskin otherwise remaining intact (Gregersen, 1996). With subincision, which is common in some tribes in central Australia, a slit is made on the lower side of the penis along its entire length and to the depth of the urethra. Urine is then excreted at the base rather than at the tip of the penis.

To say the least, the penis has been the focus of quite a lot of attention throughout history. In some cultures, the attention has become so pronounced that the male genitals have actually become the object of religious worship (phallic worship). Not surprisingly, the male genitals were often seen as symbols of fertility and thus were worshipped for their powers of procreativity. In ancient Greece, phallic worship centred on Priapus, the son of Aphrodite (the goddess of love) and Dionysus (the god of fertility and wine). Priapus is usually represented as a grinning man with a huge penis.

In contemporary Canadian society, phallic concern often focuses on the size of the penis. Internet users are bombarded with e-mail spam that promises products to increase penis size. It is commonly believed that a man with a large penis is a better lover and can satisfy a woman more than can a man with a small penis. Masters and Johnson (1966), however, found that this is not true. While there is considerable variation in the length of the penis from one man to the next—the average penis is generally somewhere between 6.5 centimetres (2.5 inches) and 11 centimetres (4.3 inches) in length when flaccid (not erect) (Wessells et al., 1996)—there is a tendency for the small penis to grow more in erection than one that starts

Supercision (superincision): A form of male genital cutting in which a slit is made the length of the foreskin on top.

Subincision: A form of male genital cutting in which a slit is made on the lower side of the penis along its entire length.

out large. As a result, there is little correlation between the length of the penis when flaccid and its length when erect. As the saying has it, "Erection is the great equalizer." The average erect penis is between 10 centimetres (4.0 inches) and 16 centimetres (6.3 inches) long, although erect penises longer than 33 centimetres (13 inches) have been measured (Dickinson, 1949; Wessells et al., 1996). Further, as noted earlier, the vagina has relatively few nerve endings and is relatively insensitive. Hence, penetration to the far reaches of the vagina by a very long penis is not essential and may not even be noticeable. Many other factors are more important than penis size in giving a woman pleasure (see Chapters 9 and 18).

Phallic concern has also included an interest in the variations in the shape of the penis when flaccid and when erect, as reflected in this limerick:

> There was a young man of Kent
> Whose kirp in the middle was bent.
> To save himself trouble
> He put it in double,
> And instead of coming, he went.

THE SCROTUM

Scrotum (SKROH-tum):
The pouch of skin that contains the testes in the male.

The other major external genital structure in the male is the scrotum; this is a loose pouch of skin, lightly covered with hair, which contains the testes ("balls" or "nuts" in slang).[7] The testes themselves are considered part of the internal genitals.

INTERNAL ORGANS

Testes: The pair of glands in the scrotum that manufacture sperm and sex hormones.

The testes are the *gonads,* or reproductive glands, of the male, which are analogous to the female's ovaries. Like the ovaries, they serve two major functions: to manufacture germ cells (sperm) and sex hormones, in particular *testosterone.* Both testes are about the same size, although the left one usually hangs lower than the right one.

Seminiferous (sem-ih-NIFF-ur-us) tubules:
Tubes in the testes that manufacture sperm.

In the internal structure of the testes, two parts are important: the seminiferous tubules and the interstitial cells (see Figure 4.13). The seminiferous tubules carry out the important function of manufacturing and storing sperm, a process called *spermatogenesis.* They are a long series of threadlike tubes curled and packed densely into the testes. There are about 1000 of these tubules, which, if they were stretched out end to end, would be several hundred metres in length.

Interstitial (int-er-STIH-shul) cells: Cells in the testes that manufacture testosterone.

The interstitial cells (or *Leydig's cells*) carry out the second important function of the testes, the production of testosterone. These cells are found in the connective tissue lying between the seminiferous tubules. The cells lie close to the blood vessels in the testes and pour the hormones they manufacture directly into the blood vessels. Thus, the testes are endocrine (hormone-secreting) glands.

One of the clever tricks that the scrotum and testes can perform, as any male will testify, is to move up close to the body or down away from it. These changes are brought about mainly by changes in temperature (although emotional factors may also produce them). If a man plunges into a cold lake, the scrotum will shrivel and move close to the body.[8] If the man is working in an extremely hot place, the scrotum will hang down and away from the body. This mechanism is important because the testes should remain at a fairly constant temperature,

---

[7]This brings to mind another limerick:
   There once was a pirate named Gates
   Who thought he could rhumba on skates.
   He slipped on his cutlass
   And now he is nutless
   And practically useless on dates.

[8]Fans of the television show *Seinfeld* may recall an episode depicting George's dismay at conclusions a woman drew about his penis size after she saw his penis while he was changing after a cold swim.

slightly lower than normal body temperature. This constancy of temperature is necessary to protect the sperm, which may be injured by extremes of temperature. Thus if the air is cold the testes move closer to the body to maintain warmth, but if the air is too hot, they move away from the body to keep cool. The mechanics of this movement are made possible by the *cremasteric reflex*, named for the cremaster muscle connecting the scrotum to the body wall. Reflex contraction of this muscle pulls the testes up.

Many people believe that taking hot baths, wearing tight athletic supporters, or having a high fever can cause infertility. Indeed, in some countries the men take long, hot baths as a method of contraception. Such a practice has some basis in biological fact, because sperm can be destroyed by heat. However, as a method of contraception, this practice has not been particularly effective. In one study, it was found that the use of a special jockstrap raised the temperature of the scrotum by nearly 1°C (1.7°F) and that wearing the device daily for seven weeks caused about a 25 percent reduction in the number of sperm produced (Robinson & Rock, 1967). Thus, such practices might decrease a man's fertility somewhat, but they are far from 100 percent effective as contraceptives. On the other hand, men with problems of infertility can sometimes increase the chance of conception by getting out of their tight jockstraps and jockey shorts.

Following initial cell division in the seminiferous tubules, the male germ cells go through several stages of maturation. At the earliest stage, the cell is called a *spermatogonium*. Then it becomes a *spermatocyte* (first primary and then secondary) and then a *spermatid*. Finally, when fully mature, it is a *spermatozoan*, or sperm. *Spermatogenesis*, the manufacture of sperm, occurs continuously in adult men. An average ejaculate contains about 200 million sperm (Bang et al., 2005).

A mature sperm is very tiny—about 60 micrometres, or 60/10 000 millimetre (0.0024 inch), long—and consists of a head, a neck, a midpiece, and a tail. A normal human sperm carries 23 chromosomes in the head. These 23 are half the normal number in the other cells of the human body. When the sperm unites with the egg, which also carries 23 chromosomes, the full complement of 46 for the offspring is produced. (See Chapter 6 for a discussion of the sperm's role in conception.)

After the sperm are manufactured in the seminiferous tubules, they proceed into the *rete testes*, a converging network of tubes on the surface of the testis toward the top. The sperm then pass out of the testis and into a single tube, the epididymis. The epididymis is a long tube (about 6 metres, or 20 feet, in length) coiled into a small crescent-shaped region on the top and side of the testis. The sperm are stored in the epididymis, in which they ripen and mature, possibly for as long as six weeks.

Upon ejaculation, the sperm pass from the epididymis into the vas deferens (it is the vas that is cut in a vasectomy—see Chapter 7). The vas passes up and out of the scrotum and then follows a peculiar circular path as it loops over the pubic bone, crosses beside the urinary bladder, and then turns downward toward the prostate. As the tube passes through the prostate, it narrows and at this point is called the *ejaculatory duct*. The ejaculatory duct opens into the *urethra*, which has the dual function of conveying sperm and transporting urine; sperm are ejaculated out through the penis via the urethra.

Sperm have little motility of their own while in the epididymis and vas. That is, they are not capable of movement on their own until they mix with the secretions of the prostate (Breton et al., 1996). Up to this point, they are conveyed by the cilia and by contractions of the epididymis and vas.

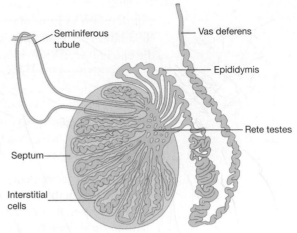

Figure 4.13 Schematic cross-section of the internal structure of the testis.

Sperm: The mature male reproductive cell, capable of fertilizing an egg.

Epididymis (ep-ih-DIH-dih-mus): A highly coiled tube located on the edge of the testis, where sperm mature.

Vas deferens: The tube through which sperm pass on their way from the testes and epididymis, out of the scrotum, and to the urethra.

The seminal vesicles are two saclike structures that lie above the prostate, behind the bladder, and in front of the rectum. They produce about 70 percent of the seminal fluid, or ejaculate. The remaining 30 percent is produced by the prostate. They empty their fluid into the ejaculatory duct to combine with the sperm.

The prostate lies below the bladder and is about the size and shape of a chestnut. It is composed of both muscle and glandular tissue. The prostate secretes a milky alkaline fluid that is part of the ejaculate. It is thought that the alkalinity of the secretion provides a favourable environment for the sperm and helps prevent their destruction by the acidity of the vagina. The prostate is fairly small at birth, enlarges at puberty, and typically shrinks in old age. It may become enlarged enough so that it interferes with urination, in which case surgery or drug therapy is required. Its size can be determined by rectal examination.

Cowper's glands, or the *bulbourethral glands,* are located just below the prostate and empty into the urethra. During sexual arousal these glands secrete a small amount of a clear alkaline fluid, which appears as droplets at the tip of the penis before ejaculation occurs. It is thought that the function of this secretion is to neutralize the acidic urethra, allowing safe passage of the sperm. Generally, it is not produced in sufficient quantity to serve as a lubricant in intercourse. The fluid often contains some stray sperm. Thus, it is possible (though not likely) for a woman to become pregnant from the sperm in this fluid even though the man has not ejaculated.

Cancer of the Sex Organs

BREAST CANCER

Cancer of the breast is the most frequently diagnosed cancer (excluding non-melanoma skin cancer) in Canadian women. About one out of every nine Canadian women is expected to develop breast cancer at some time in her life. Every year, about 22 500 women are diagnosed with and 4300 women die of breast cancer in this country (Canadian Cancer Society, 2007). The risk is higher for the woman whose mother, sister, or grandmother has had breast cancer. Although it is much more common in women, men can also develop breast cancer.

Causes

Approximately 5 to 10 percent of the cases of breast cancer in women are due to genetic factors (American Cancer Society, 2007). The remaining cases may be related to a particular virus or to diet. In countries such as Japan and Romania where the diet is low in fat, breast cancer rates are less than half that of Canada, where the diet is high in fat.

There have been great breakthroughs in research into the genetics of breast cancer. Scientists have identified two breast cancer genes, BRCA1 (for Breast Cancer 1) and BRCA2. These genes are also linked to ovarian cancer in women and prostate cancer in men (King et al., 2003). Genetic screening tests are available that detect BRCA mutations in women who have a family history of breast cancer. If a BRCA mutation is found, the woman can be monitored closely; if it is not found, she can feel relieved.

Diagnosis

The Canadian Cancer Society recommends that women examine their own breasts visually and physically. Women need to learn about how their breasts feel normally so that they can detect any changes and report them to their doctor. However, exams by clinicians and mammograms are more accurate than self-exams; research has shown that women who do routine breast self-exams are not less likely to die from breast cancer. However, many women discover their own cancer through changes in the look and feel of their breasts. Detailed information on one way to do a breast self-exam is provided in the Online Learning Centre (www.mcgrawhill.ca/olc/hyde). However, there isn't a right or wrong way to check your breasts as long as you become familiar with the whole area of breast tissue.

There are three kinds of breast lumps: *cysts* (fluid-filled sacs, also called *fibrocystic* or *cystic mastitis*), *fibroadenomas,* and *malignant tumours.* The important thing to realize is that 80 percent of breast lumps are cysts or fibroadenomas and are benign—that is, not dangerous. Therefore, if a lump is found in your breast, the chances are fairly good that it is not malignant; of course, you cannot be sure of this until a doctor has performed a biopsy.

The main technique for early detection of breast cancer is the mammography. Basically, *mammography* involves taking an X-ray of the breast. This technique is highly accurate, although some errors are still made. The major advantage, though, is that it is capable of detecting tumours that are so small that they cannot yet be felt; thus it can detect cancer in very early stages, making recovery more likely. Nonetheless, mammography involves some exposure to radiation, which itself may increase the risk of cancer. The question is: Which is more dangerous—having mammography or not detecting breast cancer until a later stage? Experts agree that the benefits outweigh the risk for women over 50. The Canadian Cancer Society recommends that women over 50 have a screening mammogram every two years. However, scientists disagree about the effectiveness of mammography screening for women who are between 40 and 49.

Once a lump is discovered, one of several diagnostic procedures may be carried out. One is *needle aspiration,* in which a fine needle is inserted into the breast; if the lump is a cyst, the fluid in the cyst will be drained out. If the lump disappears after this procedure, then it was a cyst; the cyst is gone, and there is no need for further concern. If the lump remains, it must be either a fibroadenoma or a malignant tumour.

Most physicians feel that the only definitive way to differentiate between a fibroadenoma and a malignant tumour is to do a *biopsy.* A small slit is made in the breast, and the lump is removed. A pathologist then examines it to determine whether it is cancerous. If it is simply a fibroadenoma, it has been removed and there is no further need for concern.

MASTECTOMY

Several forms of surgery may be performed when a breast lump is found to be malignant. Radiation therapy, chemotherapy, and hormone therapy may also be used. The most serious surgery is radical mastectomy, in which the entire breast and the underlying pectoral muscle and the lymph nodes are removed. In *modified radical mastectomy* the breast and lymph nodes, but not the muscles, are removed. In *simple mastectomy* only the breast (and possibly a few lymph nodes) is removed. In lumpectomy, only the lump itself and a small bit of surrounding tissue is removed. The breast is thus preserved. Research indicates that in cases of early breast cancer (when the cancer has not spread beyond the breast, e.g., to the lymph nodes), lumpectomy followed by radiation therapy is as effective as radical mastectomy (American Cancer Society, 2007) and is obviously much preferable. Drug therapy (e.g., tamoxifen first and later letrozole) is also commonly used (Pasacreta & McCorkle, 1998). Women who take tamoxifen may experience menopausal symptoms, sometimes very severe, including sexual side effects such as decreased sexual desire and pain during intercourse related to vaginal dryness (Archibald et al., 2006).

Treatments generally are highly effective and breast cancer deaths have decreased since 1986. If the cancer has not spread beyond the breast, the survival rate is more than 94 percent five years after treatment (Canadian Cancer Society, 1995).

PSYCHOLOGICAL ASPECTS

A lot more is at stake with breast cancer and mastectomy than technical details about diagnosis and surgery. The psychological impact of breast cancer and mastectomy and other treatments can be enormous (for an excellent review, see Meyerowitz, 1980). There seem

Radical mastectomy (mast-ECT-uh-mee): A surgical treatment for breast cancer in which the entire breast, as well as underlying muscles and lymph nodes, is removed.

Lumpectomy: A surgical treatment for breast cancer in which only the lump and a small bit of surrounding tissue are removed.

to be three sources of the trauma: Finding out that one has cancer of any kind is traumatic, and the surgery and possible amputation of the breast and the impact of severe menopausal symptoms are additionally stressful.

The typical emotional response of the mastectomy patient is depression, often associated with anxiety (Compas & Lueken, 2002). These responses are so common that they can be considered normal. The woman must make a number of physical and psychological adaptations, including different positions for sleeping and lovemaking and, for many women, a change to less revealing clothing. It is common for women to have difficulty showing their incisions to their sexual partners. Relationship tensions and sexual problems may increase. Many women experience a fear of recurring cancer and its treatment and of death, as well as concerns about mutilation from mastectomy and a possible loss of femininity. Our culture is very breast-oriented, and a woman who has defined her identity in terms of her beauty and voluptuous figure may have a more difficult time adjusting.

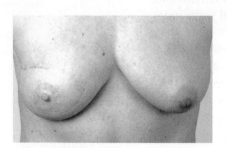

Figure 4.14 Appearance of a breast reconstructed after mastectomy.

Long-term studies, however, indicate that most women gradually adapt to the stresses they have experienced. One study found that breast cancer survivors did not differ from controls on measures of depression (Cordova et al., 2001). Many women manage to find meaning in the cancer experience, and some show post-traumatic growth such as finding new meaning in relationships and appreciating life more.

Educational classes providing relevant information can be very helpful. However, peer support groups such as those offered through the Canadian Cancer Society, although important to many women, have not fared well in tests of their effectiveness in improving mental health (Helgeson et al., 2001). For women who are more severely distressed, cognitive behavioural therapy with a trained therapist can be very effective (Antoni et al., 2001).

CANCER OF THE CERVIX, ENDOMETRIUM, AND OVARIES

Cancers of the cervix, endometrium, and ovaries are also common cancers, accounting for about 12 percent of all new cancers in women. It is estimated that 7850 Canadian women are diagnosed with and 2830 die of these cancers every year (Canadian Cancer Society, 2007). Other cancers of the female sexual-reproductive organs include cancer of the vulva, vagina, and fallopian tubes; these are all relatively rare.

Approximately 95 percent of cases of cervical cancer are caused by the human papillomavirus, HPV (see Chapter 8) (Janicek & Averette, 2001). Early initiation of heterosexual intercourse during the teenage years is a known risk factor for cervical cancer, as is intercourse with multiple partners. Both early intercourse and multiple partners, of course, increase the risk of HPV infection. Research shows that tumour-suppressor genes are active in normal cells, preventing them from becoming cancerous. HPV interferes with the activity of those tumour-suppressor genes (Janicek & Averette, 2001).

It is encouraging to note that the death rate from cervical cancer has decreased 78 percent since the mid-1960s, and more than 2 percent since 1994, mainly as a result of the Pap test (invented by G. N. Papanicolaou) and more regular checkups. The Pap test is performed during a pelvic examination (described in Figure 4.15). Because this highly accurate test can detect cancer long before the person has any symptoms, all women over age 18 to 20 should have one annually, and they should begin even earlier if they are sexually active.

There is considerable variation in the incidence of cervical and endometrial cancers across Canada. For example, the incidence of cervical cancer in some Aboriginal groups is ten times the provincial average, probably because many Aboriginal women do not have access to good health care and regular pelvic exams (Health Canada, 1998c). As with most cancers, the likelihood of a woman having a reproductive tract cancer increases with age, although cervical cancer is relatively common among women in their 20s. The most exciting news is that a vaccine is now available that prevents the most common HPV infections that cause cervical cancer (see Chapter 8). It is approved for use in Canada and is being offered free to girls in grade 7 or 8 in several provinces.

Endometrial and ovarian cancers have multiple symptoms, making diagnosis difficult. Endometrial cancer may be suspected when a woman has vaginal bleeding during times in the menstrual cycle other than her period, or after menopause. Ovarian cancer symptoms— abdominal bloating and cramping, vomiting, and diarrhea—can be (and usually are) indicative of much less serious conditions like a stomach virus or irritable bowel syndrome. Imaging techniques such as pelvic sonogram and MRI, and minimally invasive surgical techniques such as hysteroscopy, can help diagnose these cancers.

Treatment for cervical cancer varies according to how advanced it is when diagnosed. If it is detected very early, it is quite curable with methods such as cryotherapy, a non-surgical technique that uses extreme cold to destroy just the abnormal cells. Another common treatment is cone biopsy, in which a segment of the cervix is surgically removed, leaving the cervix largely intact. For women with advanced cervical cancer that has spread beyond a small, localized spot, hysterectomy (surgical removal of the uterus) is the usual treatment, although radiation therapy may be an alternative.

Hysterectomy (his-tuh- REK-tuh-mee): Surgical removal of the uterus.

For women with endometrial cancer, hysterectomy is the standard treatment. Ovarian cancer is treated by oophorectomy (surgical removal of the ovaries), often accompanied by hysterectomy. These surgeries are typically followed by radiation treatments or chemotherapy.

It is important to note some facts about hysterectomy. Although it carries risks similar to those of any major surgery, hysterectomy does not leave a woman "masculinized," with a beard and deep voice. Beard growth is influenced by testosterone, not estrogen or progesterone. And it is the ovaries that manufacture estrogen and progesterone. They are not removed in a

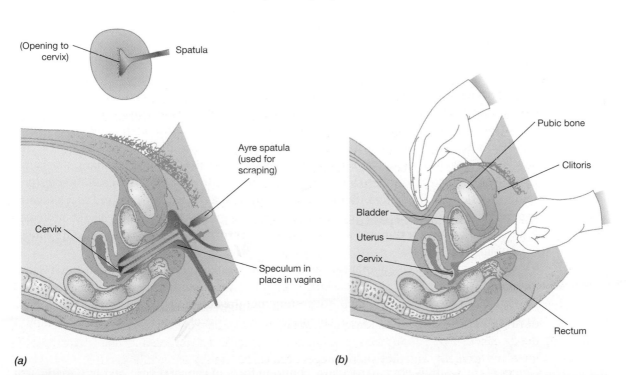

(a)   (b)

Figure 4.15 The two primary procedures used during a pelvic exam: *(a)* The speculum, a plastic or metal instrument, is inserted into the vagina to hold the vaginal walls apart to permit examination. The Ayre spatula is used to get a sample of cells for the Pap test for cervical cancer. *(b)* The bimanual pelvic exam in which the health care provider slides the index and middle fingers of one hand into the vagina and then, with the other hand, presses down from the outside on the abdominal wall in order to be able to feel the uterus, tubes and ovaries.

hysterectomy except in rare cases when the cancer has spread to them. Women who have their ovaries removed before age 50 can take hormone replacement therapy (HRT) to avoid the effects of premature menopause. Another fallacy about hysterectomy is that it prevents a woman from enjoying—or even having—sex. However, about half the women who undergo a hysterectomy for cervical or endometrial cancer report significant sexual problems (Brotto et al., 2008).

CANCER OF THE PROSTATE

Cancer of the prostate is the most common form of cancer in Canadian men. Annually, about 22 300 men are diagnosed with and 4300 die from prostate cancer in Canada (Canadian Cancer Society, 2007). About one out of every eight Canadian men is expected to develop prostate cancer at some time in his life. Most cases are not lethal, however, and survival rates are high because it generally affects older men (25 percent of men over 90 have prostate cancer), and because the tumours are small and spread (metastasize) very slowly. On the other hand, a percentage of prostate tumours do spread and are lethal. A prostate cancer gene (HPC1, for Hereditary Prostate Cancer) has been discovered, but it accounts for only about 3 percent of all cases (Pennisi, 1996; Smith et al., 1996).

Early symptoms of prostate cancer are frequent urination (especially at night), difficulty in urination, and difficulty emptying the bladder. These are also symptoms of benign prostate enlargement, which itself may require treatment by surgery or drugs but is not cancer (Oesterling, 1995). These symptoms result from the pressure of the prostate tumour on the urethra. In the early stages, there may be frequent erections and an increase in sex drive; however, as the disease progresses, there are often problems with sexual functioning.

Preliminary diagnosis of prostate cancer is by a rectal examination, which is simple and causes no more than minimal discomfort. The physician (wearing a lubricated glove) simply inserts one finger into the rectum and palpates (feels) the prostate. All men over 50 should have a rectal exam at least once a year; men with a family history of the disease should start having exams at 40. If the rectal exam provides evidence of a tumour, further laboratory tests can be conducted as confirmation. The rectal exam has its disadvantages, though. Some men dislike the discomfort it causes, and it is not 100 percent accurate. A blood test for PSA (prostate-specific antigen) is also available and should be done as well.

Treatment often involves surgical removal of some or all of the prostate, plus some type of hormone therapy, radiation therapy, or anti-cancer drugs. Because prostate cancer is often a slow-growing cancer, it may be left untreated, particularly if the man is elderly. Surgery may result in erection problems (Perez et al., 2002). Androgen-deprivation therapy is typically used for advanced prostate cancer. It results in a number of physical changes because of the loss of testosterone (Aucoin & Wassersug, 2006). In Focus 9.2 (page 268) gives one man's experience of androgen-deprivation therapy. Just as research has found that a greater number of sexual partners increases women's risk of cervical cancer, new research indicates that men with a greater number of female partners have an increased risk of prostate cancer (Rosenblatt et al., 2001).

Cancer of the penis is another cancer of the male sexual-reproductive system, but it is rare compared with prostate cancer. It seems to be much more common among uncircumcised men than among circumcised men, suggesting that the accumulation of smegma under the foreskin may be related to its cause. Treatment may consist of surgery or radiation therapy.

CANCER OF THE TESTES

Cancer of the testes is not a particularly common form of cancer. Every year in Canada, 830 men are diagnosed with this form of cancer, and about 30 men die from it (Canadian Cancer Society, 2007). However, cancer of the testes tends to be a disease of cancer in young men. The mortality rate from cancer of the testes in Canada decreased between 1987 and 2004 because, although there have been more cases of testicular cancer, treatments have improved.

IN FOCUS 4.2

Lance Armstrong: One Man's Battle with Testicular Cancer

Figure 4.16 Lance Armstrong.

Lance Armstrong was born in Plano, Texas, in 1971. Always athletic, he first competed in triathlons before turning to cycling. He began working out with the American national cycling team while still in high school. Armstrong was a top cyclist, winning a number of important races and titles before being diagnosed with testicular cancer in 1996 at the age of 25. Doctors only gave him a 40 percent chance of recovery because the cancer had already spread to his abdomen, brain, and lungs.

Armstrong had suspected that something was wrong three years before his diagnosis: he had noticed a size difference between his two testicles. However, he only sought medical attention when his testicles became so painful that he could not sit on his bike any more. He underwent surgeries to remove his testicle and lesions in his brain, as well as four cycles of chemotherapy. He was declared healthy in 1997.

Armstrong brought his attitude toward athletic training and performance to his battle with cancer:

> I prepared for my treatment like it was a bike race. I made cancer like an opponent that I hated and wanted to beat very badly. I believe the athletic approach, the athletic mentality, was very beneficial. I did everything with 100 percent efficiency, just as you must do to peak for a championship race. My research, understanding the drugs and the treatment protocol, taking care of my body, eating a healthy diet—I went 100 percent on everything.

In 1997 Armstrong founded the Lance Armstrong Foundation—you may be familiar with its "Live Strong" yellow wristband. He also has taken on an important role in informing the public about testicular cancer, in part by sharing his own story. According to Armstrong, there's still a taboo about talking about testicular cancer:

> Men don't really want to talk about it . . . at first I didn't understand . . . it's like, man, what's the big deal? But now that I have been through it and I see people's reactions . . . and people say some stupid things, there's some stupid people out there, they think it's funny some times. So now I can understand why some people might be self-conscious . . . it's still a rare cancer like compared to breast cancer. . . . "

Although many people doubted that it was possible, Lance was determined once again to be a top cyclist after his treatment, and he did it. He went on to win the Tour de France in 1999 and then won it again in the next six consecutive years.

Sources: Brewer, 1997; Kearns, 2007; www.lancearmstrong.com.

The cause of testicular cancer is not known for certain. An undescended testis has a much greater risk of developing cancer. The first sign is usually a painless lump in the testes, or a slight enlargement or change in consistency of the testes. There may be pain in the lower abdomen or groin. Unfortunately, many men do not discover the tumour, or if they do, they do not see a physician soon, so that in most cases the cancer has spread to other organs by the time a physician is consulted. When a lump is reported to a physician early, the five-year survival rate is 95 percent.[9] Therefore, the Canadian Cancer Society recommends that men do regular testicular self-examinations every month starting at puberty. The exam should be done during or right after a bath or shower because the scrotal skin is more relaxed and the contents can be felt more easily. Instructions on how to do a testicular exam are provided in the Online Learning Centre (www.mcgrawhill.ca/college/hyde). However, if the lump is not discovered or the man waits to see a physician and the cancer has progressed to Stage III, the survival rate is 75 percent (American Cancer Society, 2000).

Not every lump in the testes is cancerous. Some lumps are varicoceles; that is, varicose veins. Diagnosis is made by a physician's examination of the testes and by ultrasound. Final diagnosis involves surgical removal of the entire testis. This is also the first step in treatment. Fortunately, the other testicle remains, so that hormone production and sexual functioning can continue unimpaired. An artificial, gel-filled testicle can be implanted to restore a normal appearance.

SUMMARY

The external sexual organs of the female are the clitoris, the mons, the inner lips, the outer lips, and the vaginal opening. Collectively these are referred to as the vulva. The clitoris is an extremely sensitive organ and is very important in female sexual response. Clitoridectomy and infibulation are rituals that involve cutting of the clitoris and other parts of the vulva and are practised widely in some African nations and elsewhere. Another external structure is the hymen, which has taken on great symbolic significance as a sign of virginity, although its absence is not a reliable indicator that a woman is not a virgin. The important internal structures are the vagina; the uterus, which houses the developing fetus; the ovaries, which produce eggs and manufacture sex hormones; and the fallopian tubes, which convey the egg to the uterus. The breasts of the female also function in sexual arousal and may have great symbolic significance.

The external sexual organs of the male are the penis and the scrotum. The penis contains three spongy bodies which, when filled with blood, produce an erection. Circumcision, or surgical removal of the foreskin of the penis, is a debated practice in Canada but may have some health advantages. The scrotum contains the testes, which are responsible for the manufacture of sperm (in the seminiferous tubules) and sex hormones (in the interstitial cells). Sperm pass out of the testes during ejaculation via the vas deferens, the ejaculatory duct, and the urethra. The seminal vesicles manufacture most of the fluid that mixes with the sperm to form semen. The prostate also contributes secretions.

Breast cancer is the most common form of cancer in women. All women should do a monthly self-exam because the earlier a lump is detected, the greater the chances of complete recovery. The Pap test is used to detect cervical cancer. Prostate cancer is the most common form of cancer in men, but it generally affects older men. Cancer of the testes, although rare, is the most common cancer in men between the ages of 29 and 35. Men should do a monthly testicular self-exam.

[9]Lance Armstrong, the great cyclist, was treated for testicular cancer and went on to win the Tour de France multiple times (see In Focus 4.2 on page 103).

QUESTIONS FOR THOUGHT, DISCUSSION, AND DEBATE

1. Form two groups of students to debate the following: Resolved: Circumcision should not be performed routinely. You can draw on many resources to provide evidence for your debate, including interviews with doctors and nurses, library materials (books and journal articles on the effects of circumcision), and interviews with parents of infants.

2. You are a gynecologist practising in Toronto. An immigrant woman from Somalia makes an appointment with you. She wants you to perform infibulation on her eight-year-old daughter. She pleads with you, saying that she wants the girl to have the procedure performed under safe, sanitary conditions in a hospital. She firmly believes that she would betray her culture, to which they will return in two years, if she does not carry out this ancient custom with her daughter. What should you do?

3. Clitoridectomy and infibulation are practised widely today, particularly in East Africa. Scientific evidence indicates that these practices can cause serious negative health consequences for women and girls. Some argue that people throughout the world should work to eradicate this practice, perhaps with the help of an institution such as the World Health Organization. Others argue that these practices are deeply rooted in the cultures of these countries, and that outsiders have no right to judge it, much less try to stop it. What do you think? Why?

4. Do people you know have poor genital self-image? Why do you think so many people are interested in cosmetic genital surgery—women in vaginal enhancement surgery, men in penis enlargement surgery?

SUGGESTIONS FOR FURTHER READING

Boston Women's Health Book Collective. (2005). *Our bodies, ourselves.* New York: Simon & Schuster. A good, easy-to-read source on female biology and sexuality.

Gruenbaum, Ellen. (2000). *The female circumcision controversy: An anthropological perspective.* Philadelphia: University of Pennsylvania Press. Gruenbaum tells of her fieldwork in Sudan, where the most severe forms of FGC are practised.

Lamont, J., and Barrett, M. (Eds.). (1994). Sexuality & cancer treatment. *The Canadian Journal of Human Sexuality, 3(2),* 95–183.

Morgentaler, Abraham. (1993). *The male body: A physician's guide to what every man should know about his sexual health.* New York: Simon & Schuster. An authoritative book on men's health.

Olivotto, I., Gelmon, K., and Kuusk, U. (1995). *Intelligent patient guide to breast cancer.* Vancouver: Intelligent Patient Guide. [Available from Intelligent Patient Guide Ltd., 517–750 West Broadway, Vancouver, BC V5Z 1H4.] This book, written by three practising physicians in Vancouver and professors at the University of British Columbia Medical School, describes all aspects of breast cancer.

 Online **LearningCentre**

For review questions, web resources, and other learning and study tools, visit the *Understanding Human Sexuality* Online Learning Centre at www.mcgrawhill.ca/olc/hyde.

SEX HORMONES, SEXUAL DIFFERENTIATION, AND MENSTRUATION

Chapter Highlights

THIS WAY

I HAVE AIS, I GUESS,
BECAUSE THERE IS A GOD,
AND HE OR SHE OR BOTH,
PEERED DEEP INTO MY HEART
TO SEE
THAT ALL THAT I CAN BE
IS BEST EXPRESSED
IN FEMALE FORM.
THE ALTERNATIVE FOR ME
WOULD BE XY, AND I
WOULD BE VIRILIZED;
SO ALL THAT'S SOFT AND TENDER
WOULD INSTEAD SURRENDER

TO A STRAND OF DNA.
IN THE LIE OF X AND Y
I CAME TO CHALLENGE THE
IMMUTABILITY
OF "HE" AND THE CERTAINTY
OF "SHE." BLENDED AND INFUSED,
A RUSE OF GENDER
THAT UPENDS
A DIFFERENT FATE.
NON-FUNCTIONING RECEPTORS
HAVE RESCUED ME
NOT A FAILED MESS
BUT A SMASHING SUCCESS OF
NATURE!*

One of the marvels of human biology is that the complex and different male and female anatomies—males with a penis and scrotum; females with a vagina, uterus, and breasts—arise from a single cell, the fertilized egg, which varies only in whether it carries two X chromosomes (XX) or one X and one Y (XY). Many of the structural differences between males and females arise before birth, during the prenatal period, in a complex and delicate process called *prenatal sexual differentiation.*

Yet as the poem on this page suggests, gender is not always a simple matter. Sex and gender and their development are complex and vulnerable to disturbances. Further variety in the human condition results.

In this chapter we will examine the process of sexual differentiation both prenatally and during puberty. We will also consider the biological and psychological aspects of the menstrual cycle. Let's start, however, with another biological system, the endocrine or hormonal system, paying particular attention to the sex hormones. They play a major role in the differentiation process.

SEX HORMONES

Hormones are powerful chemical substances manufactured by the *endocrine glands* and secreted directly into the bloodstream. Because they go into the blood, their effects are felt fairly rapidly and at places in the body quite distant from where they were manufactured. The most important sex hormones are testosterone (one of a group of hormones called androgens) and estrogens and progesterone. The thyroid, the adrenals, and the pituitary are examples of endocrine glands. We are interested here in the gonads, or sex glands: the testes in the male and the ovaries in the female. The pituitary gland and a closely related region of the brain, the hypothalamus, are also important to our discussion because the hypothalamus regulates the pituitary, which regulates the other glands, in particular the testes and ovaries. Because of its role, the pituitary has been called the "master gland" of the endocrine system. The pituitary is a small gland, about the size of a pea, which projects down from the lower side

Prenatal (pree-NAY-tul) period: The time from conception to birth.

Hormones: Chemical substances secreted by the endocrine glands into the bloodstream.

Testosterone: A hormone secreted by the testes in the male (and also present at lower levels in the female).

Androgens: The group of "male" sex hormones, one of which is testosterone.

Estrogens (ESS-troh-jens): The group of "female" sex hormones.

Progesterone (pro-JES-tur-ohn): A "female" sex hormone secreted by the ovaries.

Pituitary (pih-TOO-ih-tair-ee) gland: A small endocrine gland located on the lower side of the brain below the hypothalamus; the pituitary is important in regulating levels of sex hormones.

*Sherri Groveman, an intersex individual with androgen insensitivity syndrome (AIS). In *Hermaphrodites with Attitude*, 1995, p. 2. (Contact www.isna.org/library/hwa.)

Hypothalamus (hy-poh-THAL-ah-mus): A small region of the brain that is important in regulating many body functions, including the functioning of the sex hormones.

of the brain. It is divided into three lobes: the anterior, the intermediary, and the posterior lobe. The anterior lobe is the one that interacts with the gonads. The hypothalamus is a region at the base of the brain just above the pituitary (see Figure 5.1). It plays a part in regulating many vital behaviours such as eating, drinking, and sexual behaviour,[1] and is important in regulating the pituitary.

These three structures, then—the hypothalamus, pituitary, and gonads (testes or ovaries)—function together. They influence such important sexual functions as the menstrual cycle, pregnancy, the changes of puberty, and sexual behaviour.

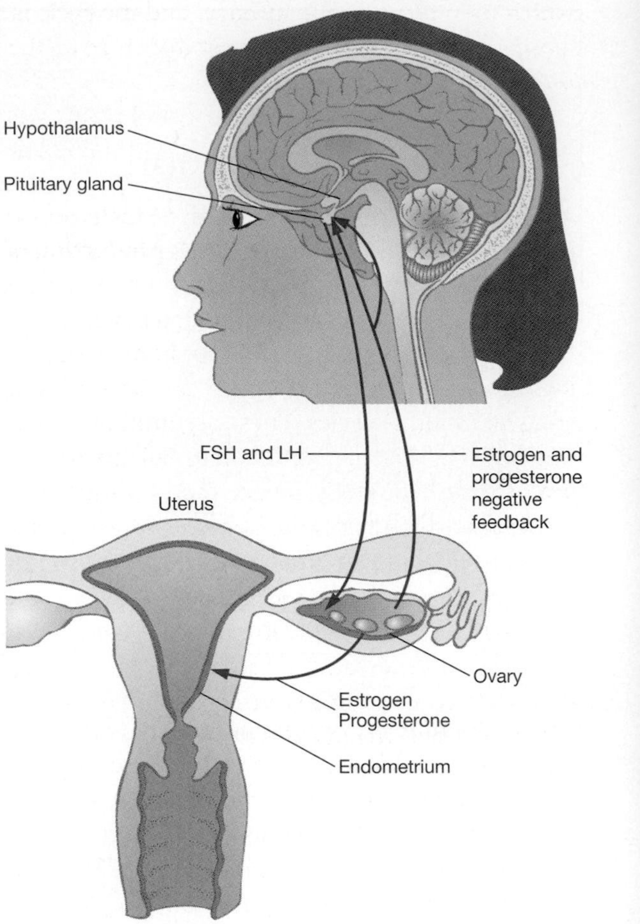

SEX HORMONE SYSTEMS IN THE MALE

The pituitary and the testes both produce hormones. The important hormone produced by the testes is *testosterone*. Testosterone, a "male" or masculinizing sex hormone, has important functions in stimulating and maintaining the secondary sex characteristics (such as beard growth), maintaining the genitals

Figure 5.1 The hypothalamus–pituitary–gonad feedback loop in women, which regulates production of the sex hormones.

Follicle-stimulating hormone (FSH): A hormone secreted by the pituitary; it stimulates follicle development in females and sperm production in males.

Luteinizing hormone (LH): A hormone secreted by the pituitary; it regulates estrogen secretion and ovum development in the female and testosterone production in the male.

Gonadotropin-releasing hormone (GnRH): A hormone secreted by the hypothalamus that regulates the pituitary's secretion of gonad-stimulating hormones.

HPG axis: Hypothalamus–pituitary–gonad axis, the negative feedback loop that regulates sex-hormone production.

and their sperm-producing capability, and stimulating the growth of bone and muscle.

The pituitary produces several hormones, two of which are important in this discussion: **follicle-stimulating hormone (FSH)** and **luteinizing hormone (LH)**. These hormones affect the functioning of the testes. FSH controls sperm production, and LH controls testosterone production.

Testosterone levels in males are relatively constant. The hypothalamus, pituitary, and testes operate in a negative feedback loop that maintains these constant levels (see Figure 5.2). The levels of LH are regulated by a substance called **gonadotropin-releasing hormone (GnRH)**, which is secreted by the hypothalamus (FSH levels are similarly regulated by GnRH). The system comes full circle because the hypothalamus monitors the levels of testosterone present, and in this way testosterone influences the output of GnRH. This feedback loop is sometimes called the **HPG axis**, for hypothalamus–pituitary–gonad axis.

This negative feedback loop operates much like a thermostat-furnace system. If a room is cold, certain changes occur in the thermostat, and it signals the furnace to turn on. The action of the furnace warms the air in the room. Eventually, the air becomes so warm that another change is produced in the thermostat, and it sends a signal to the furnace to turn off. The temperature in the room then gradually falls until it triggers another change in the thermostat,

---

[1]One psychologist summarized the functions of the hypothalamus as being the four F's: fighting, feeding, fleeing, and, ahem, sexual behaviour.

which then turns on the furnace, and the cycle is repeated. This cycle is a *negative* feedback loop because increases in temperature turn *off* the furnace, and *decreases* in temperature turn *on* the furnace.

The hypothalamus, pituitary, and testes work together in a similar negative feedback loop, ensuring that testosterone is maintained at a fairly constant level, just as the temperature of a room is kept fairly constant. The pituitary's production of LH stimulates the testes to produce testosterone. But when testosterone levels get high, the hypothalamus reduces its production of GnRH; the pituitary's production of LH is then reduced, and the production of testosterone by the testes consequently decreases. When testerone levels fall, the hypothalamus again increases the production of GnRH and the process starts again.

The traditional assumption of both laypeople and scientists has been that monthly biological and psychological cycles are the exclusive property of women and that men experience no monthly cycles. These assumptions are made, at least in part, because men have no obvious signs like menstruation to call attention to the fact that some kind of periodic change is occurring. One study, in fact, found no differences between men and women in day-to-day mood changes—men were no more or less changeable than women (McFarlane et al., 1988; see also McFarlane & Williams, 1994).

Inhibin is another hormone produced in the testes (by cells called the Sertoli cells). It acts to regulate FSH levels in a negative feedback loop just as testosterone does with LH (Plant et al., 1993). Interest in inhibin has been intense because it shows great promise, at least theoretically, as a male contraceptive. That is, because inhibin suppresses FSH production, sperm production in turn is inhibited.

Inhibin: A substance secreted by the testes and ovaries that regulates FSH levels.

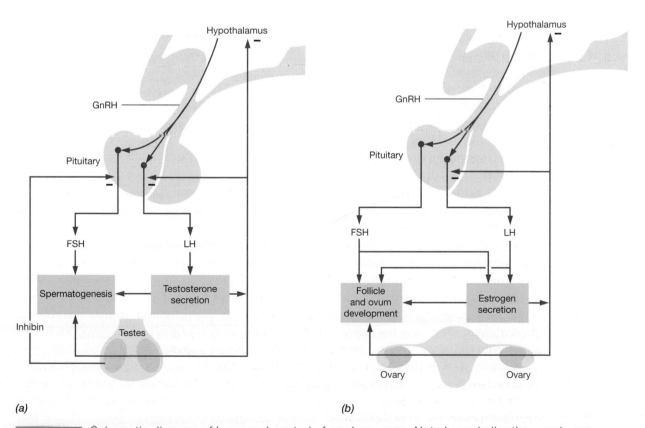

(a)   *(b)*

Figure 5.2   Schematic diagram of hormonal control of sex hormones. Note how similar they are in men and women: *(a)* Testosterone secretion and sperm production by the testes. The negative signs indicate that testosterone inhibits LH production, both in the pituitary and in the hypothalamus. *(b)* Estrogen secretion and ovum production by the ovaries (during the follicular phase of the menstrual cycle).

IN FOCUS 5.1

Is Environmental Pollution Affecting the Endocrine System?

Endocrine Disrupters

Florida panthers have low sperm counts and the same levels of estradiol as females. Frogs are born hermaphroditic, with mixed male and female organs. Male turtle doves display reduced courtship and nesting behaviours. A preschool girl begins growing pubic hair. These cases and dozens of others have appeared in the news in the last decade. Are they unrelated bizarre occurrences, or is there a common link?

Scientists believe that underlying all these troubling cases is the phenomenon of **endocrine disrupters**, which are chemicals found in the environment that affect the endocrine system, as well as the biological functioning and behaviour of animals, including humans. Evidence of the effects of endocrine disrupters (also called endocrine disrupting chemicals or EDCs) comes from both studies of animals in the wild and carefully controlled laboratory experiments.

What chemicals are the culprits? Some are pesticides such as atrazine and DDT, used by farmers and others to kill unwanted insects and weeds. Bisphenol A is another endocrine disrupter. It is used in making plastics such as baby bottles. PCBs, which were banned from production in Canada in 1977, were used in making

---

Endocrine disrupters: Chemicals found in the environment that affect the endocrine system as well as the biological functioning and behaviour of animals, including humans.

SEX HORMONE SYSTEMS IN THE FEMALE

The ovaries produce two important hormones, estrogen[2] and progesterone. Estrogen brings about many of the changes of puberty (stimulating the growth of the uterus and vagina, enlarging the pelvis, and stimulating breast growth). Estrogen is also responsible for maintaining the mucous membranes of the vagina and stopping the growth of bone and muscle, which accounts for why women generally are smaller than men.

In women the levels of estrogen and progesterone fluctuate according to the phases of the menstrual cycle and during various other stages such as pregnancy and menopause. The two pituitary hormones, FSH and LH, regulate the levels of estrogen and progesterone. In this way, the levels of estrogen and progesterone are controlled by a negative feedback loop of the hypothalamus, pituitary, and ovaries, that is similar to the negative feedback loop in the male (see Figure 5.2b). For example, as shown on the right side of Figure 5.2b, increases in the level of GnRH increase the level of LH, and the increases in LH eventually produce increases in the output of estrogen. Finally, the increases in the level of estrogen inhibit (decrease) the production of GnRH and LH.

The pituitary produces two other hormones, *prolactin* and *oxytocin*. Prolactin stimulates production of milk by the mammary glands after a woman has given birth to a child. Oxytocin stimulates ejection of that milk from the nipple. Oxytocin also stimulates contractions of the uterus during childbirth.

The female sex hormone system functions much like the male sex hormone system. The ovaries and testes produce many of the same hormones, but in different amounts. The ovaries, like the testes, produce inhibin, which in turn forms a negative feedback loop with FSH production (Burger, 1993). The functioning of the female sex hormone system and the menstrual cycle will now be described in more detail.

---

[2]We really should say *estrogens*, because they are a group of hormones. Estradiolis is one of the estrogens. To keep things simple, we will just use the term estrogen.

products such as paints, plastics, and printing ink. Some have a half-life of over 1000 years and so they are still abundant in the environment despite being banned.

How do these chemicals exert their effects on sexual biology and behaviour? All of them affect the endocrine system and, specifically, the sex hormone system. Many have multiple effects. Atrazine, for example, affects both estrogen and testosterone and inhibits their binding to estrogen receptors and androgen receptors. It also depresses the LH surge that causes ovulation. The insecticide DDT affects estrogen, progesterone, and testosterone by mimicking estrogen and binding to estrogen receptors, as well as by altering the metabolism of both progesterone and testosterone. PCBs are both anti-estrogens and anti-androgens. These chemicals are in the food we eat and the water and milk that we drink.

Why should we care about a few hermaphroditic frogs or preschoolers with pubic hair? Scientists see these cases as examples of the proverbial canary in the mine shaft. In other words, they are small signs that something terribly dangerous is happening. For example, on a Chippewa reservation in a part of Ontario that is heavily populated with chemical manufacturing plants, only 35 percent of the babies born today are boys.

Sources: Hayes et al., 2002; Iwaniuk et al., 2006; Propper, 2005; Sanghavi, 2006; Zala & Penn, 2004.

THE MENSTRUAL CYCLE

Women's sexual and reproductive lives have a rhythm of changes. One notable sign that marks the changes is menstruation. The events surrounding it are not only biological but psychological as well. The biological aspects are discussed here; the psychological aspects are discussed later in this chapter.

Humans are nearly unique among species in having a menstrual cycle. Only a few other species of apes and monkeys also have menstrual cycles. All other species of mammals (e.g., horses and dogs) have *estrous* cycles. What are the differences between estrous cycles and menstrual cycles? First, in animals that have estrous cycles, there is no menstruation; there is either no bleeding or only a slight spotting of blood (as in dogs), which is not real menstruation. Second, the timing of ovulation in relation to bleeding (if there is any) is different in the two cycles. For estrous animals, ovulation occurs while the animal is in "heat," or *estrus*, which is also the time of slight spotting. In the menstrual cycle, however, ovulation occurs about midway between the periods of menstruation. A third difference is that female animals with estrous cycles engage in sexual behaviour only when they are in heat—that is, during the estrus phase of the cycle. Females with menstrual cycles are capable of engaging in and enjoying sexual behaviour throughout the cycle.

THE PHASES OF THE MENSTRUAL CYCLE

The menstrual cycle has four phases (see Figure 5.3), each characterized by a set of hormonal, ovarian, and uterine changes. Because menstruation is the easiest phase to identify, it is tempting to call it the first phase, but biologically it is actually the last phase. (Note, however, that in numbering the days of the menstrual cycle, the first day of menstruation is counted as day 1 because it is the most identifiable day of the cycle.)

The first phase of the menstrual cycle is called the **follicular phase** (or sometimes *the proliferative phase*). At the beginning of this phase, the pituitary secretes relatively high levels of FSH. As the name of this hormone implies, its function is to stimulate follicles in the ovaries. At the beginning of the follicular phase, it signals one follicle (occasionally more than one) in the ovaries to bring an egg to the final stage of maturity. At the same time, the follicle secretes estrogen.

Follicular (fuh-LIK-you-lur) phase: The first phase of the menstrual cycle, beginning just after menstruation, during which an egg matures in preparation for ovulation.

Ovulation: Release of an egg from the ovaries; the second phase of the menstrual cycle.

The second phase of the cycle is **ovulation**, which is the phase during which the follicle ruptures open, releasing the mature egg (see Figure 5.3). By this time, estrogen has risen to a high level, which inhibits FSH production, and so FSH has fallen back to a low level. The high levels of estrogen also stimulate the hypothalamus to produce GnRH, which causes the pituitary to begin production of LH.[3] A surge of LH triggers ovulation.

Figure 5.3 Ovulation, showing the egg bursting forth from the wall of the ovary.

Luteal (LOO-tee-uhl) phase: The third phase of the menstrual cycle, following ovulation.

Corpus luteum: The mass of cells of the follicle remaining after ovulation; it secretes progesterone.

The third phase of the cycle is called the **luteal phase** (sometimes also called the *secretory phase*). After releasing an egg, the follicle, under stimulation of LH, turns into a glandular mass of cells called the **corpus luteum**[4] (hence the names *luteal phase* and *luteinizing hormone*). The corpus luteum manufactures progesterone; so, progesterone levels rise during the luteal phase. But high levels of progesterone also inhibit the pituitary's secretion of LH, and as LH levels decline, the corpus luteum degenerates. With this degeneration comes a sharp decline in estrogen and progesterone levels at the end of the luteal phase. The falling levels of estrogen stimulate the pituitary to begin production of FSH, and the whole cycle begins again.

Menstruation: The fourth phase of the menstrual cycle, during which the endometrium of the uterus is sloughed off in the menstrual discharge.

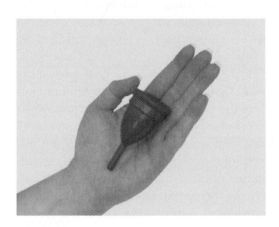

Figure 5.4 *The Keeper* menstrual cup, an environmentally friendly alternative to sanitary napkins or tampons.

The fourth and final phase of the cycle is **menstruation**. Physiologically, menstruation is a shedding of the inner lining of the uterus (the endometrium), which then passes out through the cervix and the vagina. During this phase, estrogen and progesterone levels are low and FSH levels are rising. Menstruation is triggered by the sharp decline in estrogen and progesterone levels at the end of the luteal phase.

What has been happening in the uterus while the ovaries and endocrine system were going through the four phases that we just described? During the first, or follicular, phase, the high levels of estrogen stimulate the endometrium (the inner layer) of the uterus to grow, thicken, and form glands that will eventually secrete substances to nourish the embryo. In other words, the endometrium proliferates (giving us the alternative name for this first phase, the *proliferative phase*). During the luteal phase, the progesterone secreted by the corpus luteum stimulates the glands of the endometrium to start secreting the nourishing substances (hence the name *secretory phase*). If the egg is fertilized and the timing goes properly, about six days after ovulation the fertilized egg arrives in a uterus that is well prepared to cradle and nourish it.

The corpus luteum continues to produce estrogen and progesterone for about 10 to

[3]This statement may seem to contradict the earlier statement that high estrogen levels cause a decline in LH. Both of these effects occur, but at different times in the menstrual cycle (Molitch, 1995). There are two centres in the hypothalamus, one which produces a negative feedback loop between estrogen and LH, the other which produces a positive feedback loop between the two.

[4]*Corpus luteum* is Latin for "yellow body." The corpus luteum is so named because the mass of cells is yellowish in appearance.

12 days. If pregnancy has not occurred, its hormone output declines sharply at the end of this period. The uterine lining thus cannot be maintained, and it is shed, resulting in menstruation. Immediately afterward, a new lining starts forming in the next proliferative phase.

The menstrual fluid itself is a combination of blood (from the endometrium), degenerated cells, and mucus from the cervix and vagina. Normally the discharge for an entire period is only about 60 millilitres or 2 ounces (4 tablespoons). Common practice is to use sanitary napkins, which are worn externally, or tampons, which are worn inside the vagina, to absorb the fluid. However, some women use a menstrual cup (brand names *The Keeper* or *The DivaCup*) instead of sanitary napkins or tampons (see Figure 5.4). This is a small reusable device made of flexible rubber or soft medical-grade silicone that has been approved for sale by Health Canada. It has a pull-tab to facilitate removal and can be washed in soapy water. Because it is reusable, it is more economical and environmentally friendly.

Toxic shock syndrome, sometimes abbreviated TSS, is caused by the bacterium *Staphylococcus aureus*. It is associated with tampon use, which can encourage an abnormal growth of the bacteria. Symptoms of toxic shock syndrome include high fever (39°C or greater) accompanied by vomiting or diarrhea. Any woman who experiences these symptoms during her period should discontinue tampon use immediately and see a doctor. Toxic shock syndrome leads to death in approximately 10 percent of cases. It is now recommended that women change tampons frequently, at least every six to eight hours dur-

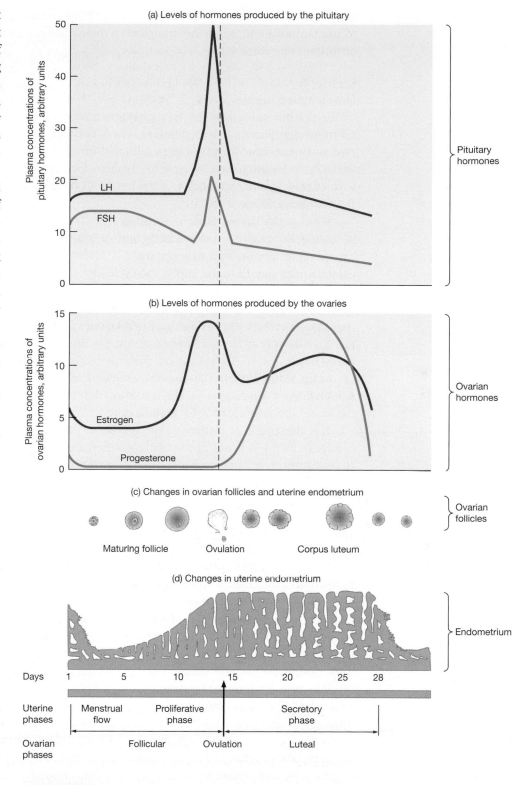

Figure 5.5 The biological events of the menstrual cycle.

Toxic shock syndrome: A sometimes fatal bacterial infection associated with tampon use during menstruation.

ing their periods (although the effectiveness of this is debated). Women are also advised not to use tampons continuously throughout a menstrual period, and to minimize use of super-absorbent tampons.

LENGTH AND TIMING OF THE CYCLE

How long is a normal menstrual cycle? Generally anywhere from 20 to 36 days is considered within the normal range. The average is about 28 days, but somehow this number has taken on more significance than it deserves. There is enormous variation from one woman to the next in the average length of the cycle, and for a given woman there can be considerable variation in length from one cycle to the next. Some recent Canadian research suggests that women with greater variability in the length of their cycle have higher levels of androgens (Van Anders & Watson, 2006).

What is the timing of the four phases of the cycle? In a perfectly regular 28-day cycle, menstruation begins on day 1 and continues until about day 4 or 5. The follicular phase extends from about day 5 to about day 13. Ovulation occurs on day 14, and the luteal phase extends from day 15 to the end of the cycle, day 28. But what if the cycle is not one of those perfect 28-day ones? In cycles that are shorter or longer than 28 days, the principle is that the length of the *luteal* phase is relatively constant. In other words, the time from ovulation to menstruation is always 14 days, give or take only a day or two. Thus, for example, if a woman has a 44-day cycle, she ovulates on about day 30. If she has a 22-day cycle, she ovulates on about day 8.

Some women report that they can actually feel themselves ovulate, a phenomenon called *Mittelschmerz (middle pain)*. The sensation described is a cramping on one or both sides of the lower abdomen, lasting for about a day.

It is also true that ovulation does not occur in every menstrual cycle. That is, menstruation may take place without ovulation. When this happens the woman is said to have an *anovulatory cycle*. Such cycles occur once or twice a year in women in their 20s and 30s and are fairly common among girls during puberty and among women during menopause.

OTHER CYCLIC CHANGES

Two other physiological processes that fluctuate with the menstrual cycle deserve mention: the cervical mucus cycle and the basal body temperature cycle.

The cervical mucus cycle involves glands in the cervix that secrete mucus throughout the menstrual cycle. One function of the mucus is to protect the entrance to the cervix, helping to keep bacteria out. These glands respond to the changing levels of estrogen during the cycle. As estrogen increases at the start of a new cycle, the mucus is alkaline, thick, and viscous. When LH production begins, just before ovulation, the cervical mucus changes markedly. It becomes even more alkaline, thin, and watery. These changes make the environment for sperm passage most hospitable just at ovulation. After ovulation, the mucus returns to its former viscous, less alkaline state. If a sample of mucus is taken just before ovulation and is allowed to dry, the dried mucus takes on a fern-shaped pattern. After ovulation, during the luteal phase, the fernlike patterning will not occur. Thus the *fern test* is one method for detecting ovulation.

A woman's *basal body temperature,* taken with a thermometer before getting up in the morning, also fluctuates with the phases of the menstrual cycle. The temperature is low during the follicular phase and takes a dip on the day of ovulation. Then, on the day after ovulation it rises noticeably, generally by 0.3°C or more, and then continues at the higher level for the rest of the cycle. Progesterone raises body temperature, so the higher temperature during the luteal phase is due to the increased production of progesterone during that time (Baker et al., 2002). This change in basal body temperature is important when a couple are using the fertility awareness method of birth control (Chapter 7) and when a woman is trying to determine the time of ovulation so that she may become pregnant (Chapter 6).

Menstrual Problems

The most common menstrual problem is painful menstruation, known as dysmenorrhea. Almost every woman experiences at least some menstrual discomfort at various times in her life, but the frequency and severity of the discomfort vary considerably from one woman to the next. Cramping pains in the pelvic region are the most common discomfort; other symptoms may include headaches, backaches, nausea, and a feeling of pressure and bloating in the pelvis.

Dysmenorrhea is caused by prostaglandins, hormonelike substances produced by many tissues of the body, including the lining of the uterus (Deligeor-Oglov, 2000). Prostaglandins can cause smooth muscle to contract and can affect the size of blood vessels. Women with severe menstrual pain have unusually high levels of prostaglandins. The high levels cause intense uterine contractions, which in turn choke off some of the uterus's supply of oxygen-carrying blood. Prostaglandins may also cause greater sensitivity in nerve endings. The combination of the uterine contractions, lack of oxygen, and heightened nerve sensitivity produces menstrual cramps.

Household remedies for painful menstruation are available and may be helpful to some women. Aspirin appears to be the best, and cheapest, painkiller available, and it can help to relieve menstrual pain. A somewhat more provocative remedy suggested by, among others, Masters and Johnson is masturbation. This makes good physiological sense because part of the discomfort of menstruation—the pressure and bloating—results from pelvic edema (a congestion of fluids in the pelvic region). During sexual arousal and orgasm, pelvic congestion increases and after orgasm, the congestion dissipates (see Chapter 9). Thus orgasm, whether produced by masturbation or some other means, should help to relieve the pelvic edema that causes menstrual discomfort. And it's a lot more fun than taking medicine!

Mefenamic acid (an antiprostaglandin drug) is a powerful and effective drug for use in the treatment of menstrual pain. The drug is sold with brand names such as Ponstan. About 80 to 85 percent of women who take this drug report significant relief from menstrual pain and symptoms such as nausea, vomiting, dizziness, and weakness (Golub, 1992). Interestingly, aspirin is also an antiprostaglandin.

Dietary changes and aerobic exercise may also be helpful (Golub, 1992; Hatcher et al., 1998). Caffeine should be avoided. A diet high in carbohydrates and low in protein during the luteal phase is helpful for some.

A menstrual problem that may be mistaken for dysmenorrhea is endometriosis. The endometrium, or lining of the uterus, grows during each menstrual cycle and is sloughed off in menstruation. Endometriosis occurs when the endometrial tissue grows in a place other than the uterus—for example, the ovaries, fallopian tubes, rectum, bladder, vagina, vulva, cervix, or lymph glands. The symptoms vary depending on the location of the growth. Very painful periods that last an unusually long time, pain during sexual activity, and infertility are the most common symptoms. Endometriosis is fairly serious and should be treated by a physician. If left untreated it can lead to sterility. Hormones are generally used in treatment, but if the problem is severe, surgery may be required. Laser surgery is a treatment option.

Another menstrual problem is amenorrhea, or the absence of menstruation. It is called *primary amenorrhea* if the girl has not yet menstruated by about age 18. It is called *secondary amenorrhea* if she has had at least one period. Some of the causes of amenorrhea include pregnancy, congenital defects of the reproductive system, hormonal imbalance, cysts or tumours, disease, stress, and emotional factors related to puberty. Amenorrhea can also result from programs of strenuous exercise and from anorexia nervosa.

Dysmenorrhea (dis-men-oh-REE-uh): Painful menstruation.

Prostaglandins: Chemicals secreted by the uterus that cause the uterine muscles to contract; they are a likely cause of painful menstruation.

Endometriosis: A condition in which the endometrium grows abnormally outside the uterus; the symptom is unusually painful periods with excessive bleeding.

Amenorrhea: The absence of menstruation.

Prenatal Sexual Differentiation

SEX CHROMOSOMES

At the time of conception the future human being consists of only a single cell, the fertilized egg. What is the difference between the fertilized egg that will become a female and the fertilized egg that will become a male? The only difference is the sex chromosomes carried in that fertilized egg. If there are two X chromosomes, the result will typically be a female; if there is one X and one Y, the result will typically be a male. While incredibly tiny, the sex chromosomes carry a wealth of information that they transmit to various organs throughout the body, giving them instructions on how to differentiate in the course of development. Because the Y chromosome is smaller, it has fewer genes and carries less information than the X. The Y chromosome has about 80 genes compared to 1090 on the X (Federman, 2006).[5]

Occasionally, individuals receive at conception a sex chromosome combination other than XX or XY. Such abnormal sex chromosome complements may lead to a variety of clinical syndromes, such as *Klinefelter's syndrome.* In this syndrome, a genetic male has an extra X chromosome (XXY). As a result, the testes are abnormal, no sperm are produced, and testosterone levels are low (Winter & Couch, 1995).

During development, the single cell divides repeatedly, becoming a two-celled organism, then a four-celled organism, then an eight-celled organism, and so on. By 28 days after conception, the embryo is about 1 centimetre (less than half an inch) long, but the male and female embryos are still identical, save for the sex chromosomes. In other words, the embryo is still in the undifferentiated state. However, by the seventh week after conception, some basic structures have been formed that will eventually become either a male or a female reproductive system. At this point, the embryo has a pair of gonads (each gonad has two parts, an outer cortex and an inner medulla), two sets of ducts (the *Müllerian ducts* and the *Wolffian ducts*), and rudimentary external genitals (the *genital tubercle*, the *urethral folds,* and the *genital swelling*) (see Figure 5.6, top).

GONADS

In the seventh week after conception, the sex chromosomes direct the gonads to begin differentiation. In the male, the undifferentiated gonad develops into a testis at about seven weeks. In the female, the process occurs somewhat later, with the ovaries developing at around 10 or 11 weeks.

Sex-determining region, Y chromosome (SRY): A gene on the Y chromosome that causes testes to differentiate prenatally.

An important gene that directs the differentiation of the gonads, located on the Y chromosome, is called sex-determining region, Y chromosome (SRY) (Page et al., 1987; Skaletsky et al., 2003). If SRY is present, it causes the manufacture of a substance called testis-determining factor (TDF), which makes the gonads differentiate into testes, and male development occurs. If TDF is not present, female development occurs, making female development the default option. The X chromosome carries a number of genes that control normal functioning of the ovaries (Winter & Couch, 1995). Surprisingly, a number of genes on the X chromosome affect cells in the testes that manufacture sperm (Wang et al., 2001).

PRENATAL HORMONES AND THE GENITALS

Once the ovaries and testes have differentiated, they begin to produce different sex hormones, which then direct the differentiation of the rest of the internal and external genital system (see Figure 5.6).

---

[5]Although all mammals have X and Y chromosomes as humans do, sex is determined in different exotic ways in different species. For example, in some reptiles, such as alligators and turtles, sex is determined by the temperature at a critical period in development: cooler nests all develop into males; warmer nests hatch as females. Some snails start out male then become female. Earthworms are hermaphrodites (have both male and female sex organs).

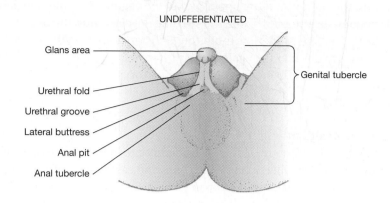

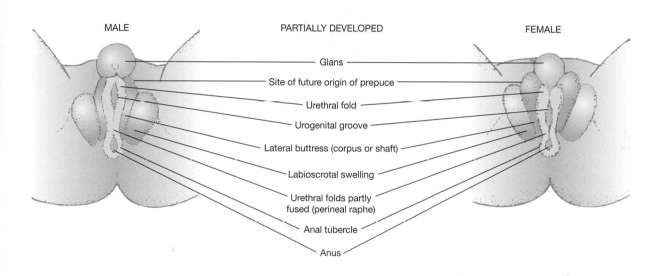

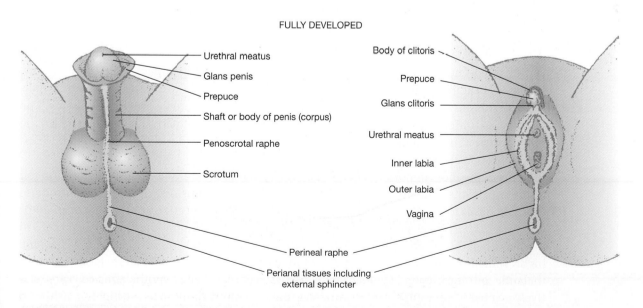

Figure 5.6 Development of the male and female external genitals from the undifferentiated stage. This occurs during prenatal development. Note homologous organs in the female and male.

Müllerian ducts: Ducts found in both male and female fetuses; in males they degenerate and in females they develop into the fallopian tubes, the uterus, and the upper part of the vagina.

In the female the Wolffian ducts degenerate, and the Müllerian ducts turn into the fallopian tubes, the uterus, and the upper part of the vagina. The tubercle becomes the clitoris, the folds become the inner lips, and the swelling develops into the outer lips.

The testes secrete Müllerian Inhibiting Substance (MIS; Vilain, 2000). MIS causes the Müllerian ducts to degenerate, while the Wolffian ducts, supported by testosterone, turn into the epididymis, the vas deferens, and the ejaculatory duct. The tubercle becomes the glans penis, the folds form the shaft of the penis, and the swelling develops into the scrotum.

Wolffian ducts: Ducts found in both male and female fetuses; in females they degenerate and in males they develop into the epididymis, the vas deferens, and the ejaculatory duct.

At least six different genes are involved in prenatal sexual differentiation. A mutation in any one of them can cause an error in development (Vilain, 2000).

By four months after conception, the gender of the fetus is clear from the appearance of the external genitals (refer again to Figure 5.6).

DESCENT OF THE TESTES AND OVARIES

As these developmental changes are taking place, the ovaries and testes are changing in shape and position. At first, the ovaries and testes lie near the top of the abdominal cavity. By the tenth week they have grown and have moved down to the level of the upper edge of the pelvis. The ovaries remain there until after birth and later shift to their adult position in the pelvis.

The male testes must make a much longer journey, down into the scrotum via a passageway called the *inguinal canal*. Normally, this movement occurs around the seventh month after conception. The inguinal canal closes off after the testes have descended.

Cryptorchidism: Undescended testes; the condition in which the testes do not descend to the scrotum as they should during prenatal development.

Two problems may occur in this process. First, one or both testes may have failed to descend into the scrotum by the time of birth, a condition known as *undescended testes*, or cryptorchidism (Santen, 1995). This condition occurs in about 2 percent of all males. Most frequently, only one testis is undescended and the other is in the normal position. In most of these cases, the testes do descend by puberty, and so only about one in 500 adult men has undescended testes. If the testes do not descend spontaneously, however, the condition must be corrected by surgery or hormonal therapy. The optimum time for doing this is before age five. Otherwise, if both testes fail to descend, the man will be sterile because, as discussed in Chapter 4, the high temperature of the testes inside the body inhibits the production of sperm.

The second possible problem occurs when the inguinal canal does not close off completely. It may then reopen later in life, creating a passageway through which loops of the intestine can enter the scrotum. This condition, called *inguinal hernia*, can be remedied by simple surgery.

BRAIN DIFFERENTIATION

During the prenatal period, when sex hormones are having a big impact on genital anatomy, they are also acting on the brain (Arnold, 2003). The results of many experiments with animals indicate that, in certain regions, there are differences between male and female brains. The primary sex-differentiated structure is the hypothalamus, particularly a region of it called the *preoptic area* (Fitch & Bimonte, 2002). The hypothalamus is gender-differentiated in humans as well (Cahill, 2005; Swaab et al., 1995).

One of the most important effects of this early sexual differentiation is the determination of the estrogen sensitivity of certain cells in the hypothalamus. Estrogen passes into these cells and binds to specific molecules in the nucleus, called *estrogen receptors* (Choi et al., 2001; McEwen, 2001). If testosterone is present during fetal development, these specialized cells in the hypothalamus become insensitive to estrogen. If estrogen is present, these cells become highly sensitive to levels of estrogen in the bloodstream. This sensitivity is crucial to the hypothalamic–pituitary–gonad feedback loop discussed earlier. Male hypothalamic cells are relatively insensitive to estrogen levels, whereas female hypothalamic cells are highly sensitive to them. Male hypothalamic cells have more androgen receptors (Donahue et al., 2000).

New magnetic resonance imaging (MRI) studies are giving us a view into the brains of alive, awake humans, in contrast to earlier techniques that dissected the brains of—well, dead people and animals. The trade-off, at least for now, is that the MRI measures are relatively crude, simple assessments of the volume or size of certain regions. One of these studies found a larger volume of the hypothalamus and amygdala—both brain regions with high densities of estrogen and androgen receptors—in men compared with women (Goldstein et al., 2001). Regions of the brain that have few estrogen and androgen receptors did not show these gender differences in size.

The brains of men and women are quite similar in many regions, but a few brain structures show some gender differentiation. These structures include the hippocampus, which is important for memory and spatial navigation, and the amygdala, which is important in emotion (Cahill, 2005).

HOMOLOGOUS ORGANS

Our discussion of sexual differentiation highlights the fact that although adult men and women appear to have very different reproductive anatomies, their reproductive organs have similar origins. When an organ in the male and an organ in the female both develop from the same embryonic tissue, the organs are said to be homologous. When the two organs have similar functions, they are said to be analogous. Table 5.1 summarizes the major homologies and analogies of the male and female reproductive systems. For example, ovaries and testes are homologous (they develop from an undifferentiated gonad) and analogous (they produce gametes and sex hormones).

Homologous (huh-MOLL-uh-gus) organs: Organs in the male and female that develop from the same embryonic tissue.

Analogous (an-AL-uh-gus) organs: Organs in the male and female that have similar functions.

Table 5.1 Homologous and Analogous Organs of the Male and Female Reproductive Systems

	Homologous Organs		Analogous Organs	
Embryonic Source	In the Adult Male	In the Adult Female	In the Adult Male	In the Adult Female
Gonad (medulla plus cortex)	Testes (from medulla)	Ovaries (from cortex)	Testes (from medulla)	Ovaries (from cortex)
Genital tubercle	Glans penis	Clitoris	Glans penis	Clitoris
Genital swelling	Scrotum	Outer lips		
Müllerian duct		Fallopian tubes, uterus, part of vagina		
Wolffian duct	Epididymis, vas deferens, seminal vesicles			
Urethral primordia	Prostate, Cowper's glands	Skene's glands, Bartholin glands	Prostate, Cowper's glands	Skene's glands, Bartholin glands

ATYPICAL PRENATAL GENDER DIFFERENTIATION

Gender is not a simple matter, as you may have noted from the preceding discussion. Most people, however, assume that it is. That is, people typically assume that if a person is female, she will be feminine; will think of herself as a woman; will be sexually attracted to men; will have a clitoris, vagina, uterus, and ovaries; and will have sex chromosomes XX. They also assume that all males are masculine; think of themselves as male; are sexually attracted to women; have a penis, testes, and scrotum; and have sex chromosomes XY.

A great deal of research over the last several decades challenges these assumptions and provides much information about sexuality and gender and their development. Before we discuss the results of this research, however, some background information is helpful.

We can distinguish among the following eight variables of gender (Money, 1987):[6]

1. *Chromosomal gender.* XX in the female; XY in the male
2. *Gonadal gender.* Ovaries in the female; testes in the male
3a. *Prenatal hormonal gender.* Testosterone and MIS in the male but not the female before birth
3b. *Prenatal and neonatal brain differentiation.* Testosterone present for masculinization, absent for feminization
4. *Internal organs.* Fallopian tubes, uterus, and upper vagina in the female; prostate and seminal vesicles in the male
5. *External genital appearance.* Clitoris, inner and outer lips, and vaginal opening in the female; penis and scrotum in the male
6. *Pubertal hormonal gender.* At puberty, estrogen and progesterone in the female; testosterone in the male
7. *Assigned gender.* The announcement at birth, "It's a girl" or "It's a boy," based on the appearance of the external genitals; the gender the parents and the rest of society believe the child to be; the gender in which the child is reared
8. *Gender identity.* The person's private, internal sense of maleness or femaleness

These variables might be subdivided into biological variables (the first six) and psychological variables (the last two). (Gender roles, or the way people of one gender are expected to behave, are discussed in Chapter 13.)

In most cases, of course, all the variables are in agreement in an individual. However, as a result of any one of a number of factors during the course of prenatal sexual development, the gender indicated by one or more of these variables may disagree with the gender indicated by others. When the contradictions are among several of the biological variables (1 through 6), the person is said to have an intersex condition or disorder of sexual development (DSD).[7] Biologically, the gender of such a person is ambiguous. The reproductive structures may be partly male and partly female, or they may be incompletely male or female. Approximately 2 percent of births have an intersex condition (Blackless et al., 2000). Individuals whose assigned gender does not match their gender identity are discussed in Chapter 13.

A number of syndromes can cause an intersex condition. Some of the most common are congenital adrenal hyperplasia, progestin-induced pseudohermaphroditism, and the androgen insensitivity syndrome. In congenital adrenal hyperplasia (CAH), also called "adrenogenital syndrome"), a genetic female develops ovaries normally as a fetus; later in the course of prenatal development, however, the adrenal gland begins to function abnormally (as a result of a recessive genetic condition unconnected with the sex chromosomes), and produces an excess amount of androgens. Prenatal sexual differentiation then does not follow the normal female course. As a result, the external genitals are partly or completely male in appearance. The labia are partly or totally fused (so there is no vaginal opening), and the clitoris is enlarged to the size of a small penis or even a full-sized one. Hence, at birth these genetic females are sometimes identified as males. Long-term follow-ups indicate that CAH girls have a female gender identity, tend toward male-stereotyped toy and game preference, and generally function well as girls and women (Meyer-Bahlburg et al., 2004, 2006).

Progestin-induced pseudohermaphroditism is a similar syndrome that resulted from a drug, progestin, which was at one time given to pregnant women to help them maintain the pregnancy if they were prone to miscarriage. (The drug is no longer prescribed because of the following effects.) As the drug circulated in the mother's bloodstream, the developing fetus

Intersex: A condition in which an individual has a mixture of male and female reproductive structures, so that it is not clear at birth whether the individual is a male or a female. Formerly called a pseudohermaphrodite.

Disorders of sexual development (DSD): A newer term for intersex conditions.

Congenital adrenal hyperplasia (CAH): A condition in which a genetic female produces abnormal levels of testosterone prenatally and therefore has male-appearing genitals at birth.

---

[6]The distinction between the terms "gender" and "sex," discussed in Chapter 1, is being maintained here.

[7]The term "hermaphrodite" is taken from Hermaphroditos, the name of the mythological son of Hermes and Aphrodite. The latter was the Greek goddess of love. A true hermaphrodite has both ovarian and testicular tissues.

was essentially exposed to a high dose of androgens. (Progestin and androgens are quite similar biochemicals, and in the body the progestin acted like an androgen.) In genetic females this produced an abnormal, masculinized genital development similar to that found in CAH.

The reverse case occurs in androgen insensitivity syndrome (AIS) (Wisniewski et al., 2000). In this syndrome a genetic male fetus produces normal levels of testosterone; however, as a result of a genetic condition the body tissues are insensitive to the testosterone, and prenatal development is feminized, although this can occur with different levels of severity. Thus, the individual is born with the external appearance of a female: a small vagina (but no internal reproductive organs) and undescended testes. The individual whose poem appeared at the beginning of this chapter has AIS.

Intersex persons provide good evidence of the great complexity of sex and gender and their development. Many variables are involved in gender and sex, and there are many steps in gender differentiation, even before birth. Because the process is complex it is vulnerable to disturbances, creating conditions such as intersex. Indeed, the research serves to question our basic notions of what it means to be male or female. In CAH, is the genetic female who is born with male external genitals a male or a female? What makes a person male or female? Chromosomal gender? External genital appearance? Gender identity?

A related phenomenon was first studied in a small community in the Dominican Republic (Imperato-McGinley et al., 1974). Due to a genetic-endocrine problem, a large number of genetic males were born there who, at birth, appeared to be females. The syndrome is called *5-Alpha Reductase Syndrome*. They had a vaginal pouch instead of a scrotum and a clitoris-sized penis. The uneducated parents, according to the researchers, were unaware that there were any problems, and these genetic males were treated as typical females. At puberty, a spontaneous biological change caused a penis to develop. Significantly, the psychological identity of these individuals also changed. Despite their rearing as females, their gender identity switched to male, and they developed heterosexual interests. In their culture, these people are called Guevodoces ("penis at 12").

Anthropologist Gilbert Herdt (1990) is critical of the research and interpretations about the Guevodoces. The major criticism is that the Western researchers assumed that this culture is a two-gender society, as in Canada, and that people have to fall into one of only two categories, either male or female. Anthropologists, however, have documented the existence of three-gender societies—that is, societies in which there are three, not two, gender categories—and the society in which the Guevodoces grow up is a three-gender society. The third gender is the Guevodoces. Their gender identity is not male or female, but Guevodoce. The 5-Alpha Reductase Syndrome has also been found among the Sambia of New Guinea, who also have a three-gender culture. Again we see the profound effect of culture on our most basic ideas about sex and gender.

SEXUAL DIFFERENTIATION DURING PUBERTY

Puberty is not a point in time, but rather a process during which there is further sexual differentiation. It is the stage in life during which the body changes from that of a child into that of an adult, with secondary sexual characteristics and the ability to reproduce sexually. Puberty can be scientifically defined as the time during which there is sudden enlargement and maturation of the gonads, other genitalia, and secondary sex characteristics (such as breasts or a beard), leading to reproductive capacity (Tanner, 1967). It is the second important period—the other being the prenatal period—during which sexual differentiation takes place. Perhaps the most important single event in the process is the first ejaculation for boys and the first menstruation for girls. Note that first menstruation is not necessarily a sign of reproductive capability since

Androgen-insensitivity syndrome (AIS): A genetic condition in which the body is unresponsive to androgens so that a genetic male may be born with a female-appearing body.

Puberty: The time during which there is sudden enlargement and maturation of the gonads, other genitalia, and secondary sex characteristics, so that the individual becomes capable of reproduction.

IN FOCUS 5.2

Can Gender Be Assigned? The Story of David Reimer

In Winnipeg in 1965, Janet Reimer gave birth to twin boys, Bruce and Brian. Six months later, the boys developed problems urinating, and their doctor suggested that they be circumcised. However, the doctor did not use the standard procedure for circumcision and botched the surgery, burning off Bruce's entire penis. The Reimers were told that Bruce would have to live without a penis. Some months later, Janet Reimer saw a television program describing the pioneering work of Dr. John Money of Johns Hopkins University in Baltimore. Money believed that gender is determined by how a child is raised, not by his or her biology, providing that assignment is done in infancy and the necessary surgeries and hormone treatments occur.

The Reimers consulted with Money and made the decision to raise Bruce as female even though they had been raising him as a boy up to that time. At the age of 21 months, Bruce's testicles were removed. The Reimers renamed their son Brenda, and following the counsel of Dr. Money resolved not to tell their child the truth. However, despite taking hormones and receiving numerous surgeries, Brenda never really fit in as a girl. She preferred stereotypically male play (e.g., climbing trees) over playing with dolls, and was frequently made fun of by other children for her masculine mannerisms. Brenda even complained of feeling like a boy. When she reached puberty, and was scheduled to have a final surgery to construct a vagina, Brenda refused, despite Money's urging, indicating she would prefer to die. A psychiatrist suggested to Mr. and Mrs. Reimer that they tell the truth to Brenda, who later commented about this revelation, "Suddenly it all made sense why I felt the way I did."

Within months of learning the truth about his sex, Bruce/Brenda cut his hair, began wearing masculine clothing, and changed his name to David. He underwent a series of surgeries to give him a more male body, including a mastectomy to remove the breasts he had grown as a result of taking estrogen. Although David was much happier with his gender, he struggled with depression, in part because he thought he would not find a partner who would love him for who he was. However, as a young adult, David met and married Jane and became the father of her three children. Yet David continued to battle depression, which worsened in his late 30s following the death of his twin brother. He also experienced marital and work-related difficulties, and failed financial investments. On May 4, 2004, at the age of 38, David committed suicide.

Babies who are born with genitals that are not clearly male or female (intersex individuals) typically are treated like David was, using a protocol that became standard in the 1960s. The treatment, which is based on Money's work, generally involves surgically altering the infant's genitals to make them clearly male or female. In Canada, such procedures are covered under medicare. However, the Intersex Society of North America (ISNA)* has argued that intersexuality represents genital variability—as opposed to genital abnormality. The medical standard is that an infant's organ that is 0.9 centimetres or less should be considered a clitoris and 2.5 centimetres or more should be considered a penis, and an infant's gender is assigned accordingly. Intersex activists argue that these cutoffs are arbitrary. What is wrong with a clitoris that is 1.7 centimetres long, for example? Ontario psychologist Morgan Holmes

girls typically do not produce mature eggs until a year or two after the first menstruation.

The physiological process that underlies puberty in both genders is a marked increase in level of sex hormones. Thus the hypothalamus, pituitary, and gonads control the changes.

Adolescence is a socially defined period of development that bears some relationship to puberty. Adolescence represents a psychological transition from the behaviour and attitudes of a child to the behaviour, attitudes, and responsibilities of an adult. In Canada it corresponds roughly to the years from age 10 to age 20. Modern Canadian culture has an unusually long period of adolescence (Steinberg, 2005). A century ago, adolescence was much shorter; the lengthening of the educational process has served to prolong adolescence. In some cultures, in fact, adolescence does not exist. Instead, the child shifts to

Figure 5.7 David Reimer underwent gender reassignment after a botched surgery when he was six months old.

believes that the surgeries are conducted because doctors and parents are uncomfortable with the idea of a child not having genitals that fit a narrow definition of what genitals should look like. Is it ethical to conduct such surgeries and gender assignments with infants who cannot give informed consent and who may later prefer another gender than that chosen for them by their parents and doctors? Should parents be encouraged to lie to their child, as David Reimer's parents were?

Sex researcher Milton Diamond conducted long-term follow-up studies on several individuals who were treated using Money's standard protocol, including David Reimer. Diamond found that, contrary to Money's published paper describing these individuals as well-adjusted, many of them had significant adjustment problems that they traced directly to the medical "management" of their condition. Diamond proposed an alternative protocol for dealing with intersex infants in which he urges physicians (1) to make their most informed judgment about the child's eventual gender identity and counsel the parents to rear the child in that gender; (2) not to perform surgeries that might later need to be reversed; and (3) to provide honest counselling and education to the parents and child as he or she grows up so that the child can eventually make an informed decision regarding treatment.

More systematic follow-up studies on intersex individuals have followed. Many individuals who underwent surgery as infants were dissatisfied with their genitals and reported poor sexual functioning (Creighton et al., 2001; Minto et al., 2003; Wisniewski et al., 2001). The results of these studies also seem to support Money's idea that gender is partly determined by environment. Recognizing these new developments, the American Academy of Pediatrics (2000) issued guidelines for pediatricians on how to care for newborns with genitals that are not clearly male or female. They include what tests to run to determine the cause of the ambiguous genitals, when the baby should be referred to a centre specializing in intersexuality, and what factors should be used to decide the sex of rearing. These factors include fertility potential (e.g., a CAH girl is potentially fertile and should be raised as a girl) and capacity for normal sexual functioning. Only with long-term studies will we learn whether these new treatments will yield better results for intersex individuals.

*For information about the ISNA and other sexuality organizations, including websites, see the Directory of Resources at the end of this book.

Sources: American Academy of Pediatrics, 2000; CBC News Online, May 10, 2004; Colapinto, June 3, 2004; Creighton & Minto, 2001; Creighton et al., 2001; Diamond, 1996, 1999; Diamond & Sigmundson, 1997; Holmes, 2002; Meyer-Bahlburg, 2004; Money & Ehrhardt, 1972; Wisniewski et al., 2000.

being an adult directly, with only a *rite de passage* in between.

Before describing the changes that take place during puberty, we should note two points. First, the timing of the pubertal process differs considerably for males and females. Girls begin the change at around 8 to 12 years of age, while boys do so about two years later. Girls reach their full height by about age 16, while boys continue growing until about age 18 or later. Second, there are large individual differences in the age at which puberty begins (Bogaert, 2005). Experiences may also affect the timing of puberty. For example, girls who have been sexually abused experience earlier puberty than do non-abused girls (Turner et al., 1999). There is no one normal time to begin menstruating or growing a beard. Thus, we give age ranges in describing the timing of the process.

CHANGES IN BOYS

A summary of the physical changes of puberty in boys and girls is provided in Table 5.2. The physical causes of puberty in boys parallel those in girls. They are initiated by increased production of FSH and LH by the pituitary. At the beginning of puberty, the increase in LH stimulates the testes to produce testosterone, which is responsible for most of the changes of puberty in the male.

The first noticeable pubertal change in males is the growth of the testes and scrotal sac, which begins at an average age of nine to ten as a result of testosterone stimulation. The growth of pubic hair begins at about the same time. About a year later the penis begins to enlarge, first thickening and then lengthening. This change also results from testosterone stimulation. As the testes enlarge, their production of testosterone increases even more leading to rapid growth of the penis, testes, and pubic hair at ages 13 and 14.

The growth of facial and axillary hair begins about two years after the beginning of pubic-hair growth. The growth of facial hair begins with the appearance of fuzz on the upper lip; adult beards do not appear until two or three years later. Indeed, by age 17, 50 percent of North American males have not yet shaved. These changes also result from testosterone stimulation, which continues to produce growth of facial and chest hair beyond 20 years of age.

Erections increase in frequency and sometimes occur at inopportune times. The organs that produce the fluid of semen, particularly the prostate, enlarge considerably at about the same time the other organs are growing. By age 13 or 14 the boy is capable of ejaculation.[8] By about age 15, the ejaculate contains mature sperm, and the male is now fertile. The pituitary hormone FSH is responsible for initiating and maintaining the production of mature sperm.

Beginning about a year after the first ejaculation, many boys begin having nocturnal emissions, or *wet dreams*. For the boy who has never masturbated, a wet dream may be his first ejaculation.

At about the same time penis growth occurs, the larynx *(voice box)* also begins to grow in response to testosterone. As the larynx enlarges, the boy's voice drops, or "changes." Typically, the transition occurs at around age 13 or 14. Because testosterone is necessary to produce the change in voice, castration before puberty results in a male with a permanently high voice.

(a)   *(b)*

| Figure 5.8 | There is great variability in the onset of puberty and its growth spurt. All these boys are the same age. Both these girls are the same age.

This principle was used to produce the *castrati*, who sang in the great choirs of Europe during the eighteenth century. They began as lovely boy sopranos, and their parents or the choirmaster, hating to see their beautiful voices destroyed at puberty, had them castrated so that they remained permanent sopranos. Contrary to popular belief, castration in adulthood will not produce a high voice, because the larynx has already grown.

A great spurt of body growth begins in boys at around 11 to 16 years of age (Figure 5.8a). Height increases rapidly. Body contours also change. While the changes in girls involve mainly the increase in fatty tissue in the breasts and hips, the changes in boys involve mainly an increase in muscle mass. Eventually testosterone brings the growth process to an end, although it permits the growth period to continue longer than it does in girls.

[8]Note that orgasm and ejaculation are two separate processes, even though they generally occur together, at least in males after puberty. But orgasm may occur without ejaculation, and ejaculation may occur without orgasm.

Table 5.2 Summary of the Changes of Puberty and Their Sequence

Girls			Boys		
Characteristic	Average Age of First Appearance (Years)	Major Hormonal Influence	Characteristic	Average Age of First Appearance (Years)	Major Hormonal Influence
1. Growth of breasts	9–10	Pituitary growth hormone, estrogens, progesterone, thyroxine	1. Growth of testes, scrotal sac	9–10	Pituitary growth hormone, testosterone
2. Growth of pubic hair	9–10	Adrenal androgens	2. Growth of pubic hair	11–12	Testosterone
3. Body growth	9.5–14.5	Pituitary growth hormone, adrenal androgens, estrogens	3. Body growth	10.5–16	Pituitary growth hormone, testosterone
4. Menarche	12–12.5	GnRH, FSH, LH, estrogens, progesterone	4. Growth of penis	11–14.5	Testosterone
			5. Change in voice (growth of larynx)	About the same time as penis growth	Testosterone
5. Underarm hair	About two years after pubic hair	Adrenal androgens	6. Facial and underarm hair	About two years after pubic hair	Testosterone
6. Oil- and sweat-producing glands (acne occurs when glands are clogged)	About the same time as underarm hair	Adrenal androgens	7. Oil- and sweat-producing glands, acne	About the same time as underarm hair	Testosterone

Source: Bernard Goldstein (1976), *Introduction to human sexuality.* New York: McGraw-Hill, pp. 80–81. Reprinted by permission of Bernard Goldstein. Sources for age: Chumlea et al., 2003; Sun et al., 2002.

Puberty brings changes and also problems. One problem is *acne,* a distressing skin condition that is stimulated by androgens and affects boys more frequently than girls. It is caused by a clogging of the sebaceous (oil-producing) glands, resulting in pustules, blackheads, and redness on the face and possibly the chest and back. Generally acne is not severe enough to require medical treatment, although its psychological impact may be great. In order to avoid scarring, severe cases should be treated by a physician. The treatment is typically ultraviolet light, the drug Retin-A, and/or antibiotics. The drug Accutane is highly effective for severe cases. However, it must be used cautiously because it may have serious side effects, including depression and thoughts of suicide.

Gynecomastia (breast enlargement) may occur temporarily in boys, creating considerable embarrassment. About 80 percent of boys in puberty experience this growth, which is probably caused by small amounts of female sex hormones being produced by the testes. Obesity may also be a temporary problem, although it is more frequent in girls than boys.

In various cultures around the world, puberty rites are performed to signify the adolescent's passage to adulthood. Many aboriginal cultures celebrate this life transition for boys and girls. In Canada the only remaining vestiges of such ceremonies are the Jewish bar mitzvah for boys and bat mitzvah for girls and, in some Christian churches, confirmation. In a sense, it is unfortunate that we do not give more formal recognition to puberty. Puberty rites probably serve an important psychological function in that they are a formal, public announcement of the fact that the boy or girl is passing through an important period of change. In the absence of such rituals, the young person may think that his or her body is doing strange things and

(a)   (b)

Figure 5.9 Most cultures celebrate puberty, but cultures vary widely in the nature of the celebration. Canadian Jewish youth celebrate a bar mitzvah (for boys) or bat mitzvah (for girls). The Samburu youth of Kenya celebrate a male circumcision ritual.

may feel very much alone. This may be particularly problematic for boys, who lack an obvious sign of puberty like the first menstruation (the first ejaculation is probably the closest analogy) to help them identify the stage they are in.

CHANGES IN GIRLS

The first sign of puberty in girls is the beginning of breast development, on average around nine to ten years of age (Sun et al., 2002). The ducts in the nipple area swell, and there is growth of fatty and connective tissue, causing the small, conical buds to increase in size. These changes are produced by increases in the levels of the sex hormones.

As the growth of fatty and supporting tissue increases in the breasts, a similar increase takes place at the hips and buttocks, leading to the rounded contours that distinguish adult female bodies from adult male bodies. Individual females have unique patterns of fat deposits, so there are also considerable individual differences in the resulting female shapes.

Another visible sign of puberty is the growth of pubic hair, which occurs shortly after breast development begins. About two years later, axillary (underarm) hair appears.

Body growth increases sharply during puberty, during the approximate age range of 9.5 to 14.5 years. The growth spurt for girls occurs about two years before the growth spurt for boys (see Figure 5.10). This is consistent with girls' general pattern of maturing earlier than boys.

Estrogen eventually applies the brakes to the growth spurt in girls. The presence of estrogen also causes the growth period to end sooner in girls, thus accounting for the lesser average height of adult women as compared with adult men.

Menarche (MEN-ar-key): First menstruation.

At about 12 to 13 years of age, the **menarche** (first menstruation) occurs. Although the average age of menarche has deceased in the past 150 years, likely due to improved nutrition, it has remained constant over the past 50 years (Posner, 2006). Girls are not capable of becoming pregnant until ovulation begins. Typically, girls do not ovulate regularly for one to two years after first ovulation (Metcalfe et al., 1983). The first menstruation is not only an important biological event but also a significant psychological one. Various cultures have ceremonies recognizing its importance. In some families, it is a piece of news that spreads quickly to the relatives. Girls themselves display a wide range of reactions to the event, ranging from negative ones, such as fear, shame, or disgust, to positive ones, such as pride and a sense of maturity and womanliness.

Some of the most negative reactions occur when the girl has not been prepared for the menarche, which is still the case surprisingly often. Parents who are concerned about preparing their daughters for the first menstruation should remember that there is a wide range in the age at which it occurs. It is not unusual for a girl to start menstruating in grade 5, and instances of the menarche during grade 4, while rare, do occur.

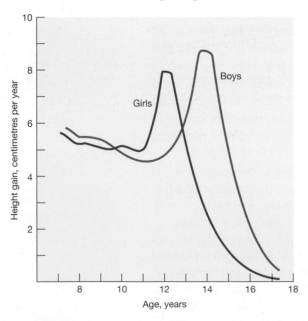

Figure 5.10 The adolescent spurt of growth for boys and girls. Note that girls experience their growth spurt earlier than boys do.

What determines the age at which a girl first menstruates? One explanation is the *percent body fat hypothesis* (Frisch & McArthur, 1974; Hopwood et al., 1990). During puberty, deposits of body fat increase in females. According to the percent body fat hypothesis, the percentage of body weight that is fat must rise to a certain level for menstruation to occur for the first time and for it to be maintained. Thus, very thin adolescent girls would tend to be late in the timing of first menstruation. Leptin, a protein manufactured in the body, seems to be related to the onset of puberty in girls and in boys, although scientists have not yet sorted out the details (Apter, 2003; Phillip & Lazar, 2003; Wilson et al., 2003). In prepubertal girls and boys, leptin levels rise as body fat increases. Leptin simulates the growth of skeletal bone and the release of LH.

The percent body fat hypothesis also helps to make sense of two related phenomena: the cessation of menstruation in women with anorexia nervosa and the cessation of menstruation in female distance runners. *Anorexia nervosa* is a condition in which the person—most commonly an adolescent girl—engages in compulsive, extreme dieting and exercise, perhaps to the point of starving herself to death. As anorexia progresses, the percentage of body fat declines and menstruation ceases. It is also fairly common for women who are runners, and all women who exercise seriously to the point where their body fat is substantially reduced, to cease menstruating. It seems that when the percentage of body fat falls below a critical value, the biological mechanisms that control the menstrual cycle shut down menstruation.[9]

Before leaving the topic of running, we should note that there is some evidence that serious exercise also affects the male reproductive system. One study of male distance runners found that their testosterone levels were only about 68 percent as high, on the average, as a control group's testosterone levels (Wheeler et al., 1984). There are some reports of male long-distance runners complaining of a loss of sex drive, but it is unclear whether this results from reduced testosterone levels or from the perpetual feelings of fatigue from their intensive training (Wheeler et al., 1984).

Other body changes in girls during puberty include a development of the blood supply to the clitoris, a thickening of the walls of the vagina, and a rapid growth of the uterus, which doubles in size between the tenth and the eighteenth years. The pelvic bone structure grows and widens, contributing to the rounded shape of the female and creating a passageway large enough for an infant to move through during birth.

The dramatic changes that occur during puberty are produced, basically, by the endocrine system and its upsurge in sex hormone production during puberty. The process begins with an increase in secretion of FSH by the pituitary gland. FSH in turn stimulates the ovaries to produce estrogen. Estrogen is responsible for many of the changes that occur; it stimulates breast growth and the growth of the uterus and vagina.

Also involved in puberty are the paired adrenal glands, which are located just above the kidneys. In the female, the adrenal glands are the major producer of androgens, which exist at low levels in females. Adrenal androgens stimulate the growth of pubic and axillary hair and are related to the female sex drive. Adrenarche—the time of increasing secretion of adrenal androgens—generally begins slightly before age eight (Grumbach & Styne, 1998).

PSYCHOLOGICAL ASPECTS OF THE MENSTRUAL CYCLE

"Why do I get so emotional?" screams the ad for Midol PMS in *Teen* magazine. It is part of the folk wisdom of our culture that women experience fluctuations in mood over the phases of the menstrual cycle. In particular, women are supposed to be especially cranky and depressed just before and during their periods. In France, if a woman commits a crime during her premenstrual phase, she may use the fact in her defence, claiming "temporary impairment of sanity."

---

[9] On the other hand, programs of moderate, regular aerobic exercise have been shown to reduce menstrual problems such as cramps (Golub, 1992).

Leptin: A protein produced in the body that is related to the onset of puberty.

Adrenal (uh-DREE-nul) glands: Endocrine glands located just above the kidneys; in the female they are the major producers of androgens.

Adrenarche (AD-ren-ar-key): A time of increased secretion of adrenal androgens, usually just before age eight.

What is the scientific evidence concerning the occurrence of such fluctuations in mood, and, if they do occur, what causes them?

FLUCTUATIONS IN MOOD: DO WOMEN BECOME EXTRA EMOTIONAL?

Premenstrual syndrome (PMS): A combination of severe physical and psychological symptoms, such as depression and irritability, occurring just before menstruation.

The term **premenstrual syndrome (PMS)** refers to those cases in which the woman has a particularly severe combination of physical, psychological, and behavioural symptoms that occur premenstrually. These symptoms may include depression, irritability, breast pain, and water retention (Stanton et al., 2002). In the last several decades, much research has been done on moods during the premenstrual period and on whether moods fluctuate during the cycle (Taylor, 2006).

Research based on women's daily self-reports throughout the cycle generally finds positive moods around the time of ovulation (that is, mid-cycle), and various symptoms, such as anxiety, irritability, depression, fatigue, and headaches, premenstrually (Golub, 1992). However, the fluctuations are not large on average. In one study, the average depression score of women was 6.8 around ovulation and 9.3 premenstrually, compared with a mean of 16.0 for depressed psychiatric patients (Gotlub, 1992).

The evidence supporting mood fluctuations and PMS has been challenged though. Of the numerous criticisms that have been made (Chrisler et al., 2006; Stanton et al., 2002), three deserve special mention here. First, much of the evidence depends on subjective retrospective reports of mood and symptoms, which are probably not very reliable. Second, we can question how the direction of the difference is interpreted. The typical interpretation is that women show a psychological "deficit" premenstrually, as compared with the "normal" state at ovulation and during the rest of the cycle. However, the opposite interpretation might also be made: that women are "normal" premenstrually and experience unusual well-being psychologically at mid-cycle. What defines "normal" or "average" mood, then? Men's moods?

Support for a reinterpretation might come from the statistics on violent crimes committed by women. While it may be true that women are somewhat more likely to commit crimes during the eight premenstrual and menstrual days, even during this period they are far less likely to commit crimes than men are. Further, most studies comparing cycles in the moods of women and men have not found differences (Stanton et al., 2002).

Third, PMS is a stereotype in our culture. The stereotype includes beliefs that premenstrual women have sharp mood swings and crying spells and are bloated from water retention. Women in fact report far fewer symptoms for themselves than they think the average woman experiences (Chrisler, 2006). PMS may therefore largely be a stereotype that does not match most women's actual experience.

Taking into account the criticisms and available evidence, it seems reasonable to conclude the following:

1. Women do, on average, experience some fluctuations in mood over the phases of the menstrual cycle.
2. Present evidence does not clearly indicate how the direction of the shifts should be interpreted—whether women's moods are unusually low premenstrually or unusually high around the time of ovulation.
3. There is a great deal of variation from one woman to the next in the size of these shifts and the way they are expressed. Some women experience no shifts or shifts so slight that they are not noticeable, whereas others may experience large shifts. It would be interesting to know how many do show mood fluctuations and how many do not. Unfortunately, the studies that have tried to provide this information themselves show substantial variation; the percentage reporting symptoms ranges between 25 percent and 80 percent in various studies (Stanton et al., 2002). It is important to make a distinction between women who have full-blown PMS and women who experience no fluctuation or only moderate fluctuations in mood over the cycle.

The American Psychiatric Association has formalized severe PMS with the diagnosis **premenstrual dysphoric disorder**, or PMDD, in the *DSM-IV* (American Psychiatric Association, 2000). It isn't in the main *DSM,* but rather in an appendix, meaning that it isn't officially "in" yet. Symptoms must occur during the last week of the luteal phase and include feeling sad or hopeless, feeling tense or anxious, tearfulness, irritability, difficulty concentrating, and changes in appetite. These symptoms have to have occurred most months for the past year. This new diagnostic category is very controversial, however (Caplan, 1995). Some argue that it represents nothing but a medicalizing and pathologizing of women's experience (Offman & Kleinplatz, 2004; Poulin & Gouliquer, 2003). Others point out that there is no scientific basis for PMDD and that some studies fail to confirm it (Gallant et al., 1992). Still others argue that the PMDD diagnosis is useful for the minority of women who experience such extreme symptoms that their quality of life is affected (DiGiulio & Reissing, 2006).

Premenstrual dysphoric disorder (PMDD): A tentative diagnostic category in the *DSM-IV,* characterized by symptoms such as sadness, anxiety, and irritability in the week before menstruation.

FLUCTUATIONS IN PERFORMANCE: SHOULD WOMEN BE PRIME MINISTER?

So far, our discussion has concentrated on fluctuations in psychological characteristics such as depression, anxiety, and irritability. However, in some situations performance is of more practical importance than mood. For example, is a female mechanic's work less accurate premenstrually and menstrually? Is a female athlete's coordination or speed impaired during the premenstrual–menstrual period?

Research on performance—such as intellectual or athletic performance—generally shows no fluctuations over the cycle. Research has found no fluctuations in academic performance, problem solving, memory, or creative thinking (Epting & Overman, 1988; Stanton et al; 2002).

In one study, 31 percent of female athletes said they believed that they experienced a decline in performance during the premenstrual or menstrual phases; yet when their actual performance was measured, they showed no deficits in strength (weight lifters) or swimming speed (swimming team members) (Quadagno et al., 1991). Thus, there is no reliable evidence indicating that the kinds of performance required in a work situation or an athletic competition fluctuate over the menstrual cycle.

FLUCTUATIONS IN SEX DRIVE

Another psychological characteristic that has been investigated for fluctuations over the cycle is women's sex drive or arousability. Women, of course, engage in sexual behaviour throughout the menstrual cycle. But might there be some subtle cycling in drive, expressed, perhaps, in fluctuations in frequency of intercourse? Studies have yielded contradictory results. Some have found a peak frequency of intercourse around ovulation, which would be biologically functional—that is, increase the chances of conception occurring. But others have found peaks just before and just after menstruation (Zillmann et al., 1994).

Of course, one should be cautious about using frequency of intercourse as a measure of a woman's sex drive. Intercourse requires some agreement between partners, and thus reflects not only a woman's desires but her partner's as well. One study assessed both heterosexual women's activity with a partner and self-rated sexual desire (Bullivant et al., 2004). The results indicated that sexual activity initiated by the woman—but not by the man—peaked during the three days before and three days after ovulation. Sexual desire showed the same pattern.

In a sophisticated study, women kept daily diaries of their moods and sexual interest and provided blood samples for hormone assays (Van Goozen et al., 1997). This study assessed testosterone levels, as well as levels of estrogen and progesterone, an important addition because the evidence is strongest for an association between testosterone and sex drive in women. The results indicated that testosterone levels peaked at ovulation. The women seemed to fall into two subgroups, with different patterns of sexual interest. About half the women reported that they suffered from premenstrual symptoms; their sexual interest peaked at ovulation, exactly when testosterone levels are high. The other half of the women said they did not suffer from premenstrual symptoms and their peak in sexual interest occurred premenstrually, perhaps in anticipation of a deprivation during menstruation.

If there is a link between phase of the menstrual cycle and sexual interest, it most likely reflects an association between testosterone levels and sexuality with a peak in sexual interest around the time of ovulation. But with humans, psychological and social factors—such as some couples' dislike of intercourse when the woman is menstruating—play a strong role as well.

WHAT CAUSES THE FLUCTUATIONS IN MOOD: WHY DO SOME WOMEN GET EMOTIONAL?

For women who do experience fluctuations in mood during the menstrual cycle, the question arises of what causes these fluctuations. This raises the nature–nurture, or biology–environment, controversy. That is, some researchers argue that mood fluctuations are caused primarily by biological factors—in particular, fluctuations in levels of hormones. Others argue that environmental factors such as menstrual taboos and cultural expectations are the primary cause.

On the biology side, changes in mood appear to be related to changes in hormone levels during the cycle. The fact that depression is more frequent in women premenstrually, at menopause, and postpartum (after having a baby) suggests that there is at least some relationship between sex hormones and depression. The exact hormone–mood relationship is not known, but low or declining levels of estrogen and/or progesterone are the likeliest culprits. Neither is it known exactly what the mechanism is by which hormones influence mood (Golub, 1992). Research does indicate that the estrogen–progesterone system interacts with the production of the neurotransmitters norepinephrine, serotonin, and dopamine, and neurotransmitter levels are linked to mood disorders such as depression (Halbreich, 1996; Mortola, 1998).

Critics of the hormone point of view note that causality is being inferred from correlational data. In other words, the data show a correlation between cycle phase (hormonal levels) and mood, but do not show that hormone levels cause the mood shift.

Those arguing the other side—that the fluctuations are due to cultural forces—note the widespread cultural expectations and taboos surrounding menstruation (for reviews, see Golub, 1992; Stanton et al., 2002). In some non-industrialized cultures, women who are menstruating are isolated from the community and may have to stay in a menstrual hut at the edge of town during their period. Often the menstrual blood itself is thought to have supernatural, dangerous powers, and the woman's isolation is considered necessary for the safety of the community. Among the Lele of the Congo, for example:

> A menstruating woman was a danger to the whole community if she entered the forest. Not only was her menstruation certain to wreck any enterprise in the forest that she might undertake, but it was thought to produce unfavorable conditions for men. Hunting would be difficult for a long time after, and rituals based on forest plants would have no efficacy. Women found these rules extremely irksome, especially as they were regularly short-handed and late in their planting, weeding, harvesting, and fishing. (Douglas, 1970, p. 179)

Such practices do not occur only among non-Western people. Note that there is a history of similar practices in our own culture as well. For example, the following passage is from the book of Leviticus in the Bible:

> When a woman has a discharge of blood which is her regular discharge from her body, she shall be in her impurity for seven days, and whoever touches her shall be unclean until the evening. . . . And whoever touches her bed shall wash his clothes, and bathe himself in water, and be unclean until the evening; whether it is the bed or anything upon which she sits, when he touches it he shall be unclean until the evening. (Leviticus 15:19–23)

Among the most common menstrual taboos are those prohibiting sexual intercourse with a menstruating woman. For example, the continuation of the passage from Leviticus just quoted is:

> And if any man lies with her, and her impurity is on him, he shall be unclean seven days; and every bed on which he lies shall be unclean. (Leviticus 15:24)

Couples who violated the taboo could be stoned. Orthodox Jews still abstain from sex during the woman's period and for seven days afterward. At the end of this time the woman goes to the *mikvah* (ritual bath) to be cleansed, and only after this cleansing may she resume sexual relations.

Advocates of the cultural explanation argue, then, that women become anxious and depressed around the time of menstruation because of the many cultural forces, such as menstrual taboos, that create negative attitudes toward menstruation. For example, in an Ontario study, one-third of the university women sampled, all of whom were in a romantic relationship, had never engaged in sexual activity during menstruation (Remple & Baumgartner, 2003). Furthermore, women's expectations may play a role (Stanton et al., 2002). Our culture is filled with teachings that women are supposed to behave strangely just before and during their periods—for example, drug company ads that ask "Why am I so emotional?" According to this line of reasoning, women are taught that they should be depressed around the time of menstruation, and because they expect to become depressed, they do become depressed. Researchers in British Columbia have proposed an additional role for expectations (McFarlane et al., 1988). Women (and men) experience variability in their moods. Because of cultural stereotypes about PMS, women attribute their negative mood to hormones when they occur premenstrually. However, they attribute their negative moods at other times in their cycle to other causes (e.g., work or family).

Figure 5.11 Does advertising for menstrual drugs contribute to negative stereotypes about women and PMS?

Surely such forces do exist in our culture. But is there any evidence that they really have an effect on women's moods and behaviour? Psychologist Diane Ruble (1977; see also Klebanov & Jemmott, 1992) did a clever experiment to determine whether women's culturally induced expectations influence their reporting of premenstrual symptoms. University students were tested on the sixth or seventh day before the onset of their next menstrual period. They were told that they would participate in a study on a new technique for predicting the expected date of menstruation using an electroencephalograph (EEG), a method that had already been successfully tested with older women. After the EEG had been run (it actually wasn't), the woman was informed of when her next period was to occur, depending on which of three experimental groups she had randomly been assigned to: (1) she was told she was "premenstrual" and her period was due in one or two days; (2) she was told she was "intermenstrual" or "mid-cycle" and her period was not expected for at least a week to ten days; or (3) she was given no information at all about the predicted date of menstruation (control group). The women then completed a self-report menstrual distress questionnaire. The results indicated that women who had been led to believe they were in the premenstrual phase reported significantly more water retention, pain, and changes in eating habits than did women who had been led to believe they were around mid-cycle. (In fact, women in these groups did not differ significantly when their periods actually arrived.) There were no significant differences between the groups in ratings of negative moods, however. This study indicates that, probably because of learned beliefs, women overstate the changes in body states that occur over the menstrual cycle. When they think they are in the premenstrual phase, they report more problems than when they think they are at mid-cycle.

This nature–nurture argument will not be easily resolved, particularly because there is evidence for both points of view. Perhaps the best solution is to say that both biology and culture contribute to women's mood fluctuations during the menstrual cycle. In other words, some women probably do experience mood shifts caused by hormonal and possibly other physical factors and, for many others, slight biological influences are magnified by psychological and cultural influences (Hampson & Moffatt, 2004). A woman's premenstrual hormonal state may act as a sort of trigger. It may, for example, provide a state conducive to depression; if the environment then provides further stimuli to depression, the woman becomes depressed.

SUMMARY

The major sex hormones are testosterone, which is produced in the male by the testes, and estrogen and progesterone, which are produced in the female by the ovaries, although both men and women have both testosterone and estrogen. Levels of the sex hormones are regulated by two hormones secreted by the pituitary: FSH (follicle-stimulating hormone) and LH (luteinizing hormone). The gonads, pituitary, and hypothalamus regulate one another's output through a negative feedback loop. Inhibin regulates FSH levels.

Biologically, the menstrual cycle is divided into four phases: the follicular phase, ovulation, the luteal phase, and menstruation. Corresponding to these phases, there are changes in the levels of pituitary hormones (FSH and LH) and in the levels of ovarian hormones (estrogen and progesterone), as well as changes in the ovaries and the uterus. A fairly common menstrual problem is dysmenorrhea, or painful menstruation.

At conception males and females differ only in the sex chromosomes (XX in females and XY in males). As the male fetus grows, the SRY gene on the Y chromosome directs the gonads to differentiate into the testes. In the absence of the SRY gene, ovaries develop. Different hormones are then produced by the gonads, and these stimulate further differentiation of the internal and external reproductive structures of males and females. A male organ and a female organ that derive from the same embryonic tissue are said to be homologous to each other.

Intersex conditions are generally the result of various syndromes and accidents that occur during the course of prenatal sexual differentiation. Currently, there is a debate over the best medical treatment of these individuals. The Guevodoces provide an interesting case of gender change at puberty.

Puberty is initiated and characterized by a great increase in the production of sex hormones. Pubertal changes in both males and females include body growth, the development of pubic and axillary hair, and increased output from the oil-producing glands. Changes in the female include breast development and the beginning of menstruation. Changes in the male include growth of the penis and testes, the beginning of ejaculation, and a deepening of the voice.

Research indicates that some, although not all, women experience changes in mood over the phases of the menstrual cycle. For those who experience such changes, their mood is generally positive around the middle of the cycle (i.e., around ovulation), whereas negative moods characterized by depression and irritability are more likely just before and during menstruation. These negative moods and physical discomforts are termed premenstrual syndrome (PMS). On the other hand, research indicates that there are no fluctuations in performance over the cycle. There is evidence suggesting that fluctuations in mood are related to changes in hormone levels as well as to cultural factors. Research attempting to document whether men experience monthly biological and/or psychological cycles is now in progress.

QUESTIONS FOR THOUGHT, DISCUSSION, AND DEBATE

1. Of the physical changes of puberty, which are the most difficult to cope with?

2. The society in the Dominican Republic in which the Guevodoces are born (see p. 121) is a three-gender society, unlike the two-gender society of the dominant Canadian culture. What would Canada be like if it were a three-gender society? Who would be classified in the third gender? Would their lives be better or worse as a result? Could we have a four-gender society? Who would be classified in the fourth gender? (For further information, see Herdt, 1990.)

3. Are women's fluctuations in mood over the menstrual cycle caused by biological factors or by environmental/cultural factors?

4. Teresa has just given birth to her first baby. The doctor approaches her with a worried expression and says that her baby's genitals are unusual and some decisions will have to be made. The phallus is too big for a clitoris, but too small for a penis. What should Teresa do? What other information should she obtain from the doctor before making a decision?

5. Your ten-year-old daughter tells you that she has heard about PMS and wonders whether she will get it when she begins her periods. What would you tell her?

SUGGESTIONS FOR FURTHER READING

Colapinto, John. (2001). *As nature made him: The boy who was raised as a girl.* Toronto: Harper Perennial Canada. This is the story of David Reimer, the Winnipeg boy who was raised as a girl after a circumcision accident.

Fausto-Sterling, Anne. (2000). *Sexing the body.* New York: Basic Books. The author, a developmental geneticist, has written a provocative book that calls into question our most basic understandings of differentiation of the sexes, both physically and psychologically.

Kessler, Suzanne J. (1998). *Lessons from the intersexed.* New Brunswick, NJ: Rutgers University Press. Kessler, a psychologist, reports on her years of research with intersex individuals and the medical and psychological professionals who treat them, and she proposes new approaches in dealing with the condition.

Larsen, P. Reed et al. (2003). *Williams textbook of endocrinology.* 10th ed. Philadelphia: Saunders. An outstanding endocrinology text, with a particularly good chapter on sexual differentiation.

Steinberg, Laurence. (2005). *Adolescence.* 7th ed. New York: McGraw-Hill. This is the definitive textbook on adolescence, written by a leading researcher.

Online LearningCentre

For review questions, web resources, and other learning and study tools, visit the *Understanding Human Sexuality* Online Learning Centre at www.mcgrawhill.ca/olc/hyde.

Chapter

6

CONCEPTION, PREGNANCY, AND CHILDBIRTH

Chapter Highlights

> I REMEMBER FEELING VERY SEXY. WE WERE TRYING ALL THESE DIFFERENT POSITIONS. NOW THAT WE WERE HAVING A BABY, I FELT A LOT LOOSER. I USED TO FEEL UPTIGHT ABOUT SEX FOR ITS OWN SAKE, BUT WHEN I WAS PREGNANT I FELT A LOT FREER.
>
> I THOUGHT IT WOULD NEVER END. I WAS ENORMOUS. I COULDN'T BEND OVER AND WASH MY FEET. AND IT WAS INCREDIBLY HOT.*

Chapter 5 described the remarkable biological process by which a single fertilized egg develops into a male or a female human being. This chapter is about some equally remarkable processes involved in creating human beings: conception, pregnancy, and childbirth.

CONCEPTION

SPERM MEETS EGG: THE INCREDIBLE JOURNEY

On about day 14 of an average menstrual cycle the woman ovulates. The egg is released from the ovary into the body cavity. Typically, it is then picked up by the fimbriae (long fingerlike structures at the end of the fallopian tube—see Figure 6.1) and enters the fallopian tube. It then begins a leisurely trip down the tube toward the uterus, reaching it in about five days if it has been fertilized. Otherwise, it disintegrates in about 48 hours. The egg, unlike the sperm, has no means of moving itself and is propelled by the cilia (hairlike structures) lining the fallopian tube. The egg has begun its part of the journey toward conception.

The woman's cervix secretes mucus that flushes the passageways to prepare for the arrival of the sperm. Meanwhile, the woman has sexual intercourse, and the man has an orgasm and ejaculates inside the woman's vagina. Alternately, the woman uses assisted insemination to place semen in the vagina.[1] Either way, the sperm are deposited in the vagina, there to begin their journey toward the egg. Actually, they have made an incredible trip even before reaching the vagina. Initially, they were manufactured in the seminiferous tubules of the testes (see Chapter 4). They then collected and were stored in the epididymis. During ejaculation they moved up and over the top of the bladder in the vas deferens; then they travelled down through the ejaculatory duct, mixed with seminal fluid, and went out through the urethra.

The sperm is one of the tiniest cells in the human body. It is composed of a *head*, a *midpiece*, and a *tail* (see Figure 6.2 on page 137). The head is about 5 micrometres long, and the total length, from the tip of the head to the tip of the tail, is about 60 micrometres (about 0.06 millimetre, or 2/1000 inch). The DNA, which is the sperm's most important contribution when it unites with the egg, is contained in the nucleus, which is in the head of the sperm. Sperm also contain RNA carrying the instructions for early embryonic development, and a large number of proteins (Ainsworth, 2005). The *acrosome*, a chemical reservoir, is also in the head of the sperm. The midpiece contains *mitochondria*, tiny structures in which chemical reactions occur that provide energy. This energy is used when the sperm lashes its tail back and forth. The lashing action (called *flagellation*) propels the sperm forward.

A typical ejaculate has a volume of about 3 millilitres, or about a teaspoonful, and contains about 200 million sperm. Although this might seem to be a wasteful amount of sperm if

---

*Boston Women's Health Book Collective. (1998). *Our bodies, ourselves for the new century.* New York: Simon and Schuster, pp. 443, 446.

[1]Increasing numbers of Canadian women are becoming pregnant using new reproductive technologies. These are described on pp. 171–175.

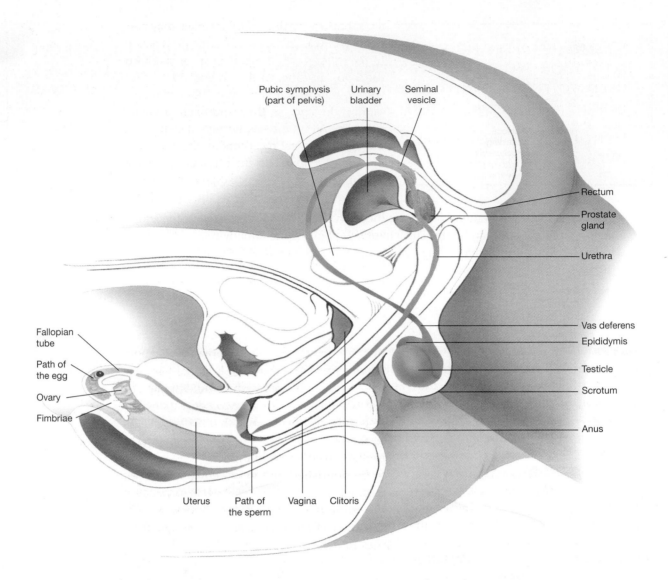

Pubic symphysis (part of pelvis)

Urinary bladder

Seminal vesicle

Rectum

Prostate gland

Urethra

Vas deferens

Epididymis

Testicle

Scrotum

Anus

Fallopian tube

Path of the egg

Ovary

Fimbriae

Uterus

Path of the sperm

Vagina

Clitoris

Figure 6.1 Sexual intercourse in the man-on-top position, showing the pathway of sperm and egg from manufacture in the testes and ovary to conception, which typically occurs in the fallopian tube.

only one is needed for fertilization, the great majority of the sperm never even get close to the egg. Some of the ejaculate, including half of the sperm, will flow out of the vagina as a result of gravity. Other sperm may be killed by the acidity of the vagina, to which they are very sensitive. Others are deformed. Of those that make it safely into the uterus, half swim up the wrong fallopian tube (the one containing no egg).

But here we are, several hours later, with a hearty band of sperm swimming up the fallopian tube toward the egg, against the currents that are bringing the egg down. Sperm are capable of swimming 1 to 3 centimetres (about 1 inch) per hour, although it has been documented that sperm may arrive at the egg within an hour and a half after ejaculation, which is much sooner than would be expected, given their swimming rate. It is thought that muscular contractions in the uterus may help speed them along. By the time a sperm reaches the egg, it has swum approximately 3000 times its own length. This would be comparable to a swim of more than 4 kilometres for a human being.

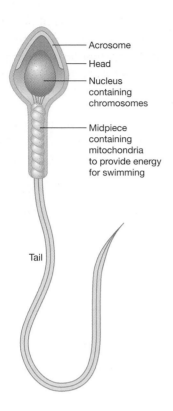

Acrosome

Head

Nucleus containing chromosomes

Midpiece containing mitochondria to provide energy for swimming

Tail

Figure 6.2 The structure of a mature human sperm.

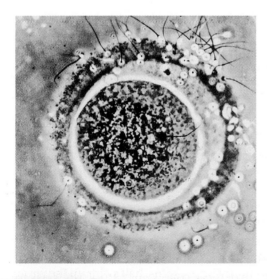

Figure 6.3 The egg is fertilized by one sperm as many sperm cluster about.

Contrary to the popular belief that conception occurs in the uterus, typically it occurs in the outer third (the part near the ovary) of the fallopian tube. Of the original 200 million sperm, only about 2000 reach the tube containing the egg. As they approach, a chemical secreted by the egg attracts the sperm to the egg. Chemical receptors on the surface of the sperm respond to the attractant, and the sperm swim toward the egg (Spehr et al., 2003). The egg is surrounded by a thin, gelatinous layer called the *zona pellucida.* Sperm swarm around the egg and secrete an enzyme called **hyaluronidase** (produced by the acrosome located in the head of the sperm—refer to Figure 6.2); this enzyme dissolves the zona pellucida, permitting one sperm to penetrate the egg.[2] Conception has occurred.

The fertilized egg, called the **zygote**, continues to travel down the fallopian tube. About 36 hours after conception, it begins the process of cell division, by which the original one cell becomes a mass of two cells, then four cells, then eight cells, and so on. About five to seven days after conception, the mass of cells implants itself in the lining of the uterus, there to be nourished and grow. For the first two weeks of gestation, the *conceptus* (product of conception) is called a zygote, between weeks two and eight it is called an **embryo**, and from then until birth it is called a **fetus**.

IMPROVING THE CHANCES OF CONCEPTION: MAKING A BABY

For couples wanting to conceive, the following are points for them to keep in mind.

The whole trick, of course, is to time intercourse so that it occurs around the time of ovulation. To do this, it is necessary to determine when the woman ovulates. For the vast majority of women, the time of ovulation can best be determined by keeping a *basal body temperature chart.* To do this, the woman takes her temperature every morning immediately upon waking (that means before getting up and moving around or drinking a cup of

Hyaluronidase: An enzyme secreted by the sperm that allows one sperm to penetrate the egg.

Zygote: The developing organism from the time of the union of the sperm and the egg to about the second week of gestation.

Embryo: The developing organism between the second and eighth weeks of gestation.

Fetus: The developing organism from the eighth week of gestation through delivery.

[2]Thus, while only one sperm is necessary to accomplish fertilization, it appears that it is important for there to be a lot of other sperm present to secrete a chemical that facilitates penetration of the egg. Therefore, maintaining a high sperm count seems to be important for conception.

coffee). She then keeps a graph of her temperature. The most reliable indicator of ovulation is the rise in temperature the day after it occurs. From this, the woman can determine the day of ovulation, and that determination should be consistent with menstruation occurring about 14 days later. Other methods for determining when a woman is ovulating are the cervical mucus and sympto-thermal methods, as well as home tests for the detection of ovulation, described in Chapter 7.

Sperm live inside the woman's body for up to five days (Wilcox et al., 1995). The egg is capable of being fertilized for about the first 12 to 24 hours after ovulation. Allowing the sperm some swimming time, this means that intercourse should be timed right at ovulation or one or two days before.

Assuming you have some idea of the time of ovulation, how frequent should intercourse be? While more may be merrier, more is not necessarily more effective. The reason for this is that it is important for the man's sperm count to be maintained. It takes a while to manufacture 200 million sperm—at least 24 hours. And, as mentioned earlier, maintaining a high sperm count appears to be important in accomplishing the task of fertilizing the egg. For purposes of conceiving, then, it is probably best to have intercourse about every 24 to 48 hours, or about four times during the week in which the woman is to ovulate. Prolonged abstinence (more than ten days) may result in low sperm quality (Levitas et al., 2005).

It is also important to take some steps to ensure that once deposited in the vagina, the sperm get a decent chance to survive and to find their way into the fallopian tubes. Position during and after intercourse is important. For purposes of conceiving, the best position for intercourse is with the woman on her back (man-on-top, or "missionary," position—see Chapter 9). If the woman is on top, much of the ejaculate may run out of the vagina because of the pull of gravity. After intercourse, she should remain on her back, possibly with her legs pulled up and a pillow under her hips, preferably for about a half hour to an hour. This allows the semen to remain in a pool in the vagina, which gives the sperm a good chance to swim up into the uterus. Because sperm are very sensitive to the pH (acidity-alkalinity) of the vagina, this factor also requires some consideration. Acidity kills sperm. Douching with commercial preparations or with acidic solutions (such as vinegar) should be avoided. Finally, lubricants and/or suppositories should not be used; they may kill sperm or block their entrance into the uterus.

DEVELOPMENT OF THE CONCEPTUS

For the nine months of pregnancy, two organisms—the conceptus and the pregnant woman—coexist. In the past the relationship between the two has been viewed as harmonious. In recent years, a new perspective has been gaining support—pregnancy as a silent struggle (Haig, 1996). Both fetus and mother need a variety of nutrients and may be competing for them. Nature should favour the development of characteristics of each that would give it the edge in such competitions, enabling it to win (e.g., struggles over calcium). Such a struggle can explain aspects of pregnancy that are inconsistent with the view of harmonious coexistence, such as gestational diabetes and pre-eclampsia. Both of these conditions carry serious risk to both the mother and the infant if not treated. Gestational diabetes is the same as other forms of diabetes in that the woman has high blood sugar because the body is not able to make and use all the insulin it needs, but appears during pregnancy. Pre-eclampsia is a condition that occurs during the third trimester that involves a sharp rise in blood pressure, the presence of protein in the urine, and swelling of the hands, feet, and face.

For nine months, the two organisms undergo parallel, dramatic changes. The changes that occur in the developing conceptus will be discussed in this section; later in the chapter we will discuss the changes that take place in the pregnant woman.

Pregnancy lasts for approximately nine months and is typically divided into three equal periods of three months, called *trimesters*. Thus, the first trimester is months 1 to 3, the second trimester is months 4 to 6, and the third (or last) trimester is months 7 to 9.

THE EMBRYO AND ITS SUPPORT SYSTEMS

We left the conceptus, which began as a single fertilized egg cell, dividing into many cells as it passed down the fallopian tube, finally arriving in the uterus and implanting itself in the uterine wall. Tendrils from the zygote begin to penetrate the blood vessels in the wall of the uterus.

During the embryonic period of development (the first eight weeks), most of the major organ systems are formed in processes that occur with amazing speed. The inner part of the ball of cells implanted in the uterus now differentiates into two layers, the endoderm and the ectoderm. Later, a third layer, the mesoderm, forms between them. The various organs of the body differentiate themselves out of these layers. The *ectoderm* will form the entire nervous system and the skin. The *endoderm* differentiates into the digestive system—from the pharynx, to the stomach and intestines, to the rectum—and the respiratory system. The muscles, skeleton, connective tissues, and reproductive and circulatory systems derive from the *mesoderm*. Development generally proceeds in a cephalocaudal order. That is, the head develops first, and the lower body last. For this reason, the head of an embryo is enormous compared with the rest of the body.

Meanwhile, another group of cells has differentiated into the *trophoblast,* which has important functions in maintaining the embryo and which will eventually become the placenta. The placenta develops out of the mass of tissues that surrounds the conceptus early in development and nurtures its growth by producing tendrils that penetrate the blood vessels in the wall of the uterus. As these tendrils become larger and more complex, they form a separate structure. The placenta has a number of important functions, perhaps the most important of which is that it serves as a site for the exchange of substances between the woman's blood and the fetus's blood. It is important to note that the woman's circulatory system and the fetus's circulatory system are completely separate. That is, with only rare exceptions, the woman's blood never circulates inside the fetus; nor does the fetus's blood circulate in the woman's blood vessels. Instead, the fetus's blood passes out of its body through the umbilical cord to the placenta (the spot where the umbilical cord attaches to the fetus becomes the navel or belly button after birth). There it circulates in the numerous *villi* (tiny fingerlike projections in the placenta). The woman's blood circulates around the outside of these villi. Thus, there is a membrane barrier between the two blood systems. Some substances are capable of passing through this barrier, whereas others are not. Oxygen and nutrients can pass through the barrier, and thus the woman's blood supplies oxygen and nutrients to the fetus, providing substitutes for breathing and eating. Carbon dioxide and waste products similarly pass back from the fetal blood to the woman's blood. Some viruses and other disease-causing organisms can pass through the barrier, including those for German measles (rubella) and syphilis. But other organisms cannot pass through the barrier; thus the woman may have a terrible cold, but the fetus will remain completely healthy. Various drugs can also cross the placental barrier, and the woman should therefore be careful about drugs taken during pregnancy (we will discuss substances during pregnancy later in this chapter).

Another major function of the placenta is that it secretes hormones. The placenta produces large quantities of estrogen and progesterone. Many of the physical symptoms of pregnancy may be caused by these elevated levels of hormones. Another hormone manufactured by the placenta is human chorionic gonadotropin (hCG). This is the hormone that is detected in pregnancy tests.

The umbilical cord is formed during the fifth week of embryonic development. The fully developed cord is about 55 centimetres (20 inches) long. Normally, it contains three

Placenta (plah-SEN-tuh): An organ formed on the wall of the uterus through which the fetus receives oxygen and nutrients and gets rid of waste products.

Human chorionic gonadotropin (hCG): A hormone secreted by the placenta; it is the hormone detected in pregnancy tests.

Umbilical cord: The tube that connects the fetus to the placenta.

blood vessels: two arteries and one vein. Some people believe that the fetus's umbilical cord attaches to the woman's navel; actually, the umbilical cord attaches to the placenta, thereby providing for the interchanges of substances just described.

Amniotic fluid: The watery fluid surrounding a developing fetus in the uterus.

Two membranes surround the fetus, the *chorion* and the *amnion,* the amnion being the innermost. The amnion is filled with a watery liquid called amniotic fluid, in which the fetus floats and can readily move. It is the amniotic fluid that is sampled when an amniocentesis (discussed shortly) is performed. The amniotic fluid maintains the fetus at a constant temperature and, most important, cushions the fetus against possible injury. Thus, the woman can even fall down a flight of stairs, and the fetus may remain undisturbed. Indeed, the amniotic fluid might be considered the original waterbed.

FETAL DEVELOPMENT DURING THE FIRST TRIMESTER

In a sense, the development of the fetus during the first trimester is more remarkable than its development during the second and third trimesters. That's because during the first trimester the small mass of cells implanted in the uterus develops into a fetus with most of the major organ systems present and with recognizable human features (see Figure 6.4).

By the third week of gestation, the embryo appears as a small bit of flesh and is about 0.2 centimetres (1/12 inch) long. During the third and fourth weeks, the head undergoes a great deal of development. The central nervous system begins to form, and the beginnings of eyes and ears are visible. The backbone is constructed by the end of the fourth week. A "tail" is noticeable early in embryonic development but has disappeared by the eighth week.

From the fourth to the eighth weeks, the external body parts—eyes, ears, arms, hands, fingers, legs, feet, and toes—develop. By the end of the tenth week they are completely formed. Indeed, by the tenth week the embryo has not only a complete set of fingers but also fingernails.

By the end of the seventh week, the liver, lungs, pancreas, kidneys, and intestines have formed and have begun limited functioning. The gonads have also formed, but the gender of the fetus is not clearly distinguishable until the twelfth week.

At the end of the twelfth week (end of the first trimester), the fetus is unmistakably human and looks like a small infant. It is about 10 centimetres (4 inches) long and weighs about 19 grams (2/3 ounce). From this point on, development consists mainly of the enlargement and differentiation of structures that are already present.

FETAL DEVELOPMENT DURING THE SECOND TRIMESTER

Around the end of the fourteenth week, the movements of the fetus can be detected ("quickening"). By the eighteenth week, the woman has been able to feel movement for two to four weeks. The fetus first opens its eyes around the twentieth week. By about the twenty-fourth week, it is sensitive to light and can hear sounds in utero. Arm and leg movements are vigorous at this time, and the fetus alternates between periods of wakefulness and sleep.

FETAL DEVELOPMENT DURING THE THIRD TRIMESTER

At the end of the second trimester the fetus's skin is wrinkled and covered with downlike hair. At the beginning of the third trimester, fat deposits form under the skin; these will give the infant the characteristic chubby appearance of babyhood. The downlike hair is lost.

During the seventh month the fetus turns in the uterus to assume a head-down position. If this turning does not occur by the time of delivery, there will be a *breech presentation*. Women

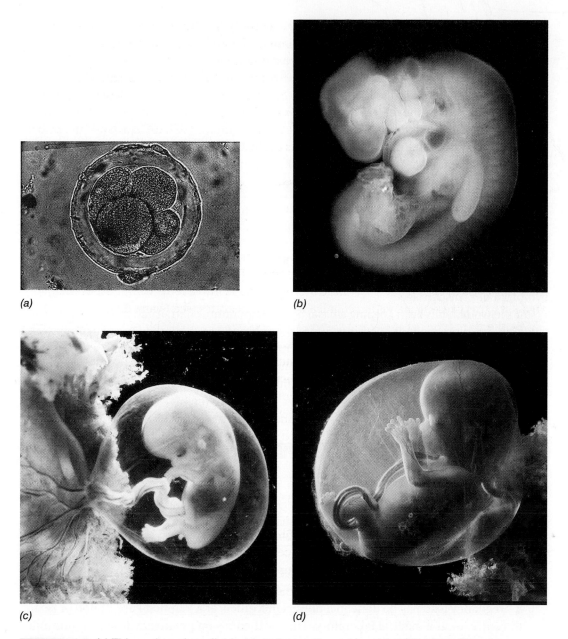

(a) (b) (c) (d)

Figure 6.4 *(a)* This embryo has divided into four cells and would still be travelling down the fallopian tube. *(b)* The embryo after four weeks of development. The major organs are forming; the bright red, blood-filled heart is just below the lower jaw. *(c)* At nine weeks the human fetus is recognizable as a primate. Limbs have formed and ears are clearly visible. *(d)* By about three months the fetus is approximately 8 centimetres long and weighs about 28 grams. Muscles have formed, which move the limbs and body.

can try assuming various positions to aid the turning (Boston Women's Health Book Collective, 2005). Physicians and midwives can also perform certain procedures to turn the fetus.

The fetus's growth during the last two months is rapid. Canadian babies born at a gestational age of 36 weeks (that is, about eight months) weigh an average of 2804 grams (6 pounds, 3 ounces) (Kramer et al., 2001). The average full-term baby (that is, 40 weeks gestational age) weighs 3562 grams (7 pounds, 14 ounces) and is 50 centimetres (20 inches) long. Interestingly, research in British Columbia found that infants of European descent weighed significantly more than infants of Chinese or South Asian descent (Janssen et al., 2007).

The Stages of Pregnancy

THE FIRST TRIMESTER (THE FIRST 12 WEEKS)

Symptoms of Pregnancy

For most women, the first symptom of pregnancy is a missed menstrual period. Of course, there may be a wide variety of reactions to this event. For the woman who has not planned the pregnancy or who feels that she already has enough children, the reaction may be negative—depression, anger, and fear. For the woman who has been trying to conceive for several months, the reaction may be joy and eager anticipation.

In fact, there are many other reasons besides pregnancy for a woman to have a late period or miss a period. Illness or emotional stress may delay a period, and women occasionally skip a period for no apparent reason.

It is also true that a woman may continue to experience some cyclic bleeding or spotting during pregnancy. This is not particularly a danger sign, except that in a few cases it is a symptom of a miscarriage.

If the woman has been keeping a basal body temperature chart, it can provide a very early sign that she is pregnant. If her temperature rises abruptly at about the time ovulation would normally occur and then stays up for more than two weeks—say, about three weeks—the chances are fairly good that she is pregnant. The increased temperature results from the high level of progesterone manufactured by the corpus luteum and, later, the placenta.

Other early symptoms of pregnancy are tenderness of the breasts—a tingling sensation and special sensitivity of the nipples—and nausea and vomiting (called "morning sickness," although these symptoms may actually happen any time during the day). More frequent urination, feelings of fatigue, and a need for more sleep are other early signs of pregnancy.

Pregnancy Tests

It is important that early, accurate pregnancy tests be available and that women make use of them. This is true for several reasons. A woman needs to know that she is pregnant as early as possible so that she can see a physician or midwife, begin getting good prenatal care, and get the nutrition she requires during pregnancy (see the section on nutrition later in the chapter). If she does not want to carry the baby to term, she needs to know as soon as possible, because abortions are much safer and simpler when performed in the first trimester than in the second.

A pregnancy test may be done in a physician's office, at a Planned Parenthood or sexual health centre, or at a medical laboratory. The most common pregnancy test is an immunologic test based on detecting the presence of hCG (human chorionic gonadotropin, secreted by the placenta) in the woman's urine. It can be done in a matter of minutes and is very accurate. It involves mixing a drop of urine with certain chemicals, either on a slide or in a tube.

The laboratory tests for pregnancy are 98 to 99 percent accurate. A laboratory test may produce a false negative (i.e., tell the woman she is not pregnant when she really is) if it is done too early or if errors are made in processing. Also, some women simply do not show positive signs in the tests, or do not do so until the second or third test. The modern urine tests are 98 percent accurate seven days after implantation (just when a period is missed).

A different type of test, called the *beta-hCG radioimmunoassay*, assesses the presence of beta-hCG in a blood sample. It can detect hCG at very low levels, so it can reliably detect pregnancy seven days after fertilization. It is much more expensive than the urine tests and is available only in laboratories associated with hospitals or large clinics.

Home pregnancy tests are also available, sold under such brand names as First Response and ClearBlue. These are urine tests designed to measure the presence of hCG; they cost $13 to $20 depending on whether they contain one test or two tests. Their charm lies in their convenience and the privacy of getting the results. Manufacturers claim the test will accurately detect a pregnancy on the first day of the missed period. Laboratory tests of 18 brands found that only one of the 18 detected low levels of hCG, and only eight detected high levels of hCG (Cole et al., 2004). Thus, 10 of 18 would produce a false negative result. This compares with an error rate of 1 to 2 percent for laboratory tests. The home pregnancy tests also have a 16 percent rate of false positives (Hatcher et al., 1994). To guard against false negatives, the manufacturers recommend repeating the test one week later if the results are negative the first time, and some of these kits contain more than one test. The reason that a high rate of false negatives is so serious is that it leads a pregnant woman to think she is not pregnant, and thus she might take substances that would harm the fetus, and she will not begin getting prenatal care; such dangerous conditions as ectopic pregnancy might therefore go undetected. Performing the tests also requires a certain amount of coordination and care.

The signs of pregnancy may be classified as *presumptive signs, probable signs,* and *positive signs.* Amenorrhea, breast tenderness, nausea, and so on, are presumptive signs. The pregnancy tests discussed previously all provide probable signs. Three signs are interpreted as positive signs, that is, as definite indications of pregnancy: (1) beating of the fetal heart, (2) active fetal movement, and (3) detection of a fetal skeleton by ultrasound. These signs cannot be detected until the fourth month, with the exception of ultrasound, which can be used in the first trimester.

Once the pregnancy has been confirmed, the woman generally is very interested in determining her expected delivery date (called EDC for a rather antiquated expression, "expected date of confinement"). The EDC is calculated using *Nägele's rule.* The rule says to take the date of the first day of the last menstrual period, subtract three months, add seven days, and finally add one year. Thus, if the first day of the last menstrual period was September 10, 2008, the expected delivery date would be June 17, 2009: subtracting three months from September 10 gives June 10, adding seven days yields June 17, and adding one year gives June 17, 2009. These days, most women have at least one ultrasound during the pregnancy. Since ultrasounds are more accurate than Nägele's rule, these results are often used to revise the due date.

PHYSICAL CHANGES

The basic physical change that takes place in the woman's body during the first trimester is a large increase in the levels of hormones, especially estrogen and progesterone, that are produced by the placenta. Many of the other physical symptoms of the first trimester arise from these endocrine changes.

The breasts swell and tingle. This results from the development of the mammary glands, which is stimulated by hormones. The nipples and the area around them (areola) may darken and broaden.

There is often a need to urinate more frequently. This is related to changes in the pituitary hormones that affect the adrenals, which in turn change the water balance in the body so that more water is retained. The growing uterus also contributes by pressing against the bladder.

Some women experience morning sickness—feelings of nausea, perhaps to the point of vomiting, and of revulsion toward food or its odour. The nausea and vomiting may occur on waking or at other times during the day. Their exact cause is not known. One theory is that nausea and vomiting cause pregnant women to expel and subsequently avoid foods containing toxic chemicals (Flaxman & Sherman, 2000). Supporting evidence includes a lower rate of miscarriage among women who experience morning sickness. While these symptoms are quite common, about 25 percent of pregnant women experience no vomiting at all.

Vaginal discharges may also increase at this time, partly because the increased hormone levels change the pH of the vagina and partly because the vaginal secretions are changing in their chemical composition and quantity.

The feelings of fatigue and sleepiness are probably related to the high levels of progesterone, which is known to have a sedative effect.

PSYCHOLOGICAL CHANGES

Our culture is full of stereotypes about the psychological characteristics of pregnant women. According to one view, pregnancy is supposed to be a time of happiness and calm. Radiant contentment, the "pregnant glow," is said to emanate from the woman's face, making this a good time for her to be photographed. According to another view, pregnancy is a time of emotional ups and downs. The pregnant woman swings from very happy to depressed and crying, and back again. She is irrational, sending her partner out in a blizzard for kosher dill pickles. One study compared 70 pregnant women (planned pregnancies) with 92 non-pregnant women. The researchers assessed both women's physical and psychological states at three points during the pregnancy (or nine months for the non-pregnant women). On the whole, they found that pregnancy is neither a time of heightened well-being nor heightened emotional turmoil (Striegel-Moore et al., 1996).

Research indicates that the situation is more complex than these stereotypes suggest. A woman's emotional state during pregnancy, often assessed with measures of depression, varies according to several factors. First, her attitude toward the pregnancy makes a difference; women who desire the pregnancy are less anxious than women who do not (Kalil et al., 1993). A second factor is social class. Several studies have found that low income is associated with depression during pregnancy. For example, a study involving interviews with 192 poor, inner-city pregnant women found that they were twice as likely as their middle-income counterparts to be depressed (Hobfoll et al., 1995). This may be due to the economic situation these women face; also, there may be more unwanted pregnancies among low-income women. A third influence is the availability of social support. Women with a supportive partner are less likely to be depressed, perhaps because the partner serves as a buffer against stressful events (Chapman et al., 1997).

During the first trimester, the symptoms that distinguish pregnant from non-pregnant women are nausea, associated with morning sickness, and fatigue (Streigel-Moore et al., 1996). Depression is not uncommon during this time. Women who led very active lives prior to becoming pregnant may find fatigue and lack of energy especially distressing. Depression during the first trimester is more likely among women experiencing other stressful life events, such as moving, changes in their jobs, changes in relationships, or illnesses (Kalil et al., 1993). In this trimester, women's anxieties often centre on concerns about miscarriage.

Figure 6.5 A generation ago, women tried to hide their pregnancies by wearing loose tops. Women now can proudly show their pregnant bellies. According to Angelina Jolie, being pregnant makes her feel womanly and sexy.

THE SECOND TRIMESTER (WEEKS 13 TO 26)

PHYSICAL CHANGES

During the fourth month, the woman becomes aware of the fetus's movements ("quickening"). Many women find this a very exciting experience.

The woman is made even more aware of the pregnancy by her rapidly expanding belly. There are a variety of reactions to this. Some women feel that it is a magnificent symbol of womanhood, and they rush out to buy maternity clothes and wear them before they are even necessary. Other women feel awkward and resentful of their bulky shape and may begin to wonder whether they can fit through doorways and turnstiles.

Most of the physical symptoms of the first trimester, such as morning sickness, disappear, and discomforts are at a minimum. Physical problems at this time include constipation and nosebleeds (caused by increased blood volume). Edema—water retention and swelling—

Edema (eh-DEE-muh): Excessive fluid retention and swelling.

may be a problem in the face, hands, wrists, ankles, and feet; it results from increased water retention throughout the body.

By about mid-pregnancy, the breasts, under hormonal stimulation, have essentially completed their development in preparation for nursing. Beginning about the nineteenth week, a thin amber or yellow fluid called colostrum may come out of the nipple, although there is no milk yet.

PSYCHOLOGICAL CHANGES

While the first trimester can be relatively tempestuous, particularly with morning sickness, the second trimester is usually a period of relative calm and well-being. The discomforts of the first trimester are past, the tensions associated with labour and delivery not yet present. Fear of miscarriage diminishes as the woman feels fetal movement (Leifer, 1980).

Depression is less likely during the second trimester if the pregnant woman has a cohabiting partner or spouse (Hobfoll et al., 1995). Furthermore, women who report more effective partner support report less anxiety in the second trimester (Rini et al., 2006). Interestingly, women who have had a previous pregnancy are more distressed during this time than women who have not (Wilkinson, 1995). This may reflect the impact of the demands associated with the care of other children when one is pregnant. Research also indicates that feelings of nurturance, or maternal responsiveness to the infant, increase steadily from the prepregnant to the postpartum period (Fleming et al., 1997). This increase does not appear to be related to changes in hormone levels during pregnancy.

THE THIRD TRIMESTER (WEEKS 27 TO 38)

PHYSICAL CHANGES

The uterus is very large and hard by the third trimester. The woman is increasingly aware of her size and of the fetus, which is becoming more and more active. In fact, some women are kept awake at night by its somersaults and hiccups.

The extreme size of the uterus puts pressure on a number of other organs, causing some discomfort. There is pressure on the lungs, which may cause shortness of breath. The stomach is also being squeezed, and indigestion is common. The navel is pushed out. The heart is being strained because of the large increase in blood volume. At this stage most women feel low in energy (Leifer, 1980).

Health Canada recommends that the amount of weight gained should range from 6.5 to 18 kilograms (15 to 40 pounds) depending on the woman's weight prior to the pregnancy. Women who are slim should gain relatively more, 12.5 to 18 kilograms, while women who are heavy should gain less, 6.5 to 11 kilograms. The average Canadian full-term infant at birth weighs 3562 grams (7.9 pounds); the rest of the weight gain is accounted for by the placenta (about 450 grams, or 1 pound), the amniotic fluid (about 900 grams, or 2 pounds), enlargement of the uterus (about 900 grams, or 2 pounds), enlargement of the breasts (about 750 grams, or 1.5 pounds), and the additional fat and water retained by the woman (3.6 kilograms, or 8 pounds, or more). Physicians recommend limited weight gain because the incidence of complications, such as high blood pressure and strain on the heart, is much higher in women who gain an excessive amount of weight. Also, excessive weight gained during pregnancy can be very hard to lose afterward.

The woman's balance is somewhat disturbed because of the large amount of weight that has been added to the front part of her body. She may compensate for this by adopting the characteristic "waddling" walk of the pregnant woman, which can result in back pains.

The uterus tightens occasionally in painless contractions called Braxton-Hicks contractions. These contractions are not part of labour. It is thought that they help to strengthen the uterine muscles, preparing them for labour.

Colostrum: A watery substance that is secreted from the breasts at the end of pregnancy and during the first few days after delivery.

Braxton-Hicks contractions: Contractions of the uterus during pregnancy that are not part of actual labour.

In a first pregnancy, around two to four weeks before delivery the head drops into the pelvis. This is called *lightening, dropping,* or *engagement.* Engagement usually occurs during labour in women who have had babies before.

Some women are concerned about the appropriate amount of activity they should engage in during pregnancy—whether some things constitute "overdoing it." Traditionally, physicians and textbooks warned of the dangers of physical activities and tried to discourage them. It appears now, however, that such restrictions were based more on superstition than on scientific fact. Current thinking holds that for a healthy pregnant woman, moderate activity is not dangerous and is actually psychologically and physically beneficial. Modern methods of childbirth encourage sensible exercise for the pregnant woman so that she will be in shape for labour (see the section on childbirth options later in this chapter). The matter, of course, is highly individual.

PSYCHOLOGICAL CHANGES

The patterns noted earlier continue into the third trimester. Psychological well-being is greater among women who have social support (often in the form of a cohabiting partner or husband), have higher incomes or are middle class, and experience fewer concurrent stressful life events. A study conducted in Montreal found that women who reported more anxiety, daily hassles, and stress during pregnancy were more likely to experience pregnancy complications (Costa et al., 1998).

What happens to the relationship of the pregnant woman with her partner? A comparison of women pregnant for the first time with women who had experienced previous pregnancies found that first-time mothers reported a significant increase in dissatisfaction with their husbands from the second to the third trimester (Wilkinson, 1995). Another study included 54 women who were pregnant for the first time and their husbands (Zimmerman-Tansella et al., 1994). Wives who reported that higher levels of affection were exchanged between husband and wife reported lower levels of anxiety and of insomnia in the third trimester.

THE FATHER'S EXPERIENCE IN PREGNANCY

PHYSICAL CHANGES

Some men experience pregnancy symptoms, including indigestion, gastritis, nausea, change in appetite, and headaches (Kiselica & Scheckel, 1995), referred to as a *couvade syndrome.* These symptoms may be caused by hormonal changes in the male. A longitudinal study of 34 couples collected blood samples from both the men and the women before and after the birth of the infant (Storey et al., 2000). Men and women displayed stage-specific hormone differences, including high levels of prolactin prenatally and low levels of testosterone postnatally. Men with more pregnancy symptoms had higher levels of prolactin prenatally.

In some cultures, this phenomenon takes a more dramatic form, known as *couvades ritual.* In this ritual, the husband retires to bed while his wife is in labour. He suffers all the pains of delivery, moaning and groaning as she does. Couvade is still practised in parts of Asia, South America, and Oceania (Gregersen, 1996).

PSYCHOLOGICAL CHANGES

In Canada in the twenty-first century, many men expect to be actively involved in fathering. Men report engaging in many activities in preparation for becoming fathers, including attending parenting classes, planning father–child activities, observing and talking to other fathers, and daydreaming about the baby. Most of these activities, of course, parallel those done by expectant mothers. It has been theorized that men who display this active involvement will do best in the father role after the baby is born (Antle, 1978). In fact, some people claim that there is a "father instinct" (Biller & Meredith, 1975). Recall our discussion in

Figure 6.6 Dad changes his daughter's diaper at a course for new fathers, which helps new or prospective fathers adjust to their new role.

Chapter 2 of the reproductive advantages of a father–infant bond. The likelihood of such a bond depends partly on the father's responsiveness to the infant. In the study of hormonal changes during pregnancy just described, men viewed videotapes with auditory and visual cues from newborns before the blood sample was drawn. Men who showed higher levels of responsiveness had higher levels of prolactin prenatally and lower levels of testosterone postnatally (Storey et al., 2000). Lower levels of testosterone may facilitate paternal behaviour.

Fathers or other partners play an important role in preparing for a baby. The birth or arrival of a first child may require finding a larger home or making physical changes to the present one. There will be visits to medical personnel, tests to be taken, arrangements to be made. Partners who participate in these activities provide support for the pregnant woman and become more involved themselves. Many couples take some form of classes in preparation for childbirth. The classes often specifically address the partner's role in late pregnancy and during labour and delivery. These joint activities contribute to the bond between the partners, which in turn provides a better foundation for the arrival of the new member of the family.

DIVERSITY IN THE CONTEXTS OF PREGNANCY

There are lots of family contexts in which women have babies these days besides the traditional one of being married to the baby's father. These include living in a common-law relationship; not living with the baby's father but seeing him regularly; being a single mother-to-be who has no contact with the baby's father; being a mother-to-be who is pregnant as a result of assisted insemination or other reproductive technologies; and being a woman in a stable relationship with another woman, who is pregnant as a result of assisted insemination or other technologies. Therefore, we use the term "partner" in the following sections.

SEX DURING PREGNANCY

Couples can and do continue to pleasure each other sexually in many ways throughout the pregnancy. However, many heterosexual couples are concerned about whether it is safe or advisable for a pregnant woman to have sexual intercourse, particularly during the latter stages of pregnancy. Traditionally, physicians believed that (1) penile–vaginal intercourse might cause an infection, or (2) sexual activity might precipitate labour prematurely or cause a miscarriage. Current medical opinion, however, is that—given a normal, healthy pregnancy—intercourse can continue safely until four weeks before the baby is due (Cunningham et al., 1993). There is no evidence that intercourse or orgasm is associated with preterm labour (Sayle et al., 2001). In fact, a study involving interviews with pregnant women at 28 weeks gestation and again following delivery found that recent intercourse and orgasm was associated with reduced risk of preterm birth (Sayle et al., 2001; Schaffir, 2006). The only exception is a case where a miscarriage or preterm labour is threatened. Whether and how frequently to engage in sexual activity is a matter for a couple to decide, perhaps in consultation with a physician or midwife.

Most pregnant women with male partners continue to have intercourse throughout the pregnancy (Reamy & White, 1987). The most common pattern is a decline in the frequency of intercourse during the first trimester, no variation in the second trimester, and an even greater decline in the third trimester (Kumar et al., 1981). One study included male partners of pregnant women; the men reported the same pattern (Bogren, 1991). In some cases, the decline in frequency in the third trimester is affected by the partner's perceptions. While some partners find the pregnant woman extremely sexy, others are not attracted to women in the later stages of pregnancy. Little is known about the sexual frequency of pregnant women with female partners.

During the later stages of pregnancy, the woman's shape makes intercourse increasingly awkward, particularly using the man-on-top position. The side-to-side position (see Chapter 9) is probably the most suitable one for intercourse during the late stages of pregnancy. Couples should also remember that there are many ways of experiencing sexual pleasure and orgasm besides having intercourse—hand–genital stimulation or oral–genital sex may be good alternatives.[3] The best guide in this matter is the woman's feelings and comfort.

NUTRITION DURING PREGNANCY

During pregnancy, another living being is growing inside the woman, and she needs lots of energy, protein, vitamins, and minerals at this time. Therefore, diet during pregnancy is extremely important. If the woman's diet is good, she has a much better chance of remaining healthy during pregnancy and of bearing a healthy baby; if her diet is inadequate, she stands more of a chance of developing one of a number of diseases during pregnancy herself and of bearing a child whose weight is low at birth. This is a result of the silent struggle for nutrients between mother and fetus discussed earlier. Babies with low birth weights do not have as good a chance of survival as babies with normal birth weights. According to a study done in Toronto, mothers in a poor-diet group had four times as many serious health problems during pregnancy as a group of mothers whose diets were supplemented with highly nutritious foods. Those with the poor diets had seven times as many threatened miscarriages and three times as many stillbirths; their labour lasted five hours longer on average (Newton, 1972).

It is particularly important that a pregnant woman get enough protein, folic acid, calcium, magnesium, and vitamin A (Luke, 1994). Protein is important for building new tissues. Folic acid is also important for growth; symptoms of folic acid deficiency are anemia and fatigue.

---

[3]There is, however, some risk associated with cunnilingus for the pregnant woman, as discussed in Chapter 9.

A pregnant woman needs much more iron than usual because the fetus draws off iron for itself from the blood that circulates to the placenta. Muscle cramps, nerve pains, uterine ligament pains, sleeplessness, and irritability may all be symptoms of a calcium deficiency. Severe calcium deficiency during pregnancy is associated with increased blood pressure, which may lead to a serious condition called eclampsia, discussed later in this chapter (Repke, 1994). Deficiencies of calcium and magnesium are associated with premature birth. Sometimes even an excellent diet does not provide enough iron, calcium, or folic acid, in which case the pregnant woman should take supplements.

EFFECTS OF SUBSTANCES TAKEN DURING PREGNANCY

We are such a pill-popping culture that we seldom stop to think about whether we should take a certain drug. The pregnant woman, however, needs to know that when she takes a drug, it not only circulates through her body, but also may circulate through the fetus. Because the fetus develops so rapidly during pregnancy, drugs may produce severe consequences, including serious malformations. Drugs that produce such defects are called teratogens.[4] Of course, not all drugs can cross the placental barrier, but many can.

> **Teratogen (ter-AH-teh-jen):** A substance that produces defects in a fetus.

There are a number of drugs and other substances that pregnant women should be cautious in using. A substantial amount of research has documented the risk to a child of maternal drinking during pregnancy. Alcohol consumed by the woman passes through the membrane barrier in the placenta and circulates through the fetus, so it can have pervasive effects on fetal growth and development (Barr et al., 1990; Jacobson et al., 1993, 1994; Streissguth et al., 1999). Health Canada (1996) has identified maternal drinking as one of the leading causes of preventable birth

(a)

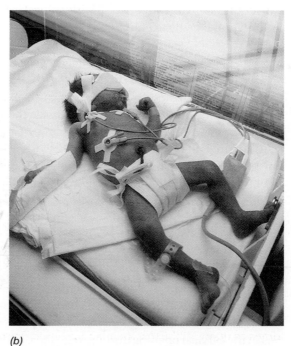

(b)

Figure 6.7   The effects of prenatal exposure to alcohol and other drugs. *(a)* A child born with fetal alcohol syndrome. *(b)* A preterm baby whose mother used crack cocaine during pregnancy.

---

[4]"Teratogen" is from the Greek words *teras*, meaning "monster," and *gen*, meaning "cause."

defects and developmental delays in children; according to the National Longitudinal Survey of Children and Youth, 15 percent of pregnant Canadian women drink some alcohol.

Fetal alcohol syndrome (FAS): Serious growth deficiency and malformations in the child of a mother who abuses alcohol during pregnancy.

The effects of prenatal alcohol consumption are dose-dependent; that is, the more alcohol the mother drinks, the larger the number and severity of effects on the child. The most serious effects are a pattern of malformations termed fetal alcohol syndrome (FAS), which is characterized by both prenatal and postnatal growth deficiencies, a small brain, small eye openings, joint, limb, and heart malformations, and mental retardation (for a review, see Mattson & Riley, 1998). It affects 1 percent of Canadians (Public Health Agency of Canada, 2005). Research indicates that "risk drinking" (seven or more drinks per week or five or more drinks on one occasion) poses a serious health threat to the fetus. However, according to the Public Health Agency of Canada (2005), there is no safe amount of alcohol during pregnancy. Perhaps understandably, there are many reports of well-intentioned bartenders, waitstaff, and patrons approaching pregnant women consuming alcohol and asking them not to drink (Moskia, 2006).

Tobacco use during pregnancy retards fetal growth and increases the risk of infant illness, disability, and death. Maternal smoking is associated with prematurity, low birth weight, cardiovascular anomalies, conditions involving arteries, veins, or the heart, and asthma (Jaakkola & Gissler, 2004; Kai & Pourier, 2001; Woods & Raju, 2001). Results from the National Longitudinal Survey of Children and Youth indicate that 23 percent of Canadian women smoke during pregnancy, although more recent Canadian data suggest that the percentage of women who smoke is lower than this (Health Canada, 2005). Other substances that may produce low birth weight, birth complications, and/or defects in the fetus include steroids, some antihistamines, long-term use of antibiotics, excessive amounts of vitamin A, D, B_6, and K, caffeine, antidepressant medication, lithium, cocaine, and marijuana. These effects are summarized in Table 6.1.

As with alcohol, the best rule for the pregnant woman considering using a prescription or over-the-counter drug, herbal product, or other substance is consult your physician. Up-to-date information on the effects of various legal substances is also available from the Motherisk Information Line by telephone at 416-813-6780 or on the Internet at www.motherisk.org.

DADS AND DRUGS

Most research has focused on the effects of drugs taken by the pregnant woman. However, new theorizing suggests that drugs taken by men before conception may also cause birth defects, probably because the drugs damage the sperm and their genetic contents (Narod et al., 1988). For example, marijuana use has been linked to a decreased sperm count, more damaged sperm, and reduced fertility (Gorzalka & Hill, 2006). In addition, one study found that not only a mother's smoking during the first trimester of pregnancy increased her offspring's risk of cancer in childhood, but a father's smoking during the pregnancy in the absence of the mother's smoking also increased this risk (John et al., 1991).

BIRTH

THE BEGINNING OF LABOUR

The signs that labour is about to begin vary from one woman to the next. There may be a discharge of a small amount of bloody mucus (the "bloody show"). This is the mucus plug that was in the cervical opening during pregnancy, its purpose being to prevent germs from passing from the vagina up into the uterus. In about 10 percent of all women the membranes containing the amniotic fluid rupture (the bag of waters bursts), and there is a gush of warm fluid down the woman's legs. Labour usually begins within 24 hours after this occurs. More commonly, the amniotic sac does not rupture until the end of the first stage of labour. The Braxton-Hicks contractions may increase before labour and actually may be mistaken for labour. Typically, they are distinct from the contractions of labour in that they are very irregular.

The biological mechanism that initiates and maintains labour is not completely understood. The progesterone-withdrawal theory is the leading hypothesis (Schwartz, 1997). Progesterone is known to inhibit uterine contractions. It has been proposed that some mechanism such as increased production of antiprogesterone reduces the inhibiting effect of progesterone and labour begins.

Table 6.1   Teratogenic Effect of Frequently Used Substances on Prenatal Development

Legal Drugs	*Potential Negative Effects*
Nicotine	Prematurity, low birth weight, delayed intellectual and behavioural development, risk of pneumonia, bronchitis, laryngitis, inner ear infections; fathers' smoking may transmit risk of cancer to offspring
Alcohol	Fetal alcohol syndrome (physical defects, short stature, mental retardation, hyperactivity, stereotypical behaviours, congenital addiction leading to withdrawal syndrome); father's abuse of alcohol may cause genetic damage that leads to birth defects
	The combination of parental smoking and drinking may cause miscarriages, prematurity, low birth weight, and sudden infant death syndrome (SIDS)
Illegal Drugs	
Heroin, morphine, methadone, oxycodone	In mother, difficulty conceiving; in infant, prematurity, low birth weight, addiction, withdrawal, death
Marijuana	In mother, difficulty conceiving; in infant, prematurity, low birth weight, high-pitched crying; no long-term effects
Cocaine	In mother, difficulty conceiving; in infant, prematurity, low birth weight, neurological deficits, small head circumference; in father may lead to reduced sperm count and decreased fertility
Lysergic acid diethylamide (LSD)	Chromosomal breakage
Medications/Treatments	
Steroids	Heart and circulatory problems; masculinization of female fetus
Diethylstilbestrol (DES)	In mother, miscarriage; in infant, prematurity, low birth weight; female child may develop cancer of the cervix; male child may have reproductive abnormalities and increased risk of testicular cancer
Reserpine (tranquillizer)	Respiratory problems in infant
Antibiotics	Defective skeletal growth in infant, hearing loss, jaundice
Aspirin	Blood disorders in infant
Some anticonvulsant medications	Cleft lip and palate in infant; failure of blood coagulation
Lithium	Cardiovascular abnormalities
SSRI antidepressant medication	Feeding and breathing difficulties at birth; low birth weight

Source: Adapted from Hetherington & Parke, 2003.

THE STAGES OF LABOUR

Labour is typically divided into three stages, although the length of the stages may vary considerably from one woman to the next. The whole process of childbirth is sometimes referred to as *parturition*.

FIRST-STAGE LABOUR

Effacement: A thinning out of the cervix during labour.

Dilation: An opening up of the cervix during labour; also called dilatation.

First-stage labour: The beginning of labour, during which there are regular contractions of the uterus; the stage lasts until the cervix is dilated 8 centimetres (3 inches).

Transition: The most difficult part of labour at the end of the first stage, during which the cervix dilates from 8 to 10 centimetres (3 to 4 inches).

First-stage labour begins with the regular contractions of the muscles of the uterus. These contractions are responsible for producing two changes in the cervix, both of which must occur before the baby can be delivered. These changes are called effacement (thinning out) and dilation (opening up). The cervix must dilate until it has an opening 10 centimetres (4 inches) in diameter before the baby can be born.

First-stage labour itself is divided into three stages: early, late, and transition. In *early first-stage labour,* contractions are spaced far apart, with perhaps 15 to 20 minutes between them. A contraction typically lasts 45 seconds to a minute. This stage of labour is fairly easy, and the woman is quite comfortable between contractions. Meanwhile, the cervix is effacing and dilating.

Late first-stage labour is marked by the dilation of the cervix from 5 to 8 centimetres (2 to 3 inches). It is generally shorter than the early stage, and the contractions are more frequent and more intense.

The final dilation of the cervix from 8 to 10 centimetres (3 to 4 inches) occurs during the transition phase, which is both short and difficult. The contractions are very strong, and it is during this stage that women report pain and exhaustion.

The first stage of labour can last anywhere from 2 to 24 hours. It averages about 12 to 15 hours for a first pregnancy and about 8 hours for later pregnancies. (In most respects, first labours are the hardest; later ones are easier.) The woman is usually told to go to the hospital when the contractions are 4 to 5 minutes apart. Once there, she is put in the labour room or birthing room for the rest of first-stage labour.

SECOND-STAGE LABOUR: DELIVERY

Second-stage labour: The stage during which the baby moves out through the vagina and is delivered.

Second-stage labour (see Figure 6.8) begins when the cervix is fully dilated and the baby's head (or whichever part comes first, if the baby is in some other position; see Figure 6.9) begins to move into the vagina, or birth canal. It lasts from a few minutes to a few hours and is generally much shorter than the first stage.

During this stage, many women feel an urge to push or bear down, and if done properly, this may be of great assistance in pushing the baby out. With each contraction the baby is pushed farther along.

(a)   *(b)*

Figure 6.8   Second-stage labour. *(a)* Baby's head crowning and then *(b)* moving out.

When the baby's head has traversed the entire length of the vagina, the top of it becomes visible at the vaginal entrance; this is called *crowning*. It is at this point that many physicians perform an episiotomy (see Figure 6.10), in which an incision or slit is made in the perineum, the skin just behind the vagina; in Canada 24 percent of vaginal deliveries involve an episiotomy (Health Canada, 2003). Most women do not feel the episiotomy being performed because the pressure of the baby against the pelvic floor provides a natural anaesthetic. The incision is stitched closed after the baby is born. The reason physicians give for performing an episiotomy are that it will prevent impaired sexual functioning in later life, reduce the severity of perineal lacerations, and reduce post-delivery pain and medication use. However, a review of relevant research conducted between 1950 and 2004 found no evidence that any of these benefits result from episiotomies (Hartmann et al., 2005). Critics claim that it is unnecessary and is done merely for the doctor's convenience, while causing the woman discomfort later as it is healing. Midwives reduce the likelihood of vaginal tears during childbirth by massaging the vaginal area and applying ointments (Maticka-Tyndale & Bicher, 1996).

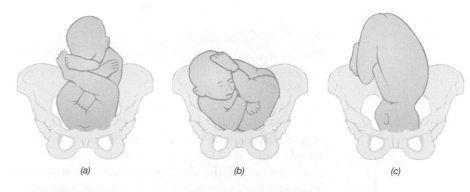

Figure 6.9 Possible positions of the fetus during birth. *(a)* A breech presentation (4 percent of births). *(b)* A transverse presentation (fewer than 1 percent). *(c)* A normal, head-first or cephalic presentation (96 percent of births).

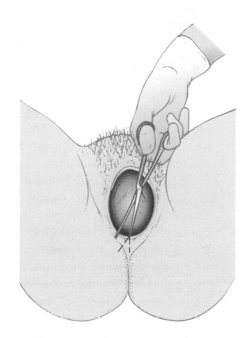

Figure 6.10 Episiotomy. A mediolateral or median cut may be performed.

Episiotomy (ih-pee-see-ah-tuh-mee): An incision made in the skin just behind the vagina, allowing the baby to be delivered more easily.

The baby is finally eased completely out of the mother's body. At this point, the baby is still connected to the mother by the umbilical cord, which runs from the baby's navel to the placenta, and the placenta is still inside the mother's uterus. As the baby takes its first breath of air, the functioning of its body changes dramatically. Blood begins to flow to the lungs, there to take on oxygen, and a flap closes between the two atria (chambers) in the heart. This process generally takes a few minutes, during which time the baby changes from a somewhat bluish colour to a healthy, pink hue. At this point, the baby no longer needs the umbilical cord, which is clamped and cut off about 7 centimetres (3 inches) from the body. The stub gradually dries up and falls off.

To avoid the possibility of transmitting gonorrhea or other eye infections from the mother to the baby, drops of silver nitrate or a similar drug are placed in the baby's eyes (see Chapter 8).

THIRD-STAGE LABOUR

Third-stage labour:
The stage during which
the afterbirth is expelled.

During third-stage labour, the placenta detaches from the walls of the uterus, and the after-birth (placenta and fetal membranes) is expelled. This stage may take from a few minutes to an hour. Several contractions may accompany the expulsion of the placenta. The episiotomy and/or any tears are sewn up.

CAESAREAN SECTION (C-SECTION)

**Caesarean section
(C-section):** A method
of delivering a baby surgically, by an incision in
the abdomen.

Caesarean section is a surgical procedure for delivery; it is used when normal vaginal birth is impossible or undesirable. Caesarean section may be required for a number of different reasons: if the baby is too large or if the mother's pelvis is too small to allow the baby to move into the vagina; if the labour has been very long and hard and the cervix is not dilating or if the mother is nearing the point of total exhaustion; if the umbilical cord *prolapses* (moves into a position such that it is coming out through the cervix ahead of the baby); if there is an Rh incompatibility (see p. 167); or if there is excessive bleeding or the mother's or the infant's condition takes a sudden turn for the worse. Another condition requiring a C-section is *placenta previa,* in which the placenta is attached to the wall of the uterus or close to the cervix.

In the Caesarean section, an incision is first made through the abdomen and then through the wall of the uterus. The physician lifts out the baby and then sews up the uterine wall and the abdominal wall.

In 2000–2001, 21 percent of Canadian births were by Caesarean section (Health Canada, 2003). The lowest rate of Caesarean delivery is in Nunavut; the highest is in the Atlantic prov-inces and British Columbia. The rate of Caesarean delivery in Canada is considerably higher than in most Western European countries. For example, the Caesarean rate is 10 percent of deliveries in the Netherlands, 12 percent of deliveries in Norway, and 10 percent of deliveries in England and Wales (Notzon, 1990).

Contrary to popular opinion, it is not true that once a woman has had one delivery by Caesarean she must have all subsequent deliveries by the same method. Vaginal births after Caesareans (VBAC) are possible (Millar et al., 1996). Up to 60 percent of women with a prior Caesarean attempt a subsequent vaginal birth (Lydon-Rochelle et al., 2001).

There is concern about the high and increasing Canadian Caesarean rates. Although the number of women affected is small, women who give birth by Caesarean are three times as likely to experience severe illness after the delivery than are women who have a vaginal deliv-ery. Reasons that have been proposed to explain them include the following: (a) There are more older women giving birth; they may have more difficult labours necessitating Caesareans; (b) fetal monitors are used increasingly; they can give the physician early warning if the fetus is in distress, necessitating a Caesarean to save the fetus; and (c) more women are requesting Caesarean without clear medical reasons for it. In fact, an analysis of 540 174 primary C-sections and 371 683 repeat Caesarean births in the United States in 2001 classified 11 percent of the former and 55 percent of the latter as potentially unnecessary (Kabir et al., 2005).

Programs in two U.S. hospitals indicate that Caesarean section rates can be decreased dramatically. In one hospital, prenatal education was expanded, guidelines for Caesareans were tightened, women were encouraged to remain active during labour (e.g., to walk at regu-lar intervals), and physicians were given statistics each month about their own deliveries. In May 1988, when the study began, the rate of Caesarean births was 31 percent. For the period January to June 1994, it was 15 percent (Hollander, 1996).

CHILDBIRTH OPTIONS

Pregnant women and their partners can choose from a variety of childbirth options. They can take childbirth classes to prepare mentally and physically for labour and delivery. There are also several options regarding the use of anaesthesia during childbirth. Finally, depending on the province, women can often choose to give birth at home, in a birthing centre, or in a hospital labour room.

THE LAMAZE METHOD

English obstetrician Grantly Dick-Read coined the term "natural childbirth" in 1932. He postulated that fear causes tension and tension causes pain. Thus, to attempt to eliminate the pain of childbirth, he recommended a program consisting of education (to eliminate the woman's fears of the unknown) and the learning of relaxation techniques (to eliminate tension).

One of the most widely used methods of *prepared childbirth* was developed by French obstetrician Fernand Lamaze. Classes teaching the Lamaze method or variations of it are now offered in most areas of the country. The Lamaze method involves two basic techniques, *relaxation* and *controlled breathing* (see Figure 6.11). The woman learns to relax all the muscles in her body. Knowing how to do this has a number of advantages, including conservation of energy during an event that requires considerable endurance and, more important, avoidance of the tension that increases the perception of pain. The woman also learns a series of controlled breathing exercises, which she will use to help her during each contraction.

Some other techniques are taught as well. One, called *effleurage*, consists of a light, circular stroking of the abdomen with the fingertips. There are also exercises to strengthen specific muscles, such as the leg muscles, which undergo considerable strain during labour and delivery. Finally, because the Lamaze method is based on the idea that fear and the pain it causes are best eliminated through education, the Lamaze student learns a great deal about the processes involved in pregnancy and childbirth.

One other important component of the Lamaze method is the requirement that the woman be accompanied during the classes and during childbirth itself by her partner or some other person, who serves as "coach." The coach plays an integral role in the woman's learning of the techniques and her use of them during labour. The coach is present during labour and delivery. The coach times contractions, checks on the mother's state of relaxation and gives her feedback if she is not relaxed, suggests breathing patterns, helps elevate her back as she pushes the baby out, and generally provides encouragement and moral support. Aside from the obvious benefits to the mother, this principle of the Lamaze method represents real progress in that it allows the partner to play an active role in the birth of the child and to experience more fully one of the most basic and

Lamaze method:
A method of "prepared" childbirth involving relaxation and controlled breathing.

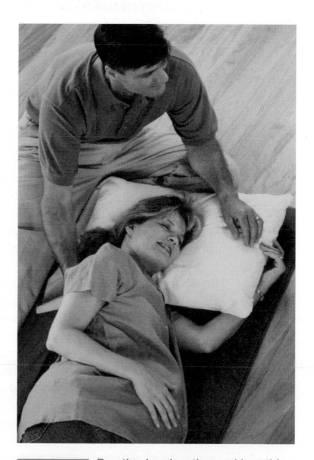

Figure 6.11 Practice in relaxation and breathing techniques is essential in preparing for a Lamaze childbirth.

moving of all human experiences. Some couples also have a *doula* (a Greek word meaning "woman's servant") present during childbirth. The doula does not perform clinical or medical tasks; her role (almost all doulas are female) is to provide physical, emotional, and informational support to the woman and her partner during labour and birth.

One common misunderstanding about the Lamaze method is that the use of anaesthetics is prohibited. In fact, the Lamaze method is more flexible than that. Its goal is to teach each woman the techniques she needs to control her reactions to labour so that she will not need an anaesthetic; however, it affirms her right to have an anaesthetic if she wants one. The topic of anaesthetics in childbirth, which has become quite controversial in recent years, is discussed in the next section.

A number of studies indicate that childbirth training, such as the Lamaze method, has several desirable results. These include reduction in the length of labour, decreased incidence of birth complications, a decrease in the use of anaesthetics, a more positive attitude after birth, increased self-esteem, and a heightened sense of being in control (e.g., Felton & Segelman, 1978; Zax et al., 1975). Lamaze training is associated with increased tolerance for pain and reduced anxiety both before birth and four weeks after birth (Markman & Kadushin, 1986; McClure & Brewer, 1980; Worthington et al., 1983).

There is no doubt that the Lamaze method has improved the childbirth experiences of thousands of women and men. On the other hand, some Lamaze advocates are so idealistic that they may create unrealistic expectations about delivery, especially for women having their first baby (primiparas). The use of the Lamaze method reduces pain in childbirth but does not eliminate it completely. For primiparas, there is often a discrepancy between their positive expectations for delivery and the actual outcomes (Booth & Meltzoff, 1984). Thus, while the Lamaze method produces excellent outcomes and helps women control pain, childbirth still involves some pain, as well as unexpected complications in some cases.

Primipara: A woman having her first baby.

THE USE OF ANAESTHETICS IN CHILDBIRTH

Throughout most of human history, childbirth has taken place without anaesthetics and in the woman's home or other familiar surroundings. The pattern in North America began to change about 250 years ago when male physicians rather than midwives began to assist during birth. Today almost all births occur in hospitals (Maticka-Tyndale & Bircher, 1996). The next major change came around the middle of the nineteenth century, with the development of anaesthetics for use in surgery. When their use in childbirth was suggested, there was some opposition from physicians, who felt they interfered with "natural" processes, and some opposition from the clergy, who argued that women's pain in childbirth was prescribed in the Bible, quoting Genesis 3:16: "In sorrow thou shalt bring forth children." Opposition to the use of anaesthetics virtually ceased, however, when Queen Victoria gave birth under chloroform anaesthesia in 1853. Since then, the use of anaesthetics has become routine (too routine, according to some) and effective. Before discussing the arguments for and against the use of anaesthetics, let us briefly review some of the common techniques of anaesthesia used in childbirth.

Tranquillizers (such as Valium) or narcotics may be administered when labour becomes fairly intense. They relax the woman and take the edge off the pain. Barbiturates (Nembutal or Seconal) are administered to put the woman to sleep. Scopolamine may sometimes be used for its amnesic effects; it makes the woman forget what has happened, and thus she has no memory afterward of any pain during childbirth. Regional and local anaesthetics, which numb only the specific region of the body that is painful, are used most commonly. An example is the pudendal block (named for the pudendum, or vulva), in which an injection numbs only the external genitals. Other examples are spinal anaesthesia (a "spinal"), in which an injection near the spinal cord numbs the entire birth area, from the waist down, and the caudal block and epidural anaesthesia, which are both administered by injections in the back and produce regional numbing from the belly to the thighs (for more information, see Coustan, 1995a). Epidurals are used in 45 percent of vaginal births in Canada.

The routine use of anaesthetics has been questioned by some. Proponents of the use of anaesthetics argue that with modern technology, women no longer need to experience pain during childbirth and that it is therefore silly for them to suffer unnecessarily. Opponents argue that anaesthetics have a number of well-documented dangerous effects on both mother and infant. Anaesthetics in the mother's bloodstream pass through the placenta to the infant. Thus, while they have the desired effect of depressing the mother's central nervous system, they also depress the infant's nervous system. Anaesthetics prevent the mother from using her body as effectively as she might to help push the baby out. If administered early in labour, anaesthetics may inhibit uterine contractions, slow cervical dilation, and prolong labour. They also numb a woman to one of the most fundamental experiences of her life. However, research shows that the negative effects of epidural anesthesia, such as the increased likelihood of the use of instruments during delivery and longer second-stage labour, can be reduced by using low dosages and techniques that allow the woman to move around (Comet, 2001).

Perhaps the best resolution of this controversy is to say that a pregnant woman should participate in prepared childbirth classes and should use those techniques during labour. If, when she is in labour, she discovers that she cannot control the pain and wants an anaesthetic, she should feel free to request it and to do so without guilt; the anaesthetic should then be administered with great caution.

HOME BIRTH VERSUS HOSPITAL BIRTH

Either a physician or a midwife (in provinces where midwifery is a legal profession) may assist in a home birth. Advocates of home birth argue that the atmosphere in a hospital—with its forbidding machines, regulations, and general lack of "homeyness"—is stressful to the woman and detracts from what should be a joyous, natural human experience. Furthermore, hospitals are meant to deal with illness, and the delivery of a baby should not be viewed as an illness; hospital births may encourage the use of procedures such as forceps deliveries and episiotomies that are themselves dangerous. Birth at home is likely to be more relaxed and less stressful; friends and other children are often present. There are some studies that indicate that—for uncomplicated pregnancies—home delivery is as safe as hospital delivery (Hahn & Paige, 1980; for a discussion, see Hoff & Schneiderman, 1985).

On the other side of the argument, if unforeseen emergency medical procedures are necessary, home birth may be downright dangerous for the mother, the baby, or both. Furthermore, hospital practices in labour and delivery have changed radically, particularly with the increased popularity of the Lamaze method; thus, hospitals are not the forbidding, alien environments they once were. Most hospitals, for example, allow partners and loved ones to be present for the entire labour and delivery, and many allow the partner to

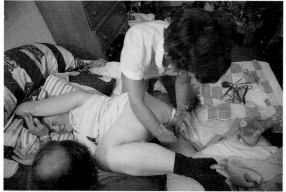

(a)

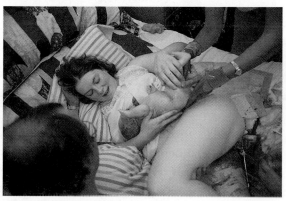

(b)

Figure 6.12 A home birth.

IN FOCUS 6.1

One Woman's Experience Giving Birth under the Care of a Midwife

I was 27 when I had my first child. I was living in British Columbia and her birth was, of course, a memorable experience. In a few words I would describe it as relaxed, personal, secure and simple.

I was under the care of a team of two midwives throughout my pregnancy; I had many opportunities to get to know them. My children's father attended many appointments as we were able to schedule some in the evening. My husband preferred one of the two midwives and I preferred the other; we each found something different in the two women that particularly appealed to us. Both my sister and my mom were encouraged to attend appointments with me. They were amazed when they got to hear my daughter's heartbeat very early on.

When my labour began, I'd been aware of having Braxton-Hicks contractions for some time, and even though it was my first childbirth experience, I could tell the difference. Although I was still in early labour, I called my midwife, then went for a walk, and took a bath. By this time I was still having regular contractions and they were still quite far apart. I called my midwife, Sylvia,

again. She said she'd come check on me, and if I were further along than she thought, she would stay. Sylvia was the midwife I had felt a stronger connection with. As it turned out, it was not her turn to take calls. However, they were so busy with other births that neither of them had had much rest in 48 hours.

Nonetheless, she stayed. We ate, we watched *Friends* on TV, and my family came by to visit with me in my home while I laboured. Apparently I was coping very well, not sounding like a woman close to active labour. At 8 p.m., I was about 5 cm dilated. I was disappointed because this hadn't changed in a while. I had tremendous back labour, and so when contractions occurred I leaned over all of the couch cushions, while family members took turns applying counter-pressure on my tailbone. In between contractions we chatted and relaxed in anticipation. Within an hour or so, my midwife suggested that we could break my waters if I wanted to because, that it might speed things up. My intention was to have a hospital birth, so it was my choice as to whether I wanted to break the water at home or head

be present in the operating room during Caesarean deliveries. Many hospitals have created birthing rooms, containing comfortable beds and armchairs, that permit labour and delivery to occur in a relaxed atmosphere and in the position the woman chooses, while being only a minute away from emergency equipment if it is required.

For any home birth, careful medical screening is essential. Only women with normal pregnancies and anticipated normal deliveries should attempt a home birth. A qualified physician or nurse-midwife must be part of the planning. Finally, there must be access to a hospital in case an emergency arises.

USE OF MIDWIVES

The status of midwives in Canada is in transition. In 2007, midwifery was a legal and regulated profession in British Columbia, Alberta, Saskatchewan, Manitoba, Ontario, Quebec, New Brunswick, Nova Scotia, and the Northwest Territories, and midwives operate as independent professionals in these provinces. Further, midwives are publicly funded in Ontario, British Columbia, Manitoba, and Quebec. However, New Brunswick and Nunavut are in the process of developing legislation and it is expected that midwifery will become a regulated profession in New Brunswick and Nunavut in the near future. According to the Canadian Midwifery Regulators Consortium (2007), registered midwives typically have an undergraduate degree in midwifery; some also have a nursing degree. There are five Canadian universities that offer this program. To be registered, a midwife must show that she (almost

in to the hospital and do it there. I thought "Now, why would I want to make all that mess at home when someone else could clean it up?"

By the time we arrived at the hospital 15 minutes later, things were already beginning to progress. As we walked past admitting, Sylvia told the staff, "She's further along than she looks, her husband will look after the paperwork," and upstairs we went. My sister helped me into the shower where I soon found that I couldn't stand up but also couldn't sit because there was too much pressure. Into the hospital bed I went, where I found myself doing squats from a reclined position. Sylvia and two nurses in the delivery room were amazing, talking me through everything, informing me of what would happen next, bringing me back down as I lost a bit of control in transition. "Lost a bit of control" is a polite way of saying that I totally lacked focus, and felt like I just couldn't manage. When I began screaming, the nurse directed me to turn inward. I remembered my yoga chanting and that helped me regain focus and, although I did a lot of moaning, I no longer felt a need to scream.

My husband was by my side holding my hand, and supporting me physically when I needed to pull up and squat with the contractions. Around 10:45 p.m. my sister was watching as my daughter's head crowned (less than an hour after being admitted), with absolute awe she looked at my husband and said, "you have to SEE this!" He took a quick peak, but dared not leave my side. I felt my daughter's hair with my fingers and her head was delivered without incident. Then she rushed out so fast that the she almost flew right past my midwife's arms, tearing me with her shoulder! With great interest Sylvia informed me that my daughter's umbilical cord was longer than she'd ever seen before. She and my husband measured it later to be approximately four feet long!

The only physician involved was when the O.B. was brought in to attend to my sutures. Within moments my daughter, Breanna, was wiped and swaddled and handed to me. I remember that feeling. It was like she opened a part of my heart I never even knew was there. The love I felt for her had been there all along, long before she was conceived, just waiting to be released. Within moments of her birth, my mother was in the delivery room to meet her first grand-daughter.

Source: Written by Trish McCourt.

---

all midwives are women) is able to deliver competent care as a primary caregiver to women who are considered low-risk.

Why do women choose to have their baby delivered by a midwife rather than a physician? First, midwives provide care from early pregnancy to six weeks after the baby is born, therefore providing continuity of care. Thus, the midwife and the family get to know each other well. Second, prenatal visits are typically 45 minutes long (longer than the typical medical visit). As part of these visits, the midwife presents information so that the woman and her family can make informed decisions about the care they receive and their birth experience. Third, midwives offer women a choice of birth place, either a home or hospital/birthing centre birth, depending on the province. Finally, the midwife stays with the woman throughout her labour and birth and manages all aspects of her care. Midwives are also trained to know when to refer to a medical specialist when complications arise that are outside their scope of practice, although they stay involved in a supportive way even if they make a referral. Midwives support birth as a normal physiological process, and are also trained to manage various emergencies.

Research suggests that women who have their baby delivered by a midwife are the most satisfied with the birth experience. A survey of Canadian women giving birth during a three-month period found that 71 percent of women who had a midwife as their primary caregiver during the birth rated their experience as "very positive," while only 53 percent of women whose primary caregiver was a physician or nurse rated it as "very positive" (Statistics Canada, 2008).

AFTER THE BABY IS BORN: THE POSTPARTUM PERIOD

PHYSICAL CHANGES

With the birth of the baby, the woman's body undergoes a drastic physiological change. During pregnancy the placenta produces high levels of both estrogen and progesterone. When the placenta is expelled, the levels of these hormones drop sharply, and thus the postpartum period is characterized by low levels of both estrogen and progesterone. The levels of these hormones gradually return to normal over a period of a few weeks to a few months. Other endocrine changes include an increase in hormones associated with breast-feeding (breast-feeding is discussed later in this chapter).

In addition, the body undergoes considerable stress during labour and delivery, and the woman may feel exhausted. Discomfort from an episiotomy is common in the first postpartum weeks.

PSYCHOLOGICAL CHANGES

On average, Canadian women remain in the hospital for two or three days after parturition; the average length of stay following a Caesarean delivery is four to five days. However, in 2001–2002, 9 percent of women had a hospital stay of less than two days. For the first two days, women often feel elated; the long pregnancy is over, they have been successful competitors in a demanding athletic event and are pleased with their efforts, and the baby is finally there, to be cuddled and loved.

Following childbirth, many women experience some degree of depression. The depressed mood and other experiences range from mild to severe; the medical literature identifies three types. In the mildest, *postpartum blues* (or "baby blues"), women experience mood swings, with periods of feeling depressed, feeling irritable, and crying, alternating with positive moods. The symptoms usually begin a few days after delivery, are most intense one week postpartum, and lessen or disappear by two weeks postpartum. Between 50 and 80 percent of women experience these mild baby blues (Kennedy & Suttenfield, 2001). Postpartum depression is more severe, characterized by depressed mood, insomnia, tearfulness, feelings of inadequacy, and fatigue. It usually begins two to three weeks postpartum but may occur anytime after delivery. Between 8 and 15 percent of women will experience it, with symptoms lasting six to eight weeks (O'Hara & Swain, 1996; Morris-Rush & Bernstein, 2002). The most severe disturbance is *postpartum psychosis*, with early symptoms including restlessness, irritability, and sleep disturbance; later ones include disorganized behaviour, mood swings, delusions, and hallucinations. Its onset can be dramatic, within 72 hours of delivery or four to six weeks postpartum. It is very rare, affecting only 1 or 2 women out of 1000 (Kennedy & Suttenfield, 2001).

It appears that many factors contribute to this depression. Being in a hospital in and of itself is stressful, as noted previously. Once the woman returns home, another set of stresses faces her. She has probably not yet returned to her normal level of energy, yet she must perform the exhausting task of caring for a newborn infant. For the first several weeks or months she may not get enough sleep, rising several times during the night to tend to a baby that is crying because it is hungry or sick, and she may become exhausted. Clearly, she needs help and support from her partner and friends at this time. Some stresses vary depending on whether this is a first child or a later child. The first child is stressful because of the woman's inexperience; while she is in the hospital she may become anxious, wondering whether she will be capable of caring for the infant when she returns home. In the case of later-born children, and some first-borns, the mother may become depressed because she did not really want the baby. Risk factors for more severe depression include personal or family history of

Postpartum depression: Mild to moderate depression in women following the birth of a baby.

psychiatric disorder, unwanted pregnancy, serious complications following birth, and lack of social support (Morris-Rush & Bernstein, 2002).

Physical stresses are also present during the postpartum period; hormone levels have declined sharply, and the body has been under stress. Thus, it appears that postpartum depression is caused by a combination of psychological, physical, and social factors.

Postpartum depression and psychosis should be treated; depression improves in response to antidepressant drugs, individual psychotherapy, partner and peer support, and nurse home visits (Gjerdingen, 2003; Mehta & Sheth, 2006). A review of the research using randomized controlled trials to assess psychological interventions reported that the most promising is intensive professional postpartum support (Dennis, 2005).

Fathers, too, sometimes experience depression after the birth of a baby. In one study, 89 percent of the mothers and 62 percent of the fathers had experienced the blues during the three months after the birth (Zaslow et al., 1985). A study in Great Britain assessed depression in both mothers and fathers eight weeks after delivery. Ten percent of the mothers and 4 percent of the fathers attained high scores. Paternal depression at eight weeks was related to adverse emotional and behavioural outcomes for children at 3.5 years of age, controlling for the mother's depression score (Ramchandani et al., 2005).

ATTACHMENT TO THE BABY

While much of the traditional psychological research has focused on the baby's developing attachment to the mother, more recent interest has been about the development of the mother's attachment (bond) to the infant. Research shows clearly that this process begins even before the baby is born. Two studies of women expecting their first child found that feelings of nurturance grew during pregnancy, and increased further at birth (Fleming et al., 1997). In this sense, pregnancy is in part a psychological preparation for motherhood.

In the 1970s, pediatricians Marshall Klaus and John Kennell popularized the idea that there is a kind of "critical period" or "sensitive period" in the minutes and hours immediately after birth, during which the mother and infant should "bond" to each other (Klaus & Kennell, 1976). Scientists later concluded that there is little or no evidence for the sensitive-period-for-bonding hypothesis (e.g., Goldberg, 1983; Lamb, 1982; Lamb & Hwang, 1982; Myers, 1984). That outcome is fortunate. Otherwise, mothers who give birth by Caesarean section (and may therefore be asleep under a general anaesthetic for an hour or more after the birth) and adoptive parents would have to be presumed to have inadequate bonds with their children. We know that, in both cases, strong bonds of love form between parents and children despite the lack of immediate contact following birth.

SEX DURING POSTPARTUM

The birth of a child has a substantial effect on a couple's sexual relationship. Following the birth, the mother is at some risk of infection or hemorrhage (Cunningham et al., 1993), so the couple should wait at least two weeks before resuming intercourse. Of course, there is no problem engaging in non-coital intimacy if both partners desire it. When coitus is resumed, it may be uncomfortable or even painful for the woman. If she had an episiotomy, she may experience vaginal discomfort; if she had a Caesarean birth, she may experience abdominal discomfort. Fatigue of both the woman and her partner also may influence when they resume sexual activity.

A longitudinal study of the adjustment of couples to the birth of a child collected data from 570 women (and 550 partners) four times: during the second trimester of pregnancy, and at one, four, and twelve months postpartum (Hyde et al., 1996). Data on the sexual relationship are displayed in Table 6.2. In the month following birth, only 17 percent had resumed intercourse. By the fourth month, nine out of ten couples had—the same percentage as reported intercourse during the second trimester. Reports of cunnilingus showed a similar

Table 6.2   Sexual Behaviours within the Previous Month, Reported by Mothers during Pregnancy and the Year Postpartum

Behaviour	Pregnancy 2nd Trimester	Postpartum		
		1 month	4 months	12 months
Intercourse	89%	17%	89%	92%
Mean frequency of intercourse/month	4.97	0.42	5.27	5.1
Fellatio	43%	34%	48%	47%
Cunnilingus	30%	8%	44%	49%
Satisfaction with sexual relationship*	3.76	3.31	3.36	3.53

*Satisfaction with the relationship was rated on a scale from 1 (very dissatisfied) to 5 (very satisfied).

Source: Hyde et al. (1996). 143–151.

pattern, while reports of fellatio did not indicate a marked decline. Note that although sexual behaviour was much less frequent in the month following birth, satisfaction with the sexual relationship remained high. A major influence on when the couple resumed intercourse was whether the mother was breast-feeding. At both one month and four months after birth, breast-feeding women reported significantly less sexual activity and lower sexual satisfaction. One reason is that lactation suppresses estrogen production, which in turn results in decreased vaginal lubrication; this can make intercourse uncomfortable. This problem can be resolved by the use of vaginal lubricants. Androgen production is also reduced, which may result in reduced sexual desire (La Marre et al., 2003).

BREAST-FEEDING

BIOLOGICAL MECHANISMS

Two hormones, both secreted by the pituitary, are involved in lactation (milk production). One, *prolactin*, stimulates the breasts to produce milk. Prolactin is produced fairly constantly for whatever length of time the woman breast-feeds. The other hormone, *oxytocin*, stimulates the breasts to eject milk. Oxytocin is produced reflexively by the pituitary in response to the infant's sucking of the breast. Thus sucking stimulates nerve cells in the nipple; this nerve signal is transmitted to the brain, which then relays the message to the pituitary, which sends out the messenger oxytocin, which stimulates the breasts to eject milk. Interestingly, research with animals indicates that oxytocin stimulates maternal behaviour (Jenkins & Nussey, 1991).

Actually, milk is not produced for several days after delivery. For the first few days, the breast secretes colostrum, discussed earlier, which is high in protein and gives the baby temporary immunity to infectious diseases. Two or three days after delivery, true lactation begins; this may be accompanied by discomfort for a day or so because the breasts are swollen and congested.

It is also important to note that, much as in pregnancy, substances ingested by the mother may be transmitted through the milk to the infant. The nursing mother thus needs to be cautious about using alcohol and other substances.

PHYSICAL AND MENTAL HEALTH

The Canadian Pediatric Society and the Public Health Agency of Canada recommend that babies be fed breast milk exclusively for the first six months, and continue breast-feeding after introduction of solid foods up to two years of age and older. This is because breast milk is the ideal food for a baby. It provides the baby with the right mixture of nutrients, it contains antibodies that protect the infant from some diseases, and may help prevent asthma and allergies. It is free from bacteria, and is always the right temperature. Breast-feeding is associated with a reduced risk of obesity at ages five and six (Von Kries et al., 1999). Researchers in Ontario recently showed that breast milk also helps boost the baby's own immune system (Filipp et al., 2001). Thus, there is little question that normally it is superior to cow's milk and commercial formulas. Nonetheless, the vast majority of babies who are not breast-fed grow up healthy.

The percentage of Canadian infants who are breast-fed, at least initially, rose from 38 percent in 1963 to 85 percent in 2003. However, there are large regional differences in breast-feeding rates, ranging from a low of 65 percent in Atlantic Canada to a high of 95 percent in British Columbia. Further, about 40 percent of mothers who initiate breast-feeding stop by three months (Health Canada, 2003). Only 19 percent of babies are fed only breast milk for their first six months. Mothers who are younger, single, and have lower education and income levels are less likely to initiate breast-feeding. Immigrant mothers are more likely to breast-feed than are non-immigrants (Health Canada, 1996a). However, individuals from Canada's ethnocultural communities often believe that North American women prefer bottle-feeding over breast-feeding. Thus, they are less likely to breast-feed as they become more acculturated (Agnew, 1997). This pattern is also seen in many Third-World countries, in which urban women are less likely to breast-feed than are rural women, even if they cannot afford to use commercial formula.

A systematic review of programs designed to promote breast-feeding concluded that educational sessions that review benefits, lactation, common problems and solutions, and provide skills training as well as in-person or telephone support programs improve initiation rates and the maintenance of breast-feeding at six months (Guise et al., 2003). Programs that involve only giving out materials at the time the new mother leaves the hospital may actually reduce the likelihood that she will breast-feed. Direct encouragement by a physician or nurse is associated with a much greater likelihood of breast-feeding. The attitudes of the partner are also important. A longitudinal study of 317 first-time mothers and their male partners in Ontario found that male partners' beliefs about breast-feeding affected the women's breast-feeding decisions (Rempel & Rempel, 2004). Women can also use a breast pump to express their milk so that the partner can give the baby a bottle. In this way, the partner can share in the experience of feeding the baby, the mother can get needed sleep if the partner takes over the night-time feeding, or the mother can go out for a few hours without fear that the baby will get hungry.

From the mother's point of view, breast-feeding has several advantages. These include a quicker shrinking of the uterus to its normal size, reduced postpartum bleeding, and more rapid loss of the weight gained during pregnancy. Breast-feeding reduces the likelihood of pregnancy by inhibiting ovulation. It may also reduce the risk of ovarian and breast cancers (Health Canada, 2003). Full breast-feeding, short intervals between feedings,

Figure 6.13   Breast-feeding.

night feedings, and the absence of supplemental feedings are all associated with greater delay in ovulation (Hatcher et al., 2004). However, it is important to note that a woman can become pregnant again before she has a period; recall from Chapter 5 that ovulation precedes menstruation. Research indicates that breast-feeding reduces negative moods and perceived stress (Mezzacappa & Katkin, 2002). Breast-feeding is also associated with reduced risk of breast cancer; the relative risk decreases by 4 percent for every 12 months of breast-feeding (Collaborative Group, 2002).

Some women report sexual arousal during breast-feeding, and a few report having orgasms. Unfortunately, this sometimes produces anxiety in the mother, leading her to discontinue breast-feeding. However, there is nothing "wrong" with this arousal, which appears to stem from activation of hormonal mechanisms. Clearly, from an adaptive point of view, if breast-feeding is important to the infant's survival, it would be wise for nature to design the process so that it is rewarding to the mother.

The La Leche League is devoted to encouraging women to breast-feed their babies and has helped spread information on breast-feeding. The organization tends to be highly enthusiastic in its advocacy of breast-feeding. A few women are physically unable to breast-feed. Others may experience difficulties with breast-feeding, such as pain during breast-feeding or feeling that the baby is nursing poorly, and need support and information to be able to overcome these difficulties. Others may feel psychologically uncomfortable with the idea, perhaps due to the prevalence of negative messages in our culture about breast-feeding, particularly in public, as well as the labelling of breasts as sexual organs. Also breast-feeding can be inconvenient for the woman who works outside the home, although working women can express their breast milk or supplement morning and evening feeding with formula while they are at work.

Problem Pregnancies

ECTOPIC PREGNANCY

Ectopic pregnancy:
A pregnancy in which the fertilized egg implants somewhere other than the uterus.

An ectopic pregnancy (misplaced pregnancy) occurs when the fertilized egg implants somewhere other than the uterus. Most commonly, ectopic pregnancies occur when the egg implants in the fallopian tube (tubal pregnancy; Schenker & Evron, 1983). In rare cases, implantation may also occur in the abdominal cavity, the ovary, or the cervix.

A tubal pregnancy may occur if, for one reason or another, the egg is prevented from moving down the tube to the uterus, as when the tubes are obstructed—for example, as a result of scarring from a chlamydia infection. Early in a tubal pregnancy, the fertilized egg implants in the tube and begins development, forming a placenta and producing the normal hormones of pregnancy. The woman may experience the early symptoms of pregnancy, such as nausea and amenorrhea, and think she is pregnant; or she may experience some bleeding which she mistakes for a period, and think that she is not pregnant. It is therefore quite difficult to diagnose a tubal pregnancy early.

A tubal pregnancy may end in one of two ways. The embryo may spontaneously abort and be released into the abdominal cavity, or the embryo and placenta may continue to expand, stretching the tube until it ruptures. Symptoms of a rupture include sharp abdominal pain or cramping, dull abdominal pain, possibly pain in the shoulder, and vaginal bleeding. Meanwhile, hemorrhaging is occurring, and the woman may go into shock and, possibly, die; thus, it is extremely important for a woman displaying these symptoms to see a doctor quickly.

The rate of ectopic pregnancy in Canada has been decreasing since 1992, going from 16 cases per 1000 reported pregnancies in 1992–1993 to 14 per 1000 pregnancies in 1999–2000 (Health Canada, 2003). The rates vary across Canada, from a low of 9 per 1000 reported pregnancies in Prince Edward Island to 26 per 1000 pregnancies in Nunavut. However, prior to

1992 the rate of ectopic pregnancy in Canada had been increasing, as it still is in a number of other countries. It is thought that high rates are due to (1) increased rates of sexually transmitted infections (STIs), particularly chlamydia, which can lead to blocking of the fallopian tubes; and (2) increased use of contraceptives, such as the IUD and progestin-only methods, that prevent implantation in the uterus but do not necessarily prevent conception. A study of pregnant women in France found that a history of STIs and heavy smoking (more than 20 cigarettes per day) were associated with ectopic pregnancy (Bouyer et al., 2003).

MOLAR PREGNANCY

A *molar pregnancy* is a mass of abnormal tissue (hydatidiform mole) inside the uterus. It is thought to be caused either by fertilization of an ovum with no genetic information or when two sperm fertilize the same egg. The woman usually thinks she is pregnant because she experiences all the same pregnancy symptoms during the first trimester as do women with a normal pregnancy, including a missed menstrual period, breast tenderness, and nausea. She may also experience a vaginal discharge, vaginal bleeding, and other symptoms that are unique to a molar pregnancy. A molar pregnancy can be diagnosed with a blood test assessing hCG levels or with an ultrasound. Women who are over age 35, who have a history of molar pregnancy or miscarriage, and who are low in vitamin A are at increased risk for a molar pregnancy.

PSEUDOCYESIS

In pseudocyesis, or *false pregnancy*, the woman believes that she is pregnant and shows the signs and symptoms of pregnancy without really being pregnant. She may stop menstruating and may have morning sickness. She may begin gaining weight, and her abdomen may bulge. The condition may persist for several months before it goes away, either spontaneously or as a result of psychotherapy. In rare cases it persists until the woman goes into labour and delivers nothing but air and fluid.

Pseudocyesis: False pregnancy, in which the woman displays the signs of pregnancy but is not actually pregnant.

PREGNANCY-INDUCED HYPERTENSION

Pregnancy may cause a woman's blood pressure to rise to an abnormal level. *Pregnancy-induced hypertension* includes three increasingly serious conditions: (1) hypertension, (2) pre-eclampsia, and (3) eclampsia. Hypertension refers to elevated blood pressure alone. Pre-eclampsia refers to elevated blood pressure accompanied by generalized edema (fluid retention and swelling) and proteinuria (protein in the urine). The combination of hypertension and proteinuria is associated with an increased risk of fetal death. In severe pre-eclampsia, the earlier symptoms persist and the woman may also experience vision problems, abdominal pain, and severe headaches. In *eclampsia*, the woman has convulsions, may go into a coma, and may die (Cunningham et al., 1993).

Pre-eclampsia: A serious disease of pregnancy, marked by high blood pressure, severe edema, and proteinuria.

Pre-eclampsia may reflect the silent struggle between mother and fetus for resources. It is hypothesized that the fetus, perhaps due to insufficient nutrition, releases a protein that increases the mother's blood pressure, and therefore the flow of nutrients to the placenta. Indeed, research finds elevated levels of the protein sFlt1 associated with pre-eclampsia (Widmer et al., 2007).

Pre-eclampsia usually does not appear until after the twentieth week of pregnancy. It is more likely to occur in women who have not completed a pregnancy before. It is especially common among teenagers. The risk of pre-eclampsia rises steadily as pregnancy body mass index increases. For overweight women, a reduction in pre-pregnancy weight may reduce the risk (Bodner et al., 2004). The possibility of pre-eclampsia emphasizes the need for proper medical care before and during pregnancy, especially for teenagers and women from ethno-cultural minority communities. Hypertension and pre-eclampsia can be managed well during their early stages. Most maternal deaths occur among women who do not receive prenatal medical care.

VIRAL ILLNESS DURING PREGNANCY

Certain viruses may cross the placental barrier from the woman to the fetus and cause considerable harm, particularly if the illness occurs during the first trimester of pregnancy. The best-known example is rubella. If a woman gets rubella during the first month of pregnancy, there is a 50 percent chance that the infant will be born deaf or have cognitive deficits, cataracts, or congenital heart defects. The risk then declines, so that by the third month of pregnancy the chance of abnormalities is only about 10 percent. While most women have an immunity to rubella because they had it when they were children, a woman who suspects that she is not immune can receive a vaccination that will give her immunity; she should do this well before she becomes pregnant.

Herpes simplex is also *teratogenic,* that is, capable of producing defects in the fetus. Usually, the infant contracts the disease by direct contact with the sore; delivery by Caesarean section can prevent this. Women with herpes genitalis also have a high risk of spontaneously aborting.

A woman who is infected with HIV, the virus that causes AIDS, can pass the virus on to her child during pregnancy, delivery, or after birth through her breast milk. In Canada, pregnant women are given the option of being tested for HIV, but testing is not required. It is important that pregnant women know if they are HIV-positive. Without treatment, 28 percent of their babies will become infected; however, if the infected mother takes AZT, an antiretrovirus drug, the likelihood of such perinatal transmission is reduced by two-thirds or more (Health Canada, 2002).

BIRTH DEFECTS

As has been noted, a number of factors, such as substances taken during pregnancy and illness during pregnancy, may cause defects in the fetus. Other causes include genetic defects (e.g., phenylketonuria, PKU, which causes cognitive impairment) and chromosomal defects (e.g., Down syndrome, which causes cognitive impairment).

About 4 to 5 percent of all babies in Canada are born with a birth defect or anomaly. About one-fourth of miscarried fetuses are malformed. The cause of more than half of these defects is unknown (O'Shea, 1995). However, amniocentesis, chorionic villus sampling, and genetic counselling are options to detect genetic defects, provided that abortion is ethically acceptable to the parents.

Amniocentesis involves inserting a fine tube through the pregnant woman's abdomen and removing some amniotic fluid, including cells sloughed off by the fetus, for analysis. The technique is capable of providing an early diagnosis of most chromosomal abnormalities, some genetically produced biochemical disorders, and sex-linked diseases carried by females but affecting males (hemophilia and muscular dystrophy), although it cannot detect all defects. If a defect is discovered, the woman may then decide to terminate the pregnancy with an abortion.

Amniocentesis should be performed between the thirteenth and sixteenth weeks of pregnancy. If a defect is discovered and an abortion is to be performed, it should be done as early as possible (see Chapter 7). Because amniocentesis itself involves some risk, it is generally thought (although the matter is controversial) that it should be performed only on women who have a high risk of bearing a child with a birth defect. A woman is in this category if (1) she has already had one child with a genetic defect; (2) she believes that she is a carrier of a genetic defect, which can usually be established through genetic counselling; and (3) she is over 35, in which case she has a greatly increased chance of bearing a child with a chromosomal abnormality.

Chorionic villus sampling (CVS) (see Figure 6.14) may eventually replace amniocentesis for prenatal diagnosis of genetic defects (Doran, 1990; Kolker, 1989). A major problem with amniocentesis is that it cannot be done until the second trimester of pregnancy; if genetic

Amniocentesis (am-nee-oh-sen-TEE-sus): A test to determine whether a fetus has birth defects; done by inserting a fine tube into the woman's abdomen in order to obtain a sample of amniotic fluid.

Chorionic villus sampling (CVS): A technique for prenatal diagnosis of birth defects, involving taking a sample of cells from the chorionic villus and analyzing them.

defects are discovered, there may have to be a late abortion. Chorionic villus sampling, in contrast, can be done in the first trimester of pregnancy, usually around 9 to 11 weeks postconception. Chorionic villus sampling can be performed in one of two ways: transcervically, in which a catheter is inserted into the uterus through the cervix, as shown in Figure 6.14; and transabdominally, in which a needle (guided by ultrasound) is inserted through the abdomen. In either case a sample of cells is taken from the chorionic villi (the chorion is the outermost membrane surrounding the fetus, the amnion, and the amniotic fluid), and these cells are analyzed for evidence of genetic defects. Studies indicate that CVS is as accurate as amniocentesis. Like amniocentesis, it carries with it a slight risk of fetal loss (due, for example, to miscarriage). According to Health Canada, for both amniocentesis and CVS, the fetal loss rate is between 1 percent and 1.5 percent, but can be as low as 0.04 percent in experienced hands.

Serious ethical questions are raised when amniocentesis and CVS are used to determine gender and are followed by an abortion if the fetus is not the desired sex.

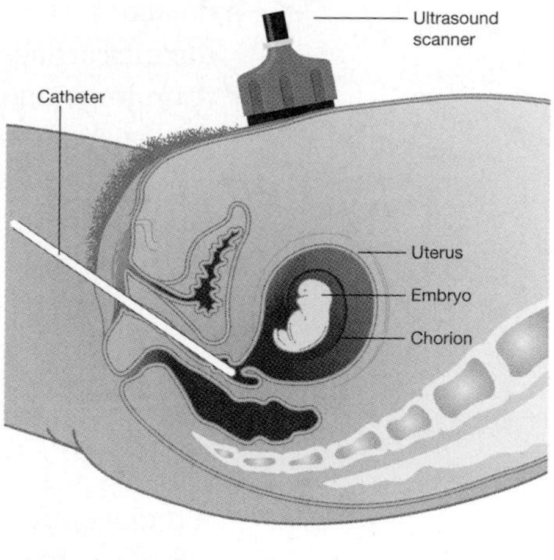

Figure 6.14 Chorionic villus sampling (CVS) and amniocentesis are both available for prenatal diagnosis of genetic defects. CVS (shown here) is able to detect chromosomal abnormalities and sex-linked diseases.

D (RH) INCOMPATIBILITY

D antigen (formerly called the Rh factor) is a substance in the blood; if it is present, the person is said to be D positive (D+); if it is absent, the person is said to be D negative (D−). The D antigen is genetically transmitted, with D+ being dominant over D−.

The presence or absence of the D antigen does not constitute a health problem except when a D− person receives a blood transfusion or when a D− woman is pregnant with a D+ fetus (which can happen only if the father is D+). A blood test is done routinely early in pregnancy to determine whether a woman is D−. Fortunately, about 85 percent of whites, 93 percent of blacks, and 99 percent of Aboriginals are D+; thus, the problems associated with being D− are not very common (Beaulieu, 1994).

If some D+ blood gets into D− blood, the D− blood forms antibodies as a reaction against the D antigen in the invading blood. During parturition there can be considerable mixing between the mother and fetus, and the blood of a D+ baby causes the formation of antibodies in a D− woman's blood. During the next pregnancy, some of the woman's blood enters the fetus and the antibodies attack the fetus's red blood cells. The baby may be stillborn, severely anemic, or developmentally delayed. Thus, there is little risk for a D− woman with the first pregnancy because antibodies have not yet formed; however, later pregnancies can be extremely dangerous.

Fortunately, techniques for dealing with this situation have been developed. An injection of a substance called *D immunoglobulin* prevents the woman's blood from producing antibodies. D− women should receive D immunoglobulin at 28 to 29 weeks gestation, within 72 hours after delivery of a D+ infant, and after induced abortion or amniocentesis (Beaulieu, 1994). If necessary, the fetus or newborn infant may get a transfusion.

MISCARRIAGE (SPONTANEOUS ABORTION)

Miscarriage, or *spontaneous abortion*, occurs when a pregnancy terminates through natural causes, before the conceptus is viable (capable of surviving on its own). It is not to be confused with *therapeutic abortion*, in which a pregnancy is terminated by mechanical or medicinal means (what is commonly called *abortion*—see Chapter 7), or with *prematurity*, in which the pregnancy terminates early, but after the infant is viable.

It is estimated that 20 percent of all pregnancies end in spontaneous abortion (Frishman, 1995). This is probably an underestimate, since very early spontaneous abortions may not be

Miscarriage: The termination of a pregnancy before the fetus is viable, as a result of natural causes (not medical intervention).

detected. The woman may not know that she is pregnant and may mistake the products of the miscarriage for a menstrual period. Thus, the true incidence may be closer to 40 percent (Cunningham et al., 1993). Most spontaneous abortions (80 percent) occur during the first trimester of pregnancy.

Most spontaneous abortions occur because the conceptus is defective. Studies of spontaneously aborted fetuses indicate that 61 percent showed abnormalities that were incompatible with life; for example, many had gross chromosomal abnormalities (Ljunger et al., 2005). Thus, contrary to popular belief, psychological and physical traumas are not common causes of miscarriage. In fact, spontaneous abortions seem to be functional in that they naturally eliminate many defective fetuses.

PRETERM BIRTH

A major complication during the third trimester of pregnancy is premature labour and delivery of the fetus. When delivery occurs prior to 37 weeks' gestation, it is considered *preterm*. Because the date of conception cannot always be accurately determined, preterm birth (prematurity) may be defined in terms of the birth weight of the infant; an infant weighing less than 2500 grams (5.5 pounds) is considered to be in the low-birth-weight category. However, this is inappropriate. The principal concern should be the functional development of the infant rather than his or her weight. It is estimated that between 8 and 9 percent of the births in Canada are preterm (Chen & Millar, 1999).

Preterm birth is a cause for concern because the premature infant is much less likely to survive than the full-term infant. It is estimated that more than half of the deaths of newborn babies in North America are due to preterm birth. Preterm infants are particularly susceptible to respiratory infections, and must receive expert care. Advances in medical techniques have considerably improved survival rates for preterm infants. About 99 percent of infants weighing 2500 grams at birth survive, as do 64 percent of those weighing 1000 grams (Cunningham et al., 1993). However, prematurity may cause damage to an infant who survives. A longitudinal study found that low-birth-weight infants scored significantly lower on math and reading tests at age 6 to 14 (Bourdman et al., n.d.).

Maternal factors such as poor health, poor nutrition, heavy smoking, cocaine use, and syphilis are associated with prematurity. Pregnancy-induced hypertension can also lead to preterm birth. Young teenage mothers, whose bodies are not yet ready to bear children, are also very susceptible to premature labour and delivery. The more risks a pregnant women is exposed to, the greater the risk of preterm birth (Ahluwalia et al., 2001).

A particularly serious cause of preterm birth is *abruptio placentae*, the premature separation of the placenta from the wall of the uterus before delivery. In some cases there is partial separation; in other cases there is complete separation. Abruptio placentae is highest in mothers over age 40 and causes between 15 and 25 percent of all stillbirths (Broers et al., 2004).

INFERTILITY

Infertility: A woman's inability to conceive and give birth to a living child, or a man's inability to impregnate a woman.

Infertility refers to a woman's inability to conceive and give birth to a living child, or a man's inability to impregnate a woman. Health Canada (2003) estimates that 12.5 percent or one in eight Canadian couples experiences infertility. When fertile couples are purposely attempting to conceive a child, about 20 percent succeed within the first menstrual cycle, and about 50 percent succeed within the first six cycles (Hatcher et al., 1994). A couple is considered infertile if they have not conceived after one year of frequent, unprotected intercourse, or after six months if the woman is over 35 (Barrett, 2006). The term "sterile" refers to an individual who has an absolute factor preventing conception.

CAUSES OF INFERTILITY

In about 40 percent of infertile couples, male factors are responsible, and female factors are responsible in an additional 40 percent. In the remaining 20 percent, either both have problems or the cause is unknown (for a detailed discussion, see Liebmann-Smith, 1987).

CAUSES IN THE FEMALE

The most common cause of infertility in women is pelvic inflammatory disease (PID) caused by a sexually transmitted infection, especially gonorrhea or chlamydia. Other causes include failure to ovulate, blockage of the fallopian tubes, and "hostile mucus," meaning cervical mucus that blocks the passage of sperm. Less common causes include poor nutrition, eating disorders, exposure to toxic chemicals such as lead or pesticides, smoking, and use of alcohol, narcotics, or barbiturates. Age may also be a factor; fertility declines in women after 35 years of age, the decline being especially sharp after age 40.

CAUSES IN THE MALE

The most common cause of infertility in men is infections in the reproductive system caused by sexually transmitted infections. Other causes include low sperm count (often due to varicoceles, varicose veins in the testes) which is defined as less than 20 million sperm per millilitre of ejaculate. Couples concerned about low sperm count may decide to abstain from vaginal intercourse in the hope of increasing the count, but research indicates that this does not work. In men with low sperm counts, the sperm become less motile and begin to show signs of becoming stale after only 24 hours of abstinence (Levitas, 2003). Another cause is low motility of the sperm, which means that the sperm are not good swimmers. Less common causes include exposure to toxic agents such as lead, smoking, alcohol and marijuana use, and use of some prescription drugs (Hatcher et al., 1994). Recent research has shown that exposure to environmental estrogens causes sperm to mature too fast, reducing their fertilizing capacity (Adoya-Osiguwa et al., 2003). Exposure to environmental estrogens comes through contact with substances such as beer and pesticides.

Research also reports that the quality of semen declines with age. As men age, the volume of the semen as well as the number and motility of the sperm decline (Eskanazi et al., 2003). Also, the rate of sperm with various genomic abnormalities increases with age (Wyrobek et al., 2006). Finally, women whose partners are over 40 are more likely to experience a spontaneous abortion (Kleinhaus et al., 2006).

COMBINED FACTORS

In some situations, a combination of factors in both the man and woman causes the infertility. One such factor is an immunologic response. The woman may have an allergic reaction to the man's sperm, causing her to produce antibodies that destroy or damage the sperm. Or her immune system may react to the fetus or placenta. According to one controversial theory, an immune reaction may create the high blood pressure that is associated with pre-eclampsia (Fox, 2002). Immune reactions occur in response to novel cells entering the body; if the body has been exposed to the cells frequently in the past, the reaction is less likely. Frequent prior exposure of a woman to a specific man's semen would reduce the likelihood of rejecting his sperm. So frequent vaginal intercourse without a condom (Robertson & Sharkey, 2001) or oral sex in which the woman swallows the ejaculate (Koelman et al., 2000) prior to the attempt to get pregnant may increase the chances of a successful pregnancy.

Sperm have a chemical sensor that causes them to swim toward the egg, attracted by a chemical on the surface of the egg (Spehr et al., 2003). Researchers have already identified one chemical that disrupts this process by shutting down the receptor. This chemical, or chemicals, that influence the surface of the egg can cause infertility. Finally, a couple may also simply lack knowledge; for instance, they may not know how to time intercourse correctly so that conception may take place.

PSYCHOLOGICAL ASPECTS OF INFERTILITY

At some point in their lives the vast majority of adults in Canadian society attempt to have a child, and infertility may put significant stresses on a couple (Daniluk, 2001a). Because in our society the male role is defined partly by the ability to father children, the man may feel that his masculinity or virility is in question. Similarly, the female role is defined largely by the ability to bear children and be a mother, so infertility may affect a woman's sense of self-worth, adequacy, and femininity (Daniluk, 1999). Historically, in most cultures fertility has been encouraged—and, indeed, demanded; hence, pressures on infertile couples may be high, particularly in traditional cultures, leading to more psychological stress. The psychological stress is greatest for the partner identified as the source of the infertility and for couples whose infertility remains unexplained (Daniluk, 2001a). Research indicates that, among couples entering fertility treatment programs, women perceive themselves as experiencing greater emotional and social stress than do men (Stanton et al., 2002). Infertility does not significantly reduce relationship satisfaction, but it can lower sexual satisfaction, pleasure, and spontaneity as couples shift from "making love" to "making babies" (Daniluk, 1999, 2001a; Zoldbrod, 1993). As emphasis on population control increases in our society, and being childfree[5] becomes an acceptable and more recognized option, the stress on infertile couples may lessen.

Treatment for infertility also can be long and stressful. British Columbia psychologist Judith Daniluk (2001a) interviewed 65 infertile couples who had received medical intervention for infertility for an average of five years. Couples described their experience with fertility treatments as an emotional rollercoaster. At first they were optimistic that the medical profession, time, and effort could fix the problem. As the process continued, they (particularly the women) experienced a sense of failure every time menstruation occurred and they had to accept that the treatment had, once again, not worked. Couples whose attempts to conceive were unsuccessful after years of medical intervention described being faced with the difficulty of deciding when "enough is enough"—that is, to stop medical interventions, and accept their infertility. They also described the stress in deciding whether to pursue other options to parenthood, a decision that caused conflict between some partners. However, they also described gains that had resulted from treatment, including strengthening their relationship and personal growth. Further, when asked whether they would make the decision to undergo fertility treatments if they had to do it again, all but one couple said yes.

TREATMENT OF INFERTILITY

There are physicians and clinics that specialize in the evaluation and treatment of infertility. An infertility evaluation should include an assessment of the couple's knowledge of sexual behaviour and conception, and lifestyle factors such as regular drug use. Infertility caused by such factors can be easily treated.

If the infertility problem stems from the woman's failure to ovulate, the treatment may involve the so-called fertility drugs. The drug of first choice is clomiphene (Clomid). It stimulates the pituitary to produce LH and FSH, thus inducing ovulation. The treatment produces a pregnancy in about half the women who are given it. Multiple births occur about 8 percent of the time with Clomid, compared with 1.2 percent with natural pregnancies. If treatment with Clomid is not successful, a second possibility is injections with *human menopausal*

---

[5]Semantics can make a big difference here. Many couples who choose not to have children prefer to call themselves "childfree" rather than "childless."

gonadotropin (HMG, a combination of LH and FSH), which may help trigger ovulation.

If the infertility is caused by blocked fallopian tubes, delicate microsurgery can sometimes be effective in removing the blockage.

If the infertility is caused by varicoceles in the testes, the condition can usually be treated successfully by a surgical procedure known as varicocelectomy.

Finally, a number of new reproductive technologies, such as in vitro fertilization, are now available for those with fertility problems, as discussed in the next section.

A Canadian study is helpful in putting issues of the treatment of infertility into perspective. Among infertile couples seeking treatment, 65 percent subsequently achieved a pregnancy with *no treatment* (Rousseau et al., 1983). For some couples conception just takes a bit longer. However, for those who meet the medical definition of infertility (unable to conceive after 12 months of unprotected intercourse), only about half will conceive a child with treatment (Daniluk, 2001b). Thus, the risks associated with treatments need to be weighed against the possibility that a pregnancy can be achieved without treatment.

New Reproductive Technologies

Reproductive technologies developed in the last three decades mean that there are many ways to conceive and birth babies besides sexual intercourse and pregnancy. These options can be used by infertile couples, single individuals, and same-sex couples. The equality provisions in the Canadian Charter of Rights and Freedoms guarantee that access to new reproductive technologies cannot discriminate on the basis of family status, marital status, sexual orientation, and so on (Law Reform Commission of Canada, 1992).

ASSISTED INSEMINATION

Assisted insemination (also called *artificial insemination*) involves artificially placing semen in the vagina to produce a pregnancy; thus, it is a means of accomplishing reproduction without having sexual intercourse. Assisted insemination in animals was first done in 1776. In 1949, when British scientists successfully froze sperm without any apparent damage to them, a new era of reproductive technology began.

There are 24 assisted insemination programs in Canada. There are two kinds of assisted insemination: assisted insemination by the male partner or husband (AIH), and donor insemination (DI). AIH can be used when the man has a low sperm count. Several samples of his semen are collected and pooled to make one sample with a higher count. This sample is then usually placed in the woman's vagina at the time of ovulation. To increase the number of sperm that reach the fallopian tubes, the sperm can also be washed, concentrated, and injected into the woman's uterus. This is called intrauterine insemination or IUI.[6] DI is used when the male partner is sterile or when the woman does not have a male partner. A donor provides semen to impregnate the woman. The success rate is about 60 percent after six months for women under the age of 35; it decreases for women who are older. The cost of each donor semen specimen sample is between $450 and $650; there are also other expenses associated with DI that can raise the cost substantially.

Of course, it is not always necessary to do DI in a fertility centre or medical facility; some people choose home insemination. The donor ejaculates into a clean glass jar and keeps the sperm at body temperature. Within one to two hours, the woman injects the sperm into her vagina while lying on her back using a non-latex syringe without a needle. Women who attempt home insemination with fresh sperm run the risk of contracting an STI just as they would if they had unprotected sex, so they should make sure that the donor has not had

Assisted insemination: Procedure in which sperm are placed into the vagina by means other than sexual intercourse.

Intrauterine insemination: A procedure in which sperm are washed, concentrated, and injected into a women's uterus.

---

[6]After taking a human sexuality course in which this textbook was used, a student contacted one of the authors to say that her mother had taken part in a pilot study involving IUI. She was born in 1981 and was one of the first, if not the first, babies born in Canada through IUI.

"I ALREADY KNOW ABOUT THE BIRDS AND THE BEES, MOM;
I WANT TO KNOW ABOUT ARTIFICIAL INSEMINATION, IN-
VITRO FERTILIZATION AND SURROGATE MOTHERING!"

Figure 6.15

unprotected sex since being tested. A study of lesbians in Victoria planning to become parents found that 44 percent were planning to use self-insemination at home (McNair et al., 2002).

Surrogacy is also called pre-conception arrangement or contract motherhood, and occurs when a woman agrees to conceive and carry a baby for someone else (Norris, 2006). Traditionally, surrogate mothers have been used by heterosexual couples in which the woman has a problem with infertility. In this case, the male partner provides the sperm and the surrogate mother becomes pregnant through assisted insemination. However, increasing numbers of gay couples are using surrogate mothers to become parents.

SPERM BANKS

Because it is now possible to freeze sperm, it is possible to store it, which is just what some people are doing: using frozen human *sperm banks*. The sperm banks open up many new possibilities for various life choices. For example, suppose that a couple decide, after having had two children, that they want a permanent method of contraception. The husband then has a vasectomy. A few years later the couple decides that they very much want to have another baby, or the couple has divorced and the man wants to have a baby with a new partner. If the man has stored semen in a sperm bank, they can.

Young men can use sperm banks to store sperm before they undergo radiation therapy for cancer. They can later father children without fearing that they will transmit damaged chromosomes (as a result of the radiation) to their offspring.

Since the mid-1990s sperm banks have gone online, making their services available to millions of people around the world (Springen & Noonan, 2003). There are an estimated 50 sperm banks in Canada (although this number may be shrinking) and 110 in the United States, and the larger ones have developed websites. These sites allow prospective parents to browse through a good deal of information about each potential donor, enabling them to select not only on the basis of height, weight, and eye and hair colour, but also education and family medical history. As recipients demand more information about prospective donors, it has become harder to maintain the donor's anonymity. Some donors of eggs or sperm advertise directly on the Internet; while the costs may be lower than the costs associated with clinic services, as is often true on the Internet, there is no guarantee that the donor has given accurate information. It is estimated that some 70 percent of the money spent on sperm-bank services in the United States in 2002 (US$65 million) was for purchases via the Internet.

EMBRYO TRANSFER

Embryo transfer:
Procedure in which an embryo is transferred from the uterus of one woman into the uterus of another.

With embryo transfer, a fertilized, developing egg (embryo) is transferred from the uterus of one woman to the uterus of another woman. Dr. John Buster of UCLA perfected the technique for use with humans, and the first two births resulting from the procedure were announced in 1984 (Associated Press, 1984; Brotman, 1984).

This technique may enable a woman who can conceive but who always miscarries early in the pregnancy to transfer her embryo to another woman who serves as the surrogate mother; that is, the person who provides the uterus in which the fetus grows (and whom the media, somewhat callously, have called a "rent-a-womb"). The embryo transfer procedure also essentially can serve as the opposite of assisted insemination. That is, if a woman produces no viable eggs, her male partner's sperm can be used to artificially inseminate another woman (who donates her egg), and the fertilized egg is then transferred from the donor to the mother.

IN VITRO FERTILIZATION

It is possible for scientists to make sperm and egg unite in a dish outside the human body. The scientific term for this procedure is in vitro fertilization, or IVF (*in vitro* is Latin for "in glass"). The fertilized egg or embryo can then be implanted in the uterus of a woman and carried to term. This technique can be of great benefit to couples who are infertile because the woman's fallopian tubes are blocked. It can also be used for cases of unexplained infertility, ovulation disorders, endometriosis, or severe male infertility. A process called *intracytoplasmic sperm injection* (ICSI) can be used if the man has no sperm or no healthy sperm in his ejaculate. This involves collecting sperm from the epididymis or testes, injecting a single healthy sperm into the ovum, and then using the fertilized egg for IVF (Pinheiro et al., 1999).

> **In vitro fertilization (IVF):** A procedure in which an egg is fertilized by sperm in a laboratory dish.

A milestone was reached with the birth of Louise Brown, the first test-tube baby, in England on July 25, 1978. Obstetrician Patrick Steptoe and physiologist Robert Edwards had fertilized the mother's egg with her husband's sperm in a laboratory dish and implanted the embryo in the mother's uterus. The pregnancy went smoothly, and Louise was born healthy and normal. The first IVF children conceived in Canada were born in Vancouver in 1983. IVF is now performed in a number of countries, with 25 clinics in Canada.

According to data from the Canadian Fertility and Andrology Society, on average in 2004, 24 percent (rates vary considerably from clinic to clinic) of all procedures were successful; that is, they resulted in a live birth; 27 percent of these were multiple births, mostly twins. The success rate is higher when the woman is under 35 and infertility is due to fallopian tube blockage. The procedure is expensive, between $7000 and $9000 per attempt. Only Ontario's medicare plan and the armed forces cover IVF, and then only in some cases (Geddes, 1999).

There is also evidence that babies born as a result of IVF are more likely to be low birth weight and have congenital abnormalities. A study in Finland found a 30 percent greater risk of abnormalities with in IVF babies (Klemetti et al., 2005). It is not clear whether the increased risk is due to the procedure, or to related factors—for example, mothers are typically older (Kovacs, 2002a). These adverse outcomes are more common in babies born after procedures using donor eggs (Wright et al., 2005).

It is also possible to freeze eggs that have been fertilized in vitro (unfertilized eggs do not freeze well), resulting in frozen embryos. This procedure creates the possibility of donated embryos; the birth of a baby resulting from this procedure was first announced in 1984 in Australia. Research finds that babies born after procedures using thawed embryos were less likely to be low birth weight but more likely to be preterm (Wright et al., 2005). The legal and moral status of the frozen embryo is a difficult question, and some worry about "embryo wastage."

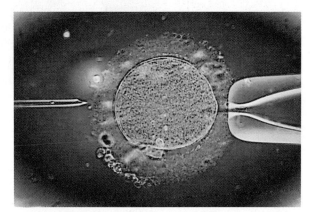

(a)

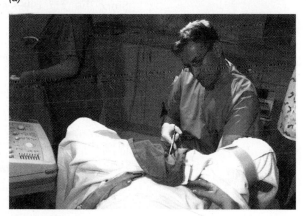

(b)

Figure 6.16 New reproductive technologies. *(a)* With in vitro fertilization, conception is more likely if the egg is scratched, allowing the sperm to enter more easily. *(b)* Vicken Sahakian, MD, medical director of a fertility centre, collects eggs from Deborah, 38. She and her husband, Eric, came in for in vitro fertilization. Out of 13 eggs produced by her, five became fertilized and were reintroduced into Deborah.

GIFT

GIFT: Gamete intra-fallopian transfer, a procedure in which sperm and eggs are collected and then inserted together into the fallopian tube.

GIFT (for gamete intra-fallopian transfer) is an improvement, in some cases, over IVF. Sperm and eggs (gametes) are collected and then inserted together into the fallopian tube, where natural fertilization can take place, followed by natural implantation. Less than 1 percent of the procedures performed in 2002 were of this type (Wright et al., 2005). Because the number is so small, success rates are not reported.

Yet another improvement is ZIFT (zygote intra-fallopian transfer), which involves fertilizing the egg with sperm in a laboratory dish and then placing the developing fertilized egg (zygote) into the fallopian tube, again allowing natural implantation. Less than 1 percent of the procedures performed in 2002 involved this technique (Wright et al., 2005).

Assisted reproduction is more likely to be successful if the woman is younger (under 34) and if fresh embryos rather than frozen ones are used. Success rates do not vary by the cause of the infertility.

CLONING

Cloning is the reproduction of an individual from a single cell taken from a "donor" or "parent." The technique, called intracellular nuclear transfer, involves replacing the nucleus of an ovum with the nucleus from a donor, thus producing an embryo that is genetically identical to the donor. Normally, of course, a child has only half of its genes in common with the mother; the other half come from the father. Therefore, children are never genetically identical to either parent. But in cloning, no sperm is necessary and the result is an individual who is genetically identical to the donor.

The first successful cloning was of a mouse, in 1981. In 1997, researchers announced the birth of Dolly, a sheep cloned from a single cell of an adult ewe. In 2000, six cloned piglets were born, significant because pigs are physiologically close to humans (Prather, 2000). Cloning has great potential—for example, as a source of organs that could be transplanted to replace failing ones, stem cells, or as an alternative in cases of infertility. But it has great risks as well; fewer than 3 percent of cloning efforts succeed, and those that do sometimes suffer from grave, unpredictable genetic defects (Kolata, 2001). In 2004, the federal government passed legislation, the Assisted Human Reproduction Act, prohibiting human cloning.

GENDER SELECTION

There is much interest in techniques that will allow couples to choose whether to have a boy or a girl. Such a technology would be useful to parents who have six girls and really want a boy, or for people who would like to have two children, one of each gender. Problems might arise, though. Some scientists fear that the result of being able to choose gender would be a great imbalance in our population, with many more males than females, because many couples prefer their first child to be a boy. This is already happening in some Asian countries, such as China and India, in which there is a particularly strong preference for sons. For example, a Canadian-led study in India examined the ratio of male to female births for women who already have a daughter compared to women who already have a son. They concluded that, even though gender selection is illegal in India, about half a million female fetuses are aborted each year in India by couples trying for a boy (Jha et al., 2006).

There is a good deal of conventional wisdom about various home methods of increasing the likelihood that a fetus will be male or female. One technique is timing intercourse in relation to ovulation, based on the belief that sperm carrying a Y chromosome swim faster; thus, intercourse at the time of ovulation should increase the chances of a male, whereas intercourse at a time before and remote from ovulation should favour the slow but hardy sperm carrying an X chromosome, resulting in a female. Several studies have tried to test these ideas, relying on indirect measures of time of ovulation (cervical mucus changes, basal body temperature). They suggest that a female is more likely when intercourse coincides with ovulation. Thus, conventional wisdom is wrong. Studies have also investigated the effect of douching; conventional wisdom has it that douching with vinegar will change the vaginal pH, increasing the chances of a boy. Neither of these (or other) "natural" methods will reliably affect the offspring's gender (Kovacs, 2002b).

As usual, entrepreneurs are taking advantage of people's desire to pick the baby's sex, and selling kits that promise results. Some of these kits capitalize on the natural methods, providing the purchaser with thermometers, douching solutions, and other paraphernalia. At least one company is selling kits via the Internet. Again, there is no evidence that these kits will produce the expected results. *Caveat emptor* (buyer beware)!

There are several scientific laboratory procedures that can be used to separate sperm containing male and female chromosomes. Older techniques involved separation based on swimming speed or immunologic characteristics; these work with 70 to 80 percent accuracy. The latest sorting technique, the Micro-Sort method, uses the fluorescence-activated sorter, which can select sperm with an X chromosome with 90 percent accuracy; this technique greatly reduces sperm count and requires assisted reproduction technology (ART). Little data exists on the long-term outcomes of using this procedure (Kovacs, 2002b).

The most reliable method of gender selection is *preimplantation genetic diagnosis* (PGD). This technique involves the removal of eggs from the woman and fertilizing them via IVF. After three days, a cell is taken from each embryo and its chromosomal makeup is determined. An embryo of the preferred type would then be implanted via ART. This method is very invasive to the woman's body and very expensive. The likelihood that the implanted egg would result in the live birth of a healthy infant is the same as for other ART pregnancies.

THE LEGAL AND ETHICAL CHALLENGES OF NEW REPRODUCTIVE TECHNOLOGIES

The technologies discussed here require expert practitioners and appropriate facilities. Further, these and other procedures raise complex legal and ethical questions (discussed in Chapter 20 on the Online Learning Centre). The federal government passed legislation in 2004 to regulate the new reproductive technologies and to deal with some of these issues. The Assisted Human Reproduction Act prohibits identifying the sex of an embryo created for reproductive purposes except for medical reasons, paying a woman to be a surrogate mother, paying a donor for sperm or eggs, and buying or selling human embryos. It also created an agency to oversee agencies providing assisted human reproduction services in Canada and to maintain a donor–offspring registry.

However, a number of other legal questions remain. One set of questions is to be found in the matter of kinship and parental rights and responsibilities. When a child is born as a result of these techniques, who exactly are the parents? What legal claim do donors and/or surrogates have to contact with "their" children after birth?

There are also a host of procedural issues. What will the standards of confidentiality be, especially with regard to the identity of non-parent donors? If something goes wrong during one of these procedures—and they are risky—who is liable? Who will take responsibility for a child with a serious disability born through one of these techniques? Finally, there is the question of who should pay for treatment of infertility. Investigations of the causes of infertility are covered by medicare. In addition, the provinces fund some costly treatments for infertility such as tubal surgery in women and repair of varicocele in men (Leader, 1999). However, DI, IVF, and drugs used to treat infertility are not covered by medicare for most Canadians. This makes most infertility treatments unavailable to the majority of Canadians, who cannot afford them.

SUMMARY

Sperm are manufactured in the testes and ejaculated out through the vas deferens and urethra into the vagina. Then they begin their swim through the cervix and uterus and up a fallopian tube to meet the egg, which has already been released from the ovary. When the sperm and egg unite in the fallopian tube, conception occurs. The single fertilized egg cell then begins dividing as it travels down the tube, and finally it implants in the uterus. Various techniques for improving the chances of conception are available.

The placenta, which is important in transmitting substances between the woman and the fetus, develops early in pregnancy. The most remarkable development of the fetus occurs during the first trimester (first three months), when most of the major organ systems are formed and human features develop.

For the woman, early signs of pregnancy include amenorrhea, tenderness of the breasts, and nausea. The most common pregnancy tests are designed to detect hCG in the urine or blood. Physical changes during the first trimester are mainly the result of the increasing levels of estrogen and progesterone produced by the placenta. Despite cultural myths about the radiant contentment of the pregnant woman, some women do have negative feelings during the first trimester. During the second trimester, the woman generally feels better, both physically and psychologically.

Despite many people's concerns, sexual intercourse is generally quite safe during pregnancy. Nutrition is exceptionally important during pregnancy because the woman's body has to supply the materials to create another human being. Pregnant women also must be very careful about ingesting substances because some can penetrate the placental barrier and enter the fetus, possibly causing damage.

Labour is typically divided into three stages. During the first stage, the cervix undergoes effacement (thinning) and dilation. During the second stage, the baby moves out through the vagina. The placenta is delivered during the third stage. Caesarean section is a surgical method of delivering a baby.

The Lamaze method of "prepared" childbirth has become very popular; it emphasizes the use of relaxation and controlled breathing to control contractions and minimize the woman's discomfort. Anaesthetics may not be necessary, which seems desirable, since they are potentially dangerous.

During the postpartum period, hormone levels are very low. Postpartum depression may arise from a combination of this hormonal state and the many environmental stresses on the woman at this time.

Two hormones are involved in lactation: prolactin and oxytocin. Breast-feeding has a number of psychological as well as health advantages.

Problems of pregnancy include ectopic (misplaced) pregnancy, pseudocyesis (false pregnancy), pre-eclampsia and eclampsia, illness (such as rubella), a defective conceptus, D (Rh) incompatibility, spontaneous abortion, and preterm birth.

The most common cause of infertility in men and women is infection related to sexually transmitted infections (STIs).

New reproductive technologies include assisted insemination, frozen sperm banks, embryo transfer, in vitro fertilization, and GIFT (gamete intrafallopian transfer), all of which are now a reality. These procedures are expensive and have low success rates.

QUESTIONS FOR THOUGHT, DISCUSSION, AND DEBATE

1. Taking the point of view of a pregnant woman, which would you prefer to have, a home birth or a hospital birth? Why?

2. For readers who are men, what role would you envision for yourself in parenting if you had a child? Do you feel that you are adequately prepared for that role? For readers who are women, what role would you ideally like an imaginary partner to take in the parenting of your imaginary children?

3. A close friend confides in you that she is afraid of pregnancy. She has heard that pregnant women experience unpleasant physical (aches and pains, fatigue, illness) and psychological (crying spells, depression) symptoms. She is especially concerned that pregnancy might have a bad effect on her relationship with her partner. What information would you give her about these fears?

SUGGESTIONS FOR FURTHER READING

Agnew, T. (1997). A *multicultural perspective of breast-feeding in Canada.* Ottawa: Minister of Public Works and Government Services Canada. Agnew gives a fascinating account of breast-feeding practices of women from ethnocultural communities both in their countries of origin and after emigrating to Canada.

Dorris, Michael. (1989). *The broken cord.* New York: Harper & Row. The true story of a man and the child he adopted, who turned out to have fetal alcohol syndrome and all the behaviour disturbances that go with it.

Kane, Elizabeth. (1988). *Birth mother: The story of America's first legal surrogate mother.* San Diego: Harcourt Brace Jovanovich. An insightful, first-person account by the woman who was the first to have a contract to bear a child for another couple but later developed serious misgivings.

Laforêt, M. (Ed.). (1993). Sexuality, infertility & assisted reproduction. *The Canadian Journal of Human Sexuality, 2(3).* This special issue of the journal reviews the literature on the major issues related to infertility and assisted reproduction, and includes a number of personal accounts.

Nilsson, A. L., et al. (1986). *A child is born.* New York: Dell. Contains exceptional photographs of prenatal development.

Zoldbrod, Aline P. (1993). *Men, women and infertility: Intervention and treatment strategies.* New York: Lexington. Explores the impact of infertility on personality, the couple's relationship, and sexuality.

For review questions, web resources, and other learning and study tools, visit the *Understanding Human Sexuality* Online Learning Centre at www.mcgrawhill.ca/olc/hyde.

Chapter

7

CONTRACEPTION AND ABORTION

Chapter Highlights

FOR A SHORT TIME I WORKED IN AN ABORTION CLINIC. ONE DAY I WAS COUNSELLING A WOMAN WHO HAD COME IN FOR AN ABORTION. I BEGAN TO DISCUSS THE POSSIBLE METHODS OF CONTRACEPTION SHE COULD USE IN THE FUTURE (SHE HAD BEEN USING RHYTHM), AND I ASKED HER WHAT METHOD SHE PLANNED TO USE AFTER THE ABORTION. "RHYTHM," SHE ANSWERED. "I USED IT FOR ELEVEN MONTHS AND IT WORKED!"*

The average student of today grew up in the pill era and simply assumes that highly effective methods of contraception are available. It is sometimes difficult to remember that this has not always been true and that previously contraception was a hit-or-miss affair at best. Contraception is less controversial than it once was. Yet the use of contraceptives was illegal until 1969 when, under Prime Minister Pierre Trudeau, Parliament amended many of the laws pertaining to sexual behaviour.

Prior to 1969, a person who sold, advertised, or published an advertisement about any "means, instructions, medicine, drug or article intended or represented as a method of preventing conception or causing abortion" could be jailed for up to two years. This statute came under the subheading "Offences Tending to Corrupt Morals" and as such was intended to protect the public and preserve social values (Appleby, 1999). The 1969 amendments to the Criminal Code of Canada also allowed abortion under certain restrictive circumstances. The process by which the abortion law was declared unconstitutional by the Supreme Court of Canada in 1988 (abortion is now legal in Canada) is discussed later in this chapter in the section on abortion. Suffice it to say that these contraception and abortion laws are clear examples of the enshrinement in the statute books of the values of another day. They arise from an understanding of reproduction as the only legitimate purpose of sex and the belief in the necessity of vigorous propagation of the species.

Today there are a variety of reasons for an individual's use of contraceptives. Both babies and mothers are healthier if pregnancies are spaced three to five years apart (Setty-Venugopal & Upadhyay, 2002). Most couples want to limit the size of their family—usually to one or two children. Single persons typically wish to avoid pregnancy. In some cases a couple know, through genetic counselling, that they have a high risk of bearing a child with a birth defect and they therefore wish to prevent pregnancy. And in this era of successful career women, many women feel that it is essential to be able to control when and whether to have children.

At the level of society as a whole, there are also important reasons for encouraging the use of contraceptives. In 2001, there were 37 622 adolescent pregnancies in Canada; 541 of these were girls under 15 years old; adolescent pregnancy is a major social problem. Physicians do not need the parents' permission to prescribe contraceptives, providing the teenager is able to understand the risks and benefits of the decision and thus provide informed consent.

On the global level, overpopulation is a serious problem. In 1900 the world's population was 1.6 billion—and it had taken millions of years to reach that level (Townsend, 2003). By 1950 it had increased to 2.5 billion. In 1999, the world population hit 6 billion, an alarming increase, and experts estimate that it will reach 8.9 billion by 2050. With the resulting destruction of the environment and increased consumption of natural resources, grave concerns arise about the ability of the planet to sustain such a large population, even in the near future. Most experts believe that we must limit the size of the world population (Upadhyay & Robey, 1999). For a summary of contraceptive practices around the world, see Table 7.1.

*Paula Weideger. (1976). *Menstruation and menopause*. New York: Knopf, p. 42.

In this chapter we discuss various methods of birth control, how each works, how effective they are, what side effects they have, and their relative advantages and disadvantages. We also discuss abortion and advances in contraceptive technology.

THE PILL, THE PATCH, AND THE RING

Combination birth control pills: Birth control pills that contain a combination of estrogen and progestin (progesterone).

With **combination birth control pills** (sometimes called *oral contraceptives*) such as Alesse and Yasmin, the woman takes a pill that contains estrogen and progestin (a synthetic progesterone), both at doses higher than natural levels, for 21 days. Then she takes no pill or a placebo for seven days, after which she repeats the cycle.

The traditional 21-on, 7-off pattern is still very common, but variations have been introduced. One is *Seasonale*, which provides 84 days of combined hormones and 7 days of placebo; this means that the woman has a period only once in three months. Seasonale was approved by Health Canada in July 2007.

Table 7.1   Contraception around the World, Reported by Currently Married Women
(The great variations reflect differences among cultures in such factors as availability of medical service, people's education about contraception, and gender roles.)

	Percentage Using Contraceptive Method						
	Voluntary Sterilization						
Region, Country	Male	Women	Pill	IUD	Male Condom	Injectables*	Vaginal Methods** & Fertility Awareness	All Methods
North America								
United States	11	28	27	1	20	4	4	—
Canada	22	11	21	1	15	1	4	88
Europe								
France	NA	NA	38	21	5	NA	NA	80
Netherlands	9	4	49	3	8	NA	NA	74
Africa (Sub-Saharan)								
Kenya	0	6	9	3	1	12	6	39
Asia								
Bangladesh	1	7	23	1	4	7	5	54
India	2	34	2	2	3	0	3	48
Latin America								
Colombia	1	27	12	12	6	4	7	77
Middle East and North Africa								
Egypt	0	1	10	36	1	6	1	56
Morocco	0	3	38	5	1	<1	3	58

NA: Statistics not available

*Includes injections such as Depo-Provera.

**Includes diaphragm, cervical cap, and spermicides.

Sources: Fisher, Borolitsky, & Morris (2003) U.S.; Bureau of the Census, International Data Base (2004), *www.census.gov/ipc/www/idbprint.html;* Zlidar et al., 2003.

HOW IT WORKS

The pill works mainly by preventing ovulation. Recall from Chapter 5 that in a natural menstrual cycle, the low levels of estrogen during and just after the menstrual period trigger the pituitary to produce FSH, which stimulates the process of ovulation. When a woman starts taking the birth control pills, estrogen levels are made high. This high level of estrogen inhibits FSH production, and the message to ovulate is never sent out. The high level of progesterone inhibits LH production, further preventing ovulation.

The progestin provides additional backup effects. It keeps the cervical mucus very thick, making it difficult for sperm to get through, and it changes the lining of the uterus in such a way that even if a fertilized egg were to arrive, implantation would be unlikely.

When the estrogen and progestin are withdrawn (after day 21 in the traditional pill), the lining of the uterus disintegrates, and withdrawal bleeding or menstruation occurs, although the flow is typically reduced because the progestin has inhibited development of the endometrium.

EFFECTIVENESS

Before the effectiveness of the pill is discussed, several technical terms that are used in communicating data on contraceptive effectiveness need to be defined. If 100 women use a contraceptive method for one year, the number of them who become pregnant during that first year of use is called the **failure rate** or *pregnancy rate*. That is, if five women out of 100 become pregnant during a year of using contraceptive A, then A's failure rate is 5 percent. *Effectiveness* is 100 minus the failure rate; thus contraceptive A would be said to be 95 percent effective. We can also talk about two kinds of failure rate: the *failure rate for perfect users* and the *failure rate for typical users*. The perfect-user failure rate refers to studies of the best possible use of the method—for example, when the user has been well-taught about the method, uses it with perfect consistency, and so on. The failure rate for typical users is just that—the failure rate when people actually use the method, perhaps imperfectly when they forget to take a pill or do not use a condom every time. The good news is that if you are very responsible about contraception, you can anticipate close to the perfect-user failure rate for yourself.

Combination pills are one of the most effective methods of birth control. The perfect-user failure rate is 0.1 percent (that is, the method is essentially 100 percent effective), and the typical-user failure rate is 3 percent (Society of Obstetricians and Gynaecologists of Canada, 2000). Failures occur primarily as a result of forgetting to take a pill for two or more days or not taking it at the same time every day. If a woman forgets to take a pill, she should take it as soon as she remembers and take the next one at the regular time; this does not appear to increase the pregnancy risk appreciably. If she forgets for two days she should do the same thing—take one as soon as possible and then continue taking one a day. If she forgets for three or more days, she should follow the same instructions taking one pill as soon as possible and then one pill a day, but in addition she should use condoms or abstain from sex until she has taken hormonal pills for seven days in a row, at which point she will again be well protected (Salem, 2005).

SIDE EFFECTS

You may have seen reports in the media on the dangerous side effects of birth control pills. Some of these reports are no more than scare stories with little or no evidence behind them. However, there are some well-documented risks associated with the use of the pill, and women who are using it or who are contemplating using it should be aware of them.

Among the serious side effects associated with use of the pill are slight but significant increases in certain diseases of the circulatory system. One of these is problems of blood clotting (thromboembolic disorders). Women who use the pill have a higher chance than non-users of developing blood clots (thrombi), particularly women over 35 who smoke. Symptoms of blood clots are severe headaches, severe leg or chest pains, and shortness of breath. For some women, the pill can cause high blood pressure.

Failure rate: The pregnancy rate occurring using a particular contraceptive method; the percentage of women who will be pregnant after a year of use of the method.

IN FOCUS 7.1

A Brief History of Birth Control in Canada

In the 1800s, in Canada and in other Western countries, birth control and abortion early in pregnancy were not illegal. However, laws were passed in the nineteenth century to prohibit the use of birth control as well as the spread of contraceptive information. In the 1892 Canadian Criminal Code, a person who sold, advertised, or published an advertisement about any "medicine, drug, or article" intended to prevent conception could be jailed for up to two years. Abortion was also made illegal.

The movement toward legalizing birth control in Canada was started by women's groups in British Columbia that recognized the toll that unwanted pregnancies were having on women's health and well-being. They joined together to form the Canadian Birth Control League. This group was influenced by Margaret Sanger, who had founded the American Birth Control League in 1914, thereby launching the birth control movement in the United States.

There were a number of other organizations that called for the legalization of birth control during the 1920s and 1930s, including the Saskatchewan section of the United Farmers of Canada, the Seventh Labour Women's Society and Economic Conference, and the National Council of Jewish Women. A. H. Tyler, a Protestant minister who wrote sex education and birth control publications in the 1930s and 1940s, was responsible for starting the birth control movement in Toronto, and founded the Canadian Voluntary Parenthood League in 1931.

The first birth control clinic in Canada was established in Hamilton, Ontario, by Mary Hawkins in 1932. This clinic, called the Birth Control Society of Hamilton, served hundreds of patients. To allay criticisms by members of the medical profession, a physician was always in attendance. Dr. Elizabeth Bagshaw, one of Hamilton's few female physicians at the time, served the clinic for more than 30 years. The clinic was so successful that the Hamilton hospital began cooperating with the clinic in 1935. By 1937 there were also birth control clinics in Windsor and Kitchener.

In 1936, Dorothea Palmer, an Ottawa social worker, was charged with distributing birth control information in poor neighbourhoods. She was acquitted in 1937, partly through the efforts of the birth control lobby. The court

Although the pill actually protects women from endometrial cancer and ovarian cancer (Hatcher et al., 2004), it may aggravate already existing cancer such as breast cancer. While these problems are relatively rare, for women who have taken the pill for more than five years, the risk of benign liver tumours increases (Hatcher et al., 2004).

The pill increases the amount of vaginal discharge and the susceptibility to vaginitis (vaginal inflammations such as monilia—see Chapter 8) because it alters the chemical balance of the lining of the vagina. Women on the pill have an increased susceptibility to chlamydia and gonorrhea (Louv et al., 1989).

The pill may cause some nausea, although this almost always goes away after the first month or two of use. Some brands of pills can also cause weight gain, by increasing appetite or water retention, but this side effect can often be reversed by switching to another brand.

Finally, there may be some psychological effects. About 20 percent of women on the pill report increased irritability and depression, which become worse with the length of time it is used. These side effects are probably related to the progesterone in the pill. There may also be changes in sexual desire. Some women report an increase in sexual interest (McCoy & Matyas, 1996). But others report a decrease in sexual desire, vaginal lubrication, and arousal (Graham et al., 1995; Seal et al., 2005). Switching brands may be helpful for these effects.

In short, the pill does have some serious potential side effects, particularly for high-risk individuals, but for many others it is an extremely effective means of contraception that poses little or no danger.

recognized that the provision of birth control information was permissible if it were done in the interest of the "public good." However, the sale and distribution of contraceptives was still technically illegal until 1969. In fact, as recently as 1960 a Toronto pharmacist was jailed for selling condoms.

In 1967, Pierre Elliott Trudeau, then the justice minister, introduced the "Omnibus Bill," making large-scale changes to the Canadian Criminal Code, including the sections related to contraception and abortion. In defending the bill, Trudeau made his now famous statement: "The state has no business in the bedrooms of the nation." The Omnibus Bill was passed in 1969 when Trudeau was prime minister. Among other changes, it made the use of contraceptives legal and allowed abortion under certain restrictive circumstances.

Figure 7.1 Dr. Elizabeth Bagshaw served as a physician for more than 30 years with the clinic run by the Birth Control Society of Hamilton, the first birth control clinic in Canada.

Sources: CARAL, n.d.; Chesler, 1992; Planned Parenthood Federation of Canada, n.d.

ADVANTAGES AND DISADVANTAGES

The pill has a number of advantages. It is close to 100 percent effective if used properly. It does not interfere with intercourse, as do some other methods, such as the diaphragm, the condom, and foam. It is not messy. Some of its side effects are also advantages; it reduces the amount of menstrual flow and thus reduces cramps. Indeed, it is sometimes prescribed for the non-contraceptive purpose of regulating menstruation and eliminating cramps. Iron-deficiency anemia is less likely to occur among pill users. The pill can clear up acne, and has a protective effect against some rather serious things, including pelvic inflammatory disease (PID) and ovarian and endometrial cancer (Hatcher et al., 2004).

The side effects of birth control pills, discussed earlier, are of course major disadvantages. Another disadvantage is the cost, which is about $24 a month for as long as they are used, although many users (41 percent) do not pay the full cost (Boroditsky et al., 1996). They also place the entire burden of contraception on the woman. In addition, taking them correctly is a little complicated; the woman must understand that they are to be taken at the same time every day, and she must remember when to take them and when not to take them. This effort would not be too taxing for a well-educated woman from a culture that is familiar with various contraceptives. However, currently available information on the use of birth control pills might be inadequate to meet the needs of a woman from a developing country. Appropriate information and direction on how to use the pill is also important for persons with intellectual disabilities.

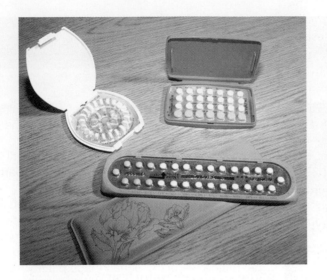

Different types of birth control pills.

One other criticism of the pill is that for a woman who has intercourse only infrequently (say, once or twice a month or less), it represents contraceptive "overkill"; that is, the pill makes her infertile every day of the month (with the side effects of taking it every day), and yet she needs it only a few days each month. Women in this situation might consider a method that is used only when needed, such as the diaphragm or condom.

Finally, it is important to recognize that, although it is an excellent contraceptive, the pill provides absolutely no protection against sexually transmitted infections.

REVERSIBILITY

When a woman wants to become pregnant, she simply stops taking pills after the end of one cycle. Some women experience a brief delay (2 or 3 months) in becoming pregnant, but pregnancy rates are about the same as for women who never took the pill.

DRUG INTERACTIONS

If you are taking birth control pills, you are taking a prescription drug and there may be interactions with other prescription drugs you take (Hatcher et al., 2004). Some of the interactions are mentioned here, but women on the pill should always consult a pharmacist before taking any new medication, including over-the-counter medication. Some anti-tuberculosis drugs, for example, decrease the effectiveness of the pill. There are 30 other drugs that may also interact with the pill; it is important for women to check with their doctor or pharmacist about possible interactions.

The pill may also increase the metabolism of some drugs, making them more potent (Hatcher et al., 2004). Examples include some anti-anxiety drugs, corticosteroids used for inflammations, and theophylline (a drug used for asthma and an ingredient in, for example, Primatene). Therefore, women using the pill may require lower doses of these drugs.

Some over-the-counter drugs may also interact with the pill. St. John's Wort, for example, can decrease the effectiveness of the pill substantially.

OTHER KINDS OF PILLS

To this point, the discussion has centred chiefly on the *combination pill,* so named because it contains both estrogen and progestin. This variety of pill is the most widely used, but there are many kinds of combination pills and several kinds of pills other than combination ones.

Combination pills vary from one brand to the next in the dosages of estrogen and progestin. The dose of estrogen is important because higher doses are more likely to induce blood-clotting problems. Most women do well on pills containing no more than 30 to 35 micrograms of estrogen such as Alesse, Demulen 30, Min-Ovral, and Minestrin (Dickey, 2000). Because of concerns about side effects due to the estrogen in the pill, current pills have considerably lower levels of estrogen than early pills; for example, Ortho 1/35 has one-third the amount of estrogen of the early pill Enovid 10. In January 2005, Yasmin, a new type of contraceptive pill that combines a low dose of estrogen with a synthetic form of progestin (drospirenone), was approved for sale in Canada by Health Canada. High-progestin brands are related to symptoms such as vaginitis and depression. Thus, depending on what side effects the woman wants to avoid, she can choose a brand for its high or low estrogen or progesterone level. (See Hatcher et al., 2004, p. 428, for a list of symptoms related to dosages of estrogen and progestin.)

The triphasic pill (e.g., Triphasil, Ortho 7/7/7) contains a steady level of estrogen like the combination pill does, but there are three phases in the levels of progesterone. The idea is to reduce total hormone exposure, although it may be more about marketing than anything else.

Progestin-only pills (Micronor is the only one available in Canada) have also been developed. They are sometimes called *mini-pills*. The pills contain only a low dose of progestin and no estrogen, and were designed to avoid the estrogen-related side effects of the standard pills. The woman takes one beginning on the first day of her period and one every day thereafter; it is important that she takes it at the same time each day. Progestin-only pills work by changing the cervical mucus such that sperm cannot get through, inhibiting implantation, and inhibiting ovulation (although while taking mini-pills about 40 percent of women ovulate consistently). Progestin-only pills have a typical-user failure rate of 5 percent, which is higher than that of combination pills. Their major side effect seems to be that they produce very irregular menstrual cycles. The mini-pill is probably most useful for women who cannot take combination pills—for example, women over 35 who smoke, or women with a history of high blood pressure or blood-clotting problems.

Progestin-only pills are also useful for women who are breast-feeding and cannot use combination pills because they reduce milk production. Neither kind of pill should be used in the first six weeks after birth when breast-feeding, because trace amounts of the hormones can reach the infant through the breast milk. After that time, though, progestin-only pills are a good choice.

THE PATCH

The patch (Evra) contains the same hormones as combination birth control pills but is administered transdermally—that is, through the skin. The patch itself is thin, beige, and about the size of a double Band-aid. It consists of an outer, protective layer of polyester, an adhesive layer that contains the hormones, and a polyester liner that is removed before applying.

The patch lasts for seven days, so the woman places a new one on once a week for three weeks, and then has a patch-free week. The very first time it is used it takes a couple of days for the hormones to reach effective levels in the bloodstream, so a backup method such as a condom should be used. One advantage of the patch is that women using it do not have to remember to take a pill every day, only to replace the patch every week. In addition, with the patch the hormones enter the body through the skin, rather than going to the stomach and needing to be digested.

The patch is new (it became available in Canada in 2004), so we do not have extensive data on it at this point. Because the hormones are the same as in the pill, the expectation is that the benefits and side effects will be quite similar to those of the pill (Hatcher et al., 2004). A trial over 13 months with real users indicated an actual-user failure rate of less than 1 percent, making it extremely effective, somewhat more so than the pill (Audet et al., 2001; Smallwood et al., 2001).

THE VAGINAL RING

It's not the latest in body piercing. Rather, the vaginal ring (NuvaRing) is a flexible, transparent ring made of plastic and filled with the same hormones as those in the

Triphasic pill: A birth control pill containing a steady level of estrogen and three phases of progesterone, intended to mimic more closely women's natural hormonal cycles.

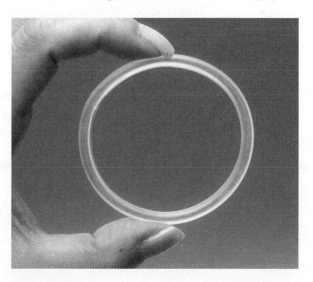

Figure 7.3   NuvaRing, the vaginal contraceptive ring.

combination pill, at slightly lower doses. The ring is placed high up in the vagina and remains in place for 21 days. It is removed and the woman goes ring-free for—you guessed it—seven days. She then inserts a new ring. This method requires even less remembering than the patch does.

The ring, too, was only recently introduced, so the scientific data on it are limited. Because the hormones in it are the same as those in the combination pill, the side effects should be the same. Research shows that it is extremely effective at stopping ovulation (Mulders & Dieben, 2001). It is expected to be even more effective than the pill because it removes the problem of missed pills. One study of 2300 women using it over a year found an actual-user pregnancy rate of less than 1 percent (21 pregnancies), with half the pregnancies resulting from major failures to use the method correctly (Dieben et al., 2002).

EMERGENCY CONTRACEPTION

Emergency contraception (EC) is available in pill form for emergencies involving unprotected intercourse that might result in an unwanted pregnancy, such as from forced intercourse or a condom breaking (Public Health Agency of Canada, 2007). In Canada, its brand name is Plan B. Plan B contains levonorgestrel (a progestin), which is also found in some regular birth control pills, although the dose is higher in Plan B (Dunn & Guilbert, 2003). The treatment is most effective if begun within 12 to 24 hours, and cannot be delayed longer than 120 hours (five days) after unprotected intercourse. Nausea is a common side effect, but Gravol can be taken to prevent it. EC may also result in irregular vaginal bleeding, fatigue, headache, dizziness, and breast tenderness (Public Health Agency of Canada, 2007).

Emergency contraception may work in any of several ways, depending on when in the cycle it is taken. It may stop ovulation, inhibit the functioning of sperm, prevent fertilization, or inhibit the development of a nourishing endometrium. Its action is to prevent pregnancy and it will not cause an abortion if the woman is already pregnant (Public Health Agency of Canada, 2007).

Emergency contraception is between 75 and 89 percent effective (Hatcher et al., 2004). Those statistics underestimate the actual effectiveness, though, because they refer to effectiveness during the most fertile part of the cycle. Actual pregnancy rates are between 0.5 and 2 percent (von Hertzen et al., 2002). That is, emergency contraception is highly effective.

As of May 2008, the emergency contraceptive pill is available over the counter without a written prescription from a physician, with the option but not a requirement of speaking with a pharmacist. Opponents of Plan B had argued that making EC widely available in this way would lead women, and especially teenagers, to become irresponsible about contraception. Research in British Columbia, where EC has been available from pharmacists without a prescription since December 2000, found that making it available without a prescription more than doubled its use (Soon et al., 2005). However, this was not because women were being irresponsible. The vast majority of these women used EC only once during the time period of the study, most often due to birth control failure. Further, research indicates that making Plan B available to teenagers has no effect on whether they have unprotected intercourse or on their number of sexual partners (Harper et al., 2005).

Insertion of a copper IUD up to seven days after unprotected intercourse is also effective as a form of EC and is more than 98 percent effective (Dunn & Guilbert, 2003).

DEPO-PROVERA INJECTIONS

Depo-Provera (DMPA) is a progestin administered by injection. The injections must be repeated every three months for maximum effectiveness. Depo-Provera was approved for use as a contraceptive in Canada only in 1997. A study of women in Saskatchewan using Depo-Provera found that most did so because of its convenience; for example, they did not have to worry about forgetting to take the birth control pill (Hampton et al., 2000).

HOW IT WORKS

Depo-Provera works like the other progestin-only methods, by inhibiting ovulation, thickening the cervical mucus, and inhibiting the growth of the endometrium. Depo-Provera is highly effective, with a typical-user failure rate of 3 percent, making it more effective than the pill.

ADVANTAGES AND DISADVANTAGES

Depo-Provera has many advantages. It does not interfere with lovemaking. It requires far less reliance on memory than birth control pills do, although the woman must remember to have a new injection every three months. It is available for women who cannot use the combination pill, such as those over 35 who smoke and those with blood pressure problems.

A disadvantage of Depo-Provera is that most users experience amenorrhea (no menstrual periods). Sometimes there is just some spotting. However, this may be an advantage. It can relieve anemia due to heavy menstrual periods, and Depo-Provera can be used in the treatment of endometriosis.

SIDE EFFECTS

No lethal side effects of Depo-Provera have been found, although long-term studies have not yet been done (Hatcher et al., 1998). However, in 2005 Health Canada put out a warning that Depo-Provera can result in irreversible bone loss after only two years on the drug and that it should only be used as a last resort.

REVERSIBILITY

The method is reversible simply by not getting another injection. Many women are infertile for 6 to 12 months after stopping its use, but then are able to become pregnant at normal rates (Lande, 1995).

Intrauterine device (IUD): A plastic device sometimes containing metal or a hormone that is inserted into the uterus for contraceptive purposes.

THE IUD

The **intrauterine device**, or **IUD**, is a small piece of plastic; it comes in various shapes. Metal or a hormone may also be part of the device. An IUD is inserted into the uterus by a doctor or nurse practitioner and then remains in place until the woman wants to have it removed. One or two plastic strings hang down from the IUD through the cervix, enabling the woman to check to see whether it is in place.

The basic idea for the IUD has been around for some time. In 1909, Burton Richter reported on the use of an IUD made of silkworm gut. In the 1920s the German physician Ernst Grafenberg reported data on 2000 insertions of silk or silver wire rings. In spite of its high effectiveness (98.4 percent), his work was poorly received. Not until the 1950s, with the development of plastic and stainless-steel devices, did the method gain much popularity. In the 1980s the use of the IUD in North America was sharply reduced by numerous lawsuits against manufacturers by persons claiming to have been damaged by the device, specifically by the IUD known as the Dalkon Shield, which was taken off the market (Hubacher, 2002). Some companies stopped

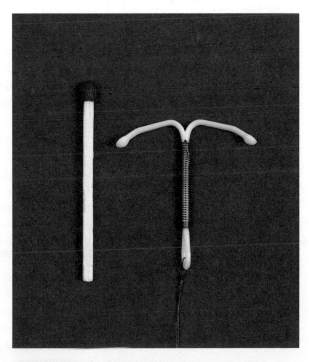

Figure 7.4 Copper T IUD (shown enlarged).

producing IUDs, and others declared bankruptcy. As a result, only two IUDs are available in Canada today. Both are T-shaped; one contains copper (Nova-T or Flex-T 200), the other progesterone (Mirena). Currently, 106 million women worldwide are using IUDs, 40 million of them in the People's Republic of China, and experts predict a resurgence of enthusiasm for them (Hubacher, 2002).

HOW IT WORKS

The IUD works by preventing fertilization. It produces changes in the uterus and fallopian tubes, and in this environment sperm that reach the uterus are immobilized and cannot move into the fallopian tube (Treiman et al., 1995). The egg may also move more swiftly through the fallopian tube, reducing the chances of fertilization.

The Mirena releases progesterone directly into the uterus. One effect is to reduce the endometrium. This results in reduced menstrual flow and reduced risk of anemia, thus overcoming two undesirable side effects of other IUDs.

The small amount of copper that is added to the copper T is thought to have an additional contraceptive effect. It seems to alter the functioning of the enzymes involved in implantation. The progestin thickens cervical mucus, disrupts ovulation, and changes the endometrium. The IUD is also used as an emergency contraceptive within seven days of unprotected intercourse.

EFFECTIVENESS

The IUD is extremely effective; it is in the same category as Depo-Provera and the pill (and sterilization) in effectiveness. The pregnancy rate for the copper T is 0.7 percent for the first year of use; after that, the failure rate is even lower. The IUD is effective for five to eight years.

Most failures occur during the first three months of use, either because the IUD is expelled or for other, unknown reasons. Expulsion is most likely in women who have never been pregnant, in younger women, and in women during menstruation. The expulsion rate is about 1 to 7 percent during the first year (Treiman et al., 1995).

SIDE EFFECTS

The most common side effects of the copper T are increased menstrual cramps, irregular bleeding, and increased menstrual flow. These symptoms occur in 10 to 20 percent of women using it and are most likely immediately after insertion. Mirena, in contrast, reduces menstruation flow and about 20 percent of users stop bleeding altogether. There is no evidence that the IUD causes cancer.

ADVANTAGES AND DISADVANTAGES

Because insertion of the IUD by a physician is covered by medicare, the initial cost is only about $75—the cost of purchasing the IUD. Thus, the IUD is a cheap means of contraception over a long period of use, since the cost is incurred only once and the copper T lasts ten years.

The effectiveness of the copper T IUD is a major advantage. The typical-user failure rate is only 0.8 percent, making it more effective than combination birth control pills and approximately as effective as Depo-Provera.

Once inserted, the IUD is perfectly simple to use. The woman has only to check periodically to see that the strings are in place. Thus it has an advantage over methods like the diaphragm or condom in that it does not interrupt intercourse in any way. It has an advantage over the pill in that the woman does not have to remember to use it. The IUD is a method that can be used safely by women after giving birth and while breast-feeding.

Contrary to what some people think, the IUD does not interfere with the use of a tampon during menstruation; nor does it have any effect on intercourse.

REVERSIBILITY

When a woman who is using an IUD wants to become pregnant, she simply has a physician remove the device. She can become pregnant immediately.

DIAPHRAGMS, CAPS, AND SHIELDS

THE DIAPHRAGM

The **diaphragm** is a circular, dome-shaped piece of thin rubber with a rubber-covered rim of flexible metal (see Figure 7.5). It is inserted into the vagina and, when properly in place, fits snugly over the cervix and does not interfere with intercourse. In order for it to be used effectively, a contraceptive cream or jelly (such as Delfen) must be applied to the diaphragm. The cream is spread on the rim and the inside surface (the surface that fits against the cervix). The diaphragm may be inserted up to six hours before intercourse; it must be left in place for at least six hours afterward and may be left in for as long as 24 hours. Wearing it longer than that is thought to increase the risk of toxic shock syndrome (see Chapter 5).

The diaphragm was the earliest of the highly effective methods of contraception for women. It was popularized in a paper in 1882 by the German researcher Mensinga. In 1925, Margaret Sanger's husband funded the first U.S. company to manufacture them, and they were the mainstay of contraception until about 1960.

> **Diaphragm:** A cap-shaped rubber contraceptive device that fits inside a woman's vagina over the cervix.

HOW IT WORKS

The primary action of the diaphragm itself is mechanical; it blocks the entrance to the uterus so that sperm cannot swim up into it. The cream kills any sperm that manage to get past the barrier. Any sperm remaining in the vagina die after about eight hours (this is why the diaphragm should not be removed until at least six hours after intercourse).

EFFECTIVENESS

The typical-user failure rate of the diaphragm has been estimated to be about 20 percent. Most failures are due to improper use: The woman may not use it every time, she may not leave it in long enough, or she may not use contraceptive cream or jelly. Even with perfectly proper use, there is still a failure rate. For example, Masters and Johnson found that expansion of the vagina during sexual arousal (see Chapter 9) may cause the diaphragm to slip. To get closer to 100 percent effectiveness, the diaphragm can be combined with a condom around the time of ovulation or throughout the cycle.

Failure rates for the diaphragm and cervical cap are often stated as ranges, for example, 17 to 25 percent because failure rates for these methods depend so much on the fertility characteristics of the user. For example, a woman under 30 who has intercourse four or more times weekly has twice the average failure rate of a woman over 30 who has intercourse fewer than four times a week.

Because the fit of the diaphragm is so important to its effectiveness, it is important that the woman be individually fitted for one by her physician. She must be refitted after the birth of a child, an abortion, extreme weight gain or loss, or any similar occurrence that would alter the shape and size of the vagina.

SIDE EFFECTS

The diaphragm has few side effects. One is the possible irritation of the vagina or the penis; this is caused by the cream or jelly and can be relieved by switching to another brand. Another side effect is the rare occurrence of toxic shock syndrome that has been reported in women who left the diaphragm in place for more than 24 hours. Therefore, users should be careful

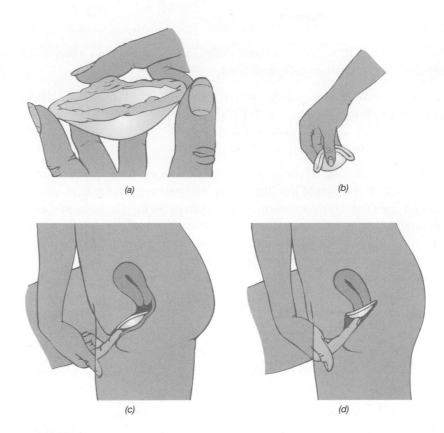

(a)

(b)

(c)

(d)

Figure 7.5   The proper use of a diaphragm. *(a)* Spermicide is applied (about 1 tablespoon in centre and around the rim). *(b)* The edges are held together to permit easier insertion. *(c)* The folded diaphragm is inserted up through the vagina. *(d)* The diaphragm is placed properly, covering the cervix. To check for proper placement, feel the cervix to be sure that it is completely covered by the diaphragm.

not to leave the diaphragm in place for much more than the necessary six to eight hours, especially during menstruation.

ADVANTAGES AND DISADVANTAGES

Some people feel that the diaphragm is undesirable because it must be inserted before intercourse and therefore ruins the "spontaneity" of sex. People with this attitude, of course, should not use the diaphragm as a means of birth control, because they probably will not use it all the time, in which case it will not work. However, a student told us that she and her partner made the preparation and insertion of the diaphragm a ritual part of their foreplay; he inserts it, and they both have a good time! Couples who maintain this kind of attitude are much more likely to use the diaphragm effectively. Moreover, the diaphragm can be inserted an hour or more before sex.

Some women dislike touching their genitals and inserting their fingers into their vagina. Use of the diaphragm is not a good method for them.

The diaphragm requires some thought and presence of mind on the woman's part. She must remember to have it with her when she needs it and to have a supply of cream or jelly. She also needs to avoid becoming so carried away with passion that she forgets about it or decides not to use it.

A disadvantage is that the cream or jelly may leak out after intercourse.

The cost of a diaphragm is about $50 plus the cost of the contraceptive cream; the office visit is covered by medicare. With proper care, a diaphragm should last about two years, and thus itself is not expensive.

The major advantages of the diaphragm are that it has few side effects and, when used properly, is very effective. For this reason, women who are worried about the side effects of the pill or the IUD should seriously consider the diaphragm as an alternative. There is also evidence of a reduction in the rate of cervical cancer among longtime users of the diaphragm. And the diaphragm provides some protection against sexually transmitted infections such as chlamydia because it covers and protects the cervix.

REVERSIBILITY

If a woman wishes to become pregnant, she simply stops using the diaphragm. Its use has no effect on her later chances of conceiving.

FEMCAP AND LEA'S SHIELD

FemCap and **Lea's Shield** are both vaginal barrier devices similar to the diaphragm. Lea's Shield is a one-size, cup-shaped silicone device that has a small one-way valve to allow air to escape as it is being inserted, and help provide suction to keep it properly in place over the cervix. FemCap is shaped like a sailor's cap (see Figure 7.6), is also made of silicone, and comes in three sizes, and so must be fitted by a physician. Both should be used with a sperm-icide or one of the new microbicides. Each was recently approved by Health Canada and both are now available.

FemCap: A method of birth control involving a rubber cap that fits snugly over the cervix.

Lea's Shield: A soft, pliable barrier contraceptive device that prevents sperm from entering the cervix.

Male condom: A contraceptive sheath that is placed over the penis.

THE MALE CONDOM

The **male condom** ("rubber," "prophylactic," "safe") is a thin sheath that fits over the penis (see Figure 7.7). It comes rolled up in a little packet and must be unrolled onto the penis before use. It may be made of latex ("rubber"), of polyurethane, or of the intestinal tissue of lambs ("skin"). The polyurethane condom (Avanti, Trojan Supra) is a recent innovation that is helpful to people who are allergic to latex (Walsh et al., 2003).

The widespread use of the modern condom, both for contraception and for protection against diseases, dates from about 1843, when vulcanized rubber was developed; however, the use of a sheath to cover the penis has been known throughout most of recorded history.[1] Casanova (1725–1798) was one of the first to popularize it for its con-traceptive ability as well as its protective value. Condoms have become increasingly popular because they help pro-tect against sexually transmitted infections (STIs).

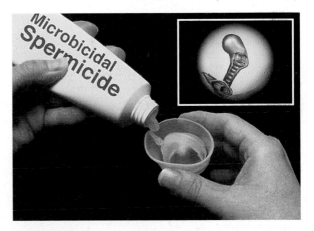

Figure 7.6 FemCap is a silicone rubber barrier contraceptive shaped like a sailor's hat, with a dome that covers the cervix and a brim that conforms to the vaginal walls.

---

[1] Condoms have also been the stimulus for humour throughout history, an example being this limerick:
There was a young man of Cape Horn
Who wished he had never been born
And he wouldn't have been
If his father had seen
That the end of the rubber was torn.

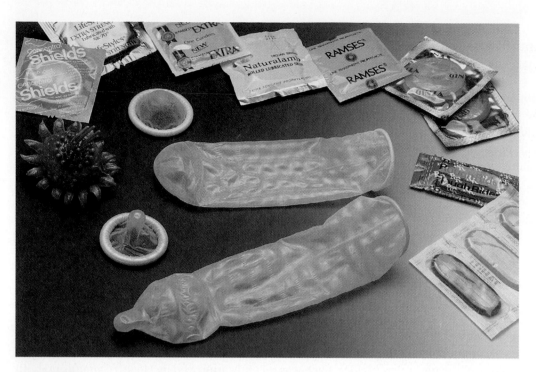

Figure 7.7   A variety of male condoms.

To be effective, the condom must be used properly. It must be unrolled onto the erect penis before the penis ever enters the vagina—*not* just before ejaculation, since long before then some drops containing a few thousand sperm may have been produced. To be effective in preventing STIs, too, it must be put on before penetration. Condoms come in two shapes: those with plain ends and those with a protruding tip that catches the semen. If a plain-ended one is used, about a centimetre or ($^1/_2$-inch) of air-free space should be left at the tip to catch the ejaculate. Care should be taken that the condom does not slip during intercourse. After the man has ejaculated, he must hold the rim of the condom against the base of the penis as he withdraws. It is best to withdraw soon after ejaculation, while the man still has an erection, in order to minimize the chances of leakage. A new condom must be used with each act of intercourse.

Condoms may be either lubricated or unlubricated. Some further lubrication for intercourse may be necessary. A contraceptive foam or jelly works well and provides additional protection. A sterile, water-based lubricant such as K-Y Jelly may also be used.

HOW IT WORKS

The condom catches the semen and thus prevents it from entering the vagina. For condoms coated with a spermicide, the spermicide kills sperm and in theory provides extra protection. Spermicide-coated condoms are not necessarily to be preferred, though. They may create allergies to the spermicide for the man or his partner, and the amount of spermicide is probably not sufficient to be very effective. For couples who want to improve on the effectiveness of the condom, it is probably wiser for the woman to use a contraceptive foam or, better yet, a diaphragm.

EFFECTIVENESS

Condoms are actually much more effective as a contraceptive than most people think. The perfect-user failure rate is about 2 percent. The typical-user failure rate is about 18 percent, but many failures result from improper or inconsistent use. Health Canada controls the quality of condoms carefully, and thus the chances of a failure due to a defect in the condom itself are small. Combined with a contraceptive foam or cream or a diaphragm, the condom is close to 100 percent effective.

SIDE EFFECTS

The condom has no side effects, except that some users are allergic to latex. For them, non-latex condoms made of polyurethane or other plastics are available.

ADVANTAGES AND DISADVANTAGES

One disadvantage of the condom is that it must be put on just before intercourse, raising the spontaneity problem again. If the couple can make an enjoyable, erotic ritual of putting it on together, this problem can be minimized.

Some men complain that the condom reduces their sensation and thus lessens their pleasure in intercourse ("It's like taking a shower with a raincoat on"). The reduction in sensation, however, may be an advantage for some; for example, it may help the man who ejaculates more quickly than he or his partner wishes. Polyurethane condoms are thinner and should provide more sensation. However, today, condoms come in all shapes, sizes, and thinness, so if one brand doesn't work well for you, try another.

There are several advantages to condoms. They are the only contraceptive currently available for men except sterilization. They are cheap (around $1.50 to $2.50 for three), they are readily available without a prescription at any drugstore and some convenience stores, and they are fairly easy to use, although the man (or woman) must plan ahead so that one will be available when it is needed.

Finally, a major advantage of condoms is that they provide protection against many sexually transmitted infections (Cates, 2001). Unlubricated condoms can also easily be made into a *dental dam* to provide protection against STIs during oral–genital activity (see Chapter 8). Over the past several years, some far-right political groups, particularly in the United States, have mounted a campaign to convince the public that condoms are completely ineffective at STI prevention. However, the scientific data say otherwise. Condoms are highly effective protection against STIs that are transmitted mainly through genital secretions (semen, cervical, and vaginal) because they keep the secretions away from the other person. STIs in this category

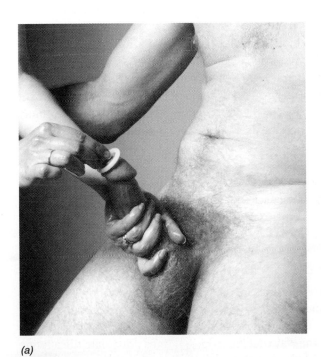

(a)

(b)

Figure 7.8 Putting on a condom correctly. *(a)* The tip is pinched to keep air out. *(b)* The condom is then rolled down over the erect penis.

include chlamydia, gonorrhea, trichomoniasis, hepatitis B, and HIV (Hatcher et al., 2004). Condoms also provide some, although not perfect, protection against STIs that are transmitted mainly by skin-to-skin contact, such as herpes, syphilis, and human papillomavirus. They won't protect against these diseases, of course, if the area producing the microbe is not covered by the condom—for example, if herpes blisters are on the scrotum. Latex and polyurethane condoms are the effective ones; animal-skin condoms are much less effective because they have larger pores that allow some viruses, such as HIV, to pass through them. For a more complete discussion of the effectiveness of condoms in STI prevention, see Chapter 8.

REVERSIBILITY

The method is easily and completely reversible. The man simply stops using condoms if conception is desired.

THE FEMALE CONDOM

The female condom, originally called Reality and now called FC, became available in 1996. It is made of polyurethane and resembles a clear balloon (see Figure 7.9). There are two rings in it, one at either end. One ring is inserted into the vagina much like a diaphragm, while the other is spread over the vaginal entrance. The inside is prelubricated, and additional lubrication may be applied if desired. The penis must be guided into the female condom so that the penis does not slip in between the condom and the vaginal wall. The condom is removed after intercourse, before the woman stands up. The outer ring is squeezed together and twisted to keep the semen inside. A new female condom must be used with each act of intercourse.

HOW IT WORKS

The female condom works by preventing sperm from entering the vagina and by blocking the entrance to the uterus.

EFFECTIVENESS

The female condom is new, so we have less data on its effectiveness compared with other methods. The data we have do not look impressive. The typical-user failure rate is 21 percent (Hatcher et al., 2004), which is unacceptably high for many women. The perfect-user failure rate is 5 percent.

SIDE EFFECTS

There are few if any side effects with the female condom. A few women experience vaginal irritation and a few men experience irritation of the penis as a result of using it.

ADVANTAGES AND DISADVANTAGES

The female condom is made of polyurethane, not the latex used in most male condoms. Polyurethane is less susceptible to tearing and does not deteriorate with exposure to oil-based substances in the way that latex does. It does not create the allergic reactions that some people have to latex.

One major advantage is that the female condom is a method

Figure 7.9 The female condom. One ring fits over the cervix, and the other goes outside the body, over the vulva, so that the condom lines the vagina and partly covers the vulva.

that a woman can use herself to reduce her risk of contracting an STI. The polyurethane is impermeable to HIV and to the viruses and bacteria that cause other STIs. Another advantage is that it can be inserted up to 8 hours before sexual intercourse.

In regard to disadvantages, the spontaneity problem presents itself again. The female condom, at least in its present form (one hopes it will be improved in the near future), is awkward to insert and makes rustling noises while in use. It makes the male condom seem sophisticated and unobtrusive by comparison. Also, it is the least effective of the methods discussed so far in this chapter. Another disadvantage is the cost, about $2.50 per condom, which is considerably higher than the cost for male condoms.

Newer female condoms are under development, including FC2, which is made of synthetic latex rather than polyurethane, and is expected to be less expensive (Upadhyay et al., 2005). Another is the VA feminine condom (also called Reddy and V-Amour), which contains a sponge to hold it in place in the vagina rather than the internal ring of FC. Yet another is PATH, which has urethane foam on the condom pouch so that the condom clings lightly to the vaginal wall.

REVERSIBILITY

The method is easily and completely reversible. The woman simply stops using the condom.

SPERMICIDES

Contraceptive foams (Delfen, Emko), creams, and jellies are all classified as spermicides— that is, sperm killers. They come in a tube or a can, along with a plastic applicator. The applicator is filled and inserted into the vagina. The applicator's plunger is then used to push the spermicide out into the vagina near the cervix, so the spermicide is inserted much as a tampon is. It must be left in for six to eight hours after intercourse. One application provides protection for only one act of intercourse.

Spermicide (SPERM-ih-side): A substance that kills sperm.

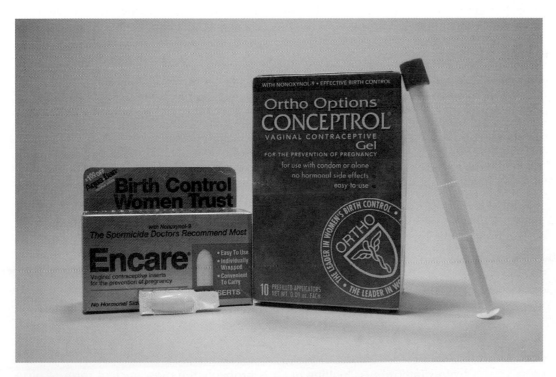

Figure 7.10 Contraceptive foams, creams, and jellies are all spermicides.

Spermicides are not to be confused with the various feminine hygiene products (vaginal deodorants) on the market. The latter are not effective as contraceptives.

HOW THEY WORK

Spermicides consist of a spermicidal chemical in an inert base, and they work in two ways: chemical and mechanical. The chemicals in them kill sperm, while the inert base itself mechanically blocks the entrance to the cervix so that sperm cannot swim into it.

EFFECTIVENESS

Failure rates for spermicides can be as high as 25 percent (Raymond et al., 2004). Put simply, they are not very effective. Foams tend to be more effective, and creams and jellies less so. Spermicidal tablets and suppositories are also available, but they are the least effective. Spermicides are highly effective only when used with a diaphragm or condom.

SIDE EFFECTS

Some people experience an allergic reaction—irritation of the vagina or penis—to spermicides. Because we couldn't find any scientific studies on the incidence of these allergies, we surveyed our sexuality classes. We found that, of the students who had used spermicides, about 2 percent of the men reported an allergic reaction, as did 26 percent of the women.

ADVANTAGES AND DISADVANTAGES

The major advantage of spermicides is that they are readily available, without a prescription, in any drugstore. Thus, they can be used as a stop-gap method until the woman can see a physician and get a more effective contraceptive. Their failure rate is so high, though, that we cannot recommend using them by themselves; always combine them with a second method such as a condom.

Spermicides provide no protection against bacterial STIs such as chlamydia and gonorrhea. Neither do they protect against HIV, and there is some evidence that their frequent use increases susceptibility to HIV (Hatcher et al., 2004).

Their major disadvantage is that by themselves, they are not very effective. They also interrupt the spontaneity of sex, although only briefly. Some women dislike the sensation of the spermicide leaking out after intercourse, and some are irritated by the chemicals. Finally, some people find that they taste terrible, and so their use interferes with oral sex.

DOUCHING

Douching (DOOSH-ing): Flushing out the inside of the vagina with a liquid.

Some people mistakenly believe that **douching** (flushing the vagina with a liquid) with any one of a variety of solutions is an effective contraceptive technique. A popular rumour among teenagers is that douching with Coca-Cola after intercourse will prevent pregnancy. Unfortunately, while it is true that acidic solutions will kill sperm, it takes only seconds for some of the sperm to reach the cervical mucus; once there, they are free to continue moving up into the uterus, and no douching solution will reach them. The woman would have to be a championship sprinter to get herself up and douched soon enough. And the douche itself may even push some sperm up into the uterus. Douching, therefore, is just not effective as a contraceptive method.

WITHDRAWAL

Withdrawal: A method of birth control in which the man withdraws his penis from his partner's vagina before he orgasms.

Withdrawal (*coitus interruptus,* "pulling out") is probably the most ancient form of birth control. (A reference to it is even found in Genesis 38:8–9.) Withdrawal is still widely used throughout the world. The man withdraws his penis from his partner's vagina before he has an orgasm and thus ejaculates outside the vagina. To be effective as contraception, the ejaculation must occur completely away from the woman's vulva.

EFFECTIVENESS

Withdrawal is not very effective as a method of birth control. The failure rate is around 27 percent. Failures occur for several reasons: The few drops of fluid that come out of the penis during arousal may carry enough sperm for conception to occur; if ejaculation occurs outside the vagina but near or on the vulva, sperm may still get into the vagina and continue up into the uterus; and sometimes the man simply does not withdraw in time.

SIDE EFFECTS

Withdrawal produces no direct physical side effects. However, over long periods of time, worry about ejaculating before withdrawal may contribute to sexual dysfunctions in the man such as premature ejaculation, and also sexual dysfunction in the woman.

ADVANTAGES AND DISADVANTAGES

The major advantage of withdrawal is that it is the only last-minute method; it can be used when nothing else is available, although if the situation is that desperate, one might consider abstinence or some other form of sexual expression such as mouth–genital sex as alternatives. Obviously, withdrawal requires no prescription and is completely free.

One major disadvantage is that withdrawal is not very effective. In addition, it requires exceptional motivation on the part of the man, and it may be psychologically stressful to him. He must constantly maintain a kind of self-conscious control. The woman may worry about whether he really will withdraw in time, and the situation is certainly less than ideal for her to orgasm.

AN EXTRA SEVEN POUNDS COULD KEEP YOU OFF THE FOOTBALL TEAM.

Become a father before you're ready and you may always wonder what else you could have been.
THE CHILDREN'S DEFENSE FUND

Figure 7.11 Male responsibility is a key issue in birth control.

FERTILITY AWARENESS (RHYTHM) METHODS

Fertility awareness (rhythm) methods, although they are not very effective, are the only form of "natural" birth control. They require abstaining from intercourse during the woman's fertile period (around ovulation). There are several fertility awareness methods, in each of which the woman's fertile period is determined in a different way: the calendar method, the basal body temperature method, and the cervical mucus method (Kambic, 1999).

The **calendar method** is based on the assumption that ovulation occurs about 14 days before the onset of menstruation. It works best for the woman with the perfectly regular 28-day cycle. She should ovulate on day 14, and almost surely on one of days 13 to 15. Three days are added in front of that period (previously deposited sperm may result in conception), and two days are added after it (to allow for long-lasting eggs); thus, the couple must abstain

Fertility awareness (rhythm) method: A method of birth control that involves abstaining from intercourse around the time the woman ovulates.

Calendar method: A type of fertility awareness method of birth control in which the woman determines when she ovulates by keeping a calendar record of the length of her menstrual cycles.

from sexual intercourse from day 10 to day 17. Therefore, even for the woman with perfectly regular cycles, eight days of abstinence are required in the middle of each cycle. Research shows that sperm can live up to five days inside the female reproductive tract and eggs live less than a day (Wilcox et al., 1995).

The woman who is not perfectly regular must keep a record of her cycles for at least six months, and preferably a year. From this she determines the length of her shortest cycle and the length of her longest cycle. The preovulatory safe period is then calculated by subtracting 18 from the number of days in the shortest cycle, and the postovulatory safe period is calculated by subtracting 11 from the number of days in the longest cycle. Thus for a woman who is somewhat irregular—say, with cycles varying from 26 to 33 days in length—a period of abstinence from day 8 to day 22 (a total of 15 days) would be required.

A somewhat more accurate method for determining ovulation is the **basal body temperature (BBT) method**. The principle behind this was discussed in Chapters 5 and 6. The woman takes her temperature every day immediately upon waking. During the preovulatory phase her temperature will be at a fairly constant low level. On the day of ovulation it drops (although this does not always occur), and on the day after ovulation it rises sharply, staying at that high level for the rest of the cycle. Intercourse would be safe beginning about three days after ovulation. Some of the psychological stresses involved in using this method have been noted previously. As a form of contraception, the BBT method has a major disadvantage in that it determines safe days only *after* ovulation; theoretically, according to the method, there are no safe days before ovulation. Thus, the BBT method is best used in combination with the calendar method or the cervical mucus method, which determine the preovulatory safe period; the BBT method determines the postovulatory safe period.

Another fertility awareness method, the **cervical mucus method**, is based on variations over the cycle in the mucus produced by the cervix. There are generally a few days just after menstruation during which no mucus is produced and there is a general sensation of vaginal dryness. This is a relatively safe period. Then there are a number of days of mucus discharge around the middle of the cycle. On the first days, the mucus is white or cloudy and tacky. The amount increases, and the mucus becomes clearer, until there are one or two *peak days*, when the mucus is like raw egg white—clear, slippery, and stringy. There is also a sensation of vaginal lubrication. Ovulation occurs within 24 hours after the last peak day. Abstinence is required from the first day of mucus discharge until four days after the peak days. After that the mucus, if present, is cloudy or white, and intercourse is safe. Combination of the cervical mucus method with BBT is called the **sympto-thermal method**.

HOME OVULATION TESTS

Recently, home tests for the detection of ovulation have been developed. Most such tests have been designed for use by couples wanting to conceive; however, a few are now available for contraception (Hatcher et al., 2004). One kind (PG53, PC 2000, and Maybe Baby) involves mini-microscopes to examine saliva or cervical mucus. Others involve temperature computers that work on the BBT method. Hormone computers (e.g., Persona) assess hormone levels in urine. Costs range between $50 and $350. The effectiveness of these tests is not yet well enough researched for us to recommend them as reliable.

EFFECTIVENESS

The effectiveness of the fertility awareness method varies considerably, depending on a number of factors, but basically it is not very effective with typical users (giving rise to its nickname, "Vatican roulette," and a number of old jokes like, "What do they call people who use the rhythm method?" Answer: "Parents"). Although the typical-user failure rate is around 25 percent for all methods, ideal-user failure rates vary considerably. They are 5 percent

Basal body temperature method: A type of fertility awareness method of birth control in which the woman determines when she ovulates by keeping track of her temperature.

Cervical mucus method: A type of fertility awareness method of birth control in which the woman determines when she ovulates by checking her cervical mucus.

Sympto-thermal method: A type of fertility awareness method of birth control combining the basal body temperature method and the cervical mucus method.

for the calendar method, 2 percent for BBT, 2 percent for the sympto-thermal method, and 3 percent for the cervical mucus method (Hatcher et al., 2004). Failure rates are lower when the woman's cycle is very regular and when the couple are highly motivated and have been well instructed in the methods.

ADVANTAGES AND DISADVANTAGES

The method has no side effects except possible psychological stress, and it is inexpensive. It is easily reversible. It also helps the woman become more aware of her body's functioning. The method requires cooperation from both partners, which may be considered either an advantage or a disadvantage.

Its main disadvantages are its high failure rate and the psychological stress it may cause. Periods of abstinence of at least eight days, and possibly as long as two or three weeks, are necessary, which is an unacceptable requirement for many couples. Actually, the fertility awareness method would seem best suited to people who do not have sex frequently.

A certain amount of time, usually several months, is required to collect the data needed to make the method work. Thus, one cannot simply begin using it on the spur of the moment.

STERILIZATION

Sterilization, or voluntary surgical contraception (VSC), is a surgical procedure whereby an individual is made permanently sterile; that is, unable to reproduce. Sterilization is a rather emotion-laden topic for a number of reasons. Some people confuse sterilization with castration, though the two are quite different. This is also an emotional topic because sterilization means the end of one's capacity to reproduce. The ability to impregnate and the ability to bear a child are very important in cultural definitions of manhood and womanhood. We hope that as gender roles become more flexible in our society and as concern about reproduction is replaced by a concern for limiting population size, the word "sterilization" will no longer carry such emotional overtones.

Sterilization: A surgical procedure by which an individual is made sterile; that is, incapable of reproducing.

Most physicians are conservative about performing sterilizations; they want to make sure that the patient has made a firm decision on his or her own and will not be back a few months later wanting to have the procedure reversed. The physician has an obligation to follow the principle of "informed consent." This means explaining the procedures involved, telling the patient about the possible risks and advantages, discussing alternative methods, and answering any questions the patient has.

Despite this conservatism, both male sterilization and female sterilization have become increasingly popular as methods of birth control. Sterilization is the most common method of birth control for fertile-aged long-term couples in Canada: 22 percent of men and 17 percent of women. As you would expect, sterilization is more common among couples who are older (Boroditsky et al., 1996).

MALE STERILIZATION

The male sterilization operation is called a vasectomy, so named for the vas deferens, which is tied or cut. It can be done in a physician's office under local anaesthesia and requires only about 20 minutes to perform. In the traditional procedure, the physician makes a small incision on one side of the upper part of the scrotum. The vas is then separated from the surrounding tissues, tied off, and cut. The procedure is then repeated on the other side, and the incisions are sewn up. For a day or two the man may have to refrain from strenuous activity and be careful not to pull the incision apart. Now a *no-scalpel vasectomy* procedure has been developed (Hatcher et al., 2004). It involves making just a tiny pierce in the scrotum and has an even lower rate of complications than a standard vasectomy (see Figure 7.12).

Vasectomy (vas-EK-tuh-mee): A surgical procedure for male sterilization involving severing of the vas deferens.

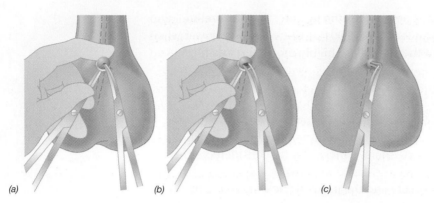

Reprinted with permission from the Population Information Program

Figure 7.12 The no-scalpel vasectomy. *(a)* The vas (dotted line) is grasped by special ring forceps and the scrotum is pierced by sharp-tipped forceps. *(b)* The forceps stretch the opening slightly. *(c)* The vas is lifted out and then tied off. The other vas is then lifted out through the same small hole and the procedure is repeated.

Typically, the man can return to having intercourse within a few days. It should not be assumed that he is sterile yet, however. Some stray sperm may still be lurking in his ducts beyond the point of the incision. Men should not rely completely on the vasectomy until three months after it was performed (Salem, 2005). Until then, an additional method of birth control should be used.

Misunderstandings about the vasectomy abound. In fact, a vasectomy creates no physical changes that interfere with erection. Neither does it interfere in any way with sex hormone production; the testes continue to manufacture testosterone and secrete it into the bloodstream. Nor does a vasectomy interfere with the process or sensation of ejaculation. As we noted earlier, virtually all the fluid of the ejaculate is produced by the seminal vesicles and prostate, and the incision is made long before that point in the duct system. Thus the ejaculate is completely normal, except that it does not contain any sperm.

How It Works
The vasectomy makes it impossible for sperm to move beyond the cut in the vas. Thus the vasectomy prevents sperm from being in the ejaculate.

Effectiveness
The vasectomy is essentially 100 percent effective; it has a failure rate of 0.1 percent. Failures occur because stray sperm are still present during the first months after surgery, because the physician did not completely sever the vas, or because the ends of the vas have grown back together.

Side Effects
The physical side effects of the vasectomy typically are minimal. In about 5 percent of cases there is a minor complication from the surgery, such as infection of the vas (Hatcher et al., 2004).

Some psychologically based problems may arise. Thus, the man's attitude toward having a vasectomy is extremely important. Only about 5 percent regret having had a vasectomy (Hatcher et al., 2004).

Reversibility
Quite a bit of effort has been devoted to developing techniques for reversing vasectomies (the surgical procedure for reversal is termed *vasovasostomy*) and to developing vasectomy techniques that are more reversible. At present, with sophisticated microsurgery techniques, pregnancy rates following reversal are around 50 percent (Hatcher et al., 2004). In making a decision about whether to have a vasectomy, though, a man should assume that it is irreversible.

After a vasectomy some men begin forming antibodies to their own sperm. Because these antibodies destroy sperm, they might contribute further to the irreversibility of the vasectomy.

Advantages and Disadvantages
The major advantages of the vasectomy are its effectiveness and its minimal health risks. Once performed, it requires no further thought or planning on the man's part. It is a permanent,

long-term method of contraception and is free. The operation itself is simple—simpler than the female sterilization procedures—and requires no hospitalization or absence from work. Finally, it is one of the few methods that allow the man to assume contraceptive responsibility.

The permanency of the vasectomy may be either an advantage or a disadvantage. If permanent contraception is desired, the method is certainly much better than something like birth control pills, which must be used repeatedly. But if the couple change their minds and decide that they want to have a child, the permanence is a distinct disadvantage. Some men put several samples of their sperm into a frozen-sperm bank so that assisted insemination can be performed if they do decide to have a child after a vasectomy.

Another disadvantage of the vasectomy is the various psychological problems that might result if the man sees sterilization as a threat to his masculinity or virility. However, long-term studies of vasectomized men provide no evidence of such psychological problems (Population Information Program, 1983). In studies done around the world, the majority of vasectomized men say that they have no regrets about having had the sterilization performed, that they would recommend it to others, and that there has been no change or else an improvement in their happiness and sexual satisfaction in marriage. Fewer than 5 percent of vasectomized men report psychological problems such as decreased libido or depression. This rate is no higher than in control samples of unvasectomized men.

Finally, if a couple use the vasectomy as a permanent method of birth control, the woman is not protected if she has intercourse with someone other than her partner. Similarly, the man is not protected from STIs.

FEMALE STERILIZATION

Several surgical techniques are used to sterilize a woman, including minilaparotomy, laparoscopy, and the transcervical approach (tubal ligation or "having the tubes tied" are terms that are also heard). These techniques differ in terms of the type of procedure used (see Figure 7.13). They are performed under local or general anaesthesia, and involve blocking the fallopian tubes in some way so that sperm and egg cannot meet.

In a **minilaparotomy** ("minilap"), a small incision (less than 3 centimetres, or about 1 inch long) is made in the abdomen. Each fallopian tube is in turn gently pulled to the opening. Each tube is blocked either by cutting and tying off the ends or by applying a small clip; the tubes are then allowed to slip back into place. With the *laparoscopy*, a magnifying instrument is inserted into the abdomen. The doctor uses it to identify the fallopian tubes and then blocks them by electrocoagulation or by clips. Either procedure takes only about 10 to 20 minutes and does not require that the woman spend the night in the hospital.

The newest procedure is the *transcervical approach*, which does not require an incision. Instead, the instruments enter through the cervix and uterus, and a blockage device is placed in the fallopian tubes. Several transcervical methods are under development

Minilaparotomy: A method of female sterilization.

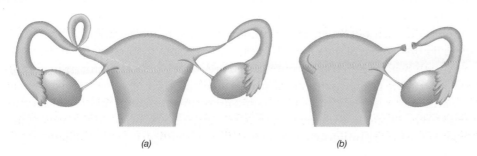

(a)   *(b)*

Figure 7.13 Two methods for performing a tubal ligation or minilaparotomy. In *(a)* the fallopian tubes are tied off and the loop is cut: the cut ends then scar over. In *(b)* the tubes are tied in two places and the section between is cut and removed.

(Upadhyay et al., 2005). One involves inserting a tiny microcoil called Essure into each fallopian tube. Scar tissue forms around it, blocking the fallopian tube.

The female sterilization procedures do not interfere with the ovaries, and therefore the production of sex hormones continues normally; thus, female sterilization does not bring on premature menopause. Some of the misunderstandings arise from confusion of female sterilization procedures with hysterectomy (surgical removal of the uterus) or oophorectomy (surgical removal of the ovaries, which does impair hormonal functioning). These latter two operations do produce sterility, but they are generally performed for purposes other than sterilization, such as treatment of cancer.

How It Works

Female sterilization procedures make it impossible for the egg to move down the fallopian tube toward the uterus. They also prevent sperm from reaching the egg.

Effectiveness

These procedures are essentially 100 percent effective. The failure rate of 0.5 percent is due to an occasional rejoining of the ends of the fallopian tubes, and rare cases in which the woman was pregnant before the sterilization procedure was performed.

Side Effects

Occasionally, there are side effects arising from the surgery, such as infections, hemorrhaging, and problems related to the anaesthetic. Generally, only 1 percent of women undergoing the surgery experience complications.

Reversibility

Highly refined microsurgery techniques make it possible to reverse female sterilization in some cases. The success rate varies considerably, depending on the method that was used to perform the sterilization. Pregnancy rates range between 38 percent and 82 percent (Hatcher et al., 2004). However, in deciding whether to have sterilization surgery, a woman should assume that it is irreversible. Five years after sterilization, only 7 percent of women regret having had the procedure (Jamieson et al., 2002).

Advantages and Disadvantages

Female sterilization has some of the same advantages as male sterilization in terms of effectiveness, permanence, and cost (it's free) when used for long-term contraception. One disadvantage is that it offers no protection from sexually transmitted infections.

New Advances in Contraception

According to some, a really good method of contraception is not yet available. The highly effective methods either are permanent (sterilization) or have associated health risks (the pill). Other, safer methods (such as the condom and the diaphragm) have failure rates that cannot be ignored. Most of the methods are for women, not men. Because of the limitations of the currently available methods, contraception research continues. Unfortunately, its pace has been slow in the last few years because pharmaceutical companies are weary of lawsuits. There is little incentive for conducting highly innovative research and much incentive for companies to be cautious. Nonetheless, research and innovation continue, even if at a slow pace. Some of the more promising possibilities for the future are discussed here.

MALE METHODS

Several possibilities for new or improved male contraception are being explored (Hatcher et al., 2004; Institute of Medicine, 2004; Wenk & Nieschlag, 2006).

New Condoms

Several new models of condoms are being tested. To deal with the problem of allergies to latex, polyurethane condoms have been developed, as noted earlier. They are thinner than latex, so they should provide more sensation. Another model is one that could be put on before erection.

Male Hormonal Methods

The basic idea underlying the development of male hormonal methods is to suppress the production of LH and FSH by the pituitary, so that sperm would not be produced or would not develop properly (Wenk & Nieschlag, 2006). Unfortunately, many of the hormone preparations that have been tried shut down sperm production but also shut down the user's sex drive, making them unacceptable to most men. Current drugs being tested involve a combination of a testosterone and a progestin (such as DMPA, used in the Depo-Provera shot for women); the latter would suppress FSH and LH production, leading to the suppression of spermatogenesis (Page et al., 2006). Another group of drugs are GnRH antagonists. By reducing GnRH activity, they would reduce the production of FSH and LH, which would stop spermatogenesis.

Immunocontraceptives

Scientists have been working on a contraceptive vaccine that would induce the individual's immune system to react in a way that would interrupt one of the steps in the fertility system, for example, one of the stages in the production or maturation of sperm. One option is a vaccine targeting sperm antigens. Another is a vaccine for men that would target pituitary FSH, which would block sperm production without stopping the manufacture of testosterone. None of these are in trials yet.

Male Contraceptive Implant

Health Canada has approved a clinical trial for an intra-vas device (IVD) in which two tiny plugs that block sperm are inserted into the vas deferens. Unlike vasectomy, for which reversal is often not successful, these devices could be removed if the man later decided he wanted to father a child.

FEMALE METHODS

Microbicides

Microbicides are substances that kill microbes (bacteria and viruses) and, preferably, sperm. Experts had hoped that current contraceptive foams and gels that contain nonoxynol-9 (N-9) would be effective microbicides, but it turns out that N-9 is ineffective and may actually make women more vulnerable to infection. What we need is a microbicide that is highly effective at killing the viruses and bacteria that cause STIs and is effective at killing sperm. Several promising microbicides are in clinical trials (Hatcher et al., 2004). They include BufferGel, Invisible Condom, Savvy, and PRO 2000. These microbicides could be used by themselves or with a diaphragm or condom.

Vaginal Rings

The NuvaRing, discussed earlier, is already available in Canada and contains a combination of estrogen and progestin. Two new progestin-only vaginal rings are under development (Upadhyay et al., 2005). They are somewhat less effective than the combination hormone ring, but they could be used by breast-feeding women.

SPRAY-ON CONTRACEPTION

The Nestorone Metered Dose Transdermal System, a progestin, is now under development in spray form (Upadhyay et al., 2005). It is sprayed on the skin (transdermally) once a day, is quickly absorbed through the skin, and then slowly diffuses into the bloodstream.

IMPLANTS AND INJECTABLES

Norplant, a progestin-only method, which involved implanting six small rods under the skin in the upper arm, is no longer available in Canada. Newer, improved implants are being developed, including Jadelle and Implanon (Upadhyay et al., 2005). They have only one or two rods or capsules implanted in the upper arm. Their initial cost, unfortunately, is high.

The contraceptive injection used in Canada today is Depo-Provera, which contains progestin only. Concerns about Depo were discussed earlier in this chapter. Newer implants, such as Cyclofem, Lunell, and Mesigyna, are being developed that contain a combination of estrogen and progestin much like the combination pill (Upadhyay et al., 2005).

NEW IUDS

Several new IUDs are under development. One, GyneFix, is similar to the copper T, but without the T—that is, it is frameless. It simply carries copper tubes on a string and would last for at least five years, but the top of it must be anchored into the fundus of the uterus. It has been approved in Europe and is available in China.

REVERSIBLE, NON-SURGICAL STERILIZATION

This method involves injecting liquid silicone into the fallopian tubes. The silicone hardens and forms a plug. The plugs could later be removed if the woman wished to become pregnant. It might also be used to plug the vas in men.

PSYCHOLOGICAL ASPECTS: ATTITUDES TOWARD CONTRACEPTION

It is a favourite old saying among Planned Parenthood workers that contraceptives are only as effective as the people who use them. That is, no contraceptive method is effective if it is not used or if it is used improperly. Thus, the user is at least as important as all the technology of contraception.

In 2003, 33 553 teenagers, or one out of every 37 women under age 20 (most of them single) became pregnant. The rate of teenage pregnancy in Canada (27.1 pregnancies per 1000 teenagers) is about the same as in England, considerably above France and the Netherlands, and much lower than the United States. Approximately 54 percent of teenage pregnancies are terminated by abortion, 44 percent result in live births (often to single teenagers), and 2 percent end in miscarriage (Dryburgh, 2000). Of the teenagers who give birth, 81 percent choose to keep their baby.

The great majority of unwanted pregnancies are the result of failure to use contraceptives responsibly. The Canada Youth Sexual Health and HIV/AIDS Study (CYSHHAS) found that between 5 and 10 percent of high school students in grades 9 and 11 had used no contraceptive method the last time they engaged in sexual intercourse (Boyce et al., 2006). Further, only about three-quarters of adolescents engaging in sexual intercourse report always using contraception (Fisher et al., 2004b). Others do not use contraceptives consistently.[2] Research in

---

[2]Myths teenagers hold about when a woman can and cannot get pregnant may contribute to their inconsistent use of contraception. For example, when she was in high school, the daughter of one of this text's authors regularly heard other kids state with certainty that a female cannot get pregnant the first time she has intercourse or if she has intercourse standing up or in water. What have you heard?

five Western countries, including Canada, indicates that in all five countries adolescents from low-income families are more likely to become pregnant (Darroch et al., 2001).

If we are to understand this issue and take effective steps to address it, we must understand the psychology of contraceptive use and non-use. Many researchers have been investigating this issue.

Why don't adolescents use contraceptives? The CYSHHAS asked Canadian high school students why they had not used condoms the last time they had sexual intercourse (Boyce et al., 2006). As shown in Figure 7.14, one important reason for both grade 9 and grade 11 students was that they did not expect to have sex. Another important reason was that they used another method of birth control. Other common reasons were having had too much alcohol or drugs, not wanting to spoil the moment, not having enough money to buy condoms, they or their partner not wanting to use condoms, and feeling that they had a faithful partner. Few students said that they did not know how to use a condom or that they were too embarrassed to talk about condom use. The study did not ask students about some other reasons that adolescents sometimes give for not using contraceptives, such as believing that they could not get pregnant, or wanting to get pregnant. However, research in Quebec has shown that people who avoid thinking about STIs are less likely to use condoms consistently (Klein & Knäuper, 2003).

Social scientists have developed several theories to explain teenagers' use and non-use of contraceptives. These theories tend to fall into one of three other categories: (1) theories that view contraceptive behaviour as a result of a decision-making process; (2) theories that view contraceptive behaviour as the outcome of psychological development; and (3) theories that focus on personality, motivation, and skills, such as William Fisher's work. Let us look at each of these three categories.

An example of a decision making theory has been formulated by Kristin Luker (1975). She argues that teenage girls essentially engage in a cost–benefit analysis—perhaps not a very deliberate one—in which they weigh (1) the costs of contraception (e.g., may be difficult to obtain, partner may not like the idea); (2) the benefits of contraception (not getting pregnant); (3) the costs of pregnancy, which may not seem large for a young woman with few bright hopes for the future; and (4) the benefits of pregnancy (feeling like a woman, having a baby who loves you). The woman also makes some estimate of the probability of getting pregnant, and generally underestimates it. As a result, she engages in contraceptive risk-taking—much like deciding not to fasten one's seatbelt in a car—because the costs of contraception seem to outweigh the benefits, or perhaps because there seem to be benefits to pregnancy.

Developmental models look at the process of psychological development during adolescence (e.g., Jorgensen, 1980; Morrison, 1985). Teenagers may find their values to be firmly in line with their parents' values, but their behaviour increasingly conforms to the norms of their peer group. A conflict between values and behaviour results (Zabin et al., 1984). More specifically, teenagers may hold their parents' conservative values about sex outside of marriage, which prize abstinence and therefore the non-use of contraceptives. Meanwhile, their actual behaviour conforms to that of their peer group and they engage in intercourse. The hope is that as adolescents mature, their behaviour and values will become more consistent with each other.

William Fisher (see In Focus 3.3 on page 70), a psychologist at the University of Western Ontario, has developed the Information–Motivation–Behavioural Skills (IMB) model to explain the psychological factors that influence sexual health behaviour such as contraceptive use (Fisher & Fisher, 1992, 1998). The first component of this model is *information*. People who lack information about contraceptives and their correct use can scarcely use them effectively. People need the information to be presented in a way that makes it easy for them to put it into practice. That is, people need basic and understandable information about fertility and contraceptives, but they also need specific, practical information about where to acquire contraceptives and how to use them correctly to prevent pregnancy.

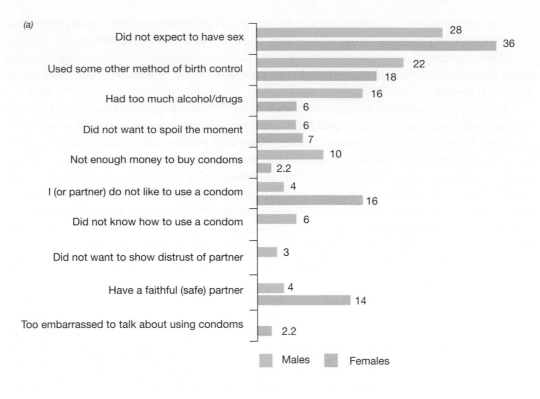

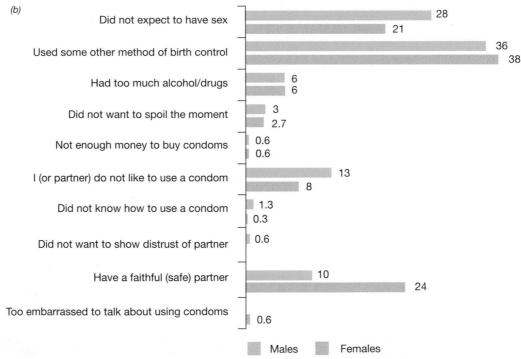

Figure 7.14   Reasons given by high school students for not using condoms the last time they had intercourse. *(a)* Grade 9 students. *(b)* Grade 11 students.

Source: Councils of Ministers of Education. (2003). *Canadian Youth, Sexual Health and HIV/AIDS Study: Factors influencing knowledge, attitudes, and behaviours.*

The second component of the IMB is *motivation*. People are more motivated to use contraceptives if they have positive attitudes toward the use of contraception, perceive that the use of contraception is socially acceptable, and have the expectation that intercourse could result in pregnancy. Individuals who believe that contraception interferes with lovemaking, think that their friends disapprove of sex or of the use of contraceptives, or believe that the chance of pregnancy is zero or close to it will be less likely to practise effective contraception. A person's motivation to engage in contraceptive behaviour is also influenced by his or her emotional responses to sexual cues, called erotophobia-erotophilia (Byrne, 1983; Fisher et al., 1983). Erotophobes don't discuss sex, have sex lives that are influenced by guilt and fear of social disapproval, have intercourse infrequently with few partners, and are shocked by sexually explicit films. Erotophiles are just the opposite—they discuss sex, they are relatively uninfluenced by sexual guilt, they have intercourse more frequently with more partners, and they find sexually explicit films to be arousing. Most people are somewhere in between. Research shows that erotophiles are more likely to be consistent, reliable contraceptive users (Fisher et al., 1988). However, extreme erotophiles may also fail to use contraceptives in the heat of the moment (Hynie & Lydon, 1996).

Erotophobe: Person with a negative orientation toward sexuality; feeling guilty and fearful about sex.

Erotophile: Person with a positive orientation toward sexuality, who feels comfortable with and positive toward sex.

The third component of the IMB is having the *behavioural skills* to engage in the actions needed to use contraceptives effectively. This includes the skills to acquire contraceptives, discuss contraceptive use with a partner, and refuse to engage in sexual intercourse if contraception is not available. Before individuals will engage in these behaviours, they must accept the fact that they are sexually active and that pregnancy (or STIs) can result from intercourse. They also need to set preventing pregnancy as a personal goal (Fisher & Fisher, 1998). Research shows that many people think the chance is zero, or close to it, that intercourse will result in pregnancy, expressing the expectation that "It can't happen to me." People with that expectation are unlikely to use contraceptives.

Research has shown that erotophobes are less likely to engage in a number of the steps essential for effective contraception (Byrne, 1983; Fisher et al., 1988):

1. *Obtaining contraceptive information.* Erotophobes have less sex information than erotophiles do, and when exposed to the same sex information, erotophobes learn less than erotophiles do.
2. *Acknowledging that sex may occur.* Because of their fearfulness, erotophobes are less likely to acknowledge that intercourse may occur, which makes contraceptive planning difficult. Gender-role socialization has made it particularly difficult for women to acknowledge such expectations (Hynie et al., 1995).
3. *Obtaining contraceptives.* Erotophobes have more difficulty going to a doctor or a drugstore to obtain contraceptives. In turn, research has shown that women who are more embarrassed about obtaining contraception are less likely to use it consistently (Herold, 1981).
4. *Communicating with a partner.* Erotophobes have more difficulty talking about sex, and therefore effective communication with their partner about use of contraceptives is unlikely to occur. Each partner may assume that the other will take care of it. An erotophobe may also have more difficulty insisting on contraceptive use with a reluctant partner.
5. *Using contraceptives every time.* Erotophobes may have trouble with actually using the contraceptive. An erotophobic male isn't going to be thrilled about putting on a condom. An erotophobic female won't be thrilled with inserting a diaphragm or thinking about sex every day as she takes her pill.

Although it is generally recognized that fantasy is an important part of sexual expression, *fantasy* may also play an important role in contraceptive behaviour (Byrne, 1983). Most of us have fantasies about sexual encounters, and we often try to make our real-life sexual encounters turn out like the "scripts" of our fantasies. An important shaper of our fantasies is the mass media. Through movies, television, and romance novels, we learn idealized techniques for kissing, holding, lovemaking. But the media's idealized versions of sex almost never include a portrayal of the use of contraceptives. In the popular series *Grey's Anatomy*, Cristina has sex for the first time with no contraception in sight and she's a doctor! There were a number of positive examples of discussion of condoms in the original *Degrassi* series (Byers, 2005). For example, Caitlin tells Joey that she's ready to have sex with him by slipping a condom into his hand while they are having a nice dinner in a romantic restaurant. More recently, positive examples have come from the series *Sex and the City*. In one sequence, Miranda has "mercy sex" with her ex-boyfriend Steve, who had just undergone treatment for testicular cancer. They don't use a condom and Miranda gets pregnant. After that, she frequently reminds her friends to use a condom, using herself as an example of the consequences of not using one. These episodes were excellent in showing that negative consequences do occur when contraception is not used, and they provide examples of honest discussions of contraception. If teenagers saw lots of instances of their heroes and heroines behaving responsibly about contraception, it would probably influence their behaviour. But right now that is not what the media give them. However, things may be slowly moving in the right direction: 25 percent of television programs that show or strongly imply sexual intercourse also include a reference to safer sex (Kaiser Family Foundation, 2001). For example, there was the episode of *Friends* in which Monica and Rachel fought over the last condom when both of their boyfriends were staying over.

What are the solutions? Can this research and theorizing on the social psychology of contraceptive use be applied to reducing unwanted teenage pregnancy? The most direct solution would be to have better programs of sex education in the schools. Although all provinces and territories have school programs that include sex education, the extensiveness of these programs varies among and within provinces (Barrett et al., 1997). Sex education programs should include a number of components that are typically missing, including legitimizing pre-sex communication about sex and contraception (Milan & Kilmann, 1987); legitimizing the purchase and carrying of contraceptives; discussing how one weighs the costs and benefits of pregnancy, contraception, and abortion; legitimizing non-coital kinds of sexual pleasure, such as masturbation and oral–genital sex; encouraging males to accept equal responsibility for contraception; and enhancing skills through role playing and other skill-building activities. Some suggestions on how to negotiate safer sex are presented in In Focus 8.3 (page 245) and sexuality education is discussed in more depth in Chapter 19.

So far we have focused only on why many adolescents do not use contraceptives consistently. Before leaving this discussion, it is important to note that it is not just single teenagers who have unwanted pregnancies, and many of the same factors just discussed also apply to older individuals. Further, some single teenage mothers make good parents, whereas some single women in their 20s and 30s do not. For example, a Nova Scotia study found no differences between the children of single teenage mothers and those of older single mothers in either parenting skills or the children's educational achievements (Bissell, 2000; Nova Scotia Department of Community Services, 1991). Research has shown that it is poverty and lack of education, rather than age per se, that create difficulties for single mothers (Hardwick & Patychuk, 1999; Maticka-Tyndale, 2001; Singh et al., 2001).

ABORTION

Abortion: The termination of a pregnancy.

In the past several decades, abortion (the termination of a pregnancy) has been a topic of considerable controversy in North America. Canada currently has no laws related to abortion and so, legally, abortion is treated like any other medical procedure. However, some groups would like to see abortion recriminalized. Opposition to abortion comes from a coalition of anti-abortion groups that prefer to call themselves "pro-life." Those seeking to preserve the right of women to legal abortions, who call themselves "pro-choice," have also organized. The organization Canadians for Choice has been active in trying ensure reproductive freedom for Canadian women.

What do most Canadians think about abortion? Alberta sociologist Reginald Bibby (2006) found that 43 percent of Canadians believe that legal abortion should be available to any woman who wants one. The percentage of Canadians favouring legal abortion for any reason is even higher among adolescents—55 percent in one study (Bibby, 2001). Most Canadians take a middle position, believing that abortion should be available under certain circumstances. What are these circumstances? Almost all (92 percent) agreed that a woman should have access to a legal abortion when her health is endangered; 86 percent supported legal abortion if conception is due to rape; 84 percent supported it when the baby is likely to have a serious defect; and 57 percent if the family had a very low income.

In 2004, more than 100 000 Canadian women obtained legal abortions (Statistics Canada, 2007). Nonetheless, all Canadian women do not have equal access to abortion services.

There are several factors that limit Canadian women's access to abortion (Shaw, 2006). One factor is a lack of availability of abortion services in many areas. In general, abortions are more available in urban than in rural areas. Further, as shown in Table 7.2, only 16 percent of hospitals perform abortions and there are no abortion services available on Prince Edward Island. There are no free-standing abortion clinics in Saskatchewan or in any of the territories, although women in these areas do have access to hospital abortions. The process for obtaining an abortion varies from province to province and may make it difficult for some women to receive abortions in a timely fashion. In some provinces, abortions are fully funded by medicare, while in other provinces only hospital abortions are covered and women have to pay between $500 and $750 for a clinic abortion. Finally, the activities of anti-abortion groups,

Table 7.2   Access to Abortion across Canada

Province	Number of Hospitals Providing Abortions	Number of Clinics Providing Abortions	Health Care Funding for Abortion
Newfoundland & Labrador	3 of a possible 14 (21%)	1	Full funding for hospitals and clinics
Prince Edward Island	0 of a possible 7 (0%)	0	Can request reimbursement for out-of-province hospital abortions; no funding for clinics
Nova Scotia	4 of a possible 30 (13%)	1	Full funding for hospitals; partial funding for clinics
New Brunswick	1 of a possible 28 (4%)	1	Full funding for hospitals; no funding for clinics
Quebec	31 out of a possible 129 (24%)	6 clinics 12 community health centers	Full funding for hospitals and community health centres; partial funding for clinics
Ontario	33 out of a possible 194 (17%)	6	Full funding for hospitals and clinics
Manitoba	2 out of a possible 52 (4%)	1	Full funding for hospitals and clinics
Saskatchewan	4 out of a possible 68 (6%)	0	Full funding for hospitals
Alberta	6 out of a possible 100 (6%)	2	Full funding for hospitals and clinics
British Columbia	26 out of a possible 88 (29%)	3	Full funding for hospitals and clinics
Yukon	1 out of a possible 2 (50%)	0	Full funding for hospitals and travel grants
Northwest Territories	2 out of a possible 3 (67%)	0	Full funding for hospitals and travel grants
Nunavut	1 out of a possible 1 (100%)	0	Full funding for hospitals and travel grants

Source: Shaw, 2006; Childbirth by Choice Trust, 2003.

IN FOCUS 7.2

A History of Abortion in Canada: Focus on Dr. Henry Morgentaler

Canada currently has no abortion legislation, and abortion is legal in Canada. However, this has not always been the case. For example, from 1969 to 1988 women could only obtain a legal abortion under certain restricted circumstances. Under this law, many women were not able to get legal abortions. Dr. Henry Morgentaler has been instrumental in bringing changes to Canada's abortion laws through a campaign of civil disobedience.

Henry Morgentaler was born in Poland in 1923. Both his parents were killed by the Nazis, and he himself was interned in two concentration camps before being liberated by U.S. forces. He immigrated to Canada and graduated with a degree in medicine from l'Université de Montréal in 1953. In 1955, he opened a general medical practice. At first, Dr. Morgentaler refused to perform abortions. However, in 1968, in violation of Canadian law, moved by the desperation of some of his poor female patients with unwanted pregnancies, he opened his first abortion clinic in Montreal. He believed that the abortion law was unjust and harmed women. At the time, physicians convicted of performing an abortion could receive a life sentence.

In 1973, he started a campaign of civil disobedience in order to challenge Canada's abortion laws and provide Canadian women with access to safe legal abortions. At the same time, in his clinics, he developed the vacuum-suction method for performing abortions; this is the procedure that is used for 97 percent of abortions in Canada today. Dr. Morgentaler was charged several times between 1973 and 1986, and was acquitted by juries in Quebec, Ontario, and Manitoba. However, he spent 10 months in Quebec prisons in 1975–1976, after the Quebec Court of Appeal overturned his jury acquittal and substituted a guilty verdict. (It is no longer legal for an appeal court to substitute a guilty verdict for a jury acquittal, due to this case.)

In 1988, after this series of court cases, the Supreme Court of Canada struck down Canada's abortion law as unconstitutional, calling it the "Morgentaler Decision." This decision effectively decriminalized abortion in Canada and provided most women with easier

Figure 7.15 Dr. Henry Morgentaler, who was instrumental in decriminalizing abortion in Canada. Legal challenges against Morgentaler began in 1970 and ended in 1988 when the Supreme Court of Canada found that the section of the Criminal Code dealing with abortion was unconstitutional.

access to a legal abortion should they want one. In June 2005, he was awarded his first honorary degree by the University of Western Ontario, and he was awarded the Order of Canada in 2008. It's because of the actions of Dr. Morgentaler that abortion is legal in Canada. He is still fighting to increase woman's access to abortion through legal action against provincial governments who refuse to fund abortions performed in clinics.

Sources: Library and Archives Canada, 2007.

Table 7.3 Abortion Rates around the World*

Country	Number of Abortions per Year	Abortion Rate*	Abortion Ratio*
Australia	63 200	16.6	20.4
Bulgaria	119 900	64.7	50.7
Canada	100 100	14.6	22.9
China	10 394 500	38.8	31.4
India[†]	588 400	3.0	2.2
Israel[†]	15 500	16.2	13.5
Italy[†]	191 500	15.3	25.7
Japan[†]	497 800	18.6	27.0
South Korea	528 000	53.0	43.0
Sweden	34 700	19.8	24.9
USSR[†]	6 818 000	111.9	54.9
U.S.	1 588 600	28.0	29.7
Vietnam[†]	170 600	14.6	8.2

*"*Abortion* rate" is the number of abortions per 1000 women aged 15 to 44. "Abortion ratio" is the number of abortions per 100 known pregnancies.

[†]*Data* from outside of Canada are from 1989 and are of unknown accuracy.

Sources: Stanley K. Henshaw, 1990, 76–89. Canadian data are from Statistics Canada, 2007. Data are from 2004.

such as picketing outside abortion clinics or the homes of physicians who provide abortions, has discouraged some physicians from providing abortion services. There is good reason for them to be fearful. At least three Canadian physicians have been wounded in their homes by snipers, and the Toronto Morgentaler clinic was destroyed by a firebomb in 1992.

In other countries, policies on abortion vary widely. Abortion is legal and widely practised in Russia and Japan, parts of eastern and central Europe, and South America. The use of abortion in the developing nations of Africa and Asia is limited because of the scarcity of medical facilities and many women in these countries undergo unsafe abortions. The World Health Organization estimates that there are 19 million unsafe abortions each year, and that 68 000 women die as a result (WHO, 2004). Table 7.3 gives rates of abortion in various countries including Canada. The Canadian abortion rate has remained fairly stable over the past decade (Statistics Canada, 2006).

This section is about methods of abortion and the psychological aspects of abortion; the ethical aspects will be discussed in Chapter 20 on the Online Learning Centre.

ABORTION PROCEDURES

Several methods of abortion are available; which one is used depends on how far the pregnancy has progressed.

VACUUM ASPIRATION

The **vacuum aspiration method** (also called *vacuum suction* or *vacuum curettage*) can be performed during the first trimester of pregnancy and up to 14 weeks' gestation. It is done on an outpatient basis with a local anaesthetic. The procedure itself takes only about 10 minutes, and the woman stays in the doctor's office, clinic, or hospital for a few hours. It is the most widely used abortion procedure in Canada today, accounting for 97 percent of abortions (Statistics Canada, 1995).

Vacuum aspiration: A method of abortion that is performed during the first trimester and involves suctioning out the contents of the uterus.

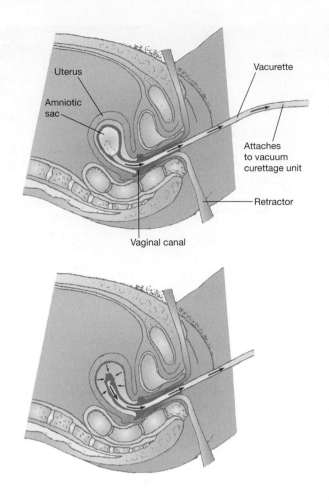

Uterus

Amniotic sac

Vacurette

Attaches to vacuum curettage unit

Retractor

Vaginal canal

Figure 7.16 A vacuum aspiration abortion.

The woman is prepared as she would be for a pelvic exam, and an instrument is inserted into the vagina; the instrument dilates (stretches open) the opening of the cervix. A tube is then inserted into this opening until one end is in the uterus (see Figure 7.16). The other end is attached to a suction-producing apparatus and the contents of the uterus, including the fetal tissue, are sucked out.

Vacuum aspiration has become the most common method of early (first trimester) abortion because it is simple and entails little risk. There are rare risks of uterine perforation, infection, hemorrhaging, and failure to remove all the fetal material.

DILATION AND EVACUATION

Dilation and evacuation (D and E) is similar to vacuum aspiration, but it must be done in a hospital under a general anaesthetic. It is used especially for later abortions, from 14 to 24 weeks' gestation (Autry et al., 2002). It is somewhat similar to vacuum aspiration, but it is more complicated because the fetus is relatively large by the second trimester.

INDUCED LABOUR

During the late part of the second trimester, abortion is usually performed by inducing labour and a miscarriage. The most commonly used version of this method is the saline-induced abortion. A fine tube is inserted through the abdomen into the amniotic sac and saline solution is injected. Within several hours, the solution causes labour to begin. A variation on this

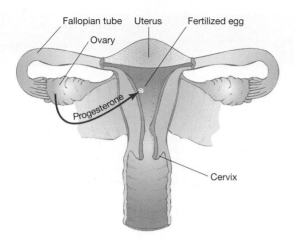

Progesterone, a hormone produced by the ovaries, is necessary for the implantation and development of a fertilized egg.

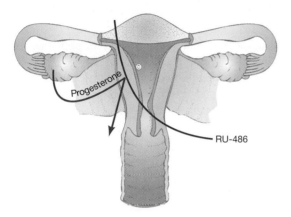

Taken early in pregnancy, RU-486 blocks the action of progesterone and makes the body react as if it isn't pregnant.

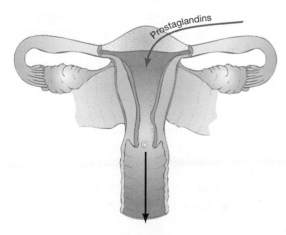

Prostaglandins, taken two days later, cause the uterus to contract and the cervix to soften and dilate. As a result, the embryo is expelled in 97% of the cases.

Figure 7.17 How RU-486, or mifepristone, works.

technique is the prostaglandin abortion. Prostaglandins (hormonelike substances that cause contractions) are injected and cause labour. Misoprostol can also be used to induce labour for second-trimester abortions (Autry et al., 2002).

Induced labour is used for abortion only if pregnancy has progressed late into the second trimester, and accounts for only 1 percent of abortions in Canada (Statistics Canada, 1995). This method is both more hazardous and more costly than the previous methods.

HYSTEROTOMY

Hysterotomy is a surgical method of abortion that can be done from 16 to 24 weeks after the woman's last menstrual period. Essentially, a Caesarean section is performed, and the fetus is removed. Hysterotomy is more serious and more expensive than the other methods, and there is greater risk of complications. It is done only rarely, but it may be used if the pregnancy has progressed to the late second trimester and the woman's health is such that the induction methods should not be used.

MIFEPRISTONE

In 1986 French researchers announced the development of a new drug called **RU-486** or **mifepristone** (Couzinet et al., 1986; Ulmann et al., 1990). It can induce a very early abortion. It has a powerful antiprogesterone effect, causing the endometrium of the uterus to be sloughed off and thus bringing about an abortion (see Figure 7.17). It is administered as a tablet followed two days later by a small dose of prostaglandin (misoprostol), which increases contractions of the uterus, helping to expel the embryo. It is used within ten days of an expected but missed menstrual period. Research shows that it is effective in 92 to 96 percent of cases when combined with prostaglandin (Silvestre et al., 1990; Spitz et al., 1998; Ulmann et al., 1990). It is most effective when the woman has been

Hysterotomy: A surgical method of abortion done in the late second trimester.

RU-486 (mifepristone): The "abortion pill."

IN FOCUS 7.3

Abortion in Cross-Cultural Perspective

Beliefs about abortion show dramatic variation in different cultures around the world. The following is a sampling from two very different cultures.

Ekiti Yoruba

The Ekiti Yoruba, many of whom have a high school or post-secondary education, live in southwest Nigeria. For them, abortion is not a distinct category from contraception but rather is on a continuum with it (Renne, 1996).

Traditionally in the Ekiti Yoruba culture, the ideal was for a woman to have as many children as possible, spaced at two- to three-year intervals. The spacing of children is made possible by a period of sexual abstinence for two years postpartum. The Ekiti Yoruba believe that sexual intercourse while a woman is still breast-feeding a baby causes illness or death to the child; men whose children have died in infancy have been blamed for breaking the postpartum sex taboo and causing the death. Because of the high value placed on fertility, use of contraceptives and abortion must be kept secret. Even though condoms, foam, and birth control pills are available at a local clinic, few people take advantage of the service because they would not want others to know that they engaged in such practices. Abortion then becomes the chief method of birth control. Estimates are that between 200 000 and 500 000 pregnancies are aborted each year in Nigeria and that about 10 000 women die each year from botched abortions.

If a woman has an unwanted pregnancy, she generally will consult a local divine healer or herbalist first, in order to "keep the pregnancy from staying." They generally provide pills or substances to insert in the vagina. If the treatment does not work, the woman then goes to a clinic and has a dilation and curettage (D&C; a procedure that is similar to D&E) abortion.

Women who abort generally fall into two categories: single high school or post-secondary students who want to finish their education, and married women who are pregnant because of an affair. Here is one woman's story:

> In 1991, when awaiting entrance into university, I became pregnant by one boyfriend whom I later decided not to marry in favor of another. Since I did not want my chosen fiancé to know of the pregnancy, I decided to abort it. I first used 3 Bee-codeine tablets, Andrew's Liver Salt, and Sprite, mixing them together and then drinking them. When this did not work, I went to a clinic in a neighboring town for D&C. The abortion cost N80 and was paid for by my boyfriend. There were no aftereffects. (Renne, 1996, p. 487)

The ease with which Ekiti Yoruba people rely on abortion is related in part to their understanding of prenatal development. Many believe that the "real child" is not formed until after the fourth month of pregnancy, and before that the being is lizard-like.

Greece

Birth control for women was legalized in Greece only in 1980, and abortion was not legalized until 1986. Yet Greece has had a sharply declining birth rate since World War II, accounted for, in large part, by abortion (Georges, 1996). Among European nations, Greece is unique in its combination of very little use of medical contraception, a low fertility rate, and the highest abortion rate in Europe.

Three powerful institutions—the government, the Greek Orthodox Church, and the medical profession—have exerted a strong pronatalist (in favour of having babies) influence. The Greek Orthodox Church equates abortion with murder and prohibits all methods of birth control except fertility awareness methods and abstinence. The government, for its part, encourages large families by a variety of measures, including paying a monthly subsidy to families with more than three children, making daycare centres widely available, and keeping female methods of contraception illegal (until 1980). Despite all this, Greek women achieved a low fertility rate, which is regarded by the government as a threat to the Greek "race," Greek Orthodoxy, and the military strength of Greece in relation to hostile neighbours, such as the extremely fertile Turks.

Despite the illegality of abortion in Greece until 1986, abortion was widespread and a very open secret. Abortions were not back-alley affairs but rather were performed by gynecologists in private offices. Physicians, as members of a powerful and prestigious profession, were successful at legal evasion. As a result, Greek women did not have to face the life-threatening risks that occur with illegal abortion in other countries. They had access to safe illegal abortion.

Why is there so much reliance on abortion and so little access to contraception in this modern European nation? As noted earlier, the Greek Orthodox Church opposes all medical contraception and the Greek government kept contraception illegal until 1980. But even then, contraception did not become widespread. In 1990, only 2 percent of women of reproductive age were using the pill. Some blame this on the medical profession, which is thought to block access to contraception in order to continue a thriving abortion practice that is more lucrative. Greek women, too, resist contraception. They distinguish between "contraception" (such as birth control pills) and "being careful" (withdrawal and condoms). They reject contraception, but being careful—especially the use of withdrawal—is widespread. Fertility awareness methods are not widely used and would not be very successful if they were, since Greek women commonly believe that they are most fertile for the four to seven days just before and after the menstrual period. The mass media have spread scare messages about the pill, and many women believe that it causes cancer.

How do Greek women, the great majority of whom are Orthodox, deal with the contradiction between their church's teaching—that abortion is murder and that a woman who has had an abortion may not receive communion—and their actual practice of having abortions? First, the Greek Orthodox Church is not as absolutist in its application of doctrines regarding abortion as the Roman Catholic Church is. Some attribute this to the fact that Orthodox priests can be married and are therefore more in touch with the realities of family life. In some cases, women do abstain from receiving communion following an abortion but then later make a confession to the priest. Priests typically are forgiving.

In Greece, motherhood is highly esteemed and idealized, yet abortion is not considered contradictory to the high value placed on motherhood. Good motherhood today is thought to require an intense investment of time and energy in one's children; by definition, then, the good mother limits family size, and abortion is a means to achieve that goal.

Cross-Cultural Patterns

Several patterns emerge from the study of abortion in these quite distinct cultures and other cultures (e.g., Gursoy, 1996; Johnson et al., 1996; Rigdon, 1996; Rylko-Bauer, 1996). First, no matter how strict the prohibitions against abortion, some women in all cultures choose and manage to obtain abortions. Second, the meaning of abortion is constructed in any particular culture based on factors such as beliefs about prenatal development, when life starts, and how much large families are valued. Third, the legality and morality of abortion in any culture is determined in part by political forces, such as the Greek government's desire to expand the size of the Greek population.

Sources: Georges, 1996; Gursoy, 1996; Johnson et al., 1996; Renne, 1996; Rigdon, 1996; Rylko-Bauer, 1996.

pregnant less than 49 days. Early research has found little evidence of side effects, although the woman experiences some cramping as the uterine contents are expelled.

In France today, more than half of women who decide to terminate an early pregnancy choose RU-486 rather than conventional abortion methods (Jones & Hensha, 2002). RU-486 is also widely used in Britain, Sweden, China, and the United States. RU-486 is not yet available in Canada.

Scientists who developed mifepristone, as well as pro-choice groups, prefer not to call it an abortion method, but rather a method for the induction of menstruation or a contragestational drug. It cannot properly be called a contraceptive because it prevents gestation, not conception. Mifepristone and the drug discussed next, methotrexate, are referred to as medical methods of abortion, compared with the more traditional surgical methods.

METHOTREXATE

Another alternative in drug-induced early abortion involves the use of a combination of the drug methotrexate, which is toxic to the embryo, with misoprostol, which causes uterine contractions that expel the dead embryo (Hausknecht, 1995). Both of these drugs are already widely used for treatment of other diseases and so are available to be used for medical abortions. Like mifepristone, they permit the early induction of abortion in a physician's office rather than an abortion clinic or hospital. Methotrexate is also used to treat ectopic pregnancy, which is a life-threatening condition.

PSYCHOLOGICAL ASPECTS

The discovery of an unwanted pregnancy triggers a complicated set of emotions, as well as a complex decision-making process. Initially women tend to feel anger and some anxiety. They then embark on the decision-making process studied by psychologist Carol Gilligan (1982). In this process women essentially weigh the need to think of themselves and protect their own welfare against the need to think of the welfare of the fetus. Even focusing only on the welfare of the fetus can lead to conflicting conclusions: Should I complete the pregnancy because the fetus has a right to life or should I have an abortion because the fetus has a right to be born into a stable family with two parents who have completed their education and can provide good financial support? Many women in Gilligan's study showed considerable psychological growth over the period in which they wrestled with these issues and made their decision.

Is there a post-abortion syndrome? Anti-abortion activists claim that women are psychologically traumatized by having an abortion (Bazelon, 2007). What do the scientific data say? The best scientific evidence indicates that most women do not experience severe negative psychological responses to abortion (Lewis 1997; Major et al., 2000; Schmiege & Russo, 2005). When women are interviewed a year or so after their abortion, most show good adjustment. Typically, they do not feel guilt or sorrow over the decision. Instead, they report feeling relieved, satisfied, and relatively happy, and say that if they had the decision to make over again, they would do the same thing. Nonetheless, some women benefit from talking about their experience, and it is important that post-abortion support groups be available (Lewis, 1997). This may be particularly true of women who have had one or more abortions in the past. An Ontario study found that women who were undergoing repeat abortions were significantly more likely to have experienced physical and sexual violence from a male partner and to have a history of child sexual abuse (Fisher et al., 2005).

Research in this area raises many interesting questions. Women generally show good adjustment after having an abortion, but good adjustment compared with what? That is, what is the appropriate control or comparison group? One comparison group that could be studied is women who requested an abortion but were denied it. It would be important to know the consequences for their adjustment.

One group that has been studied is children who were born because an abortion request was denied. It is impossible to do this research in Canada now because abortion has been legal since 1988. However, in some other countries access to abortion depends upon obtaining official approval. One such country was the former Czechoslovakia. Researchers followed up 220 children born to women denied abortion (the study group) and 220 children born to women who had not requested abortion; the children were studied when they were nine years old and again when they were 14 to 16 years old, 21 to 23, 30, and 35 (David et al., 2003). By age 14, 43 children from the study group, but only 30 of the controls, had been referred for counselling. Although there were no differences between the groups in tested intelligence, children in the study group did less well in school and were more likely to drop out. Teachers described them as less sociable and more hyperactive compared with the control group. At age 16, the boys (but not the girls) in the study group more frequently rated themselves as feeling neglected or rejected by their mothers, and felt that their mothers were less satisfied with them. By their early 20s, the study group reported less job satisfaction, more conflicts with co-workers and supervisors, and fewer and less satisfying friendships. Several other studies have found results similar to the Czech one (David et al., 2003). These results point to the serious long-term consequences for some children whose mothers would have preferred to have an abortion.

MEN AND ABORTION

Only women become pregnant, and only women have abortions, but where do men enter the picture? Do they have a right to contribute to the decision to have an abortion? What are their feelings about abortion?

A recent Swedish study surveyed 75 men ranging in age from 18 to 50 who were involved in legal abortion (Kero et al., 1999). The majority were in a long-term relationship with the pregnant woman. Among the men, 64 percent indicated that they wanted the woman to have an abortion; 27 percent felt that it was the woman's decision. The main reasons why these men wanted an abortion were related to family planning, such as conflict with life plans (e.g., schooling), feeling unable to offer a child a caring environment, or socioeconomic reasons. The second most common reason was feeling that their relationship with the woman was not stable. What were these men's reactions to the abortion? The most common words the men used to describe their feelings were *anxiety, responsibility, guilt, relief,* and *grief.* That is, more than half the men expressed both positive and negative emotions about the abortion.

Although counselling for women undergoing abortion is a standard procedure, counselling is rarely available for the men who are involved. These findings suggest that many men also need such counselling (see, for example, Cayle & Enright, 1997).

SUMMARY

Table 7.4 provides a comparative summary of the various methods of birth control discussed in this chapter.

Table 7.4   Summary of Information on Methods of Contraception and Abortion

Method	Effectiveness Rating	Failure Rate, Perfect Use,%	Failure Rate, Typical Use,%	Death Rate (per 100 000 Women)	Yearly Costs, $*	Advantages	Disadvantages
Depo-Provera	Excellent	0.3	3		170	Requires less remembering	
Combination birth control pills	Excellent	0.3	8	1.6	0–300	Highly effective; not used at time of coitus; improved menstrual cycles	Cost; possible side effects; must take daily
Patch	Excellent	0.3	1.3		0–430	Requires less remembering than the pill	
NuvaRing	Excellent	0.5	5	—	240		
IUD, Copper T	Excellent	0.6	0.8	1.0	30–175‡	Requires no remembering or motivation	May be expelled
Progesterone T	Excellent	0.1	0.1				
Condom, male	Very good	2	15	1.7	75*	Easy to use; protection from STIs	Used at time of coitus; continual expense
Condom, female	Good	5	21	2.0	375*	Protection from STIs	Awkward
Diaphragm/Lea with spermicide	Good	6	16	2.0§	100*	No side effects; inexpensive	Aesthetic objections
FemCap with spermicide							
Parous women	Fair	26	32	2.0§	100*	No side effects; inexpensive	—
Nulliparous women	Good	9	16	2.0§			
Spermicides	Fair	18	29	2.0§	50*	Easy to use; availability	Messy; continual expense
Withdrawal	Good	4	27	2.0	None	No cost	Requires high motivation
Fertility awareness	Poor to Fair	2–9	25	2.0§	None	No cost	Requires high motivation, prolonged abstinence; not all women can use
Unprotected intercourse	Poor	85	85	9§	None¶		
Legal abortion, first trimester	Excellent	0	0	0.5	0–750**	Available when other methods fail	Expense; moral or psychological unacceptability
Sterilization, male	Excellent	0.10	0.15	0.3	0–100***	Permanent; highly effective	Permanence
Sterilization, female	Excellent	0.5	0.5	1.5	None	Permanent; highly effective	Permanence

*Based on 150 acts of intercourse.
‡Based on a cost of $175 for the IUD and the assumption that the IUD will be used for two years.
§Based on the death rate for pregnancies resulting from the method. Of every 100 000 live births, 12 women die (Cheng \et al., 2003).
¶But having a baby is expensive.
**All hospital abortions are covered by Medicare. Only Newfoundland, Quebec, Ontario, Manitoba, Alberta, and British Columbia cover abortions done in free-standing clinics.
***Although vasectomy is covered by Medicare, in some provinces there is an additional fee for those done in doctors' offices.
Source: R. A. Hatcher et al., 2004.

QUESTIONS FOR THOUGHT, DISCUSSION, AND DEBATE

1. Do you think you are an erotophobe or an erotophile? In what ways do you think your erotophobia or erotophilia has affected or will affect your use of birth control?

2. Debate the following topic. Resolved: The birth control pill is a safe and effective method of birth control for most women.

3. In Canada, few IUDs are available because of lawsuits against companies that make them and concern over possible health risks. In contrast, in the People's Republic of China they are the mainstay of contraception, with 40 million in use. Which country has the better policy?

4. On your campus, as on all campuses, students probably are inconsistent in their use of birth control or use nothing even though they are engaging in sexual intercourse. Design a program to improve birth control practices on your campus.

5. Knowing that you are taking a human sexuality course and have gained a lot of expertise, Nicole, your best friend, comes to you in a state of crisis. She and her boyfriend had unprotected intercourse last night and she is terrified that she is pregnant. What options would you explain to her, and which one would you recommend?

SUGGESTIONS FOR FURTHER READING

Society of Obstetricians and Gynaecologists of Canada. (2006). *Sex sense*. 2nd ed. Ottawa. This book was developed by the Society of Obstetricians and Gynaecologists of Canada to provide practical information about all the questions people might have about the various contraceptive options available in Canada. It is user friendly and practical, containing helpful tables and illustrations.

Hatcher, Robert A., et al. (2004). *Contraceptive technology*. 18th ed. New York: Ardent Media. This authoritative book is updated frequently and provides the most recent information on all methods of contraception.

Ulmann, André, Teutsch, Georges, and Philibert, Daniel. (1990 June). RU-486. *Scientific American, 262*, 42–48. An interesting, behind-the-scenes article by three of the French scientists involved in the development of RU-486 (mifepristone).

For review questions, web resources, and other learning and study tools, visit the *Understanding Human Sexuality* Online Learning Centre at www.mcgrawhill.ca/olc/hyde.

SEXUALLY TRANSMITTED INFECTIONS

Chapter Highlights

Chlamydia
Symptoms
Treatment
Prevention?

HPV
Diagnosis
Treatment
Vaccine

Genital Herpes
Symptoms
Treatment
Long-Term Consequences
Psychological Aspects: Coping with
Herpes

HIV Infection and AIDS
An Epidemic?
Transmission
The Virus
The Disease
Diagnosis
Treatment
Women, Children, Ethnic Minorities,
and AIDS
Psychological Considerations in AIDS
Recent Progress in AIDS Research

Gonorrhea
Symptoms
Diagnosis
Treatment

Syphilis
Symptoms
Diagnosis
Treatment
Elimination of Syphilis?

Viral Hepatitis

Trichomoniasis

Pubic Lice

Preventing STIs

Other Genital Infections
Monilia
Cystitis
Prostatitis

MARIA AND LOUIS GET HOME AFTER AN EVENING ON THE TOWN AND ENTER THE HOUSE HUNGRY FOR PASSION. THE TWO EMBRACE, CLINGING TO EACH OTHER, LONGING FOR EACH OTHER. LOUIS SLOWLY UNDRESSES MARIA, HUNGRY FOR THE SILKY FLESH HE FEELS BENEATH HIM. AS THEIR PASSION GROWS, SHE BEGINS REACHING FOR HIM, RIPPING HIS CLOTHES OFF AS SHE EXPLORES HIS BODY WITH HER TONGUE. AS LOUIS GETS MORE AND MORE EXCITED, MARIA RIPS A CONDOM PACKAGE OPEN WITH HER TEETH AND SLOWLY SLIDES THE CONDOM OVER LOUIS'S ERECT PENIS. AFTER AN HOUR OF INCREDIBLE LOVEMAKING, LOUIS, EXHAUSTED WITH PLEASURE, TURNS TO MARIA AND SAYS, "YOU WERE RIGHT, THE BEST SEX IS SAFER SEX WITH LATEX!"*

As noted in Chapter 1, according to the World Health Organization, sexual health is a state of physical, emotional, mental, and social well-being related to sexuality. One aspect of this is the absence of disease, and sexually transmitted infections (STIs) are an example. Not only do STIs affect an individual's physical sexual health, but the psychological aspects of dealing with an STI also may challenge the emotional, mental, and social aspects of one's sexual health and well-being. In keeping with the Public Health Agency of Canada, we use the term STI rather than STD (sexually transmitted disease). STD refers only to infections causing symptoms. STI is more encompassing because it includes infections for which people have symptoms as well as those for which they have no symptoms—that is, are asymptomatic.

The sexual scene is not the same as it was 30 years ago. Genital warts and AIDS pose real threats. We need to do many things to combat these dangers. One is that we must rewrite our sexual scripts, as the quotation above illustrates. We also need to inform ourselves, and the goal of this chapter is to provide you with the important information you need to make decisions about your sexual activity.[1]

Your health is very important, and a good way to harm it or cause yourself suffering is to have an untreated sexually transmitted infection. Although in 1997 it appeared that there would be a continuing gradual decline in the rates of many STIs, this trend has not continued and there has been an increase in the incidence of newly acquired STIs in Canada (MacDonald & Wong, 2007). Consequently, it is very important to know the symptoms of the various kinds of STIs so that you can seek treatment if you develop any of them. Also, there are some ways to prevent STIs or at least reduce your chances of getting them, and these are certainly worth knowing about. Finally, after you have read some of the statistics on how many people contract STIs every year and on your chances of getting one, you may want to modify your sexual behaviour somewhat. If you love, love wisely.

One of the most disturbing things about the STI epidemic in Canada is that it disproportionately affects teens and young adults. For example, of 65 949 new cases of chlamydia that occurred in 2006 in Canada, 42 663 (65 percent) were among people between the ages of 15 and 24. For people in this age group, three infections—human papillomavirus, trichomoniasis, and chlamydia—account for the great majority of cases, although of these only chlamydia is a reportable infection. Worldwide, of the 60 million people who have been infected with HIV, about half became infected between the ages of 15 and 24 (Kiragu et al., 2001).

*From a student essay.

[1]The diagnosis and treatment of sexually transmitted infections is an area of furiously active research. New discoveries are announced almost monthly. Therefore, by the time you read this book, some of the statements in this chapter may have been superseded by newer research.

Prevention efforts, including sexuality education for youth, clearly must be accorded a higher priority than they have been in the past.

The STIs are presented in this chapter in the following order. First we look at three—chlamydia, HPV (genital warts), and herpes—that are all quite frequent among university students. Following that is a discussion of HIV infection and AIDS, which is less common among university students but is one of the world's major public-health problems and is generating an enormous amount of research. Next we discuss gonorrhea, syphilis, viral hepatitis, and trichomoniasis. Then comes not an infection but a bug, the pubic louse. After a practical section on preventing STIs, the chapter ends with a section about various other genital infections that, for the most part, are not sexually transmitted.

Many statistics throughout this chapter are taken from the Centre for Infectious Disease Prevention and Control (CIDPC) on the Public Health Agency of Canada (PHAC) website: www.phac-aspc.gc.ca. Data from the CIDPC are used so frequently throughout the chapter that we do not provide a citation every time. Information on STIs changes quickly, so to get the most up-to-date information, check the website. Only some but not all STIs must be reported. Therefore, there are no national data on some of the most common STIs, such as genital herpes and HPV (human papillomavirus).

Some STIs are caused by *bacteria*, some are caused by *viruses*, and a few are caused by other organisms. The distinction between bacterial infections and viral infections is important because bacterial infections can be cured using antibiotics. Viral infections cannot be cured but they can be treated to reduce symptoms. Chlamydia, gonorrhea, and syphilis are all caused by bacteria. Herpes, HIV/AIDS, genital warts, and hepatitis B are caused by viruses.

One final note before we proceed: There are a lot of illustrations in this chapter showing the symptoms of various STIs, and some of the photos may make you say "Nasty!" These illustrations are in the chapter not to scare you, but rather to help you recognize the symptoms of STIs. You should know what herpes blisters look like, for example, in case you spot them on a prospective sexual partner and in case they appear on you. However, you should consult your physician if you see a change in your genitals, even if it does not look like any of the pictures in this book.

CHLAMYDIA

Chlamydia (klah-MIH-dee-uh): An organism causing a sexually transmitted infection; the symptoms in males are a thin, clear discharge and mild pain on urination; females are frequently asymptomatic.

Chlamydia trachomatis is a bacterium that is spread by sexual contact and infects the genital organs of both males and females. Chlamydia has become the most prevalent bacterial sexually transmitted infection in Canada. The CIDPC reports that there were 43 590 reported cases in women and 22 276 reported cases in men in 2006. This is a rate of 202 cases per 100 000 people in the population, the most common reported STI in Canada. Health Canada has set a national goal of 50 cases per 100 000 population by 2010, but instead of going down, the rate of chlamydia has been rising steadily since 1997. Adolescent girls have a particularly high rate of infection, more than five times the national rate. When a man consults a physician because of a urethral discharge, his chances of having chlamydia are greater than his chances of having gonorrhea. It is important that the correct diagnosis be made since chlamydia does not respond to the drugs used to cure gonorrhea.

SYMPTOMS

The main symptoms in men are a thin, usually clear discharge and mild discomfort on urination appearing 7 to 14 days after infection. The symptoms are somewhat similar to the symptoms of gonorrhea in the male. However, gonorrhea tends to produce more painful urination and a more profuse, puslike discharge. Diagnosis is made from a urine sample in men and from a sample of cells from the cervix (or urine sample) in women. Tests are then used to detect the bacterium. Unfortunately, 75 percent of the cases of chlamydia infection are asymptomatic in women. This means that the woman never goes to a clinic for treatment, and she goes undiagnosed and untreated. The consequences of untreated chlamydia in women are discussed in the next section. Even among men, 50 percent of the cases are asymptomatic.

TREATMENT

Chlamydia is quite curable. It is treated with azithromycin or doxycycline; it does not respond to penicillin. Poorly treated or undiagnosed cases may lead to a number of complications: urethral damage, epididymitis (infection of the epididymis), Reiter's syndrome,[2] and proctitis in men who have had anal intercourse. Women with untreated or undiagnosed chlamydia may experience serious complications if not treated: pelvic inflammatory disease (PID) and possibly infertility due to scarring of the fallopian tubes (Health Canada, 1998). A baby born to an infected mother may develop pneumonia or an eye infection.

PREVENTION?

Scientists doing research on chlamydia have a major goal of developing a vaccine that would prevent infection (Berry et al., 2004). Vaccines have been developed that are effective in mice, but certain technical obstacles prevent their use with humans. An effective vaccine for humans should be available in the next decade.

Until a vaccine is available, one of the most effective tools for prevention is screening. The problem with chlamydia is that so many infected people are asymptomatic and spread the disease unknowingly. In screening programs, asymptomatic carriers are identified, treated, and cured so that they do not continue to spread the disease. More asymptomatic females are being tested routinely. However, far fewer men than women are screened, even though it is important to screen both men and women if screening is to be effective at reducing the prevalence of chlamydia (McKay, 2006).

In an innovative program in the United States, high school girls attending a school health clinic (not necessarily for STIs) collected vaginal swabs themselves, and the swabs were subjected to laboratory tests (Wiesenfeld et al., 2001). Overall, 18 percent of the girls were infected with something: 10 percent had trichomoniasis, 8 percent had chlamydia, and 2 percent had gonorrhea. None had symptoms, so these cases would have gone undetected. About half said that they would never have had a gynecological exam to get a test—yet they agreed to self-collection of vaginal swabs. This method is promising for screening teens.

On an individual level, the best method of prevention is the consistent use of a condom.

HPV

HPV stands for human papillomavirus. There are many different types of HPV; some cause genital warts, others cause cervical cancer and other genital cancers, and some have no symptoms at all. Genital warts are cauliflower-like warts appearing on the genitals, usually around the urethral opening of the penis, the shaft of the penis, or the scrotum in the male, and on the vulva, the walls of the vagina, or the cervix in the female; warts may also occur on the anus. Typically they appear three to eight months after intercourse with an infected person. The majority of people infected with HPV, however, are asymptomatic. A person without symptoms can still transmit the virus.

Infection with HPV is widespread. Although HPV is not a reportable disease and thus there are no national Canadian data, Health Canada estimates that between 20 and 33 percent of women have HPV; between 11 and 25 percent of women have the cancer-causing

---

[2]Reiter's syndrome involves the following symptoms: urethritis, eye inflammations, and arthritis.

types of HPV. Two studies tested women having routine Pap tests in Newfoundland and Ontario (Ratnam et al., 2000; Sellors et al., 2000). They found that the highest rate of HPV was among women under 25—16 percent of the young Newfoundland women and 24 percent of the young Ontario women had HPV infections. The disease is highly infectious and although condoms reduce the risk of infection, they do not eliminate it. HPV is transmitted through skin-to-skin contact most often from contact with the penis, scrotum, vagina, vulva or anus of the infected person.

HPV causes almost all cases of cervical cancer (Health Canada, 2007). In fact, there are 30 distinct types of HPV that are sexually transmitted. Some types cause genital warts and are called low risk because they do not cause cancer. Other types sharply increase the risk of cervical cancer and are called high-risk types. HPV 16 and 18 account for 70 percent of the cases of cervical cancer (Dailard, 2006). HPV infection is also associated with cancer of the penis and anus (Health Canada, 2000).

New research shows that oral sex can transmit HPV. Individuals infected this way have an increased rate of oral cancers—that is, cancer of the mouth or throat (Herrero et al., 2003; Kreimer et al., 2004).

DIAGNOSIS

Diagnosis can sometimes be made simply by inspecting the warts, because their appearance is distinctive. However, some strains of warts are flat and less obvious. Also, the warts may grow inside the vagina and may not be detected there. However, HPV is a "silent infection" because many individuals with HPV show no obvious signs of infection. Thus, for many women the first indication of HPV is abnormal cells on a Pap test. Men are not routinely tested for HPV. One new test involves analysis of the DNA from a sample of cells taken from the cervix, vagina, or other area of suspected infection and tests directly for the presence of HPV, but it may not be covered by provincial health plans.

TREATMENT

Several treatments for genital warts are available. Chemicals such as podophyllin (Podofilm) or trichloroacetic acid can be applied directly to the warts. Aldara can also be used and can be self-administered. Typically, these treatments have to be repeated several times, and the warts then fall off. With cryotherapy (often using liquid nitrogen), the warts are frozen off; again, it is typically necessary to apply more than one treatment. Laser therapy can also be used to destroy the warts. Many cases of HPV infection go away on their own, but

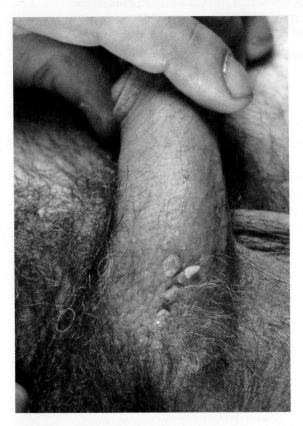

(a)

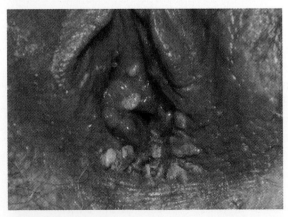

(b)

Figure 8.1   Genital warts *(a)* on the penis, and *(b)* on the vulva.

others persist for long periods. In one study of university women, HPV infection lasted, on average, only eight months (Ho et al., 1998). The duration of infection was longer with older women, and the risk of cervical cancer increases with longer infections.

VACCINE

As noted, almost all cases of cervical cancer are linked to HPV infection. Therefore, a vaccine against HPV would prevent most cases of cervical cancer. Such a vaccine is now available in Canada. The vaccine is called Gardasil and must be administered in three shots over a six-month period. Use of the vaccine does not affect existing infections; therefore, the National Advisory Committee on Immunization recommends it be administered to girls between the ages of 9 and 13—that is, before they have engaged in sexual intercourse—as well as for women between the ages of 14 and 26 who have not had an HPV infection or abnormalities on their Pap tests. The vaccine protects against HPV types 16 and 18, the ones associated with cervical cancer, as well as two other types that cause most cases of genital warts, which would also be nice to avoid. Randomized controlled trials show the vaccine to be highly effective (Villa et al., 2006).

Several Canadian provinces have school-based programs in place to administer the vaccine to girls in grade 6, 7, or 8 with parental consent. The vaccine is free. However, it is not without controversy. Some parents argue that it will encourage young girls to engage in sexual activity, or that it has not been tested sufficiently to use on young girls. Advocates for administering the vaccine point out the potential health benefits and that vaccines have been around for a long time and have been shown to be safe. They argue that the decision to make Gardasil available is no different from the decision to introduce other new vaccines (e.g., a vaccine for chicken pox was just recently made available), yet there has been no controversy about those vaccines.

GENITAL HERPES

Genital herpes is a disease of the genital organs caused by the herpes simplex virus (HSV). Genital herpes is transmitted by sexual intercourse and by oral–genital sex. Two strains of HSV are circulating: HSV-1 and HSV-2. In simpler times, HSV-2 caused genital herpes and HSV-1 caused cold sores around the mouth. Today, however, there is more crossing over. Genital herpes, then, can be caused by either HSV-1 or HSV-2.

There are no national data on the number of Canadians who have herpes. However, experts estimate that more than 20 percent of Canadian adults are infected (Steben & Sacks, 1997). For example, in British Columbia the rate of HSV-2 among women is 17 percent (Patrick et al., 2000). The rate increases with age, reaching 28 percent by age 44. The rate of HSV-2 is lower among women in Ontario than in British Columbia, reaching 16 percent by age 44. Research shows that infection rates are higher among individuals who have had more sexual partners. Of those who test positive for HSV-2 in their blood, only 14 percent report having been diagnosed with herpes. Of those with HSV-1 in their blood but not HSV-2, 2 percent report having been diagnosed with genital herpes (Xu et al., 2006). That is, the great majority of people with HSV are asymptomatic and are not aware that they are infected. These persons transmit the disease to others unknowingly.

SYMPTOMS

The symptoms of genital herpes caused by HSV-2 are small, painful bumps or blisters on the genitals. In women, they are usually found on the vaginal lips; in men, they usually occur on the penis. They may be found around the anus if the person has had anal intercourse. The blisters burst and can be quite painful. Fever, painful urination, and headaches may occur.

Genital herpes (HER-pees): A sexually transmitted infection, the symptoms of which are small, painful bumps or blisters on the genitals.

HSV: The herpes simplex virus.

The blisters heal on their own in about three weeks in the first episode of infection. The virus continues to live in the body, however. It may remain dormant for the rest of the person's life. But the symptoms may recur unpredictably, so that the person repeatedly undergoes 7- to 14-day periods of sores. HSV-1 infection tends to be less severe.

People with herpes are most infectious when they are having an active outbreak. However, people are infectious even when there is no outbreak or if they have never been symptomatic. Therefore, there is no "safe" period.

TREATMENT

Unfortunately, there is not yet any known drug that kills the virus. That is, there is no cure. Researchers are pursuing two solutions: drugs that would treat symptoms in someone who is already infected, and vaccinations that would prevent herpes. The drug acyclovir (Zovirax) prevents or reduces the recurring symptoms, although it does not actually "cure" the disease.

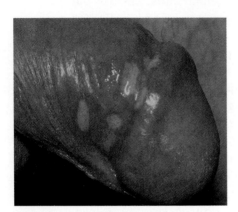

Valacyclovir (Valtrex) and famciclovir (Famvir) are newer drugs that are even more effective at shortening outbreaks and suppressing recurrences (Corey et al., 2004; Wald et al., 2006). They also reduce rates of transmission from an infected partner to an uninfected one. Scientists are actively working to create a method for immunization against herpes (Augustinova et al., 2004; Meseda et al., 2004; Milligan et al., 2004).

LONG-TERM CONSEQUENCES

Either men or women with recurrent herpes may develop complications such as meningitis or narrowing of the urethra due to scarring, leading to difficulties with urination. However, such complications do not affect the majority of those with herpes. There are two more serious long-term consequences. One is that having a herpes infection increases one's risk of becoming infected with HIV, probably because the open blisters during an outbreak make it easy for HIV to enter the body. Therefore, people who have herpes should be especially careful to use safer sex practices.

The other serious risk involves the transfer of the virus from mother to infant in childbirth, which in some cases leads to serious illness or death in the baby (Brown et al., 2005). The risk of transmission to the infant is highest in women who have recently been infected and are having their first outbreak. The risk is less with women who have had the disease longer, and is low if the woman is not having an outbreak. C-sections are therefore usually performed on women with an outbreak, but vaginal delivery is possible if there is not an outbreak.

PSYCHOLOGICAL ASPECTS: COPING WITH HERPES

The psychological consequences of herpes need to be taken as seriously as the medical consequences. The range of psychological responses is enormous. At one end of the spectrum are persons with asymptomatic herpes, who are not aware that they have the disease and are happily sexually active—and at the same time possibly unknowingly spreading the

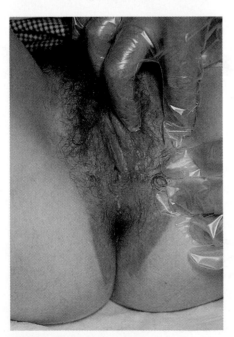

Figure 8.2 (a) Herpes blisters on the penis. (b) Herpes infection of the vulva.

disease to others. At the other end of the spectrum are persons who experience frequent, severe, painful recurrences, who feel stigmatized because of their disease, and who believe that they should abstain from sex in order to avoid infecting others. These difficulties are aggravated by the fact that outbreaks are often unpredictable, and current scientific evidence indicates that people are at least somewhat infectious even when they are not having an active outbreak. On the other hand, many people with herpes are able to cope.

Psychologists are exploring therapies for herpes patients. One highly effective treatment program consists of a combination of information on herpes, relaxation training, instruction in stress management, and instruction in an imagery technique in which the patient imagines that the genitals are free of lesions and that he or she is highly resistant to the virus (Longo et al., 1988). (See Ebel, 1994, for an excellent book on living with herpes.)

HIV INFECTION AND AIDS

In 1981, a physician in Los Angeles reported a mysterious and frightening new disease identified in several gay men. The first AIDS case in Canada was reported in February 1982. Within two years, the number of cases had escalated sharply. The disease was named **AIDS**, an acronym for **acquired immune deficiency syndrome**.

A major breakthrough came in 1984 when research teams in the United States (headed by Robert Gallo of the National Institutes of Health) and in France (headed by Luc Montagnier of the Pasteur Institute) simultaneously announced that they had identified the virus causing AIDS. The virus is called **HIV**, for human immune deficiency virus. Another strain of the virus, HIV-2, has been identified; it is found almost exclusively in Africa. HIV-1 accounts for almost all infections in North America.

As the name implies, HIV destroys the body's natural system of immunity to diseases. Once HIV has damaged an individual's immune system, opportunistic diseases may take over. In the early days of the disease, people did not have access to active antiretroviral drug therapy and would usually die within a few months to a few years.

AN EPIDEMIC?

In 1990, Ottawa launched the National AIDS Strategy, a major public health effort aimed at understanding and eradicating the disease. Nonetheless, as of the end of 2005, 20 194 persons in Canada had been diagnosed as having AIDS and 66 percent of them had died from it. However, these statistics represent only the tip of the iceberg, for they do not count persons who are infected with HIV and do not yet have symptoms of full-blown AIDS, or persons who are infected with HIV but have never been tested for it. At the end of 2005, approximately 61 000 Canadians had been diagnosed with HIV. Experts estimate that 33 million persons worldwide are infected with HIV, although the majority of them show no symptoms yet and are unaware that they are infected (Simon et al., 2006).

The hardest-hit part of the world is sub-Saharan Africa. According to UNAIDS, an agency of the United Nations, 3.2 million people in sub-Saharan Africa became newly infected with HIV in 2003 alone. This brought the total number of adults and children living with HIV/AIDS in this region to 26.6 million. In addition, it is estimated that 11 million children in the region have been orphaned by AIDS. In contrast, approximately 1.5 million people in Eastern Europe and Central Asia, 600 000 people in the Middle East and North Africa, 2 million people in Latin America and the Caribbean, 7.4 million people in Asia and the Pacific, and 1.6 million people in high-income countries (North America, Western Europe, Australia, and New Zealand) were living with HIV/AIDS in 2003. In 2005 alone, HIV infection caused approximately 2.8 million deaths worldwide. It is estimated that in the 45 countries most affected by HIV/AIDS, 68 million people will die prematurely as a result of AIDS in the next 20 years. About half of these

AIDS (acquired immune deficiency syndrome): A sexually transmitted disease that destroys the body's natural immunity to infection so that the person is susceptible to and may die from a disease such as pneumonia or cancer.

HIV: Human immune deficiency virus, the virus that causes AIDS.

IN FOCUS 8.1

Coping with Herpes

It's cliché to say, but I think at some point we all think it: "I just didn't think it could happen to me." I am an intelligent, responsible young adult living in Atlantic Canada while I complete my undergraduate degree. And I have herpes.

I had been seeing my partner exclusively for some time. We were honest and open with each other and cared very much for one another. So after some discussion, we decided to stop using condoms during sex. We both had had a number of previous partners and had both engaged in unprotected sex before. However, we also had both been tested, neither of us had symptoms, and we trusted each other.

One morning, after a particularly wonderful night together, I woke up with a small sore on my genitals. I looked at it carefully. It looked somewhat like an ingrown hair, which I had had before, but it was also somehow different. I was worried because I instantly realized it could be something sexually transmitted. I found myself thinking of my partner. I needed to tell her. I also found my thoughts drifting to her sexual history. Did I get this from her or had I given this to her? What was I going to say? How would she react? I was more scared than I thought possible about the situation.

I waited until we were alone. There wasn't really an easy way to say what I had to say. So I turned to her and just spit it out: "I have a sore." She looked a little shocked. She turned and said to me that she had one too. She had also been waiting to say something in private. We spent the next hour talking about it; what it looked like, what we knew about herpes and HPV, and what we were going to do. It seemed odd that both of us had one sore, and had gotten it at the same time. But the coincidence both relieved and worried us. We took turns that day calming each other down. I was worried but more than that, I was annoyed and I knew she was too. How could two careful people let this happen to them? We knew that if it was going to be an STI there was nothing we could do to change it. We also knew that we wouldn't know anything for sure until we saw a doctor. I called and made an appointment with my doctor right away.

As time went by, I started to get more signs that something was wrong. I had a burning sensation when I urinated which seemed to subside if I drank a lot of water. My urethral opening sometimes burned, and I felt sore in my groin area. The doctor sent me for all kinds of tests; urine tests, blood tests, and swabbed the sore. She told me that if the tests came back negative, I'd be sent to a different clinic for more tests.

The first round of tests came back negative. By the time my partner got in for tests, her sore had healed, and

---

people will be less than 25 years old when infected and less than 35 when they die. Thus, the terms *global epidemic* and *pandemic* (a widespread epidemic) have been used, with reason.

TRANSMISSION

When people speak of HIV being transmitted by an exchange of body fluids, the body fluids they are referring to are semen and blood and possible secretions of the cervix and vagina. HIV is spread in four ways: (1) by sexual intercourse (either penis-in-vagina intercourse or anal intercourse[3]); (2) by contaminated blood (a risk for people who receive a blood transfusion if the blood has not been screened); (3) by contaminated hypodermic needles (a risk for those who inject drugs or health care workers who receive accidental sticks); and (4) from an infected woman to her baby during pregnancy or childbirth.

Supporting these assertions, statistics indicate that Canadians diagnosed with HIV/AIDS are from the following exposure categories: (1) men who have sex with men (59 percent); (2) people who inject drugs (17 percent); (3) men who have sex with men and use injection drugs (2 percent); (4) heterosexuals who have had sexual contact with an infected person (17 percent);

---

[3]There is also a chance that mouth–genital sex can spread AIDS, particularly if there is ejaculation by an infected person into the mouth.

all her other tests came back negative. For over a month, we didn't know what had happened and assumed that the sores were ingrown hairs. The anxiety I felt at the onset slowly subsided. Then one day my doctor called. The swab tests had finally come back and I needed to go in for an appointment. The swab had come back positive for herpes. I couldn't believe it. Yet, I could. How did I get this? I had read a lot online, trying to sort out my symptoms and realized there was a chance I had herpes. Still, how did I get this? Again, I wonder whether I got it from my partner. If not, did I give it to her? And if not, where did I get it? I was angry; angry that the tests had taken so long, angry that they had come back positive, angry that my partner didn't have the same news, but most of all angry at myself for thinking I was okay to not use condoms in the first place. I called my partner as soon as I left the doctor's office and told her what I found out. I told her she needed to get tested. But she didn't have any sores. There was nothing she could do.

A short time later I had another outbreak. It was just like the first one, so I knew what it was. I was frustrated and upset. How could I let this happen to me? I had been cautious in so many ways. I found myself thinking of all kind of things, my future sex life, having these sores pop up whenever they wanted, knowing that I would always have to be extra careful. I was sad and worried about future partners; when and how would I let them know, how will they react, would I even be able to tell them. I spent a lot of time reading information on herpes. I thought that if I knew more I might feel better. My partner and I talked about it a lot. She was sympathetic and supportive, letting me know I had every right to be frustrated. And she apologized for the fact that we were dealing with this.

As I read about herpes, I learned that I could reinfect myself in other areas, and I could infect or reinfect my sexual partner. I had to be very careful when I had an outbreak. But I also had to be careful at other times. I read about learning to feel changes in my body, and how keeping my stress level down and living a healthy, active life could help prevent breakouts. I also read about medications that could treat symptoms, help prevent outbreaks, and help sores heal faster. After some consideration, I decided the cost of the medication was worth getting rid of my current sore and controlling future outbreaks.

For now, I've come to terms with having herpes. I still get frustrated with myself sometimes but I'm not devastated by it. The reality is that almost one in four people in Canada have it. I am cautious when I have signs of sores, making sure to use barriers for any sexual activity, and washing my hands well if they come in contact with the sore. Now, I use medications to help the sore heal and prevent future outbreaks.

Source: As told to Krystelle Shaughnessy.

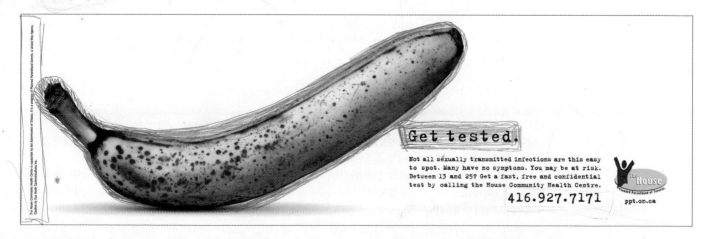

Figure 8.3 The Canadian Federation for Sexual Health and its member organizations promote sexual and reproductive health and rights through advocacy, public education, and awareness. Posters such as this one may be spotted on a passing bus.

IN FOCUS 8.2

What Is the Risk of Contracting HIV/AIDS?

Although we are constantly learning more about the relative risks of various behaviours in contracting HIV/AIDS, it is possible to categorize sexual behaviours into high-risk, low-risk, negligible-risk, and no-risk categories. High-risk practices are those that involve an exchange of body fluids and that have been shown in scientific studies to be associated with HIV infection. Low-risk practices also involve an exchange of body fluids but there are only a few reports of infection resulting from these activities, and usually only under certain conditions. Negligible-risk practices involve an exchange of body fluids but there are no confirmed reports of infection from these activities. No-risk practices do not involve the exchange of body fluids and have never been demonstrated to lead to HIV infection. Suggestions for safer sex practices that will prevent or reduce the chances of contracting HIV and other STIs can be found at the Online Learning Centre (www.mcgrawhill.ca/olc/hyde) and include thorough washing of both partners' genitals before intercourse; urination both before and after intercourse; inspecting the partner's genitals for symptoms like a wart or urethral discharge; and the use of a condom.

High Risk
- Anal or vaginal intercourse without a condom
- Sharing needles or syringes to inject drugs, steroids, or other substances
- Sharing sex toys

Low Risk
- Performing oral sex on a man or a woman without a barrier
- Anal or vaginal intercourse with a latex condom

- Injection of a substance using a used needle or syringe that has been cleaned
- Wet kissing with exchange of blood

Negligible Risk
- Performing or receiving oral sex with the use of a barrier
- Receiving oral sex without the use of a barrier
- Licking the anus
- Digital–anal intercourse or digital–vaginal intercourse (fingering someone's anus or vagina)

No Risk
- Wet or dry kissing with no exchange of blood
- Solo masturbation or being manually stimulated by a partner without using semen or vaginal fluid as a lubricant
- Using unshared sex toys
- Ejaculation on unbroken skin
- Massage, touch, body rubbing
- Injection of a substance using a new needle and syringe

What about risk of exposure to other STIs? According to the Public Health Agency of Canada, kissing and touching expose you to just a few STIs, oral sex exposes you to many STIs, and vaginal and anal sex expose you to all STIs.

Sources: AIDS New Brunswick, 2002; Canadian AIDS Society, 2001, 2004; Public Health Agency of Canada, 2007.

(5) recipients of contaminated blood transfusions (3 percent); and (6) at birth from an infected mother (1 percent). About 60 percent are under the age of 40, indicating that they were likely exposed to HIV in their early 20s (Health Canada, 2000).

In Canada in the early years of the epidemic, 11 percent of new cases were women; women accounted for 25 percent of new cases in 2005. Most of these women acquired HIV through heterosexual contact (Gatali & Archibald, 2004). Worldwide, 70 percent of the cases result from heterosexual transmission.

How great is your risk of becoming infected with HIV? In essence, it depends on what your sexual practices are (leaving aside the issues of injection drug use, which are beyond the scope of this book) (Varghese et al., 2002). *The sexual behaviour most likely to spread HIV is anal intercourse, and being the receiving partner puts one most at risk.* This is true for both men and women, regardless of sexual orientation. Penile–vaginal intercourse without a condom is a high-risk activity for contracting HIV as well. Whether you are gay or straight, statistically *the greater your number of sexual partners, the greater your risk of getting infected with HIV.* You may have heard the saying "six degrees of separation." It turns out that it is true for HIV as well. One study found that most people are just a few degrees of sexual separation from someone who is HIV-infected (Liljeros et al., 2001). The greater your number of partners, the greater your chances of connecting with that HIV-positive person. However, some people have contracted HIV from their first sexual partner. The risk varies considerably depending on whom you have sex with and whether you use a condom or a dental dam. *Penile–vaginal or anal intercourse is riskier if it is with a person who is infected with HIV (seropositive), has engaged in high-risk behaviours (unprotected anal or vaginal sex, injection drug use), is hemophiliac, is from a country where there is a high rate of HIV infection, or if condoms are not used.*

Table 8.1 shows the relative risk of becoming infected from a single act of intercourse with an infected person, using no condom. Perhaps the risk is lower than you thought for some of these STIs—researchers in Quebec have shown that a large majority of university students and health care providers are not aware of the transmissibility of HIV and chlamydia (Knäuper & Kornik, 2004; Rosen et al., 2005). However, even if the chance of contracting an STI from one unprotected sexual encounter is low, the chances add up with each additional unprotected sexual encounter. This is called the **cumulative risk**. Unfortunately, people tend to underestimate their cumulative risk of contracting an STI, particularly if the partner is appealing to them (Knäuper et al., 2005).

Cumulative risk: The likelihood of contracting an STI after repeated unprotected exposure.

Table 8.1	Risk of Being Infected with an STI as a Result of One Act of Sexual Intercourse with an Infected Person, Using No Condom

	Percentage Risk of Transmission from	
	Male to Female	Female to Male
Gonorrhea	50 to 90%	20%
Genital herpes	0.2%	0.05%
HIV	0.1 to 20%	0.01 to 10%

Source: Stone, K. M. (1994), pp. 203–212.

A study of heterosexual transmission of HIV among 415 Ugandan couples in which one partner was infected at the beginning and one was not, indicated that 22 percent of the uninfected became infected over a two-year period (Quinn et al., 2000). The male-to-female transmission rates and female-to-male rates were about equal. The higher the viral count in the infected person, the greater the rate of transmission. Interestingly, none of the circumcised men became infected. In fact, based on the results of three studies, the World Health Organization concluded that male circumcision reduces the risk of HIV transmission by as much as 60 percent.

Importantly, condoms are 87 percent effective in protecting against HIV transmission during heterosexual intercourse (Davis & Weller, 1999). This isn't perfect protection, but it's darned good, and far better than no protection. Far-right religious groups have tried to convince the public—especially school children—that condoms are totally ineffective, but the scientific studies say otherwise.

THE VIRUS

HIV is one of a group of retroviruses. Retroviruses reproduce only in living cells of the host species, in this case humans. They invade a host cell, and each time the host cell divides, copies of the virus are produced along with more host cells, each containing the genetic code of the virus. Current research is aimed at finding drugs that will prevent the virus from infecting new cells. At least two strains of HIV are found in North America, HIV-1 and HIV-2, and there are several subgroups of HIV-1 that differ genetically (Simon et al., 2006).

HIV particularly invades a group of white blood cells (lymphocytes) called CD4+ T-lymphocytes. We'll just call them T cells. These cells are critical to the body's immune response in fighting off infections. When HIV reproduces, it destroys the infected T cell. Eventually the HIV-positive person's number of T cells is so reduced that infections cannot be fought off.

Scientists have pressed hard to understand the functioning of HIV. They had identified two *coreceptors* for HIV, CCR5 and CXCR4, which allow HIV to enter T cells (Simon et al., 2006). CCR5 seems to be the important coreceptor in the early stages of the disease and CXCR4 in the later stages. This discovery may lead to advances in treatment if drugs can be used that block these coreceptors.

THE DISEASE

In 1998, the Health Canada Laboratory Centre for Disease Control Expert Working Group on Canadian Guidelines for Sexually Transmitted Disease established the following four broad classes of manifestations of HIV infection:

1. *Primary infection.* This stage begins with the initial infection with the virus and development of antibodies to it over the next two to eight weeks. Usually people who have been infected show no immediate symptoms or show symptoms that are not specific to HIV, such as a fever or sore throat. This stage lasts as long as the person keeps feeling well and the T4 cell count stays around 1000. A normal count is approximately 1000 cells per cubic millimetre of blood. People in this stage can infect other people.

2. *Asymptomatic infection.* During this stage, the person is infected with the virus but shows no symptoms, although lymphadenopathy is frequently present. These symptoms, such as swollen lymph glands and night sweats, are not immediately life-threatening. These asymptomatic carriers can infect other persons.

3. *Progressive infection.* During this stage, the person has conditions that indicate that his or her immune system is sufficiently suppressed that it is not able to fight off infections. Many infected persons go on to develop symptoms that are not immediately life threatening: fever, chronic diarrhea, unexplained weight loss, fatigue, chronic yeast infections in the throat or vagina, shingles, or abnormal or cancerous cells in the cervix. The T4 cell count drops by half, to around 500. The immune system is silently failing, however. Treatment with AZT, DDI, and other drugs may begin at this time; there is some evidence that these drug treatments (discussed shortly) are more effective if begun early.

4. *AIDS-defining opportunistic infection.* The diagnosis of AIDS is applied when the person is affected by life-threatening opportunistic infections (infections that occur only with severely reduced immunity), such as *Pneumocystis carinii* pneumonia (PCP) and Kaposi's sarcoma (KS), a rare form of skin cancer. The diagnosis is also used when other opportunistic infections or cancers of the lymph tissue are present and the person shows a positive test for HIV antibodies. Neurological problems can occur in AIDS patients because the virus can infect the cells of the brain; symptoms may include seizures and mental problems. A T cell count below 200 is by itself an indication of AIDS.

DIAGNOSIS

The blood test that detects the presence of antibodies to HIV uses the ELISA (for enzyme-linked immunosorbent assay) technique. It is easy and cheap to perform. It can be used in two important ways:

1. To screen donated blood. All donated blood in Canada is now screened with ELISA, so that infections because of transfusions should rarely occur. However, 1200 Canadians were

infected with HIV from tainted blood between 1978 and 1985 and a tiny risk remains even with ELISA.[4]

2. To help people determine whether they are infected (HIV positive) but are asymptomatic carriers.

The latter use is important because if people suspect that they are infected and find through the blood test that they are, they should either abstain from sexual activity or, at the very least, use a condom consistently, in order not to spread the disease to others. Only by responsible behaviour of this kind can the epidemic be brought under control.

ELISA is a very sensitive test; that is, it is highly accurate in detecting HIV antibodies (it has a very low rate of false negatives, in statistical language). However, it does produce a substantial number of false positives—the test saying HIV antibodies are present when they really are not. Thus, positive results on ELISA should always be confirmed by a second, more specific test.

The other major test, using the Western blot or immunoblot method, provides such confirmation. It is more expensive and difficult to perform, so it is not practical for mass screening of blood, as ELISA is. However, it is highly accurate (false positives are rare), and thus it is very useful in confirming or disconfirming a positive test from ELISA.

It should be emphasized that both tests detect only the presence of HIV antibodies. They do not predict whether the person will develop symptoms or will progress to the AIDS classification.

One of the drawbacks to the ELISA test is that it involves a long waiting period—more than a week—before test results are known. A rapid test has been approved for use in Canada. The test takes 60 seconds and only detects antibodies to HIV-1. This test is intended as a screening test and, as with the ELISA test, must be confirmed by a more accurate test. The Canadian AIDS Society (2007) has raised concerns that if these tests are done in doctors' offices rather than in sexual health centres, people may not be given enough pre-test counselling to be fully informed enough to give true consent, and will also not be given sufficient post-test counselling should they receive a positive test result.

TREATMENT

There is not yet any cure for AIDS. However, some progress is being made in developing treatments to control the disease. One antiviral drug, AZT (azidothymidine, also called zidovudine or ZDV), has been used widely. It has the effect of stopping the virus from multiplying. However, even if it stopped replication of the virus, it cannot repair the person's damaged immune system. Unfortunately, AZT has many side effects and cannot be used by some people, or can be used for only limited periods of time. Therefore, there has been a concerted effort to find new drugs that will slow or stop the progression of the disease.

DDI (dideoxyinosine or didanosine) is one such drug. Like AZT, DDI slows the progression of the disease by preventing replication of the virus. DDC (dideoxycytidine) is another drug developed in tandem with DDI; it too stops the HIV from replicating. D4T is yet another, similar drug. Collectively, these drugs are called ART, for antiretroviral therapy.

A major breakthrough came in 1996 with the availability of a new category of drugs, *protease inhibitors* (Kempf et al., 1995). Protease inhibitors attack the viral enzyme protease, which is necessary for HIV to make copies of itself and multiply. Another breakthrough came in 2006 with the introduction of darunavir, a drug that acts on viruses that are resistant to the protease inhibitors (Simon et al., 2006).

AZT: A drug used to treat HIV-infected persons; also called ZDV.

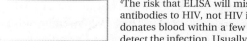

[4]The risk that ELISA will miss occasional cases of infected blood results from the fact that it detects antibodies to HIV, not HIV itself. It takes six to eight weeks for antibodies to form. Thus, if a person donates blood within a few weeks of becoming infected and before antibodies form, ELISA will not detect the infection. Usually ELISA is positive within three months of infection.

Today patients take a "drug cocktail" of one of the protease inhibitors combined with AZT and one other anti-HIV drug. This combination is called HAART, for highly active anti-retroviral therapy. Within a year of the introduction of HAART, thrilling reports emerged that the HIV count had become undetectable in the blood of persons taking the drug cocktail (Cohen, 1997). Some believed that the cure had been found. The number of deaths due to AIDS declined for the first year since the disease had been identified. Because in Canada most people with HIV/AIDS are now taking the drug cocktail, in 2005 there were only 72 deaths due to AIDS, compared to 1501 deaths in 1995 when the cocktail was not available.

HIV research, unfortunately, is much like a rollercoaster ride, with elated highs followed by plunges to the depths. HIV mutated to drug-resistant forms. And, although HIV had become undetectable in the blood of persons treated with the drug cocktail, it was hiding out in T cells and the lymph nodes and in organs such as the brain, eyes, and testes (Cohen, 1998; Finzi et al., 1997; Wong et al., 1997). In short, it is not eradicated by the drug cocktail treatment.

Today, HAART is making HIV infection a manageable disease for many persons who are surviving much longer than they would have without this treatment. A person diagnosed with HIV who receives treatment can now expect to live 20 to 30 years. For others, long-term HAART treatment causes serious side effects, such as diabetes-like problems, brittle bones, and heart disease, which means that they have to stop the treatment or switch to another one (Cohen, 2002). Others simply stop responding to the HAART regimen, and there is concern about the emergence of resistant strains.

On another front, progress is also being made with drugs that prevent the opportunistic infections that strike people living with AIDS. The drug pentamidine, for example, in aerosol form, is a standard treatment to prevent *Pneumocystis carinii* pneumonia.

WOMEN, CHILDREN, ETHNIC MINORITIES, AND AIDS

In the early days of the HIV/AIDS epidemic, men accounted for most cases in Canada, but the picture has changed considerably and the number of infected women is rapidly rising (PHAC, 2006). Whereas between 1985 and 1995 women accounted for only 11 percent of positive HIV tests, today 25 percent of individuals who test positive for HIV are women (Gatali & Archibald, 2004). Almost half of these women are under 30 years old. The urgency of addressing the needs of women with HIV infection is thus increasing.

As of 2006, new cases of women with AIDS and HIV infection were most likely to be the result of heterosexual contact (53 percent); injection drug use was the second largest category at 37 percent (PHAC, 2006).

Women need far more recognition in AIDS research. For example, intervention programs tailored to their needs should be developed. Such programs should include sexual assertiveness training, in which women are empowered to insist that their sex partners use condoms. Women also need to be included in clinical trials of drug treatments.

Some of the saddest cases are children with AIDS; these cases are known as pediatric AIDS. Babies born to infected mothers are often, but not always, infected. Although since 1985, 285 babies have been infected with HIV from their mothers, the number dropped dramatically in 2005; only five HIV-infected babies were born in Canada that year. One bright spot is the finding that using AZT to treat infected women during pregnancy can substantially reduce the rate of infection in their babies to as low as 5 percent (Harris et al., 2002). AIDS in infants has nearly been eliminated through helping pregnant women know their HIV status and the use of AZT with those who are infected.

Worldwide, people of colour have borne a disproportionate burden of the cases of AIDS. In Canada, of reported AIDS cases for whom ethnic identity was recorded, 82 percent identified their ethnic background as white, 9 percent as black, 4 percent as Aboriginal, and 3 percent as Asian. Although the annual number of reported AIDS cases has declined among

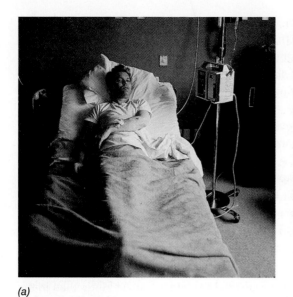

(a)

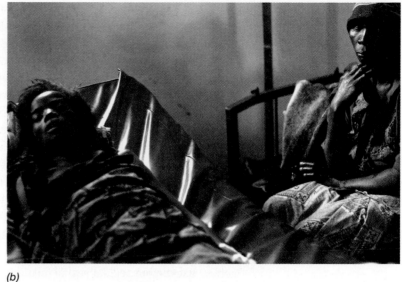

(b)

Figure 8.4 AIDS is a multicultural disease. *(a)* A North American man with AIDS. *(b)* An African woman with AIDS.

all ethnic groups since 1993, the decline has been lowest among minority groups, resulting in an increase in the proportion of AIDS cases who are black and Aboriginal. For example, the percentage of newly diagnosed cases of HIV infection among blacks went from 5 percent in 1989 to 11 percent in 2005.

The problem is particularly severe among Aboriginals. In 1989, Aboriginals constituted only 1 percent of reported AIDS cases, compared to 13 percent in 2003. However, 23 percent of new HIV/AIDS infections in Canada are among Aboriginals, even though Aboriginals make up less than 3 percent of the population (PHAC, 2006). Aboriginals also tend to be infected at an earlier age than non-Aboriginals (PHAC, 2004). The percentage of Aboriginal women with HIV/AIDS is almost twice as high as in the non-Aboriginal population.

A lack of prevention programs and poor access to testing are two factors that contribute to the increasing rate of HIV in the Aboriginal population. Some Aboriginal people also lack basic AIDS information. In a study of 658 people from First Nations communities in Ontario, 17 percent had not heard of AIDS and overall knowledge of HIV/AIDS was relatively low (Myers et al., 1994). Seventy-one percent of respondents were certain that they would never get AIDS despite the fact that there was extensive unprotected intercourse. Mobility between inner cities and rural/reserve communities is an important factor in the introduction and spread of HIV to unexposed populations (Health Canada, 2000).

There is an urgent need to develop education and prevention programs for Aboriginal and other culturally distinct Canadian communities. These programs must be culturally sensitive. There also should be substantial community involvement in program development and implementation to ensure that the programs are culturally appropriate (Brant, 1990; Health Canada, 1994a–f; Myers et al., 1993, 1999).

PSYCHOLOGICAL CONSIDERATIONS IN AIDS

Psychological issues for those infected with HIV and for AIDS patients are profound. There are some analogies to people who receive a diagnosis of an incurable cancer, for AIDS is—at least at present—incurable. Many patients experience the typical reactions for such situations, including a denial of the reality, followed by anger, depression, or both. However, the analogy to cancer patients is not perfect, for AIDS is a socially stigmatized disease in a way that cancer is not. Thus, the revelation that one has AIDS must often be accompanied by the announcement that one is gay or drug-addicted or engaged in extradyadic sex (that is, sex outside the relationship). It may make it more difficult for the person to fill the human need for emotional and physical intimacy. Also, as the patient becomes sicker, he or she is unlikely to be able to hold a job, and financial worries become an additional strain.

There is a great need to be sensitive to the psychological needs of people living with HIV/AIDS. In most cities, support groups for people living with HIV/AIDS patients and their families have formed. Social and psychological support from others is essential as people weather this crisis (Pakenham et al., 1994). Research with gay men in Alberta has shown that after sometimes years of struggle with their diagnosis, most came to viewing their lives more positively (Harris & Alderson, 2006).

Research in Ontario sheds light on the experiences with sexual intimacy of people living with HIV or AIDS (Maticka-Tyndale et al., 2002). The researchers conducted in-depth interviews with 31 men and four women who were taking combination antiviral therapies. Individuals who were living as a couple described a drop in sexual interest soon after diagnosis. For some participants sexual desire returned over time; for others it did not. According to one woman:

> Toward the very beginning, it [sex] was almost non-existent. We were afraid to. Now we're getting back to our regular sexual relationship—protected sex and it's much better than in the beginning. (p. 35)

Some single individuals worried about finding an accepting partner. Others preferred to remain single, often due to concerns about disclosing their HIV-positive status. As one man said:

> I just don't want to bother . . . You don't realize what it's like to meet someone and find them attractive physically and all and then have to one day look at them and say, "By the way, I'm HIV-positive." (p. 37)

Finally, participants discussed the negative impact of both the symptoms of HIV and the side effects of therapies on sexual intimacy.

Cognitive–behavioural therapy combined with stress-management training has been shown to be effective in improving the quality of life and decreasing anxiety and depression in HIV-infected individuals (Cruess et al., 2002; Lechner et al., 2003). The effectiveness of this therapy is important for two reasons. First, it improves the quality of life of affected people. Second, research shows that HIV-positive people who do not have symptoms but are depressed die earlier than similar people who are not depressed (Burack et al., 1993). Psychotherapy is therefore likely to have a positive impact on both mental health and physical health. Therapy also needs to focus on improving sexual satisfaction among persons living with HIV/AIDS, as this is an important aspect of quality of life (Maticka-Tyndale et al., 2002).

In Chapter 16 we discuss the phenomenon of *post-traumatic growth* following sexual assault. Between 60 and 80 percent of people living with HIV infection report positive psychological growth following diagnosis; people who experience post-traumatic growth and are optimistic tend to have higher T cell counts, helping them to fight disease progression (Milam, 2006).

RECENT PROGRESS IN AIDS RESEARCH

As this discussion makes clear, much more research on AIDS is needed. We need better treatments to control this disease, we need a cure for it, and we need a vaccine against it. Those are pretty tall orders, and it is unlikely that any of them will appear in the next few years.

VACCINE

Researchers have been working hard to develop a vaccine against HIV, but the job has turned out to be much more difficult than expected. The problem is that HIV actually has many forms and, to make matters worse, it mutates rapidly and recombines, creating even more forms. In effect, the virus doesn't hold still long enough for a vaccine to take effective aim at it.

One strategy in developing a vaccine is to first develop a vaccine that works with monkeys, which can be infected by an analogue to HIV called SIV (simian immunodeficiency virus). Progress has been made toward developing vaccines that protect monkeys from infection with SIV (Amara et al., 2001; Casimiro et al., 2003).

Yet another strategy involves the development of a vaccine to be administered to people recently infected with HIV. The goal is to boost their immune function so that they can fight off the virus. Vaccines of this type are being developed (Barouch et al., 2000; Rosenberg et al., 2000; Schooley et al., 2000).

Two other strategies involve developing a vaccine that stimulates the body to form resistance (i.e., antibodies) to HIV, or a vaccine that acts at the cellular level by stimulating the production of specialized T cells that are toxic to HIV (Luzuriaga et al., 2006). Another possibility is a vaccine that combines both. Yet another possibility is to develop a vaccine to be administered to infants that would prevent transmission through breast milk as well as later infection when they become sexually active. Several of these vaccines have moved into clinical trials with humans.

Research on Non-progressors

Some groups of people are being studied for clues to breakthroughs in the war against AIDS. One such group is *non-progressors*. Approximately 5 percent of HIV-infected people go for ten years or more without symptoms and with no deterioration of their immune system. Their T-cell count remains higher than 500. Non-progressors turn out to have less HIV in their bodies, even though they have been infected for over a decade. Why? One possibility is that these people have unusually strong immune systems that have essentially managed to contain the virus. Another is that they were infected with a weak strain of the virus. Some individuals were infected with a genetically defective strain of HIV that does not replicate; this situation is intriguing because it might be useful in producing a vaccine. Non-progressors also have particularly high levels of defensins, chemicals secreted by white blood cells (Ganz, 2002). Defensins are known to contribute to the killing of microbes such as HIV.

Chemokines

Another major scientific advance is the discovery of HIV-suppressor factors or *chemokines* (Balter, 1995; Cocchi et al., 1995; Cohen, 1997). Certain lymphocytes (CD8+ T cells) battle against HIV in the body. They do so by secreting three chemokines (which are molecules), named RANTES, MIP-1α, and MIP-1β. HIV-infected persons who are non-progressors have high levels of CD8 cells and high levels of chemokines compared with rapid progressors (Haynes et al., 1996). The chemokines can bind to the coreceptor CCR5, blocking HIV from entering cells. Scientists hope that these discoveries may lead to improved treatments for HIV-infected persons and possibly to vaccines that boost the level of chemokines and therefore boost the body's resistance to HIV infection.

Genetic Resistance

Scientists have discovered a mutation of a gene and the mutation creates strong resistance to HIV infection (Galvani & Slatkin, 2003; Novembre et al., 2005). The gene is called CCR5 because it is the gene for the CCR5 receptor that, as discussed earlier, allows HIV to enter cells. The mutation occurred some time in history as humans spread out of Africa. The evidence indicates that the mutation was strongly selected for during the bubonic plague or smallpox plagues that occurred in Europe, and the mutation is much more common there than in other parts of the world. People with two copies of the mutation (homozygotes) are resistant to infection, whereas people with one copy (heterozygotes) may become infected but show much slower disease progression.

Researchers are also pursuing gene therapy for HIV and many other diseases (Strachan & Read, 2004). This would involve injecting the patient with genetic material created to wreak havoc on HIV in any number of ways—for example, by preventing it from replicating or by inactivating proteins that HIV needs to complete its life cycle and go on infecting more lymphocytes. With all the progress made by the Human Genome Project, this approach seems quite promising.

MICROBICIDES

Microbicides are substances, usually in ointment form, that kill microbes such as HIV. These ointments could be put into the vagina or anus or spread on the penis to battle HIV transmission. The old standby nonoxynol-9 was thought to be effective in killing HIV some years ago, but today we know that it is not only ineffective but also actually makes women more vulnerable to infection by irritating the lining of the vagina (Van Damme et al., 2002). Much effort is now going into developing effective microbicides that will attack HIV as well as other sexually transmitted viruses. Some are already in clinical trials, including PRO 2000 Gel and BufferGel (Upadhyay et al., 2005). BufferGel is a vaginal defence enhancer, meaning that it boosts the vagina's natural resistance to infection; it should provide protection against HIV, chlamydia, herpes, and HPV, as well as pregnancy. PRO 2000 is an entry and fusion inhibitor, which means that it binds to viruses and bacteria so that they don't infect healthy cells; it is aimed at protecting against HIV, gonorrhea, and herpes, as well as pregnancy.

BEHAVIOURAL PREVENTION

In the last analysis, prevention is better than cure. Until we have an effective vaccine, our best hope is interventions that aim to change people's behaviour, because it is behaviour (sexual activity, injection drug use) that spreads HIV. The big success story in behavioural prevention is Uganda. In 1991, screening of pregnant women indicated that 21 percent were infected; by 1998 this figure had dropped to 10 percent (Stoneburner & Low-Beer, 2004). In the early 1990s, the Ugandan government launched a bold and forceful program called ABC—for Abstinence, Be faithful, and use Condoms. It blanketed the country with advertising about the program, which urged unmarried persons to abstain from sex, urged married people to be faithful, and urged everyone to use condoms. The whole emphasis was on behaviour change, with no need for the costly drugs that Uganda couldn't afford. It isn't completely clear which of the three components of the program had the most effect, but in any case the program worked, and the epidemic is under control in that country. Scientists have estimated that this intervention had an effect equivalent to a vaccine with 80 percent effectiveness (Stoneburner & Low-Beer, 2004).

GONORRHEA

Gonorrhea (gon-uh-REE-uh): A sexually transmitted infection that usually causes symptoms of a puslike discharge and painful, burning urination in the male but is frequently asymptomatic in the female.

Historical records indicate that **gonorrhea** ("the clap," "the drip") is the oldest of the sexual diseases. Its symptoms are described in the Old Testament, in Leviticus 15 (about 3500 years ago). The Greek physician Hippocrates, some 2400 years ago, believed that gonorrhea resulted from "excessive indulgence in the pleasures of Venus," the goddess of love (hence the term "venereal" disease). Albert Neisser identified the bacterium that causes it, the gonococcus *Neisseria gonorrhoeae*, in 1879.

Gonorrhea has always been a particular problem in wartime, when it spreads rapidly among the soldiers and the prostitutes they patronize. In the twentieth century, a gonorrhea epidemic occurred during World War I, and gonorrhea was also a serious problem during World War II. Then, with the discovery of penicillin and its use in curing gonorrhea, the disease became much less prevalent in the 1950s.

There was a resurgence in the incidence of gonorrhea in the 1970s. It is clear that one of the reasons for the resurgence was the shift in contraceptive practices to use of the pill, which (unlike the condom) provides no protection from gonorrhea and actually increases a woman's susceptibility. However, in Canada the reported rate of gonorrhea has declined 93 percent since 1980 due to use of condoms, improved diagnostic services, partner notification, and treatment. In 2006, there were 10 808 reported cases, almost half of which were among 15- to 24-year-olds. This is a rate of 27.8 per 100 000 people in the population—the rate of chlamydia is more than seven times the rate for gonorrhea. PHAC has set a goal of eliminating gonorrhea by 2010.

Figure 8.5 Symptoms of gonorrhea in men include a puslike discharge. About 80 percent of women, however, are asymptomatic.

SYMPTOMS

Most cases of gonorrhea result from penis-in-vagina intercourse. In the male, the gonococcus invades the urethra, producing *urethritis* (inflammation of the urethra). White blood cells rush to the area and attempt to destroy the bacteria, but the bacteria soon win the battle. In most cases, symptoms appear two to five days after infection, although they may appear as early as the first day or as late as two weeks after infection. Initially a thin, clear mucous discharge seeps out of the meatus (the opening at the tip of the penis). Within a day or so it becomes thick and creamy and may be white, yellowish, or yellow-green (see Figure 8.5). This is often referred to as a purulent (puslike) discharge. The area around the meatus may become swollen. About half of infected men experience a painful burning sensation when urinating. The urine may contain pus or blood, and in some cases the lymph glands of the groin become enlarged and tender.

Because the early symptoms of gonorrhea in men are obvious and often painful, most men seek treatment immediately and are cured. If the disease is not treated, however, the urethritis spreads up the urethra, causing inflammations in the prostate (prostatitis), seminal vesicles (seminal vesiculitis), urinary bladder (cystitis), and epididymis (epididymitis). Pain on urination becomes worse and is felt in the whole penis. Then these early symptoms may disappear as the disease spreads to the other organs. If the epididymitis is left untreated, it may spread to the testicles and the resulting scar tissue may cause sterility.

Asymptomatic gonorrhea (gonorrhea with no symptoms) does occur in males, but its incidence is low. In contrast, about 60 to 80 percent of women infected with gonorrhea are asymptomatic during the early stages of the disease. Many women are unaware of their infection unless they are told by a male partner. Therefore, it is extremely important for any male who is infected to inform all his contacts.

The gonorrheal infection in the woman invades the cervix. Pus is discharged, but the amount may be so slight that it is not noticed. When present, it is yellow-green and irritating to the vulva, but it is generally not heavy (it is not to be confused with normal cervical mucus, which is clear or white and non-irritating, or with discharges resulting from the various kinds of vaginitis—discussed in this chapter—which are irritating but white). Although the cervix is the primary site of infection, the inflammation may also spread to the urethra, causing burning pain on urination (not to be confused with cystitis).

If the infection is not treated, the Bartholin glands may become infected and, in rare cases, swell and produce pus. The infection may also be spread to the anus and rectum, either by a heavy cervical discharge or by the menstrual discharge.

Because so many women are asymptomatic in the early stages of gonorrhea, many receive no treatment, and thus there is a high risk of serious complications. In about 20 percent of women who go untreated, the gonococcus moves up into the uterus. From there it infects the fallopian tubes. The tissues become swollen and inflamed, and thus the condition is also called pelvic inflammatory disease (PID)—although PID can be caused by diseases other than gonorrhea. The major symptom is pelvic pain and, in some cases, irregular or painful menstruation. If PID is not treated, scar tissue may form, blocking the tubes and leaving the woman sterile. Indeed, untreated gonorrhea is one of the most common causes of infertility in women. If the tubes are partially blocked, so that sperm can get up them but eggs cannot move down, ectopic pregnancy can result, because the fertilized egg is trapped in the tube.

There are three other major sites for non-genital gonorrhea infection: the mouth and throat, the anus and rectum, and the eyes. If fellatio is performed on an infected man, the gonococcus may invade the throat. (Cunnilingus is less likely to spread gonorrhea, and mouth-to-mouth kissing rarely does.) Such an infection is often asymptomatic; the typical symptom, if there is one, is a sore throat. Rectal gonorrhea is contracted through anal intercourse and thus affects both women in heterosexual relations and, more commonly, men who have sex with men. Symptoms include some discharge from the rectum and itching, but many cases are asymptomatic. Gonorrhea may also invade the eyes. This occurs only rarely in adults, when they touch the genitals and then transfer the bacteria-containing pus to their eyes by touching them. This eye infection is much more common in newborn infants. The infection is transferred from the mother's cervix to the infant's eyes during birth. For this reason, most provinces require that silver nitrate, or erythromycin or some other antibiotic, be put in every newborn's eyes to prevent any such infection. If left untreated, the eyes become swollen and painful within a few days, and there is a discharge of pus. Blindness was a common result in the pre-antibiotic era.

DIAGNOSIS

A urine test is available for men. If gonorrhea in the throat is suspected, a swab should be taken and tested. People who suspect that they may have rectal gonorrhea should request that a swab be taken from the rectum, since many physicians will not automatically think to do this.

In women, a sample of the cervical discharge is taken from the cervix and tested. A pelvic examination should also be performed. Pain during this exam may indicate PID. Women who suspect throat or rectal infection should request that samples be taken from those sites as well.

TREATMENT

The traditional treatment for gonorrhea was a large dose of penicillin, or tetracycline for those who were allergic to penicillin. However, strains of the gonococcus that are resistant to penicillin and tetracycline have become so common that newer antibiotics such as ceftriaxone or ciprofloxacin (Cipro) must now be used. They are highly effective, even against resistant strains.

SYPHILIS

Syphilis (SIFF-ih-lis): A sexually transmitted infection that causes a chancre to appear in the primary stage.

There has been considerable debate over the exact origins of syphilis. The disease, called "the Great Pox," was present in Europe during the 1400s and became a pandemic by 1500.

The bacterium that causes syphilis is called *Treponema pallidum*. It is spiral-shaped and is thus often called a *spirochete*. In 1906, Wassermann, Neisser, and Bruck described a test for diagnosing syphilis that became known as the *Wassermann test* or *Wassermann reaction*. This test has been replaced by more modern blood tests, but the Wassermann label hangs on.

In 2005, there were 1493 cases of syphilis reported in Canada (the United States has a rate 10 times as high). Although the rate of syphilis remains low, there has been an increase in cases in the last few years; for example, there were only 174 reported cases in 2000. The increase is largely due to outbreaks in Vancouver involving sex trade workers, in the Yukon and northern Alberta among heterosexuals, and in Calgary, Ottawa, and Montreal among men who have sex with men.

Although syphilis is not nearly as common as chlamydia or gonorrhea, its effects are much more serious if left untreated. In most cases, chlamydia or gonorrhea cause only discomfort and, sometimes, sterility; syphilis, if left untreated, can damage the nervous system and even cause death. There are many cases today of coinfection, in which the person is infected with both syphilis and HIV. Syphilis infection makes one more vulnerable to HIV and vice versa.

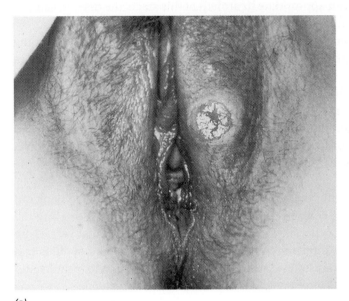

(a)

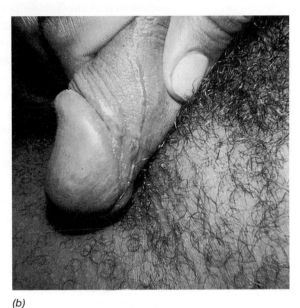

(b)

Figure 8.6 The chancre characteristic of primary-stage syphilis *(a)* on the labia majora and *(b)* on the penis.

SYMPTOMS

The major early symptom of syphilis is the chancre. It is a round, ulcerlike lesion with a hard, raised edge, resembling a crater. One of the distinctive things about the chancre is that although it looks terrible, it is painless. It appears about three weeks (as early as ten days or as late as three months) after intercourse with an infected person. The chancre appears at the point where the bacteria entered the body. Typically, the bacteria enter through the mucous membranes of the genitals as a result of intercourse with an infected person. Thus, in men the chancre often appears on the penis or scrotum. In women, the chancre often appears on the cervix, and thus the woman does not notice it and is unaware that she is infected (nature's sexism again). The chancre may also appear on the vaginal walls or, externally, on the vulva (see Figure 8.6).

If oral sex or anal intercourse with an infected person occurs, the bacteria can also invade the mucous membranes of the mouth or rectum. Thus, the chancre may appear on the lips, tongue, or tonsils or around the anus. Finally, the bacteria may enter through a cut in the skin anywhere on the body. Thus, it is possible (though rare) to get syphilis by touching the chancre of an infected person. The chancre would then appear on the hand at the point where the bacteria entered through the break in the skin.

The progress of the disease once the person has been infected is generally divided into

Chancre (SHANK-er):
A painless, ulcerlike lesion with a hard, raised edge that is a symptom of syphilis.

four stages: primary-stage syphilis, secondary-stage syphilis, latent syphilis, and late syphilis. The phase just described, in which the chancre forms, is *primary-stage syphilis*. If left untreated, the chancre goes away by itself within one to five weeks after it appears. This marks the end of the primary stage. However, the disease has not gone away just because the chancre has healed; it has only gone underground.

Beginning a few months after the original appearance of the chancre, a generalized body rash develops, marking the beginning of *secondary-stage syphilis*. The rash is variable in its appearance, the most distinctive feature being that it does not itch or hurt. Hair loss may also occur during the secondary stage. Usually, the symptoms are troublesome enough to cause the person to seek medical help. With appropriate treatment at this stage, the disease can still be cured, and there will be no permanent effects.

Even without treatment, the secondary-stage symptoms go away in a few weeks, leading people to believe mistakenly that the disease has gone away. Instead, it has entered a more dangerous stage.

After the symptoms of the secondary stage have disappeared, the disease is in the latent stage; *latent syphilis* may last for years. Although there are no symptoms in this stage, *T. pallidum* is busily burrowing into the tissues of the body, especially the blood vessels, central nervous system (brain and spinal cord), and bones. After the first year or so of the latent stage, the disease is no longer infectious, except that a pregnant woman can still pass it on to the fetus.

About half of the people who enter the latent stage remain in it permanently, living out the rest of their lives without further complications. The other half, however, move into the dangerous *late syphilis*. In *cardiovascular late syphilis* the heart and major blood vessels are attacked; this occurs 10 to 40 years after the initial infection. Cardiovascular syphilis can lead to death. In *neurosyphilis* the brain and spinal cord are attacked, leading to insanity and paralysis, which appear 10 to 20 years after infection. Neurosyphilis may be fatal.

Congenital (kun-JEN-ih-tul) syphilis: A syphilis infection in a newborn baby resulting from transmission from an infected mother.

If a pregnant woman has syphilis, the fetus may be infected when the bacteria cross the placental barrier, and the child gets congenital syphilis (meaning present from birth). The infection may cause early death of the fetus (spontaneous abortion) or severe illness at or shortly after birth. It may also lead to late complications that show up only at 10 or 20 years of age. Women are most infectious to their baby when they have primary- or secondary-stage syphilis, but they may transmit the infection to the fetus in utero as long as eight years after the mother's initial infection. If the disease is diagnosed and treated before the fourth month of pregnancy, the fetus will not develop the disease. For this reason, a syphilis test is done as a routine part of the blood analysis in a pregnancy test. In 2006 there were only eight cases of congenital syphilis in all of Canada.

DIAGNOSIS

Syphilis is somewhat difficult to diagnose from symptoms because, as noted earlier, its symptoms are like those of many other diseases.

The physical exam should include inspection not only of the genitals but also of the entire body surface. Women should have a pelvic exam so that the vagina and the cervix can be checked for chancres. If the patient has had anal intercourse, a rectal exam should also be performed.

If a chancre is present, some of its fluid is taken and placed on a slide for inspection under a dark-field microscope. If the person has syphilis, *T. pallidum* should be present.

The most common tests for syphilis are blood tests, all of which are based on antibody reactions. The VDRL (venereal disease research laboratory test) is one of these blood tests. It is fairly accurate, cheap, and easy to perform.

TREATMENT

The treatment of choice for syphilis is penicillin. *Treponema pallidum* is actually rather fragile, so large doses are not necessary in treatment. The recommended dose is two shots of benzathine penicillin, one in each of the buttocks. Latent, later, and congenital syphilis require larger doses. For those allergic to penicillin the recommended treatment is tetracycline or doxycycline, but these should not be given to pregnant women.

ELIMINATION OF SYPHILIS?

Health Canada has targeted syphilis for complete elimination in Canada. As an interim and more achievable step, the national goal is fewer than 0.5 cases per 100 000 population. On the surface, the goal may seem odd, given that syphilis is relatively rare compared with other STIs. But syphilis infection makes a person much more vulnerable to HIV infection because of the open sores produced by syphilis, and a person who is HIV-infected and then contracts syphilis may experience immediately life-threatening conditions (Wong & Jordan, 2000). For these reasons, syphilis is more serious than the small rate of infection indicates. Moreover, syphilis is completely curable with a single dose of penicillin, it is easily detectable with inexpensive laboratory tests, and it has not developed resistant strains. Experience since World War II indicates that, even when syphilis is effectively treated and brought to a low incidence, it still resurges periodically in epidemics. Therefore, total elimination is the best goal, and this seems feasible.

VIRAL HEPATITIS

Viral hepatitis is a disease of the liver. One symptom is an enlarged liver that is somewhat tender. The disease can vary greatly in severity from asymptomatic cases to ones in which there is a fever, fatigue, jaundice (yellowish skin), and vomiting, much as one might experience with a serious case of the flu. There are five types of viral hepatitis: hepatitis A, B, C, D, and E. The one that is of most interest in a discussion of sexually transmitted infections is hepatitis B. Hepatitis C and D (or delta) can also be transmitted sexually, but they are rare compared with B.

The virus for hepatitis B (HBV) can be transmitted through blood, saliva, semen, vaginal secretions, and other body fluids. The behaviours that spread it include needle sharing by people who inject drugs, sharing toothbrushes and razors, tattooing and body piercing, acupuncture, vaginal and anal intercourse, and oral–anal sex. It is most frequently transmitted through intravenous drug use (34 percent), having multiple heterosexual partners (24 percent), and male homosexual sex (7 percent) (Zhang et al., 2001). It has many similarities to AIDS, although hepatitis B is about 100 times more contagious.

Hepatitis B is more common than most people think because it receives relatively little publicity compared with AIDS and herpes. There are about 700 new cases of hepatitis B in Canada each year. People who have had the disease continue to have a positive blood test for it for the rest of their lives.

Many adults infected with HBV are asymptomatic; their bodies fight off the virus and they are left uninfected, with permanent immunity. Others develop an early, acute (short-term) illness and display a variety of symptoms but recover from the illness. A third group develops chronic (long-term) hepatitis B. They continue to be infectious and may develop serious liver disease involving cirrhosis or cancer. Fortunately, antiviral treatments are now available for those with chronic hepatitis B (PHAC, 2007).

The good news is that there is a vaccine against hepatitis B. The current recommendation is that all children be vaccinated and all provinces have school-based immunization programs. We urge you to be vaccinated if you are a person who has had a number of partners. You should be tested if there is even a hint that you have been exposed.

TRICHOMONIASIS

Trichomoniasis ("trich") is caused by a protozoan, *Trichomonas vaginalis* (Swygaard et al., 2004). The organism can survive for a time on toilet seats and other objects so it is occasionally transmitted non-sexually, but it is transmitted mainly through sexual intercourse.

For women, the symptom is an abundant, frothy, white or yellow vaginal discharge that irritates the vulva and has an unpleasant smell. In men, there may be irritation of the urethra and a discharge from the penis, but some men are asymptomatic. It is important that accurate diagnosis be made, because the drugs used to treat trichomoniasis are different from those used to treat other STIs that have similar symptoms, and the long-term effects of untreated trichomoniasis can be serious.

The treatment of choice is metronidazole (Flagyl) taken orally. If left untreated, trich can lead to pelvic inflammatory disease and problems with birth (Swygaard et al., 2004). It also increases susceptibility to HIV infection.

PUBIC LICE

Pubic lice ("crabs," or *pediculosis pubis*) are tiny lice that attach themselves to the base of pubic hairs and there feed on blood from their human host. They are about the size of a pinhead and, under magnification, resemble a crab (see Figure 8.7). They lay their eggs frequently and live for about 30 days, but they die within 24 hours if they are taken off a human host. Crabs are transmitted by sexual contact, but they may also be picked up from sheets, towels, sleeping bags, or toilet seats. (Yes, there *are* some things you can catch from toilet seats.)

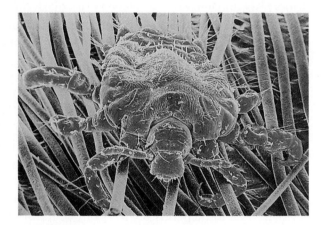

Figure 8.7   A pubic louse, enlarged. The actual size is about the same as the head of a pin.

The major symptom of pubic lice is fierce itching in the region of the pubic hair. Diagnosis is made by finding the lice or the eggs attached to the hairs.

Pubic lice are treated with the drugs Nix and Rid, which are available without prescription. Both kill the lice. After treatment, the person should put on clean clothing. Since the lice die within 24 hours, it is not necessary to disinfect clothing that has not been used for longer than 24 hours. However, the eggs can live up to six days, and in difficult cases it may be necessary to boil or dry-clean one's clothing or use a spray such as R and C.

PREVENTING STIs

While most of the literature one reads concentrates on the rapid diagnosis and treatment of STIs, prevention would be much better than cure, and there are some ways in which one can avoid getting STIs, or at least reduce one's chances of doing so. The most obvious, of course, is limiting yourself to a monogamous relationship with an uninfected person or abstaining from sexual activity. However, many people in committed monogamous relationships have engaged in behaviours that put them at risk for STIs in the past. They may not be aware that they are infected and thus can pass on the STI to their partner if they engage in unprotected sex even if both partners are monogamous (Misovich et al., 1997). As described in In Focus 8.1

IN FOCUS 8.3

Cool Lines about Safer Sex

The popular website for teens teenwire.com offers these lines for negotiating safer sex.

Partner	You
What's that?	A condom, baby.
What for?	To use when we're making love.
I don't like using them.	Why not?
It doesn't feel as good with a rubber.	I'll feel more relaxed. If I'm more relaxed, I can make it feel better for you.
But we've never used a condom before.	I don't want to take any more risks.
Condoms are gross.	Being pregnant when I don't want to be is worse. So is getting AIDS.
Don't you trust me?	Trust isn't the point. People carry sexually transmitted infections without knowing it.
Just a few dips.	Women can get pregnant and get STIs from pre-cum.
Making love with a rubber on is like taking a shower with a raincoat on.	Doing it without a rubber is playing Russian roulette.
It just isn't as sensitive.	With a condom you might last even longer, and that'll make up for it.
I don't stay hard when I put on a condom.	I can do something about that.
Putting it on interrupts everything.	Not if I help put it on.
I'll try, but it might not work.	Practice makes perfect.
But I love you.	Then you'll help me protect myself.
I guess you don't really love me.	I'm not going to prove my love by risking my life.
I'm not using a rubber, no matter what.	Well, then I guess we're not having sex.
Just this once without it.	It only takes once to get pregnant. It only takes once to get AIDS.
It won't fit.	Condoms come in all different sizes.

Source: www.teenwire.com, June 22, 2004.

(page 228), just because a partner has no obvious symptoms like herpes blisters or warts, don't assume that the person is uninfected. We have seen in this chapter how many of these infections—for example, chlamydia, herpes, and warts—can be asymptomatic. The only way to really know is to have a complete battery of tests for STIs, a choice more and more people are making. Not every STI is tested in the standard battery—for example, herpes and HPV usually are not—but it still will catch most infections.

If you are not sure that your partner is uninfected, there are other techniques available.

The latex condom, in addition to being a decent contraceptive, gives good (although not perfect) protection against HIV, HPV, chlamydia, gonorrhea, herpes, syphilis, and other STIs (Baldwin et al., 2004; Steiner & Cates, 2006; Wald et al., 2005; Winer et al., 2006). With the rise of the STI epidemic, the condom is again becoming popular. The key is to eroticize condom use (Ploem & Byers, 1997). The diaphragm also provides some protection for women, as does the female condom. In Focus 8.3 presents a possible dialogue for overcoming a partner's objections to condom use.

A dental dam gives protection from the spread of STIs during cunnilingus (oral stimulation of the vulva) or anilingus (oral stimulation of the anus). Some stores sell them or you can make them yourself from an unlubricated condom. Here's how you make a dental dam from a condom. First, carefully unroll the condom. Then cut off the tip and the rim. Finally, cut down the length of the tube and open the condom. Voila, you have a rectangular piece of latex that can be used during oral sex.

Some simple health precautions are also helpful. Successful prostitutes, who need to be careful about STIs, take such precautions. Washing the genitals before intercourse helps remove bacteria. This may not sound like a romantic prelude to lovemaking, but prostitutes make a sensuous game out of soaping the man's genitals. You can do this as part of taking a shower or bath with your partner. The other important technique is inspecting your partner's genitals. If you see a chancre, a wart, a herpes blister, or a discharge, put on your clothes and leave or, at the very least, immediately start a conversation about STI status (do not fall for the "it's only a pimple" routine). This technique may sound a little crude or embarrassing, but if you are intimate enough with someone to make love with that person, you ought to be intimate enough to look at her or his genitals. Once again, if you are cool about it, you can make this an erotic part of foreplay. Of course, you should also inspect your own genitals on a regular basis to make sure you're not inadvertently passing on an STI to a partner. Women will need to use a hand-held mirror to do so.

Urinating both before and after intercourse helps to keep bacteria out of the urethra.

Finally, each person needs to recognize that it is his or her ethical responsibility to seek out early diagnosis and treatment. Probably the most important responsibility is that of informing prospective partners if you have an STI and of informing past partners as soon as you discover that you have one. For example, because so many women are asymptomatic for chlamydia, it is particularly important for men to take the responsibility of informing their female partners if they find that they have the infection. It is important to take care of your own health, but it is equally important to take care of your partner's health.

OTHER GENITAL INFECTIONS

Vaginitis (vaj-in-ITE-is): An irritation or inflammation of the vagina, usually causing a discharge.

Vaginitis (vaginal inflammation or irritation) is very common among women and is endemic in university populations. Two kinds of vaginitis, as well as cystitis (inflammation of the urinary bladder) and prostatitis, will be considered here. None of these infections are STIs, because they are not transmitted by sexual contact; they are, however, common infections of the sex organs.

A few simple steps can help prevent vaginitis. Every time you shower or take a bath, wash the vulva carefully and dry it thoroughly. Do not use feminine hygiene deodorant sprays; they are unnecessary and can irritate the vagina. Wear cotton underpants; nylon and other synthetics retain moisture, and vaginitis-producing organisms thrive on moisture. Avoid wearing pants that are too tight in the crotch; they increase moisture and may irritate the vulva. Wipe the anus from front to back so that bacteria from the anus do not get into the vagina. For the same reason, never go immediately from anal intercourse to vaginal intercourse. Finally, if an attack of vaginitis seems to be coming on, placing some yogurt with active cultures into the vagina can help restore the good bacteria.

MONILIA

Monilia (Moh-NILL-ee-uh): A form of vaginitis causing a thick, white discharge; also called candida or yeast infection.

Monilia (also called *candida, yeast infection, fungus,* and *moniliasis*) is a form of vaginitis caused by the yeast fungus *Candida. Candida* is normally present in the vagina, but if the delicate environmental balance there is disturbed (e.g., if the pH is changed), the growth of *Candida* can get out of hand. Conditions that encourage the growth of *Candida* include long-term use of birth control pills, menstruation, diabetes or a prediabetic condition, pregnancy, and long-term use of antibiotics such as tetracycline. It is not a sexually transmitted infection, although intercourse may aggravate it.

The major symptom is a thick, white, curdlike vaginal discharge, found on the vaginal lips and the walls of the vagina. The discharge can cause extreme itching, to the point where the woman is not interested in having intercourse.

Treatment is by the drugs miconzole or clotelnazole, both available over the counter. Flucomazole, a single-dose treatment, is available by prescription.

If a woman has monilia while she is pregnant, she can transmit it to her baby during birth. The baby gets the yeast in its digestive system, a condition known as *thrush*. Thrush can also result from oral–genital sex.

Bacterial vaginosis is another vaginal infection that produces a similar discharge. The distinctive feature is that the discharge has a foul odour.

CYSTITIS

Cystitis is an infection of the urinary bladder that occurs almost exclusively in women. In most cases it is caused by the bacterium *Escherichia coli*. The bacteria are normally present in the body (in the intestine), and in some cases, for unknown reasons, they get into the urethra and the bladder. Sometimes frequent, vigorous sexual intercourse will irritate the urethral opening, permitting the bacteria to get in.

The symptoms are a desire to urinate every few minutes, with a burning pain on urination. The urine may be hazy or even tinged with red; this is caused by pus and blood from the infected bladder. There may also be backache. Diagnosis can usually be made simply on the basis of these symptoms. A urine sample should be taken and analyzed, though, for confirmation.

Treatment is usually with Bactrim or another antibiotic. The drug may include a dye that helps relieve the burning sensation on urination; the dye turns the urine bright orange-red.

To prevent cystitis or prevent recurring bouts of it, drink lots of water and urinate frequently, especially just before and after intercourse. This will help flush out any bacteria from the bladder and urethra.

Cystitis (sis-TY-tis): An infection of the urinary bladder in women, causing painful, burning urination.

PROSTATITIS

Prostatitis is an inflammation or swelling of the prostate gland. It used to be thought that it was almost always caused by an infection by the bacterium E. coli, but it is now known that it can be caused by several different conditions. It can also be caused by gonorrhea or chlamydia. The typical symptoms are fever; chills; pain above the penis or around the scrotum, anus, or rectum; difficulty starting urination; and a need for frequent urination. Research in Ontario has shown that it may produce sexual dysfunction (Smith et al., 2007). In some cases, prostatitis may be chronic (long-lasting) and may have no symptoms, or only lower-back pain. Antibiotics are used in treatment.

Prostatitis (pros-tuh-TY-tis): An infection, inflammation, or swelling of the prostate gland.

SUMMARY

Sexually transmitted infections (STIs) are at epidemic levels in Canada and worldwide. Three common STIs among college and university students are chlamydia, HPV, and herpes.

Chlamydia is often asymptomatic, especially in women. In men, it produces a thin discharge from the penis and mild pain on urination. It is quite curable with antibiotics. If left untreated in women, the possible complications include pelvic inflammatory disease and possibly infertility.

HPV (human papillomavirus) causes genital warts. Sometimes the warts are obvious, but in other cases they are small and may not be visible. HPV infection increases women's risk of cervical cancer, and a vaccine is now available.

Genital herpes, caused by the HSV virus, produces bouts of painful blisters on the genitals. These episodes may recur for the rest of the person's life, although some infected persons experience no or only a few outbreaks. Currently, there is no cure, although the drug acyclovir minimizes the symptoms. Herpes infection increases one's risk of HIV infection.

The virus HIV destroys the body's natural immune system and leaves the person vulnerable to certain kinds of infections and cancers that lead to death. The most frequent means of transmission in Canada are men who have sex with men, use of injection drugs, and having heterosexual contact with an infected person. Drugs such as AZT and ritonavir (a protease inhibitor) are used to slow the progression of the disease. More attention needs to focus on the special concerns of HIV-infected women and ethnic minorities. Several strategies for producing a vaccine are being pursued.

The primary symptoms of gonorrhea in the male, appearing two to five days after infection, are a white or yellow discharge from the penis and a burning pain on urination. The majority of women with gonorrhea are asymptomatic. Gonorrhea is caused by a bacterium, the gonococcus, and is cured with antibiotics. If left untreated, it may lead to infertility.

Syphilis is caused by the bacterium *Treponema pallidum*. The first symptom is a chancre. Penicillin is effective as a cure. If left untreated, the disease progresses through several stages that may lead to death.

Hepatitis B, caused by the virus HBV, is transmitted sexually as well as by needle sharing. Antiviral drugs are available to treat chronic cases. A vaccine is now available and is being administered widely.

Pubic lice are tiny lice that attach to the pubic hair. They are spread through sexual and other types of physical contact. Shampoos are available for treatment.

Techniques for preventing STIs include thorough washing of both partners' genitals before intercourse; urination both before and after intercourse; inspecting the partner's genitals for symptoms like a wart or urethral discharge; and the use of a condom.

Other vaginal infections include monilia, trichomoniasis, and bacterial vaginosis. Cystitis is an infection of the urinary bladder in women, leading to frequent, burning urination. Prostatitis is inflammation of the prostate gland.

QUESTIONS FOR THOUGHT, DISCUSSION, AND DEBATE

1. Contact the student health service on your campus and see whether they might be willing to share with you the number of cases of chlamydia, gonorrhea, genital warts, and herpes they diagnose per year; then share the information with your class.

2. Design a program to reduce the number of cases of sexually transmitted infections on your campus.

3. Michael has had a monogamous relationship with Sonya for six months. At her annual pelvic exam, Sonya discovers that she has chlamydia and blows up at Michael for giving it to her. Michael has never been tested for anything. What should Michael and Sonya discuss with each other, what other information do they need, and what should they do?

4. If you were designing an intervention for Aboriginal teenagers to reduce the spread of HIV, how would you make that intervention culturally sensitive? Would the approach be different for women and for men? If you feel that you don't know enough about Aboriginal culture, interview some Aboriginal students or community members to find out more.

SUGGESTIONS FOR FURTHER READING

Barrett, Michael (Ed.). (1997). *The Canadian Journal of Human Sexuality: STDs and Sexual/Reproductive Health, 6*(4). Toronto: SIECCAN. This volume of the journal contains a series of articles that summarize our current knowledge about the major STIs and make recommendations for prevention and control of STIs in Canada.

Barrett, Michael (Ed.). (1998). *The Canadian Journal of Human Sexuality: Innovative STD Prevention and Education Programs in Canada, 7*(4). Toronto: SIECCAN. This volume of the journal features articles describing innovative STI prevention programs in Canada.

Ebel, Charles, and Wald, Anna. (2002). *Managing herpes: How to live and love with a chronic STD.* Research Triangle Park, NC: American Social Health Association. People say this is the best herpes book ever.

Gallo, Roe, and McIlvenna, Ted. (2003). *Sexual strategies for pleasure and safety.* San Francisco: Specific Press. An excellent guide to creating a safer sex life.

For review questions, web resources, and other learning and study tools, visit the *Understanding Human Sexuality* Online Learning Centre at www.mcgrawhill.ca/olc/hyde.

Chapter

9

SEXUAL RESPONSE

Chapter Highlights

> HERE ARE SOME COLORS OF DIFFERENT PEOPLE'S ORGASMS: CHAMPAGNE, ALL COLORS AND WHITE AND GRAY AFTERWARD, RED AND BLUE, GREEN, BEIGE AND BLUE, RED, BLUE AND GOLD. SOME PEOPLE NEVER MAKE IT BECAUSE THEY ARE TRYING FOR PLAID.*

This chapter is about the way the body responds during sexual arousal and orgasm and the processes behind these responses. This information is very important in developing good techniques of lovemaking discussed later in this chapter and in analyzing and treating sexual problems such as rapid ejaculation or orgasmic dysfunction (see Chapter 18).

First we examine how the body responds physiologically during orgasm. Much of what we know about these processes is based on the classic research of Masters and Johnson. Their research has been criticized, though, so in the next section some alternative models to theirs are presented. Next, we focus on how hormones, the brain, and the spinal cord contribute to sexual behaviour and response. We consider research on pheromones and their influence on sexual behaviour in animals and in humans. Finally, we discuss techniques that bring people sexual pleasure.

THE SEXUAL RESPONSE CYCLE

Sex researchers William H. Masters and Virginia E. Johnson provided one of the first models of the physiology of human sexual response. Their research culminated in 1966 with the publication of *Human Sexual Response*, which reported data on 382 women and 312 men observed in more than 10 000 sexual cycles of arousal and orgasm. Recent biological research has confirmed many of their findings, while questioning a few and augmenting many. All of this research is the basis for the sections that follow.

Sexual response typically progresses in three stages, *excitement, orgasm,* and *resolution.* The two basic physiological processes that occur during these stages are vasocongestion and myotonia. Vasocongestion occurs when a great deal of blood flows into the blood vessels in a region, in this case the genitals, as a result of dilation of the blood vessels in the region. Myotonia occurs when muscles contract, not only in the genitals but also throughout the body. Let us now consider in detail what occurs in each of the stages.

EXCITEMENT

The excitement phase is the beginning of erotic arousal. The basic physiological process that occurs during excitement is vasocongestion. This produces the obvious arousal response in the male—erection. Erection results when the corpora cavernosa and the corpus spongiosum fill (becoming engorged) with blood (see Figure 9.1). Erection may be produced by direct physical stimulation of the genitals, by stimulation of other parts of the body, or by erotic thoughts. Vasocongestion occurs very rapidly, and in young men erection may occur within a few seconds of the stimulation, although it may take place more slowly as a result of a number of factors, including age, intake of alcohol, and fatigue. As the man gets closer to orgasm, a few drops of fluid (for some men quite a few) secreted by the Cowper's gland appear at the tip of the penis. Although they are not ejaculate, they may contain active sperm.

Research in the last decade—stimulated, in part, by the search for Viagra—has given us much more detailed information about the physiological processes involved in erection

Vasocongestion (vay-so-con-JES-tyun): An accumulation of blood in the blood vessels of a region of the body, especially the genitals; a swelling or erection results.

Myotonia (my-oh-TONE-ee-ah): Muscle contraction.

Excitement: The first stage of sexual response, during which erection in the male and vaginal lubrication in the female occur.

---

*Eric Berne. (1970). *Sex in human loving*. New York: Simon & Schuster, p. 238.

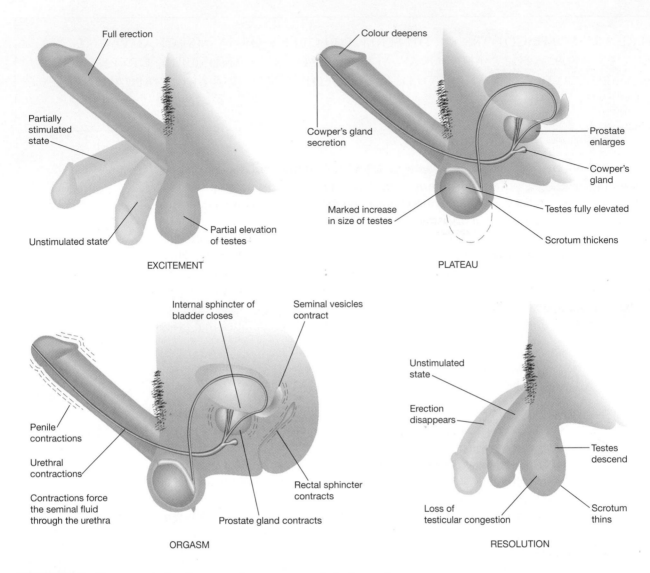

EXCITEMENT

Full erection

Partially stimulated state

Unstimulated state

Partial elevation of testes

PLATEAU

Colour deepens

Cowper's gland secretion

Marked increase in size of testes

Prostate enlarges

Cowper's gland

Testes fully elevated

Scrotum thickens

ORGASM

Internal sphincter of bladder closes

Seminal vesicles contract

Penile contractions

Urethral contractions

Contractions force the seminal fluid through the urethra

Prostate gland contracts

Rectal sphincter contracts

RESOLUTION

Unstimulated state

Erection disappears

Loss of testicular congestion

Testes descend

Scrotum thins

Figure 9.1   Changes during the sexual response cycle in the male.

(Adams, 1997; Heaton, 2000). Several arteries supply the corpora cavernosa and spongiosum. For an erection to occur, these arteries must dilate (vasodilation), allowing a strong flow of blood into the corpora. At the same time, the veins carrying blood away from the penis are compressed, restricting outgoing blood flow. The arteries dilate because the smooth muscle surrounding the arteries relaxes. Multiple neurotransmitters are involved in this process including, especially, nitric oxide (NO). Viagra acts on the NO system.

Of course, erections, nice though they are, would become a pain if they lasted forever, so there is a reverse process—vasoconstriction—that makes an erection go away—for example, following orgasm. The neurotransmitters epinephrine and norepinephrine are involved. These processes occur in the resolution phase, discussed shortly.

An important response of females in the excitement phase is lubrication of the vagina. Although this response might seem much different from the male's, actually they both result from the same physiological process: vasocongestion. During excitement, the capillaries in the walls of the vagina dilate and blood flow through them increases (Levin, 2005). Vaginal lubrication results when fluids seep through the semipermeable membranes of the vaginal walls, producing lubrication as a result of vasocongestion in the tissues surrounding the vagina. This

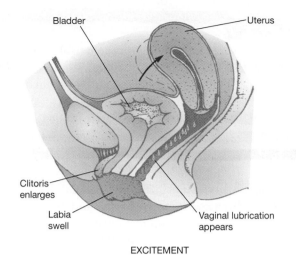

Bladder

Uterus

Clitoris enlarges

Labia swell

Vaginal lubrication appears

EXCITEMENT

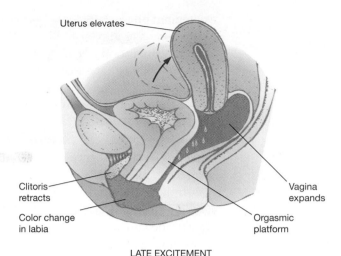

Uterus elevates

Clitoris retracts

Color change in labia

Vagina expands

Orgasmic platform

LATE EXCITEMENT

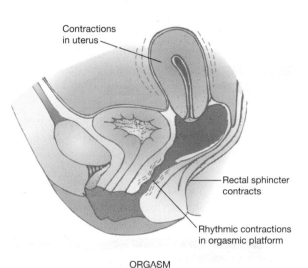

Contractions in uterus

Rectal sphincter contracts

Rhythmic contractions in orgasmic platform

ORGASM

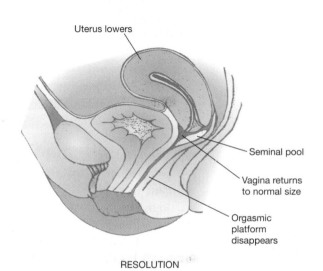

Uterus lowers

Seminal pool

Vagina returns to normal size

Orgasmic platform disappears

RESOLUTION

Figure 9.2 Changes during the sexual response cycle in the female.

response to arousal is also rapid, though not quite so fast as the male's; lubrication usually begins 10 to 30 seconds after the onset of arousing stimuli.[1] Like the male sexual response, female responding can be affected by factors such as age, intake of alcohol, and fatigue.

As the woman becomes more aroused and gets closer to orgasm, the orgasmic platform forms. This is a tightening and thickening of the wall of the outer third of the vagina (Figure 9.2). Thus, the size of the vaginal entrance actually becomes smaller, and there may be a noticeable increase in gripping of the penis.

During the excitement phase the glans of the clitoris (the tip) swells. This results from engorgement of its corpora cavernosa and is similar to erection in the male. The clitoris can be felt as larger and harder than usual under excitement. The crura of the clitoris, lying deeper in the body (refer to Figure 4.3 on page 83), also swell as a result of vasocongestion. The vestibular bulbs, which lie along the wall of the vagina, are also erectile and swell during the

Orgasmic platform: A tightening of the entrance to the vagina caused by contractions of the bulbospongiosus muscle (which covers the vestibular bulbs) that occur during the plateau stage of sexual response.

[1] Before the Masters and Johnson research, it was thought that the lubrication was due to secretions of the Bartholin glands, but it is now known that these glands contribute little if anything. At this point, you might want to go back to the limerick about the Bartholin glands in Chapter 4 (see page 85) and see whether you can spot the error in it.

excitement phase. Late in the excitement phase, elevation of the clitoris may occur. The clitoris essentially retracts or draws up into the body.

Vasocongestion in females results from the same underlying physiological processes as in males. That is, relaxation of the smooth muscles surrounding the arteries supplying the glans and crura of the clitoris and the vestibular bulbs occurs, allowing a great deal of blood flow to the region (Berman et al., 2000). As in the male, nitric oxide is a key neurotransmitter involved in the process (Traish et al., 2002). Estrogen helps the vasodilation. In the unaroused state the inner lips are generally folded over, covering the entrance to the vagina, and the outer lips lie close to each other. During excitement the inner lips swell and open up (a vaso-congestion response).

Under excitement, the nipples become erect; this results from contractions of the muscle fibres (myotonia) surrounding the nipple. The breasts themselves swell and enlarge some-what in the late part of the excitement phase (a vasocongestion response). Thus, the nipples may not actually look erect but may appear somewhat flatter against the breast because the breast has swollen. Many males also have nipple erection during the excitement phase.

The vagina shows an important change during excitement. Think of the vagina as being divided into two parts, an upper (or inner) two-thirds and a lower (or outer) one-third. In the unaroused state the walls of the vagina lie against each other, much like the sides of an uninflated balloon. During the excitement phase, the upper two-thirds of the vagina expands dramatically in what is often called a "ballooning" response; that is, it becomes more like an inflated balloon (see Figure 9.2). This helps accommodate penetration. As part of the balloon-ing, the cervix and uterus also pull up.

During excitement, a "sex flush" may appear on the skin of both men and women, though more commonly of women. The sex flush resembles a measles rash; it often begins on the upper abdomen and spreads over the chest. It may also appear later in the sexual response cycle.

Other changes that occur in both men and women include an increase in pulse rate and in blood pressure.

In men, the skin of the scrotum thickens. The scrotal sac tenses, and the scrotum is pulled up and closer to the body (Figure 9.1). The spermatic cords shorten, pulling the testes closer to the body. Late in the excitement phase, the process of vasocongestion and myotonia con-tinue to build until there is sufficient tension for orgasm.

ORGASM

Orgasm: The second stage of sexual response; an intense sensation that occurs at the peak of sexual arousal and is followed by release of sexual tensions.

In the male, orgasm consists of a series of rhythmic contractions of the pelvic organs at 0.8-second intervals. Actually, male orgasm occurs in two stages. In the preliminary stage, the vas, seminal vesicles, and prostate contract, forcing the ejaculate into a bulb at the base of the urethra (Figure 9.1). Masters and Johnson call the sensation in this stage one of *ejaculatory inevitability* ("cumming"); that is, there is a sensation that ejaculation is just about to happen and cannot be stopped. And, indeed, although men can learn to delay reaching the emission stage of ejaculation, ejaculation cannot be stopped, once the man has reached this point. In the second stage the urethral bulb, muscles at the base of the penis, and the urethra contract rhythmically, forcing the semen through the urethra and out the opening at the tip of the penis. There may also be a difference between ejaculation and the sensation of orgasm (Mah & Binik, 2001). For example, researchers in Quebec have shown that feelings of pleasure and satisfaction from orgasm were more strongly related to psychological and social factors than to physical factors (Mah & Binik, 2005).

In both males and females, there are sharp increases in pulse rate, blood pressure, and breathing rate during orgasm.[2] Muscles contract throughout the body. The face may be

---

[2]With all the current attention to aerobics and exercising the heart, we have yet to hear anyone suggest orgasm aerobics. It seems to us that it should work. Kickboxing, watch out. Here comes sexercise!

contorted in a grimace; the muscles of the arms, legs, thighs, back, and buttocks may contract; and the muscles of the feet and hands may contract in "carpopedal spasms." Generally, in the passion of the moment, one is not really aware of these occurrences.

The process of orgasm in females is basically similar to that in males. It is a series of rhythmic muscular contractions of the orgasmic platform. The contractions generally occur at about 0.8-second intervals; there may be three or four in a mild orgasm or as many as a dozen in a very intense, prolonged orgasm. The uterus also contracts rhythmically. Other muscles, such as those around the anus, may also contract.

Female orgasm typically leaves no tangible evidence (except for those women who experience emission of fluid) and women often do not reach orgasm as quickly as men do, a point to be discussed in more detail in Chapter 13. As a result, some women, particularly young women, may think they are having an orgasm when they are not; they have never had an orgasm, and they mistake intense arousal for orgasm.

Just what does orgasm in the female feel like? The main feeling is a spreading sensation that begins around the clitoris and then spreads outward through the whole pelvis. There may also be sensations of falling or opening up. The woman may be able to feel the contraction of the muscles around the vaginal entrance. The sensation is more intense than just a warm glow or a pleasant tingling. In one study, university men and women gave written descriptions of what an orgasm felt like to them (Vance & Wagner, 1976). Interestingly, a panel of experts (medical students, obstetrician-gynecologists, and clinical psychologists) could not reliably figure out which of the descriptions were written by women and which by men. This suggests that the sensations are quite similar for males and females.

Some of the men in our classes have asked how they can tell whether a woman has really had an orgasm. Their question in itself is interesting. In part it reflects a cultural skepticism about female orgasm. There is usually obvious proof of male orgasm: ejaculation. But there is no consistent proof of female orgasm except that some women do ejaculate. The question also reflects the fact that women sometimes fake orgasm. Faking orgasm is a complex issue. Basically, it probably is not a very good idea, because it is dishonest. It also leads the woman's partner to think that his or her technique of stimulation is more effective than it is. On the other hand, one needs to understand the variety of reasons women feel that this is necessary. It is sometimes difficult for women to orgasm, and our culture currently places a lot of emphasis on everyone's having orgasms. The woman may feel that she is expected to have an orgasm, and realizing that it is unlikely to happen this time, she fakes it in order to meet expectations. She may also do it to please her partner.[3] But back to the question: How can one tell? There really is not any very good way. From a scientific point of view, a good method would be to have the woman hooked up to an instrument that registers pulse rate; there is a sudden sharp increase in the pulse rate at orgasm, and that would be a good indicator. That doesn't seem like a very practical or desirable approach. Probably rather than trying to check up on each other, it would be better for partners to establish good, honest communication and avoid setting up performance goals in sex, points that will be discussed further in later chapters.

RESOLUTION

Following orgasm is the **resolution** phase, during which the body returns physiologically to the unaroused state. Orgasm triggers a massive release of muscular tension and of blood from the engorged blood vessels. Resolution, then, represents a reversal of the processes that build up during the excitement stage.

Resolution: The third stage of sexual response, in which the body returns to the unaroused state.

---

[3]Indeed, many of the old sex manuals, as well as physicians' textbooks, counselled women to fake orgasm. For example: "It is good advice to recommend to the women the advantage of innocent simulation of sex responsiveness, and as a matter of fact many women in their desire to please their husbands learned the advantage of such innocent deception" (Novak & Novak, 1952, p. 572)

The first change in women is a reduction in the swelling of the breasts. In the five to ten seconds after the end of the orgasm, the clitoris returns to its normal position, although it takes longer for it to shrink to its normal size. The orgasmic platform relaxes and begins to shrink. The resolution phase generally takes 15 to 30 minutes, but it may take much longer—as much as an hour—in women who have not had an orgasm.

In both males and females, resolution brings a gradual return of pulse rate, blood pressure, and breathing rate to the unaroused levels.

In men, the most obvious occurrence in the resolution phase is *detumescence*, the loss of erection in the penis. This happens in two stages, the first occurring rapidly but leaving the penis still enlarged (this first loss of erection results from an emptying of the corpora cavernosa) and the second occurring more slowly, as a result of the slower emptying of the corpus spongiosum and the glans.

During the resolution phase, men enter a refractory period, during which they are refractory to further arousal; that is, they are incapable of being aroused again, having an erection, or having an orgasm. The length of this refractory period varies considerably from one man to the next; in some it may last only a few minutes, and in others it may go on for 24 hours. The refractory period tends to become longer as men grow older.

Women usually do not have a refractory period, making possible the phenomenon of multiple orgasm in women, to be discussed in the next section.

Oxytocin is secreted during sexual arousal, and a surge of prolactin occurs at orgasm in both women and men (Exton et al., 1999; Levin, 2003; Krüger et al., 2002). Some think that prolactin is the off-switch to sexual arousal and that it creates the refractory period in males, although that does not explain why females do not have a refractory period. Interestingly, in both women and men, much more prolactin is secreted following orgasm from intercourse than orgasm from masturbation (Kruger, 2006).

MORE ON WOMEN'S ORGASMS

Some people believe that women can have two kinds of orgasm: clitoral orgasm and vaginal orgasm. The words "clitoral" and "vaginal" refer to the locus of stimulation: an orgasm resulting from clitoral stimulation versus an orgasm resulting from vaginal stimulation. The distinction was originated by Sigmund Freud. Freud believed that in childhood little girls masturbate and thus have orgasms by means of clitoral stimulation, or clitoral orgasms. He thought that as women grow older and mature, that is, after the Oedipal stage, they shift their erogenous zone from their clitoris to their vagina. Consequently, they shift from having orgasms as a result of clitoral stimulation to having them as a result of heterosexual intercourse, that is, by means of vaginal stimulation. Thus he considered vaginal orgasms "mature" and clitoral orgasms "immature" in a developmental sense. Not only did there come to be two types of orgasms, but "mature" has been taken to mean "better," such that many people view one kind of orgasm (orgasms through intercourse alone) as better than the other.

Freud's formulation is of more than theoretical interest. The interpretation of vaginal orgasms as more mature has had an impact on the lives of many women over several decades. Many undertook psychoanalysis and spent countless hours agonizing over why they were not able to achieve the elusive vaginal orgasm and why they enjoyed the "immature" clitoral one so much. Women who could have orgasms only through clitoral stimulation were called "vaginally frigid" or "fixated" at an infantile stage. A number of important findings on the nature of sexual response, which emerged from the Masters and Johnson research, refute Freud's views. Two of these are discussed here.

According to the results of Masters and Johnson's research, there is no difference between clitoral and vaginal orgasms. This conclusion is based on two findings. First, their results indicate that all female orgasms are physiologically the same, regardless of the site of stimulation.

Refractory (ree-FRAK-toh-ree) period: The period following orgasm during which the male cannot be sexually aroused.

Clitoral orgasm: Freud's term for orgasm in the female resulting from stimulation of the clitoris.

Vaginal orgasm: Freud's term for orgasm in the female resulting from stimulation of the vagina in heterosexual intercourse; Freud considered vaginal orgasm to be more mature than clitoral orgasm.

That is, an orgasm always consists of contractions of the orgasmic platform whether the stimulation is clitoral or vaginal. Indeed, they found a few women who could orgasm purely through breast stimulation, and that orgasm was the same as the other two, consisting of contractions of the orgasmic platform and the muscles around the vagina. Thus, physiologically there is only one kind of orgasm. (Of course, this does not mean that psychologically there are not different kinds; the experience of orgasm during intercourse may be quite different from the experience of orgasm during masturbation.) Second, clitoral stimulation is almost always involved in producing orgasm, even during vaginal intercourse. The deep structure of the clitoris (refer to Figure 4.3 on page 83) ensures that the crura of the clitoris are stimulated as the penis moves through the vaginal entrance. Thus, even the purely "vaginal" orgasm results from quite a bit of clitoral stimulation. Clitoral stimulation is usually the trigger to orgasm; the orgasm itself occurs in the vagina and surrounding tissues.

Traditionally it was believed that orgasmically, women and men can have one orgasm and then would have a refractory period before they can have another. Masters and Johnson, however, discovered that women do not enter into a refractory period, and with continued stimulation they can have **multiple orgasms** within a short period of time. Actually, women's capacity for multiple orgasms was originally discovered by Kinsey in his interviews with women (Kinsey et al., 1953; see also Terman et al., 1938). The scientific establishment, however, dismissed these reports as another instance of Kinsey's supposed unreliability.

The term "multiple orgasm," then, refers to a series of orgasms occurring within a short period of time. They do not differ physiologically from single orgasms. Each is a "real" orgasm, and they are not minor experiences. One nice thing, though, is that the later ones generally require less stimulation than the first one.

How does multiple orgasm work physiologically? Immediately following an orgasm, both males and females move into the resolution phase. In this phase, males typically enter into a refractory period, during which they cannot be aroused again. But the female usually does not enter a refractory period, perhaps because after orgasm it takes longer for vasocongestion to return to baseline in women than in men (Mah & Binik, 2001). That is, if stimulation continues she can immediately be aroused and have another orgasm if she chooses to.

Multiple orgasm with a partner is more likely to result from hand–genital or mouth–genital stimulation than from intercourse. Regarding capacity, Masters and Johnson found that women in masturbation might have 5 to 20 orgasms. In some cases, they quit only when physically exhausted. When a vibrator is used, less effort is required, and some women were capable of having 50 orgasms in a row.

It should be noted that some women who are capable of multiple orgasms are satisfied with one, particularly in intercourse,

Multiple orgasm: A series of orgasms occurring within a short period of time.

"Did you comm?"

ChENEY

Figure 9.3   Tom Cheney/Reprinted Courtesy of *Penthouse* Magazine.

and do not wish to continue. We should be careful not to set multiple orgasm as another of the many goals in sexual performance.

Some men are capable of having multiple orgasms (e.g., Hartman & Fithian, 1984; Zilbergeld, 1992). In one study, 21 men were interviewed, all of whom had volunteered for research on multiply orgasmic men (Dunn & Trost, 1989). Some of the men reported having been multiply orgasmic since they began having sex, whereas others had developed the pattern later in life, and still others had worked actively to develop the capacity after reading about the possibility. The respondents reported that multiple orgasm did not occur every time they engaged in sexual activity. For these men, detumescence did not always follow an orgasm, allowing for continued stimulation and an additional orgasm. Some reported that some of the orgasms included ejaculation and others in the sequence did not. This study cannot tell us the incidence of multiply orgasmic men in the general population, but it does provide evidence that multiply orgasmic men exist.

COGNITIVE-PHYSIOLOGICAL MODELS

Some experts on human sexuality are critical of Masters and Johnson's model. One important criticism is that the Masters and Johnson model ignores the cognitive and subjective aspects of sexual response (Zilbergeld & Ellison, 1980). That is, Masters and Johnson focused almost entirely on the physiological aspects of sexual response, ignoring what the person is thinking and feeling emotionally. Desire and passion are not part of the model, and it omits the subjective qualities of arousal and orgasm. An individual's subjective experience may be influenced by the context and the quality of the relationship in which sexual activity occurs as well as by a variety of psychological factors (Mah & Binik, 2001). The omission of the subjective element may be particularly problematic in understanding women's sexual response because women tend to emphasize subjective arousal rather than physical arousal (Working Group for a New View of Women's Sexual Problems, 2001). Women's sense of being aroused is often unrelated to awareness of genital changes (Laan et al., 1994). Research in Quebec has shown that there are two components to orgasm for both men and women: a sensory dimension, made up of the physical sensations, and a cognitive-affective dimension, consisting of pleasure, satisfaction, emotional intimacy, and feelings of ecstasy (Mah & Binik, 2002).

A second important criticism concerns how research participants were selected and how this process may have created a self-fulfilling prophecy for the outcome (Tiefer, 1991a). To participate in the research, participants were required to have a history of orgasm both through masturbation and through coitus. Essentially, anyone whose pattern of sexual response did not include orgasm—and therefore did not fit Masters and Johnson's model—was excluded from the research. As such, the model cannot be generalized to the entire population. Masters and Johnson themselves commented that every one of their participants was characterized by high and consistent levels of sexual desire. Yet sexual desire is certainly missing among some members of the general population, or it is present sometimes and absent at others. The research, in short, claims to be objective and universal when it is neither (Tiefer, 1991a).

Once these difficulties with the Masters and Johnson research and model of sexual response were recognized, several alternative models were proposed. We will examine two of them in the following sections. Both of them add a cognitive component to Masters and Johnson's physiological model.

Triphasic model: Kaplan's model of sexual response, in which there are three phases: sexual desire, vasocongestion, and muscular contractions.

KAPLAN'S TRIPHASIC MODEL

On the basis of her work on sex therapy (discussed in Chapter 18), Helen Singer Kaplan (1974, 1979) proposed a triphasic model of sexual response. Rather than thinking of the sexual response as having successive stages, she conceptualized it as having three relatively independent phases, or components: *sexual desire, vasocongestion* of the genitals, and the reflex *muscular contractions* of the orgasm phase. Notice that two of the components (vaso-congestion and muscular contractions) are physiological, whereas the other (sexual desire) is psychological. Therefore, Kaplan's model adds the desire component that was missing in Masters and Johnson's model.

There are a number of justifications for Kaplan's approach. First, the two physiological components are controlled by different parts of the nervous system. Vasocongestion—producing erection in the male and lubrication in the female—is controlled by the parasympathetic division of the autonomic nervous system. In contrast, ejaculation and orgasm are controlled by the sympathetic division.

Second, the two components involve different anatomical structures: blood vessels for vasocongestion and muscles for the contractions of orgasm.

Third, vasocongestion and orgasm differ in their susceptibility to being disturbed by injury, drugs, or age. For example, the refractory period following orgasm in the male lengthens with age. Accordingly, there is a decrease in the frequency of orgasm with age. In contrast, for many men the capacity for erection is relatively unimpaired with age, although the erection may be slower to make its appearance. An elderly man may have non-orgasmic sex several times a week, with a firm erection, although he may have an orgasm only once a week.

Fourth, the reflex of ejaculation in the male can be brought under voluntary control by most men, but the erection reflex generally cannot.

Finally, the impairment of the vasocongestion response or the orgasm response produce different disturbances (sexual disorders). Erection problems in men are caused by an impairment of the vasocongestion response, whereas rapid ejaculation and delayed ejaculation are disturbances of the orgasm response. Similarly, many women show a strong arousal and vasocongestion response, yet have trouble with the orgasm component of their sexual response.

Kaplan's triphasic model is useful both for understanding the nature of sexual response and for understanding and treating disturbances in it. Her writing on the desire phase is particularly useful in understanding problems of low sexual desire, to be discussed in Chapter 18.

Kaplan's model assumes that desire comes before arousal motivating the person toward sexual activity and excitement. Vancouver physician Rosemary Basson (2001) has developed an intimacy-based model of sexual response that does not make this assumption (see Figure 9.4). She argues that some people in long-term relationships, particularly women, may not be motivated to engage in sexual activity by their experience of spontaneous sexual desire. Rather they are motivated to engage in sexual activity in order to enhance intimacy, closeness, and commitment with their partner, to enhance their sense of attractiveness, or to share physical sexual pleasure. That is, they begin sexual activity in a sexually neutral state, but are receptive to sexual stimuli that will arouse them. Once sexual activity has begun, the person becomes aroused. This leads them to experience sexual desire and enhanced sexual arousal. Thus, according to Basson, some people may begin sexual activity for intimacy reasons, but then continue for sexual as well as intimacy reasons. Basson also acknowledges that, even in long-term relationships, both men and women can and do experience spontaneous sexual

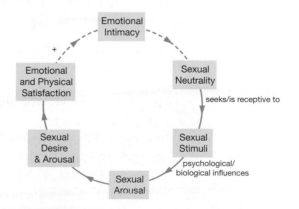

Figure 9.4 Basson's intimacy model of sexual response showing that desire sometimes comes after arousal/excitement.

desire outside of this intimacy model that may lead to sexual activity with their partner, casual sex, or self-stimulation.

A recent study described the Masters and Johnson, Kaplan, and Basson models to women and asked them which fit their experience best (Sand & Fisher, 2007). About equal numbers of women chose each of the three models.

WALEN AND ROTH: A COGNITIVE MODEL

As noted earlier, an important criticism of the Masters and Johnson model is that it ignores the cognitive and subjective aspects of sexual response. In Chapter 2 we discussed the importance of cognitive approaches in understanding the psychology of human sexuality. Walen and Roth (1987) have applied this approach to understanding the sexual response. Their model is shown in Figure 9.5.

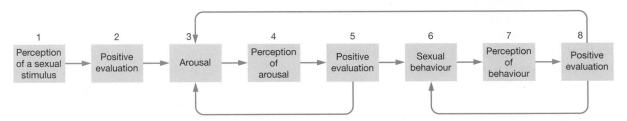

Figure 9.5 Walen and Roth's cognitive model showing the feedback loop that produces a positive sexual experience.

Recall from Chapter 2 that according to the cognitive approach, how we feel depends tremendously on what we are thinking: how we perceive what is occurring and how we evaluate it. Thus, the first step in the cognitive model is *perception:* the perception of a stimulus as sexual. What we perceive to be sexy stimuli (whether they are visual stimuli, touch stimuli, or odours) depends a great deal on the culture in which we've grown up and on our prior learning. If you've just begun a sexual relationship with someone, the very sight of that person may make you feel turned on, whereas looking at ten other people in the same room produces no turn-on. To some people, the sight of black leather, high-heeled women's boots may produce instant arousal.

The second step in the cognitive model is *evaluation.* If we feel positive about the sexual stimulus, that will lead to the next step, arousal, but if our evaluation of the stimulus is negative, the arousal cycle stops. For example, if you are a married woman and your husband, with whom you normally have a great sex life, begins to kiss you when his breath smells of a cigarette he has just smoked, your evaluation of the sexual stimulus is likely to be negative and you will not feel aroused.

Let's suppose, though, that the evaluation of the sexual stimulus is positive. Physiological *arousal*—as described in the Masters and Johnson model discussed earlier in this chapter—is the next step. But again, the cognitive approach says that it is not so much what happens physically, but whether we perceive the arousal and how we evaluate it that affects both the extent to which we get more and more aroused as well as our sexual behaviour. Similarly, our *perception of our sexual behaviour* and a *positive evaluation* of it are critical for the arousal cycle and our sexual behaviour to continue.

In sum, the cognitive model of the sexual response cycle stresses the importance of our perception and evaluation of sexual events. In many ways, the greatest erogenous zone is the brain.

Figure 9.6 Can the cognitive model of sexual arousal explain our response to this? Here a man touches a woman's breast, but it is not sexual. Why not? The context, a medical office, leads us not to perceive the woman's breast as a sexual stimulus, nor the man's touch as sexual.

HORMONAL AND NEURAL BASES OF SEXUAL BEHAVIOUR

Up to this point we have focused on the cognitive and genital responses that occur during sexual activity. We have not yet considered the underlying neural and hormonal mechanisms that make this possible; they are the topic of this section.

THE BRAIN, THE SPINAL CORD, AND SEX

The brain and the spinal cord both have important interacting functions in sexual response. First, the relatively simple spinal reflexes involved in sexual response will be discussed; then the more complex brain mechanisms will be considered.

SPINAL REFLEXES

Several important components of sexual behaviour, including erection and ejaculation, are controlled by fairly simple spinal cord reflexes (see the lower part of Figure 9.7). A reflex has three basic components: the *receptors*, which are sensory neurons that detect stimuli and transmit the message to the spinal cord (or brain); the *transmitters*, which are centres in the spinal cord (or brain) that receive the message, interpret it, and send out a message to produce the appropriate response; and the *effectors*, neurons or muscles that respond to the stimulation. The jerking away of the hand when it touches a hot object is a good example of a spinal reflex.

MECHANISM OF ERECTION

Erection can be produced by a spinal reflex with a similar mechanism, although it can also be produced by cognitive factors (McKenna, 2000). Tactile stimulation (stroking or rubbing) of

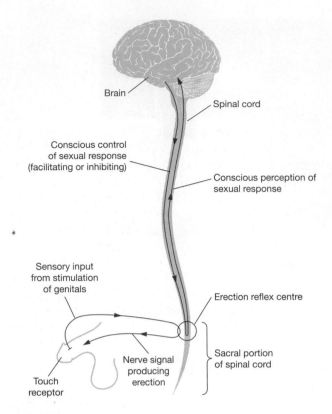

Brain

Spinal cord

Conscious control
of sexual response
(facilitating or inhibiting)

Conscious perception of
sexual response

Sensory input
from stimulation
of genitals

Erection reflex centre

Sacral portion
of spinal cord

Touch
receptor

Nerve signal
producing
erection

Figure 9.7 Nervous system control of erection. Note both the reflex centre in the spinal cord and brain control.

the penis (which has lots of receptor neurons) or nearby regions such as the scrotum or thighs produces a neural signal that is transmitted to an *erection centre* in the sacral, or lowest, part of the spinal cord (there may also be another erection centre higher in the cord). This centre then sends out a message via the parasympathetic division of the autonomic nervous system to the muscles (the effectors) around the walls of the arteries in the penis. In response to the message, the muscles relax; the arteries then expand, permitting a large volume of blood to flow into them, and erection results. Furthermore, the valves in the veins and the compression of the veins caused by the swelling in the tissue around them reduce the blood flow out of the penis (Adams et al., 1997).

The existence of this reflex is confirmed by the responses of men who have had their spinal cords completely severed, as a result of accidents, at a level above that of the reflex centre. They are capable of having erections and ejaculations produced by rubbing their genitals, although it is clear that no brain effects can be operating, since signals from the brain cannot move past the point at which the spinal cord was severed. (In fact, these men cannot "feel" anything because neural signals cannot be transmitted up the spinal cord either.) Thus, erection can be produced simply by tactile stimulation of the genitals, which triggers the spinal reflex.

Erection may also be produced by conditions other than tactile stimulation of the genitals; for example, fantasy or other purely psychological factors may produce erection. This points to the importance of the brain in producing erection, a topic that will be discussed in a later section.

Mechanism of Ejaculation

The ejaculation reflex is much like the erection reflex, except that there are two ejaculation centres and they are located higher in the spinal cord, the sympathetic and parasympathetic divisions of the nervous system are involved, and the response is muscular not vasocongestion (Giuliano & Clement, 2005; Rowland & Slob, 1997). In the ejaculation reflex, the penis responds to stimulation by sending a message to the *ejaculation centre*, which is located in the lumbar portion of the spinal cord. A message is then sent out via the nerves in the sympathetic nervous system, and this message triggers muscle contractions in the internal organs that are involved in ejaculation.

Ejaculation can often be controlled voluntarily by controlling the approach to ejaculation (see Chapter 18 for more information). This fact highlights the importance of brain influences on the ejaculation reflex (Truitt & Coolen, 2002).

The three main problems of ejaculation are rapid ejaculation, male orgasmic disorder (delayed ejaculation), and retrograde ejaculation. Rapid ejaculation, which is by far the most common problem, and male orgasmic disorder will be discussed in Chapter 18. Retrograde ejaculation occurs when the ejaculate, rather than going out through the tip of the penis,

Retrograde ejaculation: A condition in which orgasm in the male is not accompanied by an external ejaculation; instead, the ejaculate goes into the urinary bladder.

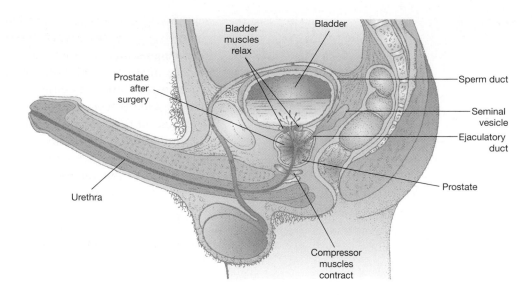

Bladder muscles relax

Bladder

Prostate after surgery

Sperm duct

Seminal vesicle

Ejaculatory duct

Prostate

Urethra

Compressor muscles contract

Figure 9.8 How a retrograde ejaculation occurs.

empties into the bladder (Kothari, 1984). A "dry orgasm" results, since no ejaculate is emitted. This problem can be caused by some illnesses, by tranquillizers and drugs used in the treatment of psychoses, and by prostate surgery. The mechanism that causes it is fairly simple (see Figure 9.8). Two sphincters are involved in ejaculation: an internal one, which closes off the entrance to the bladder during a normal ejaculation, and an external one, which opens during a normal ejaculation, allowing the semen to flow out through the penis. In retrograde ejaculation, the actions of these two sphincters are desynchronized; the external one closes, and thus the ejaculate cannot flow out through the penis, and the internal one opens, permitting the ejaculate to go into the bladder. The condition itself is quite harmless, although some men are disturbed by the lack of sensation of emitting semen.

Mechanisms in Women

Unfortunately, there is far less research on similar reflex mechanisms in women. We know that sensory input—such as touch—travels along the dorsal nerve of the clitoris and continues within the pudendal nerve to a reflex centre in the sacral portion of the spinal cord (Berman et al., 2000). Research with non-humans—mainly male and female rats—has investigated the urethrogenital reflex, which results in muscle contractions similar to orgasm in humans (Meston et al., 2004). This research suggests that the neural circuits for orgasm in women are very similar to those for orgasm and ejaculation in men. The clitoris receives both sympathetic and parasympathetic nerve fibres. The vagina, too, is supplied by both sympathetic and parasympathetic nerves. The limbic system of the brain is crucial to both female and male sexual arousal.

Research indicates that some women emit fluid during orgasm, often referred to as *female ejaculation* (Addiego et al., 1981; Belzer, 1981; Perry & Whipple, 1981). The region responsible is the Gräfenberg spot (or G-spot), also called the *female prostate* or the *Skene's glands* (Schubach, 2002). It is located on the top side of the vagina (with the woman lying on her back, which is the best position for finding it), about halfway between the pubic bone and the cervix (see Figure 9.9). Its ducts open into the urethra. Stroking it produces an urge to urinate, but if the stroking continues for a few seconds more, it begins to produce sexual pleasure. The original researchers, Perry and Whipple, argued that continued stimulation of it produces a uterine orgasm, characterized by deeper sensations of uterine contractions than the

Gräfenberg spot (GRAY-fen-berg) or G-spot: A small region on the front wall of the vagina, emptying into the urethra, and responsible for female ejaculation. Also called the female prostate or the Skene's glands.

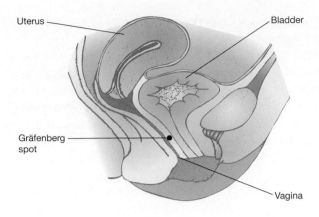

Figure 9.9 The Gräfenberg spot, or G-spot: hypothesized to produce ejaculation in some women.

clitorally induced vulvar orgasm investigated in the Masters and Johnson research.

In one survey of 1289 adult women, 40 percent reported having experienced ejaculation at the time of orgasm at least once, and 66 percent reported having an especially sensitive area on the front wall of the vagina (Darling et al., 1990). The most recent biochemical analyses indicate that the female prostate produces *prostate-specific antigen* (PSA), just as the male prostate does (Zaviačič et al., 2000).

BRAIN CONTROL OF SEXUAL RESPONSE

Sexual responses are controlled by more than simple spinal reflexes. They may be brought under voluntary control, and they may be initiated by purely psychological forces, such as fantasy. Environmental factors, such as having been taught as a child that sex is dirty and sinful, may also affect one's sexual response. All these phenomena point to the critical influence of the brain and its interaction with the spinal reflexes in producing sexual response (refer to Figure 9.7 on page 262).

Brain control of sexual response is complex and only partly understood at the present time. It appears that the most important influences come from a set of structures called the limbic system (see Figure 9.10). The limbic system forms a border between the central part of the brain and the outer part (the cerebral cortex); it includes the amygdala, the hippocampus,

Limbic system: A set of structures in the interior of the brain, including the amygdala, hippocampus, and fornix; believed to be important for sexual behaviour in both animals and humans.

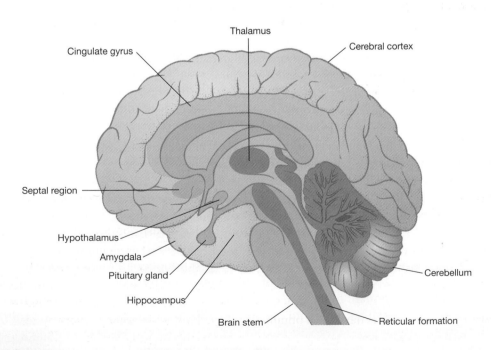

Figure 9.10 The limbic system of the brain, which is important in sexuality.

the cingulate gyrus, and the septum. The thalamus, pituitary, and reticular formation are not properly part of the limbic system, but they are closely connected to it.

Several lines of evidence point to the importance of the limbic system in sexual behaviour. A particular region of the anterior portion of the hypothalamus (the medial preoptic area, or MPOA) has been implicated in male sexual behaviour. If this area of the hypothalamus is given electrical stimulation, male rats increase their sexual behaviour; if this region is lesioned (destroyed), they no longer engage in copulation with females (McKenna, 2005). The paraventricular nucleus (PVN) of the hypothalamus is another sexual hot spot. If the genitals are stroked, cells in the PVN fire. Neurons from the PVN project down the spinal cord to sexual reflex sites (McKenna, 2005).

Exciting new research using the brain scanning technique functional MRI confirms the importance of the limbic system in sexual responding. Healthy men were shown erotic or non-erotic films while in the MRI (Park et al., 2001). Several structures in the limbic system—including the cingulate gyrus and thalamus—were activated by the erotic films (see In Focus 9.1). In another functional MRI study, the amygdala responded when men were shown sexually arousing photographs (Hamann et al., 2004).

Many of the brain centres for sex are also close to the olfactory centres. This brings us to the topic of pheromones and their role in sexual behaviour, which will be discussed later in the chapter.

HORMONES AND SEX

The sex hormones are another important physiological force that interacts with the nervous system to influence sexual response.

ORGANIZING VERSUS ACTIVATING EFFECTS

Endocrinologists generally make a distinction between the organizing effects of hormones and the activating effects of hormones. As discussed in Chapter 5, hormones present during prenatal development have important influences on genital anatomy, creating male or female genitals. Hormone effects such as these are called organizing effects because they cause a relatively permanent change in the organization of some structure, whether in the nervous system or in the reproductive system. Typically there are "critical periods" during which these hormone effects may occur.

It has also been known for some time that if an adult male mouse or rat is castrated (has the testes removed, which removes the source of testosterone), it will cease engaging in sexual behaviour (and will be less aggressive). If that animal is then given injections of testosterone, it will start engaging in sex again. Hormone effects such as these are called activating effects, because they activate (or deactivate) certain behaviours.

The organizing effects of sex hormones on sexual behaviour have been well documented (Keefe, 2002). In a classic experiment, testosterone was administered to pregnant female guinea pigs. The female offspring that had been exposed to testosterone prenatally[4] were, in adulthood, incapable of displaying "female" sexual behaviour (in particular, lordosis, which is a sexual posturing involving arching of the back and raising of the hindquarters so that intromission of the male's penis is possible) (Phoenix et al., 1959). It is thought that this result occurred because the testosterone "organized" the brain tissue (particularly the hypothalamus) in a male fashion. These female offspring were also born with masculinized genitals, and thus their reproductive systems had also been organized in the male direction. But the important point here is that the prenatal doses of testosterone had masculinized their sexual behaviour. Similar results have been obtained in experiments with many other species.

Organizing effects of hormones: Effects of sex hormones early in development, resulting in a permanent change in the brain or reproductive system.

Activating effects of hormone: Effects of sex hormones in adulthood, resulting in the activation of behaviours, especially sexual behaviours and aggressive behaviours.

---

[4]Note the similarity of these experiments to John Money's observations of human intersex individuals (Chapter 5).

IN FOCUS 9.1

What Happens in the Brain during Sex?

Exciting advances in the technology of neuroimaging are giving us inside views of the human brain during various activities. Methods such as PET (positron emission tomography) and fMRI (functional magnetic resonance imaging) show which regions of the brain "light up" (have neurons most actively firing) while the individual is solving a math problem or thinking about something sad.

Sex researchers have quickly adopted these techniques, with the goal of learning which regions of the brain are most involved in various aspects of sexuality. One of the challenges they have faced is that the subject cannot move while in an MRI scanner, making it difficult to achieve sexual arousal using most of the normal methods. Researchers have dealt with the problem by showing erotic videos to the person inside the scanner.

In one experiment, heterosexual men viewed erotic video clips, relaxing clips, and sports clips, in random order (Arnow et al., 2002). Meanwhile, their brains were being scanned in an MRI machine and the erection of the penis was measured. One has to admire these men for being able to become aroused while in an MRI scanner! Pictures from the brain scans are shown in Figure 9.11. When the men were exposed to erotic clips and were sexually aroused, as indicated by erection, intense brain activity was found in the right insula and claustrum, striatum (left caudate nucleus and putamen), cingulate gyrus, and—you guessed it—the hypothalamus! The insula is known to be involved in sensory processing, particularly of touch sensations. The cingulate cortex has been demonstrated in other studies to be involved in attentional processes and in guiding responsiveness to new environmental stimuli. Doubtless it was activated because of the men's attention to the erotic film.

Another study used fMRI to assess brain activation in both men and women while viewing erotic video segments (Karama et al., 2002). This study found brain activation in roughly the same regions as the study discussed previously. Almost all regions responded similarly in women and men. This study also found evidence of activation of the amygdala during sexual arousal. The amygdala is part of the limbic system, and as noted

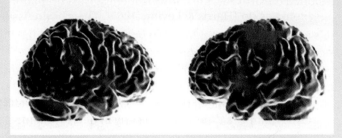

Figure 9.11 fMRI scans of the brain are opening up exciting opportunities to learn how the brain is involved in sexual response.

earlier in this chapter, plays a role in sexual responding. The amygdala is known to be involved in emotion, and its activation speaks to the strong emotions—sometimes positive, sometimes negative—that are evoked by sexual stimuli.

Research with women with spinal-cord injury indicates that they experience sexual arousal and orgasm as a result of genital stimulation (Komisaruk & Whipple, 2005). The neural signals do not travel up the spinal cord, which has been damaged, but rather pass up to the brain through the vagus nerves. fMRI scans indicate that the brain regions activated during arousal include the hypothalamus, amygdala, hippocampus, and the rest of the list of structures identified in fMRI research on able-bodied people.

These studies are fascinating in themselves as they allow us to view the workings of the brain during sexual responding. As research advances, future studies will help us understand the brain regions and associated neurotransmitters involved in sexual dysfunction, which will lead to more effective treatments for these problems. They will also allow us to better understand and treat arousal problems such as those suffered by pedophiles, who are aroused by completely inappropriate stimuli—children.

Sources: Arnow et al., 2002; Holstege et al., 2003; Karama et al., 2002; Komisaruk & Whipple, 2005; Schultz et al., 1999.

These hormonally masculinized females in adulthood displayed mounting behaviour, a male sexual behaviour.[5] When they were given testosterone in adulthood, they showed about as much mounting behaviour as males did. Thus, the testosterone administered in adulthood *activated* male patterns of sexual behaviour.

The analogous experiment on males would be castration at birth, followed by administration of ovarian hormones in adulthood. When this was done with rats, female sexual behaviour resulted; these males responded to mating attempts by other males essentially in the same way females do (Harris & Levine, 1965). Their brain tissue had been organized in a "female" direction during an early, critical period when testosterone was absent, and the female behaviour patterns were activated in adulthood by administration of ovarian hormones.

It thus seems that males and females initially have capacities for both male and female sexual behaviours; if testosterone is present early in development, the capacity for exhibiting female behaviours is suppressed. Sex hormones in adulthood then activate the behaviour patterns that were differentiated early in development.

How relevant is this research to humans? Generally, the trend is for the behaviour of lower species to be more under hormonal control and for the behaviour of higher species to be more under brain (neural) control. Thus, human sexual behaviour is less under hormonal control than rat sexual behaviour; human sexual behaviour is more controlled by the brain, and thus learning from past experiences and cultural conventions, which are stored in the brain, are more likely to have a profound effect (Wallen, 2001).

Let us now consider in more detail the known activating effects of sex hormones on the sexual behaviour of adult humans.

TESTOSTERONE AND SEXUAL DESIRE

Testosterone has well-documented effects on libido, or sexual desire, in humans (Carani et al., 1990; Carter, 1992; Everitt & Bancroft, 1991). In men deprived of their main source of testosterone by castration or by illness, there is a dramatic decrease in sexual behaviour in some, but not all, cases (Feder, 1984). Sexual desire is rapidly lost if a man is given an anti-androgen drug. Thus, testosterone seems to have an activating effect in maintaining sexual desire in men. However, in cases of castration, sexual behaviour may decline very slowly and may be present for several years after the source of testosterone is gone; this points to the importance of experience and brain control of sexual behaviour in humans.

It has also been demonstrated that levels of testosterone are correlated with sexual behaviour in boys around the time of puberty (Udry et al., 1985). Boys in grades 8, 9, and 10 filled out a questionnaire about their sexual behaviour and gave blood samples from which their level of testosterone could be measured. Among the boys whose testosterone level was in the highest quartile (25 percent of the sample), 69 percent had engaged in sexual intercourse, whereas only 16 percent of the boys whose testosterone level was in the lowest quartile had. Similarly, of the boys with testosterone levels in the highest quartile, 62 percent had masturbated, compared with 12 percent for the boys in the lowest quartile. These effects were uncorrelated with age, so it wasn't simply a matter of the older boys having more testosterone and more sexual experience. The authors concluded that at puberty, testosterone affects sexual motivation directly.

Research indicates that androgens are related to sexual desire in women also (Hutchinson, 1995; Sherwin, 1991).[6] If all sources of androgens (the adrenals and the ovaries) are removed, women lose sexual desire. Women who have undergone *oophrectomy* (surgical removal of the

[5]The term "male sexual behaviour" is being used here to refer to a sexual behaviour that is displayed by normal males of the species and either is absent in females of that species or is present at a much lower frequency. Normal females do mount, but they do so less frequently than males do. "Female sexual behaviour" is defined similarly.

[6]Lest the reader be distressed by the thought that women's considerably lower levels of testosterone might mean that they have lower sex drives, it should be noted that the sensitivity of cells to hormone levels is critical. Women's cells may be more sensitive to testosterone than men's are. Thus for women, a little testosterone may go a long way.

In Focus 9.2

Life after Castration

My daughter and I were talking about outing oneself—the act of disclosing one's inner identity. The discussion was not purely academic. "Dad, when most people out themselves, they open the closet door and just come out," she said. "You, Dad, went through the wall." I had just told my daughter that I was a eunuch.

It all started with a diagnosis of prostate cancer in 1998 when I was 52. Two years later, after failed surgery and radiation, I started hormonal therapy. This meant taking chemicals that slow the growth of prostate cancer cells by depriving them of androgen—in effect, castrating the patient. This type of chemical castration is the common treatment for advanced prostate cancer. Although more than 40,000 Canadian men are on these drugs, few people know of any men taking them. Put simply, we hide because it is shameful to be castrated.

My initial response to the therapy was typical. My mood plummeted along with my testosterone level. Hair vanished from my arms and legs. Muscle disappeared, fat appeared. My memory suffered. Not only was I now more likely to lose my car keys, I occasionally couldn't remember where I left the car.

The term *eunuch* simply means a castrated man. Given the pervasive stereotype of eunuchs as ineffective wimps, it is no surprise that men dread this label. I became curious about whether the stereotype was true, and how eunuchs functioned in the past.

The first thing I discovered was that eunuchs were anything but mindless, cowardly automatons. They were philosophers, saints, military leaders, and even assassins. They were the chamberlains, diplomats, and senior government officials in the major long-lasting, dynastic governments of Asia for the last 3,000 years. Furthermore, descriptions of the physique and psychology of eunuchs mirrored many of the anatomical and emotional changes that I experienced.

Then I discovered something even more interesting. The eunuchs of antiquity were models for our depictions of angels. God is thought to surround himself with angels as advisers and emissaries, who are identical in appearance to males castrated before puberty: tall, beardless, nonsexual beings with voices like the legendary castrati. It appears that from the Judeo-Christian standpoint, the occupants of heaven were exalted eunuchs. In turn,

---

ovaries, typically because of cancer) report marked decreases in their sexual desire. If they are treated with testosterone, their sexual desire increases (Shifren et al., 1998, 2000). Androgen levels decline with age in women, and research shows that administration of DHEA (a pre-testosterone hormone) to women over age 60 may result in their having increased sexual desire (Baulieu et al., 2000; Spourk, 2002).

PHEROMONES

Scientists and laypeople alike are intrigued by the role that pheromones play in sexual behaviour (Cutler, 1999; McClintock, 2000). Pheromones are somewhat like hormones. Recall that hormones are biochemicals that are manufactured in the body and secreted into the bloodstream to be carried to the organs that they affect. Pheromones, in contrast, are biochemicals that are secreted outside the body. Through the sense of smell, they are an important means of communication between animals. Often the pheromones are contained in the animal's urine. The dog that does "scent marking" is actually depositing pheromones. Some pheromones appear to be important in sexual communication, and some have even been called "sex attractants."

Much of the research on pheromones has been done with animals and demonstrates the importance of pheromones in sexual and reproductive functioning. For example, pheromones present in female urine have an influence on male sexual behaviour (Snowdon et al., 2006).

The sense of smell (olfaction) is essential for pheromone effects to occur. Removal of the olfactory bulbs, specifically a region called the *vomeronasal organ,* dramatically reduces the sexual

Pheromones (FARE-oh-mones): Biochemicals secreted outside the body that are important in communication between animals and that may serve as sex attractants.

earthly rulers aspired to reach this divine ideal.

The eunuch-angel connection has helped me to understand and adapt to the side effects of androgen deprivation. When I was stoked up on testosterone in the old days, for example, I would obsess about exacting revenge on those who offended me. Now I see the foolishness in such macho fury. Rather than trying to undo others, I can now willfully exercise restraint. It's not that I'm never aggressive anymore, for I'm no perfect angel, but I realize it's better to maintain a higher mission than to fight petty battles.

I don't recall crying much as an adult, but since my castration I'll weep while watching Mothers Against Drunk Driving commercials. At first, I feared my tears would be perceived as self-pity. But the truth is that I've become more sensitive to the trials and tribulations of others. I'm no longer embarrassed by my tears and I consider them to be humanizing just as they are for angels. The link to my chemical castration is obvious; testosterone fuels aggression but suppresses empathy and the ability to cry.

Understanding angel (and eunuch) psychology has even helped me to overcome the cognitive effects of hormonal therapy. Angels may be omnipotent, but they undertake just one task at a time. It seems that thousands of years ago it was already recognized that androgen deprivation makes multitasking difficult—but it doesn't prevent one from accomplishing a single task well. This realization has helped me to maintain a busy, productive academic life.

I still have a beard and sing bass: despite myths and jokes to the contrary, androgen deprivation in adulthood doesn't change those male features. Singing in a group never appealed to me before my castration because it offered little opportunity for individual advancement. But recently I joined a choir where I now enjoy the richness of the collective sound born of collaboration—and how much I've gained by accepting how much I've changed.

Angels cry. So do I. They also sing, and so do I.

Source: New York Times, March 27, 2007. Dr. Richard Wassersug is a professor of anatomy and neurobiology at Dalhousie University in Halifax.

---

behaviour of males from species such as mice and guinea pigs (Thorne & Amrein, 2003). The vomeronasal organ (VNO), located inside the nose, is a chemoreceptor—that is, it is activated by chemicals such as pheromones. Neuroscientists have even recorded the activity of single neurons in the VNO of mice and found that certain neurons fire when the animal comes into contact with another male, but different neurons fire when he comes into contact with a female (Luo et al., 2003). Activation of the VNO then activates cells in the hypothalamus (Keverne, 1999); as we have seen, the hypothalamus is crucial to sexuality. The VNO is a kind of second olfactory pathway, sometimes called the "accessory" olfactory bulb, that functions in addition to the main sense of smell.

What relevance does all this have for humans? Humans are not, by and large, "smell animals." Olfaction is much less important for us than for most other species. We tend to rely mostly on vision and, secondarily, hearing. Does this mean that pheromones have no influence on our sexual behaviour?

New research may provide an answer to this question. Researchers have discovered that there is a long-overlooked cranial nerve, called nerve zero, that sprouts from the base of the brain, connects to parts of the brain controlling reproduction, and releases gonadotropin-releasing hormone (GnRH) into the blood (Fields, 2007). Nerve zero has been found in animals and humans. Nerve zero may sense pheromones even if they do not have an odour, and thus may influence behaviour even though we are not conscious of them. However, more research is needed before the role of nerve zero in human sexual and reproductive behaviour is clear (Fields, 2007).

We now know that human pheromones exist and may play an important role in sexuality (Wyatt, 2003). Indeed, pheromones may be exactly the "body chemistry" that attracts

(a)   (b)

Figure 9.12   Pheromones. *(a)* Pheromones are a major means of communication between animals. *(b)* Are there human pheromones that are sex attractants?

people to each other. Perfumes with musky scents have become popular and presumably increase sexual attractiveness, perhaps because they smell like pheromones. The perfume industry has eagerly tried to capitalize on pheromone research, making rather large claims for the effects of their products on attraction (e.g., "makes good girls go bad.")

What scientific evidence is there regarding the existence and effects of pheromones in humans? First, although its function is not clear, the vomeronasal organ—which, as noted earlier, is related to olfaction and sexual behaviour in other species and essentially seems to function as a pheromone sensor—is present in most humans (Brennan & Zufall, 2006; Garcia-Velasco & Mondragon, 1991). This makes one wonder whether plastic surgery to create a pretty nose might inadvertently harm the person's sex life.

Second, androstenol, an odorous steroid that is well documented as a pheromone in pigs, has been isolated in the underarm sweat of humans (Gower & Ruparelia, 1993). Short-chain fatty acids that are known to be sex-attractant pheromones to male rhesus monkeys have been isolated in human vaginal secretions (Cowley & Brooksbank, 1991). It is clear, therefore, that humans do secrete pheromones.

In one experiment, a synthesized female pheromone was added to women's perfume in one group; a placebo was added to the perfume in the control group (McCoy & Pitino, 2002; Rako & Friebely, 2004). The women recorded their sexual behaviour over the next three months. Compared with the control group, pheromone-treated women showed a significantly greater frequency of intercourse, dates, sexual fondling, and kissing. They did not differ in frequency of masturbation. The researchers concluded that the pheromone had increased the women's attractiveness to men.

Classic research by Martha McClintock (1971) documented the existence of a phenomenon known as menstrual synchrony, the convergence, over several months, of the dates of onset of menstrual periods among women who are in close contact with each other (McClintock, 1998; Weller et al., 1995). This phenomenon is now thought to be due to pheromones produced by the women.

In perhaps the most dramatic experiment to date in humans, the results indicated that the timing of ovulation could be experimentally manipulated with human pheromones (Stern & McClintock, 1998). Odourless secretions from women's armpits were collected in the late follicular phase—that is, just before ovulation. Recipient women exposed to these secretions showed an accelerated appearance of the LH surge that triggers ovulation. Underarm secre-

Menstrual synchrony: The convergence, over several months, of the dates of onset of menstrual periods among women who are in close contact with each other.

tions from the same donors collected later in the menstrual cycle had the opposite effect: they delayed the LH surge of recipients and lengthened the time to menstruation.

Other pheromone research has found that preference for human body odours and brain responses to pheromones differ as a function of sexual orientation (Berglund et al., 2006; Martins et al., 2005). In one study, armpit secretions were collected from heterosexual men, heterosexual women, gay men, and lesbians (Martins et al., 2005). Odour evaluators then rated the pleasantness of these odours, not knowing the source of them. Heterosexual men, for example, gave the lowest pleasantness ratings to the pheromones from gay men, whereas gay men gave low ratings to the pheromones of heterosexual men. The researchers concluded that human "odour prints" may help us identify groups of people who are potential sexual partners.

If these speculations about the effects of pheromones on human sexual behaviour are correct, our hyperclean society may be destroying the scents that attract people to each other.

SEXUAL TECHNIQUES

In the earlier sections of this chapter, we have discussed some of the wonderful things that happen to the body during sexual arousal and orgasm. How do we get to these marvelous states, both for ourselves and our partners?

We live in the era of sex manuals. Books like *Electrify Your Sex Life*, *The Illustrated Guide to Extended Massive Orgasm,* and *The Complete Guide to Sexual Fulfillment* as well as feature articles and advice columns in many magazines and talk shows like the *Sunday Night Sex Show* with Sue Johanson give us advice on how to produce bigger and longer orgasms in ourselves and our partners. The "read all about it" boom has produced not only benefits but also problems. It may turn our attention so much to mechanical techniques that we forget about love and the emotional side of sexual expression. The sex manuals may also set up impossible standards of sexual performance that none of us can meet. On the other hand, we live in a society that has a history of leaving the learning of sexual techniques to nature or to chance, in contrast to some other societies in which adolescents are given explicit instruction in methods for producing sexual pleasure. For human beings, sexual behaviour is a lot more than "doin' what comes naturally"; we all need some means for learning about sexual techniques, and the sex manuals may help to fill that need.

In the sections that follow, we consider techniques that bring people sexual pleasure. Of course, sexual techniques are not enough to build a satisfying sexual relationship with another person. Researchers in Ontario asked people about what contributes to "great sex" for them (Kleinplatz & Ménard, 2007). Their research showed that great sex occurs when people are fully present in the moment with their minds turned off, and feel totally free to be honest and open about communicating their sexual desires. Respondents also described a strong sense of intimate connection, both at the moment, and in the relationship in general, as contributors to great sex. We discuss two of these components, loving attachment and communication, in Chapter 12.

EROGENOUS ZONES

Although the notion of erogenous zones originated in Freud's work, the term is now part of our general vocabulary. It refers to parts of the body that are sexually sensitive; stroking them or otherwise stimulating them produces sexual arousal. The genitals and the breasts are good examples. The lips, neck, and thighs are generally also erogenous zones. But even some rather unlikely regions—such as the back, the ears, the stomach, and the feet—can also be quite erogenous. One person's erogenous zones can be quite different from another's. Thus, it is impossible to give a list of sure turn-ons. The best way to find out is to communicate with your partner, verbally and non-verbally (see Chapter 12).

Erogenous (eh-RAH-jen-us) zones: Areas of the body that are particularly sensitive to sexual stimulation.

ONE-PERSON SEX

Autoeroticism: Sexual self-stimulation; for example, masturbation.

It does not necessarily take two to have sex. One can produce one's own sexual stimulation. Sexual self-stimulation is called autoeroticism.[7] Two examples are masturbation and fantasy.

MASTURBATION

Masturbation: Stimulation of one's own genitals with the hand or with some object, such as a pillow or vibrator.

Here the term hand–genital stimulation will be reserved for stimulation of another's genitals and the term masturbation for self-stimulation, either with the hand or with some object, such as a pillow or a vibrator. Masturbation is a very common sexual behaviour; almost all men and the majority of women in Canada masturbate to orgasm at least a few times during their lives. In the National Health and Social Life Survey (NHSLS), 62 percent of the men and 42 percent of the women reported that they had masturbated in the preceding year (Laumann et al., 1994, Table 3.1); 22 percent of the men and 8 percent of the women said that they had masturbated at least once a week. Although there are no national data on masturbation, our research has found that most Canadian university students (92 percent of the men and 72 percent of the women in one study) have masturbated at least once. Further, 65 percent of Canadians have positive attitudes toward masturbation (refer to Table 1.2 on page 15). A study of German university students found that the percentage of students who report masturbating was not affected by whether they had a sexual partner; rather masturbation was seen as a sexual activity in its own right (Dekker & Schmidt, 2002). The techniques used by men and women in masturbation are interesting in part because they provide information to their partners concerning the best techniques to use in lovemaking.

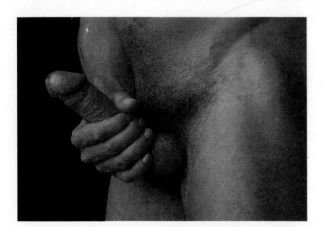

(a)

(b)

Figure 9.13 *(a)* Male masturbation using hand stimulation of the penis. *(b)* Female masturbation using clitoral stimulation.

Most commonly women masturbate by manipulating the clitoris and the inner lips. They may rub up and down or in a circular motion, sometimes lightly and sometimes applying more pressure to the clitoris. Some prefer to rub at the side of the clitoris, while a few stimulate the glans of the clitoris directly. The inner lips may also be stroked or tugged. One woman described her technique as follows:

> I use the tips of my fingers for actual stimulation, but it's better to start with patting motions or light rubbing motions over the general area. As excitement increases I begin stroking above the clitoris and finally reach a climax with a rapid, jerky circular motion over the clitoral hood. Usually my legs are apart, and occasionally I also stimulate my nipples with the other hand. (Hite, 1976, p. 20)

Of the women in Kinsey's (1953) sample who masturbated, 84 percent used clitoral and labial manipulation; inserting fingers or objects into the vagina was the second most commonly used technique, but it was practised by only 20 percent of the women. Other techniques used by women in masturbation include breast stimulation, thigh pressure exerted by crossing the legs and pressing them together rhythmically to stimulate the clitoris, and pressing the genitals against some object, such

[7]For those of you who are interested in the roots of words, "autoeroticism" does not refer to sex in the back seat of a car. The prefix "auto" means "self" (as in "autobiography"); hence self-stimulation is autoeroticism.

as a pillow, or massaging them with a stream of water while in the shower. A few women are capable of using fantasy alone to produce orgasm; fantasy-induced orgasms are accompanied by the same physiological changes as orgasms produced by masturbation (Whipple et al., 1992).

Almost all men report masturbating by hand stimulation of the penis. For those interested in speed, an orgasm can be reached in only a minute or two. Most men use the technique of circling the hand around the shaft of the penis and using an up-and-down movement to stimulate the shaft and glans. Because the penis produces no natural lubrication of its own, some men like to use a form of lubrication, such as soapsuds while showering. The tightness of the grip, the speed of movement, and the amount of glans stimulation vary from one man to the next. Most increase the speed of stimulation as they approach orgasm, slowing or stopping the stimulation at orgasm because further stimulation would be uncomfortable (Masters & Johnson, 1966). At the time of ejaculation, men often grip the shaft of the penis tightly. Immediately after orgasm, the glans and corona are hypersensitive, and men generally avoid further stimulation of the penis at that time.

MEDIA AND MASTURBATION

Some men and woman incorporate the use of mass media into their autoerotic activity. Some people masturbate as they view erotic images in magazines, on video or DVD, or on the Internet. In one survey, half of the men and one-third of the women reported viewing sexually explicit videos and erotic magazines; 32 percent of the men and 15 percent of the women reported viewing erotic material on websites (Adam & Eve, 2004). Some of these viewers used these materials as aids to sexual arousal and masturbation. Up to 10 percent of the male students in our human sexuality classes report that their most recent sexual activity was masturbation while viewing erotic materials.

The Internet plays an important role in another form of autoerotic expression. Some people have specific sexual desires or needs that they are afraid to express in their relationships. They may fear embarrassment and rejection, or risks to their physical or emotional health if they act on these needs and desires (Ross, 2005). The Internet, because of its anonymity, provides a relatively safe context in which one can explore these needs and desires. A study of 42 men and 62 women recruited in chat rooms found that persons who reported lacking real relationships and expressed fear of disclosing aspects of their sexuality were more likely to use the Internet as an important form of sexual self-expression (McKenna et al., 2001).

FANTASY

Sexual fantasy refers to sexual thoughts or images that alter the person's emotions or physiological state (Maltz & Boss, 1997). Almost all men and women report that they have experienced sexual fantasies (Leitenberg & Henning, 1995). However, many people are uncomfortable with acknowledging that they deliberately think about sex and enjoy doing so (Renaud & Byers, 2001).

Researchers studied the sexual thoughts and fantasies of heterosexual university students at the University of New Brunswick (Renaud & Byers, 1999). They found that although men think about sex more frequently than women do, for the most part, the content of their sexual fantasies is similar. The most common themes have to do with intimacy and romance. More than 90 percent of students had fantasies about having intercourse with a loved partner, kissing passionately, making love elsewhere than the bedroom such as out of doors, and giving and receiving oral sex. Compared to the women, the men's fantasies more often revolved around themes of anonymous or impersonal sex. The women had romantic fantasies and fantasies about playing a role during sexual activity—such as exposing themselves provocatively or tying their partner up—more often than the men did. In a survey of a national sample of British adults, men were more likely to report fantasies of sex with multiple and anonymous partners, whereas women reported fantasies involving a same-sex or famous male partner

Sexual fantasy: Sexual thoughts or images that alter the person's emotions or physiological state.

(Wilson, 1997). These differences are consistent with predictions based on both evolutionary theory and gender-role socialization. One study comparing the fantasies of gays and lesbians with those of heterosexual men and women found that the reported contents were very similar, except that the partner was someone of the same gender (Price et al., 1985). However, heterosexuals may fantasize sexual activity with someone of the same gender, and gay and lesbian fantasies may include persons of the other gender.

Where do sexual fantasies come from? The images may come from past experience, dreams, media portrayals, or stories someone told you. The activity may be dreamlike and sensuous, or explicit and vigorous. Like all fantasy, sexual fantasies represent a fusion of mind, body and emotions. Sexual fantasies may represent earlier or childhood experiences, pleasant or abusive (Maltz & Boss, 1997). They may be experienced as positive and pleasant or as negative and unwanted (Byers et al., 1998; Renaud & Byers, 1999).

Positive sexual fantasy can play a variety of functions for the person doing the fantasizing (Maltz & Boss, 1997). These include enhancing self-esteem and attractiveness, increasing one's own sexual arousal (e.g., during masturbation or partnered sex), and facilitating orgasm. In fact, research has shown that people who engage in more frequent sexual fantasies tend to be better adjusted sexually (Renaud & Byers, 2001). A very important role is enabling the person to mentally rehearse future possibilities. Such rehearsal may enable the person to change behaviour, initiate communication with a partner, or change partners.

Sometimes sexual thoughts or fantasies can be experienced as negative—that is, unacceptable, upsetting, and unpleasant. In fact, research in New Brunswick found that 84 percent of university students had these types of thoughts (Byers et al., 1998). The negative images most frequently reported by men were of having sex in a public place, meeting naked people, and engaging in sex with a person having authority over them. Those most frequently reported by women were of having sex in a public place, having sex with a person having authority over them, and being sexually victimized. Students who have more frequent negative sexual thoughts and fantasies are not more poorly adjusted, although some people experience anxiety and guilt because of the thought (Byers et al., 1998; Renaud & Byers, 2001).

More men than women report ever having had sexual fantasies during masturbation. The results of 13 studies indicate that about 87 percent of men and 69 percent of women fantasized during masturbation (Leitenberg & Henning, 1995). Here is an adolescent male's description of one of his favourite fantasies during masturbation:

> We would be riding in the back seat of the car and I would reach over and fondle her breasts. She would reach into my pants and begin to caress my penis and finally suck me off. (Jensen, 1976a, p. 144)

This is the fantasy of one college woman as she imagines seducing her French teacher:

> At exactly 8:00 I knocked on the door. When this guy saw what I was wearing I thought his eyes were going to pop out. Calmly he asked me to come in and sit down . . .
> "Please call me Jim." Now I was getting somewhere. . . . I slipped out of my shoes and loosened my dress. When Jim returned I was ready and waiting. . . . Well the man finally got the hint; he reached around and unzipped my dress. While I was slowly undoing his zipper, he buried his head between my breasts. As his mouth slowly descended down my body I could feel the heat rising from between my legs. . . . To add to my desire he started speaking French to me. You didn't have to be fluent to understand this. As his mouth continued to nibble away, his tongue zeroed in on my clit and sent me to a mind boggling orgasm. As my pleasure subsided I began to return the favor. . . . Although I had enjoyed several orgasms by now the night was far from over. Jim then got on top of me and made love to me for what seemed like an eternity. . . . (Moffatt, 1989, pp. 190–191)

The content of male and female sexual fantasies seems to be influenced by cultural stereotypes of male and female sexuality. However, they are also a good way to experiment with roles outside of cultural stereotypes.

SEX TOYS

Various sexual devices, such as vibrators, dildos, cock (penis) rings, and lube (lubricant), are used as *sex toys* by some people in masturbation or by couples as they have sex together. Each type of sex toy comes in endless variations. Some people consider use of sex toys to be examples of *spicy sex*, meaning a change from the usual sexual script which is sometimes called *vanilla sex* (Rye & Meaney, 2007). Here we describe a few of the more common sex toys, but there are many other devices that people can use to enhance their sexual pleasure.

Both male and female artificial genitals can be purchased. A **dildo** is a rubber or plastic cylinder, often shaped like a penis; it can be inserted into the vagina or the anus. Dildos are used by some women in masturbation, by same-sex couples, and by heterosexual couples. Some couples use a dildo with a harness, often called a *strap-on*. Artificial vaginas, and even inflatable replicas of the entire body, male or female, can also be purchased.

Dildo: A rubber or plastic cylinder, often shaped like a penis.

Some *vibrators* are shaped like a penis but others are not; there are models with a cord that plugs into an electric socket and also battery-operated, cordless models. Women may use them to masturbate, stimulating the clitoral and mons area, or may insert them into the vagina. Men may use them to stimulate the genitals or the anus. They can be purchased in "respectable" stores (where they are sometimes euphemistically called "body massagers"), in sex stores, and by mail.

Vibrators designed for woman are not recent; they were invented in the 1880s and sold as a medical device (Maines, 1999). Physicians prescribed their use for the treatment of various female "maladies," especially hysteria.[8] Vibrators disappeared from medicinal use after they were used in pornographic films in the 1920s. Today they are back in full force, with women throwing Passion Parties or Slumber Parties, which are Tupperware-style home parties where you and your friends can buy sex toys from the local salesperson (Jefferson, 2005).

Body oils are also popular for sexual use. In fact, their use has been encouraged by experts in the field; for example, sex therapists recommend them for the touching or sensate focus exercises that they prescribe for their patients in sex therapy (see Chapter 18). Oils have a sensuous quality that heightens erotic feelings. Furthermore, if you are being stroked or massaged for any extended period

Figure 9.14   Vibrators and dildos, used for sexual stimulation.

of time, the oil helps ensure that the part of your body that is being stimulated will not end up feeling like a piece of wood that has been sandpapered. Sex stores sell oils in a variety of exotic scents, but plain baby oil will also do nicely. Be aware that Vaseline and some other lubricants cause condoms to break.

[8]Some of you may have read *The Birth House*, a novel by Ami Mckay set in Nova Scotia, which features a physician's use of a vibrator with his female patients.

TWO-PERSON SEX[9]

When many of us think of techniques of two-person sex, the image that flashes across our mind generally reflects several assumptions. One assumption is that one of the people is a male and the other a female—that is, that the sex is heterosexual. This reflects a belief that heterosexual sex is normative. We also tend to assume that the man is supposed to do certain things during the act and the woman is supposed to do certain other things, reflecting the sexual scripts of our culture. He, for example, is supposed to take the initiative in deciding what techniques are used, while she is to follow his lead. Although there is nothing particularly evil in these assumptions, they do tend to impose limitations on our own sexual expression and to make people think that their own sexual behaviour is "not quite right." Therefore, we will make an attempt to avoid these assumptions in the sections that follow.

KISSING

Kissing (or what we might call, technically, "mouth-to-mouth stimulation") is an activity that virtually everyone in our culture has engaged in. In simple kissing, the partners keep their mouths closed and touch each other's lips. In deep kissing (*French kissing*), both people part their lips slightly and insert their tongues into each other's mouths (somehow these clinical descriptions do not make it sound like as much fun as it is). There are endless variations on these two basic approaches, such as nibbling at the partner's lips or tongue or sucking at the lips; they depend only on your imagination and personal preference. There are also plenty of other regions of the body to kiss: the nose, the forehead, the eyelids, the earlobes, the neck, the breasts, the genitals, and even the feet, to give a few examples.

TOUCHING

Enjoying touching and being touched is essential to sexual pleasure. Sensual touching is important to feelings of closeness and desire. In addition, caresses or massages, applied to virtually any area of the body, can be exciting. The regions that are exciting vary a great deal from one person to the next and depend on how the person is feeling at the moment; thus it is important to communicate what sort of touching is most pleasurable to you. (For specific exercises on touching and being touched, see Chapter 18.)

As noted earlier, one of the best ways to find out how to use your hands in stimulating the genitals of another person is to find out how that person masturbates (see Figure 9.15). As a technique of lovemaking, hand stimulation of the male genitals can be used as a pleasurable preliminary to intercourse, as a means of inducing orgasm itself, or as a means of producing an erection after the man has had one orgasm and wants to continue for another round of lovemaking ("rousing the dead"). Alex Comfort, in *The New Joy of Sex*, recommends the following techniques:

> If he isn't circumcised, she will probably need to avoid rubbing the glans itself, except in pursuit of very special effects. Her best grip is just below the groove, with the skin back as far as it will go, and using two hands—one pressing hard near the root, holding the penis steady, or fondling the scrotum, the other making a thumb-and-first-finger ring, or a whole hand grip. She should vary this, and, in prolonged masturbation, change hands often. (1991, p. 85)

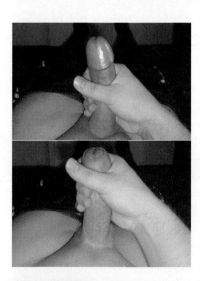

Figure 9.15 Technique of hand stimulation of the penis.

[9]Of course, some people choose to engage in sexual activities with two or more persons at the same time. This is called swinging or *un ménage à trois.* Swinging is discussed in Chapter 11.

One of the things that make hand stimulation most effective is for the man's partner to have a playful delight in, and appreciation of, the man's penis. Most men think their penis is pretty important. If the partner cannot honestly appreciate it and enjoy massaging it, hand stimulation might as well not be done.

The hands can be used to stimulate the woman's genitals to produce orgasm, as a preliminary method of arousing the woman before intercourse, or simply because it is pleasurable.

Generally it is best, particularly if the woman is not already aroused, to begin with gentle, light stroking of the inside of the thighs and the inner and outer lips, moving to light stroking of the clitoris. As she becomes more aroused, the stimulation of the clitoris can become firmer. The clitoris is very sensitive and this sensitivity can be either exquisite or painful. Some care has to be used in stimulating it; it cannot be manipulated like a piece of Silly Putty. Generally, the clitoris should not—except, perhaps, for some light stroking—be rubbed while it is dry, for the effect can be abrasive. If the woman is already somewhat aroused, lubrication can be provided by touching the fingers to the vaginal entrance and then spreading the lubrication on the clitoris. If she is not aroused or does not produce much vaginal lubrication, saliva or a water-based lube works well too. Moisture makes the stimulation not only more comfortable but also more sensuous. Some women find direct stimulation of the clitoral glans to be painful in some states of arousal. These women generally prefer stimulation on either side of the clitoris instead.

With these caveats in mind, the clitoris can be stimulated with circular or back-and-forth movements of the finger. The inner and outer lips can also be stroked or rubbed. These techniques, if done with skill and patience, can bring the woman to orgasm. Another technique that can be helpful in producing orgasm is for the partner to place the heel of the hand on the mons, exerting pressure on it while moving the middle finger in and out of the vaginal entrance. If it isn't clear by now, the partner needs to have close-trimmed nails that do not have any jagged edges. This is sensitive tissue we are dealing with.

Many couples engage in sexual activities that do not involve penetration or hand stimulation but nonetheless allow one or both partners to receive genital stimulation (the slang term for two people rubbing their bodies, usually fully clothed, together for sexual stimulation is *dry humping*). For example, a woman may lie on top of her partner and rub her clitoris against her partner's genitals (when two women do this, it is sometimes called *tribadism*). Alternatively, a man may move his penis between the thighs of his partner, a technique that has been referred to as *interfemoral intercourse*.

THE OTHER SENSES

So far, this chapter has been focused on tactile (touch) sensations in sexual arousal. However, the other senses—vision, smell, and hearing—can also make contributions.

The things you see can contribute to your arousal. Men seem, in general, to be turned on by a variety of visual stimuli, such as an attractive person, or partially dressed or nude bodies. Both men and women respond with physiological arousal to portrayals of partnered sexual activity (Laan & Everaerd, 1995). Just as erotica may be used during autoerotic activity, viewing sexual activity on a video or on the Internet may contribute to partnered sexual activities. Some men, and a few women, have mild fetishes (see Chapter 15 for more detail), and like to see their partner wearing certain types of clothing, such as leather or rubber clothing, or schoolgirl dresses. A good rule here, as elsewhere, is to communicate with your partner to find out what he or she would find arousing.

The decor of the room can also contribute to visual stimulation. Large mirrors, hung either behind the bed or on the ceiling above it, can be a visual turn-on, since they allow you to watch yourself make love. Candlelight is soft and contributes more to an erotic atmosphere than an electric light, which is harsh, or complete darkness, in which case there is no visual stimulation at all.

Perhaps the biggest visual turn-on comes simply from looking at your own and your partner's body. According to the NHSLS, watching a partner undress is one of the most appealing sexual activities (Michael et al., 1994, Table 12).

Odours can be turn-ons or turn-offs. The scent of a body that is clean, having been washed with soap and water, is a natural turn-on. It does not need to be covered up with an "intimate deodorant."[10] In a sense, the scent of your skin, armpits, or genitals is your "aroma signature" and can be quite arousing.

A body that has not been washed or a mouth that has not been cleaned or has recently been used for smoking cigarettes can be a real turn-off. Breath that reeks of garlic may turn a desire for closeness into a desire for distance. Ideally, the communication between partners is honest and trusting enough so that if one offends, the other can request that the appropriate clean-up be done.

Music—whether your preference is for rock or classical music—can contribute to an erotic atmosphere. Another advantage of playing music is that it helps muffle the sounds of sex, which can be important if you live in an apartment with thin walls or are worried about your children hearing you.

Fantasy during Two-Person Sex

Fantasies can be done solo or can heighten the experience of sex with another person. Particularly in a long-term, monogamous relationship, sexual monotony can become a problem; fantasies are one way to introduce some variety and excitement without violating an agreement to be faithful to the other person. It is important to view such fantasies in this way, rather than as a sign of disloyalty to, or dissatisfaction with, one's sexual partner.

Fantasies during two-person sex are generally quite similar to the ones people have while masturbating. In one study, 84 percent of males and 82 percent of females reported that they fantasized at least some of the time during intercourse (Cado & Leitenberg, 1990). This kind of fantasizing is quite common. Some sexual partners enjoy sharing their fantasies with each other. Describing a sexual fantasy to your partner can be a turn-on for both of you. Some couples act out all or part of a fantasy and find it very gratifying. One man says:

> I fantasized about being a fourteen-year-old girl. This is a long-lived fantasy of mine. The girl is pretty, with a petite body, probably five-one, five-two, cute ass, maybe light blond or dark brown pussy hair. Small to medium size breasts. Kind of sweet-looking, virginal. . . . Anyway, Sue got into it, like we were two girlfriends sleeping over and she was a couple years older and she was going to show me some things. I happen to be very sensitive around my nipples, so she'd say, "Oh, you have nice little nipples, you're going to have very pretty breasts." Then she'd massage my crotch like she was massaging a vagina: "Do you like it when I pet you down there?" And she'd show me what to do to pleasure her, how to masturbate her and go down on her. We played around with that for a few months. (Maurer, 1994, p. 231)

Positions of Penile–Vaginal Intercourse

Coitus: Sexual intercourse; in sertion of the penis into the vagina.

One of the most common heterosexual techniques involves the insertion of the penis into the vagina; this is called *coitus*[11] or *sexual intercourse*. Ancient love manuals and other sources illustrate many positions of intercourse.

Some authorities state that there are only four positions of intercourse. Personally, we prefer to believe that there are an infinite number. Consider how many different angles your

---

[10]With the increased popularity of mouth–genital sex, some women worry that the scent of their genitals might be offensive. The advertisements for feminine hygiene deodorant sprays prey upon these fears. These sprays should not be used because they may irritate the vagina. Besides, there is nothing offensive about the scent of a vulva that has been washed; many people, in fact, find it arousing.

[11]From the Latin word *coire*, meaning "to go together."

Figure 9.16 The man-on-top position of intercourse.

arms, legs, and torso may be in, in relation to those of your partner, and all the various ways in which you can intertwine your limbs—that's a lot of positions. We trust that given sufficient creativity and time, you can discover them all for yourself. We would agree, though, that there are a few basic positions. One basic variation depends on whether the couple face each other (face-to-face position) or whether one partner faces the other's back (rear-entry position); if you try the other obvious variation, a back-to-back position, you will quickly find that you cannot accomplish much that way. The other basic variation depends on whether one partner is on top of the other or whether the couple are side by side. Let us consider four basic positions that illustrate these variations. As cookbooks often do, we'll give you the basic recipes and let you decide on the embellishments.

The face-to-face, man-on-top position ("missionary" position—see Figure 9.16) is probably the one used most frequently by heterosexual couples in Canada. In this position the man and woman stimulate each other until they are aroused, he has an erection, and she is producing vaginal lubrication. Then he moves on top of her as she spreads her legs apart, either he or she spreads the vaginal lips apart, and he inserts his penis into her vagina. He supports himself on his knees and hands or elbows and moves his penis in and out of the vagina (pelvic thrusting). Some men worry that their heavy weight will crush the poor woman under them; however, because the weight is spread out over so great an area, most women do not find this to be a problem at all, and many find the sensation of contact to be pleasurable.

The woman can have her legs in a number of positions that create variations. She may have them straight out horizontally, a position that produces a tight rub on the penis but does not permit it to go deeply into the vagina. She may bend her legs and elevate them to varying degrees, or she may hook them over the man's back or over his shoulders. The last approach permits the penis to move deeply into the vagina. The woman can also move her pelvis, either up and down or side to side, to produce further stimulation.

The man-on-top position has some advantages and some disadvantages. It is the best position for ensuring conception, if that is what you want. It leaves the woman's hands free to stroke the man's body (or her own, for that matter). The couple may feel better able to express their love or to communicate other feelings, since they are facing each other. This position, however, does not work well if the woman is in the advanced stages of pregnancy or if either she or the man is extremely obese. Sex therapists have also found that it is not a very good position if the man wants to control his ejaculation; the woman-on-top position is better for this (see Chapter 18).

Figure 9.17 The woman-on-top position of intercourse.

For the woman-on-top position (see Figure 9.17), the woman kneels over the man, with one knee on either side of his hips. Then his hand or her hand guides the erect penis into the vagina as she lowers herself onto it. She then moves her hips to produce the stimulation. Beyond that, there are numerous variations, depending on where she puts her legs. She can remain on her knees, or she can straighten out her legs behind her, putting them outside his legs or between them. Or she can even turn around and face toward his feet.

This position has a number of advantages. It provides a lot of clitoral stimulation, and the woman can control the kind of stimulation she gets; thus many women find it the best position for them to have an orgasm. It is also a good position for the man who wants to delay his ejaculation, and for this reason it is used in sex therapy. This position is also a good one if the man is tired and it seems advisable for the woman to supply most of the movement. Furthermore, the couple face each other, facilitating better communication, and each has the hands free to stroke the other.

In the rear-entry position, the man faces the woman's back. One way to do this is to have the woman kneel with her head down; the man kneels behind her and inserts his penis into her vagina (see Figure 9.18). (This is sometimes called the "doggie position," because it is the manner in which dogs and most other animals copulate.) Another possibility is for the woman to lie on her stomach, raising her hips slightly so that the man can insert his penis while kneeling over her. Rear entry can also be accomplished when the couple are in the side-to-side position.

In this position the man's hands are free to stimulate the woman's clitoris or any other part of her body. The couple do not face each other, however, and some couples dislike this aspect of the position. A small amount of air may enter the vagina when this position is used, producing interesting noises when it comes out.

In the side-to-side position, the man and woman lie beside each other, either face to face or in a rear-entry position (see Figure 9.19). There are many variations beyond this, depending on where the arms and legs go—so many, in fact, that no attempt will be made to list them. The side-to-side position

Figure 9.18   The rear-entry position of intercourse.

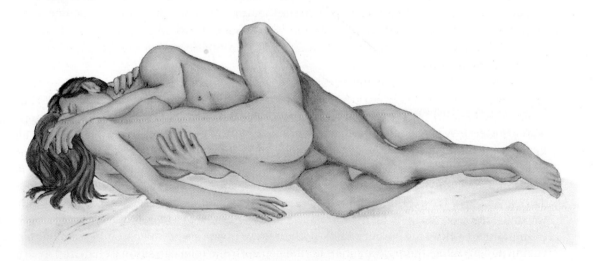

Figure 9.19   The side-to-side position of intercourse.

IN FOCUS 9.3

What Is Tantric Sex?

Many people have heard of tantric sex, particularly after Sting boasted that he and wife, Trudie Styler, were advocates of tantric sex and could make love for up to eight hours at a time. (By the way, he later clarified that this was a major exaggeration.) What exactly is tantric sex? The word *tantric* is thought to come from the Sanskrit "tantra," which means "writing or a written text." Tantric texts, also known as tantric threads or fundamentals, are ancient texts that offer sexual instructions. They come down to us from a number of ancient spiritual traditions including the *Kama Sutra* and the *Ananga Rang* from South Asia, *The Perfumed Garden* from the Middle East, *The Tao of Sex* from the Far East, and other "pillow books."

If tantric texts are simply old sex manuals, why does tantric sex seem to enjoy a kind of sexual mystique or reverence? Tantric texts have typically emerged from a spiritual approach to sex rather than biological, physiological, or empirical traditions. More than simple sexual how-to manuals, tantric texts often claim that adherents not only can have great sex, but also in so doing can attain a greater spiritual awareness of themselves, their partner, and even the universe as a whole. Sexual "energy" is a recurrent theme in tantric writings. According to these texts, sexual energy can be stored and moved from one part of the body to another through energy channels or lines (sometimes referred as *chakras*), as well as to and from sexual partners. In some tantric traditions transfer between partners is seen as particularly important, as men and women are believed to possess complementary forms of energy. Adherents believe that people can learn the skills needed to gain

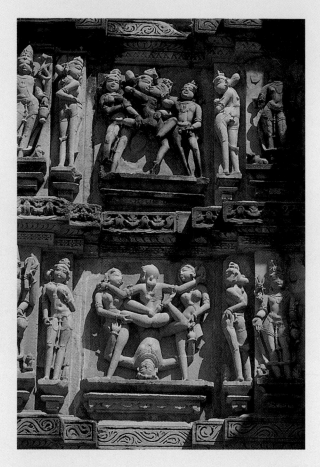

Figure 9.20 Erotic sculptures at the Temple of Kandariya Mahadevo, India, built in A.D. 1000.

is good for leisurely or prolonged intercourse or if one or both of the partners are tired. It is also good for the pregnant and the obese. At least some hands are free to stimulate the clitoris, or whatever.

Aside from the variations in these basic positions that can be produced by switching the position of the legs, there are many other possibilities. For example, the man-on-top position can be varied by having the woman lie on the edge of a bed with her feet on the floor while the man kneels on the floor. Or the woman can lie on the edge of a table while the man stands (don't forget to close the curtains first). Both of these positions produce a somewhat tighter vagina and therefore more stimulation for the penis. Or the man can sit on a chair and insert the penis as the woman sits on his lap, using either a face-to-face or a rear-entry approach. Or, with both partners standing, the man can lift the woman onto his erect penis as she wraps her

control over and manipulate this sexual energy and then use it to intensify orgasm. Summoning and discharging sexual energy through orgasm is then used to attain a "higher state of consciousness" and becomes a tool to allow contact with "universal" energies or spirits. It is claimed that long-time practitioners of tantric sex can induce orgasmic responses simply through meditation, eliminating the need for a partner and his or her energies. Unfortunately, there is little scientific evidence to support any of these claims.

Ancient tantric writings assume that sex would occur between a man and a woman; they view the combining of male and female energies as necessary to reach greater enlightenment. More contemporary tantric writers dismiss this idea and claim, for example, that men or women engaging in the sixty-nine position with a same-sex partner can achieve this same type of enlightenment.

Tantric teachings advocate delaying ejaculation and orgasm: a prolonged period of sex without ejaculation or orgasm is believed to allow "sexual energy" to be built up, manipulated, and transferred to a partner. They suggest specific techniques, often considered mystical or secret, for both men and women to use to delay orgasm and increase their chances of having multiple orgasms. These include focusing on breathing patterns and learning how to coordinate breath, thrusting movements, and other sexual acts; attending to the emotional and sexual needs of sex partners to facilitate buildup and transfer of sexual energy; and using all manner of sexual techniques and intercourse positions so that sexual activity remains exciting and playful.

Intercourse positions are frequently given metaphorical or mystical names. Sexual intercourse standing up is called Congress of the Monkey. The Large Bee position is a woman-on-top intercourse position where she leans back and, while supporting herself with her hands, twists her hips while the man is inside her. The Tail of the Ostrich intercourse position is achieved when she is on her back and he kneels between her legs. She then puts her legs over his shoulders and he lifts her up until only her head touches the ground. In the process, he enters her. The Wife of Indra, considered to be one of the most advanced positions, is achieved when, while in a sitting position, the woman puts her ankles behind her head. The man then enters her and pinches her nose, forcing her to breathe deeply from her diaphragm.

There are intriguing parallels between the advice given by sex therapists and some of the teachings in ancient tantric texts. For example, sex therapists often encourage people interested in experiencing more powerful orgasms to allow natural muscular tension or myotonia and vasocongestion to build up during sex play before orgasming. Higher levels of myotonia and vasocongestion prior to orgasm often feel more pleasurable and satisfying when released. Some of the tantric techniques are quite similar to the behavioural exercises used in contemporary sex therapy (see Chapter 18). Sex therapists emphasize the importance for sexual satisfaction of relationship satisfaction, sexual communication, adopting a mutually enjoyable sexual script that is not routine and predictable, and not focusing on orgasm. In fact, if stripped of its mysticism, colourful language, and secrecy, tantric sexual practices are not that different from what one would learn visiting a sex therapist.

Sources: Written by Guy Grenier, 2005, based on Craze, 2003; Lacroix, 2003; Tannahill, 1980.

legs around his back, or she can put one leg over his shoulder (you have to be pretty athletic to manage this one, however). For even more advanced positions, see In Focus 9.3.

MOUTH–GENITAL STIMULATION

One of the most striking features of the sexual revolution of the last few decades is the increased popularity of mouth–genital, or oral–genital, techniques (Hunt & Curtis, 2006). There are two kinds of mouth–genital stimulation ("going down on" one's partner): cunnilingus and fellatio.[12]

[12]Early marriage manuals in North America called cunnilingus and fellatio the *genital kiss*—definitely a more romantic term (Hunt & Curtis, 2006).

Cunnilingus (cun-ih-LING-us): Mouth stimulation of the female genitals.

In cunnilingus, or "eating" (from the Latin words *cunnus,* meaning "vulva," and *lingere,* meaning "to lick"), the woman's genitals are stimulated by her male or female partner's mouth. Generally, the focus of stimulation is the clitoris. The tongue stimulates it and the surrounding area with quick darting or thrusting movements, or the mouth can suck at the clitoris. A good prelude to cunnilingus can be kissing of the inner thighs or the belly, gradually moving to the clitoris. The mouth can also suck at the inner lips, or the tongue can stimulate the vaginal entrance or be inserted into the vagina. During cunnilingus, some women also enjoy having a finger inserted into the vagina or the anus for added stimulation. The best way to know what she wants is through communication between partners, either verbal or non-verbal.

Many women are enthusiastic about cunnilingus and say that it is the best way, or perhaps the only way, for them to orgasm. Such responses are well within the normal range of female sexuality. As one woman put it:

> A tongue offers gentleness and precision and wetness and is the perfect organ for contact. And, besides, it produces sensational orgasms. (Hite, 1976, p. 234)

In one large, well-sampled study of Australians, respondents reported the specific sexual practices that were used in their most recent heterosexual encounter (Richters et al., 2006). If women had intercourse only, 50 percent had an orgasm, but when they had cunnilingus plus intercourse, 73 percent had an orgasm. In contrast, among men who engaged only in intercourse, 95 percent had an orgasm. It just isn't fair.

Cunnilingus (like fellatio, discussed next) can transmit some sexually transmitted infections such as gonorrhea. Oral sex can also result in the transmission of HPV from the genitals of an infected person to the mouth of the partner or vice versa. Some cases of oral cancers involve the HPV-16 strain, which may have been transmitted by oral sex (Herrero et al., 2003). Therefore, you need to be as careful about with whom you engage in mouth–genital sex as about with whom you would engage in intercourse. A small sheet of plastic, called a dental dam, can be placed over the vulva for those wanting to practise safer sex. Unlubricated condoms can also be cut open and used in place of a dental dam.

One other possible problem should be noted, as well. Some women enjoy having their partner blow air forcefully into the vagina. While this technique is not dangerous under normal circumstances, when used on a pregnant woman it has been known to cause death (apparently as the result of air getting into the uterine veins), damage to the placenta, and embolism (Sadock & Sadock, 1976). Thus it should not be used on a pregnant woman.

Fellatio (feh-LAY-shoh): Mouth stimulation of the male genitals.

In fellatio[13] ("sucking," "a blow job") the man's penis is stimulated by his male or female partner's mouth. The partner licks the glans of the penis, its shaft, and perhaps the testicles. The penis is gently taken into the mouth. If it is not fully erect, an erection can generally be produced by stronger sucking combined with hand stimulation along the penis. After that, the partner can produce an in-and-out motion by moving the lips down toward the base of the penis and then back up, always being careful not to scrape the penis with the teeth. Or the tongue can be flicked back and forth around the tip of the penis or along the corona.

To bring the man to orgasm, the in-and-out motion is continued, moving the penis deeper and deeper into the mouth and perhaps also using the fingers to encircle the base of the penis and give further stimulation. Sometimes when the penis moves deeply toward the throat, it stimulates a gag reflex, which occurs anytime something comes into contact with that part of the throat. To avoid this, the partner should concentrate on relaxing the throat muscles while firming the lips to provide more stimulation to the penis.

When a couple are engaged in fellatio, the big question in their minds may concern ejaculation. The man may, of course, simply withdraw his penis from his partner's mouth and

---

[13]"Fellatio" is from the Latin word *fellare,* meaning "to suck." Partners should not take the "sucking" part too literally. The penis, particularly at the tip, is a delicate organ and should not be treated like a straw in an extra-thick milkshake.

Figure 9.21 Simultaneous heterosexual mouth–genital stimulation in the sixty-nine position.

ejaculate outside it. Or he may ejaculate into it, and his partner may enjoy swallowing the ejaculate. The ejaculate resembles partially cooked egg white in texture; it does not have a very distinctive flavour but often leaves a salty aftertaste. Because some people have mixed feelings about having the semen in their mouths, it is probably a good idea for the couple to discuss ahead of time (or during the activity) what they plan to do, particularly because ejaculation into the mouth is an unsafe practice in the AIDS era (see Chapter 8).

Most men find fellatio to be a highly stimulating experience, which no doubt accounts for the high frequency with which prostitutes are asked to do it. Enjoyment of fellatio is certainly within the common range of male sexuality.

Both partners can perform mouth–genital stimulation simultaneously. This is often called **sixty-nining** because the numerals "69" suggest the position of the two bodies during simultaneous mouth–genital sex. Sixty-nining may be done either side to side or with one person on top of the other, each with the mouth on the other's genitals (Figure 9.21).

Simultaneous mouth–genital sex allows both people to enjoy the pleasure of that stimulation at the same time. It can give a feeling of total body involvement and total involvement between partners. Some couples, however, feel that this technique requires doing too many things at once and is more complicated than enjoyable. For example, a woman may be distracted from enjoying the marvellous clitoral stimulation she is receiving because she has to concentrate at the same time on using her mouth to stimulate her partner's genitals. If sixty-nine is done with one partner on top, the bottom partner may feel that he or she has no control over the movement and may be choked.

Sixty-nining: Simultaneous mouth–genital stimulation; also called soixante-neuf.

Anal Intercourse

In **anal intercourse** the man inserts his penis into his female or male partner's rectum. In legal circles, anal intercourse is sometimes called sodomy (although this term may also refer to other sexual practices such as intercourse with animals), and it is sometimes referred to as having sex "Greek style."

Anal intercourse may be somewhat difficult because the rectum has no natural lubrication and because it is surrounded by fairly tight muscles. The man should therefore begin by moistening the partner's anus, either with saliva or with a sterile surgical lubricant such as K-Y Jelly (*not* Vaseline). He should also lubricate his penis. He then inserts it gently into the rectum and begins controlled pelvic thrusting. It is typically done in the rear-entry position

Anal intercourse: Insertion of the penis into the partner's rectum.

or in the man-on-top position. The more the partner can relax and be in control, the more pleasurable it is; if it is done properly, it need involve no pain. While some couples are not interested in anal sex, others delight in it. Some women report orgasm during anal intercourse, particularly when it is accompanied by hand stimulation of the clitoris. Men also report orgasms from anal intercourse, primarily due to stimulation of the prostate.

There are some health risks associated with anal intercourse. It can lead to infections with various organisms. Of greatest concern, HIV can be transmitted through anal intercourse. Thus, safer sex consists of either refraining from engaging in anal intercourse, or using a condom if one does (or doing it only in a monogamous relationship with an uninfected partner). Furthermore, for heterosexuals the penis should never be inserted into the vagina after anal intercourse unless it has been washed thoroughly. The reason for this is that the rectum contains bacteria that do not belong in the vagina and that can cause a dandy case of vaginitis if they happen to get there. Also, sex toys or other objects inserted in the anus should be thoroughly washed following removal.

Anilingus (ay-nih-LING-us): Mouth stimulation of the partner's anus.

Another variation is anilingus (*feuille de rose* in French, "rimming" in slang), in which the tongue and mouth stimulate the anus. The anus may also be stimulated by the hand, and some people report that having a finger inserted into the rectum near the time of orgasm provides a heightened sexual sensation. Anilingus carries with it some risk of HIV, hepatitis, or *E. coli* infections.

SEXUAL SCRIPTS

The sexual scripts of heterosexual, gay, and lesbian couples are quite similar, and same-sex partners and opposite-sex partners mostly engage in the same behaviours. That is, for most couples—straight and gay—hugging, kissing, caressing, and snuggling are very important. These behaviours are often precursors to oral–genital sex (fellatio and/or cunnilingus), mutual masturbation, and (less frequently) anal intercourse. For most opposite-sex couples,

Figure 9.22 Female-to-female sexual expression.

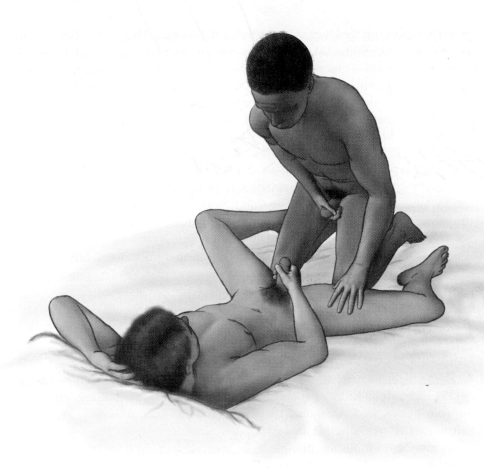

Figure 9.23   Male-to-male sexual expression.

lovemaking involves and often culminates in vaginal–penile intercourse. Among gay men, there appears to be a strong enjoyment or strong dislike of anal play, with significant numbers of men in each camp (Lever, 1994). Relative to anal sex, more gay men prefer giving and receiving oral sex (fellatio), masturbation, licking/sucking testicles, and sucking nipples. Female couples commonly engage in rubbing each other's genitals, and oral stimulation (cunnilingus). Further, many lesbians (and other couples) report using a hand-held and/or strap-on dildo—43 percent of lesbians have used a hand-held dildo and 27 percent have used a strap-on dildo, according to one survey (Lever, 1995).

Masters and Johnson (1979), in their laboratory studies, made direct observations of the lovemaking techniques of gays and lesbians and compared them with those of heterosexuals. They found that, in masturbation techniques, there were no differences. However, in couple interactions there were some substantial differences. The major one was that gays and lesbians took their time—that is, they seemed not to have any goal orientation. Heterosexual couples, on the other hand, seemed to be performance-oriented—they seemed to strive toward a goal of orgasm for each partner. In the initial approach to stimulating the female, heterosexuals and lesbians began with holding and kissing, but this lasted only about 30 seconds for the heterosexuals, who quickly moved on to genital stimulation. Lesbians, on the other hand, spent more time in holding and kissing and then went on to a long period of breast stimulation, which sometimes resulted in orgasm in the absence of genital stimulation. Lesbians also appeared to communicate more with each other. In the initial approach to stimulating the male, gay men did extensive stimulation of the nipples, generally producing erection; such a technique was rare among heterosexuals (with only three of 100 couples). Gay men were also much more likely to stimulate the frenulum (the area of the penis on the lower side, just below the corona). They also used a "teasing technique" in which the man brings his partner near orgasm, then relaxes the stimulation, then increases the stimulation again, and so on, essentially prolonging the pleasure. Among heterosexuals, the man's most frequent complaint was that his partner did not grasp the shaft of the penis tightly enough. Masters and Johnson argued that heterosexuals can learn from gays and lesbians; the technique of gays and lesbians benefits from stimulating another body like their own.

TWO-PERSON CYBERSEX

The Internet provides not only visual sexual images for people wanting to masturbate, it also creates the opportunity for two-person cybersex. People report forming relationships on the Internet that they consider to be sexually intimate, even though they have never actually met the person face-to-face (Ross, 2005). It has also created a new sexual space that is somewhere between fantasy and action. Essentially, one can type sexual acts without actually doing them (Ross, 2005). These Internet activities challenge us to think more clearly about our definitions of sexual activity. For example, a woman accuses her partner of having a cybersex affair with another woman and he replies that he was only typing. Who is right?

APHRODISIACS

IS THERE A GOOD APHRODISIAC?

An aphrodisiac is a substance—such as a food, a drug, or a perfume—that excites sexual desire. Throughout history people have searched for the "surefire" aphrodisiac. Before arousing your hopes, we should note that the search has been unsuccessful; there is no known substance that works well as an aphrodisiac.

A number of foods are thought to be aphrodisiacs, perhaps because they resemble the sex organs. These include oysters (which resemble the testes), elk antler velvet, seal penis, powdered rhinoceros horn, bananas, and asparagus (which resemble the penis). In addition, the current interest in nutrition and natural and organic foods and supplements has created a market for "natural" aphrodisiacs. According to one industry source, the popular herbs purchased for this purpose include yohimbe, cayenne, arginine, aventa sativa, and damiana. Some companies sell herbal combinations and edible syrups and "brews" that are claimed to increase sexual desire, sexual performance, sexual stamina, or all three. Again, there is no evidence that any of these foods or products affect sexual desire. However, with all these substances the belief that they will be arousing may enhance sexual functioning. Perhaps this is why people continue to believe that they are aphrodisiacs.

What about various drugs? The effects of alcohol on sexual functioning will be discussed in Chapter 18. Briefly, drinking small quantities of alcohol may, for some people, decrease psychological inhibitions and therefore increase sexual desire. Moderate to large quantities, however, rapidly lead to an inability to function sexually.

Users of marijuana report that it acts as a sexual stimulant (McKay, 2005). Probably this is due, in part, to the fact that marijuana produces the sensation that time is being stretched out, thus prolonging and intensifying sensations, including sexual sensations. There is no scientific documentation of the aphrodisiac effects of marijuana except for the reports of users. Possible negative effects of marijuana on sexual functioning are discussed in Chapter 18.

Unfortunately, some of the substances that are thought to enhance sexual functioning are quite dangerous. For example, cantharides (Spanish fly) has a reputation as an aphrodisiac, but it is poisonous and an irritant (Kaplan, 1974; Leavitt, 1974; Taberner, 1985).

Amyl nitrite ("poppers") is popular among some people. Because it relaxes the sphincter muscle of the anus, it is used by those engaging in anal intercourse (Taberner, 1985). Users report that it produces heightened sensations during orgasms (Everett, 1975). Probably it acts by dilating the blood vessels in the genitals. It may, however, have side effects,

Aphrodisiac (ah-froh-DIZ-ih-ak): A substance that increases sexual desire.

including dizziness, headaches, fainting, and, in rare cases, death; thus it can be dangerous (Taberner, 1985).

Butyl nitrite—sold under such trade names as Rush, Locker Room, and Climax—is a chemical relative of amyl nitrite. It is used to heighten sexual pleasure. Although no deaths have been reported from inhaling it, there are reported deaths from swallowing it (UPI, 1981).

In contrast to these "street" drugs, three prescription drugs (Viagra, Cialis, Levitra) have been approved by Health Canada for use in treating male sexual dysfunction. *Viagra* is designed to increase the flow of blood to the penis and maintain the resulting erection. Cialis is intended to create the ability to have a successful intercourse attempt (an erection) up to 36 hours after taking it. Note that neither drug increases desire. (For more information, see Chapter 18.) It is dangerous to combine these drugs with amyl nitrite. There is no evidence that these prescription drugs increase sexual desire or performance in women.

Anaphrodisiacs

Just as people have searched for aphrodisiacs, so they have sought **anaphrodisiacs**—substances or practices that would diminish sexual desire. Cold showers are reputed to have such effects, as is potassium nitrate (saltpetre). The latter contains nothing that decreases sexual drive, but it does act as a diuretic; it makes the person want to urinate frequently, which may be distracting enough so that he or she is not much interested in sex.

There has been some medical interest in finding drugs that would decrease sex drive for use in treating aggressive sexual offenders. One such drug is cyproterone acetate, which is an antiandrogen (for more information, see Chapter 16).

Other drugs that may lead to a loss of sexual functioning are discussed in Chapter 18.

Anaphrodisiac (an-ah-froh-DIZ-ih-ak): A substance that decreases sexual desire.

SHOULD INTERCOURSE AND ORGASM BE THE GOAL?

Western culture has traditionally held the belief that a sexual encounter should "climax" with intercourse and orgasm, at least orgasm for the man. In our modern era of multiple orgasms for women and general sexual liberation, the view that intercourse is the important part of sex and that orgasm is the goal toward which both partners must strive is pervasive. This belief system is reflected in the term *foreplay*, which implies that activities like hand stimulation of the genitals, kissing, and mouth–genital sex are only preliminaries that take place before intercourse, the latter being "real sex." In reality all of these activities and more can result in sexual pleasure (Rye & Meaney, 2007). Similar beliefs are reflected in a commonly used phrase, *achieving orgasm*, as if orgasm were something to be achieved like a promotion on the job.[14]

Psychologist Rollo May felt that men particularly, by concentrating on achieving orgasm and satisfying their desire, miss out on the more important part of the sexual experience: prolonging the feeling of desire and pleasure, building it higher and higher. As he put it:

> The pleasure in sex is described by Freud and others as the reduction of tension [orgasm]; in eros, on the contrary, we wish not to be released from the excitement but rather to hang on to it, to bask in it, and even to increase it. (1974, pp. 71–72)

Another one of the goals of sex that has emerged recently is the simultaneous orgasm. Some people consider this an event to be worked for rather than a pleasant thing that sometimes happens.

In short, our achievement drives now seem to be channelled into our sexual behaviours. There is nothing intrinsically wrong with expressing achievement drives in sex, except that any time there is an achievement situation, there is also the potential for a failure. If a woman

---

[14]To avoid this whole notion, we never use the phrase "to achieve orgasm" in this book. Instead, we prefer "to have an orgasm" or simply "to orgasm." Why not turn it into a verb so that we will not feel we have to work at achieving it?

does not have an orgasm or if a man cannot get an erection, they or their partner may feel as if the whole experience was a disaster. The problem with setting up sexual goals, then, is that the possibility of sexual failures or sexual disorders is also being set up.

The best approach is to enjoy all the various aspects of lovemaking for themselves, rather than as techniques for achieving something. We need to experience sex as a feast of the senses, rather than as an achievement competition. We need to broaden our view of sexual expression to recognize that a broad continuum of activities may provide sexual pleasure—a dream, a thought, a conversation, cuddling, kissing, sensual message, dancing, oral–genital stimulation, and intercourse (Chalker, 1995; Rye & Meaney, 2007).

Couples who delight in the process of lovemaking also spend more time pleasing each other. In one study we found that 21 percent of men and 24 percent of women in long-term relationships complained that they and their partner spent too little time in foreplay before intercourse (MacNeil & Byers, 1997). How much longer do men and women want lovemaking to last? A study of 152 Canadian heterosexual couples in long-term relationships asked the men and women how long foreplay[15] and intercourse typically last in their relationship and how long they would ideally like each to last (Miller & Byers, 2004). The researchers found that on average the women wanted foreplay to last about eight minutes longer and the men wanted it to last about five minutes longer than it typically did. They also wanted intercourse to last longer—on average women wanted about seven more minutes and men wanted about 11 more minutes of intercourse. In short, we need to view the entire body as erogenous and shift our focus to the *process* of making love and *outercourse* as much as intercourse.

FROM INEXPERIENCE TO BOREDOM

Most of us, of course, are sexually inexperienced early in our lives. However, only some people see this as a problem. Most of us also have long-term romantic and sexual relationships, and at times, feel bored with the way we are having sex. How can we deal with these problems?

SEXUAL INEXPERIENCE

In Western culture we now expect both men and women to be at least somewhat experienced and skillful in the use of sexual techniques. How can one deal with this problem of inexperience? First, it is important to question society's assumption that one should be experienced. Everyone has to begin sometime, and there is absolutely nothing wrong with inexperience. Second, there are many good books and articles on sexual techniques that are definitely worth reading, although it is important to be selective, since a few of these may be more harmful than helpful. Do not become slavishly attached to the techniques you read about in books, though; they should serve basically as a stimulus to your imagination, not as a series of steps that must be followed. Third, communicate with your partner. Because individual preferences vary so much, no one, no matter how experienced, is ever a sexual expert with a new partner. The best way to please a partner is to find out what that person likes, and communication may accomplish this better than prior experience. In fact, our research has shown that people who communicate their sexual likes and dislikes to their partner describe their sexual interactions as more pleasing than poor communicators do (Byers & Demmons, 1999). Chapter 12 gives some specific tips on communication.

BOREDOM

Boredom, of course, is not always a necessary consequence of having sex with the same person over a long period of time. Certainly there are couples who have been together for 40 or 50 years and who continue to find sexual expression exciting. However, it is not uncommon for

---

[15]We used the term "foreplay" in this study because it is easily understood by participants and has been used in other research. We don't use this term in this book, because it implies a rigid sexual script in which intercourse is the main event and other activities are merely warm-ups for the main event.

people to experience at least occasional fits of boredom. How can we deal with the problem of boredom?

Again, communication can also help solve this problem. Couples sometimes evolve a routine sexual sequence that leads to boredom and may not be what either partner wants. By communicating to each other what they would like to do and then doing it, two people can introduce some variety into their relationship. The various love manuals can also give ideas on new techniques. In addition, a couple's sexual relationship often mirrors the other aspects of their relationship, and sexual boredom may sometimes mean that they are generally bored with each other. Rejuvenating the rest of the relationship may do wonders for their sexual relationship. Our research shows that the best predictor of sexual satisfaction is satisfaction with the overall relationship, not specific sexual techniques (Byers et al., 1998; Lawrance & Byers, 1995).

One might also question the meaning of boredom. Perhaps our expectations for sexual experience are too high. Encouraged by the media, we tend to believe that every time we make love, the earth should move. We do not expect that every meal we eat will be fantastic or that we will always have a huge appetite and enjoy every bite. Yet we do tend to have such expectations with regard to sexuality. Perhaps when boredom seems to be a problem, the problem really may be unrealistically high expectations.

SUMMARY

William Masters and Virginia Johnson conducted an important program of research on the physiology of human sexual response. They found that two basic physiological processes occur during arousal and orgasm: vasocongestion and myotonia. The sexual response cycle occurs in three stages: excitement, orgasm, and resolution.

Their research indicates that there is no physiological distinction between clitoral and vaginal orgasms in women, which refutes an early idea of Freud's. They also provided convincing evidence of the existence of multiple orgasm in women.

Criticisms of Masters and Johnson's model are that (1) they ignored cognitive factors, and (2) their selection of research participants may have led to a self-fulfilling prophecy in their results.

Two cognitive-physiological models are Kaplan's three-component (desire, vasocongestion, and muscular contraction) model, and Walen and Roth's model, which emphasizes cognitive aspects of sexual response (perception and evaluation).

The nervous system and sex hormones are important in sexual response. The nervous system functions in sexual response by a combination of spinal reflexes (best documented for erection and ejaculation) and brain influences (particularly of the limbic system). There is evidence that some women ejaculate. Hormones are important to sexual behaviour, both in their influences on prenatal development (organizing effects) and in their stimulating influence on adult sexual behaviour (activating effects). Testosterone seems to be crucial for maintaining sexual desire in both men and women.

Pheromones are biochemicals secreted outside the body that play an important role in sexual communication and attraction. Much of the evidence is based on research with animals, but evidence in humans is accumulating rapidly.

Sexual pleasure is produced by stimulation of various areas of the body; these are the erogenous zones.

Sexual self-stimulation, or autoeroticism, includes masturbation and sexual fantasies. Many people have sexual fantasies while masturbating or having sex with a partner. Common themes are having intercourse with a loved partner, kissing passionately, making love elsewhere than the bedroom, and giving and receiving oral sex.

Continued on next page.

SUMMARY *cont.*

An important technique in two-person sex is hand stimulation of the partner's genitals. A good guide to technique is to find out how the partner masturbates. Touching other areas of the body and kissing are also important. The other senses—sight, smell, and hearing—can also be used in creating sexual arousal.

While there are infinite varieties in the positions in which one can have penile–vaginal intercourse, there are four basic positions: man on top (the missionary position), woman on top, rear entry, and side to side.

There are two kinds of mouth–genital stimulation: cunnilingus (mouth stimulation of the female genitals) and fellatio (mouth stimulation of the male genitals). Both are engaged in frequently and are considered pleasurable by many people. Lesbians, gay men, and heterosexuals use similar techniques (e.g., hand–genital stimulation and

oral–genital sex). Gay men and lesbians, though, seem less goal-oriented, take their time more, and communicate more than heterosexuals do.

Anal intercourse involves inserting the penis into the rectum. This activity and insertion of objects into the anus must be done carefully to avoid injury or transmission of STIs.

An aphrodisiac is a substance that arouses sexual desire. There is no known reliable aphrodisiac, and some of the substances that are popularly thought to act as aphrodisiacs can be dangerous to one's health.

We have a tendency in our culture to view sex as work and to turn sex into an achievement situation, as witnessed by expressions such as "achieving orgasm." Such attitudes make sex less pleasurable and may set the stage for sexual failures or sexual disorders.

QUESTIONS FOR THOUGHT, DISCUSSION, AND DEBATE

1. Debate the following topic. Resolved: Castration is an appropriate and effective treatment for convicted sex offenders.

2. Do you think that pheromones might play more of a role in human sexual behaviour in cultures that do not stress personal hypercleanliness as much as we do in Canada? If so, what do you think the effects of pheromones would be in those other cultures?

3. Your little sister, Katie, is a second-year university student and is in the fourth month of what looks like it will be a wonderful long-term relationship. Katie and her boyfriend now seem to have a full sexual relationship. As a benevolent older brother/sister, you want Katie to enjoy

much sexual pleasure in this relationship. What information from this chapter would you tell Katie about, if you hoped to ensure her sexual satisfaction and sexual pleasure?

4. What do you think about sexual fantasizing? Is it harmful, or is it a good way to enrich one's sexual expression? Are your ideas consistent with the results of the research discussed in this chapter?

5. You have been in an intimate relationship for two years. You find you are getting bored with your sexual activity. List five things that could make your sexual relationship more satisfying. How would you communicate your desire to do each of these to your partner?

SUGGESTIONS FOR FURTHER READING

Comfort, Alex. (1991). *The new joy of sex: A gourmet guide to lovemaking for the nineties.* New York: Crown. Alex Comfort rewrote his bestseller to maintain the joy of sex while recognizing the risk of AIDS.

Dodson, Betty. (1987). *Sex for one: The joy of self-loving.* New York: Harmony Books (Crown Publishers). An inspiring ode to masturbation.

Kaufman, Miriam, Silverberg, Cory, and Odette, Fran. (2003). *The ultimate guide to sex and disability.* San Francisco: Cleis Press. An excellent resource and self-help book with plenty of Canadian content. All three authors are Canadian.

Kroll, Ken, et al. (1995). *Enabling romance: A guide to love, sex, and relationships for the disabled (and the people who care for them).* Bethesda, MD: Woodbine House. With the recognition of disabled persons' sexuality comes a need for self-help books, and this one is designed for that purpose.

Laqueur, Thomas W. (2003). *Solitary sex: A cultural history of masturbation.* New York: Zone Books.

Maines, Rachel P. (1999). *The technology of orgasm: "Hysteria," the vibrator, and women's sexual satisfaction.* Baltimore: Johns Hopkins University Press. A delicious history of the vibrator, originally developed for physicians in the Victorian era to use in curing women of a mental disorder termed "hysteria."

Tiefer, Leonore. (2004). *Sex is not a natural act and other essays,* 2nd ed. Boulder, CO: Westview. Tiefer is both knowledgeable and a witty writer. This book contains some of her insightful criticisms of the Masters and Johnson model of sexual response.

Wyatt, Tristan. (2003). *Pheromones and animal behaviour.* New York: Cambridge University Press. The definitive book on pheromones.

For review questions, web resources, and other learning and study tools, visit the *Understanding Human Sexuality* Online Learning Centre at www.mcgrawhill.ca/olc/hyde.

Chapter

10

SEXUALITY AND THE LIFE CYCLE: CHILDHOOD AND ADOLESCENCE

Chapter Highlights

Data Sources

Infancy (0 to 2 Years)
Self-Stimulation
Infant–Infant Sexual Encounters
Non-genital Sensual Experiences
Attachment
Knowing about Boy–Girl Differences

Early Childhood (3 to 7 Years)
Masturbation
Other-Sex Behaviour
Same-Sex Behaviour
Sex Knowledge and Interests

Preadolescence (8 to 12 Years)
Masturbation
Other-Sex Behaviour
Same-Sex Behaviour
Dating and Romantic Relationships
Sexualization of Girls

Adolescence (13 to 19 Years)
Masturbation
Same-Sex Behaviour
Other-Sex Behaviour

Sexual Intercourse
How Many Youth Engage in Sexual Intercourse?
First Intercourse
Techniques in Adolescent Sex
Attitudes toward Adolescent Sexual Intercourse
Motives for Having Sexual Intercourse
Adolescent Romantic Relationships
Condom Use
Teen Pregnancy
Conflicts

Sexuality and Adolescent Development

> MY SON JEREMY . . . NAIVELY DECIDED TO WEAR BARRETTES TO NURSERY SCHOOL. SEVERAL TIMES THAT DAY, ANOTHER BOY INSISTED THAT JEREMY MUST BE A GIRL BECAUSE "ONLY GIRLS WEAR BARRETTES." AFTER REPEATEDLY ASSERTING THAT "WEARING BARRETTES DOESN'T MATTER; BEING A BOY MEANS HAVING A PENIS AND TESTICLES," JEREMY FINALLY PULLED DOWN HIS PANTS AS A WAY OF MAKING HIS POINT MORE CONVINCINGLY. THE BOY WAS NOT IMPRESSED. HE SIMPLY SAID, "EVERYBODY HAS A PENIS; ONLY GIRLS WEAR BARRETTES."*

Stop for a moment and think of the first sexual experience you ever had. Some of you will think of the first time you had sexual intercourse. New Brunswick researchers have shown that we tend to use the terms "having sex" and "sexual intercourse" synonymously (Randall & Byers, 2003). For example, fewer than 15 percent thought that genital fondling and fewer than 25 percent thought that oral sex was having sex. Nonetheless, sex is more than just having sexual intercourse. So, others will remember earlier episodes, like playing doctor with the other kids in the neighbourhood, or their first passionate kiss, or orgasms with a partner through manual or oral stimulation. Now think of the kind of sex life you had, or expect to have, in your early 20s. Finally, imagine yourself at 65 and imagine the kinds of sexual behaviour you will be engaging in then.

In recent years, scientists have begun thinking of human sexual development as a process that occurs throughout the lifespan. This process is influenced by biological, psychological, social, and cultural factors. This represents a departure from the Freudian heritage, in which the crucial aspects of development were all thought to occur in childhood. This chapter and Chapter 11 are based on the newer **lifespan**, or life-cycle, approach to understanding the development of our sexual behaviour throughout the course of our lives. The things you were asked to remember and imagine about your own sexual functioning in the preceding paragraph will give you an idea of the sweep of this approach to development. You will find a discussion of sex education across the lifespan as well as tips for parents who want to do a better job of talking to their children about sex in Chapter 19.

Lifespan development: Development from birth through old age.

DATA SOURCES

What kinds of scientific data are available on the sexual behaviour of people at various times in their lives? Most of the data come from surveys in which adults are questioned about their childhood sexual behaviour. Their responses form some of the data to be discussed in this chapter. As discussed in Chapter 3, these are self-report data and thus may be subject to reporting biases such as exaggeration and purposeful concealment. These responses may be even more problematic than some of the other kinds of data from those studies, though. For example, a 50- or 60-year-old man is asked to report on his sexual behaviour at age ten. How accurately will he remember things that happened 40 or 50 years ago? Surely there will be some forgetting. Thus, the data on childhood sexual behaviour may be subject to errors that result from adults being asked to recall things that happened a very long time ago.

An alternative would be to interview children about their sexual behaviour or perhaps even to observe their sexual behaviour. Few researchers have done either, for obvious reasons. Such a study would arouse tremendous opposition from parents, religious leaders, and

*From Bem, S.L. (1989). Genital knowledge and gender constancy in preschool children. *Child Development, 60,* 649–662.

politicians, who might argue that it is unnecessary, or that it would harm the children who were studied. These reactions reflect in part the widespread beliefs that children are not yet sexual beings and should not be exposed to questions about sex. Such research also raises ethical issues: At what age can a child give truly informed consent to be in such a study?

In a few studies children have been questioned directly about their sexual behaviour. Kinsey interviewed 432 children, aged 4 to 14, and the results of the study were published after his death by Elias and Gebhard (1969). A recent innovation is the use of a "talking" computer to interview children (Romer et al., 1997). The computer is programmed to present the questions through headphones, and the child enters his or her answers using the keyboard. This process preserves confidentiality, even when others are present, because only the child knows the question. This procedure was used to gather data from samples of high-risk youth ages 9 to 15. More children reported sexual experience to the computer than in face-to-face interviews.

Many studies of adolescent sexual behaviour and attitudes have also been done. The Canadian Youth, Sexual Health, and HIV/AIDS Study (CYSHHAS; Boyce et al., 2003, 2006) and its predecessor the Canada Youth and AIDS Study (King et al., 1988) are important national surveys. A series of surveys by Reginald Bibby and Donald Posterski (1992; Bibby, 2001) also provide some information about adolescent sexuality in Canada. In the United States, sociological studies of adolescent sexual intercourse have been done by Reiss (1967), DeLamater and MacCorquodale (1979), and Bancroft, Herbenick, and Reynolds (2002). We can have particular confidence in recent, well-sampled studies of adolescent sexuality.

The studies of child and adolescent sexual behaviour have all been surveys that have used either questionnaires or interviews. No one has made systematic, direct observations of children's sexual behaviour.

INFANCY (0 TO 2 YEARS)

Before 1890, it was thought that sexuality was something that magically appeared at puberty. Historically, we owe the whole notion that children—in fact, infants—have sexual urges and engage in sexual behaviour to Sigmund Freud.

The capacity of the human body to show a sexual response is present from birth. Male infants, for example, get erections. Indeed, boy babies are sometimes born with erections. Ultrasound studies indicate that reflex erections occur in the male fetus for several months before birth (Masters et al., 1982), and vaginal lubrication has been found in baby girls in the 24 hours after birth.

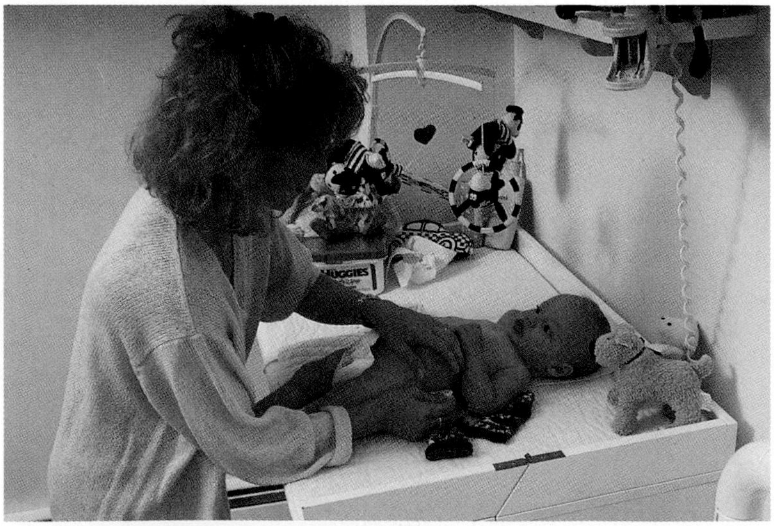

The first intimate relationship most children experience is with their mothers. The mother–infant relationship involves a good deal of physical contact and typically engages the infant's tactile, olfactory, visual, and auditory senses (Frayser, 1994).

Most activities associated with nurturing and hygienic care of babies is intimate and sensuous since it involves contact with sensitive organs—lips, mouth, anus, and genitals—that can produce in the infant a physiological response of a sensuous and sexual nature. These activities include (in addition to breast-feeding) toilet training, bathing, cleaning, and

Figure 10.1   Some activities associated with nurturing an infant are potentially sensuous, because they involve pleasant physical contact.

diapering. The highly physiological and emotionally charged first encounters of parent and infant play an indispensable part in the development process (Martinson, 1994, p. 11).

SELF-STIMULATION

Infants are often observed fondling their own genitals. There is some question as to how conscious they are of what they are doing, but at the least they seem to be engaging in some pleasurable, sexual self-stimulation. The rhythmic manipulation of the genitals associated with adult masturbation does not occur until age two-and-a-half to three years (Martinson, 1994). Ford and Beach (1951) noted on the basis of their survey of sexual behaviour in other cultures that, if permitted, most boys and girls will progress from absent-minded fingering of their genitals to systematic masturbation by ages six to eight. In fact, in some cultures adults fondle infants' genitals to keep them quiet, a remarkably effective pacifier.

Figure 10.2   Infant self-stimulation.

Orgasms from self-stimulation are possible even at this early age, although before puberty boys are not capable of ejaculation. Self-stimulation is a normal, natural form of sexual expression in infancy. It is definitely not a sign of pathology, as some previous generations believed. Indeed, in one study comparing infants who had optimal relationships with their mothers and infants who had problematic relationships with their mothers, it was the infants with the optimal maternal relationships who were more likely to stimulate their genitals (Spitz, 1949).

INFANT–INFANT SEXUAL ENCOUNTERS

Infants and young children are very self-centred (what the psychologist Jean Piaget called *egocentric*). Even when they seem to be playing with another child, they may simply be playing alongside the other child, actually in a world all their own. Their sexual development parallels the development of their other behaviours. Thus their earliest sex is typically one-person sex—self-stimulation. Not until later do they develop social, two-person sex.

Nonetheless, particularly in later infancy there may be some infant–infant encounters, either affectionate or sexual. In these encounters, children may kiss, hug, pat, stroke, and gaze at each other, behaviours that are part of erotic intimacy later in life.

NON-GENITAL SENSUAL EXPERIENCES

Many of the sensual experiences that infants and young children have are diffuse and not easily classified as some type of activity. For example, as Freud noted, infants delight in putting things in their mouths. Thus sucking at the mother's breast, or sucking on his or her own fingers, may be a sensuous experience for the infant.

Being cuddled or rocked can also be a warm, sensuous experience. Indeed, the infant's experiences in such early intimate encounters might influence her or his reactions to intimacy and cuddling in adulthood. It seems that some infants are cuddlers and some are non-cuddlers (Schaffer & Emerson, 1964). Cuddlers enjoy physical contact, while non-cuddlers show displeasure and restlessness when they are handled or held. As soon as they are old enough to do so, they show resistance to such situations or crawl or walk away from them. Cuddling and non-cuddling seem to be basically different personality patterns. It would be interesting to know whether these patterns remain consistent into adulthood.

ATTACHMENT

Attachment: A psychological bond that forms between an infant and the mother, father, or other caregiver.

The quality of the relationship with the parents at this age can be very important to the child's capacity for later sexual and emotional relationships. In psychological terms, an **attachment** (or bond) forms between the infant and the mother, father, or other caregiver. The bond begins in the hours immediately following birth and continues throughout the period of infancy (Coustan & Angelini, 1995), and is facilitated by cuddling and other forms of physical contact. Later, attachments form to other familiar people. These are the individual's earliest experiences with love and emotional attachment. The quality of these attachments—whether they are stable, secure, and satisfying or unstable, insecure, and frustrating—affects the person's capacity for emotional attachments in adulthood. Recent research with humans (discussed in Chapter 13) indicates that adults' styles of romantic attachment are similar to the kinds of attachment they remember having with their parents in childhood.

KNOWING ABOUT BOY–GIRL DIFFERENCES

By age two-and-a-half or three, children know what gender they are (see Chapter 13). This is the first step in developing a gender identity. Awareness of being a boy or a girl motivates them to be like other members of that group (Martin & Ruble, 2004). They know that they are like the parent of the same gender and different from the parent of the other gender and from other children of the other gender. At first, infants think that the difference between girls and boys is a matter of clothes or haircuts. But by age three there may be some awareness of differences in the genital region and increasing interest in the genitals of other children (Martinson, 1994). At ages four to six ideas about gender are very rigid, as reflected in the opening vignette. As the child gains experience, these gender beliefs become more flexible (Martin & Ruble, 2004).

EARLY CHILDHOOD (3 TO 7 YEARS)

Between the ages of three and seven, there is a marked increase in sexual interest and activity, just as there is in activity and interest in general. A recent Swedish survey provides detailed information about the sexual behaviour of children in this age group (Larsson & Svedin, 2002a). Parents and daycare teachers of 89 girls and 96 boys between the ages of three and six years were asked to rate the frequency of a wide range of sexual behaviour in the child during the preceding six months. In general, the children engaged in more sexual behaviours at home than in the daycare.

MASTURBATION

Children increasingly gain experience with masturbation during childhood. In a study of 1114 children ages two to five, the mothers of 60 percent of the boys and of 44 percent of the girls reported that the child touched his or her genitals (Friedrich et al., 1998). In the Swedish study, 43 percent of the girls and 71 percent of the boys had touched his or her own genitals at home; 18 percent of the girls and 28 percent of the boys had used their hand to masturbate (Larsson & Svedin, 2002).

Children also learn during this period that masturbation is something that one does in private.

OTHER-SEX BEHAVIOUR[1]

By the age of four or five, children's sexuality has become more social. There is some other-sex sex play. Boys and girls may hug each other or hold hands in imitation of adults. Playing

---

[1]We have chosen to use the rather unusual term "other-sex" instead of the more common term "opposite sex" because males and females are not opposites. In fact, as discussed in Chapter 13, males and females are more similar than they are different.

doctor can be a popular game at this age (Gundersen et al., 1981). It generally involves no more than exhibiting one's own genitals, looking at those of others, and perhaps engaging in a little fondling or touching. In the Swedish study, 64 percent of the girls and 65 percent of the boys had looked at another child's genitals; 20 percent of the girls and 34 percent of the boys had shown their genitals to other children. As one woman recalled,

> It was at the age of 5 that I, along with my three friends who were sisters and lived next door, first viewed the genitals of a boy. They had a male cousin who came to visit and we all ended up behind the furnace playing doctor. No matter what he would say his symptoms were, we were so fascinated with his penis that it was always the center of our examinations. I remember giggling as I punched it and dunked it in some red food-colored water that we were using for medicine. This

Figure 10.3 Between the ages of three and seven there is a marked increase in sexual interest.

> seemed to give him great enjoyment. One girl put hand lotion and a bandage on his penis and in the process he had an erection. We asked him to do it again, but their [sic] was no such luck. (Martinson, 1994, p. 37)

By about the age of five, children have formed a concept of marriage—or at least of its non-genital aspects. They know that a member of the other gender is the socially appropriate marriage partner, and they are committed to marrying when they get older (Broderick, 1966a, 1966b). They practise marriage roles as they "play house."

Some children first learn about heterosexual behaviour by seeing or hearing their parents engaging in sexual intercourse, or the *primal scene experience*. Freud believed that this experience could inhibit the child's subsequent psychosexual development; some contemporary writers share this belief. Limited empirical data suggest that the experience is not damaging. In surveys, about 20 percent of middle-class parents report that their child observed them when the child was four to six years of age. Parents report such reactions as curiosity ("Why are you bobbing up and down?"), amusement and giggling, or embarrassment and closing the door (Okami, 1995).

SAME-SEX BEHAVIOUR

During late childhood and preadolescence, sexual play with members of one's own gender may be more common than sexual play with members of the other gender (Martinson, 1994). Thus, it is a normal part of sexual development. Generally the activity involves no more than touching the other's genitals (Broderick, 1966a). One girl recalled:

> I encountered a sexual experience that was confusing at kindergarten age. . . . Some afternoons we would meet and lock ourselves in a bedroom and take our pants off. We took turns lying on the bed and put pennies, marbles, etc. between our labia. . . . As the ritual became old hat, it passed out of existence. (Martinson, 1994, p. 62)

SEX KNOWLEDGE AND INTERESTS

At age three or four, children begin to have some notion that there are genital differences between males and females, but their ideas are very vague. By age seven, 30 percent of North American children understand what the differences are (Goldman & Goldman, 1982). Children generally react to their discovery of genital differences calmly, though of course there are exceptions.

At age three, children are very interested in different postures for urinating. Girls attempt to urinate while standing. Children are also very affectionate at this age. They enjoy hugging and kissing their parents and may even propose marriage to the parent of the other gender.

At age four, children are particularly interested in bathrooms and elimination. Games of show are also common at this age. They become less common at age five, as children become more modest. The development of modesty likely reflects the child's learning of the restrictions that Canadian society places on sexual expression. Often as early as age three the child is taught by his or her parents not to display or touch certain parts of his or her body, at least in public. Children are often taught not to touch the bodies of others. Many parents also restrict conversation about sex. These restrictions come at precisely the time the child is becoming more aware of and curious about sexuality. As one young man recalled:

> One of my favorite pastimes was playing doctor with my little sister. During this doctor game we would both be nude and I would sit on her as if we were having intercourse. On one occasion, I was touching my sister's genital area and mother discovered us. We were sternly switched and told it was dirty and to never get caught again or we would be whipped twice as bad. So, we made sure we were never caught again. (Starks & Morrison, 1996)

As a result, children turn to sex play and their peers for information about sex (Martinson, 1994). Cross-cultural data suggest that in less restrictive societies, children continue to show overt interest in sexual activities through childhood and preadolescence (Frayser, 1994). In the rare society that puts no restrictions on childhood sex play, intercourse may occur as young as age six or seven. In Canada, first intercourse usually occurs several years later than this.

It is important to remember that children's sex play at this age is motivated largely by curiosity and is part of the general learning experiences of childhood. One man illustrated this well as he recalled:

> At the age of six or seven my friend (a boy) and I had a great curiosity for exploring the anus. It almost seemed *more like scientific research*. (Martinson, 1994, p. 59, italics added)

A longitudinal study of the impact of childhood sex play obtained reports from mothers when the child was six, and assessed the sexual adjustment of the person at age 17 or 18 (Okami et al., 1997). Forty-seven percent of the mothers reported that their child had engaged in interactive sex play. Looking at a range of outcomes, including social relationships and sexual behaviour and "problems," there were no significant differences between males and females whose mothers reported such play, and males and females whose mothers did not report such activity.

Preadolescence (8 to 12 Years)

Preadolescence is a period of transition between the years of childhood and the years of puberty and adolescence. Freud used the term *latency* to refer to the preadolescent period following the resolution of the Oedipus complex. He believed that the sexual urges go underground during latency and are not expressed. The evidence indicates, however, that Freud was wrong and that children's interest in and expression of sexuality remain lively throughout this period, perhaps more lively than their parents are willing to believe. For many, "sexual awakening" does not occur until the teens, but for others it is a very real and poignant part of preadolescence (Martinson, 1994).

At around age nine or ten, the first bodily changes of puberty begin: the formation of breast buds in girls and the growth of pubic hair. The growth of pubic hair occurs in response to *adrenarche*, the maturation of the adrenal glands, leading to increased levels of androgens. In three recent studies, one of adolescents and two of adults, the average age at which participants reported first experiencing sexual attraction to another person was at age ten (McClintock & Herdt, 1996). The samples included gay men, lesbians, and heterosexual men and women. This experience may reflect the maturation of the adrenal gland and the increases in testosterone and estradiol (a steroid responsible for the development of female reproductive organs) that result. This research suggests that "adult" sexual development starts as early as age nine or ten, not at puberty as previously thought.

The first experience of sexual attraction may lead the child to consider his or her sexual orientation. Boys and girls attracted to someone of the other gender probably conclude they are heterosexual (i.e., typical). Boys and girls attracted to someone of the same gender may experience a period of *sexual questioning*—a time of assessment and interpretation of features of their experience that violates sexual norms (Savin-Williams & Diamond, 2000). A study of students in grades 4 through 8 asked each child how likely it was that he or she would fall in love with a woman/man, marry, be a wife/husband, be a father/mother, and have a family someday. These items were used to create a scale; a low score (uncertainty that these events would occur) was interpreted as indicating that the child was questioning his or her orientation. Compared to children who were confident that these events would occur, questioning children attained lower scores on global self-worth and perceived themselves as less socially competent than their peers. They were also less attracted to same-sex activities, and rated themselves as more gender atypical (Carver et al., 2004).

MASTURBATION

During preadolescence, more and more children gain experience with masturbation. In a sample of university women, 40 percent recalled masturbating before puberty.[2] The comparable figure for men was 38 percent (Bancroft et al., 2003). Other data, as well as those on adolescents, indicate that boys generally start masturbating earlier than girls do. A study of 269 high-school seniors in Sweden inquired about solitary sexual activities in childhood. Forty-two percent of the boys and 20 percent of the girls reported masturbating to orgasm by age 12; an additional 27 percent of the boys and 18 percent of the girls reported masturbating without orgasm (Larrson & Svedin, 2002).

Interestingly, boys and girls learn about masturbation in different ways. Typically boys are told about it by their male peers, they see their peers doing it, or they read about it; girls most frequently learn about masturbation through accidental self-discovery (Langfeldt, 1981). One man recalled:

> An older cousin of mine took two of us out to the garage and did it in front of us. I remember thinking that it seemed a very strange thing to do, and that people who were upright wouldn't do it, but it left a powerful impression on me. A couple of years later, when I began to get erections, I wanted to do it, and felt I shouldn't, but I remembered how he had looked when he was doing it, and the memory tempted me strongly. I worried, and held back, and fought it, but finally I gave in. The worry didn't stop me, and doing it didn't stop my worrying. (Hunt, 1974, p. 79)

Research suggests that there is no connection between these early masturbation experiences and sexual adjustment—there were no differences in sexual satisfaction or sexual problems of students who reported masturbating during preadolescence and those who did not (Leitenberg et al., 1993).

---

[2]These are cumulative-incidence figures, to use the terminology introduced at the end of Chapter 3.

OTHER-SEX BEHAVIOUR

There is generally little sexual behaviour with the other gender during the preadolescent period, mainly because of the social division of males and females into separate groups. However, children commonly hear about sexual intercourse for the first time during this period. For example, in a sample of adult women, 61 percent recalled having learned about intercourse by age 12 (Wyatt et al., 1988). Children's reactions to this new information are an amusing combination of shock and disbelief—particularly disbelief that their parents would do such a thing. A university woman recalled:

> One of my girlfriends told me about sexual intercourse. It was one of the biggest shocks of my life. She took me aside one day, and I could tell she was in great distress. I thought she was going to tell me about menstruation, so I said that I already knew, and she said, "No, this is *worse!*" Her description went like this: "A guy puts his thing up a girl's hole, and she has a baby." The hole was, to us, the anus, because we did not even know about the vagina and we knew that the urethra was too small. I pictured the act as a single, violent and painful stabbing at the anus by the penis. Somehow, the idea of a baby was forgotten by me. I was horrified and repulsed, and I thought of that awful penis I had seen years ago. At first I insisted that it wasn't true, and my friend said she didn't know for sure, but that's what her cousin told her. But we looked at each other, and we knew it was true. We held each other and cried. We insisted that "my parents would never do that," and "I'll never let anyone do it to me." We were frightened, sickened, and threatened by the idea of some lusty male jabbing at us with his horrid penis. (From a student essay)

In the study of Swedish high-school seniors, more than 80 percent reported having consensual sexual experiences with another child when they were 6 to 12 years old (Larsson & Svedin, 2002b). The most common activities were talking about sex, kissing and hugging, looking at pornographic videos, and teasing other children sexually. With the exception of kissing and hugging, these activities were more often reported to have occurred when they were 11 and 12 than when they were ages 6 to 10. Turning to the gender of the partner, 57 percent of the boys reported such experiences with girls, 11 percent with another boy, and 33 percent with both boys and girls. For girls, the percentages were 31 with a boy, 29 with a girl, and 40 with both. Thus, sexual experiences are very common, especially at ages 11 and 12, and involve consensual experiences with both boys and girls.

The age at which youth have their first consensual sexual intercourse experience has been declining (see Figure 10.8 on page 311). Some boys and girls have their first experience during the preadolescent period. A study of American college students using computer-assisted self-interviewing found that 9 percent of the women and 16 percent of the men reported oral–genital contact, 3 percent of both reported inserting objects in the anus, 18 percent of the women and 22 percent of the men reported inserting objects in the vagina, and 2 percent of the women and 5 percent of the men reported having vaginal intercourse prior to entering high school (Reynolds et al., 2003). Five percent of male adolescents and 1 percent of female adolescents in Canada report that they had engaged in sexual intercourse by the age of 12. The majority of Canadians first engage in intercourse between the ages of 16 and 19 (Maticka-Tyndale, 1997).

For some preadolescents, heterosexual activity occurs in an incestuous relationship, whether brother–sister or parent–child. This topic is discussed in detail in Chapter 16.

SAME-SEX BEHAVIOUR

Gender-segregated social organization: A general form of social grouping in which males play and associate with other males, and females play and associate with other females; that is, the genders are separate from each other.

It is important to understand same-sex sexual activity as a normal part of the sexual development of children. In preadolescence, most children have a social organization that is **gender segregated**. That is, boys play separately from girls, and thus children socialize mainly with members of their own gender. This separation begins at around age eight. According to one study of children's friendship patterns, the segregation reaches a peak at around 10 to 12 years of age. At ages 12 to 13 children are simultaneously the most segregated by gender and the most interested in members of the other gender (Broderick, 1966b). Observational research suggests that there is greater segregation at school than in neighbourhood play groups (Thorne, 1993).

Given that children are socializing with other members of their own gender, sexual exploring at this age is likely to be with partners of the same gender. These activities generally involve masturbation, exhibitionism, and the fondling of other's genitals. Boys, for example, may engage in a "circle jerk," in which they masturbate in a group.

Girls do not seem so likely to engage in such group activities, perhaps because the spectacle of them masturbating is not quite so impressive or perhaps because they already sense the greater cultural restrictions on their sexuality and are hesitant to discuss sexual matters with other girls.

A study of psychosexual development among lesbian, gay, and bisexual youth ages 14 to 21 found that the participants reported their first experience of sexual attraction at age 10 or 11 (Rosario et al., 1996). Their first experience of sexual fantasies occurred several months to one year later. The first sexual activity with another person occurred on average at age 12 or 13. All of the young men and women reported experiencing sexual attraction to and fantasies about a person of the same gender, and one-half also reported them about a person of the other gender.

DATING AND ROMANTIC RELATIONSHIPS

Pre- and early adolescence is a period of transition in the nature of social relationships. We noted earlier that the preadolescent activities are often homosocial. Around age 10 or 11, children begin to spend time in mixed-gender or heterosexual groups. These groups engage in a variety of activities, including "hanging out" in parks or at malls, going to clubs, sporting events, or movies, and later going to parties or dances. A study of students in grades 5 through 8 in the United States found that the frequency of these mixed-gender activities increased steadily over the four grades (Connolly et al., 2004). It is in these mixed-group settings that youth typically first experience dyadic pairings and their first romantic or sexual behaviours.

According to the study, *dating*, defined as spending time or going out with a boy or girl whom the youth liked, loved, or had a crush on, emerged in grade 7. A New Brunswick study

Figure 10.4 Hanging out, group dating, and heterosexual parties emerge during preadolescence, and may include making out.

IN FOCUS 10.1

What Impact Do the Mass Media Have on Adolescent Sexuality?

A major developmental task of adolescence is learning how to manage physical and emotional intimacy in relationships with others. It is not surprising, therefore, that young people are curious about sex and about sexual intimacy. An increasingly important source of information is the mass media. Although most students identify school as their main source of information on human sexuality, 12 percent of boys and 15 percent of girls in grade 9 indicated that most of their information came from television and movies or books and magazines; 12 percent of the boys and 3 percent of the girls named the Internet as their main source (Boyce et al., 2003). Whether it is a main source of information, the mass media still provide images and information about sexuality. Further, Canadian youth are influenced by both the Canadian and the U.S. media. Youth who watch talk shows learn about erection problems, and ways to deal with them. Dramas such as *Da Vinci's Inquest* provide information about erotic dancers, sex workers, and the sex trade. Soap operas deal, sometimes explicitly, with sexual themes like sexual non-responsiveness, menopause, abortion, and extradyadic sex. How much sexual content is there in the mass media? To what extent are children and adolescents exposed to it? And what is the impact of this exposure?

Research, much of it done since 1990, has been devoted to the question of how much sexual content there is in the U.S. media. *Sexual material* is defined as verbal references to sexual activity, sexually suggestive behaviour, and explicit presentations of sex. A major project analyzed sexual material on television in 2004–2005 and found that 70 percent of programs during prime-time included sexual material; 4.6 scenes per hour included talk about sex, and 2.0 scenes per hour included sexual behaviour. Only 4 percent of the scenes containing sexual content depicted risks or responsibilities of sex (Kunkel et al., 2005). In 2000, a *Maclean's*/Global poll found that 47 percent of Canadians felt that there is too much sexually explicit programming on prime-time TV. Many adolescents also see R-rated films; these films contain more frequent and more explicit depictions of sexual behaviour, an average of 17.5 per hour, than depictions of sexual behaviour on prime-time television (Greenberg et al., 1996). Finally, there are music videos, many of which are implicitly or explicitly sexual (Brown & Steele, 1995), and frequently combine sexuality with implicit aggression (Sommers-Flanagan et al., 1993). Music videos also objectify women, presenting them in revealing clothing and portraying them as receptive to sexual advances. Further, although we are starting to see more programs

found that 70 percent of the boys and 77 percent of the girls who were 12 said that they had had a boyfriend or girlfriend (Price et al., 2000). At age 13, the figures were 82 percent for the boys and 85 percent for the girls. Many of these relationships are short-lived. For example, the CYSHHAS found that 25 percent of boys and 23 percent of girls in grade 7 reported having had a steady boyfriend/girlfriend in the last 12 months; however, 34 percent of boys and 34 percent of girls reported having had two or more steady boyfriends/girlfriends within that time period (Boyce et al., 2006). Some adolescents begin to go out at night with boys and girls, to double date, or to go on dates. However, mixed-gender activities remain very common through grade 8. Another survey of 12- and 13-year-olds in the United States f ound that about half of the 13-year-olds had held hands, hugged, or kissed (Williams et al., 2004). Fewer than 10 percent had engaged in genital fondling or intercourse; these youth were more likely to report going out on dates alone (without friends). Thus, the progression from mixed-gender activities to dyadic dating is paralleled by a progression in the development of physical intimacy.

Most lesbian and gay youth do not date those they are most attracted to out of very real fear of harassment from their peers. Further, gay and lesbian youth are more likely to be the victims of crime than are their heterosexual peers (Comstock, 1991). Many date partners of

portraying gay and lesbian adults, there are still few positive media images of gay and lesbian adolescents with whom gay and lesbian youth can identify.

There are some differences between Canadian and U.S. television shows. In particular, some topics can be introduced into Canadian television shows that would not be considered acceptable by the U.S. networks. *Degrassi Junior* (and then Senior) *High*, a popular television show of the 1980s and early 1990s, tended to portray youth sexuality in diverse ways and used story lines to explore different sexual choices such as the decision to engage in intercourse, as well as the realistic consequences of sexual behaviour (M. Byers, 2005). For example, some of the female characters became pregnant—in one case a grade 8 character decided to keep her baby and stay in school; in two other cases the characters had abortions, allowing the show to present the abortion debate. Similarly, in *Degrassi: The Next Generation*, one of the female characters became pregnant and had an abortion with no negative psychological consequences. Although these episodes were shown on the Canadian network carrying the show, the American cable station that carried it would not air the abortion episodes. Further, on American TV when abortion issues develop, it turns out to be a false alarm, the character miscarries, or she has the baby. If the character does have an abortion, negative consequences follow—she is punished or experiences extreme guilt (M. Byers, 2005). Lest we get too smug as

Canadians, it's important to note that the show included very little discussion of gay, lesbian, and bisexual youth.

What effect do these portrayals have? Research has found that media portrayals reinforce stereotyped views of sexual behaviour and sexual relationships (Brown, 2002; Ward, 2002)). The media may also influence standards of physical attractiveness and contribute to the dissatisfaction with their bodies that many, especially women, feel. For example, research has shown that viewing as little as 30 minutes of television can change women's perceptions of their bodies, which the authors term the "elastic body image" (Myers & Biocca, 1992).

The evidence that mass media portrayals have an important impact on adolescent sexual knowledge, attitudes, and behaviour is not conclusive. On the other hand, both children and adolescents believe that mass media are an important source of their knowledge. The problem lies in the fact that these portrayals are unrealistic. In sharp contrast to the high rates of non-marital sex portrayed in the media, most sexual activity involves persons who are married or living common-law (see Chapter 11). Many couples in real life are responsible users of birth control and use condoms to prevent STIs. It is unfortunate that these realities are missing from mass media portrayals of sexual behaviour. It is also unfortunate that the media have generally not taken advantage of their opportunity to provide positive sexuality education.

the other gender in order to conform to societal expectations (Savin-Williams, 1994).

Of course, these patterns are averages for Canadian preadolescents. There is great variability in the timing of these developments and between youth from different ethnocultural communities in Canada. In some cultures, boys and girls are married by age 13.

SEXUALIZATION OF GIRLS

A major concern of some parents, educators, and researchers is the sexualization of girls in our society. **Sexualization** occurs when:

- a person's value comes only from his or her sexual appeal or behaviour;
- a person is held to a standard that equates physical attractiveness with being sexy;
- a person is sexually objectified;
- sexuality is inappropriately imposed upon a person (American Psychological Association, 2007).

When children or preadolescents are sexualized, it is imposed upon them at a time when it may have wide-ranging effects.

> **Sexualization:** Occurs when a person is valued only for sex appeal or behaviour; is held to a standard that equates physical attractiveness with being sexy; is sexually objectified; or sexuality is inappropriately imposed upon a person.

An American Psychological Association Task Force report stated that sexualization of girls involves cultural contributions, including sexualized representations of girls and women on television and the Internet, in movies, MTV, cartoons, magazines, and sports media. The cultural contribution also involves sexualized products—dolls (e.g., Barbie, Bratz), toys, books, and clothing.

It also involves an interpersonal contribution, when girls are treated like sexual objects by family, friends, teachers, and other adults. "Fat talk" and expressions of concern about a girl's weight and appearance can create a self-consciousness that can be debilitating. As a result of learning to view themselves as sexual objects, many girls and women engage in self-sexualization, including purchasing clothing because it is sexy, and undergoing cosmetic surgery before they are physically mature. Research documents each of these contributions, especially in white Canadian culture.

People are concerned because sexualization may lead to reduced self-esteem (because one does not meet the standard), impaired cognitive functioning (e.g., at math) and physical performance (e.g., at athletics), anxiety about appearance in interaction with others, body-image dissatisfaction, and reduced educational and occupational aspirations. Viewing oneself as a sexual object may lead girls and young women to initiate sexual intimacy to engage in unwanted sexual activity and relationships, and to engage in risky sexual behaviour (e.g., unprotected vaginal intercourse).

The report suggests many ways to counteract sexualization. Within the schools, we can provide media literacy training programs, a broader range of athletic opportunities, and comprehensive sexuality education (see Chapter 19). Within the family, we can encourage parents to watch TV and movies and to navigate the Internet with children, commenting on appropriate and inappropriate content. Creating alternative media including "zines," blogs, and alternative magazines and books may help. Creating girl empowerment groups to support girls in a variety of ways can be very effective. Finally, parents, educators, and boys and girls can engage in activism and resistance, such as campaigning against companies that use sexualized images to sell products.

ADOLESCENCE (13 TO 19 YEARS)

A surge of sexual interest occurs around puberty and continues through adolescence (which is equated here roughly with the teenage years, ages 13 to 19). This heightened sexuality may be caused by a number of factors, including bodily changes and an awareness of them, rises in levels of sex hormones, and increased cultural emphasis on sex and rehearsal for adult gender roles. We can see evidence of this heightened sexuality particularly in the data on masturbation. But before examining those data, let's consider some theoretical ideas about how hormones and social forces might interact as influences on adolescent sexuality.

Udry (1988) has proposed a theoretical model that recognizes that both sociological factors and biological factors are potent in adolescent sexuality. He studied students in grades 8, 9, and 10 (13 to 16 years old), measuring their hormone levels (testosterone, estrogen, and progesterone) and a number of sociological factors (e.g., whether they were in a two-parent family, their parents' educational level, the teenager's response to a scale measuring sexually permissive attitudes, and the teenager's attachment to conventional institutions such as involvement in school sports and church attendance). Thirty-five percent of the males had engaged in sexual intercourse, as had 14 percent of the females.

For boys, testosterone levels had a very strong relationship to sexual activity (including coitus, masturbation, and the extent of feeling sexually turned on). Sexually permissive attitudes, a social variable, were related to sexuality among boys although they had a much smaller effect than testosterone did. For girls, the relationship between testosterone level and sexual activity was not as strong as it was for boys, but it was a significant relationship, and it was testosterone—not estrogen or progesterone—that was related to sexuality. Pubertal development (developing a curvy figure) had an effect, probably by increasing the girl's attractiveness. And the effects of testosterone were accentuated among girls in father-absent families. Testosterone level as well as social variables such as permissive attitudes and church attendance influenced the girls' plans about sexuality.

This study suggests that testosterone levels have a substantial impact on the sexuality of adolescent boys and girls. Social variables (such as permissive attitudes, father absence for girls, and church attendance) seem to interact with the biological effects, in some cases magnifying them and in some cases suppressing them. Similarly, a study with gay and lesbian youth found that increases in hormone levels with puberty resulted in increases in homo-erotic sexual feelings and behaviours (Savin-Williams, 1995).

Two longitudinal studies of 12- to 15-year-old girls (O'Sullivan & Brooks-Gunn, 2005) and girls and boys in grades 7 and 8 (L'Engle, et al., 2006) report evidence that cognitive changes mediate the effects of these biological and social changes on sexual behaviour. Girls who initiated sexual intimacy—breast fondling, genital contact—had weaker abstinence values, and lower arousability and sexual self-esteem scores. Youth who reported that they were likely to engage in sexual intimacy within the next year were more likely to initiate sexual intercourse. These measures of cognitive readiness were in turn related to reports of greater sexual feelings and competency than age-mates who were not ready.

MASTURBATION

According to the Kinsey data, there is a sharp increase in the incidence of masturbation for boys between the ages of 13 and 15. This is illustrated in Figure 10.5. Note that the curve is steepest between the ages of 13 and 15, indicating that most boys begin masturbating to orgasm during that period. By age 15, 82 percent of the boys in Kinsey's study had masturbated. Many girls also begin masturbating in adolescence, but note that the curve on the graph is flatter for them, indicating that many girls do not begin masturbating until later. Thus, the increase in their masturbation behaviour is much more gradual than for boys and continues past adolescence.

A study at the University of British Columbia asked students whether they had ever masturbated (Meston et al., 1996). Overall, 80 percent of the males and 48 percent of the females reported masturbating at least once. Asian students were significantly less likely to report having masturbated than were non-Asian students. Eighty-five percent of non-Asian males compared to 74 percent of Asian males reported that they had masturbated. The difference between non-Asian and Asian females was even greater—59 percent compared to 39 percent. A German study found that 94 percent of male university students and 74 percent of female students reported that they had masturbated in the last year; being in a satisfying sexual relationship did not affect how likely they were to report masturbating (Dekker & Schmidt, 2002). On average, female students reported masturbating about three times a month and male students about eight times a month.

More recent data indicate that children and adolescents begin to masturbate earlier today, and thus the Kinsey data need to be pushed back about one or two years. This is particularly true of girls (Dekker & Schmidt, 2002). However, the general shape of the curves still holds (Bancroft et al., 2003).

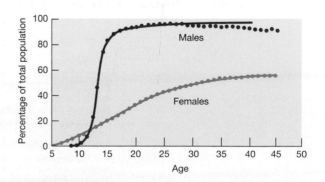

Figure 10.5 Cumulative incidence of males and females who have masturbated to orgasm, according to Kinsey's data. Current data suggest that contemporary youth begin masturbating one or two years earlier.

ATTITUDES TOWARD MASTURBATION

Attitudes toward masturbation underwent a dramatic change in the twentieth century. As a result, adolescents are now given much different information about masturbation than were earlier adolescents, and this may affect both their behaviour and their feelings about masturbation. For example, a popular handbook, *What a Boy Should Know*, written in 1913 by two doctors, advised its readers:

> Whenever unnatural emissions are produced . . . the body becomes "slack." A boy will not feel so vigorous and springy; he will be more easily tired. . . . He will probably look pale and pasty, and he is lucky if he escapes indigestion and getting his bowels confined, both of which will probably give him spots and pimples on his face. . . .
>
> The results on the mind are the more severe and more easily recognized. . . . A boy who practices this habit can never be the best that Nature intended him to be. His wits are not so sharp. His memory is not so good. His power of fixing his attention on whatever he is doing is lessened. . . . A boy like this is a poor thing to look at. . . .
>
> . . . The effect of self-abuse on a boy's character always tends to weaken it, and in fact, to make him untrustworthy, unreliable, untruthful, and probably even dishonest. (Schofield & Vaughan-Jackson, 1913, pp. 30–42)

Masturbation, in short, was once believed to cause everything from warts to insanity.[3]

Attitudes toward masturbation are now considerably more positive, and today few people would subscribe to notions like those expressed earlier. By the 1970s only about 15 percent of young people believed that masturbation is wrong (Hunt, 1974, p. 74). Indeed, masturbation is now recommended as a remedy in sex therapy. As psychiatrist Thomas Szasz said, the shift in attitudes toward masturbation has been so great that in a generation it has changed from a disease to a form of therapy. While approval of masturbation is now explicit, people can still have mixed feelings about it. Examples of lingering negative attitudes are reflected in questions that teens ask online experts about masturbation, such as "Is it bad?", "How do I stop feeling guilty after I do it?", and "Is it normal?" (Planned Parenthood Federation of America, 2002).

SAME-SEX BEHAVIOUR

Grade 9 and 11 students in the CYSHHAS were asked about their sexual attraction. About 5 percent of the girls reported being attracted to girls or to both boys and girls. Among the boys, 2 to 6 percent reported being attracted to boys or to both boys and girls. About 10 percent of men and 6 percent of women in university report having had a same-sex partner in high school (Bancroft et al., 2003). Of those who have had same-sex experiences, 24 percent had their first experience with a younger person, 39 percent with someone of their own age,

---

[3]In case you're wondering why boys' advice books were saying such awful things, there is a rather interesting history that produced those pronouncements (Money, 1986). The Swiss physician Simon André Tissot (1728–1797) wrote an influential book, *Treatise on the Diseases Produced by Onanism*, taking the term from the biblical story of Onan (Genesis 38:9). In this work he articulated a degeneracy theory, in which loss of semen was believed to weaken a man's body; Tissot had some very inventive physiological explanations for his idea. The famous American physician of the 1800s Benjamin Rush was influenced by Tissot and spread degeneracy theory in North America. The theory became popularized by Sylvester Graham (1794–1851), a religious zealot and health reformer, who was a vegetarian and whose passion for health foods gave us the names for Graham flour and Graham crackers. To be healthy, according to Graham, one needed to follow the Graham diet and practise sexual abstinence. Then John Harvey Kellogg (1852–1943) of—you guessed it—cornflakes fame entered the story. He was an ardent follower of Graham and his doctrines of health food and sexual abstinence. While experimenting with healthful foods, he invented cornflakes. His younger brother, Will Keith Kellogg, thought to add sugar and made a fortune. John Harvey Kellogg contributed further to public fears about masturbation by writing (during his honeymoon, no less) *Plain Facts for Old and Young: Embracing the Natural History and Hygiene of Organic Life*, which provided detailed descriptions of the horrible diseases supposedly caused by masturbation. These ideas then found their way into the advice books for boys of the early 1900s.

29 percent with an older teenager, and 8 percent with an adult (Sorensen, 1973). Thus, there is no evidence that adolescent same-sex experiences result from being seduced by adults; most such encounters take place between peers. In many cases the person has only one or a few same-sex experiences, partly out of curiosity, and the behaviour is discontinued. Such adolescent behaviour does not seem to be predictive of adult homosexual orientation. However, some youth who are aware of their same-sex attraction in adolescence go on to adopt a gay, lesbian, or bisexual identity, usually within five years (D'Augelli, 2002). For example, a survey of students in grades 7 through 12 in British Columbia found that 8 percent of the male students and 9 percent of the female students self-identified as bisexual, gay, lesbian, or not sure (The McCreary Centre Society, 2007). Although many youth do not disclose their sexual orientation to their parents, if they do they are more likely to tell their mothers than their fathers. Mothers also tend to react more positively to the disclosure than do fathers. Nonetheless, a study of 542 gay, lesbian, and bisexual youth found that 24 percent of mothers and 37 percent of fathers were intolerant or rejecting when they found out about their child's sexual orientation. Only 48 percent of mothers and 35 percent of fathers were accepting (D'Augelli, 2002).

Comparing the results reported by Bancroft et al. (2003) with those reported by DeLamater and Mac-Corquodale (1979), there has been no increase in the incidence of adolescent same-sex sexual behaviour. It seems safe to conclude from various studies, taken together, that about 10 percent of adolescents have same-sex sexual experiences.

Alberta sociologist Reginald Bibby (2001) surveyed 3600 teenagers across Canada, ages 15 to 19. He found that 66 percent of the girls and 41 percent of the boys approve of sexual relations between two people of the same sex. On the other hand, teenagers can be quite naïve about same-sex sexual behaviour and societal attitudes toward it. In some cases, they have been taught that sexual activity with the other gender is "bad" but same-sex activity was not mentioned; having been told nothing about same-sex sexual activity, they infer that it is permissible. In some cases, sexual relationships naïvely develop from a same-sex friendship of late childhood and adolescence. One woman recalled:

Figure 10.6 Oshawa high school student Marc Hall and his boyfriend Jean-Paul Dumond walk to their limousine on prom night. Despite the objection by the school board, the Ontario Superior Court granted Hall permission to attend his prom with his boyfriend.

> I did not even know what homosexuality was. I had never heard the term, although I had read extensively. One day at a friend's house, we were listening to music in her bedroom, she came on to me in a very surprising way. We were good friends and spent much time together, but this particular night was different. Her eyes had a new sparkle, she got very close to me, her touch lingered; she was different than she ever had been before. I was 16 and she was 15. I did not understand, but I knew that I was aroused. We were good church going kids who had never heard anything about this. (Starks & Morrison, 1996, p. 97)

OTHER-SEX BEHAVIOUR

Toward the middle and end of the adolescent years, more and more young people engage in heterosexual sex, with more and more frequency. Thus heterosexual behaviour gains prominence and becomes the major sexual outlet. Many adolescents who go on to adopt gay, lesbian, or bisexual identities report having engaged in heterosexual activity during

Figure 10.7   Sexuality in early adolescence is often playful and unsophisticated.

adolescence—74 percent of the females and 57 percent of the males in one study (D'Augelli, 2002).

In terms of the individual's development, the data indicate that there is a very regular progression from kissing, through French kissing and breast and genital fondling, to intercourse and oral–genital contact; this generally occurs over a period of years (Boyce et al., 2006; DeLamater, 2003). The progression in sexual behaviour is evident from data on the percentage of youth who have engaged in five different sexual behaviours provided in Table 10.1. Students in grades 9 and 11 were asked whether they had ever engaged in deep kissing, touching above the waist, touching below the waist, oral sex, and sexual intercourse; students in grade 7 were asked only about deep kissing, touching above the waist, and touching below the waist. In grade 7, more than a third more students had engaged in deep kissing and touching above the waist than had engaged in touching below the waist. In grade 9, almost three times as many students had engaged in deep kissing and more than twice as many had engaged in touching below the waist than had engaged in sexual intercourse. Further, more students had engaged in oral sex than had engaged in sexual intercourse. About half of grade 11 students had engaged in oral sex and sexual intercourse, but more than three-quarters had engaged in touching below the waist. The progression of sexual experience is also evident in the finding that the percentage of students who had engaged in each of the five sexual behaviours was greatest for grade 11 students, intermediate for grade 9 students, and lowest for grade 7 students. To use the terminology introduced in Chapter 2, these behaviours tend to follow a sexual script.

Table 10.1	**Percentage of Canadian Youth Who Have at Least Once Engaged in Various Sexual Behaviours**					
	Grade 7		Grade 9		Grade 11	
	Boys	Girls	Boys	Girls	Boys	Girls
Deep (open-mouth) kissing	49%	35%	65%	67%	81%	82%
Touching above the waist	46%	34%	67%	64%	81%	81%
Touching below the waist	33%	23%	57%	54%	75%	74%
Oral sex			32%	28%	53%	52%
Sexual intercourse			3%	19%	40%	46%

Source: Boyce et al., 2003.

It is interesting to compare youth involvement in sexual activity in the CYSHHAS to the results from the Canadian Youth and AIDS Study conducted in 1988 (King et al., 1988). The percentage of students reporting having engaged in deep kissing and sexual touching changed very little over the 14 years between the two studies. However, somewhat fewer students reported having engaged in sexual intercourse in 2003 than in 1988. The earlier survey did not ask about oral sex.

SEXUAL INTERCOURSE

One of the most dramatic changes to occur in sexual behaviour and attitudes in recent decades is in the area of youth sexual behaviour often called premarital sex. Note that the very term "*pre*marital sex" contains some hidden assumptions, most notably that marriage is normative and that proper sex occurs in marriage. Thus, sex among never-married (young) persons is considered *pre*marital—something done before marrying. A more neutral term would be "non-marital sex," although this fails to distinguish between premarital sex, extramarital sex, and postmarital sex and also contains the assumption of marriage. Further, premarital sex typically refers to penile–vaginal intercourse and leaves out other pleasurable sexual activities to orgasm that heterosexual, gay, and lesbian youth engage in, such as oral–genital sex and anal sex (see Chapter 9). Perhaps we should just call it "adolescent sex" or "teen sex."

HOW MANY YOUTH ENGAGE IN SEXUAL INTERCOURSE?

As shown in Table 10.1, by age 17 (grade 11) almost half of the students report that they have engaged in intercourse. Many sexually experienced youth have had two or more sexual partners (Fisher& Boroditsky, 2000). For example, almost half of the grade 9 and 11 students surveyed in the CYSHHAS who had engaged in sexual intercourse had had two or more partners (Boyce et al., 2003).

Not only are more teenagers having sex than in the 1940s, but young people today are engaging in intercourse for the first time at younger ages, compared to Canadians born 30 years earlier. Figure 10.8 gives data from the National Population Health Survey conducted by Health Canada based on interviews with more than 35 000 Canadians between the ages of 15 and 59. The figure displays the percentage of men and women who had intercourse by ages 15, 17, and 19 and is based on analyses of National Population Health Survey data by Eleanor Maticka-Tyndale, Michael Barrett, and Alexander McKay (2000b).

First, note that few women or men have intercourse at age 15 or younger, whether born in the early 1940s or in the early 1970s. Second, the younger the woman at the time of the survey,

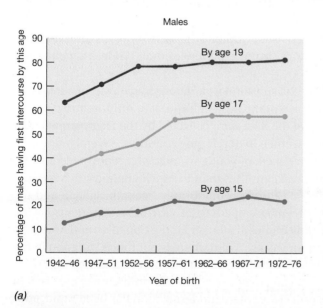

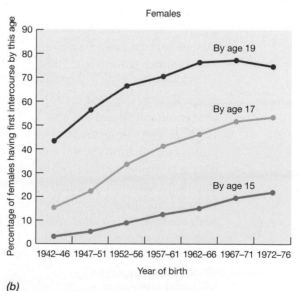

(a)   (b)

Figure 10.8 Young men and women today are engaging in first intercourse at younger ages than did people born 30 years earlier. Graph (*a*) shows data for males while graph (*b*) shows data for females (Maticka-Tyndale et al., © 2000, The Haworth Press, Inc.).

the more likely she was to have engaged in intercourse by age 17. The percentage of men who had engaged in intercourse by age 17 increases steadily for men born up to 1957 but levels off for men born after 1957. Finally, since the 1940s, there has been an increase in the percentage of men and women who have intercourse by age 19; however, this percentage has stayed steady over the past 20 years for men and over the past 10 years for women. Today 80 percent of men and 75 percent of women have intercourse by age 19.

In short, age of first intercourse decreased significantly up until the 1990s. The median age at first intercourse for people who were born between 1942 and 1946 is 18 for men and 20 for women. However, the median age of first intercourse for respondents who were teenagers at the time of the survey (that is, born between 1972 and 1976) is 17 for both males and females. Thus, while the age of first intercourse had decreased for both men and women, this change was especially pronounced for women. These trends reflect, in part, the impact of the "sexual revolution" of the 1960s and 1970s, which encouraged greater openness about sexuality and acceptance of sex between people who are not married and other forms of sexual expression, particularly for women. However, recent research has found that the average age of first intercourse is no longer decreasing and may even be increasing (Boyce et al., 2003), but, this differs from one region of Canada to the next (CFSH, 2007).

For all age groups included in the National Population Health Survey, immigrants to Canada initiated intercourse at later ages than those born in Canada did. For example, for the age group that was between 20 and 24 at the time of the survey, 41 percent of immigrant men compared to 60 percent of Canadian-born men had engaged in intercourse by age 17. The difference was even larger for women; 18 percent of immigrant women between the ages of 20 and 24 and 58 percent of Canadian-born women in that age group had engaged in intercourse by age 17 (Maticka-Tyndale et al., 2000b). Rates of sexual intercourse also differ substantially for young people who were born in Canada but who come from different ethnocultural backgrounds. For example, a study at the University of British Columbia found that 36 percent of female Asian students compared to 69 percent of female non-Asian students had engaged in intercourse. Similarly, 36 percent of Asian males compared to 63 percent of non-Asian males had engaged in intercourse (Meston et al., 1996). Length of residence in Canada or whether the student had been born in Canada did not affect the Asian students' likelihood of having engaged in sexual intercourse. However, British Columbia psychologist Lori Brotto found in a university sample that coitally experienced Asian women who were more acculturated into mainstream Canadian culture reported more sexual experiences than did less acculturated Asian women (Brotto et al., 2005).

These ethnocultural differences mirror the substantial variations in patterns of adolescent intercourse in different cultures around the world. Cross-cultural data on unmarried young women are presented in Table 10.2. Most of the data were collected by the Demographic and Health Surveys Program, which interviews women in developing countries. Several interesting points emerge from the data. First, the percentage of young women who report recent intercourse is smaller in Latin and South American countries than in African nations; this is partly due to the greater influence of the Catholic Church in the former. Second, Canada and the United States have some of the highest percentages of 20- to 24-year-old respondents having had premarital intercourse although the time frames are longer for the Canadian and American data (12 months or three months versus four weeks). Third, there is not much variation in the average age of first intercourse; it is either 16, 17, or 18 in all but one of the countries.

In many countries around the world, the incidence of adolescent intercourse has risen in the last few decades. Around the globe, especially where modernization has been rapid, adolescents are less and less under the influence of family, community, and religion and more and more responsive to peers and the mass media (Liskin, 1985).

Table 10.2   A Global Perspective on Female Adolescent Intercourse

Country and Year	Age of Respondents (Years)	Percentage Having Had Intercourse (Last Four Weeks)*	Median Age of First Coitus (Years)
Africa			
Cameroon, 1998	15–19	33.7	16.3
Kenya, 1998	15–19	19.4	17.3
Nigeria, 1999	15–19	24.6	18.1
Tanzania, 1996	15–19	28.2	17.4
Zambia, 1996	15–19	26.9	16.6
Central America			
Mexico, 1985	15–19	13.0	17.0
Nicaragua, 1998	15–19	21.7	18.1
South America			
Bolivia, 1998	15–19	8.6	19.6
Brazil, 1996	15–19	21.5	18.7
United States, 2005	15–18	34.6**	17.4[†]
Canada, 2000	15–19	52.7***	16.0

*These percentages are of all women, so some of these women are married.

**Had intercourse in the last three months.

***Had intercourse in the last 12 months.

[†]Mean age of first intercourse.

Source: Data for the United States are from the 1999 Youth Risk Behavior Survey conducted by the Centers for Disease Control and Prevention. The data for other countries are from the Demographic and Health Surveys Program, which collects comparable data from many countries around the world. The results are published in individual volumes for each country by Macro International, Inc., Calverton, MD. The typical reference is: Kenya: Demographic and Health Survey, 1998. Calverton MD: Macro International, 1999. The data for Canada are from the Canadian Community Health Survey, 2000–2001.

To summarize, the trends suggested by research about adolescent sexual intercourse in the last four decades are (1) both in Canada and in most other countries, more adolescents engaging in sexual intercourse; (2) in Canada, a greater increase in incidence for females, thereby narrowing the gap between males and females; (3) first intercourse occurring at somewhat earlier ages; (4) moderate ethnic-group variations in Canada; and (5) substantial variations from one country to another (Day, 1992; Liskin, 1985).

The increase in adolescent sexual intercourse in general and premarital intercourse in particular reflects two long-term trends. First, the age of menarche has been falling steadily since the beginning of the twentieth century; the average age is about 12.5 (Hofferth, 1990). Second, the age of first marriage has been rising. In 1960, men and women who got married for the first time tended to be in their early 20s. In 2003, it was age 28.5 for women and 30.6 for men, although many of these individuals live together before marriage (Statistics Canada, 2006). The effect is a substantial lengthening of the time between biological readiness and marriage; the gap is typically 12 to 14 years today. Recall that Udry (1988) found that hormone levels are a major influence on the initiation of sexual intercourse. Not surprisingly, many more young people are having sex before they get married now than in 1960.

It is tempting to make causal inferences from the results of these two studies—to say, for example, that permissive attitudes or drinking alcohol cause increased sexual activity. However, as discussed in Chapter 3, these data are correlational, and causality cannot be inferred from correlation.

Figure 10.9 In South American nations, the percentage of unmarried young women who engage in premarital intercourse is lower than in North America owing to the strong influence of the Catholic Church.

FIRST INTERCOURSE

First sexual intercourse is a major transition, with both psychological and social significance. Because of its significance, much research has been done in an effort to identify the influences on whether youth begin engaging in sexual intercourse. The research by Udry (1988), discussed earlier, identifies biological influences (e.g., testosterone levels) and social ones (e.g., permissive attitudes among boys and girls, and church attendance among girls) as influential.

American research using a longitudinal design measured the effects of parent–adolescent relationships on likelihood of first intercourse (Ream & Savin-Williams, 2005). Decreases in feelings of closeness to parents and in shared activities with them were associated with initiation of sexual intercourse, and followed first intercourse as well (parents may or may not have been aware that the youth had intercourse). Based on the same data set, researchers found that the higher the proportion of a youth's friends who were sexually experienced at Time 1, the more likely the person was to engage in intercourse for the first time by Time 2. Similarly, Canadian researchers have also found that having a poor relationship with one's parents and perceiving friends to be engaging in sexual intercourse are associated with engaging in sexual intercourse (Boyce et al., 2003; Hampton et al., 2005). In contrast, perceptions that their parents would disapprove of them engaging in sexual intercourse were unrelated to their behaviour (Hampton et al., 2005).

Researchers have also analyzed the emotional reactions to first coitus of university students (Sprecher et al., 1995). Men reported significantly greater pleasure and significantly less guilt than did women. Both men and women who experienced an orgasm rated the sexual experience as more pleasurable than men and women who did not. Men and women who reported a close relationship with the partner reported stronger emotional reactions than those in casual relationships.

Despite our culture's romanticized high expectations that the first intercourse experience will be like fireworks on Canada Day, it turns out to be much less thrilling than that for many people. For example, the women studied by Sprecher and her colleagues on average gave the experience only a 2.95 on a pleasure scale that ranged from 1 for "not at all" to 7 for "a great deal." Research in Alberta found that only about half the women and men in their study reported being emotionally satisfied after their first intercourse experience, and only 40 percent rated the experience as very good or excellent (Tsui & Nicoladis, 2004).

Many people assume that having penile–vagina intercourse for the first time equals losing one's virginity. However, a qualitative study involving in-depth case studies of 61 men and women found that virginity loss is socially constructed (Carpenter, 2001). Many believed that virginity could not be lost by rape, and conversely that behaviours other than penile–vaginal intercourse could constitute loss of virginity. Carpenter identified three distinct interpretations of virginity: as a gift, a stigma, or a process. Each was associated with distinctive individual choices about the transition to non-virginity. Men and women who viewed virginity as a gift were likely to lose it with a lover or "soulmate"; those who viewed it as a stigma often lost it with a stranger or non-lover.

TECHNIQUES IN ADOLESCENT SEX

Paralleling the increase in the incidence of sexual intercourse is an increase in the variety of techniques that are used during sex. One of the most dramatic changes has been the increased use of oral–genital techniques. In the Kinsey sample, 33 percent of the males had experienced fellatio premaritally and 14 percent had engaged in cunnilingus. In a British Columbia study, 64 percent of the non-Asian male students had engaged in fellatio and 59 percent had performed cunnilingus, although the rates were lower for the Asian male students (Meston et al., 1996). The CYSHHAS found that about 10 percent of high school students had engaged in fellatio and/or cunnilingus but not in intercourse (Boyce et al., 2003). Some of them may have been gay or lesbian students. Others may have chosen to engage in oral–genital sex but not intercourse because they know that mouth–genital sex cannot cause pregnancy and carries a lower risk of contracting an STI. Research has shown that most adolescents do not regard oral sex as having sex and many believe that you can be abstinent and engage in oral sex (Byers et al., in press). Thus, engaging in oral sex and not penile–vaginal or anal sex may be a way for adolescents to remain "abstinent" and maintain their "virginity" (Hunt & Curtis, 2006). The rate of oral–genital activity is only slightly higher than the rate reported in the Canada Youth and AIDS Study a decade before (McKay, 2004). Thus, despite depictions in the popular media, most high school students are not casually engaging in oral sex. Young people today also use a greater variety of positions, not just the traditional man-on-top position.

Doubtless, some of this increased variety in techniques is a result of today's "performance ethic" in sexual relations, which was discussed in Chapter 9. Adolescents and young adults may feel pressured to be gold medallists in the sexual Olympics. One man said:

> Sometimes I'm really good; I can make a girl have orgasms until she's about half dead. But if I don't like the girl, or if I'm not feeling confident, it can be hard work—and sometimes I can't even cut the mustard, and that bothers me a lot when that happens. (Hunt, 1974, p. 163)

ATTITUDES TOWARD ADOLESCENT SEXUAL INTERCOURSE

Attitudes toward adolescent intercourse have also undergone marked changes, particularly among young people. Sociologist Ira Reiss (1960) distinguished among four kinds of standards for adolescent sexual activity:

1. **Abstinence** Intercourse outside of marriage is considered wrong for both males and females, regardless of the circumstances.
2. **Permissiveness with affection** Intercourse is permissible for both males and females if it occurs in the context of a stable relationship that involves love, commitment, or being engaged.
3. **Permissiveness without affection** Intercourse is permissible for both males and females, regardless of emotional comm itment, simply on the basis of physical attraction.
4. **Double standard** Intercourse outside of marriage is acceptable for males but is not

Abstinence: A standard in which premarital intercourse is considered wrong, regardless of the circumstances.

Permissiveness with affection: A standard in which premarital intercourse is considered acceptable if it occurs in the context of a loving, committed relationship.

Permissiveness without affection: A standard in which premarital intercourse is acceptable without emotional commitment.

Double standard: A standard in which premarital intercourse is considered acceptable for males but not for females.

IN FOCUS 10.2

How Common Is Casual Sex on Holidays?

Thousands of Canadian university students go to Florida for spring break every year. Spring break involves not only warm weather but also travelling and rooming with a group of friends in a perpetual party atmosphere that includes high alcohol consumption and participating in sexually suggestive contests and displays such as wet T-shirt or hot body contests. Students perceive spring break as a time in which norms, roles, attitudes, and behaviours are more permissive and the usual expectations about behaviour, including sexual behaviour, do not apply. They also perceive that casual sex—sex with a partner whom you meet on spring break and with whom you do not expect to form a relationship—is common. As one student said, "It's not Mexico, it's sexico." Of course, perceptions and expectations do not always match reality. Is casual sex as common on spring break as students perceive it to be?

To answer this question, Ontario sociologists Eleanor Maticka-Tyndale and Edward Herold studied sexual behaviour on spring break in Florida. They sent male and female graduate students to Daytona Beach, Florida, in 1996 to administer a ten-minute questionnaire. They used three different methods of recruiting participants. Four hundred and eighty-four participants were recruited

on beaches and pool decks; 119 students completed questionnaires on return bus trips home; and 151 students were recruited through the mail. All participants were from southwestern Ontario. Given the sampling procedure, we cannot be sure that the students who participated were representative of all students on spring break. In fact, the men and women in their sample tended to be more sexually experienced than most Canadians of the same age.

The researchers asked participants about their attitudes toward casual sex on spring break, and about whether they had engaged in casual sex while in Florida. The men were more accepting of casual sex and more interested in engaging in casual sex than the women were. For example, whereas 55 percent of the men had intended to engage in intercourse while in Florida, only 11 percent of the women had had these intentions. In contrast, fairly equal numbers of male and female students actually engaged in casual sex—15 percent of the men and 13 percent of the women. Interestingly, a considerably higher percentage—46 percent—had "fooled around" sexually while on spring break; that is, engaged in casual sex that did not include intercourse. The researchers concluded that there are two

acceptable for females. The double standard may be either "orthodox" or "transitional." In the orthodox case, the double standard holds regardless of the couple's relationship, while in the transitional case, sex is considered acceptable for the woman if she is in love or engaged.

Historically in Canada, the prevailing standard has been either abstinence or the double standard. However, today, particularly among young people, the standard is one of permissiveness with affection—82 percent of youth hold this view (Bibby, 2001). What do adolescents define as affection? That is, at what point in a relationship in which two people like each other is it acceptable to engage in sexual activity? Alberta sociologist Reginald Bibby (2001) asked adolescents just this question. As shown in Table 10.3, most adolescents approved of holding hands and kissing on a first date. Male and female adolescents differed in their attitudes toward the timing of necking and petting and sexual intercourse, with the males approving of them earlier in the relationship. For example, 43 percent of males and 22 percent of females think it is acceptable to neck and pet on a first date. Similarly, 68 percent of males but only 36 percent of females think that it is acceptable to have sex on the first date or after a few dates. These different attitudes may represent a double standard with respect to the timing of initiation of sexual activity within a relationship. Interviews with youth in Nova Scotia and

different distinct sexual scripts for students who go to Florida without a relationship partner. One sexual script includes no sexual activity. The second script includes either "fooling around" or having intercourse with someone they met in Daytona.

Do students who engage in casual sex use a condom? Almost all respondents who had engaged in sex with a new partner said that they had intended to use condoms. Three-quarters of them did use a condom at least once. Apparently, condom use is part of the spring break script for casual sex.

What were the characteristics of students who engaged in casual sex? Those students who had intercourse with someone they had just met drank more alcohol, were more likely to frequent dating bars, and were more likely to have participated in spring break activities such as partying, or watching a sexually suggestive contest with someone they had just met. They were also more likely to have intended to engage in casual sex and to have engaged in casual sex on a previous spring break holiday. Females who had casual sex were more likely to have made a pact with their friends to engage in casual sex and to have friends who also engaged in casual sex. Peer influences affected men's intentions to engage in casual sex but not their behaviour.

One consistent gender difference related to sexuality is that men are more accepting of casual sex than women are (see Chapter 13). This gender difference also holds true on spring break despite a relaxation of sexual norms. Many more men than women intended to engage in casual sex. Despite the party atmosphere, participation in casual intercourse is not common—perhaps because women serve as sexual "gatekeepers" in relationships with men and few women intended to have casual sex. On the other hand, many students engage in sexual "fooling around" on spring break.

What about youth who travel for a more extended period of time? Egan (2001) found a higher incidence of casual sex among mostly European backpackers and other travellers staying in Canadian youth hostels than found by Maticka-Tyndale and Herold: 31 percent of the men and 20 percent of the women reported having had casual sex while on their current trip. Travellers who had engaged in casual sex on the current trip were more likely to have had casual sex prior to travel, be on an extended trip (more than 30 days), and expect to have casual sex on the trip.

Sources: Egan, 2001; Maticka-Tyndale & Herold, 1997, 1999; Maticka-Tyndale, Herold, & Mewhinney, 1998; Mewhinney, Herold, & Maticka-Tyndale, 1995.

British Columbia indicate that girls are still more likely to be labelled negatively for their sexual behaviour than boys are (Shoveller et al., 2004). However, a quarter of female adolescents and a third of male adolescents report two or more partners in the past year (Maticka-Tyndale, 2001). Some of these individuals are engaging in serial monogamy (discussed shortly). Others are engaging in casual sex.

Table 10.3	If two people on a date like each other, do you think it is all right for them to . . .					
	Yes on a first date		Yes, after a few dates		No	
	Males	*Females*	*Males*	*Females*	*Males*	*Females*
Hold hands	92%	87%	8%	12%	<1%	1%
Kiss	78	68	21	30	1	2
Neck and pet	43	22	50	63	7	15
Have sex	18	4	50	32	32	64

Source: Reginald W. Bibby, 2001.

IN FOCUS 10.3

What Was Your First Sexual Experience?

Think about your first sexual experience. What was it like? Where and how did it happen? How old were you? Was it planned? Are you thinking of your first kiss? The first time you had sexual intercourse? The first time you engaged in oral sex? Was it with a boyfriend/girlfriend or someone you just met? Did the two of you talk about it or did it "just happen"?

We asked youth to tell us about their first sexual experience. As you will see, no two first sexual experiences are alike.

Kirsten from Saskatchewan:

My first real sexual experience happened when I was 15. It was the long weekend in May, and a bunch of us from my high school were out drinking at a friend's cabin. There was this guy who was in the same grade as me, and he and I found ourselves walking on a gravel road alone. We sat down to "talk." We chatted awkwardly for a while, and it took him forever to slyly nudge closer to me, and finally we worked up the courage, aided in no small part by all the booze. We fooled around for a while until some friends of his came along and we jumped up (and zipped up) like frightened animals. I quickly scurried off to find the rest of the girls and tell them what had just happened. He and I couldn't look each other in the eye for months.

Trishia from Nova Scotia:

My first sexual experience was with my best friend in grade 6; we were both 12 and 13 years old at the time. She had come for a slee-pover and we were sharing my double bed. I do not recall much being said at the time, or how we both started kissing one another. It just happened, nothing ever discussed. As I recall we took turns kissing each other in various areas and moving around on top of one another. We never spoke of what happened that night.

Simon from Alberta:

As a 16-year-old, the only thing I wanted to do was to have sex, because I heard it was a great experience. I also heard that it hurt a lot at the first time but you get used to it, and that I had to be very careful. I was also told that it would make me a man. On February 7th, I found my first boyfriend. He was some years older than me, but I didn't care at the time. We dated for one week, and I was so excited that I finally found a boyfriend, and I was so glad that I could finally have sex. So the moment finally happened and it did hurt for the first time. But I felt that I was finally a man.

We can see the shift in standards by comparing data on recent attitudes to those of three decades before, as shown in Table 10.4. Two trends are particularly interesting. First, more people approve of premarital sex today than did so in 1975. Second, baby boomers are more likely to approve of premarital sex than are people who are either younger or older than them.

Table 10.4	Percentage of People Agreeing That Premarital Intercourse Is Acceptable in 1975 and 2005	
Approve of premarital sex	*1975*	*2005*
Nationally	67%	80%
By age		
18–34	90	77
35–54	63	87
55 & over	40	75

Source: Reginald W. Bibby, 2006, p.19.

Emily from New Brunswick:

The first time I had sex was a very positive experience. I was sixteen and had been with my boyfriend at the time for eight months and it was a great relationship. We were in love. We had discussed the desire to have sex for a few months and were well prepared. I went on birth control three months before we had intercourse. We wanted to make sure we were being safe. The opportunity arose one afternoon in July at my cottage; we brought blankets down to the beach and made love. It was comfortable and I felt like we were ready to go there in our relationship. I have very positive memories about the entire situation. We were together for the following two years.

Jeff from Alberta:

I was 16 years old when I had my first sexual experience. I am gay and had not come out to many people at that point. I was attending a cross-Canada high school music festival away from home. I had my eye on one guy in particular but was too shy to do anything except exchange friendly pleasantries with him. On the very last night of the festival, however, everything changed. We had been drinking, and I found the courage to come out to a small group of friends. The guy that I liked overheard our conversation, and he cornered me later in the hallway, telling me he was gay too. I was a little scared. I had never discussed my sexuality with another gay man before. It was freeing, too, to be able to talk so openly. We slept together that night, and how it felt is hard to describe. It felt really good and right to be intimate with another man, but I still felt guilty and nervous at the same time. I was still very young. I threw up afterwards because I was so nervous. It was not the most romantic ending.

Paige from New Brunswick:

I had hooked up with some guys but I had never had sex. Then I started dating Paul. The first time we had sex, we hadn't seen each other in like 2 weeks because of exams. We were hanging out at one of our mutual friends' birthday parties. We came back to my house from that. He had slept over before. He would sleep in the basement and I'd go upstairs. This time, I didn't go upstairs and it just kind of sort of happened. I'd been thinking about it for a little bit before then because we'd been together for a little bit and that was our month anniversary. There wasn't a lot of pre-planning involved.

MOTIVES FOR HAVING SEXUAL INTERCOURSE

Young people mention a variety of reasons for engaging in physical intimacy (Sprecher & McKinney, 1993). Their motives include expressing love or affection for the partner, experiencing physical arousal or desire, wanting to please the partner, feeling pressure from peers, or wanting physical pleasure. Women are more likely to mention love and affection, whereas men are more likely to mention physical pleasure. In the CYSHHAS, 60 percent of female grade 11 students but only 39 percent of male students gave love as the reason for first having sexual intercourse. Curiosity/experimentation was also an important reason given by 21 percent of males but only 14 percent of females (Boyce et al., 2006). The most common reasons for not engaging in sexual intercourse were not feeling ready, not having had the opportunity, and not having met the right person.

ADOLESCENT ROMANTIC RELATIONSHIPS

The social forces that have produced changes in adolescent sexual behaviour and standards are complex. But among them seems to be a change in courtship stages in which two people establish a special romantic relationship—in the process of meeting, and committing to the relationship. Even the terms have changed. A generation ago we talked about "dating" and "going steady." Now youth say that they are "with" somebody, or that they and their partner are "together" or just that they are "going out." Although these relationships may not last more than a few weeks or months, youth enter their first committed relationship at much younger ages now than in previous generations. Being in an exclusive relationship earlier creates both more of a demand for sexual activity and more legitimacy for it. For many, sexual intimacy is made respectable by being in a committed relationship, regardless how short-term.

Serial monogamy:
A premarital sexual pattern in which there is an intention of being faithful to the partner, but the relationship may end and the person will then move on to another partner.

Sorensen (1973) found the most common adolescent sexual pattern to be serial monogamy without marriage. In such a relationship there is an intention of being faithful to the partner, but the relationship is of uncertain duration. Of those in the sample who had engaged in sexual intercourse, 40 percent were serial monogamists. Though they averaged about four partners, nearly half of them had had only one partner, and about half of them had been involved in their current relationship for a year or more. A more recent Canadian study found that 27 percent of unmarried 15- to 17-year-olds and 82 percent of unmarried 18- to 24-year-olds had experienced sexual intercourse. More than half of these women (53 percent of the younger group and 59 percent of the older group) had had more than one intercourse partner within the previous two years (Fisher & Boroditsky, 2000).

A qualitative study of Puerto Rican youth living in New York City explored the concept of serial monogamy (Ascensio, 2002). Most of the youth endorsed monogamy and viewed infidelity as wrong. But many also believed that one was required to be faithful only in a serious relationship, with seriousness not being related to the length of the relationship or whether the couple had engaged in vaginal intercourse. The men were more likely to differentiate between merely a relationship and a serious relationship whereas many women defined their relationship as serious. As a result, men's and women's expectations of fidelity did not always coincide. Both the men and the women expressed greater tolerance for male infidelity. Thus, the attitudes of these young people are complex, reflecting their particular construction of monogamy, fidelity, and the double standard.

As described earlier, one trajectory for romantic and sexual relationships in adolescence in contemporary Canadian culture starts with mixed-gender activities, which progress to dyadic dating, and then to a series of special relationships continuing into adulthood. An alternative, increasingly common, pattern is evident in some youth subcultures. Here, many adolescents remain actively involved in mixed-gender social groupings and do not make a transition to primarily dyadic dating relationships. Instead, romantic and sexual activities occur within the context of the group, often during parties. When sexual intimacy occurs, it may involve another member of the group, another friend, or someone met on the Internet. Such relationships are often referred to as *friends with benefits* (Denizet-Lewis, 2004):

> Friends with benefits are an alternative to going steady, being in a relationship. "Being in a real relationship just complicates everything" says Brian, a 16-year-old from New England. "When you're friends with *benefits*, you go over, hook up, then play video games or something. It rocks." (Denizet-Lewis, 2004 p. 33—emphasis in original)

Brian is really describing casual sex, and that is what some adolescents and young adults say they want. Men and women with solid education and career plans want to focus on achieving their goals, and not get sidetracked by a relationship, an unintended pregnancy, or a life-threatening sexually transmitted infection. Others, however, secretly are looking for a more committed, longer-term relationship, and some admit that they are hurt by the failure of the partner to call them the next day or the next week.

Hooking up: A sexual encounter that usually occurs on one occasion involving people who are strangers or acquaintances.

These casual encounters are referred to as hooking up, a no-strings-attached sexual encounter that usually occurs on one occasion involving people who are strangers or acquaintances (Paul et al., 2000). The term "hooking up" is ambiguous and covers everything from kissing to oral sex or sexual intercourse. That is, hooking up may not involve sexual intercourse; oral sex may occur as one alternative. A study of 555 undergraduates classified each student into one of three groups: no hookup experience, hookup experience without intercourse (HU), and hookup experience including intercourse (HU-Sex). Of interest is the fact that those without hookup experience were much more likely to be in long-term romantic relationships. No-hookup persons attained significantly higher scores on a measure of self-esteem. Those who had hookup experience reported an average of 10.8 experiences in their lives. Males were significantly more likely to report hookups involving intercourse. Twenty-eight percent of the HU and 49 percent of the HU-Sex participants reported that they never saw the partner again. The major difference between those in the HU group and those in the HU-Sex group was that the latter experience significantly more symptoms of alcohol intoxication when they drink.

CONDOM USE

The CYSHHAS found that 54 percent of grade 9 students and 41 percent of grade 11 students reported using a condom the last time they had sexual intercourse (Boyce et al., 2006). Even fewer adolescents use a condom every time they have intercourse, despite the fact that condoms provide protection from sexually transmitted infections such as HIV (Calzavara et al., 1998; King et al., 1988; Langille et al., 1994). Condoms are used most frequently at the beginning of relationships or in casual encounters, and adolescents are likely to stop using condoms and switch to the birth control pill as they get to know a partner better (Fisher & Boroditsky, 2000; Maticka-Tyndale, 1997; McMahon, 2004). Despite knowledge about HIV transmission, most teens and young adults see themselves at low risk for contracting HIV infection (Levy et al., 1990, 1992; Maticka-Tyndale, 1992). Further, the CYSHHAS found that two-thirds of grade 7 students and half of grade 9 students think that there is a cure for AIDS. Therefore, adolescents' attitudes toward condoms may be especially important in determining whether they use them (Klein & Knäuper, 2003).

Research by Ontario sociologist Eleanor Maticka-Tyndale (1992) identified two beliefs that account for why young people do not perceive themselves to be at risk. First, teenagers minimize the seriousness of contracting a sexually transmitted infection such as HIV through their beliefs that medical science will find a cure "in time" should they need one. Second, they believe that by choosing partners who are like themselves and their peers they can ensure that their partners are not infected. The sexual script for an affectionate, trusting relationship does not fit with the idea that a partner can be infected and either not know it or not disclose such information, and so does not include condom use (Hynie et al., 1998). Teenagers are particularly likely to underestimate their cumulative risk (risk from repeated unprotected sex) of becoming infected with an STI from a partner if they are committed to the partner or if the partner is particularly appealing to them (Knäuper et al., 2005). Finally, teenagers are more likely to use condoms when they have positive attitudes toward condoms and when their peer group supports condom use with romantic partners (Fazakas et al., 2001; Ploem & Byers, 1997; Richardson & Beazley, 1997; Tremblay & Frignon, 2004).

People are more likely to engage in risky behaviour, including having unprotected sex, when they have been drinking. This may be because it is difficult for people who are intoxicated to pay attention to both the reasons they want to engage in the risky behaviour (impelling cues) and the reasons that it is not a good idea to do so (inhibiting cues) at the same time. According to *alcohol myopia theory*, because the impelling cues (e.g., being sexually aroused) are more immediate and vivid at the moment than are the inhibiting cues, alcohol intoxication causes people to engage in these risky behaviours even when this behaviour is not consistent with their attitudes and intentions when they are sober (MacDonald et al., 2000a, 2000b). Consistent with this theory, research in Ontario has shown that sexual arousal did not affect people's attitudes or intentions to use condoms when they are sober. Also, there

IN FOCUS 10.4

Becoming a Teen Mother: An Aboriginal Woman's Story

I am a thirty-seven-year-old First Nations mother of four sons and one daughter. I also am a third generation residential school survivor. My *Kohkum* and *Moosum* attended residential school and all of their children did as well, including my mother and all of her brothers. This was mandatory for First Nations families, so they had no choice about whether their children would go. Thankfully, when I was child, the Indian Act had changed and I was not forced to attend residential school. However, residential school not only had a direct impact on my parents and grandparents, it also has directly affected my life. I believe the legacy of their experiences attending residential school is why I became a teen mother at the age of 15.

I am the youngest of my four sisters and have a younger brother. Growing up, sexuality was not a topic of conversation at any time in my family—it was NEVER discussed. My siblings and I are trying to stop the cycle by which residential schools continue to affect generation after generation by breaking the silence about sexual health and educating our children and our nieces and nephews about sexual health. We want to make sure that the next generation can make choices about their sexuality, practice safe sex if they choose to have sex, and plan when they would like to become parents.

My older sisters and I experienced our moon time (menstruation) without the traditional supports and information required when experiencing the gift from the Creator of becoming a First Nations woman. Also our grandmothers did not tell us the traditional stories that were passed on in previous generations when a girl becomes a woman. I was not educated about my sexuality and did not know how a woman experiences her moon time or becomes pregnant. I was not taught about sexuality, sexual health, or pregnancy at home, at school or by my peers.

I twice became a teen mother in the mid-1980s, a time when sexuality as a First Nations urban young woman was not discussed. I was very ill and nauseous while visiting my boyfriend on the reserve. While he went to town with his mother, I had a discussion with one of his older brothers. I mentioned that I was not feeling well and he grabbed a book called *The Book of Home Remedies*. After consulting this book, he told me that he believed I was pregnant. I was quite confused and honestly did not understand how this happened. I later visited a doctor who confirmed that I was indeed pregnant. That day my life changed forever. From the moment I knew I was carrying a child, I changed the direction of my

were no differences between the responses of individuals who were intoxicated and those who were sober if they were not sexually aroused. However, for individuals who were sexually aroused, people who were intoxicated were more likely than sober participants to report intentions to engage in unprotected sex (MacDonald et al., 2000b). The good news is that if the inhibiting cues are made stronger, intoxicated individuals report higher intentions to use condoms than when they are sober (MacDonald et al., 2000a). Can you think of how this finding can be used to promote safer sex?

The Information–Motivation–Behavioural Skills model described in Chapter 7 (Fisher & Fisher, 1998) provides a framework to design effective interventions to increase condom use among adolescents.

TEEN PREGNANCY

Research indicates that adolescents are not consistent in using contraceptives to prevent unwanted pregnancy, although the consistency of contraceptive use varies from one ethnic group to another (Boroditsky et al., 1995; Levy et al., 1992). As a consequence, 33 553 teenagers, or about 2.7 percent of all Canadian teenage girls, became pregnant in 2003. Quebec, the three prairie provinces, and the three territories had teen pregnancy rates above the national average (SIECCAN, 2004).

life. My child is the reason why I am where I am today. I realized that I wanted to live for the future and provide for my child's needs in every way—physically, mentally, emotionally and spiritually.

At the time I became pregnant, I was attending a high school in a small town. I experienced stigma and discrimination and was shunned by many of the educators at my high school because I was pregnant. To make matters worse, I wasn't just a teen mom, I was an urban First Nations pregnant teenager. That title alone carried a tremendous amount of stigma. The way I was treated was very stressful for me. I made the choice that it was important for me to continue my education if I was to provide the needs for my unborn child. Therefore, I returned to Regina where I had grown up to complete high school. When the high school in Regina learned that I was expecting, they called a meeting with the principal, the vice principal and the student support counsellors. They informed me that I would not be able to attend school there any longer and that I would have to transfer to the pregnant mothers program. When I left the meeting I felt disappointed. However, soon my disappointment turned to anger and then to the drive and dedication to not leave the high school. I fought to remain there. I was informed that being a pregnant teen would affect all adolescents in the school and this might become "contagious" among my peers. Thankfully, in the end, I won the right to continue to attend this high school. The teen mom program that the school wanted me to attend did not provide the same level of education as I got in the regular high school.

Becoming a teen mother was a challenge, yet it was an empowering experience. I welcomed my son, Raymond into the world on January 16th, 1986. I was in labour for over 36 hours and started to have numerous complications so Raymond was delivered by Caesarean section. I brought my son home with the passion to provide for his needs the best that I could. Twenty months later, I became a teen mother again. On May 2nd, 1988, Rowan joined our family and I was a single teen mom determined to provide for both of my sons as well as to achieve all of my dreams. Having two children assisted me to make the right choices, to complete my high school education, and to work hard to follow my dreams. I am currently completing my PhD in clinical psychology and I am a professor at the First Nations University of Canada. I am living my dreams to the fullest and would not change anything in my life. My journey has been tremendously hard at times, especially as a single teen mom of two young sons, but it has been so worth it!

Source: Kim McKay-McNabb, MA, who is originally from Sakimay First Nation. Her husband Patrick is from George Gordon First Nation.

The rate of teenage pregnancy in Canada is about the same as that in Britain and less than half that of the United States, but significantly higher than France, Germany, and other northern European countries (Maticka-Tyndale, 2001; Singh & Darroch, 2000). The levels of sexual activity or the ages at which teenagers start engaging in sexual intercourse do not differ across Western countries, so what accounts for the differences in teenage pregnancy rates?

To answer this question, a team of researchers from Sweden, France, Canada, Great Britain, and the United States conducted a large-scale investigation into factors that account for the differences in teenage pregnancy rates in their five countries (Darroch et al., 2001). Of these countries, the lowest rates are in Sweden and France; Canada and Great Britain have intermediate rates; and the United States has the highest rate. The authors concluded that there are five primary factors that contribute to these differences:

1. The rates are higher in countries in which teenagers are less likely to use effective contraception.
2. Teenagers from poor and disadvantaged families are less likely to use contraception.
3. National programs that support the transition to adult economic roles and parenthood provide young people with greater incentives and means to delay childbearing.
4. Countries with lower rates have greater societal acceptance of sexual activity among young people.

5. Teenagers are more likely to use contraceptives if they know where to obtain information and services, can reach a provider easily, are assured of receiving confidential, non-judgmental services, and can obtain contraceptive supplies at little or no cost.

Canada's scores on these five factors were mixed—we scored high on some and intermediate on others compared to the other four countries. Within Canada there are differences in adolescent pregnancy rates from province to province and community to community.

The teenage pregnancy rate has dropped substantially in the past ten years. So, why is teenage pregnancy considered a major social problem in Canada? The reason is that 45 percent of these teenagers give birth to a child, and infants born to teenagers are more likely to have health problems. Most of these births are to single mothers and from low-income homes, so having a baby as a teenager may limit the mother's economic and education opportunities (Rotermann, 2007). However, some ethnocultural communities, including northern Aboriginal and First Nations communities, are accepting of teenage girls having babies (SIECCAN, 2004).

A Nova Scotia study that followed pregnant women for up to ten years after they gave birth gives us important information on the effects of teenage pregnancy on the mother and the child (Bissell, 2000; Nova Scotia Department of Community Services, 1991). This study compared 403 unmarried women to 416 married women, dividing these women into teenage mothers (19 years old or younger) and an older age group (20 or older). The study also included psychological and educational testing with the children. Unmarried mothers of all ages were most dissatisfied with their educational achievement. Women who were still in school prior to the pregnancy were most likely to return to school after the birth. Fifty-two percent of the single teenage mothers lived in poverty, but so did 54 percent of the older unmarried women and 29 percent of the young married women. The young unmarried mothers made the most economic gains over the ten years, but they never caught up to the older married group. Eighty-seven percent subsequently married. There were few differences in their children's educational achievement. There were also no differences in the ways in which teenage mothers and older mothers dealt with their children's behaviour.

Grindstaff (1988) used data from the 1981 Canadian census to study 200 000 Canadian women who had married and/or had children before the age of 20. He found that the younger women were at the birth of their first child, the less education they tended to have and the more limited their job opportunities were. However, early marriage was also associated with less successful employment outcomes even if the women delayed having their first child until they were in their early 20s. Thus, the negative consequences associated with teenage pregnancy are largely a result of the fact that teenage mothers are more likely to come from socioeconomically disadvantaged backgrounds rather than the age of the mother (Bissell, 2000; Hardwick & Patychuk, 1999; Maticka-Tyndale, 2001; Singh et al., 2001). Two critical factors for successful outcomes for adolescent mothers are finishing high school (and preferably going for even more education) and postponing other births (Furstenberg, 1987). Thus, it is important to have social programs to assist adolescent mothers in finishing high school (such as school-based daycare) as well as effective sex education programs and access to contraception.

CONFLICTS

We are currently in an era in which there are tensions between a restrictive sexual ethic and a permissive one. In such circumstances, conflicts are bound to arise. One is between parents and children, as parents hold fast to conservative standards while their children adopt permissive ones.

These conflicts within our society are mirrored in the messages of the mass media:

We are a nation that is deeply ambivalent about sex. On the one hand, sex is so much a part of the landscape that we almost take it for granted, and the message we get is that everybody else seems to be doing it and we are missing the party if we don't get moving. We should liberate our sexual natures, polish up the hot buttons, follow our hormones, and seek fulfillment somewhere across a crowded room. On the other hand, we hear just how frightening sex can be. Some of that comes from the powerful hold of our puritan heritage, but with a uniquely modern twist. AIDS, urban anonymity, sexual abuse and assault, all make sex a dangerous pastime. And this dovetails nicely with the old morality that coexists with our alleged libertine behavior. (Michael et al., 1994, p. 8)

With such conflicting messages so prevalent, it is no wonder that many young people feel conflicts about engaging in sex.

Young people may also experience conflicts between their own behaviours and their attitudes or standards. Behaviours generally change faster than attitudes do. As a result, people may engage in sexual activity while still disapproving of it. Such individuals are more likely to put themselves at risk for unwanted pregnancy or STIs by having intercourse without using condoms or other contraceptive methods.

SEXUALITY AND ADOLESCENT DEVELOPMENT

Adolescent relationships provide the context in which the individual develops the skills and learns the scripts needed to sustain long-term intimate relationships (O'Sullivan & Meyer-Bahlburg, 2003). As we discussed earlier, the process typically begins at age 9 to 12 with a first boyfriend or girlfriend; often there is little direct interaction between the two, but the relationship does provide an opportunity to assume an "adult" role. Later comes group dating, and perhaps mixed-sex social events at school. These situations provide an opportunity for conversation and for peers to observe and instruct the person in sexual scripts. In mid to late adolescence, youth begin to spend time in mixed-sex, unsupervised interaction, which provides an opportunity for physical intimacy, leading often to sexual intercourse.

Furman (2002) proposes that this behavioural sequence parallels a developmental one. Early relationships reflect simple interest. Subsequent ones fulfill primarily affiliative and sexual reproductive needs as young people explore their sexual feelings. As the person moves into late adolescence and early adulthood, longer-term relationships become the site of the fulfillment of needs for attachment and mutual care taking. One important consequence of this process is the development of a sexual identity with regard to orientation and sexual attractiveness. Obviously, the timing of this process varies from one person to another, one influence being culture and its associated variation in the degree of parental control over adolescents. Furman points out that many social and cultural arrangements facilitate the emergence of heterosexual relationships and at the same time deter gay and lesbian relationships. Mixed-sex gatherings in adolescence are usually heterosexual, and monitoring by peers would likely result in harassment of same-sex romantic activity. Gay and lesbian youth may have difficulty finding partners. Diamond's (2003) research indicates the relative fluidity of the sexual self-identities of some young women from adolescence to their mid-20s.

Thus, we can see that sexuality is an integral part of adolescent development.

SUMMARY

A capacity for sexual response is present from infancy. According to recent data, about 40 percent of children have masturbated by the time they reach puberty. Recent studies indicate that children begin masturbating at somewhat earlier ages now than a generation or so ago. Children also engage in some sex play with children of the other sex, as well as some same-sex activity.

During adolescence there is an increase in sexual activity. According to one theory, this activity is influenced by the interaction of biological factors (increasing testosterone level) and social and psychological factors (e.g., sexually permissive attitudes). By age 15, nearly all boys have masturbated. Girls tend to begin masturbating somewhat later than boys, and fewer of them masturbate. Attitudes toward masturbation are considerably more permissive now than they were a century ago. About 10 percent of adolescents have same-sex experiences to orgasm.

Today the majority of adolescent males and females have engaged in sexual intercourse. Adolescents today are considerably more likely to use a variety of sexual techniques, including mouth–genital sex. There is variation in the incidence of adolescent intercourse among various ethnocultural groups in Canada, and even greater variability from one country to another. Few adolescents use condoms or other means of contraception every time they engage in intercourse. Still, the rate of teen pregnancy in Canada has been dropping, but is higher than some European countries, yet half that of the United States.

The predominant sexual standard today is one of permissiveness with affection; that is, sex is seen as acceptable outside marriage, provided there is an emotional commitment between the partners.

Experiences with sexuality can serve important functions in a person's psychological development.

QUESTIONS FOR THOUGHT, DISCUSSION, AND DEBATE

1. What challenges do most gay, lesbian, and bisexual youth face in terms of their sexual development that most heterosexual youth do not face? What challenges are similar? How can we change Canadian society to make it easier for gay, lesbian, and bisexual youth?

2. Does permissiveness with affection characterize the standard for sexual intercourse among the 18- to 22-year-olds you know?

3. The mother of a five-year-old child tells you that her son has been masturbating while he watches TV in the family room. She asks you what she should do about his behaviour. What would you tell her?

4. You have been put in charge of designing a program to increase consistent condom use by adolescents. Based on the information provided in this chapter, and on your knowledge of the 18- to 22-year-olds you know, what would you include in the program that you design? How might you need to tailor the program differently for the different ethnocultural groups in Canada?

SUGGESTIONS FOR FURTHER READING

Eder, Donna, with Catherine Evans and Stephen Parker. (1995). *School talk: Gender and adolescent culture.* New Brunswick, NJ: Rutgers University Press. A study of adolescent peer groups and relationships in one middle school.

McCormick, Naomi B. (1979). Come-ons and put-offs: Unmarried students' strategies for having and avoiding intercourse. *Psychology of Women Quarterly, 4,* 194–211. An interesting discussion of college students' reported techniques for inviting or avoiding intercourse, and how these techniques relate to gender-role stereotypes.

Starks, Kay, and Morrison, Eleanor. (1996). *Growing up sexual* (2nd ed.). New York: HarperCollins. A fascinating view of sexual development with many first-person quotes, based on student autobiographies for a human sexuality course.

For review questions, web resources, and other learning and study tools, visit the *Understanding Human Sexuality* Online Learning Centre at www.mcgrawhill.ca/olc/hyde.

SEXUALITY AND THE LIFE CYCLE: ADULTHOOD

Chapter Highlights

> GROW OLD ALONG WITH ME!
>
> THE BEST IS YET TO BE.*
>
> LIFE BEGINS AT FORTY.**

This chapter will continue to trace the development of sexuality across the lifespan. We will look at various aspects of sexuality in adulthood: sex and the single person, cohabitation, common-law and marital sexuality, extramarital sexuality, postmarital sexuality, and sex among older adults. We consider lifestyles involving same-sex partners in Chapter 14. Each of these lifestyles is an option, reflecting the diversity of choices available in Canada today.

SEX AND THE SINGLE PERSON

SEXUAL DEVELOPMENT

Late adolescence and early adulthood are a time of continued sexual development as the individual moves toward mature, adult sexuality. First, there is a need to deal with issues of sexual orientation and define one's sexual identity. Heterosexuality is the overwhelming norm in our society, and some people slip into it easily without much thought. Others sense that their orientation is gay or lesbian and must struggle with society's **heterosexism** and negative messages about these groups. Others sense that they are attracted to both males and females. Still others feel that their orientation is heterosexual but wonder why they experience same-sex fantasies, thinking that a person's sexual orientation must be perfectly consistent in all areas (research actually shows that heterosexuals sometimes have homosexual fantasies, and vice versa). These struggles over sexual orientation seem to be more difficult for males than for females because heterosexuality is such an important cornerstone of the male role in many societies, including ours (see Chapter 13).

> **Heterosexism:** Belief that heterosexuality is the best and expected way of living.

Another step toward maturity is identifying our sexual likes and dislikes and how they vary from occasion to occasion. Learning what one likes and dislikes may occur naturally as the individual experiences various behaviours over time. Alternatively, some people intentionally seek opportunities to engage in novel behaviours or in sexual intimacy with novel partners. Of course, it is not enough to know our likes and dislikes; we must also learn to communicate them to a partner. Learning to communicate with sexual partners is difficult for many persons, perhaps because there are few role models in our society showing us how to engage in direct, honest communication with them. Effective sexual communication is described in Chapter 12.

Two more issues are important in achieving sexual maturity: becoming responsible about sex, and developing a capacity for intimacy. Taking responsibility includes being careful about contraception and sexually transmitted infections, being responsible for yourself and for your partner. Intimacy (see Chapter 12) involves a deep emotional sharing between two people that goes beyond casual sex or manipulative sex.

Our ideas of what constitutes mature sexuality are influenced by the media. Most television shows promote a rather stereotyped and heterosexist view of sex and the single person.

*Robert Browning. (1864). *Rabbi Ben Ezra*.
**Attributed to Sophie Tucker.

Recently, there has been an increase in the number of television programs that have sexuality as a major focus, and some of them are tackling topics that never used to be discussed on television. For example, in the early 1990s, the main characters in *Seinfeld* had a competition to see who could go the longest without masturbating. In an episode of *Friends*, Rachel and Monica struggle over who gets the last condom and, by implication, which one of them gets to have sex. *Queer as Folk* and *Will and Grace* introduced gay men and lesbians as central characters. In fact, *Queer as Folk*—popular among gay, lesbian, and heterosexual viewers—was one of the first television shows about the lives of gays and lesbians. It also regularly featured scenes of explicit same-sex sexual activity, often emphasizing the use of condoms. *Sex and the City* introduced single female characters who are not only comfortable with their sexuality but also actively pursue sex for pleasure and talk openly about it. Of course, most single television characters still fit societal stereotypes and, even in the more progressive shows, characters tend to fit the media ideal of young, thin, and attractive. Nonetheless, even though they are isolated examples, these shows expose and challenge the hidden and explicit media messages about sexuality and the single person.

THE NEVER-MARRIED

The term *never-married* refers to adults who have never been legally married. This group includes those who intend to marry someday and those who have decided to remain single, perhaps living in a long-term common-law relationship. People are waiting longer to get married. In the 2006 Census, 93 percent of people aged 20 to 24 and 70 percent of those aged 25 to 29 were never-married, compared to 56 percent and 21 percent, respectively, in the 1971 Census. About 20 percent of these never-married individuals are in a common-law relationship with someone of the same or other gender. Most (91 percent) expect to have children (Stobert & Kemeny, 2003).

Most adults in Canada (up to 95 percent) do marry. The average age of first marriage in 2003 was 28.5 years for women and 30.6 years for men (Statistics Canada, 2007), so the typical person who marries spends several adult years in the never-married category. Canadians are older at the age of first marriage now than in the past, largely due to the fact that most live together first and delay getting married. Some of these men and women spend this entire time in one relationship that eventually leads to marriage. According to the NHSLS, among married persons 20 to 29 years old, 46 percent of the men and 65 percent of the women are in this category (Laumann et al., 1994). Other young adults continue the pattern of *serial monogamy*, which (as we saw in Chapter 10) characterizes adolescent intimate relationships; they are involved in two or more sexually intimate relationships prior to marriage. According to the NHSLS, among married persons 20 to 29, 40 percent of the men and 28 percent of the women had two or more sexual partners before they married.

Many never-married individuals are in a romantic relationship; increasing numbers of these relationships are long-distance. This kind of geographic separation can be stressful and lonely. People in long-distance romantic relationships report greater depression and lower relationship satisfaction (Cameron & Ross, 2007). However, long-distance relationships are not necessarily less stable than other dating relationships (Cameron & Ross, 2007; Van Horn et al., 1997). What factors predict whether a long-distance relationship will survive or end? Research has shown that long-distance relationships are less likely to end if people have more trust and faith in their partner's commitment, expect more support from their partner, and are more optimistic about the future of the relationship (Cameron & Ross, 2007). Long-distance relationships are also more stable when partners see the relationship in an idealized rather than in a realistic way. They are more likely to maintain idealized notions about the relationship if they see each other less frequently (Stafford & Merolla, 2007). Interestingly, long-distance relationships often end when partners start living in the same location.

The person who passes age 30 without forming a long-term relationship gradually enters a new world. The social structures that supported meeting new people—such as college or university—are gone, and more people of the same age are married.

The attitudes of singles about their status vary widely. Some young men and women decide to live both single and sexually celibate or **chaste** (abstaining from sexual intercourse). Little research has been done on celibacy, and published studies often do not distinguish voluntary from involuntary celibates. Research using a questionnaire posted on the Internet (Donnelly et al., 2001) identified three types of involuntary celibates. *Virgins* had never had intercourse, had rarely dated, and often had not engaged in any partnered sexual intimacy; the data suggest that they failed to make the developmental transitions discussed at the end of Chapter 10. *Singles* had had sexual experience but often reported that it was not satisfying; they were unable to find and maintain long-term relationships. Both their residential and work arrangements made it difficult for persons in either group to meet potential partners. Other research suggests that one's competence in romantic relationships in adulthood—being close to and getting along with a partner—is predicted by one's competence in the social and academic domains in late adolescence (Roisman et al., 2004). The third type are *partnered* persons in sexless relationships. Typically the relationship had included sex in the past but the frequency gradually declined over time.

Some people plan to remain single but not chaste. They find the single lifestyle exciting and enjoy their freedom. A survey of 3600 Canadian adolescents found that only 88 percent expect to marry (Bibby, 2001). Other men and women are searching for a spouse, some with increasing desperation, as the years go by. How do never-married Canadians over 30 years old who expect to marry differ from those who don't expect to ever marry? The "won't marry" group are more likely to be single parents, have lower incomes, and have less education. They also view love, marriage, and family as less important (Crompton, 2005).

> **Chaste:** Abstaining from sexual intercourse; sexually celibate.

BEING SINGLE

At one extreme, there is the *singles scene*. It is institutionalized in such forms as singles apartment complexes and singles bars. Fitness centres, religious groups, and parties provide opportunities for meeting others. A recent innovation, intended for the busy urban professional, is *speed dating*. Singles attend a dating event involving 15 to 25 other singles. They are given a sticker with a number on it, and then speak to each of the other attendees for a short and fixed period of time that often depends on the number of attendees, but typically ranges between four and ten minutes. At the end of the evening they indicate their interest in seeing each individual again (yes or no) and wait to see whether there is a match. This process is not without its anxieties. Attendees may find it difficult to remember the characteristics and qualities of the many people they meet, worry about finding something interesting to say in the short period of time allotted, and feel disappointed and despondent if none of the attendees they were interested in indicate interest in them.

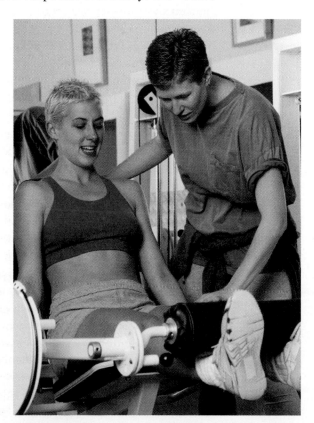

Figure 11.1 Fitness clubs are the current alternative to singles bars for some people who are hoping to meet that special someone.

The singles group, of course, is composed of the divorced and the widowed as well as the never-married. The singles bar is a visible symbol of the singles scene. Most people are there for a similar purpose: to meet that special someone. However, most will settle for a date, and it is often understood that coitus will be a part of the date. The singles bar is somewhat like a meat market; the people there try to display themselves to their best advantage and are judged and chosen on the basis of their physical appearance—and perhaps rejected for not having the type of body considered ideal in our society.

Many singles, however, do not go to singles bars. Some are turned off by the idea; some feel that they cannot compete, that they are too old or not attractive enough; and some live in rural areas where they have no access to such places. An alternative way of meeting people is through singles ads, found in most daily newspapers. As one woman said,

> Most of the men I've dated I've met . . . through personals ads. The reason I prefer guys I meet through ads is because I get to know them before meeting them. I get the chance to really get to know them before I actually see them. (Louis, 1997, p. 10)

Singles ads can also be found on the Internet as part of online dating. There are hundreds of sites where one can post ads or create a personal Web page. Some are general sites. For example, Toronto-based Lavalife.com has three separate streams for individuals seeking either partners of the same or the other gender (labelled "dating," "relationship," and "intimate encounters") and more than 1 million active members—60 percent male and 40 percent female (*Maclean's*, 2003). There also are smaller sites geared toward individuals with specific interests, such as vegetarians, pet lovers, members of particular religious groups, or seniors. Internet dating sites have been important in reducing the isolation experienced by some sexual-minority individuals—that is, gay, lesbian, bisexual, intersex, and transgender individuals.

Persons wishing to place ads are encouraged to indicate the type of partner they are searching for as well as their age, ethnicity, height, area of residence, and often a photograph. Those seeking partners can search the ads and home pages on these characteristics. Contacts made online can lead to an offline relationship or to a continuing online one. The relationship may evolve to include **cybersex**, where partners engage in sexual talk online for the purposes of sexual pleasure. It may or may not involve masturbation.

Cybersex: Online sexually oriented communication, activities, or exchanges.

A survey of 769 Canadian university students found that 18 percent of the men and 10 percent of the women had used an online dating site in the previous 12 months (Boies, 2002). Researchers in Ontario have shown that, compared to Internet users who are not online daters, Internet daters are more likely to be male, single, divorced, employed, urban, and have higher incomes (Brym & Lenton, 2003). The online daters were not socially isolated, as has sometimes been assumed. They belonged to clubs, socialized with family and friends, and saw themselves as self-confident.

The visibility of online dating, singles bars, singles tours, and other activities geared toward single adults suggests a fun-loving lifestyle with frequent sexual activity. Undoubtedly, some single persons live such a life. As Figure 11.2a indicates, 26 percent of the single men and 20 percent of the single women interviewed for the NHSLS reported having sexual intercourse two or more times per week. But the reality is different for other singles; 22 percent of the single men and 30 percent of the single women interviewed did not have sex in the year prior to the interview.

Research in Canada on sexual frequency has not used the same categories as the NHSLS. Nonetheless, the results are similar. As shown in Figure 11.2b, Bibby (1995) found that only 17 percent of single adults reported never engaging in sexual intercourse (compared to about 26 percent in the NHSLS), whereas 42 percent engage in sexual intercourse on a weekly basis or more (compared to about 49 percent in the NHSLS).

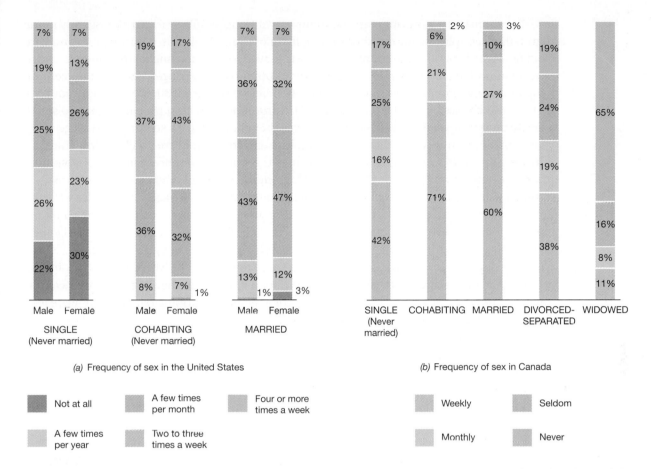

(a) Frequency of sex in the United States

(b) Frequency of sex in Canada

| | Not at all | | A few times per month | | Four or more times a week |

| | A few times per year | | Two to three times a week |

| | Weekly | | Seldom |

| | Monthly | | Never |

Figure 11.2 Frequency of sexual activity is closely related to marital status. Note that there is substantial variability in frequency within each status as well. U.S. data are from Laumann et al. (1994); Canadian data are from Bibby (1995).

COHABITATION

In early adulthood, it is common for couples to experiment with various levels of commitment, such as an exclusive dating relationship or living together. Even when living together, there are different levels of commitment, from "living together apart" to "some days and nights" to "all the time." Living together is an important turning point not only because it represents commitment but also because it is a public declaration of a sexual relationship. It is rare for two people who are going out to live together just because it will save on rent. Cohabiting is an opportunity to explore a more serious commitment, at least to some extent. Forty-two percent of Canadians have lived with a non-marital partner at some point in their lives; this percentage is even higher for people under 40 years old (Bibby, 2006). Increasingly, middle-aged and older individuals are living common-law (Statistics Canada, 2007).

Cohabitation has become an increasingly common alternative to marriage. According to the 2006 Canadian Census, the number of common-law couples grew five times faster than the number of married couples since 2001. Legally in Canada, when two people live together as a couple for 12 continuous months but are not legally married to each other, they are in a **common-law relationship**. According to the 2006 Census, 16 percent of Canadians were currently living in common-law relationships, up from 6 percent in 1981. Of these, 37 885 are same-sex couples. The rate is highest in Quebec, where 30 percent of couples are common-

Common-law relationship: Two people who have lived together as a couple for 12 continuous months but are not legally married to each other.

law. Common-law relationships are most common among people aged 20 to 24. Slightly more than half of couples living together eventually marry, although this percentage is lower in Quebec. Two-thirds of these couples marry within two years of starting to live together. However, common-law relationships break up more often than marriages. About 60 percent of people who end common-law relationships do so before the age of 30; most of these couples do not have children (Statistics Canada, 2007). Common-law relationships that end do so on average after four years, compared to marriages that end, which do so after an average of 14 years. Further, contrary to what many people think, marriages that are preceded by cohabitation are more likely to end in separation than marriages that are not preceded by cohabitation (Clark & Compton, 2006). A longitudinal study compared couples who cohabited before they got engaged, couples who cohabited after engagement/before marriage, and couples who did not live together until after marriage (Kline et al., 2004). Couples were assessed twice, following engagement and after ten months of marriage. At both times, couples who lived together before engagement had more negative interactions (e.g., criticizing their partner), lower commitment, and lower relationship quality. Thus, the seeds of divorce were sown in the pre-engagement relationship. However, these data do not mean that living together causes divorce. A related study found that men in pre-engagement cohabiting relationships were less committed to the partner than those who were not cohabiting (Rhoades et al., 2006).

The popular image of cohabitation is that it involves young, never-married couples without children. However, almost half of common-law couples have children living in the home (Statistics Canada, 2004). Canadians whose first marriage has dissolved often choose common-law over remarriage. This accounts for more than one-quarter of common-law relationships in Canada, and is especially true of people in their 30s and 40s. People living in common-law relationships "of some permanence" are entitled to most of the same legal rights as married individuals.

With respect to sexual behaviour, Bibby (1995) found that 60 percent of married persons reported having sexual intercourse once a week or more, whereas 71 percent of cohabiting persons had sexual intercourse with that frequency (see Figure 11.2b). Similarly, the NHSLS found that cohabiting men and women reported more frequent sex than did married men and women (see Figure 11.2a). However, notice the wide variation; some cohabitors report having sexual intercourse only a few times per year. It is interesting that on average cohabiting couples have sex more often than married couples. Some cohabitors are concerned about the stability of the relationship (Bumpass et al., 1991); they may have sex more frequently in the hope that it will strengthen the relationship (Blumstein & Schwartz, 1983).

MARRIAGE

In 2000, the Supreme Court of Canada ruled that under the equality provision of the Charter of Rights and Freedoms, same-sex couples (and heterosexual common-law couples) have the same rights and responsibilities as heterosexual married couples. In 2005, the federal government passed legislation that ensured that all Canadians have the right to marry, regardless of sexual orientation. According to the 2006 Census, there are 7500 same-sex married couples, which represents about 0.1 percent of all married couples (Statistics Canada, 2007). More than half (53.7 percent) of same-sex married spouses are men. Same-sex weddings in Canada are now sufficiently mainstream that they have even spawned a prime-time reality television show, *My Fabulous Gay Wedding*. However, it will probably be a number of years before we have research on sexuality within same-sex marriages. Therefore, the following sections focus on sex in heterosexual marriages.

Given that common-law couples have many of the same rights and responsibilities as married couples, why do people want to marry? Marriage is a psychological turning point for many people. The decision to get married is a real decision these days, in contrast to previous decades when everyone assumed that they would marry, and the only question was to whom. Today, most couples have had a full sexual relationship, sometimes for years, before they marry. The three most important reasons people give for getting married are that it signifies their commitment, is consistent with their moral values and beliefs, and that it reflects their belief that children should have married parents (Bibby, 2006). Some psychological pressures seem to intensify with marriage, and these pressures may result in problems where there were none previously. Marriage is a tangible statement that one has left the family of origin (the family in which you grew up) and shifted to creating one's own family (in which many people become the parents rearing children); for some, this separation from parents is difficult. The pressure for sexual performance may become more intense once people are married as sexual dissatisfactions that were easy to overlook in the early, rose-coloured-glasses phase of the relationship have more and more impact on each individual's sexual satisfaction. And finally, marriage still carries with it an assumption of a lifelong commitment to fidelity or faithfulness, a promise that is hard for some to keep.

In marriage, there is a need to work out issues of roles. Who does what? Some of the decisions are as tame as who cooks supper. But who initiates sex is far more sensitive, and who has the right to say no to sex is even more so.

This is the era of two-career couples, or at least dual-earner couples. There are issues here of finding time for sex and for just being with each other.

As a marriage progresses, it can't stay forever as blushingly beautiful as it seemed when the relationship began. The nature of love changes (see Chapter 12), and for some couples there is a gradual disenchantment with sex. Couples need to take steps to avoid boredom in the bedroom. Sexual disorders (see Chapter 18) occur in many marriages, and couples need to find ways to resolve them.

FREQUENCY OF INTERCOURSE

According to the 2006 Census, 90 percent of Canadians aged 50 to 69 are or have been legally married. However, it is expected that only 73 percent of men and 78 percent of women aged 30 to 39 will marry at some point in their lives. Of those who divorce, 70 percent of the men and 58 percent of the women remarry (Ambert, 2005). In our society, marriage is also the context in which sexual expression has the most legitimacy. Therefore, sex in marriage is one of the commonest forms of sexual expression for adults.

Research in the United States shows that the average married heterosexual couple have coitus two to three times per week when they are in their 20s, with the frequency gradually declining as they get older (there are no data on sexual frequency in same-sex marriages). The data on this point from three studies are shown in Table 11.1. Several things can be noted from the table. First, the frequency of marital sex has remained about the same from the 1940s to the 2000s. In each survey, people in their 20s reported having intercourse about every three days. Second, the frequency of intercourse declines with age; however, in 2003, among couples in their 50s, the frequency was still once per week. Social characteristics such as race, social status, and religion are generally not related to marital sexual frequency (Christopher & Sprecher, 2000).

Two general explanations have been suggested for the age-related decline in frequency: biological aging, and habituation to sex with the partner (Call et al., 1995). With regard to aging, there may be physical factors associated with age that affect sexual frequency, such as a decrease in vaginal lubrication in females, or increased likelihood of poor health. The habituation explanation states that we lose interest in sex as the partner becomes more and more familiar. Recent data indicate a sharp decline in frequency after the first year and a slow, steady decline thereafter. The decline after the first year may reflect habituation (Call et al., 1995). It is

Table 11.1 Marital Coitus: Frequency per Week (Male and Female Estimates Combined), 1938–1949, 1970, and 2003

1938–1949 (Kinsey)		1970 (Westoff)		2003 (Smith)	
Age	Median Frequency per Week	Age	Mean Frequency per Week	Age	Mean Frequency per Week
16–25	2.45	20–24	2.5	18–29	2.1
26–35	1.95	25–34	2.1	30–39	1.7
36–45	1.40	35–44	1.6	40–49	1.4
46–55	0.85			50–59	1.0
56–60	0.55			60–69	0.6
				70+	0.3

often assumed that this decline in frequency reflects a loss of interest in sex, meaning a decline in quality. However, there is an alternative possibility: that learning about your partner's sexual desires, preferences, and habits results in increased marital sexual quality, if not frequency (Liu, 2003). But analysis of the data on satisfaction with the marital sexual relationship from the NHSLS found a significant decline with length of marriage, controlling for age, consistent with the habituation hypothesis. A third factor is the arrival of children, as discussed later.

It is important to note that there is wide variability in these frequencies. For example, 2 percent of couples in their 20s report not engaging in intercourse at all; 6 percent of all married couples had not had sex in the 12 months prior to the interview (Smith, 2003). Research on a sample of 6029 married couples found that sexual inactivity was associated with unhappiness with the marriage, lack of shared activity, the presence of children, increased age, and poor health (Donnelly, 1993). In contrast, a married couple in Seattle have claimed the world record, having had intercourse more than 900 times in 700 days! Data from the NHSLS and Bibby (1995) also confirm this wide variability, as shown in Figure 11.2 on page 333.

SEXUAL TECHNIQUES

The NHSLS (Laumann et al., 1994) asked respondents to estimate the duration of their last sexual interaction. Sixteen percent of their married participants reported that sex lasted 15 minutes or less; 9 percent reported that it lasted one hour or more. Participants in the *Maclean's*/CTV poll (1994) reported on the average length of their sexual encounters; 12 percent reported that their sexual encounters lasted 15 minutes or less; 25 percent reported that they lasted more than an hour. A New Brunswick study found that, on average, sexual encounters lasted about 20 minutes (Miller & Byers, 2004).

The increased popularity of mouth–genital techniques is one of the most dramatic changes in (heterosexual) marital sex to have occurred in the past 50 years. According to Kinsey's data, about half of married women had engaged in oral sex. In the NHSLS data, 74 percent reported that their partners had stimulated their genitals orally, and 70 percent of them had stimulated their partner orally. Similarly, a Montreal study found that almost 80 percent of married and cohabiting respondents had stimulated their partner's genitals orally and that on average this occurred once a week (Samson et al., 1993). Younger respondents were more likely than older respondents to include oral sex in their sexual repertoires. For example, 90 percent of people aged 18 to 34 had stimulated their partner orally compared to only 40 percent of people in the 55 and older age group. People with higher levels of education and incomes were more likely to report engaging in oral sex, showing that there are some social-class differences.

Kinsey did not report data on anal intercourse. According to the NHSLS data, 27 percent of the married men and 21 percent of the married women reported having engaged in this activity (Laumann et al., 1994).

(a)   (b)

Figure 11.3   Sexual turning points. *(a)* Marriage and the commitment it represents is a major turning point. *(b)* The birth of a baby is a turning point that can have a negative impact on sexual aspects of the relationship, but couples who are aware of this possibility can work to overcome these problems and keep the romance going.

NEGOTIATING SEX

Before any of these techniques are executed, there is typically a "mating dance" between the man and the woman. Sexual scripts are played out in marriages as in other aspects of sex (Gagnon, 1977, pp. 208–209). Some scripts involve direct verbal statements. One person may say, "I'd love to go to bed with you right now." The partner might reply, "What are we waiting for?" or "Not now. Dinner is almost ready." Some scripts are behavioural. One woman said, "We'd get into bed, and he'd roll over to me and kind of bing me in the back end with his penis, so I'd know, Okay, tonight's the night" (Maurer, 1994, p. 180). For other couples, deciding to make love involves preliminary negotiations, which are phrased in indirect or euphemistic language, in part so that the person's feelings can be salvaged if her or his partner is not interested. For example, an individual may say, "I think I'll go take a shower" or "I think I'll go take a nap" (that means "I want to, do you?"). The partner might respond with, "I think I'll take one too" (that means "yes") or "The kids will be home any moment" or "I have a report to finish for tomorrow" (that means "no"). Or conversely, the individual may kiss their partner a bit more passionately than usual after work (that is the offer). The partner may respond with, "I had an exhausting day at work" (i.e., "no") or "I'll meet you upstairs" (i.e., "yes"). To avoid some of the risk of rejection inherent in such negotiations, some couples ritualize sex so they both understand when it will and when it will not occur—Thursday night may be their time, or perhaps Sunday afternoon.

Which of these strategies is used most frequently by heterosexual couples? A New Brunswick study found that people most frequently use a direct verbal statement to initiate sex

(Byers & Heinlein, 1989). The second most frequent strategy is more ambiguous—kissing passionately without saying anything. This study also examined the stereotype that men are more interested in sex than women are by having people in long-term relationships keep track for a one-week period of sexual initiations by the man and sexual initiations by the woman. On average the men initiated sex almost twice as often as the women did—about twice a week for the men compared to once a week for the women. Interestingly, the men and the women were equally likely to respond positively to the initiation—about three-quarters of the time. Thus, traditional gender roles persist in some areas, with men more often having the initiating role. There was also some evidence of liberation. Women initiated sex regularly (and in some couples were the usual initiator), and usually were interested in engaging in sex when their partner suggested it. Contrary to the male stereotype, the men were not always interested in sex and were equally likely to refuse their partner's initiations. There may be differences in how men and women respond when their partner refuses their initiation. According to traditional stereotypes, a woman's refusal could be attributed to her lesser sexual appetite. However, refusals by men go against traditional views of male sexuality. Therefore, a woman may conclude that the man's refusal means that he is not interested in her (Blumstein & Schwartz, 1983). Nonetheless, most of the time couples are satisfied with how they resolve disagreements about whether to have sex (Byers & Heinlein, 1989).

MASTURBATION

Many people masturbate; the NHSLS found that 63 percent of the men and 42 percent of the women reported masturbating in the past year. Seventeen percent of the married men and 5 percent of the married women masturbate at least once a week (Laumann et al., 1994).

Many adults continue to masturbate even though they are married and have ready access to sexual activity with a partner. This behaviour is perfectly normal, although it sometimes evokes feelings of guilt and may be done secretly. According to the NHSLS, married people were more likely to report that they masturbated than were single people (Michael et al., 1994). Masturbation can serve very legitimate sexual needs in long-term relationships. It feels good whether one is living with a partner or not. It can provide sexual gratification while allowing the partner to remain faithful to a spouse when they are separated or cannot have sex for some reason such as illness.[1]

Masturbation can also be a pleasant adjunct to marital sex. According to a 49-year-old man:

> One of the other things we do a lot is masturbation. We have it developed to a fine art. We rent a porno movie, take a bath, rub each other down with baby oil. My wife and I not only masturbate each other at the same time, but we get pleasure watching each other masturbate individually as well. It's a terrifically exciting thing. (Janus & Janus, 1993, p. 383)

SATISFACTION WITH MARITAL SEX

Sexual satisfaction is important to most couples. Sexual satisfaction is not just physical pleasure, nor is it simply the absence of dissatisfaction or problems. In fact, couples with sexual difficulties may feel sexually satisfied, and couples with no sexual problems may not feel satisfied at all (MacNeil & Byers, 1997). Rather, sexual satisfaction is the overall feeling we are left with after considering the positive and negative aspects (or sexual rewards and costs) of our sexual relationship. Of course, one person's reward may be another person's cost. For example, having sex every day might be a reward for someone who desires sex every day. It may be a cost for someone who prefers to have sex less frequently, say twice a week. A New Brunswick study

---

[1]An old navy saying has it, "If your wife can't be at your right hand, let your right hand be your wife." This saying probably should be updated to refer to both men and women.

found that for men in long-term relationships, the most frequently identified sexual rewards were feeling comfortable with their partner, feeling good about themselves during and after sex, and having fun during sexual activity. For women the most frequent rewards were being treated well by their partner during sex, feeling comfortable with their partner, and having sex in the context of a long-term relationship (Lawrance & Byers, 1995).

Canadian psychologists Kelli-an Lawrance and Sandra Byers developed the interpersonal exchange model of sexual satisfaction, which identifies four distinct aspects of relationships that influence sexual satisfaction (Lawrance & Byers, 1995). According to this model, we are more sexually satisfied if (1) we perceive ourselves to be getting many sexual rewards and few sexual costs, (2) we perceive that we are getting more rewards and fewer costs than we expect to get, (3) we perceive our own and our partner's rewards and costs to be relatively equal, and (4) we are happy with the non-sexual aspects of the relationship. A longitudinal study of 244 New Brunswick adults living with a partner found that these four components measured at Time 1 predicted sexual satisfaction three months later. Similar results were found in studies involving Canadian dating couples and married Chinese individuals living in Beijing and Shanghai (Byers et al., 1998; Renaud & Byers, 1997). As you might expect, we are also more sexually satisfied if our partner also experiences high sexual rewards and low sexual costs (Byers & MacNeil, 2006). Clearly, our assessment of the rewards and costs in our intimate relationships are associated with our feelings of sexual satisfaction. Our sexual satisfaction is also affected by how we get along outside the bedroom. Sexual satisfaction is an important contributor to marital quality. Longitudinal data from 283 married couples found that sexual satisfaction predicted marital quality for both men and women (Yeh et al., 2006). Sexual satisfaction and marital quality both predicted marital stability. Thus, sex and relational education programs that increase sexual satisfaction for both partners have the potential to lower the divorce rate.

In-depth interviews with 52 people, ages 12 to 69, straight, gay, lesbian, and bisexual, identified four factors that differentiate people who are happy with their sex lives (Maurer, 1994). First, there is a sense of calm about, and acceptance of, their sexuality. Second, happy people delight in giving their partners sexual pleasure. Third, these people *listen* to their partners and are aware of the partner's quirks, moods, likes, and dislikes. Fourth, they *talk*, both in and out of bed, even though it is often difficult. These interviews remind us that good communication is essential to a satisfying relationship (see Chapter 12).

SEXUAL PATTERNS

Sexual patterns in marriage are influenced by the level of sexual desire experienced by each person. A study of 24 couples obtained daily ratings of relationship affect (positive or negative), relationship status (closeness, equality of power), and lust from each partner (Ridley et al., 2006). Researchers identified four patterns in ratings of desire: (1) stable and low, (2) slight fluctuations (1 point on a 1-to-5 scale) and low, (3) moderate fluctuations, and (4) highly fluctuating. On days when positive affect toward the spouse was high, lust was high; when negative affect was high, lust was low. Interestingly, on days when people reported high closeness to spouse, the link between positive (negative) affect and lust was stronger. Finally, there was a significant positive association between own lust and partner's lust each day.

Sexual patterns can change during the course of a marriage. After ten years of marriage they may be quite different from what they were during the first year. One stereotype is that sex becomes duller as marriage wears on, and certainly there are some marriages in which that happens. In a survey of adults in the United States, 23 percent of the sexually active men and women reported that their sexual relationship was often or always "routine." Thirty-eight percent said it was never or hardly ever routine (Kaiser Family Foundation, 1998). As we noted in Chapter 9, a boring sexual relationship can be spiced up by telling each other what you really want to do and then doing it, or by consulting a how-to manual such as *The New Joy of Sex*. There are also relationships in which the sex remains very exciting. A 36-year-old engineer said:

> [Though my wife's career] is tremendously important to her, she manages to look attractive, and to dress chicly, and though she is not what many would call a beautiful woman, she is, to me, a handsome woman. In bed, she is the hottest, most exciting woman I have ever known. We have been married seven years. . . . When we get to bed, and she lets herself go, we get wild together. (Janus & Janus, 1993, p. 191)

Having a baby—what researchers call the transition to parenthood—has an impact on the sexual relationship of the couple. According to one 44-year-old mother of three children, "There's the passionate period when you can't get enough of each other, and after a few years it wanes, and after kids it really wanes" (Maurer, 1994, p. 403). Trying to get pregnant and the threat of infertility, which are so much publicized, can be potent forces on one's identity as a sexual being (Daniluk, 2001). Pregnancy itself can influence a couple's sexual interactions, particularly in the last few months (see Chapter 6).

Table 11.2   Frequency of Activities to Enhance Sexual Interactions Reported by Adults*

	Very Often	Often	Sometimes	Hardly Ever	Never	Don't Know
Do romantic things like eat by candlelight	8	18	35	30	6	3
Act out fantasies together	4	10	28	39	12	7
Wear sexy lingerie (women**)	9	10	28	35	12	6
Try different sexual positions	11	19	35	23	4	8
Read books or watch videos about improving your sex life	2	3	14	52	26	3
Go out on special evenings or dates or go away on weekends alone	11	22	37	22	5	3

Number of respondents = 1109   **Number of female respondents = 564

Source: Kaiser Family Foundation (1998).

For the first few weeks after the baby is born, intercourse is typically uncomfortable for the woman. While estrogen levels are low—which lasts longer when breast-feeding—the vagina does not lubricate well. Then, too, the mother and sometimes the father feel exhausted with 2 A.M. feedings. The first few months after a baby is born are usually not the peak times in a sexual relationship, and so that, too, must be negotiated between partners. (See Table 11.2.)

Not all couples have children. For example, data from the 2001 General Social Survey (GSS) indicate that 26 percent of Canadian women ages 30 to 34 do not have children (Stobert & Kemeny, 2003). Some of these women are delaying childbearing while they complete their education and establish their careers; 20 percent of women in the 30 to 34 age group do not have children but intend to have a child. The average age of first childbirth was 28 years in 2006, up from 24 years in the 1960s (Statistics Canada, 2007). There is some risk in this strategy; fertility declines with age, so some of these women may be unable to have a child if they want to. Other women have made a decision to remain child-free. According to the GSS, 5 percent of women do not expect to have children. A third group of women are those who choose to adopt; adopting an infant probably has effects on one's relationships and sexual activities similar to those of having a baby.

Some people will experience fundamental changes in their sexual experience at least once over the course of the marriage. The change may result from developing a capacity to give as well as receive sexual pleasure, and to expand our sexual scripts beyond traditional expectations for men and women. A man may outgrow performance anxiety and enlarge his focus to include his partner. A woman may learn that she can take care of her own sexual needs as well as her partner's. Aging may produce change in sexual experience, a topic we consider later in this chapter. There are changes due to illness, such as breast cancer or testicular cancer, which can lead to disaster or triumph depending upon how the couple copes with it.

SEX AND THE TWO-CAREER FAMILY

In our busy, achievement-oriented society, is it possible that work commitments may interfere with a couple's sex life? One couple, both of whom are professionals, commented to us that they actually have to make an appointment with each other to make love.

Research shows that there is little cause for concern. A longitudinal study followed 570 women and 550 of their husbands for one year following the birth of a baby (Hyde et al., 1998). The women were categorized according to the number of hours worked per week outside the home: homemakers, employed part time (6 to 31 hours/week), full time (32 to 44 hours), and high full time (45 or more hours). There actually were no significant differences among the four groups in frequency of sexual intercourse, sexual satisfaction, or sexual desire. It was not the number of hours of work outside the home, but rather the quality of work that was associated with sexual outcomes. Women and men who had satisfying jobs reported that sex was better, compared with people who expressed dissatisfaction with their jobs. For women, fatigue was associated with decreased sexual satisfaction, but that was true for both homemakers and employed women; and homemakers reported the same level of fatigue as employed women.

Problems may occur at the extremes, though. Two-profession couples, when both members are committed to working 60 to 80 hours per week outside the home, don't have much time for sex. The issue with such couples is not so much having a career as not making time to nurture the relationship. Quality sex requires quality time together.

(a)

(b)

Figure 11.4 Sex and the two-career family. *(a)* Research indicates that marital/sexual relationships do not suffer if the woman works outside the home. *(b)* However, for those working 60 or more hours per week, some experts are concerned because these workaholics literally take their work to bed with them.

MAINTAINING A LONG-TERM RELATIONSHIP

Most couples who establish a long-term relationship intend to stay together. However, we know that not all couples succeed. According to Statistics Canada, about 30 percent of first marriages end in divorce. The rate is even higher for first common-law relationships. A good deal of research has looked at differences between non-distressed (happy) couples and distressed (unhappy) couples. What differentiates non-distressed couples from distressed couples?

1. Non-distressed couples have good listening and communication skills. Suggestions for enhancing communication skills are outlined in Chapter 12.
2. Non-distressed couples have effective problem-solving skills. In contrast, distressed couples may discuss problems, but they rarely resolve them. As a result, the same problems tend to come up over and over again.
3. Non-distressed couples have many positive interactions and few negative interactions. For example, they have many enjoyable shared leisure-time activities, are affectionate with each other, and feel good about their communication. In fact, Gottman (1994) found that non-distressed couples have five times as much positive interaction as negative interaction.
4. Non-distressed couples tend to have realistic expectations about what relationships should be like. In contrast, distressed couples may believe that disagreements are destructive, that one must be a perfect sexual partner at all times, or that people who are in love feel intensively passionate about their partner at all times. None of these expectations are realistic.
5. Non-distressed couples tend to interpret their partner's behaviour and the causes of that behaviour positively. For example, if the woman is late for dinner, her partner is likely to assume that it was due to something beyond her control such as heavy traffic. A distressed partner is more likely to see this as an example of her being thoughtless.
6. Non-distressed couples are more likely to share a common view of roles and responsibilities within the relationship. Unhappy couples may disagree on how the relationship should work; for example, they may have different ideas about financial decision making or how involved each should be with taking care of the children.

Of course, feelings of love and intimacy are also important to maintaining a long-term relationship (see Chapter 12 for a discussion of love in long-term relationships). These feelings often are what motivates couples to work through the problems that inevitably come up. Feelings of equity in the relationship (discussed later in this chapter) are also important.

Relationship satisfaction is one of the key elements contributing to sexual satisfaction (Lawrance & Byers, 1995). Further, dissatisfaction with the relationship and conflict between spouses are associated with susceptibility to infidelity (Buss & Shackelford, 1997b). For example, one woman used her dissatisfaction with her relationship to explain her serious affair: "I'm definitely not looking for more sex. The affair I'm having is for emotional reasons. Freddie [her husband] is very self-centered. He's not an emotional support. He's distant, and we have nothing in common" (Maurer, 1994, p. 391).

What makes men and women susceptible to infidelity? A study of 107 couples married less than one year asked each partner how likely he or she was to be unfaithful in the next year (Buss & Shackelford, 1997b). Each was asked the likelihood that she or he would flirt, kiss passionately, and have a romantic date, a one-night stand, a brief affair, or a serious affair with someone of the opposite sex. Thirty-seven percent of the men and 38 percent of the women predicted they would flirt, while 5 percent of the men and 7 percent of the women said they would kiss. Two percent (of men and of women) predicted a one-night stand, and less than 1 percent (of men and women) thought they would have a serious affair. In addition, researchers measured a variety of personality, mate value, and relationship characteristics. Among the personality variables, high scorers on narcissism and impulsiveness gave a higher probability of infidelity. Characteristics of the relationship associated with greater likelihood of infidelity included reports of conflict, especially that the partner sexualized others, engaged in sexual withholding, and alcohol abuse. Finally, among both men and women, dissatisfaction with the marriage and with marital sex was associated with susceptibility to infidelity.

Our awareness of the possibility of infidelity sometimes leads us to engage in behaviours designed to preserve the relationship, or *mate retention tactics* (Buss & Shackelford, 1997a). Such tactics may be elicited by our own fear that the partner is losing interest or is dissatisfied, or because we observe some cues to infidelity. Cues thought to be associated with sexual infidelity include physical signs (partner contracting an STI), changes in "normal" sexual behaviour with the partner, increased or decreased sexual interest, and the partner disclosing his or her infidelity (Shackelford & Buss, 1997). A study of 107 American heterosexual couples married for less than one year asked about their use of mate retention tactics. Each partner was given a list of 104 behaviours and was asked how often he or she had performed each in the past year. There were marked gender differences in the reported actions. Men reported greater use of resources display (giving her money) and more frequent submission to the partner. Women reported more frequent use of enhancing their appearance or attractiveness and use of possessive verbal statements. Thus, men's and women's most frequent mate retention strategies fall along traditional gender lines. Unfortunately, these strategies do not address the problems typical of distressed couples just listed.

EXTRADYADIC SEX

Extradyadic sex refers to sexual activity between a person in a committed relationship—gay, lesbian, or straight—and someone other than that person's partner. When a person who is married engages in extradyadic sex, we call it **extramarital sex**, or adultery. Extradyadic sex can occur under several different circumstances (Pittman, 1993). Sometimes it is *accidental*, unintended and not characteristic of the person; it "just happens." One or both persons may be drunk, or having a bad day, or lonely. More serious is *romantic infidelity*, when the two people fall in love and consider or establish a long-term relationship; this situation can be very destructive to partners, children, and careers. We noted earlier in this chapter that dissatisfaction with the relationship is especially likely to lead to romantic infidelity. A third type is the *open relationship* or *open marriage*, in which the partners agree in advance that each may have sex with other persons. (In contrast, accidental and romantic infidelities begin without the partner's knowledge, and may remain secret.) Finally, there are *philanderers* who repeatedly engage in sexual liaisons outside their committed relationship. Some philanderers use dating websites to meet new sexual partners. These men and women are not motivated by the desire for sexual gratification; they are searching for self-affirmation (Pittman, 1993).

People engage in extradyadic sexual behaviour for a number of reasons. Some people believe that extradyadic sexual behaviour is acceptable, and they may have an agreement with their partner about the circumstances under which it can occur. Other people, particularly people in long-term relationships, engage in extradyadic sex because they find it particularly exciting. The excitement may be a result of being with a new partner, being found attractive and desirable, or doing something that the individual knows to be forbidden. Finally, some people may engage in extradyadic sex because there are problems in their long-term relationship.

Most of the research on extradyadic sexual behaviour has been on extramarital sex, which we turn to next. However, individuals in dating relationships also engage in extradyadic sexual behaviour, although men are more likely to do so than are women. For example, in one study of university students, 65 percent of the men and 49 percent of the women had experienced extradyadic kissing and fondling; 49 percent of the men and 31 percent of the women had experienced extradyadic sexual intercourse (Wiederman & Hurd, 1999). Many gay couples engaged in extradyadic sexual activity, often by mutual consent (Carballo-Diéguez, 2000).

Extradyadic sex: Sexual activity between a person in a serious or exclusive relationship and someone other than his or her steady partner.

Extramarital sex: Sexual activity between a married person and someone other than that person's spouse; adultery.

IN FOCUS 11.1

Have Adults Changed Their Sexual Behaviour in the AIDS Era?

In June 2006, we acknowledged the twenty-fifth anniversary of the AIDS epidemic. Beginning in 1985, the mass media published and broadcast a steady stream of features about HIV/AIDS, including its risks and recommendations for safer sex practices. Public health and community-based groups engaged in large-scale outreach efforts to educate people, particularly gay men and youth. Perhaps as a result, a recent survey of 2004 Canadians over the age of 15 found that we are generally very knowledgeable about HIV/AIDS (Ekos, 2003). However, has all this publicity and activity had any impact on people's sexual behaviour, or do people continue to engage in high-risk sexual practices? (See Chapter 8 for a discussion of high-risk and safer sex practices.)

In order to assess whether behaviour has actually changed, we need longitudinal research, in which the same people are surveyed or the same questions are asked of comparable samples over time. Unfortunately, there are few such studies; most of the data are from cross-sectional surveys at different points in time.

If you ask adults whether they have changed their behaviour because of AIDS, some say they have. In one sample of single adolescent and adult Canadians, 84 percent said that AIDS had led them to make changes in their sexual behaviour (Bibby, 1995). Interestingly, only 68 percent said that other adults they knew had made these changes. Further, the number of unmarried Canadian men who report having multiple partners has declined (Health Canada, 1998e). According to the National Population Health Survey, in 1994 and 1995, 12 to 19 percent of men and 6 to 7 percent of women had two or more sexual partners within the previous year. In 2003 only 8 percent of Canadians reported two or more partners (Ekos, 2003). Research also has shown an increase in condom use by people in high-risk groups (Catania et al., 2001). In addition, research shows that in the decade 1985 to 1995, gay men showed substantial behaviour change (Ehrhardt et al., 1991). Many gay men reduced their number of sex partners, had fewer anonymous sexual encounters, and engaged less in anal intercourse or used condoms consistently.

These changes undertaken by straights and gays contributed to a decline in the number of new cases of HIV each year from 1995 to 2000 (PHAC, 2005). Rates of several other STIs also declined in Canada through 1997 (Patrick et al., 2000). Furthermore, several studies suggest that some men and women who are diagnosed with HIV/AIDS become celibate—that is, live without a romantic or intimate relationship (Siegel & Scrimshaw, 2003). This reduces the likelihood of transmission to uninfected persons.

Perhaps because of the decline, and because of the

HOW MANY PEOPLE ENGAGE IN EXTRAMARITAL SEX?

Extramarital sexual activity is not as common as many people believe. According to the NHSLS, about 25 percent of married men and 15 percent of married women reported having engaged in extramarital sex at least once (Laumann et al., 1994). A *Maclean's*/CTV poll conducted in 1995 found a considerably lower percentage of Canadians who reported having had an affair while married—14 percent of men and 7 percent of women. These differences may reflect cultural differences between Canada and the United States. They may also reflect differences in the methodologies used in the two studies that may have affected participants' willingness to report a behaviour that is generally frowned upon (see Chapter 3).

The incidence of extramarital sex varies from one group to another and one region to another. As noted in Chapter 1, the rate of extramarital sexual activity is highest in Quebec.

All these percentages are of persons who had sex with someone other than their spouse

effectiveness of the antiretroviral therapies in reducing the impact of the illness, there has been much less media attention to HIV and AIDS in recent years, and perhaps less effort by public health and medical personnel. There are signs that this recent complacency has led to a slowing or stopping of the gains made earlier. In fact, the number of new cases of HIV and other STIs has been rising.

Nonetheless, many Canadians are not practising safer sex. For example, a survey of 2004 Canadians over the age of 15 found that only 44 percent of those who reported having had casual partners and 49 percent of those with two partners always used a condom (Ekos, 2003). Similarly, national surveys conducted in Britain found that between 1990 and 2000 there was an increase in the percentage of individuals reporting a range of behaviours that increase the risk of infection with HIV, including increased numbers of partners, anal sex, and payment for sex (Johnson et al., 2001).

An Ontario study investigated the ways that 102 gay and bisexual men justified engaging in unsafe sex (Adam et al., 2000). Some of their reasons were that not using a condom in an ongoing relationship was a way of promoting intimacy and romance; their unsafe sexual behaviour occurred in the heat of the moment and, in some cases, was involuntary; they used the high they got from engaging in risky sex as a way of escaping from negative feelings such as depression; they engaged only in lower-risk sexual behaviour (e.g., fella-

tio); and they could determine their partner's HIV status from information they had about him. Although most gay men intend to practise safer sex, some intentionally engage in unprotected sex with new partners unless condom use is initiated by the partner (Adam, 2005). This practice is referred to as *barebacking*.

The fact that the recent increase in STI rates parallels a decline in safe-sex campaigns and sex education programs suggests that continuing efforts to increase awareness of the risk of HIV/AIDS and other STIs and the importance of safer-sex practices are very important to efforts to control these illnesses. Research evaluating various intervention programs provides a solid base for designing and implementing such programs. Community-based programs targeting specific groups have demonstrated significant effects on condom use and safer sex (Ross & Williams, 2002). The use of opinion leaders and role models, and the delivery of the intervention by peer educators are associated with the success of such programs. Also important to success is the establishment of ties to the target community and a "buy-in" by the community. Clinic-based programs can also be successful in increasing consistent condom use (Fortenberry, 2002). Extensive, personal counselling can lead to some reduction in the rates of new STIs. Thus, we can further reduce the incidence of HIV/AIDS, but it requires continuing media attention and redoubled efforts by public health and medical personnel, with the active participation of the community.

while married. At the time of the surveys, some of these people were divorced. Others were remarried, perhaps for the second or third time. We can ask a more specific question: How many people engage in extramarital sex during their first marriage? Data from the NHSLS (1994) indicate that from 10 to 23 percent of the American men had extramarital sex, compared to 6 to 12 percent of the women, depending on the person's age.

There is no indication that extramarital sex is casual or frequent. In one Canadian survey, of the respondents who had had extramarital sex, 40 percent had done so with only one partner (Gallup, 1988).

ATTITUDES TOWARD EXTRAMARITAL SEX

While, as we have seen, attitudes toward premarital sex have become substantially more permissive during the past several decades, attitudes toward extramarital sex have remained relatively unchanged. Most people in Canada disapprove of extramarital sex. According to a series of well-sampled surveys conducted by Bibby and his associates (1995), in 1975 50 percent of

Canadian adults felt that it is always wrong to have sex with someone other than the marriage partner. In 1995, this figure had risen to 60 percent. A 2005 COMPAS poll found that most Canadians feel that an act of unfaithfulness would probably (27 percent) or definitely (41 percent) mean the end of a relationship. Some people view unfaithfulness to a partner in any type of committed relationship as the equivalent of adultery. And some don't limit the term to cases of sexual intimacy. "Adultery is absolutely anything," said one young woman.

A study of couples seeking therapy compared couples in which one member admitted being unfaithful with couples who did not report infidelity (Atkins et al., 2005). Couples in which one (or both) admitted infidelity reported higher levels of dishonesty, more arguments about trust, and more time spent apart. Men who reported participating in affairs were older and more sexually dissatisfied.

Attitudes toward extramarital sex are not very good predictors of extramarital sexual behaviour (Thompson, 1983). That is, the person who approves of extramarital sex is not more likely to actually engage in extramarital sex than the person who disapproves of it. Several other factors are related to attitudes toward sex outside one's primary relationship, including gender (men are more tolerant of it), education (those with more education are more accepting of it), and social class (upper-middle-class persons are more tolerant of it) (Willetts et al., 2004).

Because our society condemns extramarital sex, the individual who engages in it typically has confused, ambivalent feelings. A young married woman describes her feelings:

> I don't like the illicit part of the affair. Mostly, it's a nuisance, because it's very difficult to find time, and I don't like lying to Freddie and sneaking around. If he wouldn't mind, I'd tell him. I don't think he would go for that. He'd show up with a gun. (Maurer, 1994, p. 393)

SWINGING

Swinging: A form of extradyadic sex in which married couples exchange partners with each other.

One form of extradyadic sex is **swinging**, in which married couples exchange partners with other couples, or engage in sexual activity with a third person, with the knowledge and consent of all involved.[2]

Swingers may find their partners in several ways. Often they advertise, in tabloid newspapers, in "lifestyle" magazines such as *Maritime Connection*, or on specialized bulletin boards and websites on the Internet. The following is an example:

> We are engaged bicouple lookin to meet bim, bif and bicouples for friendship and fun . . . we are into nudism, motorcycling, fishin, volleyball, pool and campin . . . she is 22 5'5 180# 38-d blond blue . . . he is 24 5'10 145# blond green 7'' and very thick. email: (www . . . /~gnkfoxx/ nefriend.htm)

Swingers may also meet potential partners at swingers' clubs, parties, or resorts. Many of these places advertise in swingers' magazines and newsletters and are listed on specialized websites.

Several organizations and many local groups or couples sponsor parties. The date and general location of the party are publicized in magazines and on the Internet. Interested persons call or e-mail a contact person who screens them. If they pass, they are told the exact location of the party, often a private home or a hotel. A fee of $50 or more per couple may be charged for membership or entry to the party. There are estimated to be more than a dozen swinger clubs across Canada, from Dartmouth, Nova Scotia, to Prince George, British Columbia (McClelland, 1999). In 1998, a members-only swing club in Montreal was raided by police and the owner was charged with running a common bawdy house—that is, a place

---

[2]Swinging was originally called "wife-swapping." However, because of the sexist connotations of that term and the fact that women were often as eager to swap husbands as men were to swap wives, the more equitable "mate-swapping" or "swinging" was substituted.

"for the purpose of prostitution or the practice of acts of indecency." The Supreme Court eventually ruled that swinging is legal in Canada as long as it takes place in private and that "consensual sexual conduct behind code-locked doors can hardly be supposed to jeopardize a society as vigorous and tolerant as Canadian Society." A CROP poll found that 64 percent of Canadians (76 percent of Quebecers) were accepting of swingers' clubs. That is, swinging passes the community standards of tolerance test (see Chapter 17).

A man who frequently hosts parties describes what happens:

> A lot of people have the idea that swinger parties are big orgies, where everybody jumps on everybody else. It isn't that way. People are selective, like they are anyplace else. [It starts with the eyes.] So if the interest continues from eye contact to talking, and to desire, there's touching. You just go with it. So you go from talking to touching, and at a swinging party you can go from touching to bed. (Maurer, 1994, p. 120)

Swinging may be closed or open. In c*losed swinging*, the couples meet and exchange partners, and each pair goes off separately to a private place to have intercourse, returning to the meeting place at an agreed-upon time. In *open swinging*, the pairs get back together for sex in the same room for at least part of the time. In 75 percent of the cases, this includes the women having sex with each other, although two men having sex almost never occurs (Bartell, 1970; Gilmartin, 1975).

Figure 11.5 A mannequin hangs from the ceiling of this members-only swingers' club in Montreal, which was shut down by police in 1998. It later reopened after the Supreme Court ruled that swinging is legal in Canada as long as it takes place in private.

What kind of people are swingers? A review of 15 published studies, most of them involving small, convenience samples, concluded that the majority are upper or middle class, above average in education and income, and employed in the professions and in management (Jenks, 1998). Although one might expect them to be politically liberal, in one study only 27 percent described themselves as politically liberal—the rest were moderate or conservative (Jenks, 1985). The evidence indicates that at least two-thirds were raised in a religious home, but as adults they did not attend services and were not affiliated with a denomination.

Swinging appears to involve a small minority of people. Published estimates range from less than 1 to 2 percent, although none of these are current.

INTERNET INFIDELITY

The proliferation of websites designed to connect people looking for romantic or sexual partners, along with chat rooms and other forms of digital communication, has created new opportunities for people in committed relationships to engage in sexual activity with people other than their partner. A cyberaffair is a romantic or sexual relationship initiated by online contact and maintained primarily via online communication (Young et al., 2000). A new twist on cyberaffairs is when two people's avatars engage in sexual activity in virtual reality worlds such as Second Life. Most people think that people are unfaithful if they engage in cybersex with someone other than their partner, even if the two individuals never meet (Randall & Byers, 2003).

Cyberaffair: A romantic or sexual relationship initiated by online contact and maintained primarily via online communication.

There are some Internet sites set up specifically for people in relationships who wish to have affairs. Once a relationship is established online, contacts can turn into mutual erotic dialogue, which may be accompanied by masturbation. In some cases, the participants arrange to meet face-to-face and may then engage in sexual intimacy.

There has been little empirical study of cyberaffairs. Professionals engaged in relationship and sexual counselling report working with couples whose problems include loss of trust by one person over another's online relationships. Some partners define such a relationship as infidelity even if it did not involve sexual conversation or activity. Note that these can be heterosexual or same-sex couples, who are married, cohabiting, or "committed" to each other. An online survey of Internet users, recruited by a banner that appeared on a major Web portal, included questions about cybersex, the practice of engaging in sexual talk online. One-third of 1828 participants reported engaging in this activity; 46 percent of those reporting the activity—both men and women—said they were also in a committed relationship. Interestingly, those who reported engaging in cybersex reported more offline sexual partners (Daneback et al., 2005).

EQUITY AND EXTRADYADIC SEX

Social exchange theories are a type of social-psychological theory that have been used to explain sexuality in close relationships. Unlike most theories that focus on the individual, the social exchange perspective takes the interpersonal context in which most sexual activities occur into account (Byers & Wang, 2004). One such theory, **equity theory**, has been used to predict patterns of extradyadic sex (Hatfield, 1978).

Equity theory: A social exchange theory that states that people mentally calculate the benefits and costs for them in a relationship; their behaviour is then affected by whether they feel there is equity or inequity, and they will act to restore equity if there is inequity.

The basic idea in equity theory is that in a relationship, people mentally tabulate their inputs to it and what they get out of it (benefits or rewards); then they calculate whether these are equitable or not.

According to equity theory, if individuals perceive a relationship as inequitable (if they feel they are not getting what they deserve), they become distressed. The more inequitable the relationship, the more distressed they feel. In order to relieve the distress, they make attempts to restore equity in the relationship. For example, people who feel they are putting too much into a relationship and not getting enough out of it might let their appearance go, or not work as hard to earn money, or refuse to have sex or contribute to conversations. The idea is that such actions will restore equity.

If these equity processes do occur, they might help to explain patterns of extramarital sex. That is, engaging in extramarital sex would be a way of restoring equity in an inequitable relationship. Social psychologist Elaine Hatfield (1978) tested this notion. Her prediction was that people who felt underbenefited in their marriages (that is, they felt that there was an inequity and that they were not getting as much as they deserved) would be the ones to engage in extramarital sex. Confirming this notion, people who felt they were underbenefited began engaging in extramarital sex earlier in their marriages and had more extramarital partners than did people who felt equi-

Figure 11.6 Equitable sharing of household tasks—such as budgeting and paying bills—in a marriage. According to equity theory, if a person perceives that the marital relationship is inequitable and feels underbenefited, he or she is more likely to engage in extramarital sex.

tably treated or overbenefited. Apparently, feeling that one is not getting all one deserves in a marriage is related to engaging in extramarital sex. (As an aside, equitable marriages were rated as happier than inequitable ones.)

Equity theory includes rewards and costs of all kinds, as indicated by our examples. However, as noted earlier in this chapter, our perceptions of our *sexual* rewards and costs have a particular impact on our satisfaction (Lawrance & Byers, 1995). For example, people who, during sex, are happy with their communication with their partner, the level of affection, the frequency of specific techniques such as oral sex, and their ease in reaching orgasm are likely to be sexually satisfied. Individuals with a more favourable balance of sexual rewards to sexual costs are also more satisfied with the relationship in general. Greater sexual satisfaction, in turn, is associated with higher frequencies of affection and sexual behaviour, and fewer sexual concerns and problems.

Clearly, both our perceptions of equity and equality in our intimate relationships as well as our levels of sexual rewards and costs may affect our satisfaction with those relationships and the likelihood that we will become involved in extramarital (or extradyadic) sexuality.

EVOLUTION AND EXTRADYADIC SEX

Extradyadic sex is not unique to Canada. In fact, it occurs in virtually every society. When evolutionary psychologists observe a behaviour that occurs in all societies, they are inclined to explain that behaviour in terms of evolutionary processes. That is, some people engage in extradyadic sex because they carry in their genetic makeup something that motivates them to do so.

Why would some people carry these types of genes? From an evolutionary perspective, the genes that enable their bearers to produce larger numbers of offspring are more likely to survive from one generation to the next than genes that don't. A man who mates with one woman for life could produce a maximum of 6 to 12 offspring, depending on the length of time infants are breast-fed, postpartum sex taboos, and so on. If that same man occasionally has sex with a second woman (or a series of other women), he could produce 12 to 24 offspring. We think you get the picture. Historically, men who sought out other women produced more offspring, who in turn produced more offspring carrying the genetic makeup that leads to extradyadic liaisons (Fisher, 1992).

What about women? They cannot increase the number of their offspring by increasing the number of their sexual partners. However, there are ways in which having more than one sexual partner might have been biologically adaptive for women (Grailing & Buss, 2000). First, sexual liaisons with other men might have enabled a woman to acquire extra goods and services, that enhanced her offspring's chances for survival. Second, having another partner could serve as "insurance"; if her husband died, she would have another man to turn to for food, shelter, and protection. Third, a woman married to a timid, unproductive hunter could "upgrade her genetic line" by mating with another man. Finally, having children with multiple partners increases the genetic diversity of one's offspring, increasing the chances that some of them will survive. A study of 48 couples found that, as the number of similar genes at the *major histocompatibility complex* (the part of the human genetic system that has the most genes) increased, the number of extra-pair sexual partners they reported increased (Garver-Apgar et al., 2006); this suggests that couples with less genetic diversity are acting in ways that has the potential to increase the genetic diversity of their offspring.

Genetic research on species that appear to be monogamous reveals that some of the offspring being raised by a male–female pair were fathered by another male. These tests also reveal that females paired with lesser-quality males engage in extradyadic mating, whereas females paired with high-quality males do not (Morell, 1998). These results provide some support for the evolutionary hypothesis about the adaptive value of female infidelity,

POLYAMORY

Polyamory: The "non-possessive, honest, responsible and ethical philosophy and practice of loving multiple people simultaneously"; often referred to as poly.

Polyamory (often referred to as *poly*) is "the non-possessive, honest, responsible and ethical philosophy and practice of loving multiple people simultaneously" (Ve Ard & Veaux, 2003). You will notice that the definition is on love ("amory") rather than on sex, although polyamorous relationships typically are also sexual relationships. There are several forms of such relationships, including the *intentional family*, involving three or more persons; the *group relationship*, with committed, loving relationships involving three or more partners; and *group marriage*, involving three or more persons. One specific type of *group relationship* is a triad involving a married couple and an additional man or woman, all of whom share sexual intimacy; the third person and one or both members of the couple may be bisexual. Other arrangements involve two or more men and two or more women. Unlike the extradyadic affair, there is (ideally) full disclosure of the network of relationships to all participants. Unlike swinging, the emphasis is on long-term intimate relationships. Unlike polygyny, both men and women can have multiple partners. Thus, individuals in polyamorous relationships would not consider themselves to be either uncommitted or unfaithful (Ritchie & Barker, 2006). Such arrangements have even made it to popular television; you may be familiar with the television show *Big Love*, which depicts a man with three wives. What do Canadians think about people being able to have more than one marital partner at a time? Only 4 percent approve of it; an additional 16 percent do not approve but are willing to accept it (Bibby, 2004). That is, overall 80 percent of Canadians do not accept being married to more than one person; this figure is slightly lower, although still overwhelming negative, for younger Canadians.

Research involving in-depth interviews with 20 men and 20 women provided information about participants in one geographic area in the United States (Sheff, 2004). Those interviewed were in their mid-30s to late 50s, usually university educated, and employed in professional occupations; they were overwhelmingly white. Their high social status and access to resources may be a prerequisite for participating in the polyamory lifestyle. The interviewees noted that persons outside the polyamorous community, including members of their family of origin (parents, siblings), often react negatively and with hostility toward community members. Their status insulates them against some potential sanctions.

Women involved in polyamory report expanding their familial, gender, and sexual roles. For example, some of these women rejected monogamy in favour of a network of intimate partner relationships. With respect to gender roles, the women adopted a much more assertive style in their relationships with men. In the realm of sexuality, the women often recognized their high sex drive, the emotional and sexual value of intimacy with other women, and their bisexual interests or identities. Moving away from traditional roles was reported to be both liberating and frightening; creating new roles was often difficult.

In multi-ethnic settings such as Hong Kong, polyamorous relationships may cross ethnic, racial, and social class boundaries (Sik Ying Ho, 2006). For example, a 37-year-old woman described concurrent sexual relationships with both men and women, of different races and social classes. Such relationships provide novel experiences that may both be anxiety-provoking and expand one's understanding of sexual diversity.

Interestingly, research in British Columbia has shown that compared to other types of relationships, men and women in polyamorous relationships have higher testosterone levels (van Anders et al., 2007).

POSTMARITAL SEX

From the point of view of developmental psychologists, the sexual relationship in a second union, perhaps following a divorce or the death of one's partner, is especially interesting. In what ways is it the same, and how does it differ, from the sexual relationship in the first marriage? It represents the blending of things that are unique and consistent about the person with things that are unique to the new situation and new partner. As we develop sexually throughout the lifespan, these two strands continue to be intertwined—the developmental continuities (the things that are us and always will be) and the developmental changes (things that differ at various times in our lives, either because we are older or have experienced more, or because our partner or the situation is different).

THE DIVORCED AND THE WIDOWED

Almost all Canadians agree that ideally their marriage should last for the rest of their life (Bibby, 2006). Nonetheless, more than a third of Canadian marriages end in divorce. The younger people are when they marry, the more likely they are to divorce (Clark & Crompton, 2006). People who are divorced or widowed are in a somewhat unusual situation in that they are used to regular sexual expression and suddenly find themselves in a situation in which they no longer have a regular sexual partner. Partly recognizing this dilemma, our society places few restrictions on postmarital sexual activity, although it is not as approved as marital sex. However, among heterosexuals, divorced and widowed Canadians are least likely to be satisfied with their sex life; 51 percent are satisfied compared to 79 percent of people living with a partner and 75 percent of never-married individuals.

Most divorced women, but fewer widowed women, return to having an active sex life. A Canadian survey found that 25 percent of formerly married respondents had engaged in intercourse in the last seven days, compared to 72 percent of married and 45 percent of never-married participants (Gallup, 1988). An American study found that 77 percent of the widowed had not engaged in intercourse in the last year, compared with 29 percent of the divorced (Smith, 2003).

The lower incidence of postmarital sex among widows, compared with divorced women, is due in part to the fact that widows are, on the average, older than divorced women; but even when matched for age, widows are still less likely than divorcees to engage in postmarital sex. There are probably several reasons for this (Gebhard, 1968). Widows have the continuing social support system of in-laws and friends, and so they are less motivated to seek new friendships. There is also a belief that a widow should be loyal to her dead husband, and having a sexual relationship with another man is viewed as disloyalty. Many widows believe this or tell themselves that they will "never find another one like him." Widows are more likely to be financially secure than divorced women and therefore have less motivation for engaging in sex as a prelude to remarriage.

Divorced women face complex problems of adjustment (Song, 1991). These problems may include reduced income, a lower perceived standard of living, and reduced availability of social support. Some divorced men face similar problems. These problems may increase the motivation to establish a new long-term relationship.

Widowed and divorced women who have postmarital sex often begin a relationship within one year of the end of the marriage. Evidence from an American survey suggests that these are long-term relationships and that divorced men are more sexually active than divorced women (Stack & Gundlach, 1992). A survey of professional women who held teaching and administrative posts in academic institutions found that divorced women had a larger number of sexual partners and more frequent activity than their never-married counterparts (Davidson & Darling, 1988).

Earlier in this chapter we noted that substantial numbers of men and women cohabit. Like marriages, these relationships break up. What are the similarities and differences between formerly married and formerly cohabiting men and women? To answer this question, Wade and DeLamater (2002) used the NHSLS data to analyze the rate of acquisition of new partners following the dissolution of a relationship. The results indicate that these newly single men and women do not acquire new sexual partners at a high rate, and there were no significant differences between formerly married and formerly cohabiting men and women. Newly single persons acquire new partners at a significantly higher rate than single, never-married persons in the year following a breakup. Men with custody of children and men and women with low incomes have higher rates of new-partner acquisition, perhaps reflecting the impact of familial and economic instability associated with the dissolution. The results suggest that the post-dissolution experience is similar across various demographic groups; given the high rates of breaking up in Canada and the United States, dissolution may, we suggest, be considered a significant life stage with its own specific characteristics.

Elderly men and women may find the loss of a long-term partner emotionally traumatic, and may find it difficult or impossible establish a new relationship. They may also encounter resistance or hostility from their families, including their adult children, to any effort to find a new partner.

SEX AND OLDER ADULTS

When Freud suggested that young children, even infants, have sexual thoughts and feelings, his ideas met with considerable resistance. When, 50 years later, researchers began to suggest that elderly men and women also have sexual thoughts and feelings, there was similar resistance (Pfeiffer et al., 1968). This section deals with the sexual behaviour of older men and women, the physical changes they undergo, and the attitudes that influence them.

CHANGES IN WOMEN

PHYSICAL CHANGES

The climacteric is a period lasting about 15 or 20 years (from about ages 45 to 60) during which a woman's body makes the transition from being able to reproduce to not being able to reproduce; the climacteric is marked particularly by a decline in the functioning of the ovaries. But climacteric changes occur in many other body tissues and systems as well. **Menopause** (the "change of life," the "change") refers to one specific event in this process, the cessation of menstruation; this occurs, on average, over a two-year period beginning at around age 50 (with a normal menopause occurring anywhere between the ages of 40 and 60).

Biologically, as a woman grows older, the pituitary continues a normal output of FSH (follicle stimulating hormone) and LH (luteinizing hormone); however, as the ovaries age, they become less able to respond to the pituitary hormones. In addition, the brain—including the hypothalamus-pituitary unit—ages (Lamberts et al., 1997; Wise et al., 1996). With the aging of the ovaries, there is an accompanying decline in the output of their two major products: eggs and the sex hormones estrogen and progesterone. More specifically, the ovaries become less capable of responding to FSH by maturing and releasing an egg. The hormonal changes of menopause involve a decline in estrogen and progesterone levels and hormonal imbalance (see Figure 11.7).

Physical symptoms of menopause may include "hot flashes" or "hot flushes," headaches, and dizziness. For some women, a long-range effect of the decline in estrogen levels is *osteoporosis* (porous and brittle bones). The hot flash is probably the best known of the symptoms, particularly in Western cultures.

Menopause: The cessation of menstruation in middle age.

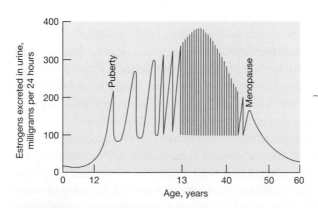

Figure 11.7 Levels of estrogen production in women across the lifespan.

Typically, it is described as a sudden wave of heat from the waist up. The woman may get red and perspire a lot; when the flush goes away, she may feel chilled and sometimes may shiver. The flashes may last from a few seconds to half an hour and occur several or many times a day. They may also occur at night, causing insomnia, and the resulting perspiration can soak the sheets. Research in Ontario also showed that women have poorer working memories after menopause. This appears to be due to decreased levels of estrogen; estrogen levels did not affect passive recall (Duff & Hampson, 2000).

Do all women experience these menopausal symptoms? About one-quarter of women do not experience hot flashes; 50 to 75 percent of women do, but the majority report that they are not bothered by them (Avis & McKinlay, 1995; McKinlay et al., 1992).

Hormone-replacement therapy (HRT) may be helpful to many menopausal women, particularly for relief of physical discomfort such as hot flashes and some sexual problems such as lack of vaginal lubrication. The treatment today typically includes both estrogen and progesterone. A recent U.S. study found that long-term use of HRT increased the risk of coronary heart disease, strokes, heart attacks, and breast cancer but reduced the risk of colorectal cancer and hip and other fractures due to osteoporosis (Writing Group for the Women's Health Initiative Investigators, 2002). There was no difference in overall mortality. However, short-term use of HRT for one or two years for the management of severe menopausal symptoms is safe for most women according to the Society of Obstetricians and Gynaecologists of Canada (SOGC, 2006). Naturopathic therapy, including black cohosh and red clover, may be effective in treating mild menopausal symptoms (Cramer et al., 2003; SOGC, 2006).

The latest development in HRT is the so-called "designer estrogens" or "tissue-specific estrogens" (Fuleihan, 1997). They are intended to provide the beneficial effects of traditional HRT without increasing the risk of breast and endometrial cancer. It is too soon to know their long-term effects on coronary heart disease, osteoporosis, and cancer. Nonetheless, a short-term, two-year study of raloxifene (one of these drugs) indicated that it increased bone density and lowered total cholesterol levels, yet it did not stimulate the endometrium—precisely the intended effects (Delmas et al., 1997). These drugs hold much promise for the future (Basson, 2007).

The decline in estrogen around menopause results in several changes in the sexual organs. The walls of the vagina, which are thick and elastic during the reproductive years, become thin and inelastic. Because the walls of the vagina are now thinner, they cannot absorb the pressure from the thrusting penis as they once did, and thus nearby structures such as the bladder and urethra may be irritated. As a result, older women may have an urgent need to urinate immediately after intercourse. Furthermore, the vagina shrinks in both width and length, and the labia majora also shrink; thus there is a constriction at the entrance to the vagina, that may make penile insertion somewhat more difficult, and the vagina may be less able to accommodate the size of a fully erect penis. By about five years after menopause, the amount of vaginal lubrication has decreased noticeably. Intercourse can then become somewhat more difficult and painful, a problem easily solved with lubricant or local estrogen therapy (SOGC, 2006). The lack of estrogen also causes the vagina to become less acidic, which leaves it more vulnerable to infections. Lest these changes sound discouraging, it is important to note that some women report that sex is even better after menopause.

Because of hormonal changes, the contractions of the uterus that occur during orgasm can become painful, to the point where the woman avoids sexual activity. Nonetheless, the woman has the same physical capacity for arousal and orgasm at 80 that she did at 30. For example, researchers in British Columbia examined premenopausal and postmenopausal women's physiological and subjective arousal to an erotic film and found no differences between the two groups (Brotto & Gorzalka, 2002).

It also appears that these changes are related in part to sexual activity—or, rather, to the lack of it. A study of healthy women with a male partner between 60 and 70 years of age found consistent differences between the 39 women who were sexually active and the 20 women who were not (Bachmann & Leiblum, 1991). Those who were sexually active reported having intercourse an average of five times per month. They reported having higher levels of sexual desire, greater comfort about expressing their sexual needs, and greater sexual satisfaction. A pelvic exam by a physician who was unaware of which women were sexually active found less genital atrophy in the sexually active women. These are correlational data, so we cannot be sure what is cause and what is effect.

One study analyzed the data from an American Association of Retired Persons (AARP) survey of persons age 45 and older (DeLamater & Moorman, 2007). The AARP survey included questions about various factors that might affect the frequency of sexual behaviour, including physical limitations such as prior stroke and arthritis, emotional problems such as depression, and use of various medications. Although some men and women reported these conditions, they were relatively uncommon and were not significantly related to the frequency of oral sexual activity or vaginal intercourse. The factors that were significantly related were high scores on an index of sexual desire (frequent sexual thoughts, desire), positive attitudes toward sex for oneself, and the presence of a partner with no limitations related to sexuality. Men and women who reported that their partner had limitations that interfered with sexual expression were significantly more likely to report masturbating.

Hysterectomy (hiss-tur-EK-tuh-mee): Surgical removal of the uterus.

Oophorectomy (OH-uh-fuh-REK-tuh-mee): Surgical removal of the ovaries.

Some people believe that having a **hysterectomy** means the end of a woman's sex life. In fact, sex hormone production is not affected as long as the ovaries are not removed (surgical removal of the ovaries is called **oophorectomy** or ovariectomy). The majority of women report that a hysterectomy has no effect on their sex lives. However, approximately one-third of women who have had hysterectomies report problems with sexual response (Zussman et al., 1981). There are two possible physiological causes for these problems. If the ovaries have been removed, hormonal changes may be responsible; the ovaries produce androgens, and they may play a role in sexual response. Alternatively, hysterectomy may change the sexual response if the cervix serves as a trigger for orgasm or if contractions of the uterus contribute to sexual pleasure.

PSYCHOLOGICAL CHANGES

Psychological problems that have been associated with menopause include depression, irritability, anxiety, and cognitive symptoms such as inability to concentrate and memory problems.

One authoritative review concluded that menopause does *not* increase the rate of depression (Stanton et al., 2002). And the Massachusetts Women's Health Study found that 85 percent of women were never depressed during the menopausal years, 10 percent were depressed occasionally, and just 5 percent were persistently depressed (Golub, 1992). Research is inconsistent and inconclusive as to whether there are significant cognitive symptoms (Stanton et al., 2002).

CHANGES IN MEN

PHYSICAL CHANGES

Although people use the term "male menopause," in the technical sense men do not experience a "menopause"; never having menstruated, they can scarcely cease menstruating. However, men do experience a very gradual decline in the manufacture of both testosterone and sperm by the testes, a mild version of the climacteric process in women (see Figure 11.8). Some refer to this time of life as **andropause**, referring to declining levels of androgens (Lamberts et al., 1997). Others prefer the term ADAM, for *androgen decline in the aging male* (Morales et al., 2000). Some experts argue that a low testosterone syndrome occurs in some older men and that testosterone treatments are beneficial, although this approach is controversial (Jan & Culberson, 2003).

Andropause: The time of declining androgen levels in middle-aged men. The male version of menopause. Also called ADAM (androgen decline in the aging male).

Vascular diseases such as hardening of the arteries are increasingly common with age in men, which may cause erection problems because good circulation is essential to erection (Riportella-Muller, 1989). A major change is that erections occur more slowly. It is important for men to know that this is a perfectly natural slowdown so that they will not jump to the conclusion that they are developing an erection problem. It is also important for partners to know about this so that they will use effective techniques of stimulating the man and will not mistake slowness for lack of interest.

The refractory period lengthens with age; thus for an elderly man, there may be a period of 24 hours after an orgasm during which he cannot get an erection. (Note that women do not

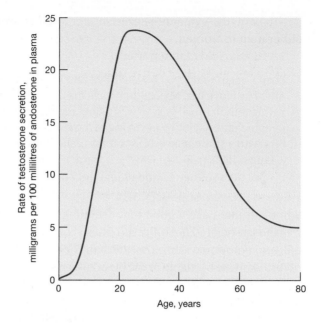

Figure 11.8 Levels of testosterone production in men across the lifespan.

undergo a similar change; most women do not enter into a refractory period and are still capable of multiple orgasm at age 80.) Other signs of sexual excitement—the sex flush and muscle tension—diminish with age.

The volume of the ejaculate gradually decreases, and the force of ejaculation lessens. The testes become somewhat smaller, but viable sperm are produced by even very old men. Ninety-year-old men have been known to father children.

One advantage is that middle-aged and elderly men may have better control over orgasm than young men; thus they can prolong sexual intercourse and may be better sexual partners.

A study of healthy men, ages 45 to 74, all married, assessed their biological, psychological, and behavioural functioning (Schiavi et al., 1994). Erectile problems, low sexual information, and low marital adjustment were associated with lower general satisfaction. Accurate information is important because it may result in more realistic expectations for sexual performance.

One of the most common physical problems for middle-aged and older men is non-cancerous enlargement of the prostate gland, which is believed to be related to changes in hormone levels. Enlargement of the prostate causes urination problems; there is difficulty in voluntarily initiating urination, as well as frequent nocturnal urination. These symptoms are usually remedied by surgery to remove the part of the gland pressing against the urethra. Unfortunately, complications of the surgery include retrograde ejaculation in about 65 percent of men and erection problems in about 10 percent (American Urological Association Practice Guidelines Committee. 2003). New treatments have recently been developed to avoid these problems, including anti-androgen drugs and laser treatments.

Some people believe that prostate surgery or removal of the prostate (**prostatectomy**) means the end of a man's sex life. It is true that the volume of the ejaculate will decrease. Prostatectomy can cause damage to the nerves supplying the penis, creating erectile problems. In other cases, retrograde ejaculation may result. Whether there are such problems depends on which of several available methods of surgery is used. Radiation, used in treating prostate cancer, may result in erectile dysfunction. Unfortunately, many men equate sex with sexual intercourse and stop engaging in all sexual activity if they develop erection difficulties as a result of prostate surgery or radiation.

Prostatectomy (pros-tuh-TEK-tuh-mee): Surgical removal of the prostate.

In sum, the evidence suggests that there need be no time limit on sexual expression for either men or women.

A 73-year-old man reported:

> I can't begin to tell you how happy I am. I am married to a wonderful woman who loves me as much as I love her. My children gave me a hard time of it at first, especially because she is a bit younger than me. [My son] was telling me that marrying again and trying to have a lot of sex—imagine that, saying to me trying to have sex—could be dangerous to the marriage. So, I said to him with a straight face, "Do you think she'll survive it?" He was so shocked, he laughed. (Janus & Janus, 1993, p. 8)

PSYCHOLOGICAL CHANGES

Some authors have argued that declining levels of testosterone in middle-aged and elderly men are associated not only with physical symptoms but also with a number of cognitive, sexual, and emotional symptoms (Urban, 1992). However, research has shown that the amount of testosterone available in the blood was not an important determinant of cognitive, psychological, or sexual functioning or quality of life in a group of men aged 55 to 76 (Tamir, 1982).

ATTITUDES ABOUT SEX AND OLDER ADULTS

Our society has a negative attitude toward sexual expression among older adults. People are uncomfortable with the idea of two 70-year-old people having sex with each other, and even more uncomfortable with the thought of a 70-year-old masturbating. These negative attitudes become particularly obvious in nursing homes, where staff members may frown on sexual activity among the residents. Somehow what is "virility" at 25 becomes "lechery" at 75. Attitudes toward sexual expression in gay, lesbian, and bisexual individuals may be even more negative, given that they face stigma associated with both their sexual orientation and their age. Some are forced to go back in the closet when they move to nursing homes.

Cross-cultural research indicates that the sexual behaviour of older adults is related to these cultural expectations (Winn & Newton, 1982). Older adults continue to be sexually active in 70 percent of societies and in precisely those societies where they are expected to be sexually active. Indeed, in 22 percent of societies, women are expected to become more uninhibited about sexuality when they become older.

Why does our society have such negative attitudes toward sex among older adults? In part, these attitudes are due to the fact that ours is a youth-oriented culture. We value youth, and the physical characteristics that are considered "sexy" are youthful ones, such as a trim, firm body and smooth skin. It is therefore hard to believe that someone with old, wrinkled skin could be sexually active. According to one youthful-looking 59-year-old woman:

> No one looks at me today with any kind of sexual interest. I mean, I don't even get the time of day from any man. I'm an older woman. I want men to be aggressive now. I'm not going to approach a man, because I'm afraid to be rejected. So I've just given up. (Maurer, 1994, p. 475)

A study of heterosexual, midlife women assessed menopausal status, self-rated attractiveness, sexual desire, and frequency of sexual intercourse (Koch et al., 2005). Regardless of menopausal status, women who perceived themselves as less attractive than ten years earlier reported a decline in both sexual desire and sexual behaviour. Women who perceived themselves as more attractive reported an increase in sexual desire, frequency of sex, and frequency of orgasm. This study demonstrates a link between feelings of attractiveness and sexual behaviour. Of course, because these data are correlational, it is not known whether changes in feelings of attractiveness caused the decline in sexual desire and behaviour.

Our negative attitudes may be a holdover from the belief that sex was for reproductive purposes only—and those past the age of reproduction should therefore not engage in it

(Pfeiffer, 1975). The incest taboo may also be involved in our negative attitudes. We tend to identify older people with our parents or grandparents, and find it hard to think of them as sexual beings. This attitude is encouraged by the fact that many parents take great pains to hide their sexual activity from their children.

These attitudes affect the way older people are treated, and older adults, whether gay or straight, may hold such attitudes themselves (Badeau & Bergeron, 1997). The current generation of older people was raised in a time in which they had little access to accurate sex information and myths about sexuality in older adults were common. Thus, older people today may be particularly affected by their own negative attitudes. For example, a Montreal study found that older men had less tolerant views about sexual expression in older people than did middle-aged men (Libman, 1989). One remedy that has been proposed for these negative attitudes is a "coming out of the closet"; as one 67-year-old commented:

> The common view that the aging and aged are nonsexual, I believe, can only be corrected by a dramatic and courageous process—the *coming-out-of-the-closet* of sexually active older women and men, so that people can see for themselves what the later years are really like. (Brecher, 1984, p. 21)

Various specific misunderstandings may influence sexuality. For example, a man might believe that sex will precipitate a heart attack or, if he has already had a heart attack, that it will bring on another one. Although heart rate accelerates during sexual intercourse, the mean heart rate during orgasm is only 117 beats per minute, which is about that attained during many common forms of daily exercise (Hellerstein & Friedman, 1969). This rate is about the equivalent of climbing two flights of stairs at a moderate pace. Thus, the demands of sex on the heart are not unreasonable. A study of patients who had had a heart attack questioned them about their activities immediately prior to the attack and in the year prior to the attack (Muller et al., 1996). The results indicate that the increase in risk caused by sexual activity is one chance in a million for a healthy individual. Furthermore, the relative risk is no greater in patients with a history of cardiac disease.

Some men also mistakenly believe that sexual activity saps their "vital strength." In some cases men may believe that they can have only a fixed number of orgasms during their lifetime (as a woman is born with a fixed number of ova) and therefore adopt a strategy of saving them now so that they will have some left later on. One woman wrote:

> My husband has reached the age of sixty-five. He has decided that, in order to ensure a longer life and health, he will no longer engage in sex activity. He is convinced that intercourse and the emission of semen are quite debilitating, particularly in his years. (Rubin, 1966, p. 258)

Ideas such as this, as well as factors such as illness or hospitalization, may lead to a period of sexual inactivity. But being sexually inactive is one of the most effective ways of diminishing sexuality. Masters and Johnson emphasized that two factors are critical in maintaining sexual capacity in old age:

1. *Good physical and mental health.* An excellent study confirms this notion (Persson, 1980). A representative sample of 70-year-olds in one town in Sweden was selected, and 85 percent agreed to participate in the detailed interviews. In the entire sample, 46 percent of the men and 16 percent of the women still had sexual intercourse; when only those who were currently married were considered, the figures rose to 52 percent for men and 36 percent for women. For both men and women, those who continued to have sexual intercourse had better mental health as rated by a psychiatrist and more positive attitudes toward sexual activity among older adults.
2. *Regularity of sexual expression.* As was noted earlier, evidence exists that some physical changes of the sex organs in old age are related to sexual inactivity. As the saying goes, "If

you don't use it, you lose it." In fact, the results of a longitudinal study suggest that, for men, frequency of orgasm is positively associated with longevity. The study involved men aged 45 to 59. At the beginning of the study, the men completed a standard medical history and a questionnaire that assessed sexual behaviour. Ten years later, the researchers found out who had died, and compared their questionnaire answers with those of the survivors. Men who reported fewer than one orgasm per month at the beginning of the study were more than twice as likely to die as the men who reported two orgasms per month (Smith et al., 1997). Of course, these data are correlational (see Chapter 3), so we cannot conclude that more frequent sexual expression causes men to live longer.

Apparently, some older people have caught on to this fact. As one 80-year-old husband said of his relationship with his 75-year-old wife,

> My wife and I both believe that keeping active sexually delays the aging process . . . if we are troubled with an erection or lubrication, we turn to oral methods or masturbation of each other. We keep our interest alive by a great deal of caressing and fondling of each other's genitals. We feel it is much better to wear out than to rust out. (Brecher, 1984, p. 33)

Reformers urge us to change our attitudes about sex and older adults. Nursing homes particularly need to revise their practices and staff need to become more comfortable discussing sexuality with residents. Changes such as knocking before entering a resident's room would help (people masturbate, you know). Other reforms would include making provisions for partners to stay overnight and allowing couples—married or unmarried—to share a bedroom.

Figure 11.9 In most cultures, older adults continue to be sexually active. This is particularly true in cultures that have positive views of sexuality and aging.

SEXUAL BEHAVIOUR OF OLDER ADULTS

Relationship satisfaction tends to be higher in older couples than in middle-aged couples (Gagnon et al., 1999). This may be because older couples engage in more positive and fewer negative interactions than their younger counterparts, perhaps because they are able to give more attention to their partner after the children have grown up. In turn, relationship satisfaction is closely linked to sexual satisfaction.

Sexual behaviour and sexual interest do decline somewhat with age. For example, a Montreal study found that 27 percent of men and women over 60 reported that sex did not interest them very much, whereas only 5 percent of participants under 60 responded this way (Trudel, 2002). Nonetheless, there are still substantial numbers of older men and women who have active sex lives, even in their 80s. In a sample of healthy 80- to 102-year-olds, 62 percent of the men and 30 percent of the women reported that they still engaged in sexual intercourse (Bretschneider & McCoy, 1988). There does not seem to be any age beyond which all people are sexually inactive.

Figure 11.10   Romance is important for many nursing-home residents.

Some older people do, for various reasons, stop having intercourse after a certain age. For women, this occurs most often in their late 50s and early 60s, while it occurs somewhat later for men (Pfeiffer et al., 1968). This is often connected to health issues (Clarke, 2006). Contrary to what one might expect, when a heterosexual couple stop having intercourse, the husband is most frequently the cause; both wives and husbands agree that this is true. For example, a Montreal study found that among older couples, age was not related to sexual frequency (Creti & Libman, 1989). However, couples in which the man lacked confidence in his own sexual response and sexual functioning had sex less frequently than other couples. The decline in women's sexual expression with age may be directly related to their male partner's decline in health.

Death of a spouse is more likely to put an end to sexual activity with a partner for women than it is for men, in part because there are far more older women than older men. Because of both men's earlier mortality and their preference for younger women, older women are more likely to be living alone and to have less access to sexual partners. Men aged 65 and older are much more likely to live with a spouse or partner than are women in that age group. For example, in the 2006 Canadian Census, among those 65 to 74, 60 percent of the women and 88 percent of the men were living with a spouse or common-law partner. Similarly, among those aged 75 to 84, 36 percent of the women and 72 percent of the men were living with a partner. Some innovative solutions have been proposed, such as elderly women forming lesbian relationships. Of course, some widowed women remarry. A British Columbia study of remarried older women found that many of them described strong sexual chemistry and a passionate sex life with their second husband that was often better than their early sexual experiences. As one woman who remarried at the age of 72 said:

There was an incredible chemical reaction with my second husband, for both of us. Quite different from the first marriage which evolves . . . there was an absolute click. Absolutely incredible!

I mean, at that age. It was like a couple of teenagers. I can't tell you. Um, oh, we had a lot of fun. (Clarke, 2006, p. 132).

A Montreal study of 144 married men ranging in age from 51 to 80 and 71 of their female spouses provides some data on how age affects sexual expression (Libman 1989). All participants were in good health and all the men had previously undergone one of two non–life-threatening surgical procedures. The sample was divided into younger (under 65) and older (age 65 and older) groups. The two groups did not differ in their frequency of sexual activity or in their satisfaction with their sex lives—both groups were generally satisfied. However, the older men and women experienced a desire for sex less often and the older men had more concerns about erectile difficulties (erectile difficulties themselves were infrequent in both male age groups, about 15 percent of the time).

The best survey to date on the sexuality of older adults was conducted in the United States in 2004 (Tessler Lindau et al., 2007). This study interviewed 3005 adults between the ages of 57 and 85. The authors used a nationally representative probability sample of people dwelling in the community; 75 percent of the people who were contacted agreed to participate. Since older adults who are sick or in care facilities are unlikely to have completed the survey, we must regard this as a survey of older adults who are above average in health and who are doubtless more sexually active than some older adults. In addition, few gay men and lesbians completed the survey, so the data apply only to heterosexual individuals. Indeed, there is little research on the effects of aging on same-sex sexual relationships. Nonetheless, it is a very important source of information about sex and older heterosexual adults, a topic about which there is a shortage of knowledge.

Some statistics from the survey, presented by age group, are included in Table 11.3. Note that women over 60 are much less likely to have a sexual partner available, so the women reported much lower frequencies of partnered activities than the men did. For both men and women, the likelihood of having engaged in sexual activity with a partner declined with age. Of those in the 64–74 age group who had engaged in sexual activity, about two-thirds had engaged in intercourse at least weekly and half had engaged in oral sex. Among individuals who had engaged in sexual activity, the frequency of sex was lower among those who were 75

Table 11.3	Sexual Activity in a Sample of Persons Aged 57 to 85		
Women	*57 to 64* *(492)*	*65 to 74* *(545)*	*75 to 85* *(513)*
Sexual activity with partner in last 12 months	61.6%	39.5%	16.7%
Have sexual activity at least once a week*	62.6%	65.4%	54.1%
Vaginal–penile intercourse*	86.8%	85.4%	74.4%
Oral sex*	52.7%	46.5%	35.0%
Masturbate in last 12 months	31.6%	21.9%	16.4%
Lack of interest in sexual activity in last 12 months	44.2%	38.4%	49.3%
Men	*(528)*	*(547)*	*(380)*
Sexual activity with partner in previous 12 months	83.7%	67.0%	38.5%
Have sexual activity at least once a week*	67.5%	65.4%	54.2%
Vaginal–penile intercourse*	91.1%	78.5%	83.5%
Oral sex*	62.1%	47.9%	28.3%
Masturbate in last 12 months	63.4%	53.0%	27.9%
Lack of interest in sexual activity in last 12 months	28.2%	28.5%	24.2%

*Of people who had engaged in sexual activity within the preceding 12 months.

Source: Tessler Lindau et al., 2007.

to 85 years of age, and one-third had engaged in oral sex. The frequency of masturbation also decreased with age, and was higher for men than for women. Having a current partner did not affect the likelihood of having masturbated in the previous 12 months.

About half of the respondents reported having at least one bothersome sexual problem. Erectile difficulties, reported by 37 percent of the men, were the most common problem for men. Low desire, reported by 43 percent of the women, was the most common problem reported by women. As shown in Table 11.3, about one-quarter of the men also reported a lack of interest in sex. Most men and women described sexual activity as an important part of their life.

We see, then, that many older people who are healthy engage in a range of sexual activities with a partner and consider sex an important part of their life.

SUMMARY

Sexuality continues to develop throughout the lifespan. It may be expressed in being single, cohabitation, common-law relationships, marriage, extradyadic relationships, relationships following divorce, or in a variety of contexts as the individual ages.

Young adults grow toward sexual maturity. Many do so in the context of a single relationship that results in marriage. Others are involved in two or more relationships before they begin to live with or marry someone. Never-married people over 30 may find themselves part of the "singles scene."

Cohabitation is a stage that up to 40 percent of people experience. People in Quebec are more likely to live common-law than are other Canadians. The time couples spend living together varies from a few months to several years. Sixty percent of cohabiting couples marry. Some cohabiting couples have children, either together or with previous partners. Men and women who are living together engage in sexual activity more often, on average, than those who are married or dating.

Marriage represents a major turning point as couples face new responsibilities and problems, and try to find time for each other. Married opposite-sex couples in their 20s engage in sexual intercourse two or three times per week on average, with the frequency declining to two or three times per month among couples over age 60. Perhaps the most dramatic change in marital sex practices in recent decades is the increased popularity of oral–genital sex. Many married people continue to masturbate. Most people today—both women and men—express general satisfaction with their marital sex life. Sexual patterns in marriage, however, show great variability. There are no data on the sexual activity of married same-sex couples.

Between 14 and 25 percent of heterosexual married men and between 7 and 15 percent of married women engage in extramarital sex at some time. Extramarital sex is disapproved of in our society and is generally carried on in secrecy. In a few cases, it is agreed that both husband and wife can have extramarital sex, as in open marriage, swinging, and polyamory. Equity theory and the sociobiological perspective may be helpful in understanding patterns of extramarital sex.

Virtually all widowed and divorced men return to an active sex life, as do most divorced women and about half of widowed women. A particular set of sexual norms characterizes the divorce subculture.

Research indicates that gay men have modified their sexual practices somewhat in the AIDS era. They have reduced their number of partners and have shifted away from risky sex practices. Among heterosexuals, there is some evidence of a reduction in the number of partners, and slight improvements in condom use.

The climacteric is the period in middle age during which the functioning of the ovaries (both hormone and egg production) declines gradually. One symptom of this process is menopause, the

Continued on next page.

SUMMARY *cont.*

cessation of menstruation. Physical symptoms, such as hot flashes, during this period result from declining levels of estrogen, and severe symptoms may be relieved by short-term use of hormone-replacement therapy. Contrary to popular belief, research does not show an increased incidence of depression at the time of menopause. Changes in sexual functioning across the menstrual cycle and at menopause are most likely related to changes in levels of testosterone.

Men experience a much more gradual decline in the functioning of their gonads leading to decreasing levels of testosterone and sperm production. Men and women may experience a psychological transition in middle age.

While sexual activity declines somewhat with age, it is perfectly possible to remain sexually active into one's 80s or 90s. Problems with sex or the cessation of intercourse may be related to physical factors. In women, declining estrogen levels result in a thinner, less elastic vagina and less lubrication; in men, there is lowered testosterone production and increased vascular disease, combined with slower erections and longer refractory periods. Psychological factors can also be involved, such as the belief that the elderly cannot or should not have sex. Masters and Johnson emphasized that two factors are critical to maintaining sexual capacity in old age: good physical and mental health, and regularity of sexual expression. A recent survey indicates that most older people who are healthy engage in sexual activity with a partner and consider it an important part of their life.

QUESTIONS FOR THOUGHT, DISCUSSION, AND DEBATE

1. What is your response when you see an elderly couple expressing affection physically with each other, perhaps kissing or holding hands? Why do you think you respond that way?

2. What is your opinion about extradyadic sex? Is it ethical or moral? What are its effects on a relationship—does it destroy or improve it, or perhaps have no effect?

3. If you are currently in a relationship, in what ways is your relationship characteristic of distressed couples? In what ways is it characteristic of non-distressed couples? What changes can you make to improve your relationship satisfaction?

4. You and your partner are talking about establishing a long-term relationship. Your partner says that his main concern is that living together will lead to a decline in how often you have sex. Is that a realistic concern? If so, what could the two of you do to prevent that from occurring?

5. Among the Yoruba of West Africa, younger women may not travel or engage in trade, but older (postmenopausal) women may. Among the Winnebago of North America, old women sit with men; they are considered to be the same as men. In some cultures, then, women gain in freedom and status after menopause. Does this happen for most women in Canada? Are there variations among ethnic groups in Canada—for example, Aboriginals, blacks, Asians, whites—in the way a postmenopausal woman is viewed and treated? Are there differences between anglophones and francophones? (For more information, see Golub, 1992.)

SUGGESTIONS FOR FURTHER READING

Barbach, Lonnie. (1993). *The pause: Positive approaches to menopause.* New York: Dutton. Barbach, a well-known therapist and author, provides many details about menopausal symptoms and positive ways to cope with them.

Brecher, Edward M. (1984). *Love, sex, and aging.* Mount Vernon, NY: Consumers Union. This large-scale survey offers a liberated view of sexuality in the elderly.

Fisher, Helen. (1992). *Anatomy of love: The mysteries of mating, marriage, and why we stray.* New York: Fawcett Columbine. This book presents a provocative, sociobiological account of human sexual behaviour, including extramarital sex.

Golub, Sharon. (1992). *Periods: From menarche to menopause.* Newbury Park, CA: Sage. This book, by a well-known researcher in the field, tells you everything you always wanted to know about menstruation and menopause.

Gould, Terry (1999). *The lifestyle: A look at the erotic rites of swingers.* Toronto: Vintage Canada. This book, written by a Vancouver-based investigative journalist, describes the lifestyle of people who engage in swinging and polyamory.

Maurer, Harry. (1994). *Sex: Real people talk about what they really do.* New York: Penguin Books. Maurer interviewed 52 people of diverse ages, preferences, and orientations about their sexual experiences. He presents lengthy excerpts organized around themes, such as Awakenings, Wild Oats, and the Long Haul.

Sarrel, Lorna, and Sarrel, Philip. (1984). *Sexual turning points: The seven stages of adult sexuality.* New York: Macmillan. This book, written for a general audience, provides an interesting theory of adult sexual development.

For review questions, web resources, and other learning and study tools, visit the *Understanding Human Sexuality* Online Learning Centre at www.mcgrawhill.ca/olc/hyde.

Chapter
12

ATTRACTION, LOVE, AND COMMUNICATION

Chapter Highlights

> THE INTIMACY IN SEX IS NEVER ONLY PHYSICAL. IN A SEXUAL RELATIONSHIP WE MAY DISCOVER WHO WE ARE IN WAYS OTHERWISE UNAVAILABLE TO US, AND AT THE SAME TIME WE ALLOW OUR PARTNER TO SEE AND KNOW THAT INDIVIDUAL. AS WE UNVEIL OUR BODIES, WE ALSO DISCLOSE OUR PERSONS.*

Many people believe that there is (or should be) a close connection between love and sex. The sexual standard of today for many is that sex is appropriate if one loves the other person (see Chapter 10). Of course, sex and love do not necessarily go together. Some people have satisfying sexual relationships without emotional involvement; other people are in love with a person with whom they do not have a sexual relationship. Nonetheless, for most people emotional passion and sexual passion are closely linked—without the sexual passion, we might be more likely to think of the person as a friend. People want to express their loving feelings to their romantic partner in a sexual way. Lovemaking, in turn, contributes to their feelings of love. In short, sex is a logical and emotional part of most romantic relationships. Therefore, it is important in a text on sexuality to spend some time considering the emotion we link so closely to sex: love. Unfortunately, much of the research on love has been restricted to studying male–female relationships and has not included same-sex relationships.

This chapter is organized in terms of the way relationships usually progress—if they progress. We begin by talking about attraction, what brings people together in the first place. Then we consider intimacy, which develops as relationships develop. Next, we look at five different views of what love is. We discuss some of the research on love, including cross-cultural research. Finally, we conclude with one of the requirements for fulfilling, long-term relationships—communication.

ATTRACTION

What causes you to be attracted to another person? Some people are attracted only to men, some only to women, some to both, and some to neither, so gender is an important component of attraction. Sexual orientation, including its causes, is discussed in Chapter 14, so it is not discussed here. However, social psychologists have done extensive research on interpersonal attraction, mostly of heterosexuals. We consider the major results of this research in this section.

THE GIRL NEXT DOOR

Our opportunities to meet people are limited by geography and time. You may meet that attractive person sitting two rows in front of you in "human sex," as the course is referred to at the University of New Brunswick, but you are unlikely to meet the wealthy, brilliant engineering student who sits in your seat two classes later. You are much more likely to meet and be attracted to the boy or girl next door than the one who lives across town. A 1988 COMPAS poll asked participants where they met their current dating partner. More than half met through friends (33 percent), at school (12 percent), through family (3 percent), or through religious settings (3 percent).

Among those who work in the same place or take the same class, we tend to be more attracted to people with whom we have had contact several times than we are to people with whom we have had little contact. This tendency has been demonstrated in laboratory studies

*Dr. Thomas Moore, "Soul mates," *Psychology Today*, March–April 1001, downloaded from http://faculty.uccb.ns.ca/pmacintyre/psych365/quotes.htm.

Mere-exposure effect:
The tendency to like a
person more if we have
been exposed to him or
her repeatedly.

in which the amount of contact between participants was systematically varied. At the end of the session, people gave higher "liking" ratings to those with whom they had had much contact and lower ratings to those with whom they had had little contact (Saegert et al., 1973). This is the mere-exposure effect; repeated exposure to any stimulus, including a person, leads to greater liking for that stimulus (Bornstein, 1989). For this reason, the chance of a man falling in love with the "girl [or boy] next door" is greater than the chance of falling in love with someone he seldom meets.

BIRDS OF A FEATHER

Homophily: The tendency
to have contact with
people who are equal in
social status.

We tend to like people who are similar to us. We are attracted to people who are approximately the same as we are in age, ethnicity, background, and economic and social status. Similarity on these social characteristics is referred to as homophily, the tendency to have contact with people equal in social status. Data on homophily from the NHSLS are displayed in Table 12.1. Note that the greatest homophily is by race/ethnicity, followed by education and age. Couples are least likely to be the same on religion. It is interesting that short-term partnerships are as homophilous as marriages and common-law relationships. These data take a somewhat liberal view of educational homophily. However, educational homophily has been increasing, and currently 54 percent of Canadian couples have the same educational level (Hou & Myles, 2007). How important is homophily to Canadians? Almost one-half (46 percent) prefer a spouse who shares their religious views and about a third (34 percent) prefer a spouse who shares their ethnic background (COMPAS, 2005). One of the reasons for homophily by ethnicity is that persons from ethnocultural minorities have tended to live in socially and economically separate communities. In communities where different racial groups have coexisted for generations, such as Nova Scotia, there tend to be more interracial relationships.

Table 12.1   Percentage of Relationships That Are Homophilous, by Type of Relationship

Type of Homophily	Type of Relationship			
	Marriages*	Cohabitations*	Long-Term Partnerships	Short-Term Partnerships
Racial/ethnic	93%	88%	89%	91%
Age[†]	78	75	76	83
Educational[‡]	82	87	83	87
Religious[§]	72	53	56	60

*Percentages of marriages and cohabitational relationships that began in the 10 years prior to the survey.
[†]Age homophily is defined as a difference of no more than five years in partners' ages.
[‡]Educational homophily is defined as a difference of no more than one educational category. The educational categories used were less than high school, high school graduate, vocational training, four-year college, and graduate degree.
[§]Cases in which either partner was reported as "other" or had missing data are omitted.
Source: Laumann et al., 1994, Table 6.4.

Social psychologist Donn Byrne (1971) has done numerous experiments demonstrating that we are attracted to people whose attitudes and opinions are similar to ours. In these experiments, Byrne typically has people fill out an opinion questionnaire. They are then shown a questionnaire that was supposedly filled out by another person and are asked to rate how much they think they would like that person. In fact, the questionnaire was filled out to show either high or low agreement with the participant's responses. Participants report more liking for a person whose responses are similar to theirs than for one whose responses are quite different. The relationship between similarity and liking may also work in the opposite direction. Research in Manitoba showed that the more satisfied individuals are with their relationship, the more they assume the other person is similar to them (Morry, 2007).

Folk sayings are sometimes wise and sometimes foolish. The interpersonal-attraction research indicates that the saying "Birds of a feather flock together" contains some truth. This tendency for men and women to choose as partners people who match them on social and personal characteristics is called the matching phenomenon (Feingold, 1988).

Despite the saying that "opposites attract," dissimilar attitudes tend to cause disliking, not liking (Pilkington & Lydon, 1997; Rosenberg, 1986). Nonetheless, we may be attracted to people whose interpersonal styles are dissimilar to our own. In one study, dominant people paired with submissive people reported greater satisfaction with their relationship than dominant or submissive people paired with a similar partner (Dryer & Horowitz, 1997).

People vary on a large number of characteristics. Perhaps similarity on some is important to attraction and relationship success, while similarity on others is not. Attitudes are one set of characteristics, personality traits are another, and attachment style is another. The research discussed so far argues that similarity in attitudes is important, but similarity in personality is not.

These predictions were tested in research involving newly married heterosexual couples (Luo & Klohnen, 2005). The average participant was 28 years old, white, fairly well educated, and Christian. The researchers calculated couple similarity scores on numerous measures in the three domains. They compared these real couple scores with the mean scores of randomly paired couples. As predicted, real couples were significantly more similar on values, religiosity, and political attitudes, but no more similar than random couples on personality. The NHSLS found that couples are similar in age, race, and education. Could this homophily account for similarity in attitudes? Researchers tried to predict similarity in attitudes and personality from similarity in background characteristics, but could not.

Finally, what is the relationship between similarity and quality of relationship? Among these couples, similarity on attachment styles was associated with indicators of marital satisfaction, but similarity in attitudes was not. Perhaps we need to revise the adage: "Birds of a feather (attitudinal similarity) may flock, but may not stick, together."

PHYSICAL ATTRACTIVENESS

A great deal of evidence shows that, given a choice of more than one potential partner, individuals will prefer the one who is more physically attractive (Hendrick & Hendrick, 1992). For example, in one study snapshots were taken of university men and women (Berscheid et al., 1971). A dating history of each person was also obtained. Judges then rated the attractiveness of the men and women in the photographs. For the women there was a fairly strong relationship between attractiveness and popularity; the women judged attractive had had more dates in the last year than the less attractive women. There was some relationship between appearance and popularity for men, too, but it was not as marked as it was for women. Research in Ontario has shown this phenomenon in children as young as three to six years of age; even young children are more attracted to children with attractive faces (Dion, 1977, 1973).

Physical attractiveness is one aspect of sex appeal; in fact, young men and women typically rate physical appearance as most important (Regan, 2004). Other aspects include general body size (measured in various ways) and certain facial features. Much of the research on attractiveness uses data from samples of white persons. One exception is research on the impact of lightness of skin on ratings of attractiveness among African Americans. Skin tone was strongly associated with the attractiveness ratings given female respondents by both male and female interviewers (Hill, 2002). Light skin was rated as more attractive, perhaps reflecting the use of white skin as the standard.

Matching phenomenon: The tendency for men and women to choose as partners people who match them, i.e., who are similar in attitudes, intelligence, and attractiveness.

In general, then, we are most attracted to good-looking people. However, among heterosexuals this effect depends on gender to some extent; physical attractiveness is more important to males evaluating females than it is to females evaluating males (Feingold, 1990). Also, our perception of attractiveness or beauty of another person is influenced by our evaluation of their intelligence, liking, and respect (Kniffin & Wilson, 2004). And this phenomenon is somewhat modified by our own feelings of personal worth, as we will discuss later in the chapter. The good news is that although Canadians on average give themselves a 6.7 out of 10 in physical attractiveness, they rate their partner significantly higher, giving their partner a 8.0 out of 10 (Harris/Decima, 2007). As a final note, a 2001 COMPAS survey asked 400 Canadians to choose whether their perfect partner would have an ordinary face and an extraordinary body or an extraordinary face and an ordinary body. Twice as many women as men choose the extraordinary face—57 percent to 29 percent.

THE INTERPERSONAL MARKETPLACE

Although this may sound somewhat callous, whom we are attracted to and pair off with depends a lot on how much we think we have to offer and how much we think we can "buy" with it. Historically, the principle seems to be that women's worth is based on their physical beauty, whereas men's worth is based on their success. There is a tendency, then, for beautiful women to be paired with wealthy, successful men.

Data from many studies document this phenomenon in heterosexual relationships. In one study, high school yearbook pictures were rated for attractiveness (Udry & Eckland, 1984). These people were followed up 15 years after graduation, and measures of education, occupational status, and income were obtained. Females who were rated the most attractive in high school were significantly more likely to have husbands who had high incomes and were highly educated (see also Elder, 1969).

In another study, female students were rated on their physical attractiveness (Rubin, 1973, p. 68). They were then asked to complete a questionnaire about what kinds of men they would consider desirable dates. A man's occupation had a big effect on his desirability as a date. Men in high-status occupations—physician, lawyer, chemist—were considered highly desirable dates by virtually all the women. Men in low-status occupations—janitor, bartender—were judged hardly acceptable by most of the women. A difference emerged between attractive and unattractive women, however, when rating men in middle-status occupations—electrician, bookkeeper, plumber. The attractive women did not feel that these men would be acceptable dates, whereas the unattractive women felt that they would be at least moderately acceptable. Here we see the interpersonal marketplace in action. Men with more status are more desirable. But how desirable a man is judged to be depends on the woman's sense of her own worth. Attractive women are not much interested in middle-status men because they apparently think of themselves as being "worth more." Unattractive women find middle-status men more attractive, presumably because they think such men are reasonably within their "price range."

FROM THE LABORATORY TO REAL LIFE

The phenomena discussed so far—feelings of attraction to people who are similar to us and who are good-looking—have been demonstrated mainly in psychologists' laboratories. Do these phenomena occur in the real world?

Donn Byrne and his colleagues (1970) did a study to find out whether these results would be obtained in a real-life situation. They administered an attitude and personality questionnaire to 420 university students. Then they formed 44 "couples." For half of the couples, both people had made very similar responses on the questionnaire; for the other half of the couples, the two people had made very different responses. The two people were then introduced and sent to the student union on a brief date. When they returned from the date, an unobtrusive measure of attraction was taken—how close they stood to each other in front of the experimenter's desk. The participants also evaluated their dates on several scales.

The results of the study confirmed those from previous experimental work. The couples who had been matched for similar attitudes were most attracted to each other, and those with dissimilar attitudes were not so attracted to each other. The students had also been rated as to their physical attractiveness both by the experimenter and by their dates, and greater attraction to the better-looking dates was reported. In a follow-up at the end of the semester, those whose dates were similar to them and were physically attractive were more likely to remember the date's name and to express a desire to date the person again in the future. This experiment was closer to real life and real dating situations and again demonstrates the importance of similarity and physical appearance.

ATTRACTION ONLINE

Technology has created a new way to meet potential partners—online (Elias, 1997). Some websites, such as Toronto-based LavaLife.com, have tens of thousands of "personal ads," and one site claims 500 000 hits per day. Surveys suggest that the people seeking partners online are educated, affluent 20- to 40-year-olds who don't have the time or the taste for "singles bars." Telephone interviews in 2005 with a sample of adults found that 11 percent of Internet users had visited an online dating site. Homophily may come into play here if people choose to visit a website specifically for people who share their ethnocultural background. According to a Canadian study, the main reasons people use online dating services are to meet people they would not otherwise meet, as well as for their privacy, confidentiality, and convenience (Brym & Lenton, 2001).

Users say that one advantage of meeting online is that the technology forces you to focus on the person's interests and values. This focus may facilitate finding a person with whom you have a lot in common; however, individuals who are in relationships that started online report lower relational intimacy than those who are in relationships that started face-to-face (Scott et al., 2006). Although in some instances you cannot see the person and so you are not influenced by his or her physical attractiveness (or lack thereof), today on many sites people are expected to post a picture. You also do not have access to body language, facial expressions, posture, and other cues that provide information. As a result, your impressions are heavily influenced by imagination, which can create a powerful attraction to the other (Ben-Ze'ev, 2004).

A major disadvantage is the risk that the other person may not be honest about his or her interests, occupation, appearance, or marital status. In fact, research suggests that one-quarter of Canadian online daters admit to having misrepresented themselves online (Brym & Lenton, 2001). Chat rooms with names like "Women with Other Men" attract people in relationships. Some of the relationships established in these rooms lead to "Divorce, Internet Style" (Quittner, 1997).

In recent years, online dating sites have enlisted the help of researchers in developing a "scientific" approach to pairing clients (Gottlieb, 2006). The most renowned is eHarmony, thanks to its outgoing founder, Neil Clark Warren. Similar sites include Chemistry.com, whose chief advisor is sociobiologist Helen Fisher, and PerfectMatch.com, whose system was developed by "Dr. Pepper" Schwartz, a sociologist. Each site uses clients' responses to an online questionnaire to match them.

How do they differ? Each site has its matching strategy. Following the research on attraction, eHarmony uses a 436-question survey to assess a broad range of attitude, value, and personality domains. Couples are matched based on relative similarity on each domain. Chemistry.com focuses on pairing adults who will experience a "spark" when they meet. Fisher argues that testosterone, dopamine, oxytocin, and vasopressin are the basis of romance

(Fisher et al., 2006). Genes associated with these hormones are associated with traits such as calmness, popularity, rationality, and sympathy. Chemistry.com uses a 146-item survey to measure these traits, and infers the clients' "chemistry."

PerfectMatch.com uses the Duet system, based on 48 questions assessing eight domains. Schwartz believes that a well-matched couple should be similar on romantic impulsivity, personal energy, outlook, and predictability, and different on flexibility, decision-making style, emotionality, and self-nurturing style. What do you think?

How successful are Internet dating sites at helping people form long-term relationships? First, in one study of Canadian online daters, only two-thirds of people using online dating services meet even one person face-to face. Of those who did meet someone face-to-face, 27 percent formed a romantic relationship with a person they met online but only 3 percent had married someone met online (Brym & Lenton, 2001). Similarly, in a British survey, 30 percent of respondents had formed a romantic relationship and 9 percent had married someone they met through an Internet dating service (Gunter, 2008).

EXPLAINING OUR PREFERENCES

The research data are quite consistent in showing that we select as potential partners people who are similar to us in social characteristics—age, race, education—and who share our attitudes and beliefs. Moreover, both men and women prefer physically attractive people, although heterosexual women place greater emphasis on a man's social status or earning potential (Sprecher et al., 1994). The obvious question is, Why? Two answers are suggested, one drawing on reinforcement theory and one drawing on sociobiology (see Chapter 2 for discussions of these theories).

REINFORCEMENT THEORY: BYRNE'S LAW OF ATTRACTION

A rather commonsensical idea—and one that psychologists agree with—is that we tend to like people who give us reinforcements or rewards and to dislike people who give us punishments. Social psychologist Donn Byrne (1997) has formulated the law of attraction. It says that our attraction to another person is proportionate to the number of reinforcements that person gives us relative to the total number of reinforcements plus punishments the person gives us. Or, simplified even more, we like people who are frequently nice to us and seldom nasty.

According to this explanation, most people prefer to interact with people who are similar to them because interaction with them is rewarding. People who are similar in age, ethnic background, and education are likely to have similar outlooks on life, prefer similar activities, and like the same kinds of people. These shared values and beliefs provide the basis for smooth and rewarding interaction. It will be easy to agree about such things as how important schoolwork is, what TV programs to watch, and what to do on Friday night. Disagreement about such things would cause conflict and hostility, which are definitely not rewards (for most people, anyway). We prefer pretty or handsome partners because we are aware of the high value placed on physical attractiveness in Canadian society; we believe others will have a higher opinion of us if we have a good-looking partner. Finally, we prefer someone with high social status or earning potential because all the material things that people find rewarding cost money.

These findings have some practical implications (Hatfield & Walster, 1978). If you are trying to get a new relationship going well, make sure you give the other person lots of positive reinforcement. Also, make sure that you have some good times together, so that you *associate* each other with rewards. Do not spend all your time stripping paint off old furniture or cleaning out the garage. And do not forget to keep the positive reinforcements (or "strokes," if you like that jargon better) going in an old, stable relationship.

A variation of the reinforcement view comes from the implicit egotism perspective (Jones, et al., 2004). It states that we are attracted to persons who are similar because they activate our

Figure 12.1 According to Byrne's law of attraction, our liking for a person is influenced by the reinforcements we receive from interacting with them. Shared activities provide the basis for smooth and rewarding interaction.

positive views of ourselves. For example, archival research found that men and women are more likcly to marry people whose names resemble their own.

SOCIOBIOLOGY: SEXUAL STRATEGIES THEORY

Sociobiologists view sexual behaviour within an evolutionary perspective and thus focus on heterosexual relationships. Historically, the function of mating has been reproduction. Men and women who selected mates according to some preferences were more successful than those who chose them based on other preferences (Allgeier & Wiederman, 1994). The successful ones produced more offspring, who in turn produced more offspring, carrying their mating preferences to the present.

Men and women face different adaptive problems in their efforts to reproduce (Buss & Schmitt, 1993). Since women bear the offspring, men need to identify reproductively valuable women. Other things being equal, younger women are more likely to be fertile than older women; hence a preference for youth, which results in young men choosing young women (homophily). Also, sociobiologists assert that men want to be certain about the paternity of offspring; hence, they want a woman who will be sexually faithful.

Sociobiologists argue that, other things being equal, a physically attractive person is more likely to be healthy and fertile than someone who isn't—thus the preference for good-looking partners. If attractiveness is an indicator of health, we would expect it to be more important in societies where chronic diseases are more prevalent. Gangestad and Buss (1993) measured the prevalence of seven pathogens, including those that cause malaria and leprosy, in 29 cultures, and also obtained ratings of the importance of 18 attributes of mates. They found that physical attractiveness was considered more important by residents in societies that had a greater prevalence of pathogens. However, one study found that there was no relationship between rated facial attractiveness (based on a photograph) and a clinical assessment of health in a sample of adolescents, suggesting that the assumed link between attractiveness and health is not there. At the same time, the raters ranked more attractive persons as healthier (Kalick et al., 1998).

Women must make a much greater investment than men in order to reproduce. They will be pregnant for nine months, and after the birth they must care for the infant and young child for many years. Thus, women want to select as mates men who are reproductively valuable; hence the preference for good-looking mates. They also want mates who are able and willing to invest resources in them and their children. Obviously, men must have resources in order to invest them; so women prefer men with higher incomes and status. Among young people, women will prefer men with greater earning potential; thus, the preference for men with greater education and higher occupational aspirations. The matter of resources is more important than the problem of identifying a reproductively valuable male, so women rate income and earning potential as more important than good looks.

Research provides some evidence that is consistent with this theory. For example, researchers presented a list of 31 tactics to a sample of undergraduate students and asked them to rate how effective each would be in attracting a long-term mate (Schmitt & Buss, 1996). Tactics that communicated sexual exclusivity or faithfulness were judged highly effective in attracting a mate for women. Tactics that displayed resource potential were judged most effective for men. Other research has shown that although there are some differences in the qualities that men and women seek in a long-term partner, there are also many similarities (Stewart et al., 2000). Further, men's and women's values are becoming more similar (Buss et al., 2001).

These two explanations—reinforcement theory and sociobiology—are not inconsistent. We can think about reinforcement in more general terms. Reproduction is a major goal for most adults in every society. Successful reproduction—that is, having a healthy child who develops normally—is very reinforcing. Following the sexual strategies that we have inherited is likely to lead to such reinforcement. Of course, sexual strategies theory is not a good explanation for same-sex attraction.

INTIMACY

What is intimacy? Intimacy is a major component of any close or romantic relationship. Today many people are seeking to increase the intimacy in their relationships. And so, in this section we will explore intimacy in more detail to try to gain a better understanding of it.

DEFINING INTIMACY

Psychologists have offered a number of definitions of intimacy, including the following (Perlman & Fehr, 1987, p. 17):

1. Intimacy's defining features include: "openness, honesty, mutual self-disclosure; caring, warmth, protecting, helping; being devoted to each other, mutually attentive, mutually committed; surrendering control, dropping defenses; becoming emotional, feeling distressed when separation occurs."
2. "Emotional intimacy is defined in behavioral terms as mutual self-disclosure and other kinds of verbal sharing, as declarations of liking and loving the other, and as demonstrations of affection."

Notice that the first definition focuses on intimacy as a characteristic of a person and the second as a characteristic of a relationship. One way to think about intimacy is that certain persons have more of a capacity for intimacy or engage in more intimacy-promoting behaviours than others. But we can also think of some relationships as being more intimate than others.

A definition of **intimacy** in romantic relationships is "the level of commitment and positive affective, cognitive and physical closeness one experiences with a partner in a reciprocal (although not necessarily symmetrical) relationship" (Moss & Schwebel, 1993, p. 33). The emphasis in this definition is on closeness or sharing, which has three dimensions—affective (emotional), cognitive, and physical. Note, too, that while intimacy must be reciprocal, it need not be equal. Many people have had the experience of feeling closer to another person than that person seems to feel toward them. Finally, note that while intimacy has a physical dimension, it need not be sexual.

In one study, university students were asked to respond to an open-ended question asking what they thought made a relationship one of intimacy (Roscoe et al., 1987). The qualities that emerged, with great agreement, were sharing, sexual interaction, trust in the partner, and openness. Notice that these qualities are quite similar to the ones listed in the definitions just given.

> **Intimacy:** A quality of relationships characterized by commitment, feelings of closeness and trust, and self-disclosure.

INTIMACY AND SELF-DISCLOSURE

One of the key characteristics of intimacy, appearing in psychologists' and university students' definitions, is self-disclosure (Derlega, 1984). Self-disclosure involves telling your partner some personal things about yourself. It may range from telling your partner about something embarrassing that happened to you at work today, to disclosing a very meaningful event that happened between you and your parents 15 years ago.

> **Self-disclosure:** Telling personal things about yourself.

Research consistently shows that self-disclosure leads to reciprocity (Berg & Derlega, 1987; Hendrick & Hendrick, 1992). In other words, if one member of the couple self-discloses, this act seems to prompt the other partner to self-disclose also. Self-disclosure by one member of the couple can essentially get the ball rolling.

Why does this occur? Psychologists have proposed a number of reasons (Hendrick & Hendrick, 1992). First, disclosure by our partner may make us like and trust that person more. Second, as social learning theorists would argue, simple modelling and imitation may occur. That is, one partner's self-disclosing serves as a model for the other partner. Norms of equity may also be involved (see Chapter 11 for a discussion of equity theory). After one partner has self-disclosed, the other person may follow suit in order to maintain a sense of balance or equity in the relationship.

Self-disclosure is closely related to satisfaction with the relationship. Research shows that there is a positive correlation between the extent of a couple's self-disclosure and their satisfaction with the relationship. In other words, couples that practise more self-disclosure are more satisfied (Hendrick, 1981). Self-disclosure of sexual likes and dislikes is associated with sexual satisfaction (Byers & Demmons, 1999; MacNeil & Byers, 2005; Purnine & Carey, 1997).

Patterns of self-disclosure can actually predict whether a couple stays together or breaks up. Research in which couples are followed for periods

© Barbara Penoyar/PhotoDisc/Getty Images

Figure 12.2 Intimacy occurs in a relationship when there is warmth and mutual self-disclosure.

ranging from two months to four years shows that the greater the self-disclosure, the greater the likelihood that the relationship will continue, and the less the self-disclosure, the greater the likelihood of breakup (Hendrick et al., 1988; Sprecher, 1987).

Self-disclosure promotes intimacy in a relationship and makes us feel close to the other person. It also is important for the partner to be accepting in response to self-disclosure. If the acceptance is missing, we can feel betrayed or threatened, and we certainly will not feel on more intimate terms with the partner.

A study of naturally occurring interactions examined the relationships between self-disclosure, perceived partner disclosure, and the degree of intimacy experienced (Laurenceau et al., 1998). Young people recorded data about every interaction lasting more than 10 minutes, for 7 or 14 days. Data were analyzed for more than 4000 dyadic (that is, two-person) interactions recorded by 158 participants. Both self-disclosure and partner disclosure were associated with the participant's rating of the intimacy of the interaction. Self-disclosure of emotion was more closely related to intimacy than was self-disclosure of facts.

Self-disclosure and intimacy, then, mutually build on each other. Self-disclosure promotes our feeling that the relationship is intimate, and when we feel that it is, we feel comfortable engaging in further self-disclosure. However, self-disclosure and intimacy don't necessarily increase consistently over time. In some relationships, the pattern may be that an increase in intimacy is followed by a plateau or even a pulling back (Collins & Miller, 1994).

MEASURING INTIMACY

Psychologists have developed some scales for measuring intimacy that can give us further insights. One such scale is the Personal Assessment of Intimacy in Relationships (PAIR) Inventory (Schaefer & Olson, 1981). It measures emotional intimacy in a relationship with items such as the following:

1. My partner listens to me when I need someone to talk to.
2. My partner really understands my hurts and joys.

Another scale measuring intimacy in a relationship includes items such as these (Miller & Lefcourt, 1982):

1. How often do you confide very personal information to him or her?
2. How often are you able to understand his or her feelings?
3. How often do you feel close to him or her?
4. How important is your relationship with him or her in your life?

If you are currently in a relationship, answer these questions for yourself and consider what the quality of the intimacy is in your relationship.

In summary, an intimate relationship is characterized by commitment, feelings of closeness and understanding, and self-disclosure. We can promote intimacy in our relationships by engaging in self-disclosure and being accepting of the other person's self-disclosure. However, we are unlikely to be willing to self-disclose unless we trust our partner.

LOVE

At the beginning of this chapter, we noted that there is a connection between love and sex in our society. In everyday life and in theories of love, this connection lies along a continuum (Hendrick & Hendrick, 2004). At one end are "hookups," short-term sexual relationships on a Saturday night, spring break, or a singles cruise, with little romance (Lambert et al., 2003; Maticka-Tyndale et al., 2003; Grello et al., 2006). In theories of love, this is the "love is really

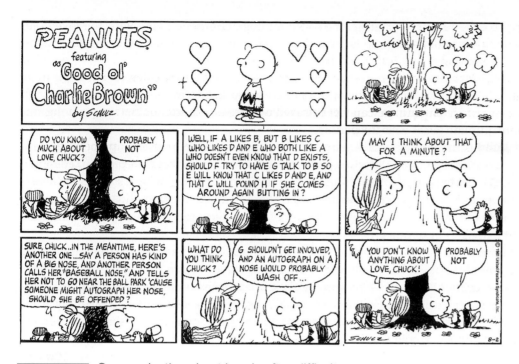

Figure 12.3 Communicating about love is often difficult.
PEANUTS reprinted by permission of United Feature Syndicate, Inc.

sex" view found, for example, in evolutionary theory. At the other end are romantic love relationships in which sex is non-existent or incidental, as for example in a non-sexual affair. In theories, this is the view found, for example, in the theory of love as a story. Toward the middle is the "sex is really love" view, as in the theory of passionate love. In the centre is a relationship that balances the two, and theories that recognize both, such as the triangular theory.

THEORIES OF LOVE

In this section, we will consider four views of love: the triangular theory, the attachment theory, the love-as-a-story perspective, and the passionate love view and its connection to the biology of love.

THE TRIANGULAR THEORY OF LOVE

Robert Sternberg (1986) has formulated a triangular theory of the nature of love. According to his theory, love has three fundamental components: intimacy, passion, and commitment. He calls it a triangular theory because he depicts these three components graphically in a love triangle.[1] As shown in Figure 12.4, the top point is intimacy, the left point is passion, and the right point is decision or commitment.

Three Components of Love. Intimacy is the emotional component of love. It includes our feelings of closeness or bondedness to the other person. The feeling of intimacy usually involves a sense of mutual understanding with

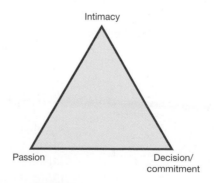

Figure 12.4 The triangle in Sternberg's triangular theory of love.

[1]This terminology should not be confused with the popular use of the term "love triangle," which refers to a situation in which three people are involved in love, but the love is not reciprocated and so things don't work out quite right. For example, A loves B, B loves C, and C loves A, but A doesn't love C and B doesn't love A. Alas.

the loved one; a sense of sharing one's self; intimate communication with the loved one, involving a sense of having the loved one hear and accept what is shared; and giving and receiving emotional support to and from the loved one. Intimacy, of course, is present in many relationships besides romantic ones. Intimacy here is definitely not a euphemism for sex (as when someone asks, "Have you been intimate with him?"). The kind of emotional closeness involved in intimacy may be found between best friends and between parents and children, just as it is between lovers.

Passion is the motivational component of love. It includes physical attraction and the drive for sexual expression. Physiological arousal is an important part of passion. Passion is the component that differentiates romantic love from other kinds of love, such as the love of best friends or the love between parents and children. Passion is generally the component of love that is faster to arouse, but in the course of a long-term relationship it is also the component that fades most quickly.

Intimacy and passion are often closely intertwined. In some cases passion comes first, when a couple experience an initial, powerful physical attraction to each other; emotional intimacy may then follow. In other cases, people know each other only casually, but as emotional intimacy develops, passion follows. Of course, there are also cases where intimacy and passion are completely separate. For example, in cases of casual sex, passion is present but intimacy is not.

The third component is the cognitive component, decision or commitment. This component actually has two aspects. The short-term aspect is the decision that one loves the other person. The long-term aspect is the commitment to maintain that relationship. Commitment is what makes relationships last. Passion comes and goes. All relationships have their better times and their worse times, their ups and their downs. When the words of the traditional marriage ceremony ask whether a person promises to love his or her partner "for better or for worse," the answer "I do" is the promise of commitment.

According to Sternberg, people who have high levels of all three components—intimacy, passion, and commitment—experience consummate love. What term would you use to describe a person who only experiences commitment and intimacy, for example, but not passion? What about someone who has high commitment but low intimacy and passion?

Comparing Love Triangles. Sternberg's (1986) triangle metaphor allows us to show how the two people in a couple can be well matched or mismatched in the love they feel toward each other. In Figure 12.5(a), Pat and Robert feel the same levels of intimacy, they both feel equal levels of passion, and they both have the same level of commitment. According to the theory, that is a perfect match. Figure 12.5(b) shows a situation in which the couple are slightly mismatched, but not seriously, and 12.5(c) shows a moderate mismatch. Figure 12.5(d) shows a situation in which there is a severe mismatch. Both partners are equally committed, but Pat feels significantly more intimacy and passion than Robert.

Sternberg's research indicates that when there is a good "match" [as shown in Figure 12.5(a) or (b)] between the two partners' love, both tend to feel satisfaction with the relationship. When there is a mismatch in the triangles, they feel dissatisfied with the relationship.

Thinking about practical applications of the theory, if a relationship seems to be in trouble, it may be because there is a mismatch of the

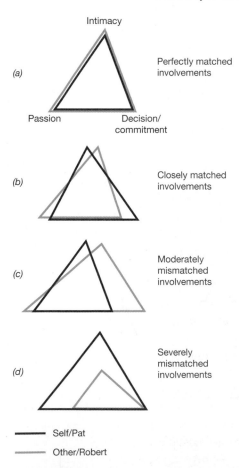

Figure 12.5 Partners can be well matched or mismatched, depending on whether their levels of intimacy, passion, and decision/commitment match.

triangles. We could analyze the love in the relationship in terms of the three components (intimacy, passion, and commitment) to see where the partners are mismatched. It could be that they are well matched for passion, but that one feels and wants more intimacy or commitment than the other person does.

Love in Action. Sternberg also argues that each of the three components of love must be translated into action. The intimacy component is expressed in actions such as communicating personal feelings and information, offering emotional (and perhaps financial) support, and expressing empathy for the other. The passion component is expressed in actions such as kissing, touching, and making love. The decision or commitment component is demonstrated by actions such as saying "I love you," getting married, and sticking with a relationship through times when it isn't particularly convenient.

As the great psychoanalyst Erich Fromm wrote in his book *The Art of Loving* (1956), love is something one *does*, not a state one is *in*. Fromm believed that loving is an art, something that one must learn about and practise. And as Sternberg says, "Without expression, even the greatest of loves can die" (1986, p. 132).

Evidence for Sternberg's Triangular Theory of Love. What kind of support is there for Sternberg' theory? Sternberg has developed a questionnaire, the Sternberg Triangular Love Scale (STLS), to measure the three components in his theory. Several studies have been done on the characteristics of the scale itself (e.g., Sternberg, 1987, 1997; Whitley, 1993). The scale provides good measures of the components, especially of passion and commitment. Scores for the same relationship are stable for up to two months.

Sternberg makes several predictions about how scores ought to change over time. Acker and Davis (1992) recruited 204 adults, ages 18 to 68; 65 percent were married. The average length of the relationship was 9.5 years. As predicted, commitment scores increased as relationships progressed from dating to marriage. Sternberg expects intimacy to decrease over time as familiarity with the partner increases; sure enough, behavioural intimacy (sharing inner feelings, trying to understand the partner) decreased as predicted. However, contrary to prediction, two other measures of intimacy (including Sternberg's) increased.

A study of a sample of German adults assessed the relationship between the three components and sexual activity and satisfaction (Grau & Kimpf, 1993). The theory predicts that the amount of passion should be most closely related to sexual activity, but the results indicated that intimacy was most closely related to sexual behaviour and sexual satisfaction.

THE ATTACHMENT THEORY OF LOVE

In Chapter 10 we discussed the earliest attachment that humans experience, the attachment between infant and parent. One hypothesis is that the quality of this early attachment—whether secure and pleasant or insecure and unpleasant—profoundly affects us for the rest of our lives, and particularly affects our capacity to form loving attachments to others when we are adults.

The *attachment theory of love* is based on these ideas (Hazen & Shaver, 1987; Simpson, 1990). According to the most recent formulation proposed by British Columbia psychologist Kim Bartholomew, adults are characterized in their romantic relationships by one of four attachment styles (Bartholomew & Horowitz, 1991). These attachment styles are based on our perceptions of ourselves as well as our expectations of how others will respond to us. As shown in Figure 12.6, we either see ourselves in a positive way as worthy of love and support or we see ourselves in a negative way as unworthy of love. Similarly, we either see other people in a positive way as trustworthy and available or we see them in a negative way as unreliable and rejecting. *Secure lovers* have a sense of their own lovability and the expecta-

IN FOCUS 12.1

What Is Jealousy?

Jealousy—the green-eyed monster—is an unpleasant emotion often associated with romantic and sexual relationships. Intense cases of jealousy may result in violence, including partner abuse, assault, and homicide. As a result, it has been the focus of considerable scholarly work. Several perspectives contribute to our understanding of this emotion.

Jealousy is a cognitive, emotional, and behavioural response to a threat to an interpersonal relationship (Guerrero et al., 2004). The cognitive appraisal perspective suggests that jealousy occurs when an individual *interprets* some stimulus as representing a threat to a valued relationship; in reality, there may or may not be a threat to the relationship. A variety of behaviours by the partner may be interpreted as a threat; in one study, individuals in dating relationships said that having their partner just spend time with another person was one of the top three acts of betrayal (Roscoe et al., 1988). Interaction with someone via the Internet, behaviour or remarks by third parties, or coming home late may arouse suspicion and elicit jealousy from a partner.

There are two types of jealousy that may occur together or separately: emotional and sexual. *Emotional jealousy* occurs when one person believes or knows that the partner is emotionally attached to or in love with another. *Sexual jealousy* occurs when the person believes or knows that the partner wants to engage in or has engaged in sexual intimacy with another. A study of heterosexual and homosexual adults found that although both women and men are concerned about both types of infidelity, they are more concerned about the emotional infidelity of a partner (Harris, 2002). Which would concern you more, emotional infidelity or sexual infidelity?

Psychologists Gregory White and Paul Mullen (1989) see jealousy as a constellation including thoughts, emotions, and actions. Two situations, according to their research, activate jealousy. One is a situation in which there is a threat to our self-esteem. For example, in a good relationship, our romantic partner helps us feel good about ourselves—makes us feel attractive or fun to be with, for example. If a rival appears and our partner shows interest, we may think things like "He finds her more attractive than me" or "She finds him more fun to be with than me." We then feel less attractive or less fun to be with—that is, our self-esteem is threatened.

The second situation that activates jealousy is a threat to the relationship. If a rival appears on the scene, we may fear that our partner will separate from us and form a new relationship with the rival. Jealousy is activated because of our negative thoughts and feelings about the loss of a relationship that has been good for us and the loss of all the pleasant things that go along with that relationship, such as companionship and sex.

According to White and Mullen, we go through several

MODEL OF SELF

	Positive	Negative
Positive MODEL OF OTHER	SECURE Comfortable with intimacy and autonomy	PREOCCUPIED Preoccupied with relationships
Negative	DISMISSING Dismissing of intimacy	FEARFUL Fearful of intimacy Socially avoidant

Figure 12.6 Bartholomew and Horowitz's (1991) four-category, two-dimensional model of adult attachment.

tion that other people are generally accepting and responsive. *Preoccupied lovers* have a sense of their own unlovability but a positive evaluation of other people. They try to achieve self-acceptance by gaining the acceptance of people they value. They want desperately to get close to a partner but are so worried that the partner does not love them that they may scare them away. *Fearful lovers* have a negative expectation of both themselves and other people. They expect to be rejected by others and so avoid romantic relationships. They are uncomfortable feeling close to, trusting, or depending on another person, or having that person feel close to them. Finally, *dismissing lovers* feel themselves to be worthy of love, but have negative views of other people. These people may protect themselves against disappointment by avoiding close relationships and maintaining a sense of independence.

Dismissing and fearful lovers are similar in that both avoid intimacy. Preoccupied and

Figure 12.7 One situation that activates jealousy is a perceived threat to the relationship.

stages in the jealousy response, sometimes very quickly. The first is cognitive, in which we make an initial appraisal of the situation and find that there is a threat to our self-esteem or to the relationship. Next we experience an emotional reaction that in itself has two phases. The first is a rapid stress response, the "jealous flash." To use the terminology of the two-component theory of love discussed later in this chapter, this stress response is the physiological component of the jealous emotion. The second phase of emotional response occurs as we reappraise the situation and decide how to cope with it. In the reappraisal stage, we may shift from seeing the situation as a threat to seeing it as a challenge, for example. The intense initial emotions quiet down and may be replaced by feelings of moodiness.

Attempts to cope with jealousy lead to a variety of behaviours. Some of these are constructive, such as effective communication with one's partner. Such communication may lead to an evaluation of the relationship, and attempts to change some of the problematic aspects of it. If the problems seem sufficiently serious, a couple may seek help from a mediator or therapist. Other behavioural responses to jealousy are destructive. The threat to one's self-esteem may lead to depression, substance abuse, or suicide. Aggression may be directed at the partner, the third person, or both, and may result in physical or sexual abuse or even murder.

Research suggests that a person's attachment style may be an important influence on how he or she responds to jealousy (Sharpstein & Kirkpatrick, 1997). Undergraduates were asked how they had reacted in the past to jealousy. Those with a secure attachment style reported that they had expressed their anger to the partner and maintained the relationship. Those with a preoccupied or anxious style reported the most intense anger, but they were most likely to say they did not express their anger. People with a fearful or avoidant style were more likely to direct their anger toward the third person.

Sources: Fisher, 1992; Guerrero et al., 2004; Reiss, 1986; White & Mullen, 1989.

fearful lovers are alike in that both depend on acceptance from others to feel good about themselves. Research shows that about 49 percent of adults have a secure attachment style, 12 percent a preoccupied style, 21 percent a fearful style, and 18 percent a dismissing style (Bartholomew & Horowitz, 1991). The research also shows that separation from parents in childhood—perhaps because of divorce or death—is not related to adult attachment styles (Hazen & Shaver, 1987). That is, children of divorced parents are no more or less likely to be secure lovers than are children from intact marriages (a finding that is probably fortunate, given the high divorce rate in Canada). What does predict adult attachment style is the person's perception of the *quality* of the relationship with each parent. Recent research has shown that the quality of friendships in childhood and adolescence also affects adult attachment styles. For example, research using a sample of 191 gay and bisexual men in Vancouver found that both the quality of parental relationships (particularly relationships with fathers) and the quality of peer relationships were associated with adult attachment style (Landott et al., 2004).

This research has some important implications. First, it helps us understand that adults bring to any particular romantic relationship their own personal history of love and attachment. The forces of that personal history can be strong, and one good and loving partner may not be able to change a dismissing lover into a secure lover. This does not mean that people who have insecure attachment relationships with their parents cannot have a secure attachment relationship with their romantic partner. Research in New Brunswick has shown that although many people form a particular type of attachment relationship with all of the important people in their lives, some people with insecure attachment relationships with family have secure attachment relationships with their romantic partner (Ross & Spinner, 2001). Second, it helps us understand that conflict in some relationships may be caused by a mismatch of attachment styles. A secure lover who wants a close, intimate relationship is likely to feel frustrated and dissatisfied with a dismissing or fearful lover who is uncomfortable with feeling close. Attachment theory suggests that an important form of similarity is similarity in attachment style (Latty-Mann & Davis, 1996). Third, this theory provides some explanation for jealousy, which is most common among preoccupied lovers (although present among the others) because of their early experience of feeling anxious about their attachment to their parents. Finally, attachment style may help to explain high-risk sexual behaviour. Research in Ontario showed that women who have insecure attachment styles engage in intercourse at a younger age and have more sexual partners than do women with secure attachment styles (Bogaert & Sadava, 2002).

Attachment style affects relationships by affecting the way the partners interact. A study of 128 established couples (average length of relationship 47 months) assessed attachment style, patterns of accommodation, and satisfaction with the relationship (Scharfe & Bartholomew, 1995). Individuals with a secure attachment reported responding constructively to potentially destructive behaviour by the partner, for example, with efforts to discuss and resolve the problem. People who were fearful of attachment to another responded with avoidance or withdrawal. This may affect relationship satisfaction. A longitudinal study of university students in Ontario showed that, over a four-month period, participants with a secure attachment style did not change their feelings about the relationship. In contrast, participants with one of the insecure attachment styles reported lower levels of satisfaction and commitment over time (Keelan et al., 1994).

LOVE AS A STORY

When we think of love, our thoughts often turn to the great love stories: Romeo and Juliet, Cinderella and the Prince (Julia Roberts and Richard Gere), King Edward VIII and Wallis Simpson, and *Pygmalion/My Fair Lady*.[2] According to Sternberg (1998), these stories are much more than entertainment. They shape our beliefs about love and relationships, and our beliefs in turn influence our behaviour:

> Zach and Tammy have been married 28 years. Their friends have been predicting divorce since the day they were married. They fight almost constantly. Tammy threatens to leave Zach; he tells her that nothing would make him happier. They lived happily ever after.

> Valerie and Leonard had a perfect marriage. They told each other and all of their friends that they did. Their children say they never fought. Leonard met someone at his office, and left Valerie. They are divorced. (Adapted from Sternberg, 1998)

Wait a minute! Aren't those endings reversed? Zach and Tammy should be divorced, and Valerie and Leonard should be living happily ever after. If love is merely the interaction between two people, how they communicate and behave, you're right; the stories have the wrong endings. But there is more to love than interaction; what matters is how each partner *interprets* the interaction. To make sense out of what happens in our relationships, we rely on our love stories.

A love story is a story about what love should be like; it has *characters*, a *plot*, and a *theme*.

Love story: A story about what love should be like, including characters, a plot, and a theme.

----
[2]Notice that all of these stories are heterosexual.

Every love story has two central characters who play roles that complement each other. The plot details the kinds of events that occur in the relationship. The theme is central; it provides the meaning of the events that make up the plot and gives direction to the behaviour of the principals.

The story guiding Zach and Tammy's relationship is the War story. Each views love as war; a good relationship involves constant fighting. The two central characters are warriors, doing battle, fighting for what they believe. The plot consists of arguments, fights, threats to leave—in other words, battles. The theme is that love is war. One may win or lose particular battles, but the war continues. Zach and Tammy's relationship endures because they share this view, and because it fits their temperaments. (Can you imagine how long a conflict-avoider would last in a relationship with either of them?)

According to this view, *falling in love* occurs when you meet someone with whom you can create a relationship that fits your love story. Further, we are satisfied with relationships in which we and our partner match the characters in our story (Beall & Sternberg, 1995). Valerie and Leonard's marriage looked great on the surface but it didn't fit Leonard's love story. He left when he met his "true love"—that is, a woman who could play the complementary role in his primary love story.

Where do our stories come from? Many of them have their origins in the culture, in folktales, literature, theatre, films, and television programs. The cultural context interacts with our personal experience and characteristics to create the stories that each of us has (Sternberg, 1996). As we experience relationships, our stories evolve, taking into account unexpected events. Each person has more than one story; the stories often form a hierarchy. One of Leonard's stories was "House and Home," where home was the centre of the relationship, and he (in his role of Caretaker) showered attention on the house and kids (not on Valerie). But when he met Sharon, with her aloof air, ambiguous past, and dark glasses, he was hooked—she elicited the "Love Is a Mystery" story, which was more salient to Leonard. He could not explain why he left Valerie and the kids; like most of us he was not consciously aware of his love stories.

You can see from these examples that love stories derive their power from the fact that they can be self-fulfilling. Our love story affects the way we think about and behave in our relationship. That is, we create in our relationships events according to the plot and then interpret those events according to the theme. Our love relationships are literally social constructions. Because our love stories are self-confirming, they can be very difficult to change. Many people are not aware of their love story (Sternberg et al., 2001).

Sternberg and his colleagues have identified five categories of love stories found in North American culture, and several specific stories within each category. They have also developed a series of statements that reflect the themes in each story. People who agree with the statements "I think fights actually make a relationship more vital," and "I actually like to fight with my partner" are likely to believe in the War story. Sternberg and Hojjat (cited in Sternberg, 1998) studied samples of 43 and 55 couples. They found that couples generally believed in similar stories. The more discrepant the stories of the partners, the less happy the couple was. Some stories were associated with high satisfaction; for example, the Garden story, in which love is a garden that needs ongoing cultivation. Two stories associated with low satisfaction were the Business story (especially the version in which the roles are Employer and Employee), and the Horror story, in which the roles are Terrorizer and Victim. If you watch *The Simpsons*, what do you think Marge and Homer's love story is?

THE BIOLOGY OF PASSIONATE LOVE

The three theories considered so far define love as a single phenomenon. A fourth perspective differentiates between two kinds of love: passionate love and companionate love (Berscheid & Hatfield, 1978). Passionate love is a state of intense longing for union with the other

Passionate love: A state of intense longing for union with the other person and of intense physiological arousal.

person and of intense physiological arousal. It has three components: cognitive, emotional, and behavioural (Hatfield & Sprecher, 1986a). The cognitive component includes preoccupation with the loved one and idealization of the person or of the relationship. The emotional component includes physiological arousal, sexual attraction, and desire for union. Behavioural elements include taking care of the other and maintaining physical closeness. Passionate love can be overwhelming, obsessive, all-consuming.

Passionate love can also lead to overly optimistic predictions about the likelihood that the relationship will last. Researchers in Ontario asked university students who were in a dating relationship of between one month and one year, their roommates, and their parents to predict how long the students' dating relationships would last (MacDonald & Ross, 1999). The students described their relationship more positively than did the other two groups, because they tended to focus on the strengths and minimize the negative aspects of the relationship. Students predicted that the relationship would last longer than did parents and roommates. Who was right? The results indicated that roommates were the most accurate about whether the couple would still be together one year later; the students were the least accurate.

Companionate love: A feeling of deep attachment and commitment to a person with whom one has an intimate relationship.

By contrast, companionate love is a feeling of deep attachment and commitment to a person with whom one has an intimate relationship (Hatfield & Rapson, 1993b).

Passionate love is hot; companionate love is warm. Passionate love is often the first stage of a romantic relationship. Two people meet, fall wildly in love, and make a commitment to each other. But as the relationship progresses, a gradual shift to companionate love takes place (Cimbalo et al., 1976; Driscoll et al., 1972). The transformation tends to occur when the relationship is between 6 and 30 months old (Hatfield & Walster, 1978).

Some may find this perspective a rather pessimistic commentary on romantic love because it does not fit the societal love story in which people see stars and hear bells when they fall in love, and continue to do so forever after. But it may actually describe a good way for a relationship to develop. Passionate love may be necessary to hold a relationship together in the early stages, while conflicts are being resolved. But past that point, most of us find that what we really need is a friend—someone who shares our interests, who is happy when we succeed, and who empathizes when we fail—and that is just what we get with companionate love. However, even when passionate love has evolved to companionate love, it helps to continue to see our partner and our relationship in somewhat idealized ways. An Ontario study found that couples with these positive relationship "illusions" were more satisfied with their relationship (Murray & Holmes, 1997; Murray et al., 1996). Of course, illusions are not sufficient to maintain a relationship if they are not based on common needs and goals.

Sexual desire and romantic love may often be independent processes (Diamond, 2004). Sexual desire is a motivational state leading to a search for opportunities for sexual activity. It motivates proximity seeking and contact, and leads to feelings of passion (passionate love). Sexual desire responds to reproductive cues such as physical attractiveness and high status. Romantic love is a motivational state leading to attachment and commitment. It promotes self-disclosure and intimacy leading to long-term relationships (companionate love).

Research involving observation of romantic couples identified distinctive non-verbal displays of affiliation (smiling, leaning toward partner), and of sexual cues (licking the lips, lip puckering) (Gonzaga, et al., 2006). Displays of affection were associated with subjective reports of feeling love and of happiness. Displays of sexual cues were associated with subjective reports of sexual arousal and desire.

From an evolutionary perspective, successful reproduction requires mating, and the establishment of a pair-bond to ensure parental care of offspring (see Chapter 2). Fisher and colleagues (2006) propose that there are three internal systems involved in this process: desire to mate, pairing (mating), and parenting. They believe that each system involves reward pathways in the brain and associated hormonal changes. The sex drive motivates a person to seek a partner. Processes of attraction lead to pairing, a focusing of energies on a specific partner. Processes of attachment lead to long-term relationships which facilitate parenting.

What causes the complex phenomena of passionate and companionate love? Where does the rush of love at first sight come from? Research suggests that it is caused by bodily chemistry and neural activity in the brain. Studies of the prairie vole, a small rodent, have identified specific patterns of neurochemical activity that are associated with mating and pair bonding (preference for a specific partner) (Curtis & Wang, 2003). In female prairie voles, dopamine is released during mating; in both male and female voles, the dopamine appears to enhance the likelihood of pair bonding. Dopamine is associated with euphoria and craving. A surge of dopamine in the human body can produce increased energy, focused attention, and reduced need for food and sleep; these are common experiences of people in the early stages of love.

The frequent presence of the loved one, produced initially by passionate love, triggers the production of two other chemicals, prolactin and oxytocin. The levels of prolactin rise following orgasm in humans and are also related to pair bonding in voles.

Oxytocin may contribute to long-term relationships. It has been shown to play an important role in pair-bonding in some animals (McEwen, 1997). In humans it is stimulated by touch, including sexual touching and orgasm, and produces feelings of pleasure and satisfaction. Research indicates that levels of interpersonal trust correlate positively with oxytocin as well (Zak et al., 2004). In an experiment, researchers administered either oxytocin or a placebo to young men through the nose. Compared to the men who received a placebo, the men who received oxytocin were more likely to take social risks during interactions with another person but not other types of risks (Kosfeld et al., 2005).

The newest research with humans involves the use of magnetic resonance imaging (MRI) to study brain activity related to love. Bartels and Zeki (2004) recruited young men and women who were in love. While their brain activity was being measured, each participant was shown photos of the romantic partner and of a close friend. The picture of the partner activated specific areas of the brain. Which ones? The areas rich in dopamine pathways were enervated, lending weight to the neurochemical findings that suggest dopamine is important in the experience of love. Furthermore, when measures of levels of brain activity in response to the picture of the lover were correlated with scores on the Passionate Love Scale (discussed shortly), the scores were positively correlated.

RESEARCH ON LOVE

So far the discussion has focused on theoretical definitions of various kinds of love. You can see that various theorists—Sternberg, Bartholemew, Berscheid, and Hatfield—mean different things when they use the term love. One of the ways psychologists and sociologists define terms is by using an **operational definition**. In an operational definition, a concept is defined by the way it is measured. Thus, for example, in the attraction experiment described earlier in the chapter, one of the ways that attraction was operationally defined was how close people stood to each other (Byrne et al., 1970). Operational definitions are very useful because they are precise and because they help clarify exactly what a scientist means by a complex term such as love.

Operational definition: Defining some concept or term by how it is measured—for example, defining intelligence as those abilities that are measured by IQ tests.

MEASURING LOVE

We introduced the concept of *passionate love* earlier. Hatfield and Sprecher (1986a) decided to develop a paper-and-pencil measure of passionate love. They wrote statements intended to measure the cognitive, emotional, and behavioural components of passionate love. The respondent rates each statement on a scale from 1 (not true at all) to 9 (definitely true of him or her). If you feel that you are in love with someone, think about whether you would agree with each of the following statements, keeping that person in mind.

1. *Cognitive component:*

   Sometimes I feel I can't control my thoughts; they are obsessively on _____.

   For me, _____ is the perfect romantic partner.

2. *Emotional component:*

   I possess a powerful attraction for _____.

   I will love _____ forever.

3. *Behavioural component:*

   I eagerly look for signs indicating _____'s desire for me.

   I feel happy when I am doing things to make _____ happy.

Hatfield and Sprecher administered their questionnaire along with some other measures to students who were in relationships ranging from casually dating to engaged and living together. The results indicated that scores on the Passionate Love Scale (PLS) were positively correlated with other measures of love and with measures of commitment to and satisfaction with the relationship. These correlations give us evidence that the PLS is valid—in other words, measures what it is supposed to measure. The findings confirm that the scale measures passion. For example, students who got high scores on the PLS reported a stronger desire to be with, held by, and kissed by the partner, and said that they were sexually excited just thinking about their partner. These findings confirm that the scale is measuring passion. Finally, the passionate love scores increased as the nature of the relationship moved from dating to dating exclusively. Hatfield and Sprecher's research is a good example of how to study an important but complex topic, such as love, scientifically.

LOVE AND ADRENALINE

Two-component theory of love: Berscheid and Walster's theory that two conditions must exist simultaneously for passionate love to occur: physiological arousal and attaching a cognitive label ("love") to the feeling.

Two-Component Theory of Love. Social psychologists Ellen Berscheid and Elaine Walster (1974a) proposed a two-component theory of love. According to their theory, passionate love occurs when two conditions exist simultaneously: (1) the person is in a state of intense *physiological arousal*, and (2) the situation is such that the person applies a particular label—"love"—to the sensations being experienced. Their theory is derived from an important theory developed by Stanley Schachter (1964).

Suppose that your heart is pounding, your palms are sweating, and your body is tense. What emotion are you experiencing? Is it love—has reading about passionate love led to obsessive thoughts of another person? Is it fear—are you frantically reading this text because you have an exam tomorrow morning? Is it sexual arousal—are you thinking about physical intimacy later tonight? It could be any of these, or it could be anger or embarrassment. A wide variety of emotions are accompanied by the same physiological states: increased blood pressure, a higher heart rate, increased myotonia (muscular tension), sweating palms. What differentiates these emotions? The key is the way we interpret or label what we are experiencing.

Schachter's (1964) two-component theory of emotion says just this; an emotion consists of a physiological arousal state plus the label the person assigns to it (for a critical evaluation of this theory, see Reisenzein, 1983). Berscheid and Walster have applied this to the emotion of "love." They suggest that we feel passionate love when we are aroused and when conditions are such that we identify what we are feeling as love.

Evidence for the Two-Component Theory. Several experiments provide evidence for Berscheid and Walster's two-component theory of love. In one study, male research participants exercised vigorously by running in place; this produced the physiological arousal response of pounding heart and sweaty palms (White et al., 1981). Afterward they rated their liking for an attractive woman, who actually was a confederate of the experimenters.

Men in the running group said they liked the woman significantly more than did men who were in a control condition and had not exercised. This result is consistent with Berscheid and Walster's theory. The effect is called the misattribution of arousal; that is, in a situation like this, the men misattribute their arousal—which is actually due to exercise—to their liking for the attractive woman. An analysis of 33 experiments found that arousal affects attraction even when the source of the arousal is unambiguous (Foster et al., 1998).

A study conducted in North Vancouver suggests that fear can increase a man's attraction to a woman (Dutton & Aron, 1974). An attractive female interviewer approached male passersby either on a fear-arousing bridge (you may be familiar with the Capilano Bridge) or on a non–fear-arousing bridge. The fear-arousing bridge was constructed of boards, attached to cables, and had a tendency to tilt, sway, and wobble; the handrails were low, and there was a 70-metre drop to rocks and shallow rapids below. The "control" bridge was made of solid cedar; it was firm, and there was only a 3-metre drop to a shallow rivulet below. The interviewer asked subjects to fill out questionnaires that included projective test items. These items were then scored for sexual imagery.

Misattribution of arousal: When a person in a stage of physiological arousal (e.g., from exercising or being in a frightening situation), attributes these feelings to love or attraction to the person present.

Figure 12.8 The misattribution of arousal. If people are physically aroused (e.g., by jogging), they may misattribute this arousal to love or sexual attraction, provided the situation suggests such an interpretation.

The men in the suspension-bridge group should have been in a state of physiological arousal, while those in the control-bridge group should not have been. In fact, there was more sexual imagery in the questionnaires filled out by the men in the suspension-bridge group, and these men made more attempts to contact the attractive interviewer after the experiment than the men on the control bridge. Intuitively, this result might seem to be peculiar: that men who are in a state of fear are more attracted to a woman than men who are relaxed. But in terms of the Berscheid and Walster two-component theory, it makes perfect sense. The fearful men were physiologically aroused, while the men in the control group were not. And according to this theory, arousal is an important component of love or attraction.[3]

Now, of course, if the men (most of them heterosexuals) had been approached by an elderly man or a child, probably their responses would have been different. In fact, when the interviewer in the experiment was male, the effects discussed above did not occur. Society tells us what the appropriate objects of our love, attraction, or liking are. That is, we know for what kinds of people it is appropriate to have feelings of love or liking. For these men, feelings toward an attractive woman could reasonably be labelled "love" or "attraction," while such labels would probably not be attached to feelings for an elderly man.

---

[3]According to the terminology of Chapter 3, note that the Dutton and Aron study is an example of *experimental* research.

The physical arousal that is important for love need not always be produced by unpleasant or frightening situations. Pleasant stimuli, such as sexual arousal or praise from the other person, may produce arousal and feelings of love. Indeed, Berscheid and Walster's theory does an excellent job of explaining why we seem to have such a strong tendency to associate love and sex. Sexual arousal is one method of producing a state of physiological arousal, and it is one that our culture has taught us to label as "love." Thus both components necessary to feel love are present: arousal and a label. On the other hand, this phenomenon may lead us to confuse love with lust (that is, sexual desire), an all-too-common error.

CROSS-CULTURAL RESEARCH

In the past two decades, researchers have studied people from various ethnic or cultural groups to see whether they experience attraction, intimacy, and love in similar ways. Three topics that have been studied are the impact of culture on how people view love, on whom people fall in love with, and on the importance of love in decisions to marry.

Cultural Values and the Meaning of Love. Cross-cultural psychologists have identified two dimensions on which cultures vary (Hatfield & Rapson, 1993a). The first is individualism–collectivism. *Individualistic cultures,* like those of Canada, the United States, and Western European countries, tend to emphasize individual goals over group and societal goals and interests. *Collectivist cultures,* like those of China, Africa, and southeast Asian countries, emphasize group and collective goals over personal ones. Several specific traits have been identified that differentiate these two types of societies (Triandis et al., 1990). In individualistic cultures, behaviour is regulated by individual attitudes and cost–benefit considerations; emotional detachment from the group is accepted. In collectivist cultures, the self is defined by group membership; behaviour is regulated by group norms; attachment to and harmony within the group are valued.

The two types of cultures have different conceptions of love. The majority group in Canadian society, for example, emphasizes passionate love as the basis for marriage (Dion & Dion, 1993b). Individuals select mates on the basis of such characteristics as physical attractiveness, similarity (compatibility), and wealth or resources. We look for intimacy in the relationship with our mate. In Chinese society, by contrast, many marriages are arranged; the primary criterion is that the two families be of similar status. The person finds intimacy in relationships with other family members.

The second dimension on which cultures differ is independence–interdependence. Many Western cultures view each person as independent, and value individuality and uniqueness. Many other cultures view the person as interdependent with those around him or her. The self is defined

Figure 12.9 Whether a culture is individualistic or collectivistic determines its views on love and marriage. In Canada, which is an individualistic culture, individuals choose each other and marry for love. In India, a collectivistic culture, marriages are arranged by family members to serve family interests.

in relation to others. Canadians value standing up for one's beliefs. The people of India value conformity and harmony within the group.

Dion and Dion (1993a) studied university students in Toronto, representing four ethnocultural groups. Students from Asian backgrounds were more likely to view love as companionate, as friendship, in contrast to those from English and Irish backgrounds. This tendency is consistent with the collectivist orientation of Asian cultures.

Cultural Influences on Mate Selection. Buss (1989) conducted a large-scale survey of 10 000 men and women from 37 societies. The sample included people from four cultures in Africa, eight in Asia, and four in eastern Europe, in addition to 12 Western European and 4 North American ones. Each respondent was given a list of 18 characteristics one might value in a potential mate and asked to rate how important each was to him or her personally. Regardless of which society they lived in, most respondents, male and female, rated intelligence, kindness, and understanding at the top of the list; note that these are characteristics of companionate love. Men worldwide placed more weight on cues of reproductive capacity, such as physical attractiveness; women rated cues of resources as more important. The results support the sociobiological perspective and suggest that there are not large cultural differences in mate selection.

Many people prefer mates who are physically attractive. We often hear that "beauty is in the eye of the beholder." This saying suggests that standards of beauty might vary across cultures. In one study, researchers had students from varying cultural backgrounds rate 45 photographs of women on a scale ranging from very attractive to very unattractive (Cunningham et al., 1995). The photographs portrayed women from many different societies. Overall, Asian, Hispanic, and white students did not differ in their ratings of the individual photographs. However, Asian students' ratings were less influenced by indicators of sexual maturity (such as facial narrowness) and expressivity (such as the vertical distance between the lips when the person smiled). In a separate study, black men and white men gave similar ratings to most aspects of female faces, but black men preferred women with heavier bodies than did white men. Again, the results indicate more similarities than differences across cultures, in this case in standards of physical attractiveness.

Love and Marriage. We noted earlier that individualistic cultures place a high value on romantic love, while collectivist cultures emphasize the group. The importance of romantic love in North American society is illustrated by responses to the question, "If a man (woman) had all the other qualities you desired, would you marry this person if you were not in love with him (her)?" Over time, increasing percentages of North American men and women answer no. The change has been greater for women.

Researchers asked this question of men and women in 11 different cultures (Levine et al., 1995). We would predict that members of individualistic cultures would answer no, whereas those in collectivist cultures would answer yes. Research has shown that, as predicted, many—about half of Indians and Pakistanis—would marry even though they didn't love the person (Levine et al., 1995). In Thailand, which is also collectivist, 19 percent said yes. In the individualistic cultures of Australia, England, and the United States, less than 7 percent of people would marry someone they did not love.

When we look at the findings of the cross-cultural research on love, attraction, and marriage, the pattern that emerges is one of *cross-cultural similarities and cross-cultural differences*, a theme we introduced in Chapter 1. That is, some phenomena are similar across cultures; for example, valuing intelligence, kindness, and understanding in a mate. Other phenomena differ substantially across cultures; for example, whether love is a prerequisite for marriage. However, even in Asian (collectivist) societies young people are increasingly seeing love as a basis for marriage (Dion & Dion, 1993a). However, they may see love as developing after marriage rather than as a prerequisite for marriage.

IN FOCUS 12.2

Why I Chose to Have an Arranged Marriage

On my wedding day, I remember thinking that my choice of wanting an arranged marriage was rare for someone living in the West, but I later realized that having an arranged marriage is not atypical for many individuals in North America and around the world.

I was born in Fiji Islands and immigrated at the age of seven to Vancouver, Canada, with my parents and younger brother. Though I was raised in a traditional, Muslim home, I was nonetheless still affected by Western, social ideals. The clash of cultures became more apparent as I matured.

My mother, a strong member of our religious community, travels the world in her efforts to spread Islam. Ever since I turned 18, she had been sending me photographs and "résumés" of girls (i.e., potential wives) she had met during her journeys. As usual, I would return the photos to my mother, with a lengthy explanation of what I considered to be the many limitations to an arranged marriage and how I would marry a girl I fall in love with and have known for some time.

Luckily for me, my denials and many "rejections" fell on deaf ears. In the Spring of 1997, my mother sent me a package. It contained some souvenirs from her recent visit of Pakistan and four pictures of Ayesha, a young woman from Peshawar. As I looked carefully at the photos of this person, studying the softness of her complexion, the welcoming nature of her smile, the innocence of her gaze, something inside me wanted to know more about her.

I telephoned my mother and began asking her about the mysterious woman in the photos. At my very utterance of Ayesha's name, my mother let out a slightly audible sigh, one, which if given words to, would say, "Yes! I finally got him!"

This was one of the longest phone conversations I had with my mother. I learned that Ayesha was a caring, loving and family-oriented person (qualities I admire), who, like me, also majored in English Literature and Psychology. The more I heard, the more I liked.

Of course, being raised in Canada, in a society where mothers and sons do not always prefer the same girl, I had to find out for myself. I asked my mother for Ayesha's phone number, but was met with resistance: "Her parents will not allow a strange man to speak with her on the phone." Is this for real, I thought. Do the parents really expect me to marry their daughter without getting to know her? At this point I felt like abandoning this whole fantasy I had of meeting this "Pakistani Princess."

My mother then suggested that I fly to Peshawar to meet Ayesha and her family. Trusting my mother's good intentions and my own inner voice, I took time off from my practice and flew to Pakistan. Somewhere over the Atlantic Ocean, I remember thinking about stories I had heard of other men traveling overseas to meet women. The stories were similar. When they visited the home of the women, these women were adorned in their finest clothes, wore copious amounts of make-up and even cooked the meal, behavior aimed at impressing their potential husbands.

I was no doubt surprised, then, when I met Ayesha, who greeted me with not a speck of make-up on. She had on clothes, which, while pleasant-looking, were not anything extraordinary. And she did not cook, nor help, with dinner.

What happens when an individual from a collectivist culture is raised in Canada? In Focus 12.2 tells the story of a Canadian man's decision to enter into an arranged marriage.

COMMUNICATION

Consider the following situation involving Chris and Donna (we have purposely left Chris's gender ambiguous—Chris and Donna could be a lesbian or a heterosexual couple.)

> Chris and Donna have been living together for about three years. Donna had had sex with only one other person before Chris, and she had never masturbated. Since they've been together, she has had orgasms only twice during lovemaking, despite the fact that they make love three or four times per week. She has been reading some magazine articles about female sexuality and is beginning to think that she should be experiencing more sexual satisfaction. As far as she knows, Chris is unaware that there is any problem. Donna feels lonely and a bit sad.

What should Donna do? She needs to communicate with Chris. They apparently have not

Ayesha was different from the rest. She was unique and real. In trying not to peak my interest, she did just that.

Our interest for each other developed with our first lone conversation. I didn't want to tell Ayesha of my academic or professional achievements and question her on her domestic acumen (as is the typical queries in such meetings). I wanted to know about her interests, her passions, about her. As we felt more comfortable with each other, I asked her what types of books she liked to read, to which she responded with every relationship therapist's idea of romance—"love stories," she said, modestly looking at me for a response. I accepted Ayesha's openness and courage with an appreciative smile.

Realizing that my mother had told Ayesha's family that I was a psychologist, it was important for me that Ayesha know of my specialization. In telling her that I am a Clinical Sexologist, not only did she not judge me, she in fact grew curious about my career and later shared that I must be helping many people in need.

It was obvious to us that we had already begun to satisfy each other's needs. That night, the night of our first meeting, I shared with my mother my intentions of wanting to marry Ayesha. The next morning, my mother took a formal proposal to Ayesha's mother, who discussed the proposal with Ayesha. Ayesha accepted the proposal and we were wed ten days later.

I returned to Canada shortly after our wedding (our Nikka) and began the sponsoring process. Ayesha and I talked almost every day for about one year. In fact, we dated by phone and fell in love, long-distance, after we got married. Imagine that.

On May 2nd, 2007, Ayesha and I, along with our two beautiful daughters, Malaika and Alishba, celebrated our tenth year of wedded bliss. So, is having an arranged marriage the secret to our happiness? Maybe and maybe not. Ayesha and my relationship is based on six key qualities: love, openness, a non-judgmental attitude, respect, commitment and trust (I, till this day, have never broken a promise to her). When you consider that these same qualities also result in happy non-arranged marriages, it makes us wonder about the deeper meaning of the institution of marriage, regardless of how the individuals meet.

Her Perspective

I come from a traditional, yet open-minded family. Since it is typical for parents in Pakistan to arrange a marriage for their children, when my parents asked me if they could do the same for me, I had no objections. I trusted my parents and put my faith in God to find the "right" person for me.

When my parents told me that a family from Canada was coming to visit us, I sensed that they would be special because my parents had never asked me to meet any other families who were also interested in meeting me.

When I first met Faizal, I didn't even clearly see his face because it is a custom for women to not make eye contact with a man who is not related to them. However, from the way he spoke, I could sense his gentle personality and caring ways. Though we talked alone for an hour, I remember time just flying by—it was so easy and so much fun to talk to him that I could imagine my married life with him being full of love and happiness.

I hardly knew Faizal when we first got married. Soon afterward, I began to slowly fall in love with him, and ever since I am falling more and more in love with him every day.

Source: Faizal Sahukhan, Ph.D., sex therapist, university instructor, advice columnist, radio host, author. www.multiculturalromance.com

---

communicated much about sex in the last three years, and they need to begin. The following sections will discuss the relationship between sex, communication, and relationships and provide some suggestions on how to communicate effectively.

COMMUNICATION AND RELATIONSHIPS

A good deal of research has looked at differences in communication patterns between non-distressed (happy) couples and distressed (unhappy, seeking relationship counselling) heterosexual couples. This research shows, in general, that distressed couples tend to have communication deficits (Gottman, 1994). Further, research in Quebec has shown that heterosexual, gay male, and lesbian couples do not differ in their communication skills or in the contribution of communication deficits to their relationship adjustment (Julien et al., 2003). Research also shows that couples with sexual problems have poorer sexual and non-sexual communication than couples without sexual problems (Kelly et al., 2006). Of course, many other factors contribute to relationship conflict or sex problems, but poor communication

IN FOCUS 12.3

Sexuality and Disability: Constructing a Sexual Blueprint

For most people, coming out as a sexual being is just assumed. It isn't something they have to declare and take a stand for—that is, unless they live with a disability like I do. Whenever I talk about sexuality and disability the "elephant in the room" that tends not to get named, but is so very much part of the conversation, is that sex for people with a disability is somehow not the "real thing" or that we really don't have the same feelings when we're kissed, touched or fucked. I'm here to tell you that we do have the same sensations, wants and desires as anyone else, kink, vanilla or otherwise. And when you have a disability and declare that you're queer, well, that's a whole other story!!

Part of my work in the community is that of a sexual health educator and I have been educating people about sexuality and disability more than 10 years. I began to do this work because of my own journey discovering how to be sexual in a world that overtly says that people with disabilities shouldn't have sex, relationships and all the trimmings or "trappings" that go with them. My interest in talking to groups about sexuality and disability is personal—it's important to me to remove the mystery and misconceptions that people have about what sex is like for disabled folks. I want to connect with people on a very real level that acknowledges the fragility of the body and that disability or difference is something that can enter into anyone's life whether through aging, illness or accident. People with disabilities actually have lots to teach about pushing the boundaries surrounding conventional ideas about sex, how to make love, and notions of intimacy with oneself and with another person. I felt that it was so important to get the message out that I also co-authored a book on sexuality and disability entitled *The Ultimate Guide to Sex and Disability*.

In my own journey of sexual discovery, I experimented sexually with my male and female friends, all of whom lived with disabilities. My first sexual relationship was with a man when I was 18. We both lived with physical disability. Negotiating a sexual relationship was challenging but most of all it was fun, exciting, and very hot. I later had relationships with other men, some living with some form of physical disability and others not. I had to learn to create opportunities for communication because each sexual experience forced me and my partner to confront our assumptions. This meant that both of us had to ask questions about our desires as well as about what felt pleasurable and what didn't. Communication is important, although not easy, for everyone but particularly for people with a disability.

In one of the chapters of *The Ultimate Guide to Sex and Disability*, we wrote:

> Despite what people actually experience, many still view sex as something that is the same for everybody "normal", and inferior for the rest of us. Every person needs to discover what sex is to her/him, how it feels, what she/he respond to. Constructing a sexual blueprint, an understanding of where you have more or less sexual sensation, what your body looks like (inside and out), its textures and rhythms, leads to a healthier sexuality for anyone.

Whether my partner is someone living with disabilities or not, I am reminded that I can't rely on what I know from previous experiences. I have to be open to really exploring what's pleasurable and hot with this new person.

In my twenties through to my late thirties, my primary sexual relationships were with men. When I was 37, I fell in love and fell hard for a woman younger than myself. Although we were only together for a short period of time, I had previously never felt the depth of emotional and physical connection in a relationship that I had with her. I felt that I really had found where I belonged. Since then, my primary relationships have been with women, again some living with disability and others not. It really doesn't matter to me whether they have a disability. What does matter is how we feel together: whether the chemistry is there; whether we can make each other laugh; and, what we each bring to the relationship that keeps it alive, interesting and hot.

The bottom line is that people with disabilities, straight or queer, *are* sexual—and as often as possible.

Source: Fran Odette is Program Manager of the Women with Disabilities and Violence Program at Springtide Resources (formerly Education Wife Assault) in Toronto.

patterns are certainly among them. The problem with this research is that it is correlational (see Chapter 3 for a discussion of this problem in research methods); in particular, we cannot tell whether poor communication causes unhappy relationships or whether unhappy relationships create poor communication patterns.

An elegant longitudinal study designed to meet this problem provides evidence that unrewarding, ineffective communication precedes and predicts later relationship problems (Markman, 1979, 1981). Heterosexual dating couples who were planning marriage were studied for 5.5 years. Couples with better communication at the beginning of the study were more satisfied with their relationship when they were followed up 2.5 and 5.5 years later.

On the basis of this notion that communication deficits cause communication problems, relationship counsellors and therapists often work on teaching couples communication skills. Recent research suggests that distressed couples do not always differ from non-distressed couples in their communication skills or ability; rather, some distressed couples use their skills as weapons, to send negative messages (Burleson & Denton, 1997; Gottman & Notarius, 2002). These results suggest that therapists should focus on the intent of the partners as they communicate with each other, not just on techniques.

But what are these negative messages? Gottman (1994) used audiotape, videotape, and monitoring of physiological arousal to answer this question. He identified four destructive patterns of interaction: criticism, contempt, defensiveness, and withdrawal. *Criticism* refers to attacking a partner's personality or character: "You are so selfish; you never think of anyone else." *Contempt* is intentionally insulting or orally abusing the other person: "How did I get hooked up with such a loser?" *Defensiveness* refers to denying responsibility, making excuses, replying with a complaint of one's own, and other self-protective responses, instead of addressing the problem. *Withdrawal* involves such activities as responding to the partner's complaint with silence, turning on the TV, or walking out of the room in anger. You can probably see that these types of communication are likely to lead to an escalation of the hostility rather than a solution to the problem. In fact, a Quebec study found that a pattern of withdrawal was associated with a decrease in relationship adjustment (Guay et al., 2003).

On the other hand, positive communication is important in developing and maintaining intimate relationships. In the following discussions, we describe some of the skills involved in positive sexual communication.

SEXUAL SELF-DISCLOSURE

As discussed earlier in this chapter, one of the keys to building a good relationship is self-disclosure. One of the keys to building a satisfying *sexual* relationship is *sexual* self-disclosure. Sexual self-disclosure involves telling personal sexual things about yourself. It may range from sharing your sexual likes and dislikes to disclosing about an unwanted sexual experience you had with a previous partner.

Sexual self-disclosure: Telling personal sexual things about yourself such as your sexual likes and dislikes.

How much do couples self-disclose about their preferences? In a survey of more than 3000 Canadian men and women, 97 percent said that they were sometimes or always able to discuss sex with their partner openly; however, only 28 percent had had one or more serious discussions in the past year (Auld et al., 2002). According to one New Brunswick study of individuals in heterosexual dating relationships, although people do talk to their dating partner about their sexual likes and dislikes, they do not fully reveal their personal feelings about them (Byers & Demmons, 1999). Both the men and the women in this study revealed more to their partner about their non-sexual feelings than about their sexual feelings and more about what they liked sexually than about what they didn't like. However, the more one member of the couple self-disclosed sexually, the more they reported that their partner did so too. That is, the sexual self-disclosure by one partner was reciprocated by the other partner, perhaps because self-disclosure by a partner assures us that he or she is comfortable talking about sex and shares similar values (Herold & Way, 1988).

Sexual self-disclosure leads to sexual satisfaction in two ways (MacNeil & Byers, 2005). First, it increases intimacy between partners. Talking about sexual likes and dislikes allows partners to feel closer to each other and see themselves as compatible (Offman & Matheson, 2005). Feeling closer and more satisfied with the non-sexual aspects of the relationship leads to higher sexual satisfaction. Second, sharing what pleases and displeases us sexually with our partner allows them to learn about our sexual preferences. This kind of understanding helps partners to negotiate mutually enjoyable sexual interactions. That is, by telling our partner what we like and don't like sexually, we receive more of what we want and less of what we don't want during sexual interactions (Byers & Demmons, 1999; MacNeil & Byers, 1997; Purnine & Carey, 1997). In turn, having more pleasing sexual interactions is associated with enhanced sexual satisfaction.

Sexual self-disclosure is especially important for maintaining sexual satisfaction in long-term relationships. In contrast, early in a relationship, sex is new and exciting and may feel satisfying even though our partner is not fully aware of what pleases and displeases us sexually (Byers, 1999).

BEING AN EFFECTIVE COMMUNICATOR

Back to Donna and Chris: One of the first things to do in this type of situation is to decide to talk to one's partner, admitting that there is a problem. Then the issue is to resolve to communicate, and particularly to be an *effective* communicator. Suppose Donna begins by saying,

> You're not giving me any orgasms when we have sex.   (1)

Chris gets angry and walks away or gets upset. Donna meant to communicate that she wasn't having any orgasms, but Chris thought she meant that Chris was a lousy lover.

Intent: What the speaker means.

Impact: What someone else understands the speaker to mean.

Effective communicator: A communicator whose impact matches his or her intent.

It is important to recognize the distinction between **intent** and **impact** in communicating (Gottman et al., 1976; Purnine & Carey, 1997). Intent is what you mean. Impact is what the other person thinks you mean. An **effective communicator** is one whose impact matches her or his intent. Donna wasn't an effective communicator in the above example because the impact on Chris was considerably different from her intent. Notice that effectiveness does not depend on the content of the message. One can be as effective at communicating contempt as communicating praise.

Many people value spontaneity in sex, and this attitude may extend to communicating about sex. It is best to recognize that to be an effective communicator, you may need to plan your strategy. It often takes some thinking to figure out how to make sure that your impact will match your intent. Planning also allows you to make sure that the timing is good—that you are not speaking out of anger, or that your partner is not tired or preoccupied with other things.

In the last few decades public communication about sex has become relatively open, but private communication remains difficult (Crawford et al., 1994). This doesn't mean that Donna can't communicate. But she shouldn't feel guilty or stupid if it is difficult for her. And she will be better off if she uses some specific communication skills and has some belief that they will work. The sections that follow suggest some skills that are useful in being an effective communicator and how to apply these to sexual relationships.

GOOD MESSAGES

"I" language: Speaking for yourself, using the word "I"; not mind reading.

Every couple has problems. The best way to voice them is to complain rather than to criticize (Gottman, 1994). Complaining involves the use of **"I" language**, in which you speak about your own thoughts and feelings rather than about your partner. Research has shown that non-distressed couples are more likely to self-disclose thoughts and feelings during problem-solving (Gottman & Notarius, 2002). By using "I" language, your partner is less likely to

Figure 12.10

become defensive. "I" language uses soft emotions such as feelings of unhappiness or concern rather than hard emotions such as anger. Thus, if Donna were to use this technique, she might say,

I feel a bit unhappy because I don't have orgasms very often when we make love.   (2)

Notice that she focuses specifically on herself. There is less cause for Chris to get angry, upset, or defensive than there was in message 1.

One of the best things about "I" language is that it avoids mind reading (Gottman et al., 1976). Suppose Donna says,

I know you think I'm not much interested in sex, but I really wish I had more orgasms.   (3)

She is engaging in **mind reading**. That is, she is making certain assumptions about what Chris is thinking. She assumes that Chris believes she isn't interested in sex or having orgasms. Research shows that mind reading is more common among distressed couples than among non-distressed couples (Gottman et al., 1977). Worse, Donna doesn't *check out* her assumptions with Chris. The problem is that she may be wrong, and Chris may not think that at all. "I" language helps Donna avoid this by focusing on herself and what she feels rather than on what Chris is doing or failing to do. Another important way to avoid mind reading is by giving and receiving feedback, a technique discussed in a later section.

Documenting is another important component of giving good messages (Brenton, 1972). In documenting you give specific examples of the issue. This is not quite so relevant in Donna's case, because she is talking about a general problem; but even here, specific documenting can be helpful. Once Donna has broached the subject, she might say,

Last night when we made love, I enjoyed it and it felt really good, but then I didn't have an orgasm, and then I felt disappointed.   (4)

Now she has gotten her general complaint down to a specific situation that Chris can remember.

Suppose further that Donna has some idea of what Chris would need to do to bring her to orgasm: she would like more sensual touching or more oral stimulation of her clitoris. Then she might do specific documenting as follows:

Last night when we made love, I enjoyed it, but I didn't have an orgasm, and then I felt disappointed. I think what I needed was for you to stimulate my clitoris with your mouth a bit more. You did it for a while, but it seemed so brief. I think if you had kept doing it for two or three minutes more, I would have had an orgasm.   (5)

Now she has not only documented to Chris exactly what the problem was, but she has given a specific suggestion about what could have been done about it, and therefore what could be done in the future.

Mind reading: Making assumptions about what your partner thinks or feels.

Documenting: Giving specific examples of the issue being discussed.

Another technique in giving good messages is to offer *limited choices* (Langer & Dweck, 1973). Rather than asking a question that can be answered with a "yes" or a "no," she might say,

> I've been having trouble with orgasms when we make love. Would you like to discuss it now, or would you rather wait until tomorrow night?   (6)

Now, either answer Chris gives will be acceptable to her; she has offered a set of acceptable limited choices.[4] She has also shown some consideration for Chris by recognizing that this might not be a good time for a discussion.

LEVELLING AND EDITING

Levelling: Telling your partner what you are feeling by stating your thoughts clearly, simply, and honestly.

Levelling means telling your partner what you are feeling by stating your thoughts clearly, simply, and honestly—that is, self-disclosing your feelings (Gottman et al., 1976). This is often the hardest step in communication, especially when the topic is sex. It is especially difficult for adults to reach shared understandings about sex, since there is great secrecy about it in our society (Crawford et al., 1994). In levelling, keep in mind that the purposes are:

1. To make communication clear
2. To clear up what partners expect of each other
3. To clear up what is pleasant and what is unpleasant
4. To clear up what is relevant and what is irrelevant
5. To notice things that draw you closer or push you apart (Gottman et al., 1976)

Editing: Censoring or not saying things that would be deliberately hurtful to your partner or that are irrelevant.

When you begin to level with your partner, you also need to do some editing. Editing involves censoring (not saying) things that would be deliberately hurtful to your partner or that would be irrelevant. You must take responsibility for making your communication polite and considerate. Levelling, then, should not mean a "no holds barred" approach. Ironically, research indicates that married people are ruder to each other than they are to strangers (Gottman et al., 1976). This is likely also true of all partners in long-term relationships.

Donna may be so disgruntled about her lack of orgasms that she's thinking of having sex with someone else to jolt Chris into recognizing her problem, or perhaps in order to see if another partner would stimulate her to orgasm. Donna is probably best advised to edit out this line of thought and concentrate on the specific problem: her lack of orgasms. Having sex with someone else is not likely to magically solve her problem. If she and Chris can work it out together, Donna will not only be more sexually satisfied but their relationship also will be stronger.

The trick is to balance levelling and editing. If you edit too much, you may not level at all, and there will be no communication. If you level too much and don't edit, the communication will fail because your partner will respond negatively, and things may get worse rather than better.

LISTENING

Up to this point, we have been concentrating on techniques for you to use in sending messages about sexual relationships. But, of course, communication is a two-way street, and you and your partner will exchange responses. It is therefore important for you and your partner to gain some skills in listening and responding constructively to messages. The following discussion will suggest such techniques.

One of the most important things is that you must really *listen*. This means more than just

---

[4]The technique of limited choices is useful in a number of other situations, including dealing with children. For example, if your two-year-old daughter had finished watching *Sesame Street* and you wanted the TV turned off, you wouldn't say, "Would you turn the TV off?" (she might say "no") but, rather, "Do you want to turn off the TV, or would you like me to?"

removing the headphones from your ears. It means actively trying to understand what the other person is saying. Often people are so busy trying to think of their next response that they hardly hear what the other person is saying. Good listening also involves positive non-verbal behaviours, such as maintaining eye contact with the speaker and nodding one's head when appropriate. Be a *non-defensive listener,* focus on what your partner is saying and feeling, and don't immediately become defensive, or counterattack with complaints of your own.

The next step, after you have listened carefully and non-defensively, is to give *feedback.* This often involves brief vocalizations—"Uh-huh," "Okay"—nodding your head, or facial movements that indicate you are listening (Gottman et al., 1998). It may involve the technique of paraphrasing—that is, repeating in your own words what you think your partner meant. Suppose, in response to Donna's initial statement, "You're not giving me any orgasms when we have sex," Chris hadn't gotten upset and instead had tried to listen and then gave her feedback by paraphrasing. Chris might have responded,

> I hear you saying that I'm not very good at making love to you, and therefore you're not having orgasms.   (7)

At that point, Donna would have had a chance to clear up the confusion she had created with her initial message, because Chris had given her feedback by paraphrasing. At that point she could have said, "No, I think you're a good lover, but I'm not having any orgasms, and I don't know why. I thought maybe we could figure it out together." Or perhaps she could have said, "No, I think you're a good lover. I just wish you'd do more of some of the things you do, like going down on me and stimulating my clitoris with your tongue."

It's also a good idea to *ask for feedback* from your partner, particularly if you're not sure whether you're communicating clearly.

Body Talk: Non-verbal Communication

Just as it is important to be a good listener to your partner's verbal messages, so too is it important to be good at reading your partner's non-verbal messages. Often the precise words we use are not so important as our **non-verbal communication**—the way we say them. Tone of voice, expression on the face, position of the body, whether you touch the other person—all are important in conveying the message.

As an example, take the sentence "So you're here." If it is delivered "So *you're* here" in a hostile tone of voice, the message is that the speaker is very unhappy that you're here. If it is delivered "So you're *here*" in a pleased voice, the meaning may be that the speaker is glad and surprised to see you here in Newfoundland, having thought you were in Europe. "So you're here" with a smile and arms outstretched to initiate a hug might mean that the speaker has been waiting for you and is delighted to see you.

Suppose that in Donna and Chris's case, the reason Donna doesn't have more orgasms is that Chris doesn't stimulate her firmly enough or in the spot that feels best to her. During sex, Donna is worried that it is taking her too long to reach orgasm and that Chris is getting tired or bored stimulating her. (Notice that Donna is mind reading again.) As a result, Donna does not enjoy the stimulation she does get as much as she could, and her body language communicates that she's not really into it. Chris already believes that Donna does not really like sex and the response (or rather non-response) of her body confirms these assumptions. Chris reads Donna's body language as communicating that she's not really enjoying having her clitoris stimulated. Although she would like to have an orgasm and for Chris to keep stimulating her, her body is saying "I'm not into this. Let's get it over with." And that's exactly what Chris does.

To correct this situation, Donna might adopt a more active, encouraging approach. She might take Chris's hand and guide it to her clitoris, showing exactly where and how firmly she likes to have it rubbed. She might give Chris verbal feedback, saying "That's good" when

Paraphrasing: Saying in your own words what you think your partner meant.

Non-verbal communication: Communication not through words, but through the body (e.g., eye contact, tone of voice, touching).

Chris touches her in a way that she likes, or "Please don't stop" if she wants oral stimulation to continue.

The point is that in communicating about sex, we need to be sure that our non-verbal signals help to create the impact we intend rather than one we don't intend. It is also possible that non-verbal signals are confusing communication and need to be straightened out. "Checking out" is a technique for doing this that will be discussed in a later section.

Interestingly, research shows that distressed couples differ from non-distressed couples more in their non-verbal communication than in their verbal communication (Gottman et al., 1977; Vincent et al., 1979). For example, even when a person from a distressed couple is expressing agreement with his or her partner, that person is more likely to accompany the verbal expressions of agreement with negative non-verbal behaviour. Distressed couples are also more likely to be negative listeners—while listening, the individuals are more likely to display frowning, angry, or disgusted facial expressions, or tense or inattentive body postures. Contempt is often expressed non-verbally, by sneering or rolling the eyes, for example. In contrast, harmonious relationships are characterized by closer physical distances and more relaxed postures than are found in distressed couples (Beier & Sternberg, 1977). Once again, it is not only what we say verbally but how we say it, and how we listen, that makes the difference.

VALIDATING

Validation: Telling your partner that, given his or her point of view, you can see why he or she thinks a certain way.

Another good technique in communication is validation (Gottman et al., 1976), which means telling your partner that, given his or her point of view, you can see why he or she thinks a certain way. It doesn't mean that you agree with your partner or that you're giving in. It simply means that you recognize your partner's point of view as legitimate, given his or her set of assumptions, which may be different from yours.

It is important to recognize that all couples will have disagreements. What is important is how you handle these disagreements. If they lead to fights because one partner thinks the other is "wrong," these will likely damage the relationship. It is much better to try to understand the other person's viewpoint. In a study of 76 couples, understanding of the partner's preferences for such things as sexual techniques, use of erotica, and use of contraception (not agreement with them) was associated with satisfaction with the sexual aspects of the relationship (Purnine & Carey, 1997).

Suppose that Donna and Chris have gotten into an argument about cunnilingus. Donna thinks it would bring her to orgasm. Chris doesn't want to do it and feels very uncomfortable with the idea. If Donna tried to validate Chris's feelings, she might say,

> I can understand the way you feel about going down on me, especially given the way you were brought up to think about sex.   (8)

Chris might validate Donna's feelings by saying,

> I understand how important it is for you to have an orgasm.   (9)

Validating hasn't solved their disagreement, but it has left the door open so that they can now make some progress.

DRAWING YOUR PARTNER OUT

Suppose it is Chris who initiates the conversation rather than Donna. Chris has noticed that Donna doesn't seem to get a lot of pleasure out of sex, and would like to find out why and see what they can do about it. Chris needs to draw Donna out and might begin by saying,

> I've noticed lately that you don't seem to be enjoying sex as much as you used to. Am I right about that?   (10)

That much is good because Chris is checking out an assumption. Unfortunately, the question leads to a "yes" or "no" answer, and that can stop the communication. So, if Donna replies "yes," Chris had better follow it up with an *open-ended* question like

> Why do you think you aren't enjoying it more?   (11)

If Donna can give a reasonable answer, good communication should be on the way. One of the standard—and best—questions to ask in a situation like this is

> What can we do to make things better?   (12)

ACCENTUATE THE POSITIVE

We have been concentrating on negative communications, that is, communications in which some problem or complaint needs to be voiced. It is also important to communicate positive things about the relationship in general and sex in particular (Gottman & Notarius, 2002). If that was a great episode of lovemaking, or the best kiss you've ever experienced, say so. A learning theorist would say that you're giving your partner some positive reinforcement. As discussed earlier in this chapter, social psychologists' research shows that we tend to like people better who give us positive reinforcements. Recognition of the strengths in a relationship offers the potential for enriching it (e.g., Miller et al., 1975). And if you make a habit of positive communications about sex, it will be easier to initiate the negative ones and they will be better received.

Most communication during sex is limited to muffled groans, or "Mm-m's," or an occasional "Faster, John" or "Did you, Michèle?" It might help your partner greatly if you gave frequent verbal and non-verbal feedback, such as "That was great" or "Let's do that again." This would make the positive communications and the negative ones far easier.

Research shows that non-distressed couples make more positive and fewer negative communications than distressed couples (Billings, 1979). In fact, Gottman's (1994) research with married couples found that there is a *magic ratio* of positive to negative communication. In stable marriages, there is five times as much positive interaction—verbal and non-verbal, including hugs and kisses, as there is negative. Not only do happy couples make more positive communications; they are more likely to respond to a negative communication with something positive (Billings, 1979). Distressed couples, on the other hand, are more likely to respond to negative communication with more negative communication, escalating into conflict. We might all take a cue from the happy couples and make efforts not only to increase our positive communications but even to make them in response to negative comments from our partner.

FIGHTING FAIR

Even if you use all the techniques just described, you may still get into arguments with your partner. Arguments are a natural part of a relationship and are not necessarily bad. Given that there will be arguments in a relationship, it is useful if you and

(a)

(b)

Figure 12.11 *(a)* A couple with good body language (good eye contact and body position); *(b)* A couple with poor body language (poor eye contact and body position).

Fighting fair: A set of rules designed to make arguments constructive rather than destructive.

your partner have agreed to a set of rules called fighting fair (Bach & Wyden, 1969) so that the arguments may help and won't hurt.

Here are some of the basic rules for arguing that may be useful to you (Brenton, 1972; Creighton, 1992). Many of them relate to the four destructive communication patterns identified by John Gottman (1999).

1. Edit what you say. Don't make sarcastic or insulting remarks about your partner's sexual adequacy. This generates resentment, opens you to counterattack, and is just a dirty way to fight.
2. Don't bring up the names of former partners, lovers, boyfriends, or girlfriends to illustrate how all these problems didn't happen with them. Stick to the issue: your relationship with your partner.
3. Don't play amateur psychologist. Don't say things like "The problem is that you're a compulsive personality" or "You acted that way because you never resolved your Oedipus complex." You really don't have the qualifications (even after reading this book) to do so. Even if you did, your partner is likely to think you are biased and so would not be apt to recognize your expertise in the middle of an argument.
4. Don't engage in dumping. Don't store up gripes for six months and then dump them on your partner all at one time.
5. Don't hit and run. Don't bring up a serious negative issue when there is no opportunity to continue the discussion, such as when you're on the way out the door going to work or when guests are coming for dinner in five minutes.
6. Don't focus on who's to blame. Focus on looking for solutions, not on who's at fault. If you avoid blaming, it lets both you and your partner save face, which helps both of you feel better about the relationship.

Figure 12.12 Arguments are not necessarily bad for a relationship, but it is important to observe the rules for "fighting fair," unlike this couple.

CHECKING OUT SEXY SIGNALS

One of the problems with verbal and non-verbal sexual communications is that they are often ambiguous. This problem may occur more often with couples who don't know each other well, but it can cause uncertainty and misunderstanding in couples in long-term relationships as well.

Some messages are very direct. Statements like "I want to have sex with you" are not ambiguous at all. Unfortunately, such directness is not common in our society. Two New Brunswick studies show that only a minority of people in opposite-sex relationships—22 percent in dating relationships and 41 percent in long-term relationships—use a direct verbal statement to initiate sex (Byers & Heinlein, 1989; O'Sullivan & Byers, 1992). The rest use ambiguous verbal or non-verbal messages. Similarly, Ontario researchers found that men and women in same-sex relationships are more likely to initiate sex using non-verbal than using verbal behaviours (Beres et al., 2004). Consider George, who stands up, stretches, and says "It's time for bed." Does he mean he wants to engage in sexual activity or to go to sleep?

Ambiguous messages can lead to feelings of hurt and rejection, or to unnecessary anger and perhaps complaints to third parties. If George wants to have sex but his partner interprets his behaviour as meaning that George is tired, George may go to bed feeling hurt, unattractive, and unloved. A woman who casually puts her arm around the shoulders of a co-worker and gives him or her a hug may find herself explaining to her supervisor that it was a gesture of friendship, not a sexual proposition.

When we confront ambiguous messages, we should check out their meaning. The problem is that most of us are reluctant to do that. Somehow we assume that we ought to know exactly what the other person meant, and that we are dumb or naïve if we don't. It is important to recognize that many "sexy signals"—like putting an arm around someone's shoulders, inviting a date to your apartment for coffee, or french-kissing while rubbing your date's (clothed) buttocks—really are ambiguous. Ideally, each of us should be effective communicators, making sure our message clearly matches our intent. It helps to be clear yet also subtle and seductive as messages that are too direct/polite may be a turn-off (Graham et al., 2004). As recipients of ambiguous messages, we need to make an effort to clear them up. In response to an invitation to a woman's apartment for coffee, a man might reply, "I would like some coffee, but I'm not interested in sex this time." Or he might draw her out with a question: "I'd like some coffee; is that all you have in mind?" Check out sexy signals. Don't make any assumptions about the meaning of ambiguous messages.

GENDER DIFFERENCES IN COMMUNICATION

Some authors argue that men and women have radically different verbal communication styles (Tannen, 1991). We should not be led astray by flashy claims that men and women are so different that they belong to different linguistic communities. Research generally has shown that although there are some gender differences in communication, in general these differences are small (see Chapter 13). So whether an individual is in a relationship with a partner of the same gender or of the other gender, with a little effort couples should be able to engage in clear, accurate sexual communication.

SUMMARY

For most people—heterosexual, gay, and lesbian—emotional passion and sexual passion are closely linked. Unfortunately, much of the research on love has been restricted to heterosexuals and has not included gay men, lesbians, or bisexuals.

Research indicates that mere repeated exposure to another person facilitates attraction. We tend to be attracted to people who are similar to us socially (age, race or ethnicity, economic status) and psychologically (attitudes, interests). In first impressions, we are most attracted to people who are physically attractive; we also tend to be attracted to people whom we believe to be "within reach" of us, depending on our sense of our own attractiveness or desirability.

According to reinforcement theory, we are attracted to those who give us many reinforcements. Interaction with people who are similar to us is smooth and rewarding; they have similar outlooks and like the same things we do. According to sexual strategies theory, we prefer young, attractive people because they are likely to be healthy and fertile. Men prefer women who are sexually faithful; women prefer men with resources who will invest in them and their children.

Intimacy is a major component of a romantic relationship. It is defined as a quality of a relationship characterized by commitment, feelings of closeness and trust, and self-disclosure.

According to the triangular theory, there are

Continued on next page.

SUMMARY cont.

three components to love: intimacy, passion, and decision or commitment. Love is a triangle, with each of these components as one of the points. Partners whose love triangles are substantially different are mismatched and are likely to be dissatisfied with their relationship.

According to the attachment theory of love, adults vary in their capacity for love as a result of their love or attachment experiences in infancy. The theory says that there are four types of lovers: secure lovers, preoccupied lovers, fearful lovers, and dismissing lovers.

Love can also be viewed as a story, with characters, a plot, and a theme. People use their love stories to interpret experiences in relationships. Falling in love happens when a person meets someone who can play a compatible role in his or her story.

Love may have a neurochemical component. Passionate love, a state of intense longing and arousal, may be produced by dopamine. Like all chemically induced "highs," passionate love eventually comes to an end. It may be replaced by companionate love, a feeling of deep attachment and commitment to the partner. This type of love may be accompanied by elevated levels of prolactin and oxytocin, which may be produced by physical closeness and touch.

Hatfield and Sprecher have constructed a scale to measure passionate love. Such scales make it possible to do scientific research on complex phenomena like love. Scores on this scale were correlated with measures of commitment to and satisfaction with romantic relationships.

Researchers have hypothesized that there are two basic components of romantic love: being in a state of physiological arousal and attaching the label "love" to the feeling. Several studies report evidence consistent with the hypothesis.

Cross-cultural research indicates that individualistic cultures like that of Canada emphasize love as the basis for marriage and encourage intimacy between partners. Collectivist cultures emphasize intergroup bonds as the basis for marriage, and discourage intimacy between partners. Culture influences the importance of various characteristics in choosing a mate; it also affects our standards of beauty and the likelihood that we would marry someone we didn't love.

Research reveals clear differences in communication patterns between happy, non-distressed couples and couples who are unhappy, seeking counselling, or headed for divorce. Destructive patterns of interaction include criticism, contempt, defensiveness, and withdrawal. The key to building a good relationship is reciprocal self-disclosure. The key to maintaining a good relationship is being a good communicator.

Specific tips for being a good communicator include using "I" language; avoiding mind reading; documenting your points with specific examples; using limited-choice questions; levelling and editing; being a non-defensive listener; giving feedback by paraphrasing; being aware of your non-verbal messages; validating the other's viewpoint; drawing your partner out; and engaging in positive verbal and non-verbal communication. When you do fight, fight fair. Finally, it is important to check out ambiguous sexy signals to find out what they really mean.

QUESTIONS FOR THOUGHT, DISCUSSION, AND DEBATE

1. If you are currently in love with someone, how would you describe the kind of love you feel, using the various concepts and theories of love discussed in this chapter?

2. Resolved: Selecting mates on the basis of individualistic considerations, such as whether you love the person, contributes to the high rates of divorce and single-parent families.

3. Your best friend has been dating another person exclusively for the past year. One day you ask how the relationship is going. Your friend replies, "I don't know. We get along really well. We like to do the same things, and we can tell each other everything. But I feel like something is missing. How do you know if you are in love?" How would you answer her question?

4. If you are in a long-term relationship, think about the kind of communication pattern you have with your partner. Do you use the methods of communication recommended in this chapter? If not, do you think that there are areas in which you could change and improve? Would your partner cooperate in attempts to improve your communication pattern?

SUGGESTIONS FOR FURTHER READING

Fisher, Helen. (1992). *Anatomy of love.* New York: Fawcett Columbine. Fisher explains sexual anatomy, sexual emotions, mate selection, adultery, and the sexual double standard, among other topics, using evolutionary perspectives. A provocative book.

Gottman, John. (1994). *Why marriages succeed or fail.* New York: Simon & Schuster. Summarizes the results of 20 years of research on communication in marriage. The book includes self-assessment questions and specific suggestions to help couples enhance their communication.

Grenier, G. (2007). *The 10 conversations you must have before you get married (and how to have them).* Toronto: KeyPorter Books. This book by a Canadian author and sex and relationship therapist includes a discussion of 15 rules of communication.

Hendrick, Susan, and Hendrick, Clyde. (1992). *Liking, loving and relating.* 2nd ed. Pacific Grove, CA: Brooks/Cole. This textbook explains psychologists' research on interpersonal attraction, love, and the formation and maintenance of relationships.

Lerner, Harriet G. (1989). *The dance of intimacy.* New York: Harper & Row. Lerner, a prominent psychotherapist, gives tips on how to promote intimacy in our relationships.

Sternberg, Robert. (1998). *Love is a story: A new theory of relationships.* New York: Oxford University Press. Sternberg describes his theory and the 27 love stories he has identified. The book includes items from a scale designed to identify which stories a person holds.

For review questions, web resources, and other learning and study tools, visit the *Understanding Human Sexuality* Online Learning Centre at www.mcgrawhill.ca/olc/hyde.

Chapter

13

GENDER AND SEXUALITY

Chapter Highlights

> THE MAJORITY OF WOMEN (HAPPILY FOR THEM) ARE NOT VERY MUCH TROU-
> BLED WITH SEXUAL FEELINGS OF ANY KIND. WHAT MEN ARE HABITUALLY,
> WOMEN ARE ONLY EXCEPTIONALLY.*
>
> I CAN'T MATE IN CAPTIVITY.**

When a baby is born, what is the first statement made about it? "It's a boy" or "It's a girl," of course. Children learn what gender they are early in development—by age two-and-a half most children can correctly identify their own gender (Campbell et al., 2002; Thompson, 1975). Sociologists tell us that gender is one of the most basic of status characteristics. That is, in terms of both our individual interactions with people and the position we hold in society, gender is exceptionally important. Many people experience consternation in the rare cases when they are uncertain of a person's gender. They may not know how to interact with the person, and may feel flustered, not to mention curious, until they can ferret out some clue as to whether the person is a male or a female. In this chapter we explore gender roles and the impact they may have on sexuality. We also discuss transgender, an incongruity between gender identity and physical sex.

GENDER ROLES AND STEREOTYPES

One of the basic ways in which societies codify this emphasis on gender is through gender roles.[1] A gender role is a set of norms, or culturally prescribed expectations, that define how people of one gender ought to behave. A closely related phenomenon is a stereotype, which is a rigid set of beliefs about a group of people (e.g., men) that distinguishes those people from others (e.g., women) and is applied to all members of that group. Research shows that even in modern North American society, and even among university students, there is a belief that males and females do differ psychologically in many ways, and the stereotypes have not changed much since 1972 (Bergen & Williams, 1991).

Children as young as six are aware of these stereotypes. Researchers in Nova Scotia showed children pictures containing a man and a woman and told them brief stories about the pictures (Edwards & Williams, 1982). Each story described a gender stereotype. The researchers then asked the children which person in the picture the story was about. The children responded with the appropriate stereotype most of the time. More than 85 percent of eight-year-olds identified the woman in the picture as appreciative, gentle, weak, soft-hearted, sentimental, emotional, excitable, and meek and mild. They identified the man in the picture as aggressive, strong, coarse, cruel, loud, and ambitious.

Heterosexuality is viewed as an important part of gender roles (Hyde & Jaffee, 2000). The "feminine" woman is expected to be sexually attractive to men and in turn to be attracted to them. Women who violate any part of this role—for example, lesbians—are viewed as violators of gender roles and are considered masculine (Storms, 1980). Heterosexuality is equally important in the male role.

Gender role: A set of norms, or culturally defined expectations, that define how people of one gender ought to behave.

Stereotype: A rigid set of beliefs about a group of people (e.g., men) that distinguishes them from others (e.g., women) and is applied to all members of that group.

---

*Dr. William Acton. (1857). *The functions and disorders of the reproductive organs.*
**Gloria Steinem, in answer to the question why she never married.
[1]The distinction between sex and gender will be maintained in this chapter. Male–female roles—and thus gender roles—are being discussed here.

(a)

(b)

Figure 13.1   Children are very interested in achieving adult gender roles.

GENDER SCHEMA THEORY

In Chapter 2 we discussed gender schema theory, a cognitive approach to understanding gender stereotypes. Recall that according to that theory, a gender schema is the set of ideas (about behaviours, personality, appearance, and so on) that we associate with males and females (Bem, 1981; Martin et al., 2002). Our gender schema influences how we process information. It causes us to tend to dichotomize information on the basis of gender. It also leads us to distort or fail to remember information that is stereotype-inconsistent. As a result, it is relatively difficult to change people's stereotyped notions because we tend to filter out information that contradicts stereotypes. Of course, people do not process information using gender schema in every situation. Research in Ontario has shown that both our own gender roles (i.e., how traditional we are) and the situation we are in affect how likely we are to process information in terms of gender schema (McKenzie-Mohr & Zanna, 1990). In this study the researchers found that traditionally masculine men who were exposed to a non-violent erotic film treated the female confederate in a more sexist way than did non-traditional men or men who saw a control film, suggesting that the erotic film activated a traditional gender schema for this group of men.

THE TRADITIONAL SEXUAL SCRIPT

Scripts are cognitive frameworks for how people are expected to behave in social situations. The sexual script that is most pervasive in North America is a heterosexual script, termed the *traditional sexual script* or TSS. The TSS specifies how men and women are expected to behave in (heterosexual) sexual situations (Byers, 1996; Striepe & Tolman, 2003). Some aspects of the TSS and the underlying gender schema are that:

1. Men are "oversexed" and women are "undersexed." As such, men are seen as having strong sexual needs and being highly motivated to engage in sexual activity at any opportunity. Women are depicted as being sexually reluctant, slow to arouse, and interested in sex only in the context of love and commitment.
2. High sexual experience enhances men's but decreases women's perceived status. That is, for men, sexual experience is perceived as reflecting positive characteristics such as masculinity and attractiveness. In women, highly sexual experience is attributed to undesirable characteristics such as non-selectivity and lack of values. Think of the differences in the values attached to the words used to describe the sexually experienced man ("macho," "stud") compared to those used for the sexually experienced woman ("slut," "whore").
3. Men are expected to be "sexperts" and to take responsibility for both their own and their female partner's sexual pleasure and orgasm. Women are expected to be sexually naïve.

Thus, they may be afraid to share their sexual preferences with their partner out of fear that he will take this as evidence that they have had many sexual partners (something that is evaluated negatively in women). They also may fear that their partner will think they are criticizing him for not being the sexpert he is supposed to be.

4. Men, because of their greater sexual interest, are supposed to be the initiators in sexual situations.

5. In order to avoid being judged negatively by being "too" sexually available, women are expected to be sexual gatekeepers and place limits on sexual activity, particularly with a new partner. Thus, even when they are interested in engaging in sexual activity, females are expected to offer at least initial token resistance to their partner's sexual advances.

How much evidence is there that heterosexuals follow the TSS? Research conducted in New Brunswick sheds some light on this question (Byers, 1996). Participants in two studies (one of dating relationships, the other of long-term relationships) kept a diary in which they recorded sexual initiations and responses to initiations in their relationships. The results indicated that in heterosexual relationships, men initiate sex more often than women do both in dating and long-term relationships. This is consistent with the TSS. However, men are not always the initiators—on average women initiated sex more than once a week. Responses to initiations also did not follow the TSS. The research showed that men and women are equally likely to accept or refuse an initiation—they respond positively about 83 percent of the time in dating relationships and about 74 percent of the time in long-term relationships (Byers & Heinlein, 1989; O'Sullivan & Byers, 1992). Further, when one partner is reluctant to engage in sexual activity, men and women use the same strategies to try to change their partner's mind—most often flirting or touching/stroking the partner (O'Sullivan & Byers, 1996).

These results indicate that some aspects of the TSS, such as the expectation that it is the male role to initiate sex, continue to characterize heterosexual relationships. However, women regularly initiate sexual activity, albeit less frequently than their male partners. Further, research does not support other aspects of the TSS. Women are no more reluctant to engage in sexual activity than men are. To this extent, men's and women's roles in heterosexual sexual interactions appear to be converging. Nonetheless, as discussed in Chapter 16, adherence to the TSS may be a cause of some men's sexual coercion of women in dating relationships (Byers, 1996).

SOCIALIZATION

Many adult women and men do behave as gender roles say they should. Why does this happen? Psychologists and sociologists believe that it is a result of gender-role socialization. Socialization refers to the ways in which society conveys to the individual its norms or expectations for his or her behaviour. Socialization occurs especially in childhood, as children are taught to behave as they will be expected to in adulthood. Socialization may involve several processes. Children may be rewarded for behaviour that is appropriate for their gender ("What a brave little man he is"), or they may be punished for behaviour that is not appropriate to their gender ("Nice young ladies don't do that"). The adult models they imitate—whether these are parents of the same gender, teachers, or women and men on television—also contribute to their socialization. In some cases, simply telling children what is expected of males and females may be sufficient for role learning to take place. Socialization continues in adulthood, as society conveys its norms of appropriate behaviour for adult women and men. These norms extend from appropriate jobs to who initiates sexual activity.

Gender socialization comes from multiple sources, including parents, peers, and the media (Leaper & Friedman, 2007). Certainly parents have an early, important influence, from buying dolls for girls and footballs or baseball bats for boys, to giving boys more freedom to explore. Research indicates that parents treat girls and boys similarly in many ways, with the exception that parents strongly encourage gender-typed activities (Lytton & Romney, 1991).

Socialization: The ways in which society conveys to the individual its norms or expectations for his or her behaviour.

The peer group also can have a big impact in socializing for gender roles. In an Ontario experiment, children in grades 3 to 6 read stories about boys and girls who engaged in traditionally masculine, traditionally feminine, or a combination of masculine and feminine behaviours. The boys preferred to be friends with the exclusively masculine boy and girls preferred the exclusively feminine girl (Zucker et al., 1995). Teenagers may be particularly effective at exerting pressure for gender-role conformity (Maccoby, 1998).

The media are also important socializing agents. Many people assume that things have changed a lot in the last 20 years and that gender stereotypes are a thing of the past. On the contrary, various media—from television to teen magazines—continue to show females and males in stereotyped roles. An analysis of gender stereotyping in children's picture books published from 1980 to 2001 showed no decline over time in stereotyping (Hamilton et al., 2006). For example, most of the adults in the books were shown engaged in gender-stereotyped occupations.

An analysis of popular American television situation comedies (sitcoms) from the 1950s to the 1990s indicated that there were small trends toward more egalitarian gender roles, but traditional stereotyping was still common (Olson & Douglas, 1997). *The Cosby Show* of the late 1980s earned the highest ratings for equality of gender roles of spouses and equality of gender roles of children (Olson & Douglas, 1997). In contrast, the 1990s series *Home Improvement* earned the lowest scores on equality of gender roles—lower even than the *Father Knows Best* series of the 1950s.

Dozens of studies show that gender stereotypes shown on television affect children's stereotyped ideas (reviewed by Signorielli, 1990). For example, three- to six-year-olds who view more TV have more stereotyped ideas about gender roles than do children who view less. In a naturalistic experiment in British Columbia, children in a town with little availability of television showed less gender-stereotyped attitudes than children in a town with great availability of television. Television then became more available in the first town; two years later, the children in that town were as stereotyped in their attitudes as the children in the town in which television was available all along (Kimball, 1986).

But picture books and TV are old-fashioned media. One might expect the new media to be less stereotyped. To the contrary, however, video games show patterns of extreme gender stereotyping, including violence against women. In the Duke Nukem video game, Duke enters a strip club and guns down nearly nude women (Dill et al., 2005). The average grade 8 or 9 boy plays computer games 13 hours per week, compared with five hours for girls (Gentile et al., 2004). In short, boys' exposure to these games and their gender stereotypes is massive.

Although gender roles themselves are universal (Rosaldo, 1974)—that is, all societies have gender roles—the exact content of these roles varies from one culture to the next, from one ethnic group to another, and from one social class to another. Gender roles in the major ethnocultural Canadian communities are described now.

GENDER ROLES AND ETHNICITY

Ethnicity refers to a sizeable group of people who share a common and distinct racial, national, religious, linguistic, or cultural origin or heritage. Although people of British and French backgrounds make up the largest ethnic groups in Canada, 28 percent of Canadians report only origins other than British or French (Statistics Canada, 1998a). Between 23 and 41 percent of the population in Toronto, Vancouver, and Montreal were born outside of Canada. Changing immigration patterns since the 1980s have increased the ethnocultural diversity of Canada and have introduced a wide range of attitudes and traditions surrounding gender roles (Barrett et al., 1997). In some ways, the gender roles of members of these communities reflect the values and norms of their country of origin. However, gender roles are also influenced by the majority Canadian culture through the process of acculturation—the

Acculturation: The process of incorporating the beliefs and customs of a new culture.

Figure 13.2 Gender roles in Canada's ethnocultural communities reflect aspects of the majority as well as aspects of the minority culture, such as this arranged Hindu marriage in Montreal.

process of incorporating the beliefs and customs of a new culture. For example, in keeping with traditional values, immigrant parents may allow their sons but not their daughters to engage in unsupervised dating. However, the same parents may encourage their daughters to obtain professional degrees and take up careers even though women in their culture traditionally did not work outside the home (Mackie, 1991).

The study *Ethnocultural Communities Facing AIDS* examined sexuality within six Canadian ethnocultural communities (see Chapter 1 for a description of this study). Groups were chosen based on ethnicity, not race. Large, cohesive communities with a large proportion of young people and people who had immigrated to Canada since 1986 were chosen (Cappon et al., 1996). The researchers found a number of cross-cultural similarities in gender roles. Generally, men and women in these communities are seen as having distinct roles in that men are expected to be the head of the family and women are expected to be the caregivers. However, economic realities often mean that women must work outside the home, and these role changes often create conflict within the family. There tends to be a double standard with respect to sexual behaviour. Dating and premarital sex are accepted and often encouraged in sons but not tolerated in daughters. Men are expected to be active in sexual relationships, whereas women are expected to be passive and to meet men's needs (Singer, 1996).

There also are differences in gender role expectations between various ethnocultural groups, as the following descriptions of the Chinese, South Asian, and Caribbean communities in the aforementioned study demonstrate (Health Canada, 1994a–f). As you will see, gender roles in Canada are not uniform. Different ethnic groups define gender roles differently.

THE CHINESE COMMUNITY

In 2001 there were 1 029 395 Chinese Canadians, the largest visible minority group in the country. Chinese culture emphasizes responsibility to the family and the community over self-fulfillment and individualism as in the majority Canadian culture. Marriage is highly valued so that couples are reluctant to separate or divorce even when experiencing signifi-

Figure 13.3 Gender roles in Canada's Asian community are becoming more diverse as people move away from their traditional background.

cant marital problems. In most families, the man is considered the head of the household; the woman is the primary caregiver and is expected to adopt a submissive role with her male partner. It is not acceptable for females to engage in premarital or extramarital sexual activity, and premarital sex is also discouraged for males. However, extramarital sexual activity by men may be accepted, particularly in "astronaut families" in which the man works away from home in Hong Kong or Taiwan. Today gender roles within the community are becoming more diverse as people move away from their traditional roles. As achievement and education are considered important within the Chinese community, women who were born in Canada may experience conflict between the traditional gender roles of Chinese culture and those of Canadian culture, which increasingly prizes independence and assertiveness in women. Men may also experience conflict between family values and individual achievement.

THE SOUTH ASIAN COMMUNITIES

In 2001 there were 917 070 South Asians (e.g., Indians and Pakistanis) living in Canada. In South Asian communities, religion is a major focus of community life. Hard work, education, and achievement are seen as important. Respect for traditional values, which in some cases includes arranged marriages even for women born in Canada, is also highly valued. South Asian men and women tend to be assigned different roles, and women are expected to be submissive to men. Boys tend to be given privileges and freedom, dating is allowed, and it is expected that they will have some sexual experience. However, girls may not be allowed to date because female virginity prior to marriage is highly valued. Men are expected to take the lead in the sexual encounter; women are expected to be passive, submissive, and uninformed about sex. As a result of women's prescribed sexual passivity, some men visit sex workers for casual sex before and during marriage. The women are not supposed to question the behaviour of their husbands or to complain about extramarital sexual activity.

ENGLISH-SPEAKING CARIBBEAN COMMUNITIES

In 2001 there were 662 215 blacks in Canada, many with roots in the Caribbean. English-speaking Caribbean (e.g., Jamaican) communities have a strong sense of family and community. Traditionally, the man was expected to be the provider and the woman was expected to care for the children and the household while also working outside the home. Today there are many single-parent families in the Caribbean communities, usually headed by women. More restrictions are placed on girls than on boys, in part as an attempt to prevent adolescent pregnancy. In adolescence and into adulthood, women's focus is on developing relationships and they may engage in serial monogamy. Both having a male partner and having a child are considered important aspects of the female role and indicators of success. In contrast, young men are more likely to want to have many sexual partners. It also is not uncommon for married and cohabiting men to have multiple partners.

ABORIGINAL COMMUNITIES

In the 2001 Canadian Census, 976 305 people reported Aboriginal ancestry (Statistics Canada, 2003). The Aboriginal peoples constitute important ethnocultural minority groups in Canada. Before contact with Europeans, at least some of the First Nations peoples in North America had relatively egalitarian gender roles (Kinsman, 1996; LaFramboise et al., 1990). That is, their roles were more egalitarian than those of the European culture of the same period. The process of acculturation and adaptation to the majority culture seems to have resulted in increased male dominance among North American Aboriginal peoples.

Among the more than 200 Aboriginal languages spoken in North America, at least two-thirds have a term that refers to a third (or more) gender beyond male and female (Tafoya & Wirth, 1996). European anthropologists termed this additional category *berdache*, a term rejected by Aboriginal peoples, who prefer the term *two-spirit* (Jacobs et al., 1997). These same anthropologists concluded that the people were homosexuals, transsexuals, or transvestites, none of which are accurate from an Aboriginal point of view (Kinsman, 1996). A man might be married to a two-spirit male, but the marriage would not be considered homosexual because the two are of different genders (Tafoya & Wirth, 1996).

There was also a role of the "manly hearted woman," a role that a woman who was exceptionally independent and aggressive could take on. There was a "warrior woman" role among the Apache, Crow, Cheyenne, Blackfoot, Pawnee, and Navajo tribes (e.g., Buchanan, 1986; House, 1997). In both cases, women could express masculine traits or participate in male-stereotyped activities while continuing to live and dress as women.

Figure 13.4 Among some First Nations there are three gender roles, the third being known as a "manly hearted woman" or "warrior woman." Chiricahua Tah-des-te was a messenger and warrior in Geronimo's band. She participated in negotiations with several U.S. military leaders and surrendered with Geronimo in 1886.

GENDER DIFFERENCES IN PSYCHOLOGICAL FUNCTIONING

Gender differences in personality and behaviour have been studied extensively by psychologists (e.g., Hyde, 2007). Here we will focus on gender differences in two areas that are particularly relevant to gender and sexuality: aggressiveness and communication styles.

Males and females differ in *aggressiveness.* Males are generally more aggressive than females, and this difference is found cross-culturally (Best, 2001). This is true for virtually all indicators of aggression (physical aggression such as fighting, verbal aggression, and fantasy aggression) (Hyde, 1984). It is also true at all ages; as soon as children are old enough to perform aggressive behaviours, boys are more aggressive, and men dominate the statistics on violent crimes. The gender difference in aggression tends to be largest among preschoolers, but it gets smaller with age so that gender differences in adults' aggression are small (Hyde, 1984).

Researchers have found that there are some differences between men and women in their style of communicating, both verbally and non-verbally. This research was reviewed in Chapter 12. Of particular relevance to sexuality, within dating relationships, women self-disclose more than men do about both sexual and non-sexual issues (Byers & Demmons, 1999).

Norms about self-disclosure are changing, though. Traditional gender roles favoured emotional expressiveness for females, but emotional repressiveness and avoidance of self-disclosure for males. There is a contemporary ethic, though, of good communication and openness that demands equal self-disclosure from males and females (Rubin et al., 1980). Research with university students in New Brunswick indicates that traditional gender roles persist in that women are more emotionally expressive than men are both in non-sexual and in sexual situations (Lawrance et al., 1996). However, this research also shows that we are moving toward a norm of greater emotional expressiveness for men. Men were described as ideally equally expressive as women in sexual situations. Thus, the traditional expectation that men should not express their feelings seems to be gradually shifting toward the expectation that they be open and communicative.

There are gender differences in people's ability to understand the non-verbal behaviours of others. The technical phrase for this is "decoding non-verbal cues"—that is, the ability to read others' body language correctly. It might be measured, for example, by one's accuracy in interpreting facial expressions. Research shows that women are better than men at decoding such non-verbal cues and discerning others' emotions (Hall, 1998). Certainly, this is consistent with the gender-related expectation that women will show greater interpersonal sensitivity.

What are the implications of these gender differences in communication styles for sexuality? For example, if men are less able to disclose personal information about themselves, consider whether this might not hamper their ability to communicate their sexual needs to their partners.

GENDER DIFFERENCES IN SEXUALITY

In this section, the discussion will focus on areas of sexuality in which there is some evidence of male–female differences. As we will point out, differences do exist, but they are in a rather small number of areas—masturbation, attitudes about casual sex, arousal to erotica, consistency of orgasm during sex, and sex drive. There is a danger in focusing on these differences to the point of forgetting about gender similarities. Keep in mind that men and women are in many ways quite similar in their sexuality—for example, in the physiology of their sexual response (Chapter 9)—as you consider the evidence on male–female differences that follows. Also bear in mind that most of the scientific evidence described here is based on North

American samples. Only a few cross-cultural surveys are available. The gender differences discussed in the next sections characterize mainstream North American culture. Gender patterns may be similar or different in other cultures.

MASTURBATION

A review of 177 studies of gender differences in sexuality found that the largest gender difference was the incidence of masturbation (Oliver & Hyde, 1993).

Recall that in the Kinsey data, 92 percent of the men had masturbated to orgasm at least once in their lives, as compared with 58 percent of the women. Not only did fewer women masturbate, but in general, those who did masturbate had begun at a later age than the men. Virtually all men said they had masturbated before age 20 (most began between ages 13 and 15), but substantial numbers of women reported masturbating for the first time at age 25, 30, or 35. This gender difference shows no evidence of diminishing, according to more recent studies. The NHSLS, although it did not collect data on lifetime incidence of masturbation, did ask about masturbation in the last year; 63 percent of the men, compared with 42 percent of the women, reported that they had masturbated (Laumann et al., 1994). Similarly, 80 percent of male students but only 48 percent of female students at the University of British Columbia reported masturbating at least once (Meston et al., 1996). The data suggest, then, that there is a substantial gender difference in the incidence of masturbation, with men considerably more likely to have masturbated than women.

ATTITUDES ABOUT CASUAL SEX

In the review just mentioned, the second largest gender difference noted was in attitudes toward casual sex—that is, sexual intercourse in a situation, such as a "one-night stand," in which there is no emotionally committed relationship between the partners (Oliver & Hyde, 1993; Yost & Zurbriggen, 2006). Men are considerably more approving of such interactions, and women tend to be disapproving. Many women feel that sexual intercourse is ethical or acceptable only in the context of an emotionally committed relationship. For many men, that is a nice context for sex, but it isn't absolutely necessary. As one man in a column in *Cosmopolitan* magazine said,

> Being male, I find that sometimes your groin can take over and it's only after the deed is actually done that you regret sleeping with the particular girl. (quoted in Farvid & Braun, 2006, p. 301).

In Canada, 68 percent of male adolescents, but only 48 percent of female adolescents, approve of having sex before marriage with someone you like (Bibby, 2001). Further, adolescent females are more likely to believe that sex without love is not satisfying. Gender differences in attitudes toward casual sex were even greater; in the Canada Youth Sexual Health and HIV/AIDS Study, 66 percent of grade 11 boys but only 32 percent of grade 11 girls agreed that it was all right to have casual sex (Boyce et al., 2003).

One study asked male and female university students about their motives for having sex (Meston & Buss, 2007). Participants identified 237 reasons for having sex, ranging from wanting to experience physical pleasure to wanting to express love for the person, feel closer to God, improve their sexual skills, or make their partner happy. Twenty of the top 25 reasons were the same for the men and the women. Consistent with traditional gender roles, the men were more likely to have sex due to the physical desirability of their partner (e.g., "The person had a desirable body"), opportunity (e.g., "The person was available"), physical pleasure (e.g., "I wanted to achieve an orgasm"), and insecurity (e.g., "I felt obligated to"). Contrary to stereotypes, for the most part, the women were not more likely to endorse emotional and commitment motives for having sex, although the women were more likely to say that they had sex to express their love for their partner.

AROUSAL TO EROTICA

Traditionally in our society most erotic material—sexually arousing pictures, movies, or stories—has been produced for a male audience. The corresponding assumption presumably has been that women are not interested in such things. Does the scientific evidence bear out this notion?

Laboratory research shows that men are more aroused by erotic materials, but the gender difference is not large (Murnen & Stockton, 1997). A classic study by psychologist Julia Heiman (1975; for a similar study with similar results, see Steinman et al., 1981) provides a good deal of insight into the responses of males and females to erotic materials. The participants were sexually experienced university students, and Heiman studied their responses as they listened to tape recordings of erotic stories. Not only did she obtain the participants' self-ratings of their arousal, as other investigators have done, but she also got objective measures of their physiological levels of arousal. To do this, she used two instruments: a penile strain gauge and a photoplethysmograph (see Figure 13.5). The penile strain gauge (which our students have dubbed the "peter meter") is used to get a physiological measure of arousal in men; it is a flexible loop that fits around the base of the penis. The photoplethysmograph, or photometer, measures physiological arousal in the female; it is an acrylic cylinder, about the size of a tampon, that is placed just inside the entrance to the vagina. Both instruments measure vasocongestion in the genitals, which is the major physiological response during sexual arousal (see Chapter 9). A problem with these devices is that they are intrusive and neither can be used with both women and men. New technology has come to the rescue. Researchers in Quebec have shown that thermal imaging technology (i.e., changes in the temperature of the genital area due to sexual arousal are detected by a remote camera focused on the genital region) may be useful in assessing physiological genital arousal in both women and men (Kukkonen et al., 2007). Genital arousal in women can also be measured using a labial thermistor clip, which also assess changes in temperature (Payne & Binik, 2006).

Research participants heard one of four kinds of tapes depicting heterosexual couples. There is a stereotype that women are more turned on by romance, whereas men are more aroused by "raw sex." The tapes varied according to which of these kinds of content they contained. The first group of tapes was *erotic*; they included excerpts from popular novels giving explicit descriptions of heterosexual sex. The second group of tapes was *romantic*; a couple were heard expressing affection and tenderness for each other, but they did not actually engage in sex. The third group of tapes was *erotic-romantic*; they included erotic elements of explicit sex but also romantic elements. Finally, the fourth group of tapes served as a control; a couple were heard engaging in conversation but nothing else. The plots of the tapes also varied according to whether the man or the woman initiated the activity and whether the description centred on the woman's physical and psychological responses or on the man's. Thus, the tapes were either male-initiated or female-initiated and either female-centred or male-centred. Three important results emerged from the study:

1. Explicit heterosexual sex (the erotic and erotic-romantic tapes) was most arousing, both for women and for men. The great majority of both men and women responded most strongly, both physiologically and in self-ratings, to the erotic and erotic-romantic tapes. Women, in fact, rated the erotic tapes as more arousing than men did. Neither men nor women responded—either physiologically or in self-reports—to the romantic tapes or to the control tapes (except for a couple of men who were aroused by a discussion of the relative merits of an anthropology major versus pre-med—ah, well).
2. Both men and women found the female-initiated, female-centred tape to be most arousing. Perhaps the female-initiated plot was most arousing because of its somewhat forbidden or taboo nature.

Penile strain gauge:
A device used to measure physiological sexual arousal in the male; it is a flexible loop that fits around the base of the penis.

Photoplethysmograph (foh-toh-pleth-ISS-moh-graf): An acrylic cylinder that is placed inside the vagina in order to measure physiological sexual arousal in the female. Also called a photometer.

Thermal imaging:
A method of detecting genital arousal using a remote camera focused on the genital region to measure the temperature of the genital area.

3. Women were sometimes not aware of their own physiological arousal. Generally there was a high correlation between self-ratings of arousal and objective physiological measures of arousal, for men. When men were physically aroused, they never made an error in reporting this in their self-ratings—it is pretty hard to miss an erection. But when the women were physically aroused, about half of them did not report arousal in their self-ratings (see also Laan et al., 1994). (One might assume that women who were sophisticated enough to volunteer for an experiment of this nature and who were willing to insert a photoplethysmograph into their vagina would not suddenly become bashful about reporting their arousal; that is, it seems likely that these women honestly did not perceive themselves to be aroused.)

In sum, then, Heiman's study indicates that women and men are quite similar in their responses to erotic materials but that women can sometimes be unaware of their own physical arousal.

In statistical terms, Heiman found a low correlation between women's self-reports of arousal and the physiological measures of their arousal. In an interesting follow-up study, one experimental group of women was instructed to attend to their genital signs of sexual arousal ("While rating these slides, I would like you to attend to various changes that may occur in your genital area such as vaginal lubrication, pelvic warmth, and muscular tension"), and a second group was told to attend to non-genital signs of arousal ("While rating these slides, I would like you to attend to various changes that may occur in your body. These are heart rate increase, nipple erection, breast swelling, and muscular

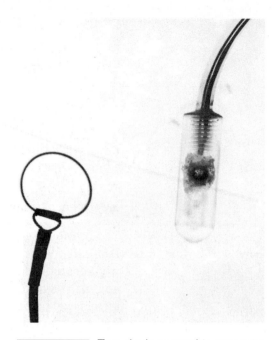

Figure 13.5 Two devices used to measure physiological sexual response in males and females. The penile strain gauge (left) consists of a flexible band that fits around the base of the penis. The photoplethysmograph (right) is an acrylic cylinder containing a photocell and a light source, which is placed just inside the vagina.

tension"), while a control group was given no instructions (Korff & Geer, 1983). Both experimental groups showed high correlations between self-reports and physiological measures of arousal, while the control group showed the same low correlation that Heiman found. This shows that women can be quite accurate in realizing their physical arousal if they are simply told to focus their attention on it. The broader culture, of course, does not give women such instructions, but rather tells them to focus on the environment outside themselves—the love, romance, partner—so that many women have not learned to focus on their body. But the experiment described here shows quite clearly that they can.

Heiman studied sexual arousal to preferred sexual stimuli. Recent research has shown that physiological sexual arousal is category specific in men but not in women. That is, heterosexual men are more physiologically aroused by stimuli depicting women than by stimuli depicting men, whereas gay men are more aroused of stimuli depicting men than by stimuli depicting women. In contrast, both heterosexual women and lesbians show similar arousal to male and female stimuli (Chivers, 2005; Chivers et al., 2004). This does not necessarily mean that women are inherently bisexual, just that there are a wide range of stimuli that can turn women on. In contrast, subjective arousal for both women and men was greatest to their preferred sex.

ORGASM CONSISTENCY

Men are more consistent than women at having orgasms during sex. For example, according to the NHSLS, 75 percent of men, but only 29 percent of women, always have an orgasm during sex with their partner (Laumann et al., 1994, p. 116). The gap is narrower for orgasm consistency during masturbation, but even here men seem to be more effective: 80 percent of men, compared with 60 percent of women, report that they usually or always have an orgasm when masturbating (Laumann et al., 1994, p. 84).

SEX DRIVE

Evidence from a number of sources indicates that men, on average, have a stronger sex drive than women do (Baumeister et al., 2001; Peplau, 2003). Men think about sex more often and have more frequent and varied fantasies than women do (Renaud & Byers, 1999). Compared with women, men desire more sexual partners and a greater frequency of intercourse. In a study across 52 nations, the gender difference in the preferred number of partners was found in all regions of the globe (Schmitt, 2003). It is important to remember, of course, that these are average differences. For a particular heterosexual couple, it is quite possible that the woman's level of desire would exceed the man's.

WHY THE DIFFERENCES?

The previous section reviewed the evidence on differences in male and female sexuality. Four differences—the lower percentage of females, compared with males, who masturbate; women's more disapproving attitudes toward casual sex; women's lesser orgasm consistency; and men's greater sex drive—are fairly well documented and in need of explanation. What factors lead to these differences? Many possible explanations have been suggested by a wide variety of scholars.

ARE THE DIFFERENCES BOGUS?

One possibility is that many of these gender differences, typically documented by self-report, are not true differences. Instead, it could be that people report what is expected of them, shaped by gender norms. Men are expected to want lots of sex, so they exaggerate their desire in self-reports, or women minimize theirs.

A clever study used the bogus-pipeline method to investigate this possibility (Alexander & Fisher, 2003). University students were brought to the lab to fill out questionnaires about their sexual attitudes and behaviours. They were randomly assigned to one of three experimental conditions. In the *bogus-pipeline condition*, the student was hooked up to a fake polygraph or lie-detector machine and told that the machine could detect false answers. People should respond very honestly in this condition. In the anonymous condition, the student simply filled out the questionnaire anonymously, as is typical of much sex research, and placed the questionnaire in a locked box when finished. In the exposure threat condition, respondents were instructed to hand their completed questionnaires directly to the experimenter, who was an undergraduate peer, and the experimenter sat in full view while the respondents completed their questionnaires, serving as a reminder that this other person would easily be able to see their answers. Figure 13.6 shows the results for reports of the number of sexual partners the respondents had had.

When people were in the bogus-pipeline condition and gave the most honest reporting, men's and women's reports of their number of partners were nearly identical—in fact, women's were slightly higher than men's. In the standard conditions of anonymity used in most sex research, women reported fewer partners than men did. Under a threat that responses would be made public, the largest gap between women and men appeared. In the anonymous condition and the exposure

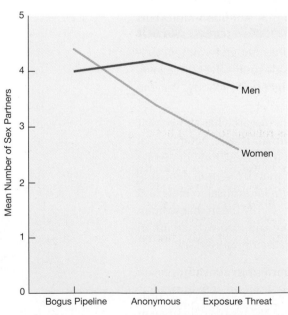

Source: Alexander & Fisher (2003).

Figure 13.6 Mean number of sexual partners reported by men and women in the Bogus Pipeline Study (see text for further details).

threat condition, differences emerged that were consistent with gender roles. Women confirmed the expectation that they have fewer partners.

What are the implications of this study? Does it mean that all the differences described in the previous section are bogus? Probably not, but it means that findings of gender differences obtained by self-reports are probably exaggerations of the truth. And it is important to note that findings obtained from physiological measures, such as those used in Heiman's study, are not vulnerable to these reporting biases.

Let's assume that the gender differences discussed in the previous section are real, although perhaps not as dramatically large as the research suggests. How can these differences be explained?

BIOLOGICAL FACTORS

Gender differences in sexuality might be created, in part, by two biological factors: anatomy and hormones.

ANATOMY

The male sexual anatomy is external and visible and has a very obvious response: erection. While the male is nude, he can easily see his sexual organs, either by looking down or by looking in a mirror. The female sexual organs, in contrast, are hidden. The nude female looks down and sees nothing except pubic hair (which really is not very informative); she looks in a full-length mirror and sees the same thing. Only by using a hand-held mirror can she get a good view of her own genitals. To make matters worse, the word *clitoris*—but not *penis*—is often missing from books about sexuality, from parents' talk about sex, and from students' knowledge about sexuality (Ogletree & Ginsburg, 2000). Furthermore, the female's genitals do not have an obvious arousal response like the male's erection. As a result, she may be less aware of her own arousal, a notion that is supported by Heiman's research.

The anatomical explanation, then, is that because the woman's genitals are not in plain view and because their arousal response is less obvious than that of the man's genitals, she is less likely to masturbate and less likely to be fully aware of her own sexual response (Baldwin & Baldwin, 1997). If this explanation is correct, or at least part of the answer, could steps be taken to help women become more aware of their own sexuality? Perhaps parents can help their daughters to become more aware of their own sexual organs by naming the parts of their genitals including their clitoris and encouraging them to look at their genitals in the mirror. And parents might want to discuss the idea of masturbation with their daughters.

HORMONES

The hormonal explanation rests on the finding that testosterone is related to sexual behaviour. This evidence was reviewed in Chapter 9. Basically, the evidence comes from studies in which male animals are castrated (and thus lose their natural source of testosterone), with the result that their sexual behaviour disappears, presumably reflecting a decrease in sex drive. If replacement injections of testosterone are given, the sexual behaviour returns.

Females generally have lower levels of testosterone in their tissues than males do. Human females, for example, have about one-tenth the level of testosterone in their blood that human males do (Janowsky et al., 1998).

The hormonal explanation, then, is that if testosterone is important in activating sexual behaviour and if females have only one-tenth as much of it as males have, this might result in a lower level of sexual behaviour such as masturbation in women, or a lower "sex drive."

There are at least two problems with this logic. First, it may be that cells in the hypothalamus or the genitals of women are more sensitive to testosterone than the comparable cells in men; thus a little testosterone may go a long way in women's bodies. Second, we must be cautious about making inferences to human males and females from studies done on animals. Although some recent studies have demonstrated the effects of testosterone on sexual interest and behaviour in humans, the effects are less consistent and more complex than in other species (Chapter 9).

CULTURAL FACTORS

Our culture has traditionally placed tighter restrictions on women's sexuality than it has on men's, and vestiges of these restrictions linger today. It seems likely that these restrictions have acted as a damper on female sexuality, and thus they may help to explain why some women do not masturbate, why some women have difficulty having orgasms, and why some women are wary about casual sex.

One of the clearest reflections of the differences in restrictions on male and female sexuality is the double standard. As we saw in Chapter 10, the double standard says that the same sexual behaviour is evaluated differently, depending on whether a male or a female engages in it. The sexual double standard gives women less sexual freedom than men (Crawford & Popp, 2003). An example is adolescent sexual activity. Traditionally in our culture, sexual activity, including premarital intercourse, has been less acceptable for adolescent girls than for adolescent boys. Indeed, sexual activity with multiple partners might be a status symbol for a man but a sign of undesirable characteristics for a woman. The sexual double standard is alive and well on prime-time television, where negative consequences (e.g., rejection or humiliation) are more common in scenes in which female characters initiate sex than scenes in which male characters initiate (Aubrey, 2004).

Generally, there seems to be less of a double standard today than there was in earlier times. For example, as the data in Chapter 10 indicate, people now approve of premarital intercourse for females about as much as they do for males. This change in attitudes is reflected in behaviour. A much higher percentage of young single women report having engaged in intercourse now than in the 1940s. There is much less of a difference between females and males now than there was a generation ago; as reported in Chapter 10, the vast majority of both women and men are now engaging in intercourse during adolescence.

The decline of the double standard may help to explain why some of the gender differences found in older studies of sexual behaviour have disappeared in more recent studies. When cultural forces do not make such a distinction between male and female, males and females become more similar in their sexual behaviour. Yet vestiges of the double standard remain today in regard to casual sex, which is considered less acceptable for women than for men. For example, a Quebec study showed that university women rate females who have sex in an uncommitted relationship more negatively, and believe a male partner will see her more negatively if the woman supplies the condom than if the man supplies the condom (Hynie & Lydon, 1995; Hynie et al., 1997). This suggests that women perceive a double standard.

Gender roles, particularly as prescribed by the traditional sexual script described earlier in this chapter, also contribute to differences in male and female sexuality. For example, the expectation is that in heterosexual relationships males are the initiators and females are the passive objects of men's advances. This makes the man responsible both for his own response and for the woman's response, and may lead men to experience a lot of pressure. Further, the male role discourages men from expressing emotions such as tenderness or communicating feelings and teaches men that touching is a means to an end, sex intercourse (Zilbergeld, 1999). Women have not been encouraged to be active in producing their own pleasure or bringing about their own orgasms.

In keeping with these gender role expectations, research has shown that men are more active in sexual situations than women are (Lawrance et al., 1996). In fact, women with traditional views of gender roles are the most passive in sexual situations. Research has shown that women (and men) who are sexually passive have more difficulty becoming aroused and report lower sexual satisfaction (Kiefer & Sanchez, 2007; Sanchez et al., 2006).

Research in New Brunswick has shown that the cultural sexual script affects perceptions of a partner's sexual preferences (Miller & Byers, 2004). The researchers had 152 heterosexual couples report their actual and ideal duration of foreplay and intercourse, as well as their perceptions of their partner's desired duration of foreplay and intercourse. They found that men's estimates of their partner's ideals were more similar to their estimates of what the average woman would want than they were to the actual preferences stated by their partner. Similarly, women's estimates of their partner's ideals were more similar to their estimates of what the average man would want than they were to their partner's stated preferences. This suggests that people use stereotypes to guide their understanding of their partner's sexual preferences (and possibly the way they make love) more than they use explicit or implicit information provided by the partner. This is more evidence for the need for better sexual communication (see Chapter 12 for a discussion of good sexual communication).

Marital and family roles may play a part. When children are born, they can act as a damper on the parents' sexual relationship. The couple lose their privacy when they gain children. They may worry about their children bursting through an unlocked door and witnessing them making love. Or they may be concerned that their children will hear the sounds of love-making. Generally, though, the woman is assigned the primary responsibility for childrearing, so she may be more aware of the presence of the children in the house and more concerned about the effects on them of witnessing their parents engaging in sex. Once again, her worry and anxiety do not contribute to her having a satisfying sexual experience.

OTHER FACTORS

A number of other factors, not easily classified as biological or cultural, may also contribute to differences between male and female sexuality.[2]

Many Canadian adolescent girls who are sexually active do not use contraceptives or do not use them consistently—32 percent in one study (Fisher et al., 1999; Levy et al., 1992). A woman who is worried about whether she will become pregnant—and, if she is single, about whether others will find out that she has been engaging in sexual activity—is not in a state conducive to the enjoyment of sex, much less the experience of orgasm (although this scarcely explains why more women than men do not masturbate).

Ineffective techniques of stimulating the woman may also be a factor, particularly in heterosexual relationships. The heterosexual techniques of intercourse, with the penis moving in and out of the vagina, may provide good stimulation for the man but not the woman, since she may not be getting sufficient clitoral stimulation. Perhaps the problem, then, is that women are expected to orgasm as a result of intercourse, when that technique is not very effective for producing orgasms in women. Although some lesbians also use ineffective techniques, Masters and Johnson (1979) found that lesbians benefited from stimulating another body like their own.

A relationship probably exists between the evidence that fewer women masturbate than men and gender differences in orgasm consistency. Childhood and adolescent experiences with masturbation are important early sources of learning about sexuality. Through these experiences we learn how our bodies respond to sexual stimulation and what the most effective techniques are for stimulating our own bodies. This learning is important to our experience of adult, two-person sex. For example, Kinsey's data suggested that women who masturbate to orgasm before marriage are more likely to orgasm in intercourse with their husbands;[3] 31 percent of the women who had never masturbated to orgasm before marriage

---

[2]Other possible causes of orgasm problems in women are discussed in Chapter 18.

[3]Note that this is in direct contradiction to the old-fashioned advice given in manuals that suggested that "getting hooked" on masturbation might impair later marital sexuality; if anything, just the reverse is true.

had not had an orgasm by the end of their first year of marriage, while only 13 to 16 percent of the women who had masturbated had not had orgasms in their first year of marriage (Kinsey et al., 1953, p. 407). One woman spoke of how she discovered masturbation late and how this may be related to her orgasm capacity in heterosexual sex:

> I thought I was frigid, even after three years of marriage, until I read this book and learned how to turn myself on. After I gave myself my first orgasm, I cried for half an hour, I was so relieved. Afterwards, I did it a lot, for many months, and I talked to my doctor and to my husband, and finally I began to make it in intercourse. (Hunt, 1974, pp. 96–97)

Women's relative inexperience with masturbation may not only lead to a lack of sexual learning, but it also may create a kind of "erotic dependency" on men. Typically, boys' earliest sexual experiences are with masturbation, which they also hear about from other boys. More important, they learn that they can produce their own sexual pleasure. Girls typically have their earliest sexual experiences in opposite sex touching and fondling. They therefore learn about sex from boys, and they learn that their sexual pleasure is produced by the male. As sex researcher John Gagnon commented:

> Young women may know of masturbation, but not know *how* to masturbate—how to produce pleasure, or even what the pleasures of orgasm might be. . . . Some young women report that they learned how to masturbate after they had orgasm from intercourse and petting, and decided they could do it for themselves. (1977, p. 152)

Once again, such ideas might lead to a recommendation that girls be given information about masturbation.

Numerous factors that may contribute to shaping male and female sexuality have been discussed. Our feeling is that a combination of several of these factors produces the differences that do exist. The early differences in experiences with masturbation are very important. Although these differences may result from differences in anatomy, they could be eliminated by giving girls information on masturbation. Women may enter into adult sexual relationships with a lack of experience in the bodily sensations of arousal and orgasm, and they may be unaware of the best techniques for stimulating their own bodies. Put this lack of experience together with various cultural forces, such as the double standard and ineffective techniques of stimulation, and it is not too surprising that there are some gender differences in sexuality.

BEYOND THE YOUNG ADULTS

One of the problems with our understanding of gender differences in sexuality is that so much of the research has concentrated on heterosexual university students or other groups of young adults (as is true of much behavioural research). For example, the 52-nation study of gender differences in preferred number of partners discussed earlier tested university students at nearly all sites (Schmitt, 2003). Using this population may provide a very narrow view of male–female differences; they are considered during only a very small part of the lifespan. In reality, female sexuality and male sexuality change in their nature and focus across the lifespan. Indeed, our culture's common belief that men reach their sexual "peak" at around age 19, whereas women do not reach theirs until they are 35 or 40 has some scientific support (Barr et al., 2002). Kinsey (1953) found, for example, that women generally had orgasms more consistently at 40 than they did at 25.

Psychiatrist Helen Singer Kaplan, a specialist in therapy for sexual disorders, advanced an interesting view of differences between male sexuality and female sexuality across the lifespan (Kaplan & Sager, 1971). According to her analysis, the teenage male's sexuality is very intense and almost exclusively genital in its focus. As the man approaches age 30, he is still highly interested in sex, but not so urgently. He is also satisfied with fewer orgasms compared with the adolescent male. With age the man's refractory period becomes longer. By the age of 50, he is typically satisfied with two orgasms a week, and the focus of his sexuality is not so completely genital; sex becomes a more sensuously diffuse experience and has a greater emotional component.

In women, the process is often quite different. Their sexual awakening may occur much later; they may, for example, not begin masturbating until age 30 or 35. While they are in their teens and 20s, their orgasmic response often is slow and inconsistent. However, by the time they reach their mid-30s, their sexual response has become quicker and more intense, and they orgasm more consistently than during their teens and 20s. They initiate sex more frequently than they did in the past. Also, the greatest incidence of extradyadic sex for women occurs among those in their late 30s. Vaginal lubrication takes place almost instantaneously in women in this age group.

Men, then, seem to begin with an intense, genitally focused sexuality and only later develop an appreciation for the sensuous and emotional aspects of sex. Women have an early awareness of the sensuous and emotional aspects of sex and develop the capacity for intense genital response later. To express this in another way, we might use the terminology suggested by Ira Reiss: person-centred sex and body-centred sex. Adolescent male sexuality is body-centred, and the person-centred aspect is not added until later. Adolescent female sexuality is person-centred, and body-centred sex comes later.

It is important to remember, though, that these patterns may be culturally, rather than biologically, produced. In some other cultures—for example, the Mangaia in the South Pacific (see Chapter 1)—all females reportedly have orgasms during coitus, even when they are adolescents.

TRANSGENDER

Most people experience their gender identity—that is, their internal sense of femaleness or maleness—as the same as or consistent with their physical sex. However, some individuals experience incongruity between their physical sex and their internal sense of gender. In the medical literature, such a person is described as having gender dysphoria. Keeping in mind the distinction between sex and gender, it is important to understand that this is an issue not of sexual behaviour but of gender and gender identity.

Transgender, or trans, is an all-inclusive term that refers to people who cross the strict lines of the sex they were assigned at birth. It is used to describe a number of different groups of people, including:

- Two-spirit persons: A term used by some Aboriginal people to describe people with alternative gender and sex expressions (discussed earlier in this chapter).
- Intersex persons: Persons born with mixed indicators of biological sex (discussed in Chapter 5).
- Individuals who cross-dress—that is, dress in clothing traditionally associated with the other sex. People cross-dress for a range of reasons. For trans-identified individuals it is often to express their gender identity. However, most women can also identify situations when they prefer to express their more feminine side by dressing in more traditionally feminine clothing (e.g., dresses and high heels) and wearing makeup (in the queer community this is often referred to as *femme*) and other times when they prefer to express their more masculine side by dressing in more traditionally masculine clothing (e.g., jeans and a t-shirt) and look more *butch*. Indeed some people cross-dress in order to perform (drag queens and drag kings; discussed in Chapter 15). For some

Person-centred sex: Sexual expression in which the emphasis is on the relationship and emotions between the two people.

Body-centred sex: Sexual expression in which the emphasis is on the body and physical pleasure.

Gender dysphoria (dis-FOR-ee-uh): Unhappiness with one's gender.

Transgender: A category including transsexuals (those who think of themselves as a third gender), gender benders, and others.

Cross-dressing: Dressing in the stereotypic clothing of the other gender.

IN FOCUS 13.1

Matt: A Transman's Story

Matt is a 29-year-old man who lives in Ottawa. He describes himself as a "different kind of man," in that he was born and raised as a female.

Matt grew up in a small town in Southern Ontario. Unlike his sisters, Matt was not interested in being a Brownie or taking ballet. He had short hair and wore mainly T-shirts. He recalls feeling little pressure to behave like a girl until grades 7 and 8, when he started to feel a need to conform to what was expected of him. Matt remembers thinking that he looked better as a boy than a girl, yet knowing that he would need to change to fit in. He started wearing more feminine clothing and grew his hair. As a teenager, Matt knew he was not interested in boys, yet living in a small town he had no idea of what it meant to be gay.

At 20, Matt moved to Ottawa to attend university. He became involved in the queer community, and gradually began to change how he presented himself. He cut his hair, wore more masculine clothing, and expressed him-

self in more masculine ways. He felt comfortable with this gender presentation. More and more often, Matt was perceived and responded to as male. He recalled that one year he had two jackets. When he wore one of them, he would be perceived as female; when he wore the other, he would be perceived as male. It felt like society was presenting the idea of transitioning to him.

The decision to transition was very difficult for Matt. On the one hand, he did not find being a woman aversive, and was concerned about the social consequences of not conforming to his biological gender and the physical consequences of taking testosterone. On the other hand, Matt felt more comfortable presenting as male. There was also the matter of how others responded to his gender presentation. Most often, people would initially perceive him as male, but then—often after noticing that Matt had breasts—see him as female. Some people were apologetic, which could be uncomfortable for Matt; others were hostile and, in many cases,

people, cross-dressing is not related to their sexual identity. Transvestites (discussed in Chapter 16) are men who dress in feminine clothing for purposes of sexual arousal, and their gender identity typically closely matches their biological sex.

- People who present both masculine and feminine characteristics.
- **Transsexuals:** Individuals whose physical sex does not match their gender identity.

Transsexual: A person whose physical sex does not match their gender identity.

Many transgender individuals describe experiencing an incongruity between their gender identity and their physical sex since early childhood. They may experience particular difficulty when they reach puberty, feeling "betrayed" by their developing body. Further, adolescents are increasingly expected to conform to the gender role expected of their assigned gender. Given the lack of role models, information, and social support, many gender-variant youth are likely to feel confused, isolated, and depressed. According to British Columbia sociologist Aaron Devor, recognizing and accepting oneself as transgender takes place over a number of years. He identified a series of stages in coming to terms with a new gender. In Stage 1, individuals experience anxiety about their gender and sex, which leads them to question their assigned gender in Stage 2. In later stages, they change genders and sexes—some by undergoing gender reassignment surgery, others through taking hormones or just living as the other gender—and come to accept and experience themselves as the new gender.

Although many trans individuals regard their physical sex as opposite to their gender identity, others view the binary categories of female and male as restrictive, and see themselves as neither female nor male, both female and male, or another gender altogether (Hill, 2000). In fact, researchers have proposed several alternatives to our current two-gender system. For example, Eyler and Wright (1997) conceptualized gender as occurring along a nine-point continuum with female-based identities on one end, male-based identities on the other, and

verbally insulted him. He found public washrooms to be particularly difficult because of how others would respond to him. It was the fear for his physical safety and the stress associated with these daily interactions that prompted Matt to transition: "It took up so much energy not to conform to society's expectation that I present as one gender or the other. I had to choose."

At 25, Matt started taking testosterone. So that the changes would be gradual, he started on a low dose and slowly increased it. He grew facial hair and his voice deepened. Taking the testosterone enabled Matt to be more confident in his interactions with others. He did not have to be constantly vigilant about his personal safety or be concerned about how others would respond to him. Matt has since had a hysterectomy and a double mastectomy and now feels very happy with his body.

Matt feels like his family transitioned with him. Initially, they were concerned that he was transitioning only because he had been influenced by a friend's example. They worried that he would have difficulty establishing a career, finding a long-term partner, and having a secure and happy future. However, when they recognized that Matt was becoming happier and healthier as he transitioned, they became less concerned. Matt feels his relationship with his parents is much closer than before he transitioned because they have become much more open with each other.

At present, Matt is completing the last year of an accounting diploma. He is in a four-year relationship with a woman, in which he is very happy. He feels that because of his experiences he is much more critical of society's messages about gender and other social categories. He has also developed much closer relationships with others as a result of his personal experiences of discrimination. Matt regards being trans and his decision to alter his body as a function of societal pressure to act a certain way based on sex. He believes that we would all benefit from treating people in accordance with their personality, not their gender presentation.

Source: Based on an interview with Jacqueline Cohen.

bigendered identities in the middle. They considered people whose feelings and behaviours alternated between male and female as having a bigendered identity. Further, trans activists and authors such as Aaron Devor (1989), Leslie Feinberg (1996), and Kate Bornstein (1994) have called for the recognition of identities that transcend current gender boundaries, putting forward terms such as *gender outlaw* and *hir* (rather than *his* and *her*) and *ze* (rather than *he* or *she*) to draw attention to the need for language that is more inclusive of all genders. In fact, Devor coined the term *gender blender*. Other new terms have emerged, including *gender bender* and *gender free* (Bockting, 1999).

Among transsexuals, some choose to present in accordance with their gender identity in only some situations; for example, with a specific group of friends. Others may live in accordance with their gender identity without undergoing physical changes to make their body more in line with their gender. Many choose to alter their physical sex, a process known as sex change, or more recently *gender transition*, or just *transitioning* (discussed shortly). They may take hormones to bring their physical sex more into alignment with their gender

Figure 13.7 Harisu is the stage name of Lee Kyung-eun, a transsexual pop singer, model, and actress from South Korea.

Gender reassignment: The surgery done on transsexuals to change their anatomy to match their gender identity.

Male-to-female transsexual (MtF) or transwoman: A person who is born with a male body but who has a female identity and wishes to undergo gender reassignment.

Female-to-male transsexual (FtM) or transman: A person born with a female body whose gender identity is male and who wishes to undergo gender reassignment.

identity. Further, some transsexuals pursue gender reassignment, in which their physical anatomy is surgically altered to reflect their gender identity. In the medical literature, individuals who do not pursue surgery are sometimes referred to as non-operative; those who are planning surgery are called pre-operative; and those who have had the surgery are described as post-operative.

We use the terms "male-to-female" and "female-to-male" to identify the direction of the transition and the identity that the transsexual has shown. Thus, those born with male bodies whose identity is female are called male-to-female transsexuals, transwomen, or MtFs; those born with female bodies whose gender identity is male are called female-to-male transsexuals, transmen, or FtMs.

In addition to the distinction between MtF and FtM transsexuals, Ontario psychologist Ray Blanchard has proposed that we can also make a distinction between *gynephilic* and *androphilic* transgender individuals (Blanchard et al., 1985).[4] Those who are gynephilic are sexually attracted to women, and those who are androphilic are sexually attracted to men. For example, if we think of a female-to-male transsexual, he[5] would be classified as androphilic if he is attracted to men and as gynephilic if he is attracted to women. Androphilic MtFs tend to be shorter and lighter in weight compared with gynephilic MtFs and compared with men in the general population (Blanchard et al., 1995). This may be one reason why androphilic MtFs are more successful in their new gender—they are more convincing as women because they are smaller. Gynephilic MtFs, in contrast, often marry women and have children in young adulthood. They have a history of eroticized cross-dressing in childhood and adolescence. Masculine in appearance, they often make the transition to the new gender after they are 40. Among FtMs, those who are gynephilic are typically more interested in surgery to construct a penis (phalloplasty) compared with those who are androphilic (Chivers & Bailey, 2000). Some transsexuals, too, are bisexual. In one sample of MtFs recruited through the Internet, 32 percent said they were attracted to men, 31 percent to women, and 28 percent to both (Bockting, 2004).

References to transgender individuals are found in much of recorded history, although of course they are not referred to by this term (Devor, 1997). For example, in the early centuries of Christianity, a number of women presented and lived as men. One example is Pelagia, a woman who declined marriage and, presenting as a man, entered a monastery. Pelagia became Pelagius, a man, and was later elected prior of a convent. A woman at the convent became pregnant and accused Pelagius of being the father. Of course, this was not possible; however, Pelagius was not in a position to offer his strongest defence. Consequently, he was expelled from the convent and died in disgrace. When he died, it was discovered that he had a female body.

Some societies consider transgender individuals to be members of a third gender, and they live comfortably in that category. Examples are the *two-spirit people* among Native North Americans, the *acault* from Burma, *hijras* and *jōgappa* from India, *xanīth* from Oman, *bantut* from the Phillipines, *kathoey* from Thailand, and *fa'afāfine* from Somoa (Poasa et al., 2004).

Most of our current understanding of transsexual issues is based on research with MtF transsexuals. This is because MtFs have been more than twice as likely than FtMs to seek sex reassignment surgery (Olsson & Moller, 2003). This may be because male prenatal development is more complex and error-prone, or because preschool boys spend so much more time with their mothers than with their fathers. Alternatively, as about half of gender-dysphoric

[4]A heated debate is being waged about the best terminology for these two types. We won't drag you into it. Part of the complexity derives from the issue of, for example, describing an MtF's sexual orientation as "homosexual." Does that refer to same-sex attraction according to the gender before or after surgery? *Gynephilic* and *androphilic* get around this problem.

[5]In keeping with the preferences of transgender individuals to use pronouns consistent with their gender identities, we refer to MtF individuals as "her" or "she" and FtM individuals as "him" or "he."

females do not make use of official gender clinics, the numbers may in reality be more equal (Devor, 1996, 1997). There are several reasons for this. The surgery required to transform male into female genitalia is easier than the surgery required to transform female into male genitalia. In addition, transmen often pass as men more readily than transwomen pass as women. Finally, our society tends to be much more tolerant of women who cross-dress than men who cross-dress. As such, MtFs may be more strongly motivated to pursue surgery in order to live as their chosen gender.

THE GENDER REASSIGNMENT PROCESS

Gender reassignment, sometimes called *sex change* or, more recently, *gender transition*, is complex and proceeds in several stages (Bockting, 1997; Levine et al., 1998; Peterson & Dickey, 1995). Some members of the transsexual community refer to the process as *crossing*. Programs in Montreal, Toronto, and Vancouver offer a range of services to transgender individuals; most of the gender-reassignment surgery is conducted at a private clinic in Montreal. Ontario has recently announced plans to resume coverage of sex-reassignment surgery. However, in most provinces, gender-reassignment surgery is not typically covered by Medicare except on a case-by-case basis, although procedures such as hysterectomy and chest reconstruction that are performed in-province may be covered.

The first step is very careful counselling and psychological evaluation. It is important to establish that the person is a true transsexual—that is, someone whose gender identity does not match his or her body type. Some people mistakenly seek sex reassignment; for example, a man who is simply poorly adjusted, unhappy, and not very successful might think that things would go better for him if he were a woman. It is important to establish that the person is a true transsexual or has a core transgender identity before going ahead with a procedure that is irreversible.

Next comes the "real life experience," which is the requirement that the person live as a member of the new gender for a period of one or two years. This is done to ensure that the person will be able to adjust to the role of the new gender; once again, the idea is to be as certain as possible that the person will not regret having had the operation. Many MtF transsexuals, even before consulting a physician, start dressing as women. Most transgender individuals encounter transphobia, sometimes to the point of violence (Monro, 2000; Lombard et al., 2001).

The next step is hormone therapy. The MtF is given estrogen and must remain on it for the rest of her life. The estrogen gradually produces some feminization. The breasts enlarge. The pattern of fat deposits becomes feminine; in particular, the hips become rounded. Balding, if it has begun, stops. Secretions by the prostate diminish, and eventually there is no ejaculate. Erections become less and less frequent, a phenomenon that pleases the transsexual, since they were an unpleasant reminder of the unwanted penis. The FtM is given androgens, which bring about a gradual masculinization. A beard may develop, to varying degrees. The voice deepens. The pattern of fat deposits becomes more masculine. The clitoris enlarges, although not nearly to the size of a penis, and becomes more erectile. The pelvic bone structure cannot be reshaped, and breasts do not disappear except with surgery. New MRI studies suggest that the brain may change as well. In FtMs given androgen treatment, the size of the hypothalamus enlarged from a typical female size to a typical male size (Hulshoff et al., 2006).

The final step for many people seeking gender reassignment is the surgery itself, which some transgender individuals decide to skip. For the MtF transsexual, the penis and testes are removed, but without severing the sensory nerves of the penis. The external genitalia are then reconstructed to look as much as possible like a woman's (see Figure 13.8). The glans of the penis is used to form a clitoris with sexual sensitivity. Next, an artificial vagina—a pouch 15 to 20 centimetres (6 to 8 inches) deep—is constructed. It is lined with the skin of the penis. For about six months afterward, the vagina must be dilated with a plastic device so that it does not reclose. Other cosmetic surgery may also be done, such as reducing the size of the Adam's apple.

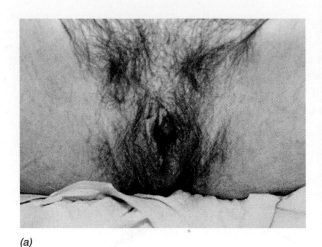

(a)

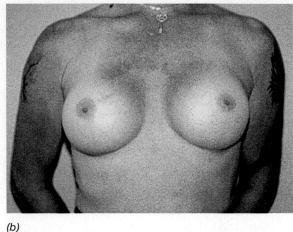

(b)

Figure 13.8   *(a)* The appearance of the genitals following MtF surgery. *(b)* Breast augmentation for the MtF transsexual. Photos courtesy of Dr. Daniel Greenwald.

The female-to-male change is more complex and generally less successful. In one procedure, a penis and scrotum are constructed from tissues in the genital area and the forearm (see Figure 13.9). The new penis does not have erectile capacity; in some cases a rigid silicone tube is implanted in the penis so that it can be inserted into a vagina, making coitus possible. In a new procedure called *metoidioplasty* a penis is created from an enlarged clitoris (Perovic & Djordjevic, 2003). Using this procedure, the penis is between 4 and 10 centimetres and thus is not large enough for sexual intercourse but does have a male-like appearance and allows the FtM to urinate standing up. Some FtMs choose not to have genital surgery and just go through breast removal and possibly hysterectomy.

An important experience for transgender individual is *passing* (Bockting, 1999). For a MtF, this might mean going into a bank or supermarket dressed as a woman and having no one notice anything unusual, simply believing she is a woman.

WHAT CAUSES TRANSSEXUALISM?

Scientists have not found a definite cause of transsexualism. One likely reason is that there may be more than one path to it. As usual, both biological and environmental theories have been proposed.

On the biological side, John Money (1986) has argued that the issue is a critical period during prenatal development. Some event, not yet known, may lead to atypical development of some brain structure—possibly the hypothalamus, corpus callosum, or anterior commissure (Devor, 1997). Other theorists, following this same line of thinking, have proposed that during prenatal development, the fetus, if it is to become a male, must be both defeminized and masculinized (Pillard & Weinrich, 1987). A failure of either process could produce a person with a male body but a female identity. To understand this distinction between defeminization and masculinization, at least for anatomy, recall from Chapter 5 that in a normally developing male the Müllerian ducts degenerate (defeminization) and the Wolffian ducts thrive (masculinization). If some process failed, though, both might thrive. The same might be true of cells in other brain regions having to do with gender identity. Consistent with this view, two studies have found differences between MtFs and typical men in the bed nucleus of the *stria terminalis* (BST), part of the limbic system (Kruijver et al., 2000; Zhou et al., 1995). As noted in other chapters, the limbic system is important in sexuality.

Again on the biological side, one recent genotyping study showed that MtFs differed from

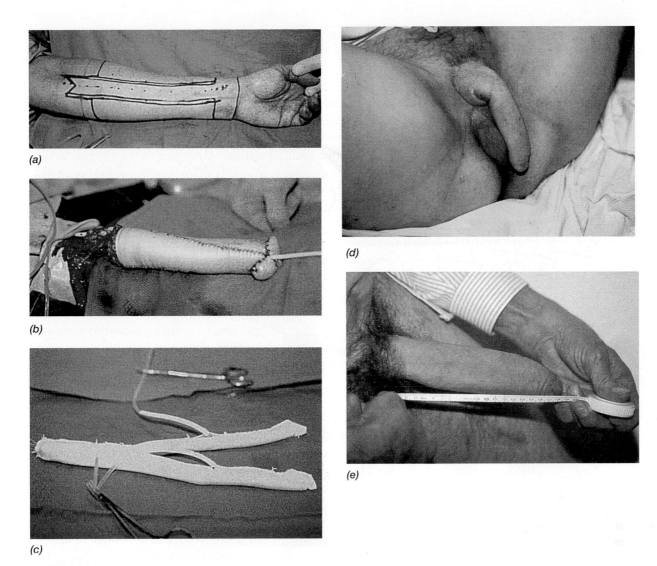

Figure 13.9 FtM surgery. *(a)* Skin on the forearm marked before transfer to the groin. *(b)* The penis is constructed (blood vessels and nerves shown on the left). *(c)* An inflatable prosthesis, wrapped in Goretex and ready for insertion. *(d)* Penis before insertion of the implant. *(e)* Erect penis. Photos courtesy of Dr. Daniel Greenwald.

male controls in the gene that creates androgen receptors and in another gene that creates estrogen receptors (Henningsson et al., 2005). This study will need to be repeated, and FtMs will need to be studied as well before we can be certain of these genetic effects, but they may represent one pathway by which people become transsexual.

An Ontario study found that the appearance of boys with gender identity disorder is less masculine and rugged, whereas girls with gender identity disorder appear more masculine and rugged than their same-gender peers (McDermid et al., 1998).

On the environmental side, noted sex researcher Richard Green (1987) has extensively studied the phenomenon of extreme femininity in boys, which might be a forerunner of either homosexuality or transgenderism. He has found that the parents of these boys basically treat them as if they were girls; for example, they dress them in girls' clothing and then tell them how cute they look. In the case of female-to-male transsexuals, he believes the origins lie in parental practices that include giving the child a gender-ambiguous name and encouraging rough play, and a family constellation in which the mother is unpleasant and emotionally distant (thereby discouraging identification with her) and the father is pleasant and warm (thus encouraging identification with him). However, research suggests that not all parents do so (Zucker & Green, 1993).

Gender variation is found in children as young as two or three years of age. For example, research by Ontario psychologist Kenneth Zucker (1999, 2000, 2002) indicates that some children insist that they are the other gender, show a preference for dressing in the clothes of the other gender, demonstrate an intense desire to participate in the stereotypical play of the other gender, and express dislike for their sexual anatomy. According to the *Diagnostic and Statistical Manual of Mental Disorders*, a diagnostic manual put forward by the American Psychiatric Association (1994), children who express a strong and persistent cross-gender identification as well as discomfort with their own biological sex or gender role have gender identity disorder (GID). This diagnostic category as well as the question of how and whether to treat children with GID has been very controversial (Gender Identity Research and Education Society [GIRES], 2006). On the one hand, proponents of the diagnosis argue that cross-gender behaviour will result in social isolation and ostracism that, in turn, may lead to avoidance of school and participation in activities with peers, and may lead to depression, substance abuse, and suicide. Indeed, such advocates present a strong argument to intervene to help the child become more comfortable with his or her biological sex. Other experts note that if GID persists throughout childhood and sex reassignment seems almost certain to be called for, then treatment will be much more effective if the youth does not go through the pubertal processes of his or her original gender (Delemarre-van de Waal & Cohen-Kettenis, 2006). Puberty can be delayed for three to four years and the treatment is reversible should the child change his or her mind.

Gender identity disorder (GID): A strong and persistent cross-gender identification.

(a)

(b)

Figure 13.10 *(a)* Hilary Swank as Brandon Teena in the film *Boys Don't Cry*, the true story of an FtM transsexual who was murdered because of the ignorance and prejudice of those around him; *(b)* the real Brandon Teena.

On the other hand, there are a number of problems with the GID diagnosis. First, longitudinal studies suggest that most children who are diagnosed with GID do not persist in identifying as the opposite to their biological sex in adulthood; rather, many children with GID identify as gay or lesbian in adulthood (GIRES, 2006; Zucker, 2000, 2002). In fact, as discussed in Chapter 14, many gays and lesbians recall engaging in cross-gender behaviours as children. Thus, these behaviours may be part of a normal developmental pathway for gays and lesbians. Giving children a diagnosis of GID pathologizes them (Hill et al., 2007). Second, Canadian psychologist Nancy Bartlett and her colleagues have pointed out that even though the diagnosis of GID is intended for children who experience strong discomfort with their biological sex, it may also be misused to diagnose children who are dissatisfied with their gender role (Bartlett et al., 2000). As such, it may be more appropriate to regard such children as simply not fitting into the two gender categories prescribed by our culture rather than seeing them as having a disorder. Behaviour that violates cultural norms about how girls and boys are supposed to behave should not be considered disordered. Such advocates argue that what is needed is not treatment for the children so much as support groups for the parents to help them accept and provide supportive guidance to their gender-variant children. From their research with the fa'afāfine in Samoa, they found that cross-gender behaviours or identities do not cause distress in children who are raised in cultures where they are accepted as members of a third gender (Vasey & Bartlett, 2007). Clearly, both sides are concerned with the welfare of the child. The key question appears to be whether the child benefits from a diagnosis of and treatment for GID.

OTHER ISSUES

The phenomenon of transsexualism raises a number of interesting psychological, legal, and ethical questions for our contemporary society.

One case that attracted attention was that of Dr. Renée Richards, formerly Richard Raskind, a physician who had her gender reassigned to that of a woman. When she was a man, she was a successful tennis player. In 1976 she attempted to enter a women's tennis tournament. The women players protested that she was not a woman, and she protested that she was. Officials subsequently decided to use the buccal smear test for gender, which is also the one used in the Olympics, and is a test of genetic gender. Richards protested that this was not the appropriate test to be used on her. Psychologically she is a female, she has female genitals, and she functions socially as a female, and she feels that these are the appropriate criteria. She does, though, have a male pelvic bone structure and other bone structures that are masculine, and these may have important consequences for athletic performance. The important question raised by this case is: What should the criteria be for determining a person's gender? Should it be chromosomal gender (XX or XY) as tested by the buccal smear? Should it be the gender indicated by the external genitals? Should it be psychological gender identity? In 2000, the International Olympic Committee suspended its use of gender verification for female athletes (Genel, 2000). It seemed not to be accomplishing anything except to embarrass some women who turned out to have genetic anomalies.

Buccal smear: A test of genetic sex, in which a small scraping of cells is taken from the inside of the mouth, stained, and examined under a microscope.

Another question that might be raised concerns institutions that are all male or all female. In 1999, a MtF transsexual who was receiving hormone therapy at the time of her conviction for murder was given permission by Correctional Services Canada to undergo gender-reassignment surgery and be transferred to a women's prison. Similarly, in 2000 a member of the Canadian Armed Forces was probably the first soldier in the world to undergo a gender-reassignment operation while continuing to serve in the military.

The transsexual also encounters a number of practical problems when undergoing gender reassignment. Official records, such as the social insurance card and birth certificate, must be changed to show not only the new name but also the new gender.

Transsexuals are able to give us, through their personal accounts, new insights into the nature of sex and gender.

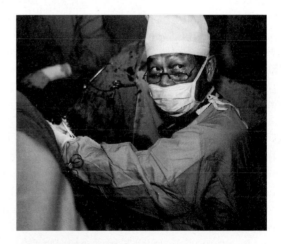

Figure 13.11 Thailand has a booming medical tourism industry featuring male-to-female gender reassignment surgery.

CRITICISMS OF GENDER-REASSIGNMENT SURGERY

A number of criticisms of sex-reassignment surgery for transsexuals have been raised. One of these came from a study by Johns Hopkins researcher Jon Meyer (1979). He did a follow-up study of the adjustment of 50 transsexuals, 29 who received surgery and 21 who did not. His conclusion, much publicized, was that there were no significant differences in the adjustment of the two groups. If that is the case, he claimed, then gender-reassignment surgery is unnecessary and should not be done.

Then criticisms of Meyer's study appeared (e.g., Fleming et al., 1980). Meyer's adjustment scale was somewhat peculiar and involved debatable values. After the Meyer study and the criticisms of it, some clinics ceased doing gender-reassignment surgery, but most continue to do it.

According to more recent research, the adjustment of transsexuals is significantly better following surgery (Bolund & Kullgren, 1996; Green & Fleming, 1990). In one study, 86 percent of MtFs were satisfied with their surgery to create a vagina and 89 percent of FtMs were satisfied with their surgery to create a penis (de Cuypere et al., 2005). In another study of 232 MtFs, none expressed regret at having had the surgery (Lawrence, 2003). Further, Ontario psychologist Ray Blanchard has shown that gender reorientation results in greater involvement in love relationships and reduced emotional distress for both FtMs and MtFs (Blanchard et al., 1983, 1985). However, as society becomes increasingly aware of and accepting of the range of gender presentations, we may see fewer people pursuing surgery in order to fit into one of two discrete gender categories.

SUMMARY

A gender role is a set of norms, or culturally defined expectations, that specify how people of one gender ought to behave. Children are socialized into gender roles first by parents and later by other forces such as peers and the media.

Gender roles are not uniform in Canada. They vary according to ethnic group and other factors. Gender roles in ethnocultural communities such as the Chinese, South Asian, and Caribbean communities tend to reflect the traditional values of the country of origin. Although most Aboriginal people have adopted gender roles similar to those of the majority Canadian culture, some Aboriginal people traditionally had more egalitarian gender roles in comparison with European culture.

The traditional sexual script specifies how males and females are expected to behave in sexual situations. Research suggests that male and female roles in sexual situations differ in some respects but are converging.

Psychological gender differences have been documented in aggressiveness and communication styles.

The two largest male–female differences in sexuality are in the incidence of masturbation (males having the higher incidence) and attitudes toward casual sex (females being more disapproving). Heiman's study of arousal to erotic materials illustrates how males and females are in some ways similar and in others different in their responses. Males are more consistent at having orgasms, especially during heterosexual intercourse, than females are.

Three sets of factors have been proposed to explain gender differences in sexuality: biological factors (anatomy, hormones); cultural factors (gender roles, the double standard); and other factors (fear of pregnancy, differences in masturbation patterns creating other gender differences).

Most research on gender and sexuality has been done with university-age samples. There is reason to believe that patterns of gender differences in sexuality change in middle age and beyond.

Transgender is a broader category of people whose gender identity does not match their anatomy. Transgender individuals respond in different ways including some who seek surgery (transsexuals) and those who do not seek surgery or who see themselves as being in a third gender category. Generally, the adjustment of transsexuals following the gender reassignment is good.

QUESTIONS FOR THOUGHT, DISCUSSION, AND DEBATE

1. Do you think that gender-reassignment surgery is the appropriate treatment for transsexuals? Why or why not?

2. Recalling your childhood, do you think you were socialized in a stereotyped masculine or feminine way? What impact do you think those socialization experiences have had on your current sexual attitudes and behaviours?

3. Do you think there is still a double standard for male and female sexuality today? Explain your answer.

4. Dominic is a strong advocate of equality between men and women, yet his six-year-old daughter's favourite television program shows both the parents and the children in very stereotyped roles. The mother is a secretary and the father is a physician. The teenage daughter is a cheerleader and thinks of nothing else, while the son plays football. What should Dominic do? Why?

SUGGESTIONS FOR FURTHER READING

Devor, Holly (1997). *FTM: Female-to-male transsexuals in society*. Bloomington: Indiana University Press. FtMs are the understudied group of transsexuals, and Devor's book fills the gap in an exceptional and fascinating way.

Feinberg, Leslie (1997). *Transgender warriors: Making history from Joan of Arc to RuPaul*. Boston: Beacon Press. This historical account of transgender individuals throughout history who defied gender boundaries is written from the personal perspective of this well-known transgender activist.

Howey, Noelle (2002). *Dresscodes: Of three girlhoods—my mother's, my father's, and mine*. New York: Picador USA. This is Howey's extraordinary memoir about growing up with a father who proved to be a male-to-female transsexual.

Hyde, Janet S. (2007). *Half the human experience: The psychology of women* (7th ed.). Boston, MA: Houghton Mifflin. We are not in a very good position to give an objective appraisal of this book, but for what it's worth we think it is an interesting, comprehensive summary of what is known about the psychology of women and gender roles.

Zilbergeld, Bernie. (1999). *The new male sexuality* (Revised Edition). New York: Bantam Books. Zilbergeld's original *Male sexuality* was a great success, and this updated version is every bit as insightful.

For review questions, web resources, and other learning and study tools, visit the *Understanding Human Sexuality* Online Learning Centre at www.mcgrawhill.ca/olc/hyde.

Chapter

14

SEXUAL ORIENTATION AND IDENTITY: GAY, LESBIAN, BI, OR STRAIGHT?

Chapter Highlights

> THE STATE HAS NO BUSINESS IN THE BEDROOMS OF THE NATION.*
>
> JEFFREY AND I MET WHEN HE RESPONDED TO AN ONLINE MESSAGE I POSTED, SEEKING GAY TEENAGERS WILLING TO DISCUSS THEIR ONLINE LIVES. . . . HE MADE IT CLEAR THAT HE COULD ALLOW NO OVERLAP BETWEEN HIS ONLINE GAY LIFE AND THE LIFE HE LED IN THE "REAL WORLD." . . . HE FEARED THAT IF WORD OF HIS SEXUAL ORIENTATION WERE TO REACH HIS PARENTS, THEY MIGHT REFUSE TO SUPPORT HIM OR PAY FOR COLLEGE. FROM HIS PEERS AT SCHOOL HE DREADED VIOLENCE.**

Every summer, cities across North America hold a Gay Pride Day, usually including a parade. This is to commemorate the first time that gay, lesbian, and transgender individuals openly fought back against police harassment; this occurred in June 1969 in the Stonewall, a gay bar in New York City's Greenwich Village. Gay liberation was born. The first gay liberation group in Canada was formed in Vancouver in 1970 (Kinsman, 1996). Eight months later, 200 protesters on Parliament Hill demanded equal rights for gays and lesbians (Smith, 1999). In 1981, 3000 people rallied in Toronto to protest the arrest of 300 men during police raids on gay bath houses (Kinsman, 1996).

The purpose of this chapter is to try to provide a better understanding of people's sexual orientations, whether homosexual, heterosexual, or bisexual. First, though, several concepts need to be clarified. A distinction has already been made between sex (sexual behaviour) and gender (being male or female)[1] and between gender identity (the psychological sense of maleness or femaleness) and sexual orientation (heterosexual, homosexual, or bisexual). To this, the concept of sexual identity should be added; this refers to one's self-label or self-identification as heterosexual, gay, lesbian, or bisexual.

There may be contradictions between people's sexual identity (which is subjective) and their actual choice of sexual partners viewed objectively (Mathieson & Enicott, 1998). For example, a woman might identify herself as a lesbian yet occasionally have sex with men. Objectively, her choice of sexual partners is bisexual, but her identity is lesbian. More common are persons who think of themselves as heterosexuals but who engage in sex with both male and female partners. A good example of this is the tearoom trade discussed later—the successful, heterosexually married men in gray flannel suits who occasionally stop off at a public restroom to have another male perform fellatio on them. Once again, the behaviour is objectively bisexual, in contradiction to the heterosexual identity. Another example is the group of women who claim to have bisexual identities but who have experienced only heterosexual sex. These women claim bisexuality as an ideal they are capable of attaining at some later time. Once again, identity contradicts behaviour.

Given these contradictions, sexual orientation is best defined by whom we are sexually attracted to and also have the potential for loving. Thus a homosexual is a person whose sexual orientation is toward members of her or his own gender; a heterosexual is a person whose sexual orientation is toward members of the other gender; and a bisexual is a person

Sexual identity: One's self-identity as homosexual, heterosexual, or bisexual.

Sexual orientation: A person's erotic and emotional orientation toward members of his or her own gender or members of the other gender.

Homosexual: A person whose sexual orientation is toward members of the same gender.

Heterosexual: A person whose sexual orientation is toward members of the other gender.

Bisexual: A person whose sexual orientation is toward both men and women.

*Pierre Trudeau, 1967, when defending his bill to overhaul the Criminal Code of Canada, including statutes that had criminalized consensual homosexual acts.

**Jennifer Egan. (2000). Lonely gay teen seeking same. *The New York Times Magazine*, December 10, 2000, p. 113.

[1]As discussed in Chapter 13, these two gender categories do not fit for some people who would identify as transgender.

whose sexual orientation is toward both genders. Again, however, a person's attraction may not match his or her behaviour and/or sexual identity. The word *homosexual* is derived from the Greek root *homo,* meaning "same" (not the Latin word *homo,* meaning "man"). The term "homosexual" may be applied in a general way to homosexuals of both genders or specifically to male homosexuals. The term lesbian, which is used to refer to female homosexuals, can be traced to the great Greek poet Sappho, who lived on the island of Lesbos (hence "lesbian") around 600 B.C. She is famous for the love poetry that she wrote to other women.

However, use of the term *homosexual* to refer to lesbians and gay men is problematic for three main reasons (American Psychological Association, 1991). First, in the past it has been associated with negative stereotypes such as deviance, mental illness, and criminal behaviour, and thus can be used as a derogatory label. Second, it emphasizes sexual behaviour rather than sexual identity. As discussed later in this chapter, many women and men engage in same-sex[2] behaviour, yet do not consider themselves to be lesbian, gay, or bisexual. Third, it is ambiguous because even though it is a general term, it has often been used to refer exclusively to gay men. For these reasons, it is preferable to use the terms *lesbians, gay men, bisexual women,* and *bisexual.* A heterosexual is then referred to as straight. In this chapter, we will use the abbreviation "LGB" for lesbians, gays, and bisexuals whenever possible because it is awkward to repeat the phrase "gays and lesbians," and even that phrase omits bisexuals.

In recent years, some members of the gay, lesbian, and bisexual communities have reclaimed terms that have historically been used as derogatory terms against LGBs. Examples of such terms include *dyke, fairy, fag* or *faggot,* and *queer.* For example, the term *queer* has now been taken back by gay and lesbian activists and scholars, who use it as a proud term encompassing gays, lesbians, and transgender persons. As an umbrella term, it has the advantage of not forcing people to adopt a narrow societally defined label that may not reflect their experience or the fluidity of sexual identity (Bower et al., 2002). Queer theory is prominent in lesbian–gay–bisexual studies. However, although some people are comfortable using these terms to refer to themselves, other people are not, perhaps because the terms have been used to belittle them in the past. Thus, while LGBs may use these terms themselves, it is probably not a good idea to impose these terms on them.

HOW MANY PEOPLE ARE GAY, LESBIAN, BI, OR STRAIGHT?

Most people believe that homosexuality is rare. What percentages of people in North America are gay, lesbian, or bisexual? As it turns out, the answer to this question is complex. Basically, it depends on the definition we use.

Several well-sampled surveys in Canada, the United States, the United Kingdom, and France have given us estimates (Savin-Williams, 2006). Data from the (American) National Survey of Family Growth (NSFG) and the Canadian Community Health Survey (CCHS) are shown in Table 14.1. The 2003 CCHS surveyed adults aged 18 to 59 and was the first Statistics Canada survey to ask respondents to indicate whether they considered themselves to be homosexual, bisexual, or heterosexual; that is, it assessed sexual identity. Of the men surveyed, 1.3 percent considered themselves to be homosexual; 0.6 percent to be bisexual. Of the women surveyed, 0.7 percent self-identified as homosexual; 0.9 percent as bisexual. These data are similar to the sexual identity question in the NSFG (Mosher et al., 2005).

Lesbian: A woman whose sexual orientation is toward other women.

Straight: Heterosexual.

[2]To be consistent with the definitions of "gender" and "sex" adopted in this book, we should use the terms "same-gender" or "other-gender" when describing sexual behaviour or relationships. However, we have used the term "same-sex" because it is the term most people use—for example, there has been considerable public debate about same-sex marriage.

Table 14.1   The NSFG and CCHS Statistics on Same-Sex Behaviour, Identity, and Attraction

	NSFG		CCHS	
	Men	Women	Men	Women
Behaviour				
Ever had sexual contact with same-sex partner	6.0%*	11.2%		
Same-sex partner, last 12 months	2.9*	4.4		
Only same-sex partners, last 12 months	1.6	1.3		
Sexual Identity				
Heterosexual	90.2	90.3	97.1	98.4
Bisexual	1.8	2.8	0.6	0.9
Homosexual	2.3	1.3	1.3	0.7
Queer, questioning, etc.	3.9	3.8		
Sexual Attraction				
Only to same sex	1.5	0.7		
Mostly to same sex	0.7	0.8		
Both	1.0	1.9		
Mostly to opposite sex	3.9	10.2		
Only opposite sex	92.2	85.7		

Sources: Moser et al., 2006; Statistics Canada, 2004.

The statistics from the NSFG are more complex, because the survey asked several questions about sexual orientation and much depends on how *gay, lesbian,* and *bisexual* are defined. Should the definition be based on self-identification alone or also on behaviour? In terms of behaviour, does the definition of gay or lesbian require someone to have had exclusively same-sex sexual experiences, or just some same-sex experiences, or perhaps just to have experienced sexual attraction to members of his or her own sex without ever acting upon it? We will return to this point. What we can say here is that, according to the NFSG, about 2 percent of men and 1 percent of women are exclusively homosexual in their sexual behaviour and in their identity. About 10 percent of both men and women have had at least one same-sex sexual experience in adulthood, and about 4 percent of both men and women experience sexual attraction to members of their own sex. Slightly more than 2 percent of men and 1 percent of women have a homosexual identity.

However, estimates based on the NSFG may not be perfectly accurate. We can expect underreporting on any kind of sensitive topic like homosexuality, and the NSFG asked non-equivalent questions on behaviour to men and women, making gender comparisons inaccurate.

The NSFG statistics are comparable to those found in a well-sampled international survey. The results indicated that 6.2, 4.5, and 10.7 percent of males in the United States, United Kingdom, and France, respectively, had engaged in sexual behaviour with someone of their own gender in the last five years (Sell et al., 1995). The comparable statistics for women were 3.6, 2.1, and 3.3 percent. These and other surveys confirm that the incidence of same-sex sexual activity among men is higher than the incidence among women. Probably twice as many men as women have a same-sex experience to orgasm in adulthood, and the same ratio is probably true for the percentage of people who have exclusively engaged in same-sex sexual activity.

What about youth? The CYSHHA survey asked grade 7, 9, and 11 students whether they were attracted to males, attracted to females, attracted to both males and females, or attracted to no one. Somewhat fewer than 3 percent indicated that they are attracted to members of their own gender. Interestingly, 9 percent of grade 7 students but fewer than 2 percent of grade 9 and 11 students said they were attracted to no one.

After reading these statistics, though, you may still be left wondering how many people are gay, lesbian, and bisexual. As Kinsey soon realized in trying to answer this question, it depends on how you count. A prevalent notion is that like black and white, homosexual and heterosexual are two quite separate and distinct categories. This is what might be called a *typological conceptualization* (see Figure 14.1). Kinsey made an important scientific break-through when he decided to conceptualize opposite-sex and same-sex not as two separate categories but rather as variations on a continuum (Figure 14.1, section 2). The black and white extremes of heterosexuality and homosexuality have a lot of shades of gray in between: people who have had both some opposite-sex and some same-sex experience, in various mixtures. To accommodate all this variety, Kinsey constructed a scale running from 0 (exclusively heterosexual) to 6 (exclusively homosexual), with the midpoint of 3 indicating equal amounts of heterosexual and homosexual experience.

1. The typology

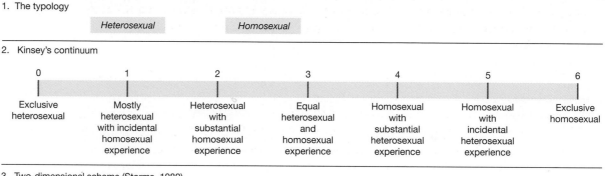

2. Kinsey's continuum

3. Two-dimensional scheme (Storms, 1980)

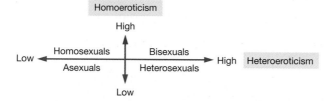

Figure 14.1   Three ways of conceptualizing homosexuality and heterosexuality.

Many sex researchers continue to use Kinsey's scale today, but the question remains, When is a person a homosexual? If you have had one same-sex experience, does that make you gay or lesbian, or do you have to have had substantial same-sex experience (say, a rating of 2 or 3 or higher)? Or do you have to have exclusively same-sex experience to be a homosexual? Kinsey dealt with this problem in part by devising this scale, but he also made another important point. He argued that we should not talk about *homosexuality* but rather about *homosexual behaviour*. *Homosexuality*, as we have seen, is exceedingly difficult to define. *Homosexual behaviour*, on the other hand, can be scientifically defined as a sexual act between two people of the same gender. Therefore, we can talk more precisely about people who have engaged in varying amounts of same-sex behaviour or who have had vary-ing amounts of same-sex experience.

Other theorists have suggested that Kinsey's one-dimensional scale is too simple (Sell, 1997; Storms, 1980). The alternative is to form a two-dimensional scheme. The idea here is to have one scale for heteroeroticism (the extent of one's arousal to members of the opposite gender), ranging from low to high, and another for homoeroticism (the extent of arousal to members of one's own gender), ranging from low to high (see Figure 14.1, section 3). Thus if one is high on both heteroeroticism and homoeroticism, one is a bisexual; the person high on heteroeroticism and low on homoeroticism is heterosexual; the person high on homo-eroticism and low on heteroeroticism is homosexual; and the person low on both scales is asexual. According to a large British study, 1 percent of people reported that they have no sexual attraction to men or women although they did engage in a low level of sexual activity with a partner (Bogaert, 2004). In another study completed on the Internet, 3.6 percent of respondents chose to identify themselves with the label "asexual" (Prause & Graham, 2007). These persons reported less desire for partnered sex, but not necessarily no desire for sex. This scheme allows even more complexity in describing homosexuality and heterosexuality than Kinsey's scale does.

The answer to the original question—How many people are gay, lesbian, and bisexual?—is complex. Probably about 90 percent of men and 90 percent of women are exclusively heterosexual. About 10 percent of men women have had at least one same-sex sexual experience in adulthood. About 2 percent of men and 1 percent of women are exclusively homosexual and/or identify themselves as homosexual. These figures are based on the NSFG and the NHSLS, but adjusted somewhat to allow for concealment by some respondents.

ATTITUDES

Your sexual orientation has implications for the attitudes people have toward you. In Canadian culture there is the belief that all people are heterosexual, that heterosexuality is the norm. Furthermore, just as there are stereotypes about other minority groups, there are stereotypes (usually negative) about gays and lesbians. These stereotypes and negative attitudes lead to discrimination and hate crimes against gays and lesbians. In this section we will examine some of the scientific data on these negative attitudes.

ATTITUDES TOWARD GAYS AND LESBIANS

What are Canadians' attitudes towards homosexuality? As shown in Table 14.2, most Canadians (74 percent) are in favour of equal rights for gays and lesbians. However, Canadians are more divided on same-sex marriage (43 percent are in favour) and adoption by same-sex couples (46 percent are in favour). Further, 63 percent of respondents thought that being homophobic was as bad as or worse than being racist or anti-Semitic. Note that the attitudes of Canadians toward gays and lesbians are becoming increasingly accepting. For example, in 1995 only 34 percent were in favour of same-sex marriage and adoption by same-sex couples. The research found that respondents who were women, younger, had more education, and were living in Quebec and British Columbia were more accepting of issues such as same-sex marriage and adoption by same-sex couples. Canadians also are much more accepting of homosexuality than Americans are. For example, whereas more than two-thirds of Canadians approve of homosexuality, only 38 percent of Americans do (Bibby, 2006). It's important to note that many Canadians accept same-sex relationships, same-sex marriage, and adoption by same-sex couples even if they are not "in favour" of them. For example, Bibby (2006) found that 22 percent of Canadians were accepting of same-sex marriage even if they didn't approve of it.

Table 14.2 Attitudes of Adult Canadians toward Homosexuality		
	In Favour	*Not in Favour*
Do you think homosexuals should have the same rights as heterosexuals?	74%	30%
Are you in favour or not of same-sex marriage?	43	47
Are you in favour or not with same-sex couples adopting children?	46	47

Source: Leger Marketing, 2004.

Homophobia: A strong, irrational fear of homosexuals; negative attitudes and reactions to homosexuals.

Homonegativity: Negative attitudes and behaviours toward gays and lesbians; sometimes called anti-gay prejudice or sexual prejudice.

Heterosexism: The belief that everyone is heterosexual and heterosexuality is the only legitimate, acceptable and healthy way for people to be; homosexuality is denigrated.

Homophobia may be defined as a strong, irrational fear of homosexuals and, more generally, as fixed negative attitudes and reactions to gay men and lesbians. Some scholars dislike the term homophobia because, although certainly some people have anti-gay feelings so strong that they could be called a phobia, what is more common is negative attitudes and prejudiced behaviours. Therefore, some prefer the term homonegativity, anti-gay prejudice, sexual prejudice, heterosexism, or heterocentrism (Herek, 2000; Morrison & Morrison, 1999). **Heterosexism** is the belief that everyone is heterosexual and that heterosexuality is the only legitimate, acceptable and healthy way for people to be; homosexual people and behaviours are denigrated (Berkeman & Zinberg, 1997). Some LGBs experience multiple forms of prejudice. Lesbians may face sexism as well as homonegativity. LGBs from visible minority groups may face racism as well as anti-gay prejudice.

Homonegativity and heterosexism can have serious emotional consequences for LGB individuals. This may be a particular problem for adolescents establishing their sexual identity. Overt acts of anti-gay prejudice, as well as more subtle negative messages such as those contained in anti-gay humour, and the widespread insult "that's so gay," can cause significant pain and suffering. The message is that there is something really bad about acting in any way that might suggest being gay (Adam, 2007). Some—but not all—lesbian, gay, and bisexual youth adopt the negative attitudes they see around them, called internalized homonegativity, and this may make it difficult for them to accept their sexual orientation. Cultural homonegativity as well as internalized homonegativity may also affect some LGB individuals' self-esteem. In some cases, LGB youth so devalue their self-worth that they contemplate or attempt suicide (D'Augelli, 2006).

The most extreme expressions of anti-gay prejudice occur in *hate crimes* against LGBs. One horrifying case occurred in Wyoming (Loffred, 2000). Matthew Shepard, a University of Wyoming student, was found tied to a fence, savagely beaten and comatose. Two young men had led Shepard to believe that they, too, were gay and lured him from a bar to ride in their pickup truck, where they began beating him with a revolver. They later tied him to a fence, beat him more, and left him for dead. He died five days later. Similarly, in 2001, Aaron Webster, a prominent photographer and a gay man, was beaten to death in Vancouver by four males wielding baseball bats, a golf club, and a pool cue after they found him naked in an area widely known as a stroll for gay men looking for casual sex.

A survey of Canadian LGBs found high rates of violence (Faulkner, 1997). Seventy-eight percent had experienced verbal assaults, 21 percent had been physically assaulted, 21 percent reported harassment by the police, and 7 percent had been assaulted with a weapon. A study of LGBs in Vancouver found similar results: 74 percent had been verbally abused, 32 percent had been physically assaulted, and 9 percent had been physically and sexually assaulted (*Vancouver Sun*, 1995). Indeed, according to Statistics Canada (2004), Canadians over the age of 15 who identify themselves as gay or lesbian are 2.5 times as likely to be victims of violent victimization than heterosexual Canadians.

In a survey of LGB youth between the ages of 15 and 19, 80 percent reported that they had received verbal harassment because of their sexual orientation, 11 percent had been the objects of physical assault, and 9 percent had been the objects of sexual assault (D'Augelli et al., 2006). Similarly, a survey of students in grades 7 through 12 in British Columbia found that sexual-minority youth were more likely than their heterosexual counterparts to experience physical and sexual victimization, verbal harassment, and discrimination (McCreary Centre Society, 2007). These studies show that hate crimes against and harassment of LGB youth are not rare, isolated incidents. These incidents exact a psychological toll; for example, the LGB youth were less likely to feel safe at school. One Canadian high school student described one of his experiences of violence:

> At school I was attacked a couple of times in the hallway. Once I was walking down the hallway and a guy jumped on me and pretended to fuck me. It was a big joke for him and his friends.

After throwing him off me, I collapsed. I couldn't believe that I had been violated in such a sexual way in front of the school. I had to deal with the students going around and saying I was going to take him to court. I had to deal with total strangers coming up to me and saying, "What are you doing to my friend? How come you are taking him to court?" These people didn't even recognize that I was the victim. I was not the one at fault. (Grace & Wells, 2007, p. 7)

In 1995, Parliament passed a hate crimes sentencing bill, which specifies longer sentences for hate-motivated crimes—that is, crimes motivated by hate, bias, and prejudice against specific groups. The list of unacceptable hate crimes includes those committed against gays and lesbians. In 2004, Parliament passed a private member's bill introduced by former MP Svend Robinson that bans hate propaganda that targets gays and lesbians. Although this is a step in the right direction of providing some legal protection to LGBs, it may seem like cold comfort to a person who has been the victim of such a crime. Further, police have some discretion in what charges are laid and do not always identify assaults against LGBs as motivated by hate unless there is clear evidence that these are in fact hate crimes.

But we should also recognize the other side of the coin. As we can see from the statistics in Table 14.2 on page 435, most Canadians are tolerant or supportive of LGB individuals. For example, 67 percent of Canadians approve of overt gay and lesbian teachers in middle school, and 86 percent approve of openly gay MPs. Thus while some Canadians are bigots on the issue of homosexuality, most Canadians are not. As one woman said,

Figure 14.2 Svend Robinson became the first openly gay member of Parliament, having come out publicly in 1988. As an MP he worked for gay and lesbian human rights. A Gallup poll conducted in 2000 indicated that 86 percent of Canadians approve of openly gay members of Parliament.

> I really don't feel that I've ever been oppressed as a lesbian or suffered any abuse. I've been careful who I've told, but those people have been really accepting. (Jay & Young, 1979, p. 716)

ATTITUDES TOWARD BISEXUALS

Bisexuals experience a different kind of stigma than do lesbians and gay men. If you are asked to imagine a lesbian or gay couple, you can likely come up with a mental image—two women kissing or two men holding hands or dancing together are easily recognizable as a lesbian or gay couple. Now what do you imagine when you are asked to think of a bisexual couple? The point is that we have few cultural images of bisexuality (Trynka & Tucker, 1995). As such, bisexuality is rarely even recognizable. A study of 22 self-identified bisexual Canadian women found that all participants felt that bisexuality was misunderstood by the straight, lesbian, and gay communities (Bower et al., 2002).

There are a great many negative stereotypes about bisexuals (Herek, 2002). Bisexuals are often thought of as internally conflicted or psychologically immature (Rust, 2000a). They are stereotyped as non-monogamous, needing both same-sex and opposite-sex partners to satisfy both the "gay/lesbian" and "heterosexual" sides of their sexualities (Spalding & Peplau, 1997). In contrast, research has found that few bisexuals have both female and male partners at the same time (although some do), and bisexuals do not differ from lesbians and gay men in their relationship status and length (Balsam, 2004; Rust, 2000b). Further, few bisexuals report that they "need" both male and female partners to think of themselves as bisexual (Rust, 2001).

Similarly, bisexuals may be viewed with suspicion or downright hostility by the gay and lesbian communities (Bower et al., 2002; Mathieson & Endicott, 1998; Rust, 2002). Bisexual-identified women are often told they are denying their true identity, which must be lesbian or heterosexual. Young women who have sexual involvements with other women are often regarded as heterosexuals who are merely experimenting with women because lesbianism is chic (Rust, 2000a). Bisexual women who are involved in lesbian communities may be told they are really lesbians who have not yet realized it. Bisexuality is sometimes seen as "fence-sitting," a way to get the "best of both worlds" without having to commit to a particular identity. Some gay men and lesbians even argue that there is no such thing as a true bisexual (Rust, 2002).

In contrast, proponents of bisexuality argue that it has some strong advantages. It allows more variety in one's sexual and human relationships than does exclusive heterosexuality or exclusive homosexuality. The bisexual does not rule out any possibilities and is open to the widest variety of experiences.

GAYS, LESBIANS, AND BISEXUALS AS A MINORITY GROUP

From the foregoing discussion, it is clear that LGB people are the subject of many negative attitudes, just as other minorities are (Meyer, 2003). Like members of other minority groups, they can experience job discrimination, even though this is illegal. Wage discrimination occurs as well. According to research in the United States, gay men are more educated than straight men, but gay men earn less (Black et al., 2000). Researchers in Ontario assessed university students' attitudes toward homosexuals, English Canadians, French Canadians, Aboriginal peoples, and Pakistanis. Their attitudes were significantly more negative toward homosexuals than toward any of the other groups (Haddock et al., 1993).

Same-sex sexual activity used to be illegal in Canada. For example, in 1967 Everett Klippert was sent to prison as a "dangerous sex offender" after he told police that he had had sex with men over a 24-year period and was unlikely to change. However, consensual same-sex activity was decriminalized in 1969, when, under Prime Minister Pierre Trudeau, Parliament passed a bill introducing widespread changes to laws regulating sexual behaviour in the Criminal Code of Canada. Before 1969, "homosexual offences" included some outdated and derogatory terms such as "buggery (anal intercourse), attempted buggery, indecent assault on a male by a male or female on a female, acts of gross indecency between men, procuring and attempting to procure acts of gross indecency between males" (Lahey, 1999, p. 135). These changes to the Criminal Code were a turning point in the recognition and increasing acceptance of LGBs in Canada. However, at that time, the offence of anal intercourse was added to the Criminal Code. Anal sex is illegal only if it involves children or is not done in private. However, the age of consent for anal sex is 18, whereas the age of consent for vaginal intercourse is 14. Further, anal sex is deemed not to be done in private (and therefore illegal) if more than two persons are present. There is no similar provision for vaginal intercourse. This puts gay (and straight) youth who want to experiment sexually with anal intercourse (many gay males do not engage in anal intercourse) in a difficult situation. Thus, the Criminal Code still discriminates against gay men in this way. However, recent court rulings have suggested that the higher age of consent for anal intercourse violates the equality provisions of the Charter of Rights and Freedoms.

Activists also argue that there has been more vigorous enforcement of the bawdy-house and obscenity laws against LGBs and same-sex erotic materials. For example, following the

1969 changes to the Criminal Code, police continued to lay "indecent act" and "bawdy-house" charges against men for engaging in consensual sex with other men. Nor were gay men and lesbians legally protected from discrimination (Kinsman, 1996). Before the Charter of Rights and Freedoms, virtually no human rights complaints by gays and lesbians were successful (Lahey, 1999; Smith, 1999). For example, prior to 1992, homosexuality was grounds for dishonourable release from the military (Gouliquer, 2000). In the early 1980s, men and women who were suspected of being gay or lesbian were investigated, interrogated, and sometimes released by the military. However, in 1992 Canadian Forces policy concerning sexual orientation was found to violate the Charter of Rights and Freedoms. LGBs can no longer be denied the right to join the military or serve in the military.

Recent decisions by the Supreme Court of Canada recognize that the equality rights guaranteed in the Canadian Charter of Rights and Freedoms include sexual orientation and that provincial human rights codes must recognize sexual orientation as a prohibited ground for discrimination. In 1996, Parliament amended the Human Rights Act to specifically prohibit discrimination based on sexual orientation (the act already prohibited discrimination on the basis of other characteristics such as gender, race, and disability). The act also bars "hate speech" against gay men and lesbians. This means, among other things, that gay men and lesbians cannot be fired because of their sexual orientation, they cannot be refused housing, and they are entitled to adopt children. In fact, Parliament recently passed the Modernization of Benefits and Obligations Act, which amended existing federal statutes to ensure that they apply equally to couples in same-sex and other-sex relationships. The majority of Canadians support such entitlement (refer to Table 14.2 on page 435). In contrast, in the United States, gays and lesbians do not have legal protection against discrimination, and fewer Americans support equal rights for gay men and lesbians.

The most recent area in which gay men and lesbians have attained equal rights is marriage. In 2003, courts in Ontario and Quebec were the first to legalize same-sex marriage, ruling that federal laws restricting marriage to one man and one woman violated the Charter of Rights and Freedoms. In 2004, courts in Quebec, Manitoba, Nova Scotia, Saskatchewan, Newfoundland and Labrador, and the Yukon made the same ruling. On June 28, 2005, the House of Commons passed a bill ensuring that marriage is a right for all Canadians regardless of sexual orientation, so that all Canadians are treated as equal under the law; the bill was given royal assent and became law less than a month later, on July 20, 2005. Marriage is now defined as "the union of two people to the exclusion of all others." Canada was the fourth country in the world to legalize same-sex marriage. In 2007, the Ontario Court of Appeal ruled that a child can have three parents— in this case, a biological mother and father as well as the mother's same-sex partner.

Canadians are fairly evenly split in their attitudes toward same-sex marriages: A poll conducted in 2004 found that 53 percent are in favour of same-sex marriages (refer again to Table 14.2). An additional 22 percent of Canadians accept same-sex marriage as a matter of civil rights even if they don't personally approve of it (Bibby, 2006). The attitudes of Canadians on same-sex marriage are similar to those of the British but more liberal

Figure 14.3   Michael Stark and Michael Leshner of Toronto. Together for more than 20 years, this couple was instrumental in getting Ontario courts to recognize same-sex marriage. The federal government legalized same-sex marriage in June 2005.

than those of Americans. Only 35 percent of Americans are in favour of same-sex marriage. Conversely, 59 percent of Americans favour amending the U.S. constitution to ban same-sex marriages.

Discrimination goes hand in hand with stereotypes. One such stereotype is that gay men are child molesters. As with many stereotypes, this one is false. Research shows that the vast majority of child abusers have a heterosexual orientation; only 2 to 3 percent are gay (Jenny et al., 1994).

There is an important way in which LGBs differ from other minorities, though. In the case of most other minorities, appearance is a fairly good indicator of minority-group status. It is easy to recognize a Chinese Canadian or a woman, for example, but one cannot tell simply by looking at a person what his or her sexual orientation is. Thus LGBs, unlike other minorities, can hide their status. There are certain advantages to this. It makes it fairly easy to get along in the heterosexual world—to "pass." However, it has the disadvantage of encouraging the person to conceal her or his true identity to avoid homonegativity; this may be psychologically stressful (Meyer, 2003). A study of gay men (all of whom were uninfected with HIV) indicated that those who concealed their identity had a significantly higher incidence of cancer and infectious diseases than those who did not conceal their identity (Cole et al., 1996). Concealing a stigma—whether it is one's sexual orientation, mental illness, illiteracy, or a history of child sexual abuse—exacts a psychological toll (Pachankis, 2007).

We shouldn't leave this discussion of discrimination and prejudice against LGBs without asking a crucial question (Rothblum & Bond, 1996): What can be done to prevent or end this prejudice? Change must occur at many levels: the individual, the interpersonal, and the organizational levels (e.g., corporations, educational institutions), as well as society as a whole and its institutions (e.g., the federal government). At the individual level, all of us must examine our own attitudes toward LGBs to see if they are consistent with basic values we hold, such as a commitment to equality and justice. Some people may need to educate themselves or attend anti-homonegativity workshops to examine their attitudes. Research in Ontario has shown that workshops for university students that include imagery exercises, coming out stories, and discussion significantly reduce homonegativity and increase comfort with sexual matters (Rye & Meaney, in press). These attitudes, though, were formed as we grew up—influenced by our parents, our peers, and the media. Parents must consider the messages they convey to their children about gay men and lesbians. The adolescent peer group is strongly homophobic. What can be done to change it? How can the media change in order not to promote anti-gay prejudices and stereotypes? At the interpersonal level, people must recognize that LGBs are often a hidden minority. Eric, for example, just told a joke that ridiculed gay men. What he didn't know was that one of his three listeners is gay—just not "out" with him (for obvious reasons). We must examine our interactions with other people, recognizing the extent to which many of us assume that everyone is heterosexual until proven otherwise. At the institutional level, how can education be changed in order to reduce anti-gay discrimination? A strong program of sex education across the grades, with open discussion of sexual orientation, would be a good start (see Chapter 19). In fact, schools have a responsibility to ensure that homophobic harassment and name-calling does not occur. Azmi Jubran filed a complaint against his school with the B.C. Human Rights Commission. Year after year he had been harassed verbally and physically by his school peers because they believed he was gay. In 2005, the B.C. Court of Appeal ruled that it is not enough for schools to discipline the offending students. Schools must provide preventive anti-homophobic education to prevent this kind of harassment. In addition, gay–straight alliances can work to combat heterosexism and anti-gay prejudice in organizations. Such alliances have been established at many high schools and universities across Canada (including the University of Manitoba). They are open to all students and staff who want to work toward a more inclusive and supportive environment for LGB and trans students.

LIFE EXPERIENCES OF LGB INDIVIDUALS

In understanding the lives of LGBs, it is important to recognize that there is a wide variety of experiences. An important aspect of this variability is whether the person is covert (in the closet) or overt (out of the closet) about his or her sexual identity. As discussed earlier, some people may be heterosexually married and have children, but spend a few hours a month engaging in secret same-sex sexual behaviour or sexual fantasies.[3] Other gay men and lesbians may live almost entirely within an LGB community, particularly in a large city like Toronto or Vancouver where there is a large gay subculture. There are also various degrees of overtness (being "out") and covertness. Many lesbians and gays are out with trusted friends but not with casual acquaintances, or in some situations but not others. The lifestyle of gay men differs from that of lesbians, perhaps as a result of the different roles assigned to males and females in our society and the different ways that boys and girls are reared. In addition, there is different discrimination against gay men than there is against lesbians. For example, it is considered quite natural for two women to share an apartment, but if two men over a certain age do so, eyebrows are raised.

The lifestyles of LGBs are thus far from uniform. They vary according to whether one is male or female and overt or covert about one's sexual identity and also according to social class, occupation, personality, and a variety of other factors.

COMING OUT

Toronto's Marc Leduc won a silver medal in boxing for Canada at the 1992 Olympic Games in Barcelona as well as a gold medal at the North American International Boxing Tournament. In the same year, Leduc came out to the public as gay—he felt he could not be open about his sexual orientation until he retired. Similarly, although statistics suggest that there likely are many gay men in professional sports, not one of 3850 men currently playing professional football, basketball, and hockey in North America is openly gay. By the time he was 12, Leduc was aware that he was gay. He was also aware of his love for boxing. As a youth, he was involved in petty crime, used cocaine and speed, and spent six years in jail for robbery:

> I was a problem kid. I think a lot of it snowballed from not dealing with my sexuality, not accepting it. Socially, you're just not accepted. And as an adolescent, you don't feel like a man if you're gay. [told to a reporter]

Since he came out, Leduc has been an advocate for the lesbian and gay communities. He has also appeared in two documentaries on lesbians and gay men in sports, *For the Love of the Game* and *The Last Closet*. He is happy to help dispel stereotypes. His earlier life, though, reveals the emotional toll of being in the closet.

As we noted earlier, there are significant variations in the gay experience, depending on whether or not one is out of the closet. The process of coming out of the closet, or coming out, involves acknowledging to oneself, and then to others, that one is gay or lesbian. The person is psychologically vulnerable during this stage. Whether the person experiences acceptance or rejection from friends and others to whom he or she comes out can be critical to self-esteem.

Following the period of coming out, there is a stage of exploration, in which the person experiments with the new open sexual identity; during this time the person makes contact with the LGB community and practises new interpersonal skills. Typically, next comes a stage of forming first relationships. These relationships are often short-lived and characterized by jealousy and turbulence, much like many heterosexual dating relationships. Finally, there is the integration stage, in which the person becomes a fully functioning member of society and is capable of maintaining a long-term, committed relationship (Coleman, 1982).

Covert homosexual: A homosexual who is "in the closet," who keeps his or her sexual orientation a secret.

Overt homosexual: A homosexual who is "out of the closet," who is open about his or her sexual orientation.

Coming out: The process of acknowledging to oneself, and then to others, that one is gay or lesbian.

---

[3]Men who secretly have sex with other men while in a sexual relationship with a woman are sometimes said to be on the "down low" or "d" for short.

Figure 14.4 Today many Canadian cities have an annual Gay and Lesbian Pride March as part of Gay Pride Week, such as this June 2008 parade in Toronto. In the early 1990s, mayors of Fredericton, Hamilton, London, and Saskatoon refused to declare Gay Pride Week. In each case, the provincial Human Rights Commission found the mayors at fault, fined them, and ordered them to issue gay pride proclamations.

Of course, before the coming out process can occur, the person must have arrived at a gay identity. Researchers have proposed different models of identity development. Some have suggested that people proceed through a series of stages that occur in a fixed sequence. Others criticize the stage approach for reasons detailed later. Advocates of the stage approach argue that identity development typically proceeds in six stages (Cass, 1979):

1. *Identity confusion.* The person most likely began assuming a heterosexual identity because heterosexuality is so normative in our society. As same-sex attractions or behaviours occur, there is confusion. Who am I?
2. *Identity comparison.* The person now thinks, "I *may* be homosexual." There may be feelings of alienation because the comfortable heterosexual identity has been lost.
3. *Identity tolerance.* At this stage the person thinks, "I probably am homosexual." The person now seeks out gay men and/or lesbians and makes contact with the gay subculture, hoping for affirmation. The quality of these initial contacts is critical.
4. *Identity acceptance.* The person now can say, "I am homosexual," and accepts rather than tolerates this identity.
5. *Identity pride.* The person dichotomizes the world into gays and lesbians (who are good and important people) and heterosexuals (who are not). There is a strong identification with the gay group, and an increased coming out of the closet.
6. *Identity synthesis.* The person no longer holds an "us versus them" view, recognizing that there are some good and supportive heterosexuals as well as some LGBs who hold distorted attitudes. In this final stage, the person is able to synthesize public and private sexual identities.

What are the criticisms of this stage approach? First, recent research has found that some people do not go through one or more of these stages, and not everyone goes through the stages in this order (Diamond, 2000; Harvey et al., 2001). Second, the traditional view, particularly based on men, has been that sexual orientation once established does not change. However, there is new evidence that women's sexuality may be more fluid and may be capable of change over time (Baumeister, 2000; Diamond, 1998; Garnets & Peplau, 2001). Thus a woman may change her identity from heterosexual to lesbian if she falls in love with a woman, or vice versa. Research in Quebec with men who have sex with men found that over an 18-month period 10 percent changed their identity from gay to bisexual or vice versa (Engler et al., 2005). Third, the stage model suggests that to be fully developed a person must reach the final stage; that is, there is only one positive ending. This may not be accurate. Finally, it does not fit for many individuals who ultimately adopt a bisexual identity (see In Focus 14.1, about a bisexual woman). As a result, a number of theorists have proposed alternative, non-stage models (Alderson, 2003; Diamond, 2007).

The Internet is having an impact in some crucial aspects (Egan, 2000; McKenna & Bargh, 1998). For a teenage boy who is just realizing that he is gay, the Internet provides boundless information and the opportunity to "chat" with others, while remaining safe in his home and not acknowledging his identity publicly in ways that could be at best embarrassing and at worst dangerous. Interactions with others on the Internet can foster a positive identity and self-acceptance; research in Ontario identified contact with other LGB youth as a particularly important factor in establishing a positive identity (Schneider, 1991).

BISEXUAL IDENTITY

Bisexual men and women generally begin to think of themselves as bisexual in their early to mid-20s (Fox, 1995; Weinberg, 1994). There are some gender differences in the sequence of behaviours, though. Bisexual women typically have their first opposite-sex attraction and sexual experiences before their first same-sex ones. Bisexual men, in contrast, are more likely to have same-sex experiences first, followed by opposite-sex ones. What do bisexuals base their identity on? Sexual behaviour, feelings of attraction, or something else?

Research has shown that most bisexual men and women base their sexual identity on their feelings of sexual attraction or capacity to fall in love with either women or men regardless of whether they have expressed these feelings through sexual behaviour (Rust, 2001). Many describe their sexual attractions to women and men as different from each other. Those respondents who have had sexual experiences with both women and men generally report having these experiences serially over a period of time, often including lengthy monogamous relationships. They indicate that they do not cease being bisexual when they became monogamously involved with either a woman or a man, just as heterosexuals do not cease to be straight after a period of celibacy (Rust, 2000a). Some individuals adopt bisexual identities to reflect their politics. They may see bisexuality as a challenge to the importance of gender in defining sexuality, viewing their bisexual identity not as a combination of their attractions to women and men, but an attraction to specific people regardless of their gender.

LESBIAN, GAY, AND BISEXUAL COMMUNITIES

A loose network of lesbian, gay, and bisexual communities extends around the world (Esterberg, 1996). As one woman put it,

> I have seen lesbian communities all over the world (e.g., South Africa, Brazil, and Israel) where the lesbians of that nation have more in common with me (i.e., they play the same lesbian records, have read the same books, wear the same lesbian jewelry) than the heterosexual women of that nation have in common with heterosexual women in North America. (Rothblum, 2007)

These links have been cemented in the past decade by increases in international travel, globalization, and the international reach of the Internet (Puar, 2001).

IN FOCUS 14.1

Being Bisexual

Coming out as bisexual has been a long process for me, and at this point I feel that my sexuality is more a journey or a story that is continuing to unfold rather than a fixed label.

When I first felt sexual attraction, around 12 or 13, it was towards men. It was only in my late teens that I became aware of any attraction to women. This blossomed at age 21, when I had my first sexual experience with a woman and came out as a lesbian. Over the next few years I dated, had sex with, and fell in love with women. But at the same time I also found myself feeling some attraction to men again, and I gradually started exploring this renewed interest. I entered a serious relationship with a man at age 24, which forced the identity issue for me. It was a struggle to let go of my lesbian identity for many reasons. My main fear centred around the possibility of being rejected by the lesbian community I had come to call home and not finding another community which would accept me. I began identifying as bisexual but wasn't totally comfortable with it. It was the most accurate term to use, but I didn't have a strong connection to it or feel any pride in being bisexual.

About two years later I attended a Toronto Bisexual Network event and was introduced for the first time to a bisexual community. The connection with other bisexual people was very powerful for me, and allowed me to move towards a comfort and joy with my bisexual identity that I hadn't been able to achieve on my own.

Right now I live in Toronto's gay village with my bisexual male partner of four years. At different times during our involvement we've been either monogamous or open to outside sexual partners. It's all about whatever feels right for both of us at any given time, and about being able to communicate with each other about our wants

Distinct LGB communities became visible in Canada in the 1970s in Toronto, Vancouver, and Montreal (Kinsman, 1996). During this period, there was a flourishing of businesses catering to a gay clientele, including bars, clubs, bath houses, restaurants, bookstores, theatres, and social organizations. Many of these establishments also cater to a lesbian and bisexual clientele, although generally there are fewer businesses geared specifically toward lesbians. The lesbian community in particular has been involved in creating a lesbian culture, expressed in music and literature, and celebrated at festivals and women's sporting events. LGB residential areas grew up close to these commercial establishments, creating LGB neighbourhoods in these cities, although most gays and lesbians do not live in these "gay villages" (Kinsman, 1996).

LGBs tend to be less visible in smaller Canadian communities, but they nonetheless tend to have strong social networks. Some people move to large urban centres seeking greater anonymity, acceptance, and perhaps distance from their families.

Several symbols are used as representations of gay, lesbian, and bisexual pride. That is, they are used to indicate that being gay is something to be proud of, not to hide. An upside-down pink triangle, which is what the Nazis used to label gay men, has been reclaimed by the gay community. The lowercase Greek letter lambda is also used. However, perhaps the most easily recognizable symbol is the rainbow flag, used by the gay community since 1978, and a representation of diversity and multiculturalism. A pink, purple, and blue striped flag is used to symbolize bisexual pride, with the pink representing attraction to members of the same gender, the blue representing attraction to people of the other gender, and the purple (the middle stripe) representing attraction to both men and women. Pride celebrations, which celebrate the anniversary of the Stonewall rebellion mentioned earlier, take place in various cities across Canada each summer. The Pride parade, in particular, is considered an important celebration of what it means to be gay, lesbian, or bisexual. The use of slang is another sign of solidarity among LBGs (see Table 14.3).

and desires as well as our insecurities and limits. For me this has less to do with bisexuality than it has to do with not holding monogamy as an ideal and being open to exploring other possibilities for respectful and responsible sexual living. Sometimes I find myself feeling a bit apologetic because I worry that my life reflects the stereotype of the bisexual who can't be monogamous, although intellectually I realize that I don't have an obligation to live my life in ways that challenge every stereotype that exists about bi people. If people think that I'm a reflection of every bisexual person out there that isn't actually my problem.

As an out bisexual, I get hit with both homophobia and biphobia. The specific challenges of being bisexual include invisibility, not being taken seriously, and dealing with all the myths and stereotypes that exist about bi people. Biphobia hurts the most when it comes from other queer people. The queer community is where I feel most at home, and yet it isn't always that accepting of bi folks. We get excluded on a regular basis, even when the "B" is listed in an organization or event's name.

In spite of the challenges, I'm proud to be bisexual. It means I'm coming from a very authentic place and I can talk openly about my struggles and the changes I've gone through. My pride has now grown into activism. I teach courses and lead workshops about bisexuality, I facilitate numerous support groups and I publish a bi women's zine called "The Fence." I'm also involved in many different lesbian, gay, bisexual and transgender organizations as an out bisexual and I advocate for bi inclusivity in these organizations. I'm committed to challenging people's ideas about bisexuality and also to helping provide bisexuals with ways of expressing themselves, connecting with others, and learning that it's possible to be bisexual and proud of it.

Cheryl Dobinson is a writer, bisexual activist, and zine-maker (www.thefence.ca) living in Toronto.

Table 14.3	Some Slang Terms from LGB Culture
In the closet	Keeping one's sexual orientation hidden, not being open or public
Coming out	Coming out of the closet, or becoming open about one's sexual orientation
Queen	An effeminate gay man
Nellie	An effeminate gay man
Drag queen	A man who dresses in women's clothing ("drag") for fun or performance reasons
Drag king	A woman who dresses in men's clothing ("drag") for fun or performance reasons
Butch	A masculine gay man or a masculine lesbian
Dyke	Slang term for lesbian
Femme	A feminine lesbian
Straight	A heterosexual
Trick	A casual sexual partner
Cruising	Looking for a sexual partner
Tearoom	A public washroom where gay men engage in casual sex

Gay bars are one aspect of the LGB social life. These are gay-friendly clubs in which drinking, perhaps dancing, talking, socializing with friends, and, sometimes, the possibility of finding a romantic or sexual partner are important elements. In large cities, some gays bars cater to either gays or lesbians. However, many gay bars, particularly in smaller Canadian cities, are mixed gender and mixed orientation. This means that they cater to both gay men and to lesbians, as well as to gay-positive heterosexuals. What makes them gay bars is that they are accepting of same-sex relationships. Thus, patrons can be open about their sexual orientation and feel free to socialize and dance with whomever they wish without fearing verbal or physical harassment from other customers. Some gay bars look like any other bar from the outside, while others may have names—for example, The Open Closet—that indicate to the

Gay bar: A gay-friendly bar or club frequented by lesbians and gays.

alert that they are gay bars. LGB community dances and parties are other important avenues for socializing, particularly in small centres.

Gay baths are another aspect of some gay men's social and sexual lives. The baths are clubs with many rooms in them, generally including a swimming pool or whirlpool, as well as rooms for dancing, watching television, and socializing; most areas are dimly lit. Once a man has found a sexual partner, they go to one of a number of small rooms furnished with beds, where they can engage in sexual activity. The baths feature casual, impersonal sex, since a partner can be found and the act completed without the two even exchanging names, much less making any emotional commitment to each other.

Gay baths: Clubs where gay men can socialize; features include a swimming pool or whirlpool and access to casual sex.

In many parts of Canada, there are no or relatively few bath houses (Myers et al., 1993). However, there are 15 in Montreal and about six in Toronto. There is some controversy in the gay community about whether they encourage risky sexual practices. Some see the baths as an aspect of gay culture that spreads HIV and will continue to do so, killing thousands; they believe the baths must be closed and the destructive practices they encourage should stop (Rotello, 1997; Signorile, 1997). Others celebrate the liberated sexuality fostered by the baths and see it as an essential part of gay men's lifestyle. Today many bath houses emphasize safe sex—for example, by supplying condoms and handing out safer sex information.

Today, of course, a major way for LGB individuals to meet each other is through the Internet. Cyberspace is also a place where gay men and lesbians can find community when, geographically, they do not live in a place that has a gay community (Brown et al., 2005). Gay-related websites provide chat rooms and have ways for LGBs to form online relationships and perhaps find partners for casual sex or a long-term relationship (Brown et al., 2005).

Certainly, in the last three decades the *gay liberation movement* has had a tremendous impact on the gay lifestyle and community. In particular, it has encouraged LGBs to be more overt and to feel less guilty about their behaviour. The gay liberation movement has given rise to a number of provincial and national organizations committed to ending discrimina-

Figure 14.5 The comedic television series *G-Spot*, produced by Serendipity Point Films and Barna-Alper Productions, is an example of a mainstream show that often deals with gay-friendly storylines.

tion against LGBs. For example, EGALE (Equality for Gays and Lesbians Everywhere) is a national organization committed to advancing equality and justice for lesbian, gay, bisexual, and transgender individuals and their families across Canada. The organization does so by fighting for justice in the courts as well as by building communication and action networks. There are also many LGB organizations at the provincial and local levels. Some address social justice issues; others provide community service and education. For example, large Canadian cities and most Canadian universities have pride centres. The Canadian Lesbian and Gay Archives serves as a central clearinghouse for LGB information.

There are thus many places for LGBs to socialize besides bars, including the Metropolitan Community Church (a gay and lesbian church), gay athletic organizations, and gay political organizations.

Among other accomplishments, members of the gay liberation movement have founded numerous gay newspapers and magazines. These have many of the same features as other newspapers: forums for political opinions, human-interest stories, and fashion news. In addition, the classified ads feature advertisements for sexual partners; similar ads for same-sex and other-sex partners can be found in non-mainstream newspapers in most cities as well as on the Internet. Today there are many regional LGB publications, including *Wayves* published in Halifax, *Fugues* published in Montreal, *Outwords Inc* published in Winnipeg, *Perceptions* published in Saskatoon, *Outlooks* published in Calgary, and *Xtra* published in Toronto, Ottawa (*Capital Xtra*), and Vancouver (*Xtra West*). There are also several publications that list gay-owned or gay-friendly businesses, including information about bars, accommodations, shops, services, and tours. The Canadian Gay, Lesbian, and Bisexual Resource Directory distributes information relevant to LGB communities across Canada through its website www.gaycanada.com.

SAME-SEX RELATIONSHIPS

Contrary to stereotypes, a substantial number of lesbians, gay men, and bisexuals form long-term relationships. One such relationship is described in In Focus 14.2. Some bisexuals are in a relationship with a person of the other gender; others are in a same-sex relationship. Across numerous surveys, between 8 and 21 percent of lesbian couples had been together for 10 years or more, as had between 18 and 28 percent of the gay male couples (Kurdek, 2005).

In the 2006 Census, there were 7465 same-sex married couples and 37 885 same-sex common-law couples in Canada (Statistics Canada, 2007). Of these, 55 percent were male couples and 45 percent were female couples. About 15 percent of female same-sex couples but only 3 percent of male same-sex couples have children living with them. One study asked same-sex Canadian couples why they wanted to be married (Alderson, 2004). For some, it was important to publically declare their life-long commitment to each other. For others marriage was part of a spiritual journey, including feeling that marriage brings greater depth to a relationship. Some felt that the legal protection provided by marriage (e.g., if their partner got sick) was important. Finally, for some it was about equality rights and making things better for gay and lesbian youth in the future. For example, here's what one 41-year-old woman said:

> You can't represent the essence of it and that's the spiritual part that I'm talking about—that indescribable experience of being a family. And now that we're being recognized by the outside state as a family. It's very powerful to be recognized. (Alderson, 2004, p. 113)

All couples—gay or straight—must struggle to find a balance that suits both persons. Three aspects of the relationship typically have to be negotiated and can be sources of conflict: money, housework, and sex (Solomon et al., 2005).

Figure 14.6 A gay male couple. A large percentage of lesbians and gay men report currently being in a steady romantic relationship.

IN FOCUS 14.2

Carolyn and cj: A Same-Sex Couple

Carolyn is 29 and cj is 31. They have been together for eight years. They live in Ottawa, where Carolyn works for the federal government and cj works as a researcher for an online activist organization.

Carolyn has always had close relationships with her parents and younger sister. They were her best friends when she was growing up, and she has many fond memories of working on family craft activities. In school, she was active in almost every non-sports extra-curricular club. In middle school she wanted to have a boyfriend, mainly for the social status. In grade 12, she had an impassioned relationship with a young man, and his openness about sexual identity influenced her own ideas on the subject. After this relationship, Carolyn wanted to balance her romantic experiences by having a relationship with a woman. She dated two women before cj and found that she was more able to be herself with women. Carolyn's nuclear family was supportive when

she came out to them; they indicated that the gender of her partner was not an issue. She delayed coming out to her extended family, fearing that they would be less supportive. Carolyn identifies as a dyke: For her, the term lesbian assumes an attraction to women only, whereas the term dyke does not negate her past relationship with a man and recognizes her attraction to trans people.

cj's family is also close. She has two brothers and a sister. She had an active childhood and adolescence, spending much of it horseback riding and at the family cottage. Classism was a particular challenge for cj in school. She felt that there were certain expectations of her because she was from an upper-middle-class home. She rejected these expectations and purposefully sought out like-minded friends. Although cj had boyfriends in high school, including a couple of long-term relationships, she now recognizes that she was always attracted to women. In first-year university, cj had crushes on some

In one Quebec study, gay couples, lesbian couples, and heterosexual couples were brought to the laboratory and told to discuss a problem (Julien et al., 2003). Each couple's interactions were videotaped and later coded for both positive and negative behaviours by each partner. The results showed no differences among lesbian, gay, and heterosexual couples on any of the interaction measures.

What is striking about all the research on gay and lesbian relationships is how similar all relationships are, regardless of sexual orientation, in their satisfactions, loves, joys, and conflicts (Patterson, 2000; Peplau et al., 1996).

LESBIAN AND GAY FAMILIES

Increasingly, gay and lesbian couples are creating families that include children (Bowe, 2006). In the past, the courts have tended to grant custody to the non-gay or -lesbian parents and have often restricted visitation by the gay or lesbian parent (Barrett et al., 1997). However, legislation in most provinces allows same-sex adoption either by the partner of a parent or of an unrelated child. In provinces where there has not been such legislation, the courts have ruled that provincial acts that prevent same-sex couples from applying to adopt are unconstitutional. The Canadian Charter of Rights and Freedoms prohibits discrimination on the basis of sexual orientation, and this applies to adoption, custody, and access. This legislation appears to recognize the result of research on the effects on children of living in a gay or lesbian family.

It is important to recognize that these families are not all the same. In some, the children were born to one of the partners in a previous heterosexual relationship. In others, the children were adopted or, in the case of lesbian couples, born by means of assisted insemination. Some have even said that a "lesbian baby boom" is underway (Patterson, 1995). Some are single-parent families, with, for example, a lesbian mother rearing her children from a previous heterosexual marriage.

of the women in her classes, yet did not know how to act on her feelings. She dated one woman before Carolyn. When cj came out to her family, her father was immediately accepting. Her mother found it harder to come to terms with cj's sexual identity, however. Her minister and cj's sister were instrumental in helping her accept her daughter's identity. cj identifies as pansexual—that is, she is not exclusively attracted to women; rather, she is attracted to people regardless of their gender.

cj and Carolyn were both raised in Fredericton, where they attended the same high school. Although they knew each other by name, they travelled in different circles. When cj returned to Fredericton after university, she and Carolyn kept running into each other and had some awkward flirtatious moments. Yet they were not certain of each other's sexual identity or their mutual attraction until they saw each other at an LGBT event. Following this, they went on a coffee date, and within a few months were dating exclusively. Approximately 18 months later, they moved to Ottawa together so that Carolyn could complete a degree in art history and cj could do a masters degree in legal studies.

In Spring 2000, three years before same-sex marriage was legalized in Ontario, Carolyn and cj applied for a marriage licence. Although they do not regard marriage as necessary to affirm their relationship, it was important for them to have the legal benefits and protections associated with marriage. They wanted to buy a house together and did not want to wait until same-sex marriage was legalized. So they took the necessary steps to ensure they would have as close to a legal equivalent to marriage as possible.

Most of Carolyn and cj's disagreements relate to household chores. Important aspects of their relationship are having similar politics and values, enjoying discussing such issues, and finding each other interesting. Their trust that the other person will be there to support them is also very important to them.

Source: Based on an interview by Jacqueline Cohen.

(a)

(b)

Figure 14.7   Lesbian and gay parents and their children. It is illegal to discriminate against gay men or lesbians in adoption, custody, or access decisions.

Heterosexuals often make the assumption, based on their homonegativity, that it is better for children to grow up in heterosexual families than in gay or lesbian families. Based on this assumption, they raise three questions about how children fare. First, will they be less healthy psychologically than children who grow up with two heterosexual parents? Second, will they have difficulties in relationships with their peers, perhaps being stigmatized or teased because of their unusual family situation? Third, will they show "disturbances" in gender identity or sexual identity? Will they become gay or lesbian? What has research found?

Research on children growing up in lesbian or gay families, compared with those growing up in heterosexual families, dismisses these assumptions. For example, the adjustment and mental health of children in lesbian and gay families are no different from those of children in heterosexual families (Golombok et al., 2003; Patterson, 2006).They fare about as well in terms of social skills and popularity as children growing up in heterosexual families (Patterson, 1992). Finally, the overwhelming number of children growing up in lesbian or gay households have a heterosexual orientation (Allen & Burrell, 2002).

In conclusion, although some people have raised concerns about children growing up in lesbian and gay families based on their negative assumptions, research consistently shows no difference between these children and those in heterosexual families in psychosocial development, gender identity, or sexual orientation (Canadian Psychological Association, 2003). As one expert in clinical psychology concluded, "It appears that traditional family structures, including [mother and] father presence and heterosexuality, are not essential for healthy child development. Well-adjusted children of both sexes can be reared in families of varying configurations with the most crucial ingredient appearing to be the presence of at least one supportive, accepting caregiver" (Strickland, 1995).

LGB Sexual Orientation and Mental Health

Some Canadians believe that homosexuality is a kind of mental illness. Is this really true? Do psychologists and psychiatrists agree that LGBs are poorly adjusted or deviant? What are the implications of sexual orientation for a person's adjustment?

SIN AND THE MEDICAL MODEL

Actually, the belief that homosexuality is a form of mental illness is something of an improvement over previous beliefs about homosexuality. Before the last century, the dominant belief in Europe and North America was that homosexuality was a sin or a heresy. During the Inquisition, people who were accused of being heretics were also frequently accused of being homosexuals and were burned at the stake. Indeed, in those times, all mental illness was regarded as a sin. In the twentieth century, this view was replaced by the **medical model**, in which mental disturbance, and homosexuality in particular, is viewed as a sickness or illness (Bullough & Bullough, 1997).[4] This view is still held by some members of the general public but is not accepted by mental health professionals.

Medical model: A theoretical model in psychology and psychiatry in which mental problems are thought of as sickness or mental illness; the problems in turn are often thought to be due to biological factors.

RESEARCH EVIDENCE

What do the scientific data say? Early research compared a group of gays and lesbians in therapy with a group of randomly chosen heterosexuals not in therapy. Not surprisingly, these studies tended to find more problems of adjustment among the gay and lesbian group than among the heterosexual group (Rosen, 1974). However, the reasoning was circular in assuming that LGBs were abnormal (in therapy) and that heterosexuals were normal (not in therapy), and then finding exactly that.

A major breakthrough came with the next group of studies, which involved non-patient research. In these studies, a group of gays and lesbians not in therapy (non-patients) were compared with a group of heterosexuals not in therapy. The non-patient gays and lesbians were generally recruited through LGB organizations, advertisements, or word of mouth. Such non-patient research has found no differences between the groups (Ross et al., 1988; Rothblum, 1994). That is, gays, lesbians, and heterosexuals were equally well adjusted. This finding is

---

[4]As one gay comedian quipped, "If homosexuality is an illness, hey, I'm going to call in queer to work tomorrow."

quite remarkable in view of the very negative attitudes that members of the general public tend to hold toward LGBs (Gonsiorek, 1996).

On the basis of these studies, it must be concluded that the evidence does not support the notion that gay men and lesbians by definition are "sick" or poorly adjusted. This position has received official professional recognition by the American Psychiatric Association (APA). Prior to 1973, the APA had listed homosexuality as a disorder in its authoritative *Diagnostic and Statistical Manual of Mental Disorders* (which Canadian psychiatrists also use). In 1973, the APA voted to remove homosexuality from that listing; thus, it is no longer considered a psychiatric disorder by the APA or by the Canadian Psychiatric Association. Other countries were slower to make these changes. Homosexuality was removed from the list of mental disorders by the World Health Organization only in 1993, by Japan in 1995, and by China in 2001.

In the last decade a new set of studies has emerged using even better designs that, for example, obtain a random sample of the general population and then compare the gays and lesbians and the heterosexuals in the sample on indices of mental health (Cochran et al., 2003; Meyer, 2003; Wichstrøm & Hegna, 2003). These studies find higher rates of depression among gays and lesbians compared with heterosexuals, and suicide attempts are more common among LGB youth than among heterosexual youth.

However, scientists vigorously debate the meaning of the statistics. One controversy concerns how big or meaningful the differences are. For example, in one study 9.1 percent of LGB adolescents had made a suicide attempt, compared with 3.6 percent for heterosexual adolescents (Wichstrom & Hegna, 2003). We could focus on the fact that LGB youth were nearly three times as likely to attempt suicide. Alternatively, we could say that it's a gap of less than 6 percentage points and 90.9 percent of the LGBs had *not* attempted suicide (Savin-Williams, 2001; Savin-Williams & Ream, 2003). Should we view the glass as half full or half empty?

Beyond that, scientists agree that higher rates of depression and suicide among LGBs do not indicate that homosexuality per se indicates mental illness. Rather, the higher rates reflect the greater exposure of LGBs to prejudice and hate crimes, and the stress of concealing their true sexual identity (Meyer, 2003). In contrast, high levels of social support from the LGB community and from family and friends are associated with better mental health (Fenaughty & Harré, 2003; Russell & Richards, 2003).

CAN SEXUAL ORIENTATION BE CHANGED BY PSYCHOTHERAPY?

Conversion therapy or **reparative therapy**—treatments designed to change LGBs into heterosexuals—have been around for more than 100 years (Shidlo et al., 2001; Haldeman, 1994). The latest versions come from far-right religious groups. Many earlier techniques were downright inhumane. They included crude behaviour therapy that involved giving gay men electrical shocks while they viewed slides of nude men, as well as surgeries ranging from castration to brain surgery. All these treatments rested on the assumption that homosexuality was an illness that should and could be cured.

Conversion or reparative therapy: Any one of a number of treatments designed to turn LGBs into heterosexuals.

Investigations of reparative therapies today reveal that many individuals undergoing reparative therapy do so because of pressures from their family. They also identify the personal agonies that people experience as they are forced into, or perhaps choose, to change their orientation. One man, who is now a psychologist, quoted from his diary:

> I am going to meet with the counselor tomorrow. I don't really know what to think. I feel that I need help but I also feel that I'm trying to do away with a part of myself. I know I should look at it as sinful and ugly, like a wart that needs to be burned off. Is it possible that those emotions are what allow me to be a sensitive caring male? Is it possible that God has allowed this in my life to build certain characteristics? Is it really ugly and sinful that I want to hold and be held by a man and that I want to have a relationship with a man that includes sex? It sure sounds ugly on paper

I don't like admitting these things. I really don't. What is it that causes me to think and feel this way? Is it Satanic? Am I possessed? (Ford, 2001, p. 77)

The consequences of reparative therapies can be ugly because they do not actually change people's sexual orientation but do make them feel awfully guilty about it. Thus, reparative therapy itself can create mental health problems. As a result, some gay men and bisexuals subsequently seek psychotherapy to help them recover from conversion therapies (Haldeman, 2001).

Given the evidence discussed earlier in this section supporting the argument that LGBs are not mentally ill, reparative therapies make no sense. In addition, they do not work. Ethical issues are raised as well: Should a person be changed from gay to straight against his or her will? Why do we only try to change people from gay to straight, and not the reverse? By 2000, the scandals associated with conversion therapies had become so great that the American Psychiatric Association issued an official position statement opposing them (American Psychiatric Association, 2000).

WHAT DETERMINES SEXUAL ORIENTATION?

A fascinating psychological question is: Why do people become homosexual, heterosexual, or bisexual? Several theoretical answers to this question, as well as the relevant evidence, are discussed in this section. You will notice that the older theorists and researchers considered it their task to explain homosexuality; more recent investigators, realizing that heterosexuality needs to be explained as well, are more likely to consider it their task to understand the developmental pathways for all orientations.

BIOLOGICAL THEORIES

A number of scientists have proposed that sexual orientation is caused by biological factors. Interestingly, this is also the view of the majority of Canadians—54 percent believe that homosexuality is something a person is born with and an additional 8 percent believe that it results from a combination of biological factors and environment (Gallup, 2004). The likeliest candidates for these biological causes are genetic factors, prenatal factors, differences in brain structure, and an endocrine imbalance.

GENETIC FACTORS

One study recruited gay and bisexual men who had a twin brother or an adopted brother (Bailey & Pillard, 1991). Among the 56 gay men who had an identical twin brother, 52 percent of the co-twins were themselves gay (in the terminology of geneticists, this is a 52 percent concordance rate). Among the 54 gay men who had a non-identical twin brother, 22 percent of the co-twins were themselves gay. Of the adoptive brothers of gay men, 11 percent were gay. The same research team later repeated the study with lesbians (Bailey et al., 1993). Among the 71 lesbians who had an identical twin, 48 percent of the co-twins were also lesbian. Among the 37 lesbians who had a non-identical twin sister, 16 percent of the co-twins were lesbian. Of the adoptive sisters of lesbians, 6 percent were lesbian. The statistics for women were therefore quite similar to those for men. Later studies using improved methods have found similar results (Kendler et al., 2000; Kirk et al., 2000).

The fact that the rate of concordance is substantially higher for identical twins than for non-identical twins argues in favour of a genetic contribution to sexual orientation. If genetic factors absolutely *determined* sexual orientation, however, the concordance rate would be 100 percent for the identical twin pairs, and the rates are far from that. The implication is that factors other than genetics also play a role in influencing sexual orientation.

A milestone came in 2005 with the first full genome scan for sexual orientation in men, using modern genotyping methods (Mustanski et al., 2005). The sample consisted of 456 individuals from 146 different families, all of which had two or more gay brothers. It included many heterosexual siblings and parents from those families, as well as the gay siblings. This design is ideal for spotting regions of DNA that are the same for two gay brothers but that differ from the heterosexual siblings or parents. The findings indicated possible influence by three genes, found on chromosomes 7, 8, and 10. It seems likely that multiple genes contribute to sexual orientation. This research is still in its infancy but should yield important findings in the next decade.

PRENATAL FACTORS

Another possible biological cause is that homosexuality develops as a result of factors during the prenatal period. As we suggest in Chapter 5, exposure to inappropriate hormones during fetal development can lead a genetic female to have male genitals, or a genetic male to have female genitals. It has been suggested that a similar process might account for homosexuality (and also for transsexualism—see Chapter 13).

According to one theory, homosexuality is caused by a variation in prenatal development. There is a critical time of fetal development during which the hypothalamus differentiates and sexual orientation is determined (Ellis & Cole-Harding, 2001). Any of several biological variations during this period will produce homosexuality.

One line of animal research that supports this theory has found evidence that severe *stress to a mother* during pregnancy tends to produce homosexual offspring. For example, exposing pregnant female rats to stress produces male offspring that assume the female mating posture, although their ejaculatory behaviour is normal (Ward et al., 2002). The stress to the mother reduces the amount of testosterone in the fetus, which is thought to produce homosexual rats. Research with humans designed to test the prenatal stress hypothesis reports mixed results. Some studies find effects like those in the rat studies and others do not (Bailey et al., 1991; Ellis & Cole-Harding, 2001).

Another research group has suggested that prenatal *exposure to abnormally high levels of estrogen* produces human female offspring who are more likely to be lesbian (Meyer-Bahlburg, 1997; Meyer-Bahlburg et al., 1995). To test this hypothesis they studied adult women who had been exposed to DES before birth. DES, or diethylstilbestrol, is a powerful estrogen that was used to prevent miscarriage until 1971, when its use was discontinued because of harmful side effects. More DES-exposed women than controls were rated as homosexual or bisexual (Kinsey ratings of 2 through 6).

Canadian researchers have been leaders in examining prenatal factors that may determine a person's sexual orientation. For example, Ontario psychologists Ray Blanchard and Anthony Bogaert have studied the birth order of gay men. Their research shows that consistently, across many samples, in a number of countries, compared with heterosexual men, gay men are more likely to have a late birth order and to have more older brothers but not more older sisters (Blanchard, 1997, 2004; Bogaert, 2003). This effect is only found in right-handed men (Blanchard & Lippa, 2006). The researchers find no birth order or sibling effects for lesbians compared with heterosexual women. They believe that they have uncovered a prenatal effect, hypothesizing that, with each successive pregnancy with a male fetus, the mother forms more antibodies against an antigen (H-Y antigen) produced by a gene on the Y chromosome (Blanchard 2001). Because H-Y antigen is known to influence prenatal sexual differentiation, the hypothesis is that the mother's antibodies to this antigen may affect sexual differentiation in the developing fetal brain, and subsequent sexual attraction (Bogaert, 2003). These researchers estimate that between 15 and 30 percent of gay men had their sexual orientation created in this manner (Cantor et al., 2002; Blanchard & Bogaert, 2004).

Other researchers have documented an odd, but potentially important pattern concerning the 2D:4D finger-length ratio. This refers to the ratio of the length of the index finger to the length of the ring finger. In general, men have lower 2D:4D ratios than women; that is, men's index fingers are relatively shorter than their ring fingers, compared with women's. Lesbians have a lower 2D:4D ratio than heterosexual women. Results across studies are inconsistent for comparison of gay men and heterosexual men (McFadden et al., 2005). Similarly, Alberta researcher Martin Lalumière has found that gay men and lesbians are more likely to be left-handed than are heterosexuals; gay men are about 40 percent more likely than straight men to be left-handed, and lesbians are nearly twice as likely as heterosexual women to be left-handed (Lalumière et al., 2000). Both patterns suggest some kind of prenatal hormone effect on the developing brain.

These theories of prenatal influence are intriguing and show much promise for the future.

Brain Factors

Another line of theorizing argues that there are anatomical differences between the brains of gays and straights that produce the differences in sexual orientation. A number of studies have pursued this possibility, all looking at somewhat different regions of the brain (Swaab, 2005). A highly publicized study by neuroscientist Simon LeVay (1991) is an example. LeVay found significant differences between gay men and straight men in certain cells in the anterior portion of the hypothalamus. Anatomically, the hypothalamic cells of the gay men were more similar to those of women than to those of straight men, according to LeVay. However, the study had a number of flaws: (1) The sample size was very small: only 19 gay men, 16 straight men, and six straight women were included. This small sample size was necessitated by the fact that the brains had to be dissected in order to examine the hypothalamus, so that the brains of living persons could not be studied. (2) All of the gay men in the sample, but only six of the straight men and one of the straight women, had died of AIDS. The groups are not comparable, then. Perhaps the brain differences were caused by the neurological effects of AIDS. (3) Lesbian women were omitted from the study, making them invisible in the research—as they often have been in psychological and biological research. (4) The gay men were known to have been gay based on records at the time of death; the others, however, were just "presumed" to be heterosexual—if there was no record of sexual orientation, the assumption was that the person had been heterosexual, scarcely a sophisticated method of measurement.

It is difficult to know how much confidence to place in LeVay's findings. Other scientists who looked for this effect found no differences in this region of the hypothalamus as a function of the person's sexual orientation (Byne et al., 2000; Swaab, 2005). Yet animal researchers believe that they have identified a similar region in the hypothalamus of the rat that does seem to be involved in sexual behaviour (Swaab, 2005).

Hormonal Factors

Investigating the possibility that endocrine factors are the cause of homosexuality, many researchers have tried to determine whether the testosterone levels of gay men differ from those of straight men. These studies have not found any hormonal differences between the two groups (Banks & Gartrell, 1995; Gooren et al., 1990).

Despite these results, some clinicians have attempted to cure male homosexuality by administering testosterone therapy (Glass & Johnson, 1944). This therapy fails; indeed, it seems to result in even more same-sex sexual activity than usual. This is not an unexpected result, since, as we saw in Chapter 9, androgen levels seem to be related to sexual responsiveness. As a clinician friend of two of the authors replied to an undergraduate male who was seeking testosterone therapy for his homosexuality, "It won't make you heterosexual; it will only make you horny."

In conclusion, of the biological theories, the genetic theory and the prenatal theory have new supporting evidence, but much more research is needed.

LEARNING THEORY

Behaviourists emphasize the importance of learning in the development of sexual orientation. They note the prevalence of bisexual behaviour both in other species and in young humans, and they argue that rewards and punishments shape the individual's behaviour into predominant homosexuality or predominant heterosexuality. The assumption, then, is that humans have a relatively amorphous, undifferentiated pool of sex drive which, depending on circumstances (rewards and punishments), may be channelled in any of several directions. In short, people are born sexual, not heterosexual or homosexual. Only through learning does one of these behaviours become more likely than the other. For example, if early sexual experiences are with a same-sex partner and pleasant, the person may become gay. Same-sex sexual activity has essentially been rewarded and therefore becomes more likely.

Another possibility, according to a learning-theory approach, is that a person who has early heterosexual experiences that are very unpleasant might develop toward homosexuality. Heterosexuality has essentially been punished and therefore becomes less likely. This might occur, for instance, in the case of a girl who is sexually assaulted by a male at an early age; her first experience with a male was extremely unpleasant, so she avoids it and turns to homosexuality.

The learning-theory approach treats same-sex sexual activity as a normal form of behaviour and recognizes that both heterosexuality and homosexuality are not necessarily inborn but must be learned.

The evidence on learning theory's explanation of sexual orientation is mixed. A comprehensive study of the influences on sexual orientation in humans disconfirmed some essential arguments. The idea that homosexuality results from early unpleasant heterosexual experiences was not supported by the data. Lesbian women, for example, were no more likely to have been sexually assaulted than were heterosexual women (Bell et al., 1981). Yet recent research using an animal model does point to the importance of early learning. Zebra finches are small birds that are monogamous, mate for life, and are almost invariably heterosexual. If the fathers are removed from the cages, though, so that the young birds grow up without adult males or male–female pairs, in adulthood these birds pair with either males or females (Adkins-Regan, 2002). That is, their behaviour, which is bisexual, is a result of early experience.

In contrast to the bird research, research with humans indicates that children who grow up with a gay or lesbian parent are not themselves more likely as a result to become gay (Allen & Burrell, 2002; Bailey et al., 1995; Patterson, 2006). In this sense, then, sexual orientation is not "learned" from one's parents.

INTERACTIONIST THEORY

BEM: THE EXOTIC BECOMES EROTIC

Psychologist Daryl Bem (1996) proposed a theory of the development of sexual orientation that encompasses the interaction of biological factors and experiences with the environment. Bem's theory is diagrammed in Figure 14.8.

The theory begins with biological influences, relying on the evidence discussed earlier about biological contributions to sexual orientation (box A in Figure 14.8). However, Bem does not believe that genes and other biological factors directly and magically determine a person's sexual orientation. Rather, he theorized that biological factors exert their influence on sexual orientation through their influence on temperament in childhood (box A to box B). Psychologists have found abundant evidence that two aspects of temperament have a biological basis: aggression and activity level. Moreover, these two aspects of temperament show reliable gender differences. According to Bem, most children show levels of aggression and activity level that are typical of their gender; boys are generally more aggressive and more active than girls. These tendencies lead children to engage in gender-conforming activities (B to C). Most boys play active, aggressive sports, and most girls prefer quieter play activities. These play patterns also

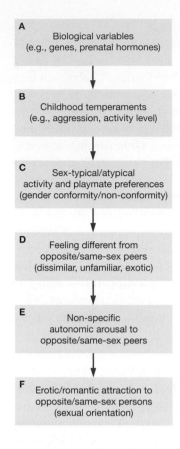

A Biological variables
(e.g., genes, prenatal hormones)

B Childhood temperaments
(e.g., aggression, activity level)

C Sex-typical/atypical
activity and playmate preferences
(gender conformity/non-conformity)

D Feeling different from
opposite/same-sex peers
(dissimilar, unfamiliar, exotic)

E Non-specific
autonomic arousal to
opposite/same-sex peers

F Erotic/romantic attraction to
opposite/same-sex persons
(sexual orientation)

Figure 14.8 Daryl Bem's theory of the development of sexual orientation: The exotic becomes erotic.

lead children to associate almost exclusively with members of their own gender. The boy playing tackle football is playing in a group that consists either entirely or almost entirely of boys. This chain of events will eventually lead to a heterosexual orientation in adulthood.

A minority of children, however, have temperamental characteristics that are not typical of their gender: some boys are not particularly active or aggressive and some girls are. These children are then gender–non-conforming in their play patterns. The boys prefer quieter, less active play and have more girls as friends, and the gender–non-conforming girls prefer aggressive sports and have more boys as friends.

These experiences with childhood play and playmates create a feeling in children that certain other children are different from them and therefore are exotic (box C to D). For the boy who spends most of his time playing active, aggressive sports with other boys, girls are different, mysterious, and exotic. For the gender–non-conforming girl who plays active sports with boys, most girls, too, seem different and exotic to her.

The presence of an exotic other causes a person to feel generalized arousal, whether in childhood, adolescence, or adulthood (box D to E). Those of you who are heterosexual certainly remember many instances in your past when you felt ill at ease and nervous in the presence of a member of the other gender.

In the final link of the model, this generalized arousal is transformed into erotic/romantic attraction. Essentially, the exotic becomes erotic. This transformation may be a result of processes described in Berscheid and Walster's (1974) two-component theory of arousal, discussed in Chapter 12. Generalized arousal can easily be transformed into sexual arousal and attraction if the conditions are right. For heterosexual persons, the exotic people are members of the other gender, with whom they had less contact in childhood and who have become eroticized. For gay men and lesbians, the exotic people are members of their own gender, from whom they felt different in childhood and who have become eroticized. For most individuals, then, members of the other gender are exotic. Thus, one virtue of the theory is that it is designed to explain both homosexual and heterosexual sexual orientations.

One body of evidence that is consistent with Bem's theory indicates that gay men and lesbians, on average, are more likely than heterosexuals to have had a childhood history of gender non-conformity (Bailey & Zucker, 1995; Cohen, 2002). This pattern has been found cross-culturally in cultures as diverse as Brazil, Peru, the Philippines, Somoa, and the United States (Bartlett & Vasey, 2006; Whitam & Mathy, 1991). Although findings of gender non-conformity are consistent with Bem's theory, they are also consistent with the biological theories.

At the same time, Bem's theory and evidence have been criticized (Peplau et al., 1998; for Bem's response, see Bem, 1998). Two criticisms have been raised: (1) evidence not discussed by Bem contradicts some central propositions of the theory; and (2) the theory reflects male experience and neglects female experience. Regarding the evidence, Bem noted that, in one major study, lesbians (70 percent) were significantly more likely than were heterosexual women (51 percent) to recall feeling somewhat or very different from other girls their age

(Bell et al., 1981). The difference is significant, but perhaps more important is the finding that a majority of heterosexual women felt different from other girls. Other girls seemed different or exotic to them. Why didn't they become lesbian, then?

SOCIOLOGICAL THEORY

Sociologists emphasize the effects of *labelling* in explaining homosexuality. The label "homosexual" has a big impact in our society. For example, one of the biggest insults used by middle school students is calling a classmate a "fag" (McFarland, 2001). The label "homosexual" often has derogatory connotations, reflecting our society's predominantly negative attitudes toward homosexuality.

But the label "homosexual" may also act as a self-fulfilling prophecy. Suppose that a young boy—possibly because he is slightly effeminate or poor in sports, or for no reason at all—is called "gay." He reacts strongly and becomes more and more anxious and worried about his problem. He becomes painfully aware of the slightest homosexual tendency in himself. Finally, he convinces himself that he is gay. He begins engaging in same-sex sexual activity and associates with a gay group. In short, a gay man has been created through labelling.

Recall that in Chapter 2 we discussed Ira Reiss's sociological theory of human sexuality. In his theorizing he addresses the issue of sexual orientation, focusing particularly on gay men. Recognizing the need to explain cross-cultural differences in sexual patterns, he contends that it is male-dominant societies with a great rigidity of gender roles that produce the highest incidence of homosexuality. In such societies, there is a rigid male role that must be learned and conformed to, but young boys have little opportunity to learn it from adult men precisely because the gender roles are rigid, so that women take care of children and men have little contact with them. It is therefore difficult to learn the heterosexual component of the male role. In addition, because the male role is rigid, there will be a certain number of males who dislike it and reject its heterosexual component. Cross-cultural studies support his observations (Reiss, 1986). Societies that have a great maternal involvement with infants and low father involvement with infants and that have rigid gender roles are precisely those that have the highest incidence of same-sex sexual behaviour in males.

This pattern describes the negative pathway to becoming gay or lesbian. Reiss argues that there is also a positive pathway. It exists in less gender-rigid societies with more permissiveness about sexuality. In such societies, individuals feel freer to experiment with same-sex behaviour and may find it satisfying. Examples are provided by several First Nations peoples in which three gender roles have been recognized (see Chapter 13).

THE BOTTOM LINE

We have examined a number of theories of sexual orientation and the evidence supporting or refuting them. What is the bottom line? Which theory is correct? The answer is, we don't know yet. We do not know what causes sexual orientation. Several theories have strong evidence supporting them, but no one theory accounts for all cases. We believe that a good lesson can be learned from this conclusion.

It has generally been assumed not only that gays form a distinct category (which, we have already seen, is not very accurate) but also that they form a homogeneous category; that is, that all gays are fairly similar. Not so. Probably there are many different kinds or "types" of gay men, lesbians, bisexuals, and heterosexuals. Indeed, one psychologist has suggested that we should refer not to "homosexuality" but rather to "homosexualities" (Bell, 1974b; Bell & Weinberg, 1978). If this is the case, then one would not expect a single "cause" of sexual orientation but rather many causes, each corresponding to its type. The next step in research, then, should be to identify the various types of LGBs and heterosexuals and the different pathways of development that lead to each.

DIFFERENCES BETWEEN GAY MEN AND LESBIANS

Although gay men and lesbians are commonly lumped together in one category and called homosexuals, evidence from a number of sources indicates that there are some important differences between the two groups that go beyond one group being male and the other female.

Women are more likely to be bisexual, and less likely to be exclusively homosexual, than men are. In the NSFG data set, 2 percent of women and 1 percent of men indicated that they were sexually attracted to both women and men, whereas 1.5 percent of women and 2.2 percent of men rated themselves as being attracted exclusively to members of their own gender (Mosher et al., 2005).

In related research, among both heterosexuals and homosexuals, women show more flexibility or change over time in their sexual orientation (Kinnish et al., 2005). In laboratory research, men are specific in their sexual arousal, whereas women tend not to be (Chivers et al., 2004). That is, heterosexual men tend to be aroused, physiologically, by female stimuli and not male stimuli, and gay men show the reverse pattern. Women, however, whether lesbian or heterosexual, show arousal to both male and female stimuli.

Some of the theories discussed earlier in this chapter seem to work for gay men or for lesbians but not for both. For example, the birth order effect has been found repeatedly; compared with heterosexual men, gay men are more likely to have a late birth order and an excess of older brothers. Lesbians, however, are no more or less likely to have a late birth order compared with heterosexual women (Blanchard, 1997; Bogaert, 2003).

We will almost certainly need somewhat different theories to explain the development of sexual orientation in women and in men (Hyde & Jaffee, 2000).

SEXUAL ORIENTATION IN MULTICULTURAL PERSPECTIVE

Different cultures around the world hold different views of same-sex sexual behaviour. For example, as described in In Focus 2.1 (page 34), among the Melanesians of the southwest Pacific same-sex behaviour is ritualized such that boys are expected to engage in exclusively homosexual relations for about ten years but then marry women and become exclusively heterosexual. As one anthropologist observed about the Sambia of Papua New Guinea:

> Semen is also necessary for young boys to attain full growth to manhood. . . . They need a boost, as it were. When a boy is eleven or twelve years old, he is engaged for several months in homosexual intercourse with a healthy older man chosen by his father. (This is always an in-law or unrelated person, since the same notions of incestuous relations apply to little boys as to marriageable women.) Men point to the rapid growth of adolescent youths, the appearance of peach fuzz beards, and so on, as the favorable results of this child-rearing practice. (Schieffelin, 1976, p. 124)

Similarly, various Canadian ethnic minority groups differ in their cultural definitions for same-sex behaviours.

Generally, members of Canadian ethnocultural communities have less tolerance for homosexuality than members of the majority culture do. There tends to be a stigma attached to being a gay man, a denial of the existence of homosexuality within the community, and considerable pressure to conform to community norms. As a result, many LGBs feel forced to stay in the closet with respect to their sexual orientation in order to be accepted within their family and community (Singer et al., 1996).

For example, in both the Caribbean and African communities in Canada, gay and bisexual men may keep their activities secret for fear of being ostracized if they are open about their sexual orientation (Health Canada, 1994b, 1994c). Similarly, because of strong negative attitudes in the community, many gay and bisexual men in the South Asian community keep their same-sex relationships hidden. They may comply with family pressure to get married to avoid causing conflict in the family. South Asian men who were born in Canada are more likely to be open about their sexual orientation (Health Canada, 1994e).

Members of some ethnic groups, including men from the Caribbean and Latin American communities, may engage in extensive same-sex sexual behaviour while still considering themselves to be heterosexual (Singer et al., 1996). An interesting example of these different cultural definitions comes from a study of Mexican and Mexican-American men (Magaña & Carrier, 1991). In Mexico, there is a dichotomizing of same-sex sexual behaviours that parallels traditional gender roles. Anal intercourse, because it most resembles penis-in-vagina intercourse, is the preferred behaviour, and fellatio is practised relatively little. A man adopts the role either of receptive partner or inserting partner and does this exclusively. Those who take the receptive role are considered unmanly, feminine, and "homosexual." Those who take the inserting role are considered masculine, are not labelled "homosexual," and are not stigmatized. Research with Latin American men living in Montreal also found that men who take the inserting role during anal intercourse with men often consider themselves to be

Figure 14.9 Ethnicity and sexual orientation. Among Latin American and Caribbean women, warmth and physical closeness are very acceptable, but there are strong taboos against female–female sexual relationships.

heterosexual (Health Canada, 1994a). In contrast, men who take the receptive role are considered homosexual and are marginalized in the community. This approach differs substantially from that in the gay Canadian majority, where men commonly switch roles and both are considered gay.

Such different definitions of homosexuality are not limited to Latin American cultures. One researcher described the scene in contemporary Egypt as follows:

> In Egypt, because there was so little sense of homosexuality as an identity, what position you took in bed defined all. Between men, the only sex that counted was anal sex. . . . In the minds of most Egyptians, "gay," if it meant anything at all, signified taking the receptive position in anal sex. On the other hand, a person who took the insertive role—and that seemed to include virtually all Egyptian men, to judge by what my acquaintances told me—was not considered gay. . . . Many of the insults in the Arabic language concern being penetrated anally by another man. (Miller, 1992, p. 76)

As for lesbians, Latin American women and Caribbean women experience conflicts in the complexities of ethnicity and sexual orientation (Espin, 1987; Gonzalez & Espin, 1996; Silvera, 1990). In both cultures, emotional and physical closeness among women is considered acceptable and desirable. However, attitudes toward lesbianism are extremely restrictive. The emphasis on family—defined as mother, father, children, and grandparents in Latin American cultures—and the emphasis on attracting a man and bearing a child in Caribbean cultures makes the lesbian even more of an outsider. Women who are openly lesbian may be stigmatized and ostracized in these communities.

Among the Chinese communities in Canada, two features of the culture shape attitudes toward homosexuality and its expression: (1) a strong distinction between what may be expressed publicly and what should be kept private; and (2) a stronger value placed on loyalty to one's family and on the performance of family roles than on the expression of one's own desires (Chan, 1995). Sexuality is something that must be expressed only privately, not publicly. And having an identity, much less a sexual identity or a gay lifestyle, apart from one's family is almost incomprehensible to traditional Chinese. As a result, a relatively small proportion of LGB members of the Chinese communities in Canada are "out" in their community. Nonetheless, there is an active gay Asian community in Vancouver. However, these individuals often remain in the closet within the Chinese community because of fear of bringing shame to their families (Health Canada, 1994f). As with other ethnocultural communities in Canada, members of the Chinese community who are out tend to be more acculturated—that is, influenced by Canadian culture.

In sum, when we consider sexual orientation from a multicultural perspective, two main points emerge: (1) The very definition of homosexuality is set by culture. In Canada, we would say that a man who is the inserting partner in anal intercourse with another man is engaging in homosexual behaviour, but other cultures (such as Mexico and Egypt) would not agree. (2) Many ethnocultural communities are more disapproving of homosexuality than is the majority Canadian culture. In those cases, LGBs feel conflicts between their sexual identity and loyalty to their ethnic group.

A FINAL NOTE

Deprivation homosexuality: Homosexual activity that occurs in certain situations, such as prisons, when people are deprived of their regular heterosexual activity.

As we have seen in this chapter, most theory and research rests on the assumption that sexual orientation is determined by conditions in childhood, or by prenatal or genetic factors. Yet some people have their first heterosexual and then their first homosexual experience in their 20s. It is difficult to believe that these behaviours were determined by some pathological condition at age five. Deprivation homosexuality, or situational homosexuality, is also a good example of the influence of late-occurring experience. A heterosexual man may engage in same-sex sexual behaviour while in prison but return to exclusive heterosexuality after his release. Once again, it seems likely that such a man's same-sex sexual behaviour was determined by his circumstances (being in prison) rather than by some problem years before. Unlike gender identity, which seems to be fixed in the preschool years, sexual identity continues to evolve. This contradicts some scientists' assertion that sexual orientation is determined before adolescence (Bell et al., 1981). We think that when sexual orientation is determined is still an open question. For some it may be determined by genetic factors or experiences early in life, but for others it may be determined in adulthood.

Second, a question is raised as to whether heterosexuality is really the "natural" state. The pattern in some theories has been to try to discover the pathological conditions that cause homosexuality (e.g., a father who is an inadequate role model or a homoseductive mother)— all on the basis of the assumption that heterosexuality is the natural state and that homosexuality must be explained as a deviation from it. As we have seen, this approach has failed; there appear to be multiple causes of homosexuality, just as there may be multiple causes of heterosexuality. The important alternative to consider is that bisexuality is the natural state, a point acknowledged by Freud, the learning theorists, and sociological theorists (Weinberg et al., 1994). This chapter will close, then, with some questions. Psychologically, the real question should concern not the conditions that lead to homosexuality but rather the causes of exclusive homosexuality and exclusive heterosexuality. Why do we eliminate some people as potential sex partners simply on the basis of their gender? Why isn't everyone bisexual?

SUMMARY

Sexual orientation is defined as a person's erotic and emotional attraction toward members of his or her own gender, toward members of the other gender, or both.

The most recent well-sampled surveys indicate (when corrected for some underreporting) that about 2 percent of men and 1 percent of women are exclusively homosexual and that roughly 10 percent of men and 10 percent of women have had at least one same-sex sexual experience in adulthood. Kinsey devised a scale ranging from 0 (exclusively heterosexual) to 6 (exclusively homosexual) to measure this diversity of experience. A person's sexual identity may be discordant with his or her actual behaviour.

Although many Canadians believe that homosexuality is wrong, the vast majority are in favour of equal rights for LGBs and a slim majority favour same-sex marriage. In some cases homonegativity and anti-gay prejudice may be so strong that they result in hate crimes and harassment directed at gays and lesbians.

Lesbian, gay, and bisexual communities can be found around the world. These communities are defined by a common culture and social life and by rituals such as pride marches.

In surveys, the majority of gay men and lesbians report being in a steady romantic relationship. Although people with negative attitudes toward LGBs have voiced concerns about the psychological well-being of children who grow up in lesbian and gay families, these concerns are unfounded, according to the available studies.

Well-conducted research indicates that homosexuality per se is not a sign of poor adjustment. Research does show somewhat elevated rates of depression and suicide among LGBs, which is almost certainly due to exposure to prejudice and hate crimes. Although some groups claim success in "reparative" therapy to change the sexual orientation of LGBs, there is no scientific evidence that one's sexual orientation can be changed, and many indications that these therapies are psychologically harmful. Most therapists believe that it is impossible to change a person's sexual orientation (that is, their erotic and emotional attraction) although people can and do change their sexual identity.

Continued on next page.

SUMMARY *cont.*

In regard to the causes of sexual orientation, biological explanations include genetic factors, hormone imbalance, prenatal factors, and brain factors. The genetic explanation has some support from the data, and there is new evidence of prenatal factors. Learning theorists stress that the sex drive is undifferentiated and is channelled, through experience, into heterosexuality or homosexuality. Bem's interactionist theory proposes that homosexuality results from the influence of biological factors on temperament, which in turn influences whether a child plays with boys or girls; the less familiar (exotic) gender becomes associated with sexual arousal. Sociologists emphasize the importance of roles and labelling in understanding homosexuality. They also note that gender-rigid, male-dominant societies are likely to produce a higher incidence of gay men. Available data do not point to any single factor as a cause of sexual orientation but rather suggest that there may be many types of homosexuality ("homosexualities") and heterosexuality with corresponding multiple causes.

Gay men and lesbians differ in some important ways. Women are more likely to be bisexual, and theories that are effective in explaining men's sexual orientation are not supported for women.

Different ethnic groups in Canada, as well as different cultures around the world, hold diverse views of same-sex sexual behaviours.

Bisexuality may be more "natural" than either exclusive heterosexuality or exclusive homosexuality.

QUESTIONS FOR THOUGHT, DISCUSSION, AND DEBATE

1. Debate the following topic. Resolved: LGBs should not be discriminated against in employment, including such occupations as high school teaching.

2. Do you feel that you are homonegative or homophobic, or do you feel that your attitude toward gays is positive or tolerant? Why do you think your attitudes are the way they are? Are you satisfied with your attitudes or do you want to change them?

3. Does your university, in addition to prohibiting discrimination on the basis of race and sex, also specifically prohibit discrimination on the basis of sexual orientation? Do you think it should?

4. Imagine that you are a gay man employed at a managerial level in an advertising agency in Calgary. You and your partner have been together for 11 years and intend to stay that way. It is becoming increasingly awkward for you to pretend that you have no partner and that you are straight when you attend parties for the staff or when people ask you how your weekend was. Should you come out to your colleagues at work? Why or why not?

SUGGESTIONS FOR FURTHER READING

Besen, Wayne R. (2003). *Anything but straight: Unmasking the scandals and lies behind the ex-gay myth.* Binghamton, NY: Harrington Park Press. Besen, a journalist, conducted investigative reporting on conversion therapies for gays that are led by far-right religious groups.

Herek, Gregory M., Kimmel, Douglas C., Amaro, Hortensia, and Melton, Gary B. (1991). Avoiding heterosexist bias in psychological research. *American Psychologist, 46,* 957–963. This stimulating article on research methodology points out ways in which heterosexist bias can enter research and suggests ways to avoid this bias.

Janoff, D. V. (2005). *Pink blood: Homophobic violence in Canada.* Toronto: University of Toronto Press. This book describes violence against gay, lesbian, bisexual, and transgender individuals in Canada, including 120 homicides and more than 350 gay-bashings.

Lahey, K. A., and Alderson, K. (2004). *Same-sex marriage: The personal and political.* Toronto: Insomniac Press. This book presents the political events and legal victories that led to the legalization of same-sex marriage in Canada and several other countries, and presents the stories of 16 married gay couples.

Miller, Neil. (1992). *Out in the world: Gay and lesbian life from Buenos Aires to Bangkok.* New York: Random House. The author travelled around the world, observing gay and lesbian communities. The accounts are fascinating.

Savin-Williams, Ritch C. (2005). *The new gay teenager.* Cambridge, MA: Harvard University Press. Savin-Williams, a leading researcher on sexual orientation, argues that today's teenagers are not caught up in the rigid ideas of previous generations and instead think more flexibly about sexuality. The result—gay teenagers who are thriving!

Warner, Tom. (2002). *Never going back: A history of queer activism in Canada.* Toronto: University of Toronto Press. This book by one of Canada's leading gay activists chronicles the history of lesbian and gay liberation in Canada.

For review questions, web resources, and other learning and study tools, visit the *Understanding Human Sexuality* Online Learning Centre at www.mcgrawhill.ca/olc/hyde.

VARIATIONS IN
SEXUAL BEHAVIOUR

Chapter Highlights

> NO KIND OF SENSATION IS KEENER AND MORE ACTIVE THAN THAT OF PAIN;
> ITS IMPRESSIONS ARE UNMISTAKABLE.*

Most laypeople, as well as most scientists, have a tendency to classify behaviour as normal or abnormal. There seems to be a particular tendency to do this with regard to sexual behaviour. Many terms are used for abnormal sexual behaviour, including "sexual deviance," "perversion," "sexual variance," and paraphilias. The term "sexual variations" will be used in this chapter because it is currently favoured in scientific circles.

This chapter will deal with some behaviours that more people might consider to be abnormal, so it seems advisable at this point to consider exactly when a sexual behaviour is abnormal. Which of the following would you consider abnormal? A man who has difficulty getting aroused unless he is wearing women's panties? A woman who enjoys being tied up as part of sex play? A man who gets turned on watching someone undress without that person's knowledge? To be able to answer this question, we start with a discussion of what is a reasonable set of criteria for deciding what kinds of sexual behaviour are abnormal?

WHEN IS SEXUAL BEHAVIOUR ABNORMAL?

DEFINING ABNORMAL

As we saw in Chapter 1, sexual behaviour varies a great deal from one culture to the next. There is a corresponding variation across cultures in what is considered to be "abnormal" sexual behaviour. Given this great variability, how can one come up with a reasonable set of criteria for what is abnormal? Perhaps it is best to begin by considering the way others have defined "abnormal" sexual behaviour.

One approach is to use a *statistical definition*. According to this approach, an abnormal sexual behaviour is one that is rare, or not practised by many people. Following this definition, then, standing on one's hands while having intercourse would be considered abnormal because it is rarely done, although it does not seem very abnormal in other ways. This definition, unfortunately, does not give us much insight into the psychological or social functioning of the person who engages in the behaviour.

In the *sociological approach*, the problem of culture dependence is explicitly acknowledged. A sociologist might define a deviant sexual behaviour as a sexual behaviour that violates the norms of society. Thus, if a society says that a particular sexual behaviour is deviant, it is—at least in that society. This approach recognizes the importance of the individual's interaction with society and of the problems that people must face if their behaviour is labelled "deviant" in the culture in which they live.

A *psychological approach* was stated by Arnold Buss in his text entitled *Psychopathology* (1966). He says, "The three criteria of abnormality are discomfort, inefficiency, and bizarreness." The last of these criteria, bizarreness, has the problem of being culturally defined; what seems bizarre in one culture may seem normal in another. However, the first two criteria are good in that they focus on the discomfort and unhappiness sometimes felt by the person with a truly abnormal pattern of sexual behaviour and also on inefficiency. For example, a male clerk in a Minneapolis supermarket was having intercourse with willing shoppers in

---

*Marquis de Sade, *Philosophy in the Bedroom*.

their cars several times a day. This apparently compulsive behaviour led to his being fired. This is an example of inefficient functioning, a behaviour that can reasonably be considered abnormal.

The *medical approach* is exemplified by the definitions included in the *Diagnostic and Statistical Manual of Mental Disorders (DSM-IV-TR)* (American Psychiatric Association, 2000). It recognizes eight specific paraphilias: fetishism, transvestic fetishism, sexual sadism, sexual masochism, voyeurism, frotteurism, exhibitionism, and pedophilia (there is also a category for paraphilias that are not listed). The general definition of paraphilia is:

> Recurrent, intense, sexually arousing fantasies, sexual urges, or behaviors involving non-human objects (Fetishism, Transvestic Fetishism), the suffering or humiliation of oneself or one's partner (Sexual Sadism, Sexual Masochism), children (Pedophilia), or other non-consenting person (Voyeurism, Frotteurism, Exhibitionism). (DSM-IV-TR, p. 566)

Additional diagnostic criteria are stated for each of the specific disorders; these generally include that (a) the fantasies, urges, or behaviours have occurred over a period of at least six months, and (b) they cause "clinically significant distress or impairment in social, occupational, or other important areas of functioning." These definitions are very influential; they are used in many situations to determine who receives treatment.

However, some of these paraphilias that involve two consenting adults, such as sexual sadism and masochism, are also controversial. Canadian psychologist Peggy Kleinplatz and her colleague Charles Moser believe that these sexual interests do not represent mental disorders and should therefore not be listed in the *DSM-IV-TR* (Moser, 2001; Moser & Kleinplatz, 2005). They argue that as there is no agreed upon definition of healthy sexuality, it is difficult to be clear about what behaviours should be classified as paraphilic. Rather behaviours that involve unusual sexual interests, but not coercion, may be healthy expressions of sexuality for some individuals. They argue that the fact that they are labelled as pathological is due to sociopolitical and historical factors, and that many of these assumptions behind the diagnoses are not supported by research (Moser & Kleinplatz, 2005).

Note that some paraphilias and most atypical sexual behaviours are not against the law (e.g., fetishism and sexual masochism). However, some are. For example, pedophilia, the most serious paraphilia, is against the law because it involves exploitation and force. It is discussed in Chapter 16. Other behaviours do not involve exploitation or force but do violate community standards of taste. In this area we find laws against indecent exposure, voyeurism, indecent acts in a public place, and public nudity (refer to In Focus 2.2 on page 44 for a complete list of sex crimes contained in the Criminal Code of Canada).

An interesting case that demonstrates how community standards of taste can impact on laws regulating sex crimes arose when Gwen Jacobs walked topless through the town of Guelph in 1991. She was charged with committing an indecent act in a public place. However, in 1996, the Ontario Court of Appeal ruled that women have a right to go topless as long as

Paraphilia (par-uh-FILL-ee-uh): Recurring, unconventional sexual behaviour that is obsessive and compulsive.

Indecent exposure: Showing one's genitals in a public place to passersby; exhibitionism.

Figure 15.1 Gwen Jacobs and Mary Lou Schloss protested Ontario laws against women going topless in their walk over the Peace Bridge in 1992. In 1996, the Ontario Court of Appeal ruled that going topless is not an indecent act under the Criminal Code.

it is not for commercial gain or sexual purposes. What are the attitudes of Canadians towards women going topless? One study found that 72 percent of Canadians think it should be illegal for women to go topless on city streets and 48 percent think it should be illegal for them to go topless on a public beach (Fischtein et al., 2005).

In this chapter we discuss a number of atypical sexual behaviours, including the seven behaviours that can be diagnosed as paraphilias. As discussed next, all of these behaviours occur along a continuum. Thus, even these seven behaviours can be considered paraphilic only if the person meets the diagnostic criteria just listed; that is, these fantasies, urges, or behaviours are intense, have persisted for six months or longer, and have resulted in significant impairment or distress in important areas of functioning.

THE NORMAL–ABNORMAL CONTINUUM

Each of the approaches just described provides criteria that attempt to distinguish what is "normal" from "abnormal." While such distinctions may be made in theory, they are often difficult to make in reality. For example, lingerie is often sexually arousing for both men and women. For a woman who is wearing a low-cut bra and silk thong panties, the sensuous feel of the material against her skin may be arousing; for a man it might be the sight of the woman wearing the lingerie. At the same time, lingerie is a common sexual fetish object. This is an excellent example of the continuum from normal to abnormal sexual behaviour. That is, normal sexual behaviour and abnormal sexual behaviour—like other normal and abnormal behaviours—are not two separate categories but rather gradations on a continuum. Many people have mild fetishes, finding things such as silk underwear arousing, and that is well within the range of normal behaviour; only when the fetish becomes extreme is it abnormal. Indeed, in one sample of university men, 42 percent reported that they had engaged in voyeurism and 35 percent had engaged in *frottage* (sexual rubbing against a woman in a crowd) (Templeman & Stinnett, 1991). Unfortunately, the researchers did not ask about fetishes. But the point is that many of these behaviours are common even in "normal" populations.

This continuum from normal to abnormal behaviour might be conceptualized using the scheme shown in Figure 15.2. A mild preference, or even a strong preference, for the fetish object (say, silk panties) is within the normal range of sexual behaviour. When the silk panties become a necessity—when the man cannot become aroused and engage in sexual activity unless they are present—we have crossed the boundary into abnormal behaviour. When the man becomes obsessed with white silk panties and shoplifts them at every opportunity, so that he will always have them available, the fetish has become a paraphilia. In extreme forms, the silk panties may become a substitute for a human partner, and the man's sexual behaviour consists of masturbating with the silk panties present. In these extreme forms, the man may commit burglary or even assault to get the desired fetish object, which would certainly fit our definition of abnormal sexual behaviour.

The continuum from normal to abnormal behaviour holds for many of the sexual variations discussed in this chapter, such as voyeurism, exhibitionism, and sadism.

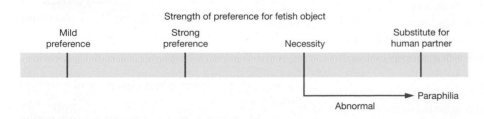

Figure 15.2 The continuum from normal to abnormal behaviour in the case of fetishes.

SEXUAL ADDICTIONS AND COMPULSIONS

Patrick Carnes (1983) advanced the theory that some sexual variations are a result of an addictive process much like alcoholism. One definition of alcoholism or other drug dependency is that the person has a pathological relationship with the mood-altering substance. In the case of sexual addiction, the person has a pathological relationship to a sexual event or process, substituting it for a healthy relationship with others. However, there are some differences between chemical addictions that create a physiological dependency and behavioural "addictions." For example, if a person suddenly abstains from an addictive sexual behaviour, there are no physiological withdrawal symptoms as there are from abstaining from using alcohol. A second criticism is that use of the term "addiction" may affect perceptions of these behaviours and thus become an excuse for illegal, destructive behaviour. For example, a sex offender might say: "I'm sexually addicted to forced sex and therefore can't stop myself." Therefore, some experts recommend that we use the term *compulsive sexual behaviour* instead of *sexual addiction* (e.g., Coleman, 1991).

COMPULSIVE SEXUAL BEHAVIOUR

Compulsive sexual behaviour: A disorder in which the person experiences intense sexually arousing fantasies, urges, and associated sexual behaviour.

How do we define compulsive sexual behaviour? Compulsive sexual behaviour

is a disorder in which the individual experiences intense sexually arousing fantasies, urges, and associated sexual behaviors that are intrusive, driven, and repetitive. Individuals with this disorder (a) are lacking in impulse control, (b) often incur social and legal sanctions, (c) cause interference in interpersonal and occupational functioning, and (d) create health risks. (Coleman et al., 2001, p. 326)

It can be paraphilic (i.e., involve the sexual behaviours listed in the *DSM-IV-TR*) or non-paraphilic (involve conventional sexual behaviours such as compulsive masturbation or compulsive use of the Internet for sexual purposes) (Coleman et al., 2003). Note that this perspective differs from the addiction approach in emphasizing that the person may experience social and legal sanctions and take health risks. Coleman et al. (2003) estimate that approximately 5 percent of the population—more men than women—suffer from compulsive sexual behaviour.

The chief distinguishing feature of sexual addictions or compulsions is that the person has lost control of the behaviour. Thus, not all sexual variations are addictions or compulsions. Some people have intense urges to engage in behaviours, such as masturbation or Internet sexuality, that in and of themselves are normal. Thus, for example, the man who masturbates every day in the privacy of his own home while looking at pornographic magazines or at pornography on the Internet is probably not experiencing a compulsion/addiction and the behaviour is well within the normal range. However, the married man who (and this is based on a real person) rushes from his desk at work several times a day to lock himself in the supply closet to masturbate and can think of little else than the next time he will masturbate, probably does have a sexual compulsion/addiction. The key is the compulsiveness, the lack of control, the obsession (constant thoughts of the sexual scenario), and the obliviousness to danger or harmful consequences.

Some researchers emphasize the out-of-control aspects of problematic sexual behaviour (Bancroft & Vikadinovic, 2004). Whereas most people lose interest in sex when anxious or depressed, a minority experience increased sexual interest. When coupled with low sexual inhibition (self-control), the person may engage in compulsive sexual behaviour in an attempt to improve/escape from the negative mood. This intensive study of 31 self-defined "sex addicts" provided evidence supporting this perspective.

People who have sexual compulsions or addictions—like alcoholics—often hold faulty beliefs that can contribute to the problem because they involve a denial or distortion of reality. These beliefs allow these people to "justify" their behaviour before engaging in it. For example, they may deny the possibility of contracting a sexually transmitted infection. They also engage in self-justification, such as "If I don't have it every few days, the pressure builds up." Like alcoholism, the compulsive behaviour leads to many self-destructive behaviours. The person with a sexual compulsion or addiction may spend money that he or she doesn't have (e.g., for payment to prostitutes), may neglect work or family in order to engage in the behaviour (e.g., by spending many hours on the Internet), or may risk arrest (e.g., for indecent exposure).

According to Carnes's (1983) analysis, each episode of the sexually compulsive behaviour proceeds through a four-step cycle, which intensifies each time it is repeated.

1. *Preoccupation.* The person can think of nothing other than the sexual act to which he or she is addicted.
2. *Rituals.* The person enacts certain rituals that have become a prelude to the addictive act.
3. *Compulsive sexual behaviour.* The sexual behaviour is enacted and the person feels that he or she has no control over it.
4. *Despair.* Rather than feeling good after the sexual act is completed, the addict falls into a feeling of hopelessness and despair.

For example, consider the story of a man who engaged in compulsive exhibitionism—let's call him Sam. Often after a stressful interpersonal event, Sam would become preoccupied with (unrealistic) thoughts of women's positive reactions if he exposed himself. He would then put on certain clothes, go for a walk, "just happen" to walk by a coffee shop, and "just happen" to stop for coffee, all without acknowledging to himself that he intended to expose himself. Sam would look around until he identified a woman who did some small thing that he could misinterpret as indicating that she was interested in him sexually. He would follow her out to the parking lot and expose himself, feeling he had no control over the behaviour. He would feel good at the time, but shortly thereafter would feel really bad about himself and about his lack of control over his behaviour. Interestingly, there is often a history of alcoholism or other types of addictions in the families of people with compulsive sexual behaviour. Sometimes, too, there is a family history of the same compulsive sexual behaviour.

FETISHISM

Fetishism is characterized by sexual fantasies, urges, or behaviours involving the use of non-living objects to produce or enhance sexual arousal with or in the absence of a partner. In extreme cases the person is incapable of becoming aroused and having an orgasm unless the fetish object is present. Typically, the fetish item is something closely associated with the body, such as clothing. Inanimate-object fetishes can be roughly divided into two subcategories: media fetishes and form fetishes.

MEDIA FETISHES AND FORM FETISHES

In a **media fetish**, the material out of which an object is made is the source of arousal. An example would be a leather fetish, in which any leather item is arousing to the person. Media fetishes can be subdivided into hard media fetishes and soft media fetishes. In a hard media fetish, the fetish is for a hard substance, such as leather or rubber (see, for example, In Focus 15.2 on page 476). Hard media fetishes may often be associated with sadomasochism (discussed later in this chapter). In a soft media fetish, the substance is soft, such as fur or silk.

In a **form fetish**, it is the object and its shape that are important. An example would be a

Fetishism: A person's sexual fixation on some object other than another human being and attachment of great erotic significance to that object.

Media fetish: A fetish whose object is anything made of a particular substance, such as leather.

Form fetish: A fetish whose object is a particular shape, such as high-heeled shoes.

IN FOCUS 15.1

A Case History of a Shoe Fetishist

The following case history is taken directly from the 1886 book *Psychopathia Sexualis*, by Richard von Krafft-Ebing, the influential early investigator of sexual deviance. It should give you the flavour of his work.

Case 114. X., aged twenty-four, from a badly tainted family (mother's brother and grandfather insane, one sister epileptic, another sister subject to migraine, parents of excitable temperament). During dentition [teething] he had convulsions. At the age of seven he was taught to masturbate by a servant girl. X. first experienced pleasure in these manipulations when the girl happened to touch his member [penis] with her shoe-clad foot. Thus, in the predisposed boy, an association was established, as a result of which, from that time on, merely the sight of a woman's shoe, and finally, merely the idea of them, sufficed to induce sexual excitement

and erection. He now masturbated while looking at women's shoes or while calling them up in imagination. The shoes of the school mistress excited him intensely, and in general he was affected by shoes that were partly concealed by female garments. One day he could not keep from grasping the teacher's shoes—an act that caused him great sexual excitement. In spite of punishment he could not keep from performing this act repeatedly. Finally, it was recognized that there must be an abnormal motive in play, and he was sent to a male teacher. He then revelled in the memory of the shoe scenes with his former school mistress and thus had erections, orgasms, and, after his fourteenth year, ejaculation. At the same time, he masturbated while thinking of a woman's shoes. One day the thought came to him to increase his pleasure by using such a shoe for masturbation. Thereafter

Figure 15.3 A common fetish is for leather, often in association with sexual sadism and masochism. This store caters to clientele interested or involved in those activities.

shoe fetish, in which shoes are highly arousing (see In Focus 15.1). Some shoe fetishes require that the shoes be high-heeled; this fetish may be associated with sadomasochism, in which the fetishist derives sexual satisfaction from being walked on by a woman in high heels. Other shoe fetishes require that the shoes be leather boots that have been worn. Other examples of form fetishes are nylon stockings, garters, and lingerie.

WHY DO PEOPLE BECOME FETISHISTS?

Psychologists are not sure what causes fetishes to develop. Here we will consider three theoretical explanations: learning theory, cognitive theory, and the sexual addiction model. These theories can be applied equally well to explaining many of the other sexual variations in this chapter.

According to learning theory (e.g., McGuire et al., 1965), fetishes result from classical conditioning, in which a learned association is built between the fetish object and sexual arousal and orgasm. In some cases a single learning trial

he frequently took shoes secretly and used them for that purpose.

Nothing else in a woman could excite him; the thought of coitus filled him with horror. Men did not interest him in any way. At the age of eighteen he opened a shop and, among other things, dealt in ladies' shoes. He was excited sexually by fitting shoes for his female patrons or by manipulating shoes that came for mending. One day while doing this he had an epileptic attack, and, soon after, another while practicing onanism in his customary way. Then he recognized for the first time the injury to health caused by his sexual practices. He tried to overcome his onanism, sold no more shoes, and strove to free himself from the abnormal association between women's shoes and the sexual function. Then frequent pollutions, with erotic dreams about shoes occurred, and the epileptic attacks continued. Though devoid of the slightest feeling for the female sex, he determined on marriage, which seemed to him to be the only remedy.

He married a pretty young lady. In spite of lively erections when he thought of his wife's shoes, in attempts at cohabitation he was absolutely impotent because his distaste for coitus and for close intercourse in general was far more powerful than the influence of the shoe-idea, which induced sexual excitement. On account of his impotence the patient applied to Dr. Hammond, who treated his epilepsy with bromides and advised him to hang a shoe up over his bed and look at it fixedly during coitus, at the same time imagining his wife to be a shoe. The patient became free from epileptic attacks and potent so that he could have coitus about once a week. His sexual excitation by women's shoes also grew less and less.

Source: Von Krafft-Ebing, 1886, 1965.

might serve to cement the association. For example, one adult male recalled:

I was home alone and saw my uncle's new penny loafers. I went over and started smelling the fresh new leather scent and kissing and licking them. It turned me on so much that I actually ejaculated my first load into my pants and have been turned on ever since. (Weinberg et al., 1995, p. 22)

In this case, shoes were associated with sexual arousal as the result of an early learning experience. Another example appears to be the shoe fetishist described in In Focus 15.1. This case clearly exemplifies the *DSM-IV-TR* criteria for paraphilia. The youth/man experienced sexual fantasies and urges associated with women's shoes for years, experienced arousal and ejaculation only when they were present, and experienced significant impairment in his academic and social life as a result. There was even an experiment that demonstrated that males could, in the laboratory, be conditioned to become sexually aroused when viewing pictures of shoes (Rachman, 1966).

A second possible theoretical explanation comes from cognitive psychology, discussed in Chapter 2 (Walen & Roth, 1987). According to cognitive theorists, people with fetishes (or other paraphilias) have a serious cognitive distortion in that they perceive an unconventional stimulus—such as black leather boots—as erotic. Further, their perception of arousal (link 4 in the model; refer to Figure 9.5 on page 260) is distorted. They feel "driven" to the sexual behaviour when aroused, but the arousal may actually be caused by feelings of guilt and self-loathing. Thus, there is a chain in which there are initial feelings of guilt at thoughts of the unconventional behaviour, which produces arousal, which is misinterpreted as sexual arousal, which leads to a feeling that the fetish ritual must be carried out; it is, there is orgasm and temporary feelings of relief, but the evaluation of the event is negative, leading to further feelings of guilt and self-loathing, which perpetuates the chain.

A third theory that has been advanced to explain some atypical sexual behaviours, especially those that seem compulsive, is the theory of sexual addiction, discussed earlier in this chapter.

Whatever the cause, fetishism typically develops early in life. In one sample of foot or shoe fetishes, the mean age at which respondents reported first being sexually aroused by feet or shoes was 12 years (Weinberg et al., 1995).

TRANSVESTISM

Transvestism: The practice of deriving sexual gratification from dressing as a member of the other gender; tranvestic fetishism.

Drag queen: A gay man who dresses in women's clothing.

Female impersonator: A man who dresses up as a woman as part of a job in entertainment.

Cross-dressing refers to wearing clothes stereotypically associated with the other gender. Transvestism ("trans" = "cross"; "vest" = "dressing") refers to cross-dressing for erotic purposes (Moser & Kleinplatz, 2002).

Cross-dressing may be done by a variety of people for a variety of reasons. As discussed in Chapter 13, transgender individuals cross-dress to express a more feminine or masculine side of themselves. Further, transsexuals live as the other gender as part of transitioning. Some gay men—drag queens—dress up as women, and some lesbians dress in masculine clothes (drag kings); these practices, though, are basically caricatures of traditional gender roles. Female impersonators are men who dress as women, often as part of their jobs as entertainers. For example, Robin Williams in *Mrs. Doubtfire* and Dustin Hoffman in *Tootsie* won praise from critics and big box office profits for their impersonations of women. Finally, some—perhaps many—adolescent boys cross-dress, usually only once or a few times (Green, 1975). This behaviour does not necessarily mean that the boy will continue to cross-dress throughout his life; it may simply reflect exploration of his sexuality; it may also reflect the sexual drives, confusions, and frustrations of adolescence.

In contrast to people who engage in cross-dressing for the reasons just discussed, a transvestite is a heterosexual man who dresses in female clothing to produce or enhance sexual arousal (American Psychiatric Association, 2000).[1] If his fantasies, urges, or behaviours meet the *DSM-IV* diagnostic criteria for paraphilia, the man is said to have a transvestic fetish. The cross-dressing is often done in private, perhaps by a married man without his partner's knowledge. Transvestic fetishism is almost exclusively a male sexual variation; it is essentially unknown among women. There may be a number of reasons for this difference, including our culture's tolerance of women who wear masculine clothing and intolerance of men who wear feminine clothing. The phenomenon illustrates a more general point, namely, that many sexual variations are defined for, or practised almost exclusively by, members of one gender; the parallel practice by members of the other gender is often not considered deviant. Most sexual variations are practised mainly by men.[2]

A survey of a national sample in Sweden asked each participant whether she or he had ever dressed in clothing of the other gender and experienced sexual arousal (Långström, & Zucker, 2005). Almost 3 percent of men and 0.4 percent of women reported at least one such experience. Among men, this behaviour was associated with being easily sexually aroused (in general, not just by cross-dressing), more frequent masturbation, and same-sex sexual experience.

A common means of studying persons with atypical sexual behaviour patterns is to place ads in specialty newsletters and magazines, and to solicit participants at meetings and

---

[1]A common abbreviation for transvestism, used both by scientists and by members of the transvestite subculture, is TV.

[2]Several theories have been proposed to explain why there are so many more men than women with paraphilias (Finkelhor & Russell, 1984). Sociobiologists believe that the difference lies in the evolutionary selection of males to inseminate many partners and to be aroused by sexual stimuli devoid of emotional content (Wilson, 1987). Sociologists point to gender role socialization, which teaches males to be instrumental and to initiate sexual interactions. Females, on the other hand, are taught to be nurturing and to empathize with others; for example, with the vulnerability of children (Traven et al., 1990). Moser and Kleinplatz (2005) argue that diagnosis of certain paraphilias, such as transvestism, results from the tendency in our culture to define masculinity very narrowly as well as to pathologize unconventional behaviour.

(a)   (b)

Figure 15.4 Two examples of cross-dressing: *(a)* Lead actors in several films have portrayed a cross-dresser (e.g., the three leads from *To Wong Foo, Thanks for Everything! Julie Newmar*). *(b)* Men in drag.

conventions attended by such persons. Using these procedures, researchers gathered survey data from 1032 cross-dressers (Docter & Prince, 1997). The sample did not include drag queens or female impersonators. The vast majority of the men (87 percent) were heterosexual, 60 percent were married, 65 percent had a university education, and 76 percent reported being raised by both parents through age 18. Sixty-six percent reported that their first cross-dressing experience occurred before age ten. Sexual excitement and orgasm were reported by 40 percent as often or almost always associated with cross-dressing. This indicates that this sample included men who cross-dress for a variety of reasons—not just men who do so to enhance sexual arousal. Almost all (93 percent) preferred complete cross-dressing, but only 14 percent frequently went out in public dressed as a woman.

Another survey was conducted by mailing questionnaires to 1200 members of a U.S. cross-dressing organization (Bullough & Bullough, 1997). There were 372 questionnaires returned. The median age at which the men began to cross-dress was 8.5; 32 percent reported that they first dressed as a female before they were six. Most of them reported cross-dressing as children, and 56 percent said they were never caught.

How do the partner and children of the cross-dresser react to his unusual behaviour? In one sample of 50 heterosexual transvestites, 60 percent of the wives were accepting of their husband's cross-dressing (Talamini, 1982). Most of these women commented that he was a good husband. Some of the wives felt fulfilled being supportive of the husband, and some even helped him in dressing and applying makeup. In the same sample, 13 of the couples had told their children about the cross-dressing. They claimed that the relationship with the children was undamaged and that the children were tolerant and understanding. However, given societal attitudes toward cross-dressing and gender roles, the partner may have problems with it—particularly if she did not know about the cross-dressing before they became involved.

Transvestism is one of the harmless, victimless sexual variations. Like other fetishes, it is a problem only when it becomes so extreme that it is the person's only source of erotic gratification, or when it becomes a compulsion the person cannot control and therefore causes distress in other areas of the person's life.

SADISM AND MASOCHISM

DEFINITIONS

Sexual sadist: A person who derives sexual satisfaction from inflicting pain, suffering, or humiliation on another person.

A **sexual sadist** is a person who derives sexual satisfaction from inflicting pain, suffering, or humiliation on another person. The term "sadism" derives from the name of the Marquis de Sade, who lived around the time of the French Revolution. Not only did he practise sexual sadism—several women apparently died from his attentions (Bullough, 1976)—but he also wrote novels about these practices (the best known is *Justine*), thus assuring his place in history.

Sexual masochist: A person who derives sexual satisfaction from experiencing pain.

A **sexual masochist** is a person who is sexually aroused by fantasies, urges, or behaviours involving being beaten, humiliated, bound, or tortured to enhance or achieve sexual excitement. This variation is named after Leopold von Sacher-Masoch (1836–1895), who was himself a masochist and who wrote novels expressing masochistic fantasies. Notice that the definitions of these variations make specific their *sexual* nature; the terms are often loosely used to refer to people who are cruel or to people who seem to bring misfortune on themselves, but these are not the meanings used here. These two are often referred to as a pair since the two behaviours or roles (giving and receiving pain) are complementary.

Bondage and discipline: The use of physical or psychological restraint to enforce servitude, from which both participants derive sensual pleasure.

There are two other styles of interaction that are related to sadism-masochism (S-M). These are bondage and discipline (B-D) and dominance and submission (D-S) (Ernulf & Innala, 1995). **Bondage and discipline** refers to the use of physically restraining devices or psychologically restraining commands as a central aspect of sexual interactions. These devices or commands may enforce obedience and servitude without inducing any physical pain. **Dominance and submission** refers to interaction that involves a consensual exchange of power; the dominant partner uses his or her power to control and sexually stimulate the submissive partner. Both B-D and D-S encompass a variety of specific interactions that range from atypical to paraphilic.

Dominance and submission: The use of power consensually given to control the sexual stimulation and behaviour of the other person.

SEXUAL SADOMASOCHISTIC BEHAVIOUR

Sadomasochism (S-M) is a rare form of sexual behaviour, although in its milder forms it is probably more common than many people think. In fact, discussion of spanking and use of handcuffs during sexual activity has made it to such prime-time television shows as *Friends, Sex and the City*, and *Seinfeld*. Kinsey found that about one-quarter of both males and females had experienced definite or frequent erotic response as a result of being bitten during sexual activity (Kinsey et al., 1953). Sadistic or masochistic sexual fantasies are more common; a New Brunswick study found that 65 percent of university students have sexual fantasies of being tied up and 62 percent have fantasies of tying someone up (Renaud & Byers, 1999).

In one study, 178 men who responded to an ad in an S-M magazine or belonged to an S-M support group filled out a questionnaire (Moser & Levitt, 1987). The majority were heterosexual, well educated, and interested in both dominant and submissive roles (switchable). The following are behaviours that the majority of them had both tried and enjoyed: humiliation, bondage, spanking, whipping, fetish behaviour, tying up with ropes, and master-and-slave role playing.

Another study administered questionnaires to 130 men and 52 women who responded to ads placed in S-M magazines; the study focused particularly on the women respondents (Breslow et al., 1985). Thirty-three percent of the men and 28 percent of the women preferred the dominant role; 41 percent of the men and 40 percent of the women preferred the submissive role; and 26 percent of the men and 32 percent of the women were versatile. The majority of these S-M respondents were heterosexual. Men involved in S-M frequently report having been interested in such activity since childhood; women are more likely to report having been introduced to the subculture by someone else (Weinberg, 1994). Women prefer bondage, spanking, and master-and-slave role playing (Levitt et al., 1994).

Thus, there is a spectrum of activities that constitute S-M. People who become involved in it often have tried a variety of these behaviours and find only some of them satisfying. They develop a script of activities that they prefer to enact each time they engage in S-M. One group of researchers (Santilla et al., 2002) identified 29 individual sexual behaviours associated with S-M. They administered questionnaires to 184 Finnish men and women who were members of S-M clubs. Each participant was asked which of the behaviours he or she had participated in during the preceding year. Four clusters or themes were identified: hypermasculinity (e.g., dildo, enema), administering and receiving pain (e.g., clothespins attached to nipples, caning, hot wax), physical restriction (e.g., handcuffs, straitjackets), and humiliation (e.g., verbal humiliation, face slapping). Further analyses of participation in the behaviours within each cluster identified a continuum in frequency from very common to very rare, with the order of the behaviours suggesting that this continuum reflects a dimension from least to most intense. For example, the humiliation continuum ranges from flagellation (reported by 81 percent; least intense) to verbal humiliation (70 percent) to gagging (53 percent) and face slapping (37 percent), to using knives to make surface wounds (11 percent; most intense). The results suggest that the S-M activities within each cluster are *scripted*, with the less intense behaviours being much more common.

Some observers note that S-M is about play, as in the theatre. S-M sexual activities are organized into "scenes"; one "plays" with one's S-M partners. In addition to the activities such as those just discussed, roles, costumes, and props are an important part of each scene. The roles include slave and master, maid and mistress, and teacher and pupil. The costumes range from simple to elaborate. The props may include tight leather clothing, pins and needles, ropes, whips, and hot wax. In S-M clubs, which may be heterosexual or homosexual, there are often rules governing the social and S-M interaction, particularly the creation and enactment of scenes. According to one website, the rules include no touching of another's body without consent, giving players the room they need to enact a scene, not intruding physically or verbally on a scene in progress, and sometimes no sexual penetration.

Interestingly, sexual sadists and masochists do not consistently find experiencing pain and giving pain to be sexually satisfying. For example, the masochist who smashes a finger in a car door will yell and be unhappy just like anyone else. Pain is arousing for such people only when it is part of a carefully scripted ritual. As one woman put it,

> Of course, he doesn't *really* hurt me. I mean quite recently he tied me down ready to receive "punishment," and then by mistake he kicked my heel with his toe as he walked by. I gave a yelp, and he said, "Sorry love—did I hurt you?" (Gosselin & Wilson, 1980, p. 55)

CAUSES OF SEXUAL SADOMASOCHISM

Most experts view sexual sadomasochism as a variation on other forms of healthy sexuality. The causes of why people come to prefer sexual activities that involve sexual sadism and masochism (and equally most other sexual preferences) are not precisely known. The theories in our discussion of fetishes can be applied here as well. For example, learning theory points to conditioning as an explanation. A little boy is being spanked over his mother's knee; in the process, his penis rubs against her knee, and he gets an erection. Or a little girl is caught masturbating and is spanked. In both cases, the child has learned to associate pain or spanking with sexual arousal, possibly setting up a lifelong career as a masochist. On the other hand, in one sample of sadomasochists, more than 80 percent did *not* recall receiving erotic enjoyment from being punished as a child (Moser, 1979, cited in Weinberg, 1987). Thus, forces besides conditioning may be at work.

Another psychological theory has been proposed to explain sexual masochism specifically, although not sadism (Baumeister, 1988a, 1988b). According to the theory, the masochist is motivated by a desire to escape from self-awareness. That is, the masochistic behaviour helps the

IN FOCUS 15.2

The Pleasure of Kinky Sex: Trevor Jacques, a BDSM Practitioner and Advocate

Trevor Jacques is 52 years old, single, and living in Toronto. He was born in England, the eldest of four children of middle-class parents. As a child, he was the "good son," even serving as an altar boy for a while. His parents raised him to ask questions and "do the right thing." This allowed him to chart his own course in life, both in his career and, in his words, his "kink."

In terms of his career, Trevor is a physicist who became an engineer. He worked on avionic missile systems in Great Britain, infra-red surveillance technology for the Canadian and U.S. navies, and as a database consultant. However, he identifies a strong passion for educating people about safer BDSM and conducting research about the experiences of members of the BDSM community. (Note how Trevor uses "safer" rather than "safe," in that nothing, even breathing, is entirely safe.)

Trevor uses the term BDSM to describe the practices of the community because it encompasses multiple meanings and roles, and is almost free of the baggage that comes with words used in clinical diagnosis. That is, B and D, interpreted together, refer to bondage and discipline, D and S together refer to dominance and submission, and S and M together refer to sadism and masochism. Trevor also subscribes to the term "kinky," because he feels it describes what BDSM practitioners like to do, while making it clear that they only are interested in consensual partners and do not want to hurt anyone who does not clearly want and consent to it. For Trevor "hurt" refers to the application of intense stimulation, which may or may not include pain, but which does not entail injury.

As an adolescent, Trevor does not recall being particularly interested in girls and sex, yet his father assured him "it would come." He had his first sexual experience when he was 21, with a woman. He describes it as conventional and very enjoyable, yet "was missing something." Trevor came out as gay at 26. He also realized that he was attracted to more than conventional sex when he found himself gravitating toward erotica that depicted hypermasculine men and men representing or engaged in BDSM activities. He describes coming out as kinky as a far faster process than coming out as gay, because he had already been through the coming out process once. He realized that being kinky was "simply who he is and how he was born," in the same way one is gay.

Since openly identifying as kinky, Trevor has been very active in the BDSM community which he regards as one of his two chosen families (the other being his "LGBTIQ" family). He finds "vanilla" (non-BDSM) sex enjoyable, yet also looks for opportunities for BDSM play. He particularly enjoys social events organized by and for the BDSM community. Many of these are social functions that raise money for local charities. Some are similar to any other reception or dinner; others have people "dressed to the gills" in leather/rubber/PVC or other role-playing clothes and accessories." There are other categories of BDSM gatherings that he likes, including BDSM conferences and sex events—the for-

individual escape from being conscious of the self in the same way that drunkenness and some forms of meditation do. In an era dominated by individualism and self-interest, why would anyone want to escape from the self? Probably because high levels of self-awareness can lead to anxiety as a result of a focus on pressures on the self, added responsibilities, the need to keep up a good image in front of others, and so on. Sexual masochistic activity allows the person to escape from being an autonomous, separate individual. Sexual masochism may be an unusually powerful form of escape because of its link to sexual pleasure. This theory can also explain why sexual masochism is more common among males than among females (Baumeister, 1988b). According to the theory, the male role is especially burdensome because of the heavy pressures for autonomy, separateness, and individual achievement. Sexual masochism accomplishes an escape from these aspects of the male role. Some men cross-dress while engaging in sexual masochistic activity, a finding that tends to support this theory (Chivers & Blanchard, 1996).

mer referring to open public events, and the latter being very private events, limited to self-identified members of BDSM organizations.

What does Trevor like about these events? He enjoys the opportunity to meet new people who share his interests. He does not feel a need to have sex or BDSM play during (in the case of the private sex/BDSM events) or after the event, although he certainly enjoys it when it does happen. He also enjoys being able to express what he refers to as the "exhibitionist" and "voyeuristic" parts of himself at these events. Note that what he is referring to as exhibitionism is the desire to "show off" and be admired by other men when he is dressed up in his BDSM gear and, potentially, showing off his kinky prowess (e.g., by flogging a consenting partner). This is very different from exhibitionism that involves displaying one's genitals, for example, to a *non*-consenting person in a public venue (all of Trevor's teaching of BDSM strongly stresses consent and the avoidance of harm. He practises what he teaches). Similarly, Trevor enjoys being able to see and watch other men, who know they are being watched, dressed up and engaging in the activities that turn him on.

Trevor describes himself as a "fetishistic switch." This means that he has a fetish for specific clothing/gear—in his case, leather, rubber, and other clothing—and that he likes to switch between being the top (the dominant/disciplining/"sadistic" partner) and the bottom (the submissive/receiving/"masochistic" partner). Pain may be part of his play; however, it is not essential. Indeed, he is very uncomfortable with the myth that "BDSM necessarily equals pain," and that all pain is undesired (e.g., stubbing one's toe during a heavy flogging is a good example of unwanted pain during desired pain). He enjoys many kinky pleasures, such as bondage, "artfully applied pain" for sexual pleasure, fetishes, control, and so on. However, consistent with the basic tenets of safer BDSM play, his limits extend to the agreed play, respect for his partner(s), and ensuring that harm does not occur. Like most BDSM practitioners, he is a proponent of what is termed Safe, Sane, and Consensual (SSC) play. What Trevor enjoys at any point in time depends, among other factors, on the person with whom he's playing, how he and they feel at the time, and what his day has been like. One of the things he likes about BDSM is that he becomes immersed in the play, and that his brain switches off the minutiae of daily life.

In 1991, Trevor and his co-authors of the best-selling *On the Safe Edge: A Manual for SM Play* designed and began to deliver a series of seminars on SM safely, under the auspices of the AIDS Committee of Toronto (ACT). Since that time, more than 3500 people have attended these courses. He also is frequently invited to talk about BDSM on television and radio and to university classes. One of his main messages is that people need to be honest with themselves and others about their practices and the pleasure they get from them: they should not let other people define them. Otherwise, they may miss out on years of pleasure and enjoyment. Further, people interested in BDSM need to learn what is safe. That is, they need informed consent while having their own kind of fun.

Source: As told to Sandra Byers.

BONDAGE AND DISCIPLINE

Sexual bondage, the use in sexual behaviour of restraining devices that have sexual significance, has been a staple of erotic fiction and art for centuries. Current mainstream and adult films and videos portray this activity. In some communities, individuals interested in B-D have formed clubs. There are many B-D sites on the Internet that may also advertise BDSM "play parties" as well as BDSM *munches*. A BDSM munch is an informal gathering of people who are interested in BDSM, often at a restaurant (hence the term munch), so they can eat, socialize, and meet other people with similar interests.

We noted earlier the difficulty of gathering data on participation in variant forms of sexual expression. One innovative study downloaded all the messages about bondage mailed to an international computer discussion group (Ernulf & Innala, 1995). Of the messages in which senders indicated their gender, 75 percent were male. Of those indicating a sexual

Figure 15.5   Bondage.

orientation, most were heterosexual; 18 percent said they were gay, and 11 percent said they were lesbian. The messages were coded for discussion of what the person found sexually arousing about B-D. Most frequently mentioned (12 percent) was play: "sex is funny, and sex is lovely, and sex is PLAY." Next was the exchange of power (4 percent): "It is a power trip because the active is responsible for the submissive's pleasure." The next most common themes were intensified sexual pleasure, tactile stimulation associated with the use of ropes and cuffs, and the visual enjoyment experienced by the dominant person.

There is a marked imbalance in preferences for the active ("top") and passive ("bottom") roles. Most men and women, regardless of their sexual orientation, prefer to be "bottom." This may be the reason why there are an estimated 2500 professional dominatrices in the United States.

DOMINANCE AND SUBMISSION

Sociologists emphasize that the key to S-M is not pain, but rather dominance and submission (D-S) (Weinberg, 1987). Thus it is not an individual phenomenon, but rather a social behaviour embedded in a subculture and controlled by elaborate scripts.

Sociologists feel that to understand D-S one must understand the social processes that create and sustain it (Weinberg, 1987). There is a distinct D-S subculture, involving magazines (such as *Corporal*), clubs, and bars. It creates culturally defined meanings for D-S acts. Thus a D-S act is not a wild outbreak of violence, but rather a carefully controlled performance with a script (recall the concept of scripts in Chapter 2). One woman reported that:

> we got into dominance and submission. Like him giving me orders. Being very rough and pushing me around and giving me orders, calling me a slut, calling me a cunt. Making me crawl around . . . on all fours and beg to suck his cock. Dominance-submission is more important than the pain. I've done lots and lots of scenes that involve no pain. Just a lot of taking orders, being humiliated. (Maurer, 1994, pp. 253, 257)

Within the play, people take on roles such as master, slave, or naughty child. Thus men can play the submissive role in D-S culture, even though it contradicts the male role, because it is really not they who are the naughty child, just as an actor can play the part of a murderer and know that he is not a murderer.

One interesting phenomenon, from a sociological point of view, is the social control over risk taking that exists in the D-S subculture (Weinberg, 1987). That is, having allowed oneself to be tied up or restrained and then whipped, one could be seriously injured or even murdered, yet such outcomes are rare. Why? Research shows that complex social arrangements are made in order to reduce the risk (Lee, 1979). First, initial contacts are usually made in protected territories, such as bars or meetings, that are inhabited by other people involved in D-S who play by the same rules. Second, the basic scripts are widely shared, so that everyone understands what will and will not occur. When the participants are strangers, the scenario may be negotiated before it is enacted. Third, as the activity unfolds, very subtle non-verbal signals are used to control the interaction (Weinberg, 1994). By using these signals, the person playing the submissive role can influence what occurs. Thus, as two people enact the master and slave script, the master is not in complete control and the slave is not powerless. So it is the *illusion* of control, not actual control, that is central to D-S activity for both the master and the slave.

VOYEURISM

There are two types of voyeur ("Peeping Tom").[3] In scoptophilia, sexual pleasure is derived from observing sexual acts and the genitals; in *voyeurism*, technically, the sexual pleasure comes from viewing nudes, often while the voyeur is masturbating. The most recent strategy of voyeurs is to secretly install small video cameras so that they can observe women using the washroom or changing their clothes. Surreptitiously observing or recording a naked person who is in a private place are both criminal offences (see In Focus 2.2 on page 44).

Voyeurism provides another good illustration of the continuum from normal to abnormal behaviour. Although voyeurism can be a paraphilia, it is also of interest to many individuals without paraphilias. The appeal of watching is illustrated by an Ontario study that asked university students whether they would watch an attractive person undress and an attractive couple having sex (Rye & Meaney, 2007). The likelihood of getting caught was specified as 0, 10, or 25 percent. Two-thirds said they would watch someone undress; 45 percent said they would watch the couple. The likelihood of watching the person undress increased as the risk decreased; the likelihood of watching the couple did not vary by risk. There were no differences between the men and the women in the study.

Voyeurs are typically men who want the woman they view to be a stranger and do not want her to know what they are doing (Yalom, 1960). The element of risk is also important; while one might think that a nudist camp would be heaven to a peeper, it is not, because the elements of risk and forbiddenness are missing (Sagarin, 1973).

A study of 561 men who sought treatment for paraphilias included 62 voyeurs (Abel & Rouleau, 1990). One-third reported that their first experience occurred before they were 12 years old. One-half said they recognized their interest in peeping prior to age 15. These men estimated that, on average, they had peeped at 470 persons.

In one study of arrested (male) voyeurs, it was found that they were likely to be the youngest child in their family and to have good relationships with their parents but poor ones with their peers (Gebhard et al., 1965). They had few sisters and few female friends. Few were married. These studies, however, point out one of the major problems with the research on sexual variations: much of it has been done only on people who have been arrested for their behaviour or sought treatment. The "respectable" person with a paraphilia who has the behaviour under somewhat better control or who is skilled enough or can pull enough strings not to get caught is not studied in such research. Thus, the picture that research provides for us of these variations may be very biased.

EXHIBITIONISM

The complement to voyeurism is exhibitionism ("flashing"), in which the person derives sexual pleasure from exposing his genitals to others in situations where this is clearly inappropriate. In the Criminal Code this is referred to as indecent exposure. The pronoun "his" is used advisedly, since exhibitionism is primarily associated with men. When a man exposes himself, his behaviour is likely to be considered offensive. On the other hand, a man who notices that a woman wearing a skirt is not wearing underwear is more likely to be turned

Voyeur: A person who becomes sexually aroused from secretly viewing nudes.

Scoptophilia: A sexual variation in which the person becomes sexually aroused by observing others' sexual acts and genitals.

Exhibitionist: A person who derives sexual gratification from exposing his genitals to others in situations in which this is inappropriate.

---

[3]"Voyeur" comes from the French word *voir*, meaning "to see." "Peeping Tom" comes from the story of Lady Godiva; when she rode through town nude to protest the fact that her husband was raising his tenants' taxes, none of the townspeople looked except one, Tom of Coventry.

Figure 15.6   Exhibitionism.

on than offended. Here again, whether a sexual behaviour is considered abnormal depends greatly on whether the person doing it is a male or a female. Homosexual exhibitionism is also quite rare; so the prototype we have for exhibitionism is a man exposing himself to a woman. Research in New Brunswick found that in 1996, 6 percent of male sex offenders were convicted for exhibitionism (Byers et al., 1997). Many of the men convicted for exhibitionism, 48 percent in one Canadian study, commit another offence involving indecent exposure within the next few years (Marshall et al., 1991). In addition, 6 percent of the exhibitionists in an Ottawa study were subsequently convicted of a hands-on sexual offence such as sexual touching or sexual assault (Greenberg et al., 2002). According to one survey, 33 percent of university women have been the objects of indecent exposure (Cox, 1988).

According to the study of men seeking treatment for paraphilias (Abel & Rouleau, 1990), 15 percent of the exhibitionists had exposed themselves at least once by age 12; one-half had done so by age 15. According to other research (Blair & Lanyon, 1981), exhibitionists generally recall their childhoods as being characterized by inconsistent discipline, lack of affection, and little training in appropriate forms of social behaviour. An analysis of ten studies of the social skills of sexual offenders (rapists, child molesters, incest offenders, pedophiles, and exhibitionists) found that sexual offenders possess fewer social skills than non-offenders (Emmers-Sommer et al., 2004).

The causes of exhibitionism are not known, but a social learning-theory explanation offers some possibilities (Blair & Lanyon, 1981). According to this view, the parents might have subtly (or perhaps obviously) modelled such behaviour to the person when he was a child. In adulthood, there may be reinforcements for the exhibitionistic behaviour because the man gets attention when he performs it. In addition, even if he is married, the man may lack the social skills to form an intimate adult relationship (Marshall, 1989). As a result he receives little reinforcement from interpersonal sex.

The learning-theory approach has been used to devise some programs of therapy that have been successful in treating exhibitionists. For example, exhibitionists may be shown photos of scenes in which they typically engaged in exhibitionism; while experiencing arousal to the scene, an unpleasant-smelling substance is placed at their nostrils (Maletzky, 1997). After 11 to 19 twice-weekly sessions of this conditioning and some self-administered home sessions, all but one of the men passed a temptation test in which they were placed in a naturalistic situation with a volunteer female and managed not to flash at her. Therapists typically also apply a variety of cognitive techniques. For example, most exhibitions have a number of cognitive distortions such as "Many girls find this amusing" or "These women are older than me and therefore cannot be harmed." The therapist would help the man identify and alter these cognitions as one focus of therapy (Maletzky, 1997).

Many women, understandably, are alarmed by exhibitionists. But since the exhibitionist's goal is to produce shock or some other strong emotional response, the woman who becomes extremely upset is gratifying him. Probably the best strategy for a woman to use in this situation is to remain calm and make some remark indicating her coolness, such as suggesting that he should seek professional help for his problem.

A study of 62 female sex offenders in Great Britain identified five women who had exhibited themselves (O'Connor, 1987). One 21-year-old woman stripped off her clothes and masturbated in public on several occasions. A 25-year-old single woman exposed her genitals and invited passersby to have sex with her. A 40-year-old woman entered private residences, took off her clothes, and invited any male present (including one child) to have sex with her. Two women were arrested while urinating in public. All five women had histories of unusual behaviour and had been diagnosed with alcohol or psychiatric problems. Their atypical sexual behaviours appear to reflect these problems, rather than sexual motivations.

Notice that both voyeurism and exhibitionism are considered problematic behaviour when the other person involved is an unwilling participant. A man who derives erotic pleasure from watching his partner undress or a woman who is aroused by exhibiting her body in new lingerie to her partner are not engaging in criminal or paraphilic behaviour.

The term exhibitionism is also used to refer to people who get sexually aroused by having other people watch them engage in sexual activity, although this is not the way the term is used in the *DSM-IV-TR*. Conversely, the "voyeurs" are turned on by watching people engaged in sexual activity. Thus, this is a consensual activity between "exhibitionists" and "voyeurs" and may occur in a private home or in an outdoor location. In Britain, the term used to describe all kinds of outdoor sexual activity watched by others is called "dogging."

HYPERSEXUALITY

We turn now to several variations that are not explicitly listed in the *DSM-IV-TR*; however, each of these also may vary from atypical through compulsive to paraphilic, depending on their frequency, duration, and consequences.

Hypersexuality includes nymphomania and satyriasis, conditions in which there is an extraordinarily high level of sexual activity and sex drive; the person is apparently insatiable and, at the extreme, sexuality overshadows all other concerns and interests. When it occurs in women, it is called nymphomania; in men it is called satyriasis[4] (or Don Juanism). While this definition seems fairly simple, in practice it is difficult to say when a person has an abnormally high sex drive. As was seen in Chapters 10 and 11, there is a wide range in the

Nymphomania (nim-foh-MANE-ee-uh): An excessive, insatiable sex drive in a woman.

Satyriasis (sat-ur-EYE-uh-sis): An excessive, insatiable sex drive in a man.

Figure 15.7 Historical painting of a satyr, which gives the name to satyriasis, a sexual variation in which a man has an excessive, insatiable sex drive.

[4]Satyriasis is named for the satyrs, who were part-human, part-animal beasts in Greek mythology. A part of the entourage of Dionysus, the god of wine and fertility, they were jovial and lusty and have become a symbol of the sexually active male.

frequencies with which people engage in sexual activity; therefore, the range we define as "normal" should also be broad. In real life, "nymphomania" or "satyriasis" is often defined by the spouse who thinks his or her partner wants sex "too" frequently. In particular, our society is not accepting of highly sexual women and they are likely to be labelled in negative ways (Blumberg, 2003).

Hypersexuality: An excessive, insatiable sex drive in either men or women.

Because these two terms are imprecise, some researchers prefer the term hypersexuality. **Hypersexuality** refers to an excessive, insatiable sex drive in either a man or a woman—not just to a high level of sexual desire or of sexual activity. It leads to compulsive sexual behaviour in the sense that the person feels driven to it even when there may be very negative consequences (Goldberg, 1987). The person is also never satisfied by the activity, and she or he may not be having orgasms, despite all the sexual activity. Such cases meet the criteria for abnormal behaviour discussed at the beginning of this chapter: The compulsiveness of the behaviour leads it to become extremely inefficient, with the result that it impairs functioning in other areas of the person's life. While most people use sexuality sites on the Internet in healthy ways, some people feel driven toward online sexual pursuits. Compulsive cybersex use is discussed shortly.

A study of 100 male patients with paraphilias or related disorders focused on creating an operational definition of hypersexuality (Kafka, 1997b). The results supported the use of the criterion of seven or more orgasms per week for a minimum duration of six months. The men reported an average of 7.4 to 8.0 orgasms per week in the preceding six months; the modal time per day the men spent in unconventional sexual activity was one to two hours. The most common unconventional behaviours were compulsive masturbation (67 percent of the sample), protracted promiscuity (56 percent), and dependence upon pornography (41 percent). The most common paraphilias were exhibitionism, voyeurism, and pedophilia.

This research provides a useful operational definition for men, although numbers alone do not capture the compulsive aspect of the behaviour or the extent to which it is interfering with the person's life and relationships. In addition, the suggested criterion should not be applied to women. The criterion is stated as the number of orgasms per week. Some women rarely or never experience orgasms; in fact, their anorgasmia might cause them to engage in compulsive sexual behaviour. Another problem is that women who are orgasmic are capable of multiple orgasms during a single session of activity (see Chapter 9). A woman

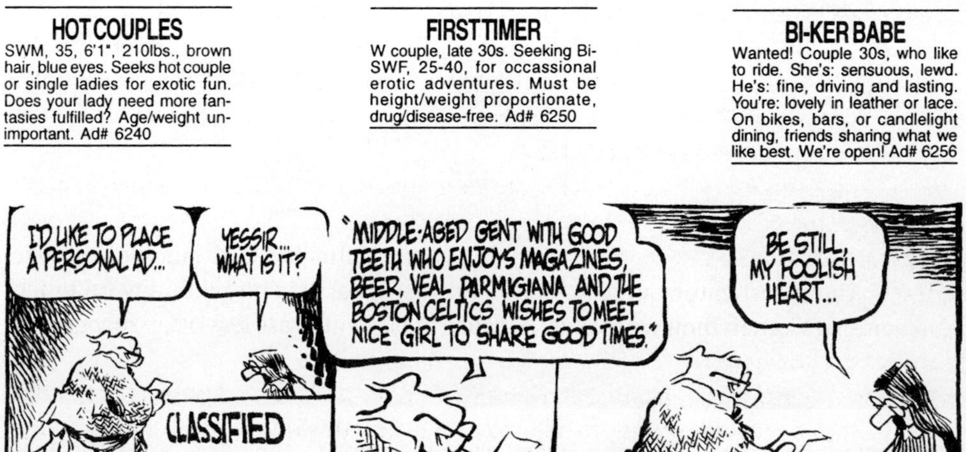
HOT COUPLES
SWM, 35, 6'1", 210lbs., brown hair, blue eyes. Seeks hot couple or single ladies for exotic fun. Does your lady need more fantasies fulfilled? Age/weight unimportant. Ad# 6240
FIRST TIMER
W couple, late 30s. Seeking Bi-SWF, 25-40, for occassional erotic adventures. Must be height/weight proportionate, drug/disease-free. Ad# 6250
BI-KER BABE
Wanted! Couple 30s, who like to ride. She's: sensuous, lewd. He's: fine, driving and lasting. You're: lovely in leather or lace. On bikes, bars, or candlelight dining, friends sharing what we like best. We're open! Ad# 6256
I'D LIKE TO PLACE A PERSONAL AD...
YESSIR... WHAT IS IT?
CLASSIFIED
"MIDDLE-AGED GENT WITH GOOD TEETH WHO ENJOYS MAGAZINES, BEER, VEAL PARMIGIANA AND THE BOSTON CELTICS WISHES TO MEET NICE GIRL TO SHARE GOOD TIMES."
BE STILL, MY FOOLISH HEART...
©Jefferson Communications, Inc. 1982 Distributed by Tribune Company Syndicate, Inc.

Figure 15.8 Advertising for partners. Many newspapers and magazines carry such "personal ads."

who engages in sexual activity three times a week could experience seven or eight orgasms, which would not be atypical or abnormal. Once again, we see that a person's gender is very important in defining abnormality. A valid criterion for hypersexuality in men thus may not be valid for women.

One study recruited women from volunteers at presentations about highly sexual women, and via newspaper ads in alternative newspapers (Blumberg, 2003). The authors used the term *highly sexual* to refer to women who desire sexual stimulation to orgasm six or seven times per week, or who think of themselves as highly sexual and their sexuality frequently strongly affects their lives. Forty-four women were interviewed, ranging in age from 20 to 82, from such diverse occupations as janitor and corporate CEO; 41 of the 44 were white. Twenty-five percent were married; 48 percent were separated or divorced. The preferred weekly frequency of sexual episodes—again, not orgasms—ranged from 3 to 70. The women reported that the internal demand for sexual excitement and satisfaction was too strong to be ignored; for many of them, it shaped their daily lives. This demand led to challenges in the areas of their feelings about themselves, their relationships with partners, and their relationships with female friends. Some of the women found it impossible to form a single relationship that could fulfill their needs, leading to multiple partners or the frequent forming of new relationships. The researcher believes that neither the term *sexual addiction* nor *compulsive sexual behaviour* should be applied to this behaviour. These women did not feel that their behaviour was out of control, and they did not report an increase in frequency of behaviour or the impact of it on their lives over time.

ASPHYXIOPHILIA

Asphyxiophilia is the desire to induce in oneself a state of oxygen deficiency in order to create sexual arousal or to enhance sexual excitement and orgasm (Zaviačič, 1994). A variety of techniques are used, including temporary strangulation by a rope around the neck, a pillow against the face, or a plastic bag over the head or upper body. Obviously, this is very dangerous behaviour; a miscalculation can lead to death.

> **Asphyxiophilia:** The desire to induce in oneself a state of oxygen deficiency in order to create sexual arousal or to enhance excitement and orgasm.

Little is known about asphyxiophilia. Most of the deaths attributed to the practice involve men, about three men for every woman (Sauvageau & Racette, 2006). There were 118 recorded deaths due to asphyxiophilia in Alberta and Ontario (the only provinces that record this information) between 1974 and 1987; only one was female (Hucker & Blanchard, 1992). The average age of death was 26 but ranged from 10 to 56 years. Such cases are often obvious to the trained investigator. Characteristics that distinguish these deaths from intentional suicides include a male who is nude, cross-dressed, or dressed with genitals exposed, and evidence of sexual activity at the time of death (Hucker & Blanchard, 1992). Pornography or other props such as mirrors are often present (Zaviačič, 1994).

Some cases have been identified involving women (Byard et al., 1993). A review of eight fatal cases among women found that only one involved unusual clothing, and none involved pornography or props. Two of the cases were initially ruled homicide, one suicide, and five accidental death. The investigators suggest that death due to asphyxiophilia may be much more common among women than we realize, because these deaths are less often recognized for what they are by investigators.

Men and women engage in asphyxiophilia in the belief that arousal and orgasm are intensified by reduced oxygen. There is no way to determine whether this is true. If the experience is more intense, it may be due to heightened arousal created by the risk rather than by reduced oxygen. Some believe that certain women may experience an orgasm accompanied by urethral ejaculation; this belief has been identified as one reason women engage in asphyxiophilia. Again, there is no evidence.

There is probably a range, from those who try this activity once out of curiosity to those who engage in it repeatedly and compulsively. Obviously, practitioners don't want to kill themselves; most include a self-release mechanism, but these safeguards sometimes fail.

CYBERSEX USE AND ABUSE

A major concern in recent years has been whether the use of the Internet to access sexually oriented materials, chat rooms, and bulletin boards can become compulsive, addictive, or paraphilic. Recall that compulsive behaviour involves (a) a lack of impulse control, (b) a tendency to lead to social and legal sanctions, (c) interference in interpersonal and occupational functioning, and (d) the creation of health risks. The term addictive behaviour is sometimes used because these behaviours typically involve an addictive cycle: preoccupation, ritual, loss of control, and despair. Paraphilias are behaviours defined as lasting six months or more and causing significant distress. This concern has been raised by therapists and clinicians, who report cases of Internet use leading to job loss, relationship difficulties leading to divorce, and other adverse consequences (Galbreath et al., 2002).

If we think about Internet sexual behaviour as falling on a continuum from healthy and normal to unhealthy and abnormal, most people who use the Internet for sexually related activities are cybersex users, not cybersex abusers, addicts, or compulsives (Cooper et al., 1999a, 1996b). However, the Internet is thought to be especially likely to be involved in leading to addictive or compulsive behaviour because it is characterized by the three A's: anonymity, accessibility, and affordability. Unlike face-to-face behaviours such as cruising for a partner or buying or renting X-rated DVDs, Internet users are anonymous. The Net is available 24/7, and its use is relatively cheap—you can download almost any kind of sexual material for as little as $2.95, and often for free. The latter enhances its appeal; even if your ideal partner is 5'1", weighs 140 lbs, has red hair and green eyes, and dresses in black leather with an opening exposing the genitals, you can find him or her online.

British psychologist Mark Griffith (2000, 2001) has argued that cybersex becomes an addiction or compulsion when it has the following six characteristics. These characteristics are similar to those proposed by Carnes (1983) for sexual addictions more generally:

1. *Salience*. Cybersex becomes the most important activity in the person's life and he or she becomes preoccupied with thinking about it.
2. *Mood modification*. The person reports that cybersex alters his or her negative mood by producing either an arousing "buzz" or "high" or a calming feeling of "escape" or "numbing" and thus is used as a coping strategy.
3. *Tolerance*. The person requires greater and greater amounts of cybersex to achieve the former changes in mood. As a result, he or she spends more and more time engaging in Internet sex.
4. *Withdrawal symptoms*. The person experiences unpleasant feelings and physical effects when he or she stops engaging in cybersex or suddenly decreases its use.
5. *Conflict*. As a result of spending a great deal of time on the Internet, the person experiences conflicts with the significant people in his or her life (e.g., not spending time with his or her partner), with other activities (such as job, social life, school), or within him- or herself.
6. *Relapse*. If the person begins to engage in cybersex again after a period of not doing so, he or she quickly returns to his or her most extreme pattern of use.

Research on Internet use has utilized convenience samples of persons who respond to invitations on websites and agree to complete an online questionnaire. Obviously, such samples consist of persons with access to computers who possess basic online skills. Thus, these samples may underrepresent lower-income and minority persons, although though they may be representative of people engaging in cybersex. Early research found that almost one-half of the participants spent less than one hour per week in online sexual pursuits (Cooper et al.,

1999). Of concern was the 8 percent who reported spending 11 or more hours per week in such activity. These heavy users were more likely to go online both at home and at work and to report that their online sexual behaviour interfered with their lives. A study based on more than 40 000 users assessed the relationship between the frequency and duration of Internet use and mental health. The results indicated that the number of months that had passed since participants first went online was positively associated with a history of mental health problems and treatment, as well as with current behavioural difficulties involving alcohol, gambling, food, and sex. Spending more hours per week online was associated with a history of mental health problems and treatment (Mathy & Cooper, 2003).

A Swedish study focused on cybersex or online sexual activity (OSA), which is two or more persons engaging in sexual talk for the purposes of sexual pleasure (Daneback et al., 2005). Researchers placed a banner soliciting participation on a Web portal. The banner appeared randomly during a two-week period; 1835 persons completed the survey. Almost one-third reported that they had engaged in cybersex; the most common location was in a chatroom. Participants in OSA were young, and homosexual men were four times more likely to report OSA than were heterosexual men. Those who reported OSA spent more time online and reported more offline sexual partners than did people who did not report OSA.

Research using a sexual compulsivity scale sought to determine what percentage of users were compulsive users (Cooper et al., 2000). The study found that 83 percent of the participants were not problematic users. Eleven percent attained moderate scores on the scale, 4.6 percent were *sexually compulsive*, and 1 percent were *cybersex compulsives*—that is, they attained the highest scores on compulsivity and spent more than 11 hours per week in online sexual pursuits. Persons in the cybersex compulsive group were more likely to be male, to be single and dating, and to report that they were bisexual; they reported spending 15 to 25 hours per week in online sexual pursuits. Twenty-one percent of the respondents reported that their online activities had jeopardized at least one area of their life, the most common being personal relationships. The researchers concluded that bisexuals, and perhaps other sexually marginalized groups, may be especially at risk for online sexual compulsivity.

OTHER SEXUAL VARIATIONS

A review of the literature identified more than 100 sexual variations (Federoff, 2007). Some of these just describe unusual sexual interests; the individual involved may not actually have a paraphilia. Most of the paraphilias are too rare to have had much research devoted to them. Nonetheless, some of them are described here.

Saliromania is a variation found mainly in men; there is a desire to damage or soil a woman or her clothes or the image of a woman, such as a painting or statue. The man becomes sexually excited and may ejaculate during the act.

Coprophilia and **urophilia** are both variations having to do with excretion. In coprophilia the feces are important to sexual satisfaction. In urophilia it is the urine that is important. The urophiliac may want to be urinated on as part of the sexual act. Insiders refer to urination as "golden showers."

Frotteurism is the seventh paraphilia identified by the *DSM-IV-TR*. It is defined as sexual fantasies, urges, or behaviours involving touching or rubbing one's genitals against the body of a non-consenting person. It must occur over a period of at least six months and cause marked distress or interpersonal difficulty. Milder forms of this activity are common. A man may approach a woman from the rear and press his penis against her buttocks; or a woman may approach a man from the side and rub her genitals against his leg or hip. The target may be unaware of it if it occurs in a crowded elevator or subway train, or in the crush of a crowd at a sports event or concert. We noted earlier that 35 percent of a sample of university men reported having engaged in this activity.

Saliromania: A desire to damage or soil a woman or her clothes.

Coprophilia (cop-roh-FILL-ee-uh): Deriving sexual satisfaction from contact with feces.

Urophilia (YUR-oh-fill-ee-uh): Deriving sexual satisfaction from contact with urine.

Frotteurism: Rubbing one's genitals against the body of a non-consenting person.

Necrophilia: Deriving sexual satisfaction from contact with a dead person.

Zoophilia: Sexual contact with an animal; also called bestiality or sodomy.

Necrophilia is sexual contact with a dead person. It is a very rare form of behaviour and is considered by experts to be psychotic and extremely deviant. Necrophiliacs derive sexual gratification from viewing a corpse or actually having intercourse with it; the corpse may be mutilated afterward (Thorpe et al., 1961).

Zoophilia is sexual contact with an animal; this behaviour is also called *bestiality* or *sodomy*, although the latter term is also sometimes used to refer to anal intercourse or even mouth–genital sex between humans. About 8 percent of the men in Kinsey's sample reported having had sexual experiences with animals. Most of this activity was concentrated in adolescence and probably reflected the experimentation and diffuse sexual urges of that period. Not surprisingly, the percentage was considerably higher among boys on farms; 17 percent of boys raised on farms had had animal contacts resulting in orgasm. Kinsey found that only about 3 to 4 percent of all females have had some sexual contact with animals. Contemporary therapists report cases of men and women engaging in sexual activity with household pets. Activities include masturbating the animal, oral–genital contact, and intercourse. A preference for sexual contact with animals over humans is extremely rare (Earls & Lalumière, 2002).

Researchers posted a questionnaire online and recruited participants through a letter to members of a network of people with sexual interests in animals (as we said, you can find anything on the Web—that's accessibility). Those who volunteered were asked to refer others who had interests similar to those assessed by the questionnaire (Williams & Weinberg, 2003). Data were obtained from 114 men, all white, with a median age of 27; 64 percent were single, never married, and 83 percent had at least some university education. These characteristics undoubtedly reflect in part the fact that the sample was obtained via the Web. Ninety-three percent defined themselves as "zoophiles" and said this identity involved a concern for the animal's welfare and an emphasis on consensual sexual activity. They compared themselves favourably with "bestialists," whom they said were not concerned about an animal's welfare. Given a list of possible reasons for sexual interest in animals, the two most common were a desire for affection and pleasurable sex. The type of sexual contact reported by the men varied by the type of animal. Receiving oral sex and receiving anal intercourse were the most frequent activities with dogs, whereas performing vaginal and anal intercourse were most frequent with horses. Only one man preferred sheep. Many of the men had not had a human partner of either sex in the preceding year. The researchers suggest that a preference for sexual activity with animals can be explained by learning theory in that the rewards offered by sex with animals are immediate, easy, and intense, and thus extremely reinforcing. They suggested that the respondents' choice of animal is explained by their early conditioning; most men preferred the type of animal they first had sex with.

PREVENTION AND TREATMENT OF HARMFUL SEXUAL VARIATIONS

For many of the variations discussed in this chapter, there is a continuum from normal to abnormal. People whose behaviour falls at the normal end enjoy these activities at no expense to self or others. Some may need reassurance that there is nothing wrong with engaging in these behaviours but do not need treatment to change their behaviour. They may, however, need treatment to accept themselves and to question pressure by family members and/or society to fit a narrow definition of normality. It is important that therapists are able to accept that there are a range of normal sexual behaviours. Individuals with atypical sexual interests may be reluctant to see a therapist out of fear that their interests will be pathologized. As a result, some therapists in Canadian cities are advertising themselves as "kink friendly" or "kink positive" in order to communicate their accepting attitudes.

However, some people engage in behaviours that fall at the abnormal end. Some people engage in sexual variations that they find highly distressing, causing them significant unhappiness. Their sexual interests (e.g., in the case of a person with a sexual compulsion or addiction) may interfere with having healthy relationships or completing their day-to-day responsibilities. Yet they may find these sexual interests extremely difficult to change or control. Other sexual variations—for example, pedophilia—cause significant harm to other people. However, some pedophiles do not see their behaviour as harmful. Thus, the issue of whom to treat is extremely complex. Nonetheless, it is important to develop programs to prevent and treat these types of harmful sexual variations (Qualls et al., 1978).

PREVENTION OF HARMFUL SEXUAL VARIATIONS

In preventive medicine, a distinction is made between primary prevention and secondary prevention. Applied to the sexual variations, primary prevention would mean intervening in home life or in other factors during childhood to help prevent problems from developing, or trying to teach people how to cope with crises or stress so that problems do not develop. In secondary prevention, the idea is to identify people who are at high risk to develop a problem as early as possible, so that difficulties are minimized.

It would be highly advantageous to do primary prevention of harmful or distressing sexual variations—that is, to head them off before they even develop. Unfortunately, this is proving to be difficult, for a number of reasons. One problem is the diagnostic categories. The categories for the diagnosis of sexual variations are not nearly so clear-cut in real life as they may seem in this chapter, and multiple diagnoses for one person are not uncommon. That is, a given man might have engaged in incest, pedophilia, and exhibitionism. If it is unclear how to diagnose sexual variations, it is going to be rather difficult to figure out how to prevent them. If one is not sure whether there is a difference between chicken pox and measles, it is rather difficult to start giving inoculations.

An alternative approach that seems promising—rather than figuring out ways to prevent each separate variation—is to analyze the *components of sexual development*. Disturbance in one or more of these components in development might lead to different sexual variations. Two such components are arousal to appropriate stimuli and formation of relationships with others (Bancroft, 1978). Thus, for example, a disturbance in attachment relationships in childhood might lead to exhibitionism or to compulsive cybersex. The idea would then be to try to ensure that as children grow up, their development in each component is healthy (primary prevention). We might have specific programs for children who demonstrate characteristics or behaviour that is known to lead to harmful sexual variations (secondary prevention). Ideally, harmful sexual variations would not occur then. However, this task is made more difficult by the fact that we have little scientific knowledge about either what constitutes unusual sexual behaviours among children or what components of development lead to harmful sexual variations (Moser et al., 2004).

Interest in developing preventive programs targeting children partly stems from the number of youth charged with sexual offences. For example, in 2003 in Canada there were 392 youth charged with sexual assault and 268 youth charged with other sexual offences in youth court (many more youth were charged with other crimes such as physical assault and theft than were charged with sexual offences). Research with 45 adolescent sex offenders in Toronto indicated that 42 percent showed equal or more arousal to film clips of children than to film clips of adults—that is, had pedophilic interests (Seto et al., 2003). One study of American adolescents incarcerated for sexual offences found that 46 percent committed their first offence before the age of 12 (Burton, 2000). Childhood victimization was positively associated with later sexual aggression by the youth, suggesting that social learning can help explain the development of sexual offending.

We have a long way to go in preventing harmful sexual variations, to say the least.

TREATMENT OF HARMFUL SEXUAL VARIATIONS

Despite our best efforts, it is unlikely that we will be successful at preventing all harmful sexual variations. Treatments are needed for this category of variations. Many different treatments have been tried, each based on a different theoretical understanding of the causes of sexual variations. We will look at four categories of treatments: medical treatments, cognitive–behavioural therapies, skills training, and AA-type 12-step programs.

MEDICAL TREATMENTS

Inspired by the notion that sexual variations are caused by biological factors, various medical treatments for sexual variations have been tried over the last century. Some of them look today like nothing other than cruel and unusual punishment. Nonetheless, people would love to have a "pill" that would cure some of these complex and painful or dangerous paraphilias, so the search for such treatments continues.

Surgical castration has never been commonly used in Canada as a treatment for various kinds of uncontrollable sexual urges, although it was used extensively in Europe. However, a few sex offenders in Canada do "voluntarily" undergo surgical castration. Indeed, a study of 134 men interested in castration found that 41 percent of them indicated that the reason that they wanted to be castrated was to have more control over their sexual urges (Wassersug et al., 2004). Such treatments are based on the notion that removing a man's testosterone by removing the testes will lead to a drastic reduction in sex drive, which will in turn erase urges to commit sex offences. However, as we saw in Chapter 9, a reduction in testosterone levels in humans does not always lead to a reduction in sexual behaviour (Federoff & Moran, 1997). Surgical castration cannot be recommended as a treatment for sex offenders either on humanitarian grounds or on grounds of effectiveness.

Hormonal treatment involves the use of drugs to reduce sexual desire. Sexual arousability is heavily dependent on maintaining the level of androgen in the bloodstream above a given threshold. Two ways to reduce this level are to administer (1) drugs that reduce the production of androgen in the testes ("chemical castration"), or (2) antiandrogens that bind to androgen receptors in the brain and genitals, blocking the effects of androgen. The use of either should produce a sharp decline in sexual desire. Several drugs have been tried in the past 40 years. The most commonly used in Canada is *medroxyprogesterone acetate* (MPA), which binds to androgen receptors. The drug is given by injection, often weekly. A review of the literature shows that the use of MPA results in reduced sexual interest and a lower level of sexual fantasies, along with decreased erections and ejaculation (Miner & Coleman, 2001). However, "the drop-out rate is extremely high and re-offense rates have been found to exceed 65 percent of those who discontinue antiandrogen treatment" (p. 8). Recently, clinicians have started using leuprolide acetate, a synthetic analogue of gonadotropin-releasing hormone (GnRH; see Chapter 5); its continued use suppresses androgen production and reduces sexual fantasies and drive. It has fewer side effects than MPA. One study reports its use with 12 adults with paraphilic or other sexual disorders (Krueger & Kaplan, 2001). These individuals were followed for between six months and six years. Treatment resulted in significant suppression of deviant sexual interests and behaviour. Similar results were found in a study of six young juveniles/young adults (Saleh et al., 2004).

The use of alternative, *psychopharmacological treatment* increased dramatically in frequency in the 1990s. Here, psychotropic medications are administered to offenders. These medications influence patients' psychological functioning and behaviour by their action on the central nervous system. The newness of the drugs being used means there is little research on the effectiveness of this technique.

There is a great deal of interest in the use of the newer antidepressants known as selective serotonin reuptake inhibitors (SSRIs). Case reports indicate that SSRIs reduce paraphilic fantasies and urges (Raymond et al., 2002). They appear to change the compulsive sexual behaviour rather than sexual desire (Bradford, 2000; Federoff, 1994). As these drugs have been successfully used to treat non-sexual compulsive behaviours, their success with paraphilias suggests that these conditions may be a type of obsessive-compulsive disorder (Miner & Coleman, 2001).

Both hormonal and psychopharmacological treatment should be used as only one element in a complete program of therapy, which would include counselling and treatment for other emotional and social deficits (Bradford, 2000; Saleh & Berlin, 2003). For example, Eli Coleman (Coleman et al., 2003) recommends that in addition to psychopharmacological treatment, individuals with compulsive sexual behaviour should (1) receive psychotherapy to deal with issues from the families-of-origin and learn to better deal with their stress, anxiety, and depression that can trigger the compulsive sexual behaviour; (2) participate in group therapy in order to learn from others with similar problems and overcome feelings of shame and guilt; and (3) receive couple therapy that is aimed at improving the couple's intimacy and sexual functioning. The best results are obtained with men who are highly motivated to change their behaviour and therefore comply with the prescribed treatment regimen. If the man with the paraphilia stops taking the drug or participating in other aspects of treatment, the program will fail. Unfortunately, one of the limitations of research on the effectiveness of these treatments is the dropout rate, which was 46 percent in one study.

COGNITIVE–BEHAVIOURAL THERAPIES

Compared to other therapeutic approaches, cognitive–behavioural therapy is effective at reducing recidivism among sex offenders (Hanson et al.,2002; Marshall et al., 1991; Marshall et al., 2006). Cognitive programs are used extensively to treat incarcerated sex offenders in Canadian prisons (Byers et al., 1997). Comprehensive programs target offender needs and risks factors. However, they also aim to reduce the need to reoffend by helping the offender attain the skills and self-beliefs (including self-esteem) needed to attain a "good life" (Marshall et al., 2006). As such, most programs include:

1. Behaviour therapy to reduce inappropriate sexual arousal and enhance appropriate arousal.
2. Learning more effective ways of coping and managing moods.
3. Social skills training to increase intimacy skills that are needed to form satisfying and effective interpersonal relationships.
4. Increasing capacity to accept responsibility for ones actions, for example, through modification of distorted thinking and challenging the rationalizations that the person uses to justify the undesirable behaviour.
5. Relapse prevention; helping the person identify and control or avoid whatever triggers the behaviour and to identify sources of support.
6. Finding other, less problematic ways of meeting the needs and desires fulfilled by the behaviour.

One technique that is often used is *covert sensitization*. It involves pairing aversive imagery (thoughts) with fantasies of the target behaviour. In the treatment of an exhibitionist, for example, he repeatedly practises a vivid fantasy in which, just as he imagines getting ready to expose himself, he experiences waves of nausea and vomiting. The details, of course, are individualized to the person and his particular problem. Reports indicate that this approach has been effective in some cases of sexual sadism, exhibitionism, and pedophilia (Barlow et al., 1969; Walen & Roth, 1987).

Another approach is *orgasmic reconditioning* (Marquis, 1970; Walen & Roth, 1987). With this method, the patient is told to masturbate to his usual paraphilic fantasies. Then, just at the moment of orgasm, he switches to an acceptable fantasy. After practising this for some time, he becomes able to orgasm regularly while having an acceptable fantasy. He then is told to move the fantasy progressively to an earlier phase of masturbation. Gradually he becomes conditioned to experiencing sexual arousal in the context of acceptable behaviour.

One program designed for female offenders combined cognitive–behavioural with psycho-dynamic techniques, and relied on one-on-one rather than group therapy (Traven et al., 1990). Male offenders typically deny responsibility for their behaviour, so the initial stage of treatment may focus on acknowledging one's behaviour and its consequences. Women in this program readily acknowledged what they had done and were overwhelmed by guilt and shame, so the initial stage focused on self-esteem. Thus, different treatment programs may be needed for men and women with paraphilias.

SKILLS TRAINING

According to yet another theoretical understanding, persons with paraphilias engage in their behaviour because they have great difficulty forming relationships, and so do not have access to appropriate forms of sexual gratification. This perspective is consistent with data on IQ differences between sex offenders and controls. A meta-analysis included results from 75 studies involving 236 independent samples and more than 25 000 persons (Cantor et al., 2005). Men who committed sex offences scored significantly lower than non-offenders, and lower than those who committed non-sexual offences. Among sex offenders, the younger the age of the victims, the lower the IQ score. Many of these people do not have the skills to initiate and maintain conversation. They may find it difficult to develop intimacy (see Chapter 12) (Keenan & Ward, 2000). Such people may benefit from a treatment program that includes social skills training. Such training may include how to carry on a conversation, how to develop intimacy, how to be appropriately assertive, and identifying irrational fears that are inhibiting the person (Abel et al., 1992). These programs may also include basic sex education.

If a person needs to learn and practise sexual interaction skills, one approach would be to have him interact with a trained partner. This is the basis for a controversial practice, the use of *sex surrogates* as part of a treatment program. The surrogate works with the therapist, interacting socially and sexually with the client to provide opportunities for using the newly acquired information and skills. Some therapists believe that the use of surrogates is ethical, but others see it as a type of prostitution. Just as the definition of "abnormal" depends on one's point of view, so does the definition of "sex therapy."

12-STEP PROGRAMS

Sexual addictions theory argues that many people who engage in compulsive, inappropriate sexual patterns are addicted to their particular sexual practice. The appropriate treatment, according to this approach, is one of the 12-step programs modelled on Alcoholics Anonymous. Several groups have adapted the AA program for sexual addictions, among them Sexaholics Anonymous (SA), Sexual Addicts Anonymous (SAA), and Sex and Love Addicts Anonymous (SLAA). These groups can usually be found by calling the local phone number for Alcoholics Anonymous or by looking up their websites on the Internet. Some of the programs are run by group members, whereas others are affiliated with professional health care facilities.

Twelve-step programs combine cognitive restructuring, obtaining support from other members who have the same or similar problem behaviours, and enhancing spirituality. This last aspect involves increasing one's awareness of a "higher power" who can be relied on to help one recover. The first step in the process of recovery is admitting that one is sexually addicted, that the behaviour is out of control, and that one's life has become unmanageable. These are hard admissions to make for someone who has spent years denying the existence of a problem. There are frequent meetings with a support group, and there is a strong emphasis on building feelings of self-worth. AA for alcohol or drug addiction demands that the addict

Figure 15.9 The centrepiece of 12-step programs such as Sex Addicts Anonymous are group meetings in which participants confront their addiction with the support of other group members.

abstain from contact with the substance. Similarly, programs for sexual addicts adopt a definition of "sexual sobriety." They cannot adopt an abstinence model, however, because sexual expression is a basic human need. Thus, they attempt to differentiate addictive sexual behaviour from healthy sexual behaviour. For some groups, although not all, only marital sex (and not other partnered sex or masturbation) is considered to fit the definition of sexual sobriety.

Groups using 12-step programs are generally unwilling to cooperate with researchers, believing that to do so would prevent group members from concentrating on recovery. As a result, there is little research data on the effectiveness of these programs.

WHAT WORKS?

What is needed is carefully controlled research on the effectiveness of various approaches to the treatment of sexual variations (Miner & Coleman, 2001). Research to date has tended to apply one method to a heterogeneous group of people. It is likely, however, that each method will be more effective with some paraphilias than with others. Research involving drugs should systematically assess side effects; some drugs have severe side effects on some people, especially if used for more than six months. Research should consider the relative likelihood of relapse; some people with paraphilias pose grave danger to themselves (e.g., asphyxiophiliacs) or to others if they resume their problematic behaviour.

SUMMARY

It seems reasonable to define "abnormal sexual behaviour" as behaviour that is uncomfortable for the person, inefficient, bizarre, or physically or psychologically harmful to the person or others. The American Psychiatric Association defines paraphilias as recurrent, intense, sexually arousing fantasies, urges, or behaviours that are obsessive and compulsive. A behaviour is compulsive if the person is obsessed with it, feels compelled to engage in it, and has experienced personal, relationship, medical, or legal difficulties as a result of it. Some of these behaviours are against the law, but most are not.

Four theoretical approaches have been used in understanding the paraphilias: learning theory, cognitive theory, the sexual addiction/compulsion model, and sociological theory. Several explanations have been proposed for the fact that there are many more males than females with paraphilias.

A fetishist is a person who becomes erotically attached to some object other than another human being. Most likely, fetishism arises from conditioning, and it provides a good example of the continuum from normal to abnormal behaviour.

The transvestite derives sexual satisfaction from dressing as a member of the other gender. Like many other sexual variations, transvestism is much more common among men than among women. Survey data suggest that many men who later become transvestites begin cross-dressing in childhood.

Three styles of sexual interaction involve differences in control over sexual interactions. Dominance and submission involve a consensual exchange of power, and the enacting of scripted performances. Bondage and discipline involve the use of physical restraints or verbal commands by one person to control the other. Both D-S and B-D may occur without genital contact or orgasm. Sexual sadism and masochism involve deriving sexual gratification from giving and receiving pain. Both are recognized as paraphilias if they become compulsive.

The voyeur is sexually aroused by looking at nudes. The exhibitionist displays his or her sex organs to others. Both are generally harmless.

Nymphomania and satyriasis are terms used to describe women and men with an extraordinarily high sex drive. Both terms are ambiguous and subject to misuse. The term hypersexuality is potentially more precise, particularly if it is defined behaviourally.

Other sexual variations include asphyxiophilia, zoophilia, and necrophilia. A recent concern is cybersex abuse, which is facilitated by the anonymity, accessibility, and affordability of the Internet.

The possibility of programs to prevent sexual variations is being explored.

Four types of programs to treat sexual variations are medical treatments including hormonal and psychopharmacological interventions; cognitive–behavioural therapies; social skills training; and AA-type 12-step programs. We need careful research to determine which programs work best in the treatment of given behaviours.

QUESTIONS FOR THOUGHT, DISCUSSION, AND DEBATE

1. What do you think of the idea about preventing sexual variations presented in this chapter? Do you think the schools or some other agency should institute a program to screen children, trying to detect those with characteristics that might indicate they would develop a sexual variation later in life, and then give therapy to those children?

2. Of the sexual variations in this chapter, which seem to you to be the most abnormal? Why? Do the ones you have chosen fit the criteria for abnormality discussed at the beginning of the chapter?

3. A common phenomenon in medical school is for medical students to think they have contracted one of the diseases they are studying. The analogous phenomenon would be for students who read this chapter to think that they have one or more of the paraphilias. Did you notice yourself becoming sexually aroused as you read about one (or more) of the variations? If so, do you think you are abnormal? Why, or why not?

4. Most persons who seek treatment or are arrested for atypical or paraphilic behaviours are white men. Do you think that this is an accurate picture of our society, or are we just unaware of non-whites who engage in these behaviours? Based on the data presented and the causes discussed, would you expect black, Asian, or Aboriginal men to engage in these behaviours? Why, or why not?

5. Which of the behaviours in this chapter would you consider to be abnormal? Which would you consider to be atypical but normal?

SUGGESTIONS FOR FURTHER READING

Griffin-Shelley, Eric. (1991). *Sex and love: Addiction, treatment, and recovery.* Westport, CT: Praeger. This book describes the addiction model as it is applied to sex and love. It also describes treatment programs.

Wilson, Glenn D. (Ed.). 1987. *Variant sexuality: Research and theory.* Baltimore: Johns Hopkins University Press. The chapters in this book review different theoretical explanations for sexual variations, from genetics and sociobiology to cross-cultural perspectives.

For review questions, web resources, and other learning and study tools, visit the *Understanding Human Sexuality* Online Learning Centre at www.mcgrawhill.ca/olc/hyde.

SEXUAL COERCION

Chapter Highlights

Sexual Assault
Incidence Statistics
Sexual Assault of Women by Acquaintances
Spousal Sexual Assault of Women
The Impact of Sexual Assault on Women
Causes of Sexual Assault against Women
Men Who Are Sexually Aggressive against Women
Ethnicity and Sexual Assault against Women
Sexual Assault against Men
Sexual Assault in Prison
Preventing Sexual Assault

Child Sexual Abuse
Patterns of Child Sexual Abuse
Patterns of Intrafamilial Sexual Abuse
Impact on the Victim
The Offenders
Treatment of Sex Offenders
Mandatory Notification of the Release of Sex Offenders
Preventing Child Sexual Abuse

Sexual Harassment
Sexual Harassment at Work
Sexual Harassment in Education: An A for a Lay
Sex between Professionals and Patients

EBONI'S BASIC EDUCATION ABOUT SEX CAME FROM WHAT SHE SAW AND THE DIRECT EXPERIENCES THAT SHE HAD. WHEN SHE WAS 5, SHE AND HER BROTHER WERE WRESTLING WITH THEIR UNCLE. SUDDENLY HER UNCLE LOCKED HER BROTHER OUT OF THE ROOM AND BEGAN TAKING OFF EBONI'S CLOTHES. HE HELD HER DOWN ON THE BED AND BEGAN TO PENETRATE HER BUT STOPPED ABRUPTLY. EBONI WAS FRIGHTENED OF HIM FROM THEN ON. SHE DIDN'T REALLY UNDERSTAND WHAT HE INTENDED TO DO OR WHY HE WANTED TO DO IT, BUT SHE KNEW THAT HIS BEHAVIOR WAS UNEXPECTED AND STRANGE.

. . . EBONI'S GRANDMOTHER AND FATHER INSISTED THAT SHE NOT TALK TO STRANGERS OR TAKE MONEY FROM THEM. EBONI UNDERSTOOD WHY—SHE KNEW THAT BEING MOLESTED MEANT BEING RAPED. BUT STRANGERS WERE NOT THE PREDATORS.*

This chapter is about sexual activity that involves coercion and is not between consenting adults; specifically, we will consider sexual assault; child sexual abuse; and sexual harassment at work, in education, and by professionals. All these topics have been highly publicized in the last 20 years, and much good scientific research on them has appeared.[1]

SEXUAL ASSAULT

In the last two decades, there has been a movement toward seeing crimes involving force in sexual relations as crimes of violence and victimization rather than as sex crimes. In 1983, the Criminal Code of Canada was amended to accommodate this different understanding and to protect the victims. Prior to 1983, the Criminal Code had four statutes that prohibited forced sexual activity: rape, attempted rape, indecent assault against a female, and indecent assault against a male. At that time, the legal definition of rape was heterosexual intercourse by a man with a woman who was not his wife (see Table 16.1). The rape law was criticized on a number of grounds. First, rape was limited to forced heterosexual intercourse. Second, it defined the assailant as male and the victim as female. Thus, women could not be charged with rape, and men could not be victims of rape. Third, husbands could not be charged with raping their wives, meaning that a woman could not legally refuse her husband's demands (Hughes, 2001). Fourth, the victim's prior sexual activities could be considered as evidence of her consent and of the credibility of her testimony, effectively putting her past on trial. In addition, the law had a number of provisions that made the criminal justice system unresponsive to sexual assault complaints. It specifically required corroboration that the crime of rape actually took place. The judge was obliged to inform the jury that they should not convict only on the basis of the complainant's testimony (Los, 1994). Finally, rape complaints that were not made immediately after the attack were invalidated. These provisions meant that it was extremely difficult to get a conviction if there was no physical evidence (such as physical injury) or when the complaint was not filed immediately. In fact, the majority of complaints of rape did not result in a conviction (Clark & Lewis, 1977; Siegel & McCormick, 1999).

---

*Wyatt, 1997, pp 72–73.
[1]Portions of this chapter are excerpted from J. S. Hyde. (1996). *Half the human experience. The psychology of women*, 5th ed. Boston: Houghton Mifflin.

Table 16.1   The Offence of "Rape" in the Criminal Code of Canada in 1968. This offence was replaced with three sexual assault offences in 1983.

A male person commits rape when he has sexual intercourse with a female person who is not his wife,

a. Without her consent, or
b. With her consent if the consent
    (i) Is extorted by threats or fear of bodily harm
    (ii) Is obtained by impersonating her husband, or
    (iii) Is obtained by false and fraudulent representations as to the nature and quality of the act.

In 1983, the Criminal Code was amended so that the offences of rape and indecent assault were replaced with three gender-neutral crimes of sexual assault. These crimes depend on the amount of force used to carry out the assault and the degree of injury sustained by the victim, not on the nature of the forced sexual activity. The purpose of these changes was to de-emphasize the sexual nature of the offence, to stress their violent nature, to encourage victims to report these crimes to the police, and to improve the court procedure so as to reduce trauma to victims and increase the rate of convictions (Roberts & Gebotys, 1992). The three levels of sexual assault parallel the three levels of physical assault in the Criminal Code: (simple) sexual assault, sexual assault with a weapon causing serious injury or endangering the life of the victim or causing bodily harm, and aggravated sexual assault (refer to In Focus 2.2 on page 44 for a description of these statutes).

Sexual assault[2] includes a wide range of non-consensual sexual experiences ranging from unwanted touching to forced oral, anal, or vaginal intercourse and sexual violence causing serious physical injury or disfigurement to the victim. In keeping with the equality provisions of the Charter of Rights and Freedoms, the law is written in gender-neutral terms so that either men or women can be the victim of a sexual assault and can be charged with sexual assault, and the statute no longer discriminates against married people. The crucial point is that the activity is non-consensual—that is, the victim did not consent to it. The Criminal Code also defines "consent" for the purposes of sexual assault offences. Consent must be actively established. Silence, inaction, or ambiguous conduct is not consent. There is no consent if the complainant is drunk or unconscious, if the complainant shows by his or her actions that he or she is not in agreement, or if the complainant consents to engage in sexual activity and then changes his or her mind. Children under 16 cannot be considered to have consented to sexual activity as this is considered child sexual abuse (discussed later in this chapter).

There were also some provisions that related to court proceedings, such as limiting the questioning of victims in sexual assault trials about their sexual history (often referred to as the "rape shield laws") and no longer requiring corroboration of the victim's testimony. However, due to court challenges, there are now some conditions under which the judge can allow the victim's sexual history to be admitted as evidence. Advocacy groups such as the Women's Legal Education and Action Fund (LEAF) argue that many judges are still influenced by myths and stereotypes about sexual assault, such as the mistaken belief that many women make false allegations about sexual assault, and thus, contrary to the will of Parliament, judges frequently permit sexual history evidence (Busby, 1999).

INCIDENCE STATISTICS

In 1993, Statistics Canada conducted the Violence Against Women Survey, a nationwide survey of 12 300 women aged 18 and over. It used the definition of sexual assault in the Criminal

Sexual assault: Any non-consensual sexual activity ranging from unwanted touching, to forced oral, anal, or vaginal intercourse, to sexual violence in which the victim is wounded or maimed or his or her life is endangered or when the victim is incapable of giving consent.

---

[2]Although many Canadians still use the term "rape" in everyday conversation—usually meaning forced sexual intercourse—in keeping with the Canadian Criminal Code we have chosen to use the term "sexual assault" in this chapter, except when studies specifically used the term rape.

Code of Canada to determine its incidence. Thirty-nine percent of women reported having been sexually assaulted by a man since the age of 16; 5 percent (corresponding to 572 000 women) in the previous 12 months. Only 6 percent of the women had reported the assault to the police. Victims of sexual assault by a stranger are most likely to report the incident to authorities (Renner & Wackett, 1987). In 2004, there were more than 22 000 sexual assaults reported to the police (Silver, 2007). The rate of reported sexual assault has been decreasing since the 1990s. However, according to the 2004 General Social Survey, only 8 percent of sexual assault victims reported the crime to the police. Some of the reasons why women chose not to report their sexual assault to the police were believing that the police could not do anything, wanting to keep the event private, feeling ashamed or embarrassed, being afraid of not being believed, fearing the perpetrator, and not wanting the perpetrator to be arrested (Kong et al., 2003; Lievore, 2003).

Women with disabilities are at greater risk to experience sexual assault than are women without disabilities—more than four times more likely in one study (Martin et al., 2006).

There has been no Canadian national survey of the incidence of sexual assault against men. However, the NHSLS conducted in the United States showed that men are victims of sexual aggression, although much less frequently than women are. According to the NHSLS, 1 percent of men reported having been victims of forced sex with a woman, compared to 22 percent of women who reported having been the victims of forced sex with a man (Laumann et al., 1994). It is more common for a man to have been forced to have sex by another man (1.9 percent of men) than by a woman (1.3 percent of men).

In 1999, the Canadian General Social Survey asked both women and men under age 65 about their experiences of sexual aggression: 1.8 percent of the women but only 0.3 percent of the men reported that someone had touched them against their will in the previous 12 months. Respondents in married or common-law relationships were asked about forced sexual activity by their partner within the last five years: 0.7 percent of the women and 0.2 percent of the men reported that their partner had forced them to engage in unwanted sexual activity by threatening them, holding them down, or hurting them in some way. The sexual assault provisions of the Criminal Code of Canada apply equally to men and to women as victims. However, data from 166 police departments across Canada in 2000 indicate that 98 percent of adult victims who reported the assault to the police were women (Brzozowski, 2004).

The following discussion starts with sexual assault by men against women, because this is the most common type of sexual assault.

Figure 16.1 Many women experience severe emotional distress after a sexual assault, and it is important that crisis counselling be available to them.

SEXUAL ASSAULT OF WOMEN BY ACQUAINTANCES

Sexual assault by someone who is known to the victim, often called "date rape" or sexual assault by an acquaintance, is much more frequent than sexual assault by a stranger (Renner & Wackett, 1987; Statistics Canada, 1994). Studies in this area typically ask respondents about a range of unwanted sexual activity due not only to threats or physical force, but also to verbal coercion such as continual arguments and pressure. Thus, some but not all of these unwanted experiences would meet a legal definition of sexual assault.

How many people report these types of unwanted sexual experiences? A national survey found that 28 percent of female university and college students had experienced sexual coercion in the past year (DeKeseredy & Kelly, 1993). Similarly, 19 percent of middle school and high school girls in New Brunswick reported having had a sexually coercive experience with a boyfriend that they found highly upsetting; 17 percent of boys reported that they had been sexually abusive (Price et al., 2000; Sears et al., 2007). Many women do not recognize that what happened to them was sexual assault because it occurred in a dating situation, often after the couple had engaged in consensual sexual activity at a lower level (e.g., kissing). Nonetheless, research in Ontario has demonstrated that sexual coercion by a dating partner is associated with higher depression, lower self-esteem, and more negative sexual self-perceptions (Offman & Matheson, 2004).

Miscommunication may contribute to sexual assault in dating relationships. Research has shown that many men still hold to the traditional view that a woman who says "no" really means "yes" (Byers et al., 1987; Osman, 2003). This myth is too often reinforced in films that portray women as enjoying sex resulting from sexual coercion by men. Men need to learn that "no" means "no." Consider this example of miscommunication and different perceptions in a case of sexual assault by an acquaintance:

> *Bob:* Patty and I were in the same statistics class together. She usually sat near me and was always very friendly. I liked her and thought maybe she liked me, too. Last Thursday I decided to find out. After class I suggested that she come to my place to study for midterms together. She agreed immediately, which was a good sign. That night everything seemed to go perfectly. We studied for a while and then took a break. I could tell that she liked me, and I was attracted to her. I was getting excited. I started kissing her. I could tell that she really liked it. We started touching each other and it felt really good. All of a sudden she pulled away and said "Stop." I figured she didn't want me to think that she was "easy" or "loose." A lot of girls think they have to say "no" at first. I knew once I showed her what a good time she could have, and that I would respect her in the morning, it would be OK. I just ignored her protests and eventually she stopped struggling. I think she liked it but afterward she acted bummed out and cold. Who knows what her problem was?

> *Patty:* I knew Bob from my statistics class. He's cute and we are both good at statistics, so when a tough midterm was scheduled, I was glad that he suggested we study together. It never occurred to me that it was anything except a study date. That night everything went fine at first, we got a lot of studying done in a short amount of time, so when he suggested we take a break I thought we deserved it. Well, all of a sudden he started acting really romantic and starting kissing me. I liked the kissing but then he started touching me below the waist. I pulled away and tried to stop him but he didn't listen. After a while I stopped struggling; he was hurting me and I was scared. He was so much bigger and stronger than me. I couldn't believe it was happening to me. I didn't know what to do. He actually forced me to have sex with him. I guess looking back on it I should have screamed or done something besides trying to reason with him but it was so unexpected. I couldn't believe it was happening. I still can't believe it did. (Hughes & Sandler, 1987, p. 1)

Several explanations have been proposed for why sexually aggressive men misperceive women's communications. The first proposes that aggressors lack competence in "reading" women's negative emotions. The second suggests that sexually aggressive men fail to make subtle distinctions between women's friendliness and seductiveness. The third proposes that they have a "suspicious schema" and automatically doubt that women are communicating truthfully and accurately, particularly when the woman rejects a sexual advance. Research supports the third explanation (Malamuth & Brown, 1994). These findings have important implications for prevention and treatment programs for sexual aggressors. They suggest that the programs that use cognitive therapy to get the man to change his suspicious schema are likely to be most effective. Such programs might be used as part of a comprehensive program with convicted sex offenders, or as prevention programs with high school or university men who have been identified as potential sexual aggressors.

A frightening problem today is the emergence of the so-called "date-rape drugs." There are three major types: Rohypnol, GHB, and ketamine. Numerous cases have been reported of men who slipped the drug into a woman's drink and then sexually assaulted her. Rohypnol (row-HIP-nawl; "roofie," "roachie," "La Rocha," "forget pills," "pasta," "peanuts," "whiteys," "ropes") is the drug name for flunitrazepam. The drug causes drowsiness or sleep and the man sexually assaults the woman while she is asleep. The drug also causes the woman not to remember the event the next day. GHB ("liquid G," "G," "Georgia home boy," "easy lay," "grievous bodily harm"), the drug name for gamma hydroxyl butyrate, produces similar effects to alcohol but can cause hallucinations in larger doses and when mixed with alcohol can lead to loss of consciousness. Ketamine ("K," "vitamin K," "special K") causes a combination of amnesia and hallucinations. Ecstasy ("Adam," "XTC," "bean," "E," "M," "roll") and Foxy Methoxy are also sometimes used as a date rape drug. Several strategies for avoiding this situation have been suggested, including, especially, not accepting a drink from a stranger, and never leaving your drink unattended.[3]

SPOUSAL SEXUAL ASSAULT OF WOMEN

The definition of sexual assault in the Criminal Code of Canada includes non-consensual sex with a spouse or common-law partner. How common is spousal sexual assault? The Violence Against Women Survey found that 8 percent of respondents had been sexually assaulted by a current or former spouse (Statistics Canada, 1993). According to the 2004 General Social Survey, 3 percent of women reported being sexually assaulted by their spouse (legal or common-law) in the previous 12 months.

One phenomenon that emerges from the research is an association between non-sexual and sexual violence in long-term relationships—that is, the man who batters his female partner is also likely to force her to have sex (CDC, 2004).

A man might sexually assault his female partner for many motives, including anger, power and domination, sadism, or a desire for sex regardless of whether she is willing (Russell, 1990). In some cases the man is extremely angry, perhaps in the middle of a family argument, and he expresses his anger toward his partner by sexually assaulting her. In other cases, power and domination of the female partner seem to be the motive; for example, the woman may be threatening to leave him. Finally, some sexual assaults appear to occur because the man is sadistic—enjoys inflicting pain—and is psychiatrically disturbed.

> **Spousal sexual assault:** The sexual assault of a person by his or her current or former marital or common-law spouse.

THE IMPACT OF SEXUAL ASSAULT ON WOMEN

A large number of studies have investigated the psychological reactions of women following sexual assault (Frazier et al., 2004; Koss, 1993). This research shows that sexual assault is a time of crisis for a woman and that the effects on many victims persist for a year or more. This

[3]An enterprising U.S. company claims to have developed a coaster that detects Rohypnol and other drugs. Customers put a drop of their drink on the coaster and if it changes colours, the drink contains one of the drugs. Although a good idea, it does not detect all the drugs. Further, it is another preventive strategy that focuses on women taking responsibility for their own safety rather than on educating and punishing potential aggressors.

IN FOCUS 16.1

A Sexual Assault Victim Tells Her Story

During my second year at university, I realized that I wanted to socialize more. I broke up with my hometown honey, began attending college parties, started drinking, and dated other guys at my school. I was a virgin and didn't want to be anymore. I met my second boyfriend in physics. "G" was a football player and a big, handsome man, the best-looking man I'd ever met. We began to date and at first it was wonderful. He even carried me home once from a party, and I thought, "This is the one." Our first attempt at intercourse was difficult and I began to beg him to stop, but he just kept trying until he was successful and there was blood everywhere. It was awful.

I continued to date G, but he began to act very differently. When he drank, he became extremely violent, and on different occasions I watched him break a vending machine, and pull a toilet out of a wall at a university residence. He was unhappy with the way he was treated on the football team, and I tried to console him. He became angrier and paranoid. He demanded to know where I was at all times and accused me of cheating on him. I wanted to break up with him, especially since sex was rough and not always consensual, but I was scared of him. I tried avoiding him but he always found me.

One night, G arrived very drunk at a party I was attending. He threatened a guy who was there talking to me. I tried to sneak out of the party. He noticed I left and ran out after me. Another guy slowed me down to try to persuade me to let him drive me home since I had been drinking. G accused me of trying to pick this guy up and threatened the guy, who even volunteered to drive both of us home. But G wouldn't let him and said I would take him home. I didn't want trouble so I drove him to his dorm. He claimed he was too drunk to walk to his dorm, so I tried to help him into his room. When I turned around to leave, he sprang up and locked me in. He attacked me. I tried fighting him, but he wouldn't listen or stop. He hit my head into the wall several times and tried to force me to perform oral sex. I bit him, and that made him more angry. He then tried to force anal sex, and I fought as hard as I could. I finally started crying, and he stopped when he lost his erection. The rest of the night, I felt completely trapped in his dorm room. I lay awake all night and tried to leave, but he would wake up and stop me. I've never forgotten how scared I felt that entire night. He got up that morning and showered and acted as if nothing had happened. He was in all my classes for the rest of my university career.

is true of both women sexually assaulted by a stranger as well as those sexually assaulted by an acquaintance or date (Koss, 1993; Neville & Heppner, 1999).

Emotional reactions immediately after a sexual assault can be severe (Burgess & Holmstrom, 1974). The high levels of distress generally reach a peak three weeks after the assault and continue at a high level for the next month. There is then gradual improvement beginning two or three months after the assault (Koss, 1993; Rothbaum et al., 1992). Many differences between assaulted and non-victimized women disappear after three months, except that assaulted women continue to report more fear, anxiety, self-esteem problems, and sexual problems. These effects may persist for 18 months or longer (Koss, 1993). Sexually victimized women have a somewhat higher risk of suicidal behaviour (Ullman, 2004).

Some women experience self-blame (Cairns, 1993). A woman may spend hours agonizing over what she did to bring on the sexual assault or what she might have done to prevent it: "If I hadn't worn that tight sweater . . ."; "If I hadn't been dumb enough to walk on that dark street . . . "; "If I hadn't been stupid enough to trust that guy . . ." This is an example of a tendency on the part of both the victim and others to *blame the victim* and excuse the perpetrator. Self-blame is linked to worse long-term psychological outcomes for victims (Koss & Figueredo, 2004). People are particularly likely to blame the victim if she voluntarily used alcohol or drugs, even when the perpetrator used physical force (Girard & Senn, 2008).

Researchers are finding increased evidence of the damage to women's *physical health*

I began to drink very heavily afterward. I told my roommate, J, and another woman on my floor, D. I never thought to report it, since he was my "boyfriend."

A year and a half later, I began to hear voices. It was a male voice calling me a fucking bitch, whore, and other names. I thought I was going crazy and became very depressed. I decided I must be schizophrenic and decided to kill myself.

Soon after, I was shopping in a bookstore. I saw this title staring right at me, *I Never Called It Rape*. I started reading it right there in the store, and I began crying and thinking, "This is what happened to me." I spoke with a faculty member, who arranged for immediate counselling.

The first time I went to see the counsellor, I couldn't even speak. I sat in her office and cried for the entire hour. She kept saying, "It's not your fault, it's not your fault." I couldn't believe it. Later we discussed how most of the times G and I had sex had actually been sexual assault, including the first and the last. I participated in a "Take Back the Night March." Members of one male residence threw bottles at us.

I went through medical school and residency. During my first year of residency, I was assaulted again, this time by a man in a stairwell during a New Year's Eve party at a hotel. I started screaming, "You're raping me, you're raping me!" He stopped and I got away! But

I didn't go to the ER, I just went home and crawled in bed. My old shame came back. I began to drink heavily again. One night I drank all night and never showed up to work that next morning. I finally rolled into my director's office, depressed, hung over, and still smelling of alcohol, and my boss said I had to stop and straighten up right away or he wouldn't let me back for the next year. So I stopped drinking. I also made two very good friends around the same time. Through their support, I really turned my life around.

Three years later, I moved to a different city. I was living alone for the first time and had a great deal of anxiety. I joined a Sexual Assault Survivors Support Group. Then in the spring, I was invited to speak at my old university for Career Day for high school students, so I went back there ten years after the incidents. I was finally successful in my career, had strong, loving relationships with my friends and parents, and was happy. I look back at what happened now and think that I really survived a lot. I feel it helps me to be a better physician because I can empathize with how bad life can be for people.

Source: Based on an interview conducted by Janet Hyde.

---

that may result from sexual assault (Golding, 1999; Heise, 1993; Koss et al., 1991; Koss & Heslet, 1992). Women may suffer physical injuries, such as cuts and bruises, and vaginal pain and bleeding. Women who have been forced to have oral sex may suffer irritation or damage to the throat; rectal bleeding and pain are reported by women forced to have anal intercourse. A sexually assaulted woman may contract a sexually transmitted infection such as HIV/AIDS or herpes. In about 5 percent of cases involving forced intercourse, pregnancy results (Koss et al., 1991). Women who have been sexually or physically assaulted at some time in the past visit their physician twice as often per year as non-victimized women (Koss et al., 1991).

Some women who experience severe long-term psychological symptoms following sexual assault are actually experiencing **post-traumatic stress disorder (PTSD)** (Koss, 1993; Ullman et al., 2007). Symptoms can include persistently re-experiencing the traumatic event (flashbacks, nightmares), avoiding stimuli associated with it (avoiding certain locations or activities), and hyperarousal (sleep difficulties, difficulty concentrating, irritability). According to a cognitive–behavioural view of PTSD, people who have experienced a terrifying event form a memory schema that involves information about the situation and their responses to it (Foa et al., 1989). Because the schema is large, many cues can trigger it and therefore evoke the feelings of terror that occurred at the time; the schema is probably activated at some level all the time. Schemas also affect how we interpret new events, so the consequences are far-reaching and long-lasting (see In Focus 16.1). The strongest predictors of which sexual assault survivors

Post-traumatic stress disorder (PTSD): Long-term psychological distress suffered by someone who has experienced a terrifying event.

IN FOCUS 16.2

What Should I Do after a Sexual Assault?

If You Have Been Sexually Assaulted

Tell someone you trust. Sexual assault is a traumatic violation of the person. Especially in the beginning it is helpful to be with someone who will listen to your feelings and help you carry out your decisions. If you can't tell a friend or a family member, call a sexual assault crisis line. This will help you know that you are not alone.

Decide whether to report the assault to the police. This is your decision. If you decide to report, call the police as soon as possible and preserve evidence of the crime. Do not wash, change your clothes, bathe, shower, or douche until you have a medical exam. Save anything that was involved as it may be needed as evidence.

Seek medical attention. Whether or not you decide to report the assault to the police, it is important that you see a doctor to treat any physical injuries and check for STIs and/or pregnancy. If pregnancy seems likely, emergency contraception can be used (see Chapter 7). If you have made a police report, the hospital will use a sexual assault forensic kit to collect evidence such as scrapings, semen, blood, and hair. It is important that this be done within 24 hours of the assault.

Understand that it is normal to experience a wide range of emotions. Emotions such as anger, sadness, detachment, depression, fear, and being out of control are normal responses to sexual assault. It will take time to recover. Taking control over the little things in your life, and later the bigger things, can be one step on the road to recovery.

Understand that the assault was not your fault. You may feel guilty or that the attack was somehow your fault. Sexual assault is a crime, and it was not your fault.

If Someone You Know Has Been Sexually Assaulted

Believe them. A sexual assault survivor may fear not being believed. Accept their version of the facts and be supportive. Sexual assault survivors react differently; no

---

develop PTSD are negative reactions and lack of support from others, and avoidance coping—that is, avoiding thinking about and resolving the issue (Ullman et al., 2007).

It is important to recognize that sexual assault affects many people besides the victim. Most women routinely do a number of things that stem from fears of sexual assault. For example, a single woman is not supposed to list her full first name, but rather her first initial or a man's name, in the telephone book, so as not to reveal that she lives alone. Many women, when getting into their car at night, almost reflexively check the backseat to make sure no one is hiding there. Most university women avoid walking alone through dark parts of the campus at night. In the Violence Against Women Survey (Statistics Canada, 1993), 60 percent of women reported feeling worried when walking alone in their neighbourhood after dark. The point is that most women experience the fear of sexual assault, if not sexual assault itself (Burt & Estrep, 1981; Senn & Dzinas, 1996), and this fear restricts their activities.

Spouses or partners of victims may also be profoundly affected. At the same time, they can provide important support for the woman as she recovers (see In Focus 16.2).

Post-traumatic growth: Positive life changes and psychological development following exposure to trauma.

New research in psychology indicates that not everyone who experiences a serious traumatic event develops PTSD. Some, in fact, display **post-traumatic growth**—that is, positive life changes and psychological development following exposure to trauma (Tedeschi et al., 1998). Research with sexual assault victims—or, more accurately, sexual assault survivors—confirms that some do report positive life changes, such as an increased ability to take care of themselves, a greater sense of purpose in life, and greater concern for others in similar situations (Frazier et al., 2004).

emotional reaction may indicate that they are in shock.

Listen to them. Find somewhere to be alone with them, and let them talk. Be patient. Let them tell their story at their own speed and in their own way. They may need to talk at odd hours, or a great deal in the beginning.

Comfort them. Try to calm and ground them if they are anxious or upset. Do this in a soothing, not a disapproving, way. They may not want to be held or touched, but you can still nurture them by offering tea, a blanket, a comfortable chair, a favourite object, and so on.

Tell them it was not their fault. Do not judge. Avoid questions that seem to blame them for their actions. Avoid "why" questions such as "Why didn't you fight harder?" or "Why did you go to their room?" Let them know that it was the aggressor's fault, not theirs.

Provide security. Help them feel safe by offering to find them a secure place to sleep and companionship when they return home.

Encourage action. Suggest calling a sexual assault crisis centre. A sexual assault crisis worker is experienced in talking to survivors, and can understand the survivor's needs and offer useful resources. Medical assistance also may be important, depending on the nature of the assault. If they agree to medical assistance, go with them to the hospital, clinic, or doctor's office. Stay during the examination if they want you to.

Let them make the decisions. A sexual assault survivor needs to regain their feeling of control. You can help with this by giving referrals and resources, but letting them make the decisions.

Help them decide whether to report the assault. If they decide to report the assault, encourage them to preserve any evidence. They should not take a shower or remove their clothes until they talk to the police.

Recognize your own limitations. Take time out when you need it. Recognize when you have reached the limits of your abilities. Help them create a network of support and referrals. Put aside your feelings and deal with them elsewhere. If you have strong feelings, talk to another friend or a local hotline.

Source: Condensed from Hughes and Sandler (1987) and from materials developed by the Fredericton Sexual Assault Crisis Centre.

CAUSES OF SEXUAL ASSAULT AGAINST WOMEN

To provide a perspective for the discussion that follows, we can distinguish among four major theoretical views of the nature of sexual assault (Albin, 1977; Baron & Straus, 1989):

1. *Victim-precipitated sexual assault.* This view holds that a sexual assault is always caused by a woman "asking for it." Sexual assault, then, is considered basically the woman's fault. This view represents the tendency to "blame the victim."

2. *Psychopathology of sex offenders.* This theoretical view holds that sexual assault is an act committed by a psychologically disturbed man. His deviance is responsible for the crime occurring.

3. *Feminist.* Feminist theorists and learning theorists view sexual assault as the product of gender-role socialization in our culture, which reinforces and legitimizes male aggression in general and sexual coercion specifically. Feminists also have theorized about the complex links between sex and power: In some assaults, men use sex to demonstrate their power over women; in other assaults, men use their power over women to get sex. Feminists also point to the eroticization of violence in our society. Gender inequality is both the cause and the result of sexual assault in this view.

4. *Social disorganization.* Sociologists believe that crime rates, including sexual assault rates, increase when the social organization of a community is disrupted. Under such conditions the community cannot enforce its norms against crime.

You personally may subscribe to one or more of these views. It is also true that researchers in this area have generally based their work on one of these theoretical models, which may influence their research. You should keep these models in mind as you read the rest of this chapter.

What do the data say? Research indicates that a number of factors contribute to sexual assault, ranging from forces at the cultural level to factors at the individual level. These factors include the following: cultural values, sexual scripts, early family influences, peer-group influences, characteristics of the situation, miscommunication, sex and power motives, and masculinity norms and men's attitudes. The data on each of these factors are considered here.

Cultural values can serve to support sexual assault. Cross-culturally, in preliterate societies, sexual assault is significantly more common in cultures that are characterized by male dominance, a high degree of general violence, and an ideology of male toughness (Sanday, 1981). Within the United States, states with greater gender inequality and social disorganization tend to have higher rates of sexual assault (Baron & Straus, 1989). This emphasizes how important cultural context is in creating a social climate that encourages or discourages sexual assault.

Sexual scripts play a role in sexual aggression as well (Byers, 1996). Adolescents quickly learn society's expectations about dating and sex through culturally transmitted sexual scripts. These scripts support sexual assault when they convey the message that the man is supposed to be oversexed and be the sexual "aggressor." By adolescence, both girls and boys endorse scripts that justify sexual aggression. A New Brunswick study of almost 1700 middle school and high school students found that about 11 percent of boys believe that it is acceptable for boys to be sexually coercive with a girlfriend (Price & Byers, 1999; Sears et al., 2007). Boys who were sexually abusive but not abusive in other ways (i.e., physically or psychologically) were more accepting of sexual dating violence and had friends who were sexually abusive. This suggests that these boys see sexual coercion as a normal part of the sexual script.

Early family influences may play a role in shaping a man into becoming a sexual aggressor. Specifically, young men who are sexual aggressors are more likely to have been sexually abused themselves in childhood (Friedrich et al., 1988; Koss et al., 1994).

The peer group can be a powerful factor in men's sexually aggressive behaviour. For example, a national study of 1300 Canadian male college and university students found that men who had abusive friends were more likely to have used sexual aggression (DeKeseredy & Kelly, 1993; DeKeseredy & Schwartz, 1999). It may be that aggressive friends encourage men to be sexually aggressive. It also may be that sexually aggressive men choose friends who have similar attitudes.

Characteristics of the situation play a role. Sexual assault is more likely to occur in secluded places or at parties at which excessive alcohol is used (Koss et al., 1994). Another situational factor is social disorganization, as noted earlier. An extreme example is war, in which sexual assault of women is common (Brownmiller, 1975). In the 1990s we saw graphic examples of this in the war in the former Yugoslavia. Bosnian women—Croats and Muslims—were frequently sexually assaulted by the attacking Serbs.

Miscommunication between women and men is a factor. In our discussion of sexual assault in dating relationships we saw a case in which the man and the woman had totally different understandings of what had occurred. Because many people in Canada find it difficult to discuss sex directly, they try to infer sexual interest from subtle non-verbal cues, a process that is highly prone to errors (Abbey, 1991). Specifically, some men have a predisposition to interpret a woman's friendly behaviour or sexy clothing as carrying a sexual message that she did not intend.

Sex and power motives are involved in sexual assault. Feminists have stressed that sexual violence is an expression of power and dominance by men over women (Brownmiller, 1975; Clark & Lewis, 1977). Current theory emphasizes that sexual motives and power motives are both involved and interact with each other. For example, using phallometric assessment, researchers in Ontario examined differences in physiological arousal to consenting and non-consenting sexual scenarios between a group of men convicted of sexual assault, a group of men convicted of non-sexual crimes, and a group of men from the community. The violent non-sexual criminals and men from the community were more aroused by hearing about consensual sex than by hearing about forced sex. However, the sex offenders showed little difference in their arousal to consenting and sexual assault scenarios (Lalumière et al., 2003). Research by Ontario psychologists Howard Barbaree and William Marshall (1991) has identified a number of processes that may be involved. For example, sexually aggressive and non-aggressive men may differ in their ability to suppress sexual arousal when it occurs under inappropriate circumstances. Hostile aggression may inhibit sexual arousal in non-aggressive men but not in sexually aggressive men.

Finally, *masculinity norms and men's attitudes* are another factor (Abram et al., 2003; Koss et al., 1994), as we will see in the next section. Supporting the feminist theoretical view, research shows that men who have more hypermasculine attitudes are more likely to have a history of sexual aggression (Murnen et al., 2002).

Thus, research has supported the theories that propose that socialization, social inequality, and social disorganization contribute to sexual assault. However, research has not found that women cause their own sexual assault (victim-precipitated theory) or that most men who commit sexual assault have psychological disorders. The very commonness of sexual assault, especially in dating relationships, argues against the psychopathology of sexual offenders. Hypermasculinity is a far more common cause than psychopathology.

MEN WHO ARE SEXUALLY AGGRESSIVE AGAINST WOMEN

There is no "typical" sexually aggressive man. Men who commit sexual assault against women vary tremendously in occupation, education, relationship status, previous criminal record, and motivation for committing sexual assault. One thing we do know about sexually aggressive men is that they tend to be repeat offenders. In one study of men who admitted to rape on a survey but had never been prosecuted, the majority had committed the crime more than once (Lisak & Miller, 2002). Those who were repeat offenders averaged about six rapes each. Men who repeatedly commit sexual assault have especially high scores on hostility toward women and have a history of delinquency (Abbey & McAuslan, 2004; Hall et al., 2006). A massive program of research by Neil Malamuth, Mary Koss, and their colleagues identified four factors that predispose men to engage in sexual coercion of women (Malamuth, 1998; Malamuth et al., 1991; see also Hall et al., 2005, 2006):

1. *A violent home environment.* A boy who grows up in a hostile home environment has a higher likelihood of engaging in sexual aggression against women. Factors that create a hostile home environment include violence between the parents or abuse directed toward the child, whether battering or sexual abuse.
2. *Delinquency.* Being involved in delinquency is itself made more likely by coming from a hostile home. But the delinquency in turn increases the likelihood of engaging in sexual coercion—the boy associates with delinquent peers who, for example, encourage hostile attitudes and rationalizations for committing illegal acts and reward a tough, aggressive image.
3. *Sexual predatory orientation.* The male, often in the context of the delinquent peer group, develops a heavy emphasis on sexual conquests to bring him self-esteem and status with the peer group. For example, Alberta sex researcher Martin Lalumière and his colleagues found that sexually coercive men highly value having many new partners and engaging in casual sex (Lalumière et al., 1996; Lalumière & Quinsey, 1996). Coercion may seem to them a reasonable way of making conquests.
4. *A hostile masculine personality.* This personality constellation involves deep-seated hostility toward women together with negatively defined, exaggerated masculinity—masculinity defined as rejecting anything feminine such as nurturance, and emphasizing power, control, and "macho" characteristics.

Perhaps surprisingly, this research was not based on convicted sex offenders but rather on a national representative sample of U.S. male university students.

Similarly, research in Ontario using a community sample of men between the ages of 19 and 82 found that childhood abuse and having a large number of sexual partners in adolescence increased the likelihood of using sexual coercion (Senn et al., 2000). In addition, the researchers found that men who had trouble expressing their feelings were more likely to have used sexual coercion. In contrast, empathy for other people's feelings seems to attenuate or reduce a man's likelihood of being sexually aggressive. That is, a man who has several of the risk factors just listed, but who also is sensitive to others' feelings and needs and is not self-centred, is not likely to use sexual coercion, compared with a man who has the risk factors and lacks empathy and is self-centred (Baumeister et al., 2002). These research findings have important implications for programs of therapy for convicted sex offenders. Empathy training should be emphasized, as it is in the most modern programs (Marshall, 1993; Pithers, 1993).

ETHNICITY AND SEXUAL ASSAULT AGAINST WOMEN

We have seen how cultural context can promote or inhibit sexual assault. The cultural heritages of various ethnocultural groups in Canada provide different cultural contexts for people of those groups, so it is important to consider the incidence of sexual assault in Canadian ethnocultural communities. Participants in three of the communities that participated in the *Ethnocultural Communities Facing AIDS* study were asked whether they had ever been coerced or forced to have sex with someone against their will. The incidence of sexual coercion differed markedly from one community to the other. In the English-speaking Caribbean communities, 37 percent of the women and 19 percent of the men reported that they had experienced sexual coercion, compared to 8 percent of the women and 1 percent of the men in the Latin American communities and 5 percent of the men from the South Asian communities (Maticka-Tyndale et al., 1996). Interestingly, in the English-speaking Caribbean communities, people who had been in Canada longer were more likely to indicate that they had experienced sexual coercion. This suggests that sexual coercion is a more common experience in Canada than it is in the Caribbean.

Sometimes ethnicity can help. In Asian cultures, saving face is very important. For men from Asian communities in Canada, the potential for loss of face by committing sexual assault is a deterrent to such activity (Hall et al., 2005).

Historical factors may also affect the meaning of sexual assault. Many recent Canadian immigrants are refugees from places such as Bosnia, where invading military forces instituted systematic campaigns of sexual violence against women (Valentich, 1994). Similarly, sexual assault has a highly charged meaning in the history of African Americans (Wyatt, 1992). In the period following the American Civil War, a black man convicted of rape or attempted rape of a white woman was typically castrated or lynched. In sharp contrast, there was no penalty for a white man who raped a black woman.

In some cultures, it is considered a wife's duty to have sex with her husband when he wants to. Might these cultural expectations affect how sexual assault—particularly spousal assault—is defined in these countries?

SEXUAL ASSAULT AGAINST MEN

The sexual assault provisions in the Criminal Code of Canada apply equally to men and to women as victims. However, in 2000 only 1.5 percent of adults convicted of sexual assault were women. Some authors believe, based on self-report studies, that there are more women sex offenders than indicated by police reports (Denov, 2003). It is important for counsellors and others in helping professions to recognize the possibility of male victims of sexual assault.

It is possible for a woman to force a man to engage in intercourse; research shows that men may respond with an erection in emotional states such as anger and terror. In a study of 115 men who had been sexually assaulted, 7 percent had been assaulted by a woman or group of women and an additional 6 percent by both a man and a woman (King & Woollett, 1997). Forced vaginal intercourse occurred in only two of the cases.

Research in New Brunswick has investigated males' and females' experiences of unwanted sexual activity due to pressure or force (Byers & O'Sullivan, 1998; O'Sullivan et al., 1998). The results showed that sexual coercion of men by women is not rare—19 percent of men had experienced unwilling sexual activity in the previous year; 9 percent of women reported having used sexual coercion. Further,14 percent of the men who had experienced sexual coercion were extremely upset by the incident. In a study of New Brunswick middle school and high school students, 4 percent of the boys had experienced unwanted sexual activity that they found upsetting; 5 percent of the girls reported that they had been sexually abusive (Price et al., 2000; Sears et al., 2007). Although both these studies showed that females are more likely to experience sexual coercion than males are, the results indicate that sexual coercion of males by females is not that infrequent. Further, these experiences are very upsetting for some males, and some men (straight and gay) who have been sexually assaulted experience symptoms of PTSD (Dunmore et al., 2001; Gold et al., 2007).

Some of the same factors that contribute to sexual aggression by men also contribute to sexual aggression by women. They occur in similar heterosexual dating situations, and men and women use similar strategies to influence their partner to engage in the unwanted sexual activities, most often verbal forms of pressure or ignoring requests to stop (O'Sullivan & Byers, 1999). Sexual scripts play a role as well. Research in Ontario has shown that many women believe the stereotype that men are always interested in sex (Clements-Shreiber et al., 1998). Thus, they may not believe that when a man says "no" he really means "no." For example, in a study of sexual coercion in a sample of university students, 58 percent of the men (and 78 percent of the women) reported being the objects of sexual persistence after they had refused sexual advances (Struckman-Johnson et al., 2003). Sexual persistence included using any of a number of tactics to have sexual contact with the respondent despite their initial refusal of the sexual advances. The persistence tactics assessed included persistent kissing and touching, the perpetrator taking off his or her own clothes, telling lies, and using physical restraints. One man said,

> At a party, she came up and began talking to me. I was already drinking some at the time. While playing cards, she talked me into finishing several of her drinks and beers. She said there was another party and convinced me to go. I was too drunk to drive so she drove us. The "party" seemed to lack other people. After about a half-hour of kissing/making out, I was tired and wanted to go home. She said no and told me she wanted to have sex. I said no, but she continued to kiss me and try to talk me into it. When she produced a condom, I gave in. (Struckman-Johnson et al., 2003, p. 83)

However, research in Ontario found that male victims tend to be blamed more harshly for their victimization than female victims and female perpetrators blamed more leniently for their behaviour than male perpetrators (Rye et al., 2006). Men may be particularly unlikely to report a sexual assault if they are aware that they may be blamed for their own victimization.

Having recognized that some men are sexually coerced by women, it is important to note that the great majority of male victims of forced intercourse are sexually assaulted by men, not women (Calderwood, 1987). Men who have been sexually assaulted by other men experience very negative psychological consequences (Walker et al., 2005).

SEXUAL ASSAULT IN PRISON

According to a study of 516 men and women prisoners in U.S. prisons, 22 percent of the men and 7 percent of the women had been the objects of sexual coercion (Struckman-Johnson et al., 1996). Prison staff were the perpetrators in 18 percent of the cases, fellow prisoners in the remainder. Among the male victims, 53 percent had been forced to have receptive anal sex, sometimes with multiple male perpetrators, and 8 percent were forced to have receptive oral sex. The men reported severe emotional consequences. Inmates offered a number of suggestions for ending prison sexual violence. The most frequent was to segregate the most vulnerable: those who are young, non-violent, new in prison, and white. Many also favoured allowing conjugal visits.

Sexual assault in prison is a particularly clear example of the way in which sexual assault is an expression of power and aggression; prisoners—most of whom would identify as heterosexual—use it as a means of establishing a dominance hierarchy.

PREVENTING SEXUAL ASSAULT

Strategies for preventing sexual assault need to be aimed at both men and women. Although most programs are aimed at teaching women ways to avoid victimization, it is perhaps more important to develop programs for men. To eliminate sexual assault of women, our society would need to make a radical change in the way it socializes males (Hall & Barongan, 1997). If little boys were not so pressed to be aggressive and tough, and were encouraged to express their feelings and to be nurturant, there would be far fewer sexually aggressive men. If adolescent boys did not have to demonstrate that they are hypersexual, perhaps there would be few sexually aggressive men.

We also need prevention programs aimed at changing attitudes that contribute to sexual assault. These programs need to stress the importance of obtaining verbal consent as well as to provide behavioural strategies for doing so. Research in Ontario has shown that women more than men stress a need for active verbal consent in both new and ongoing relationships (Humphreys, 2007; Humphreys & Herold, 2007). They need to foster a climate in which sexually coercive behaviour is seen as unacceptable in such a way that men don't perceive the presenters to be "male bashing." These types of perceptions can result in a backlash

Figure 16.2   Young people today are challenging stereotypes about female weakness and passivity. This photo shows a protest by more than 800 students in Welland, Ontario, against violence against women.

Figure 16.3 Self-defence classes for women. Many experts believe that all women should take such classes to gain the skills necessary to defend themselves in the case of an attempted sexual assault.

that increases attitudes and statements justifying men's use of sexual coercion. An infamous example is the response of some men to a "No means No" campaign at Queen's University in Kingston—they hung banners out of the windows of male residences that read "No means more beer" and "No means tie her up."

Unfortunately, until large changes are made in society, we still need to teach women to be vigilant. These strategies fall into two categories: (1) avoiding situations in which there is a high risk of sexual assault; and, (2) if the first strategy has failed, knowing some self-defence techniques if a sexual assault attempt is actually made. Here are some ways for women (and men) to avoid high-risk situations (Hughes & Sandler, 1987, p. 3):

Set sexual limits. No one has a right to force you to do something with your body that you don't want to do. If you don't want to be touched, for example, you have a right to say, "Don't touch me," and to leave if your wishes are not respected.

Decide early if you would like to have intercourse. The sooner you communicate your intentions firmly and clearly, the easier it will be for your partner to understand and accept your decision.

Do not give mixed messages; be clear. Say "yes" when you mean "yes" and "no" only when you mean "no."

Be forceful and firm. Do not worry about being polite if your wishes are being ignored.

Do not do anything you do not want to do just to avoid a scene or unpleasantness. Do not be assaulted because you are too polite to get out of a dangerous situation or because you are worried about hurting your date's feelings. If things get out of hand, be loud in protesting, leave, and go for help.

Be aware that alcohol and drugs are often related to sexual assault by dating partners. They compromise your ability (and that of your date) to make responsible decisions.

Trust your gut-level feelings. If the situation feels risky to you, or if you feel you are being pressured, trust your feelings. Leave the situation or confront the person immediately.

Be careful when you invite someone to your home or you are invited to your date's home. These are the most likely places for sexual assaults to occur.

If this first set of strategies—avoiding sexual assault situations—does not work, self-defence strategies are needed. Always remember that the goal is to get away from the attacker and run for help.

Many universities and other organizations offer self-defence classes for women, and we believe that every woman should take at least one such course. Many techniques are available and the exact method the woman chooses is probably not too important. Research shows that fighting back—fighting, yelling, fleeing—increases a woman's likelihood of thwarting a sexual assault attempt (Brecklin & Ullman, 2005; Zoucha-Jensen & Coyne, 1993). However, we also need to change how girls are socialized so that women are more comfortable being assertive and using self-defence.

Finally, to prevent sexual assault of men by women, we need to combat the cultural stereotype that men are always interested in sex. This belief may make it difficult for men to clearly and repeatedly refuse a sexual invitation, and may make women less likely to believe men when they do say no. However, for men and women to be honest and open about their sexual interests, they will first need to become more comfortable talking about sex and less reliant on non-verbal communication.

Sexual assault prevention programs have been attempted over the past several decades. Often they are designed for a mixed audience of male and female first-year university students. Sadly and frustratingly, evaluations of these programs typically show only small changes in attitudes that do not last long, and no changes in actual sexual assault rates (Breitenbecher, 2000; Rozee & Koss, 2001). Experts in the field are trying to develop more effective prevention programs for both women and men; we need to put our best energies into these efforts (Lonsway & Kothari, 2000; Rozee & Koss, 2001).

CHILD SEXUAL ABUSE

In this section we discuss the broad category of child sexual abuse and one specific subcategory, intrafamilial sexual abuse—sexual abuse that occurs within the family.

There are currently several statutes related to the sexual exploitation of children in the Criminal Code of Canada, including sexual assault, sexual interference, invitation to sexual touching, and sexual exploitation (refer to In Focus 2.2 on page 44). These offences apply to any type of sexual contact with a child by a man or a woman, showing pornography to a child, having a child witness sexual intercourse, or using a computer to facilitate committing a sexual offence against a child. Making, possessing, and distributing child pornography is also illegal and is discussed in Chapter 17.

The laws that seek to prevent the sexual exploitation of children and young people were amended in 1985. Prior to 1985, there was an offence for sexual intercourse with a female under 14. There were also offences for sexual intercourse with a female 14 to 16 years old and for seduction of a female 16 to 18 years old "of previously chaste character" (Mohr & Roberts, 1994). Many of the criticisms of the repealed rape law also applied to the laws pertaining to sexual exploitation of children. For example, in most cases they applied only to girls (Busby, 1999). In contrast, the current provisions are gender-neutral and based on a combination of age, whether the accused is in a position of trust, and the specific activities that occurred. For example, the age of consent is normally 16. This means that a person accused of engaging in sexual activity with someone under 16 cannot defend him- or herself on the basis that the child agreed to the sexual activity. However, a child who is 14 or 15 can legally have sex with someone who is less than five years older than him or her. The age of consent for anal intercourse is 18 and thus is higher than for vaginal intercourse, although the Supreme Court has ruled that this constitutes discrimination against gay youth. The age of consent is also higher if the adult is in a position of trust or authority with a child, such as a teacher or sports coach.

Under the sexual exploitation provision, it is an offence for a person in a position of trust to have sex with a child who is under 18 years old, whether or not the child consents to it.

Finally, the Criminal Code includes a law against incest. This statute prohibits sexual intercourse with a person who is a blood relative—that is, a parent, child, brother, sister, grandparent, or grandchild. Most prosecutions are cases involving children and adult relatives although the incest statute is not specific to child sexual abuse. The nearly universal taboo against incest seems to have as its purpose the promise to children that the home will be a place where they can be free from sexual pressure and the prevention of the alleged genetic problems of inbreeding.

PATTERNS OF CHILD SEXUAL ABUSE

How common is child sexual abuse in Canada? The 1983 National Population Survey (often called the Badgley Report) found that 18 percent of women and 8 percent of men had experienced unwanted sexual contact (touching or intercourse) by age 16 (Bagley, 1989). A more recent survey of 9953 individuals aged 15 and over living in Ontario found that 11 percent of the women and 4 percent of the men reported that they had experienced severe sexual abuse as children (threats, touching, or intercourse) (MacMillan et al., 1997). Similarly, in the United States the NHSLS found rates of 17 percent for women and 12 percent for men (Laumann et al., 1994). It seems clear that child sexual abuse is not rare, and that girls are more often its victims than boys are. Worldwide, roughly 20 percent of women and 5 to 10 percent of men report sexual contact with an adult when they were a child (Freyd et al., 2005). Most cases are never reported. In the National Population Survey, only about 20 percent of the victims had told anyone.

How many of these incidents get reported to the authorities? In 2005, there were 2.1 reported cases of child sexual abuse per 1000 children in Canada (Brzozowski, 2007). Reported sexual assaults for girls were four times as high as for boys; reports for youth between the ages of 12 to 17 were twice as high as for younger children. Of those complaints that are substantiated by police, most involve touching and fondling of the genitals (68 percent), attempted or completed sexual activity (35 percent), or adults exposing their genitals (12 percent) (Trocmé et al., 2001).

The great majority of perpetrators of child sexual abuse are men. According to the NHSLS, for girls almost all the reported cases involved sexual contact with men; for boys, most cases involved men although some cases involved women. A number of factors probably account for this great imbalance. Men in our culture are socialized more toward seeing sexuality as focused on sexual acts rather than as part of an emotional relationship. The sexual script for men involves partners who are smaller and younger than themselves, whereas women's sexual script involves partners who are larger and older than they are.

In the great majority of cases, both for boys and girls, the sexual activity involves only touching of the genitals (Laumann et al., 1994). However, for girls,

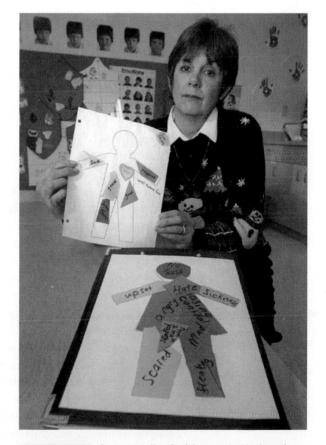

Figure 16.4   A counsellor holds art depicting the "before" and "after" feelings of an abused child. On the limbs of the "after" image words such as "mad," "hate," "scared," "upset," and "angry" are written.

10 percent of cases involved forced oral sex, 14 percent of cases involved forced vaginal intercourse, and 1 percent involved forced anal sex. For boys, 30 percent of cases involved forced oral sex and 18 percent involved forced anal sex.

Reports from 122 police departments in 2005 provide information regarding reported cases of sexual assault of children and youth in Canada (Brzozowski, 2007). Most (79 percent) of the child and youth victims of sexual assault were girls. Some of the sexual abuse was of children at very young ages, although the rates for youth between the ages of 12 and 17 were double those of children between 3 and 11 years old. Table 16.2 shows the relationship between these adults and their victims. Notice that sexual assault by a stranger is least common, accounting for only 12 percent of sexual assaults of girls and 8 percent of sexual assaults of boys. In contrast, 34 percent of the girls and 37 percent of the boys were sexually assaulted by a family member, including parents, siblings, and extended family members such as stepparents or grandparents.

Table 16.2	Categories of People Who Were Accused of Child Sexual Assault in 2005	
	Percentage of Victims	
Perpetrators	Girls	Boys
Acquaintance*	44%	45%
Family	34	37
Stranger	12	8
Unknown	10	10

*Acquaintance includes any relationship in which the perpetrator and victim were familiar with each other, but were not related or in a legal guardianship arrangement.

Source: Brzozowski, 2007.

Of particular concern is sexual abuse of children by a person in a position of trust or authority. One of the most publicized cases of this type of abuse was that of eight Roman Catholic priests and ten lay members of the Christian Brothers of Ireland in Canada who were convicted of sexually abusing 77 boys at Mount Cashel Orphanage in St. John's, Newfoundland, in the 1970s. A number of priests in other parts of Canada and in the United States have also been convicted of child sexual abuse. Many First Nations children attending residential schools and Aboriginal and non-Aboriginal boys in youth detention centres were also sexually abused by persons charged with their care.

PATTERNS OF INTRAFAMILIAL SEXUAL ABUSE

Intrafamilial sexual abuse: Sexual contact between a child and an adult who is the child's relative or caregiver, such as a stepfather.

Incest is defined in the Criminal Code of Canada as sexual contact between blood relatives. Of particular concern is sexual abuse of children by an adult family member, often called **intrafamilial sexual abuse**. Intrafamilial abuse includes both child sexual abuse by a blood relative and by a non-relative who is the child's caregiver (e.g., between stepfather and stepdaughter) and are typically prosecuted under the sexual assault provisions of the Criminal Code (see In Focus 2.2 on page 44).

The overwhelming majority of cases of intrafamilial child sexual abuse go unreported to authorities and unprosecuted. Nonetheless, court statistics (see Table 16.2) show that in 2005 family members were accused of 34 percent of the sexual assaults against children (Brzozowski, 2007). Data from the NHSLS based on adult recollections of incidents of sexual abuse in childhood, most of which were never reported, also show that a large percentage of cases are perpetrated by family members. Researchers found that 54 percent of the women and 20 percent of the men reported that the perpetrator was a family member.

IMPACT ON THE VICTIM

Many therapists who are experienced with cases of child sexual abuse feel that the effects on the victim are serious and long-lasting. Consider the following case:

> A 25-year-old office worker was seen in the emergency room with an acute anxiety attack. She was pacing, agitated, unable to eat or sleep, and had a feeling of impending doom. She related a vivid fantasy of being pursued by a man with a knife. The previous day she had been cornered in the office by her boss, who aggressively propositioned her. She needed the job badly and did not want to lose it, but she dreaded the thought of returning to work. It later emerged in psychotherapy that this episode of sexual harassment had reawakened previously repressed memories of sexual assaults by her father. From the age of 6 until mid-adolescence, her father had repeatedly exhibited himself to her and insisted that she masturbate him. The experience of being entrapped at work had recalled her childhood feelings of helplessness and fear. (Herman, 1981, p. 8)

In a major review of studies of children who were sexually abused (either by family members or by non-relatives), the researchers concluded that there is strong evidence of a number of negative effects on these children, compared with control groups of non-abused children (Kendall-Tackett et al., 1993; but see Rind et al., 1998). Sexually abused children are significantly more likely to have symptoms of anxiety, post-traumatic stress disorder (PTSD), depression, poor self-esteem, health complaints, aggressive and antisocial behaviour, inappropriate sexual behaviour, school problems, and behaviour problems such as hyperactivity. Victims had more severe symptoms when (1) the perpetrator was a member of the family; (2) the sexual contact was frequent or occurred over a long period of time; and (3) the sexual activity involved penetration (vaginal, oral, or anal). The child's gender did not seem to be a factor; that is, there were no differences in symptoms between boys and girls. However, the researchers noted that gender was not investigated in many studies, probably because so few boys appeared in most samples. Research in Quebec has shown that sexually abused children experience more PTSD symptoms than do children who have experienced other life stressors, such as an orthopedic problem (Collin-Vézina & Hébert, 2005; Tremblay et al., 2000). The trauma of sexual abuse may also trigger early puberty. Note that although children who have experienced sexual abuse are more likely to experience each of these symptoms, some of these children do not experience any severe negative consequences.

If a case is reported and prosecuted, the child may be as traumatized by testifying in court as by the abuse itself. Repeatedly testifying about severe abuse is associated with worse mental health outcomes (Quas et al., 2005). Interestingly, the perpetrator receiving a light sentence is also associated with worse mental health outcomes for the child.

Research has demonstrated that many of the negative effects of child sexual abuse persist into adulthood. Canadian research has shown that adults who were sexually abused as children display more depression, anxiety, eating disorders, and alcohol and drug dependence, compared with controls (Gold, 1986; Lemieux & Byers, 1996; Runtz & Roche, 1999). They also have more negative feelings about sexuality, more sexual difficulties, and difficulty forming stable, safe romantic relationships (Lemieux & Byers, 2008; Testa et al., 2005). The risk of these difficulties is greater if attempted or completed intercourse occurred, if the abuse was by a relative, and if the victim told someone and received a negative response from that person (Bulik et al., 2001; Kendler et al., 2000; Lemieux & Byers, 2008). Adult survivors of child sexual abuse are also more likely to experience sexual assault as an adult as well as sexual disorders such as fears of sex (sexual aversion), lack of sexual desire, and lack of arousal (Leonard & Follette, 2002; Loeb et al., 2002). Women who were sexually abused as children are also more

(a)

(b)

Figure 16.5 Sexual abuse outside the family is most often perpetrated by a person in a position of trust such as *(a)* the sexual abuse of Sheldon Kennedy by his junior hockey coach; *(b)* the sexual and physical abuse of Aboriginal children attending native residential schools run by several different Christian churches—the subject of an Edmonton-to-Ottawa walk for justice by Robert Desjarlais in June 2000.

likely to be preoccupied with sex, younger at the time of their first voluntary intercourse, and more likely to be teen mothers (Noll et al., 2003). Their sexuality is ambivalent—they experience both sexual aversion and a preoccupation with sex. Again, though, not all adults who report sexual contact with an adult as a child show these long-term negative consequences.

Child sexual abuse has effects not only on mental health, but on physical health as well. Adults who were victims of child sexual abuse are one and a half times as likely as those who weren't abused to have had health problems in the past year (Sachs-Ericsson et al., 2005).

In most cases child sexual abuse is psychologically damaging and may lead to symptoms such as depression and PTSD. The evidence indicates that the extent of distress is associated with a number of factors including, especially, the severity of the abuse (Kallstrom-Fuqua et al., 2004). Patterns of sexual abuse can range from five minutes of fondling by a neighbour to repeated forced intercourse by a father or stepfather over a period of several years. The effects of sexual abuse are most severe when it involved intercourse, occurred repeatedly over years, and was committed by a father or stepfather (Fleming et al., 1999; Kendler et al., 2000). In addition, two Canadian studies have shown that adjustment is affected by both the abused child's coping style as well as the quality of family relationships (Hébert et al., 2006; Runtz & Schallow, 1997; Tremblay et al., 1999).

In contrast, some women with a history of child sexual abuse perceive some benefit from the adverse life experience. They believe that it made them better at protecting their own children from abuse and made them stronger people (McMillen et al., 1995). This is another example of post-traumatic growth.

Treatments such as cognitive–behavioural therapy are available and effective in treating adults with PTSD following child sexual abuse (McDonagh et al., 2005).

THE OFFENDERS

Many child molesters abuse more than one child. In particular, child sexual abusers who abuse boys outside the family are likely to have multiple victims (Abel et al., 1987). For example, in 2000, Carl Toft came up for parole after serving eight years of a 13-year sentence for molesting more than 200 boys at the New Brunswick Training Centre. In 2005, he was released into the community after completing his 13-year sentence. Critics argued that he should be denied parole because, by his own admission, he was not cured.

What do the data say about child sexual abusers? Are they likely to repeat the offence? Are there effective treatments for them?

Pedophilia involves an adult who has a sexual preference for prepubescent children, generally age 13 or younger (American Psychiatric Association, 2000). Although the vast majority of pedophiles are male, some women also sexually abuse young children (Seto, 2004). To meet the official criteria for diagnosis as a paraphilia (see Chapter 15), the person must have intense sexually arousing fantasies, sexual urges, or behaviours, over a period of at least six months, that involve sexual activity with a prepubescent child. For example, an Alberta study of convicted adolescent sex offenders showed a high frequency of deviant sexual fantasies (Aylwin et al., 2005). Not all pedophiles are child molesters—that is, have sex with children. Not all child molesters are pedophiles—that is, have a sexual preference for prepubescent children. Research in Ontario has shown that most men convicted of child pornography offences are pedophiles—that is, show a preference for prepubescent children (Seto et al., 2006). Child pornography is discussed in Chapter 17. Note that people with a sexual preference for pubescent children are correctly called *hebophiles*.

Pedophiles fall into a number of categories, depending on the gender of the children they are attracted to and other factors. In one study of 678 pedophiles, all of them men, 27 percent were attracted to boys, 47 percent to girls, and 25 percent to both (Blanchard et al., 1999). Child molesters also differ in whether their victims are their biological children, stepchildren, children they know, or children they do not know (Guay et al., 2001). Pedophiles who molest children tend to be repeat offenders and their patterns of preference tend to be stable over time.

Pedophiles score low on measures of heterosocial competence (Dreznick, 2003). That is, they lack the interpersonal skills to function well in adult heterosexual relationships. Canadian research shows that pedophiles have poorer cognitive functioning than controls and are more likely than controls (11 percent compared to 5 percent) to have had accidents involving head injury and unconsciousness before the age of six (Blanchard et al., 2002; Cantor et al., 2004, 2005). This suggests that problems with early brain development and/or some injury to the developing brain may create this disorder in some cases.

Researchers are very interested in developing measures that might identify pedophiles who have not been arrested, and perhaps have not even offended yet (Seto, 2004). Sophisticated cognitive tests using reaction times indicate that pedophiles have a strong mental association between children and sex, whereas non-pedophiles have an association between adults and sex (Gray et al., 2005). Research in Ontario using phallometric measures, such as those discussed in Chapter 11, indicate that men who are attracted to child pornography but have not sexually offended against children show greater arousal to child photos than to adult photos, and their arousal to child photos is even greater than the arousal of men who have actually sexually offended against children (Seto et al., 2006). Possession of child pornography itself might be an indicator of pedophilia (Seto, 2004). Measures such as these may provide ways to identify men who are likely to offend even before they commit their crime.

Pedophilia: Paraphilia in which an adult has a sexual preference for prepubescent children.

IN FOCUS 16.3

False Memory Syndrome? Recovered Memory?

A topic that is extremely controversial concerns the issue of what some call recovered memory and others call false memory syndrome. The issue is whether the child victim of sexual abuse or other severe trauma can forget (suppress) the memory of the event and later recover that memory.

On one side of the argument, the *recovered memory* side, psychotherapists see adult clients who display serious symptoms of prior trauma, such as severe depression and anxiety. Sometimes these clients have clear memories of being sexually abused in childhood and have always remembered the events but have never told anyone until they told the therapist. In other cases, the client doesn't remember that any abuse occurred but, during the process of therapy, or sometimes spontaneously before therapy, something triggers the memory and the client then recalls the sexual abuse.

On the other side, some psychologists believe that these memories for events that had been forgotten and then are remembered are actually *false memories;* that is, the events never occurred. They argue that unscrupulous or overzealous therapists may induce these memories by hypnotizing clients or strongly suggesting to clients that they had been abused in childhood.

What do the data say? First, there is evidence from laboratory studies that information associated with unpleasant emotions is more likely to be forgotten (e.g., Bootzin & Natzoulas, 1965). Research directly on the issue of child sexual abuse also provides support for the idea that forgetting does occur in some cases. In one study, 129 women who were known to have been sexually abused as children—they had been brought to a hospital for treatment at the time and the abuse had been medically verified—were interviewed 17 years later; 38 percent did not remember their prior abuse (Williams, 1994). The possible flaw in this study is that some of the respondents may have remembered but not have reported it to the interviewer. However, they were reporting many other intimate sexual experiences, so it seems likely that they would report accurately about this one, too. In a number of studies of adult women who reported that they had been victims of child sexual abuse, between 19 and 40 percent said that they forgot the abuse for some period of time and then remembered again (Feldman-Summers & Pope, 1994; Gold et al., 1994; Loftus et al., 1994).

Abuse was more likely to have been forgotten when it was more severe. It has been theorized that amnesia for traumatic events of this kind, particularly when the child has been betrayed by someone in a position of trust like a parent, is an adaptive response that helps the child survive in a terribly distressed family situation (Freyd, 1996).

Two Ontario researchers attempted to answer the question of recidivism (repeat offending) by sex offenders by conducting a review of research conducted in six different countries, including Canada (Hanson & Bussière, 1998). They found that the recidivism rate was only about 13 percent for child molesters within four to five years after the offence. This is no doubt an underestimate of the actual rates of reoffending, because so much child sexual abuse goes unreported (Hanson, 2000). Further, recidivism was much higher for sex offenders who had not received treatment (participation in treatment was voluntary). It was also higher for certain subgroups of child molesters such as those men who had committed previous sexual offences, had begun sexual offending at an early age, and had targeted male victims. The strongest predictor of recidivism was phallometric measures of sexual deviance (recall the penile strain gauge discussed in Chapter 13). Offenders are shown slides of children and their arousal (erection) is measured. Several Canadian studies have found that men who show greater sexual arousal to children as measured through phallometric assessment are more likely to commit another sexual offence (Firestone et al., 2000; Proulx et al., 1997; Rice et al., 1991; Seto et al., 2000). Ontario researchers have also demonstrated that the recidivism

The other question is, can memories of events that did not occur be "implanted" in someone? In one study, the researcher was able to create false memories of childhood events in 25 percent of the adults given the treatment (Loftus, 1993). Certain conditions seem to increase the chances that people will think they remember things that did not actually occur, including suggestion by an authority figure and suggestion under hypnosis.

Two recent studies shed additional light on this debate. One was a study of women admitted to a hospital unit specializing in the treatment of trauma-related psychological disorders (Chu et al., 1999). Among those reporting childhood sexual abuse, 26 percent had partial amnesia for it and 27 percent had complete amnesia for a period of time before recalling it. These patients also displayed dissociative symptoms. *Dissociative amnesia* is an inability to recall important personal information, usually of a traumatic nature (American Psychiatric Association, 2000). The great majority of those who suffered child sexual abuse had been able to corroborate the occurrences by some method such as medical records. Importantly, most of them first remembered the abuse while at home, and about half were not involved in any kind of treatment or counselling at the time they remembered, ruling out the possibility of suggestion by a therapist.

In another study, normal participants' brains were scanned using fMRI (functional magnetic resonance imaging) while they were suppressing unwanted memories (Anderson et al., 2004). Neural systems underlying suppression were clearly identified and included a region in the prefrontal cortex and the hippocampus. From this study we can see that suppression of memories is not just hocus-pocus, but has a real basis in the brain.

What is the bottom line? There is evidence that some people do forget childhood sexual abuse and remember it later. There is also evidence that some people can form false memories based on suggestions made by another person. It seems likely that most of the cases of recovered memory of child sexual abuse are true, but that some are false and the product of suggestion. It is also probably true that false accusations of past child abuse are made, often by a well-intentioned "victim" who is highly suggestible to press reports of other cases or who has been misled by an overly zealous therapist. As a result, an accused person who is actually innocent may be arrested. There are errors of justice on both sides. Nonetheless, there are many more cases of unreported and unpunished perpetrators than of falsely convicted persons.

Sources: Anderson et al., 2004; Bootzin & Natsoulas, 1965; Chu et al., 1999; Feldman-Summers & Pope, 1994; Freyd, 1996; Gold, Hughes, & Hohnecker, 1994; Loftus, 1993; Loftus, Polonsky, & Fullilove, 1994; Williams, 1994.

rate is higher for extrafamilial offenders than for intrafamilial offenders, as well as for offenders with general feelings of hostility (Firestone et al., 1999, 2000, 2005; Greenberg et al., 2000). Therefore, depending on the particular case, there may be a very low or very high risk of repeating the offence, and we know some of the factors that predict which category a particular offender might belong in. It is also true that, in the studies that were reviewed, many of the offenders had been given some treatment. The low recidivism rate might tell us more about the success of the treatment programs than about natural rates of recidivism among those who have not been given some treatment.

TREATMENT OF SEX OFFENDERS

Canadian researchers have been leaders in the development of assessment and treatment strategies for child sexual abusers (Bradford & Greenberg, 1996; Hall, 1995; Marshall & Barbaree, 1988; Marshall & Pithers, 1994). Among the treatments in use in Canada are antiandrogen drugs, hormones, antidepressants drugs (SSRIs such as Prozac), and cognitive–behavioural therapy. Cyproterone acetate (CPA) is an antiandrogen drug—that is, it reduces

Figure 16.6 Sex offenders in a therapy group. Research shows that treatment of sex offenders, whether with the drug Cyproterone acetate or not, should include cognitive–behavioural therapy.

the action of testosterone in the body with the hope that the sexually aggressive behaviour will be sharply reduced—that has been used in the treatment of child sexual abusers and other sex offenders. Research indicates that CPA greatly reduces pedophiles' sexual arousal to children (Bradford & Greenberg, 1996). Results with a new anti-GnRH drug are quite promising (Rosler & Witztum, 1998). By blocking the action of GnRH, pituitary and gonadal functioning is inhibited, again reducing levels of testosterone. One problem is that reducing the level of testosterone does not necessarily reduce sexual behaviour, including sexually aggressive behaviour. Further, sex offenders have to voluntarily agree to this treatment. Few sex offenders are willing to continue to take antiandrogens because they also suppress normal sexual arousal.

To be successful at reducing recidivism, a comprehensive program needs to target both risk factors such as deviant arousal as well as enhance offenders overall functioning by improving intimacy skills and effective coping (Marshall et al., 2006). A program for sex offenders in Kingston, Ontario, is an example of a successful comprehensive cognitive–behavioural treatment program. This program reduced recidivism from 35 percent among untreated sex offenders to less than 10 percent among treated offenders (Marshall, 1992; Marshall & Eccles, 1991). Cognitive–behavioural therapy has advantages over drug treatment because offenders often refuse or discontinue hormone treatment, as it reduces both normal and deviant sexual arousal (Barbaree & Seto, 1997). Between 30 and 100 percent of men who start hormonal treatment later drop out.

MANDATORY NOTIFICATION OF THE RELEASE OF SEX OFFENDERS

Many Canadians are concerned that sex offenders who are released into the community after serving their sentence will reoffend—that is, commit another sexual assault or molest another child. Media coverage of high-profile cases in which offenders have reoffended after their release adds to public fears and has resulted in a call from some people for mandatory public notification of the release of sex offenders. They argue that if people are aware that there is a released sex offender in their community, they can protect themselves and their children from sexual violence.

Since 1994, organizations (but not individuals) have been able to have potential employees and volunteers screened by police to ensure that they do not have a prior conviction for child sexual abuse. In addition, in December 2004 the federal government, with unanimous support of the provinces and territories, implemented the National Sex Offender Registry that is available only to law enforcement officials and is intended to help them investigate unsolved crimes of a sexual nature. This information is not available to the general public.

The registry is not without controversy (Friscolanti, 2008). For example, although the idea was that all convicted sex offenders would be required to register, the prosecutor must ask a judge to add a defendant to the database. Thus, many sex offenders are not on it. In addition, although offenders are required to register with police, not all of them do so, and their whereabouts are not known. Offenders are required to inform the police if they are taking a vacation, but only if the vacation is longer than two weeks. Also police can only use the registry to solve a crime, not to prevent one. Critics argue that the law needs to be changed to better balance the rights of offenders with protection of the public.

Some people argue that there should be a comparable registry of child molesters available to the public (Canadian Centre for Justice Statistics, 1999). Most authorities raise a number of concerns related to establishing a national registry of sex offenders available to the public. These include problems related to misidentification of innocent people and sex offenders' rights to privacy if they do not pose a risk to the public. They also fear that some citizens may take the law into their own hands. Finally, public notification may drive sex offenders underground so that it becomes more difficult for police to keep track of them (Federoff & Moran, 1977). The issue of public warnings about the release of sex offenders pits the rights of the community to be informed about the risk of significant harm against the privacy rights of the offender (Canadian Centre for Justice Statistics, 1999). Therefore, at present community notification is restricted to offenders who are believed to pose an immediate risk to the public. The police are left with a great deal of discretion in determining which offenders pose such a risk, leaving the issue open to continued public debate.

PREVENTING CHILD SEXUAL ABUSE

With increasing awareness of the prevalence and potential negative consequences of child sexual abuse, most elementary schools in Canada have implemented a sexual abuse prevention program (these often go by names such as "personal safety"). The goal of these programs is to empower children to resist people who attempt to abuse them sexually as well as to provide them with the skills they will need to do so. Most programs share certain concepts (Hébert et al., 2001; Hébert & Tourigny, 2004). For example, they help children to distinguish between good touches and bad touches, as well as to recognize potentially abusive situations. They teach them strategies to deal assertively with potential abuse, such as yelling "No." They emphasize the importance of the child telling a trusted adult about the abuse or attempted abuse. Finally, they reassure children that they are not to blame in the event that sexual abuse does occur. However, the programs differ in their length, the way the program is delivered (e.g., video, puppets, books, etc.), and who delivers it (teachers, parents, police officers) (Hébert & Tremblay, 2000; Hébert et al., 2001). A few programs offer concurrent programs for parents to assist them in talking to their own children about sexual abuse. Researchers in Quebec evaluated the impact of such a parent workshop (Hébert et al., 2002). They found that the workshop had a positive impact on parents' knowledge as well as on their reactions to a hypothetical situation involving child sexual abuse, compared to parents who did not attend the workshop. However, only 20 percent of the invited parents chose to attend the workshop.

How effective are these programs? Do children learn the concepts? Do they remember them? A review of studies on the effectiveness of child sexual abuse prevention programs found that these programs do increase elementary school children's knowledge (Hébert & Tourigny 2004). Further, in role-play situations, the children are better able to identify potentially abusive situations and implement the skills that they learned. Older children tend to show greater gains than younger children do. However, the gains are sometimes small and tend to decrease over time. This suggests that children will need to have booster sessions— that is, have sexual abuse prevention skills reviewed regularly—if they are to retain their skills. Longer programs and programs that allow children to practise and role-play their self-protection skills, rather than relying only on instruction, tend to be more effective. For example, evaluation of child abuse prevention programs in Quebec and Calgary found that the children who received the program increased their knowledge and skills at the end of the program more than a control group (Hébert et al., 2001; Tutty, 1997).

There are some concerns that are often raised about child abuse prevention programs. First, are children able to put the skills they learn into practice (Finkelhor & Daro, 1997)? That is, how many children actually use the skills they learned in a sexual abuse prevention program when faced with a sexual abuser, particularly when the abuser is a family member? Second, will the program have negative effects on the children, such as increasing their anxieties or their fear of appropriate physical affection (Reppucci et al., 1999)? Although some children do show these types of responses, according to parental reports most children do not (Hébert et al., 2001; Tutty, 1997).

Sexual Harassment

Under Canadian federal and provincial law, sexual harassment is a form of sex discrimination. However, unless it involves sexual assault, it is not a Criminal Code offence and is not dealt with in a court of law. Rather, victims can lodge a complaint with the Human Rights Commission. The issue is a powerful one—it can interfere with a person's ability to do a job or obtain a service. It may force a victim out of a job, but it can also force a perpetrator from a job.

Canadian courts and human rights tribunals have used the following definition of sexual harassment developed by the U.S. Equal Employment Opportunity Commission (Aggarwal, 1992):

> Unwelcome sexual advances, requests for sexual favors, and other verbal or physical conduct of a sexual nature constitute sexual harassment when
>
> A. Submission to such conduct is made either explicitly or implicitly a term or condition of an individual's employment or academic advancement,
>
> B. Submission to or rejection of such conduct by an individual is used as the basis for academic or employment decisions affecting that individual, or
>
> C. Such conduct has the purpose or effect of unreasonably interfering with an individual's work or academic performance or creating an intimidating, hostile, or offensive working or educational environment.

According to the New Brunswick Human Rights Commission, sexual harassment is any "vexatious comment or conduct of a sexual nature, that is known or ought reasonably to be known to be unwanted"—that is, that a reasonable person should have known was unwelcome. Sexual harassment can be divided into two categories: sexual coercion and sexual annoyance (Aggarwal, 1992). The key ingredient for sexual coercion is that compliance with the sexual advances has some direct link to employment or educational status or opportunity, or to receipt of a public service. This is termed "quid pro quo harassment" (*quid pro quo* meaning "I'll do something for you if you do something for me"). Sexual annoyance or environmental harassment is sexually related behaviour that creates a hostile, intimidating work environment so that the person cannot work effectively, such as constant lewd innuendoes, verbal intimidation, or practical jokes that cause embarrassment. Gays and lesbians are particularly likely to experience sexual harassment based on their sexual orientation. In one study, more than half of gay and lesbian youth had experienced verbal abuse on more than three separate occasions (D'Augelli, 2006).

Sexual harassment can occur at work and in education, as well as in other contexts such as psychotherapy or on the street.

SEXUAL HARASSMENT AT WORK

Sexual harassment at work may take a number of different forms. A prospective employer may make it clear that sexual activity is a prerequisite to being hired. Stories of such incidents are rampant among actors. Once on the job, sexual activity may be made a condition for continued employment, for a promotion, or for other benefits such as a raise. Or it can involve creating a hostile work environment. Here is one case:

> I work at a family-owned restaurant. Because I am a bartender, it is often just me behind the bar. On numerous occasions, I have caught one of the owners staring at my backside as I am getting things out of the refrigerator behind the bar. He has also blatantly stared at my legs, if I am wearing a skirt, while I am trying to speak with him. This owner also enjoys standing at the end of the counter so he partially obstructs the walkway that allows me to move from behind the bar. When I try to get out and say "Excuse me," he leans forward on the counter so I have to squeeze between him and the wine rack. He has also shown me how to clean the nozzle used to foam milk for coffee drinks, but does so in a fashion that looks much like someone manually stimulating a certain piece of the male anatomy, and then looks at me with a grin on his face. There have been times when the dishwasher wasn't working and he made comments to the male bartender, as I was standing right there, such as, "Be gentle with her . . . you have to go slowly so you don't hurt it . . . it needs lubrication." He has walked up behind me and blown on my neck.
>
> All of the comments and actions are very unnerving. (From a student essay)

Figure 16.7   This man has positioned himself so that the woman cannot avoid contact, and if he is her supervisor, she may be hesitant to protest.

It is clear how psychologically damaging such environments are to the victim.

Surveys indicate that sexual harassment at work is far more common than many people realize, although the estimates vary depending on how sexual harassment is defined. An Angus Reid-Southam News telephone survey in 1991 found rates of 37 percent for women and 10 percent for men (Aggarwal, 1992). A more recent survey of 1990 Canadian women between the ages of 18 and 65 found that 56 percent had experienced sexual harassment in the last year; the overall lifetime rate was 77 percent (Crocker & Kalemba, 1999). Averaged over many studies, between 25 and 50 percent of women have been sexually harassed at work, counting harassment both by supervisors and by co-workers (Ilies et al., 2003; Welsh, 1999). The preponderance of harassers are male.

Both female and male victims report that harassment has negative effects on their emotional and physical condition, their ability to work with others on the job, and their feelings about work (Sbraga & O'Donohue, 2000). However, men are more likely to feel that the overtures from women ended up being reciprocal and mutually enjoyable. Women, on the other hand, are more likely to report damaging consequences, including being fired or quitting their job (Gutek, 1985). There is evidence linking the experience of sexual harassment to depression, anxiety, and PTSD (Rederstorff et al., 2007). Even subtle sexual harassment such as asking, "Do you have a boyfriend?" in a job interview can damage women's performance in the interview (Woodzicka & LaFrance, 2005).

Why does sexual harassment at work occur? According to a theory proposed by psychologists Susan Fiske and Peter Glick (1995), it results from a combination of gender stereotyping and men's ambivalent motives. Stereotypes of women in our culture are complex and include three distinct clusters: "sexy," "non-traditional" (e.g., feminist), and "traditional" (e.g., mother). Many men have ambivalent motives in their interactions with women because they desire both dominance and intimacy. Fiske and Glick argue that there are four types of harassment of women by men. With the first, *earnest harassment,* the man is truly motivated by a desire for sexual intimacy, but he won't take "no" for an answer and persists with unwelcome sexual advances. He stereotypes women as sexy. With the second type, *hostile harassment,* the man's motivation is domination of the woman, often because he perceives her as being competitive with him in the workplace. He holds the stereotype of women as non-traditional and therefore competitive with him. His response to rejection by a woman is increased harassment. The third and fourth types of harassment involve ambivalent combinations of the two basic motives, dominance and a desire for intimacy. In the third type, *paternalistic-ambivalent harassment,* the man is motivated by a desire for sexual intimacy but also by a paternalistic desire to be like a father to the woman. This type of harassment may be particularly insidious because the man thinks of himself as acting benevolently toward the woman. Finally, the fourth type, *competitive-ambivalent harassment,* mixes real sexual attraction and a stereotype of women as sexy with the man's hostile desire to dominate the woman, which is based on his belief that she is non-traditional and competitive with him. This theory gives us an excellent view of the complex motives that underlie men's sexual harassment of women.

Social psychologists have developed a clever method for studying sexual harassment experimentally in the laboratory, called the Computer Harassment Paradigm (Maass et al., 2003). In one study, university men were first exposed to a female confederate of the experimenters, who expressed either strong feminist beliefs (intentions to get a high-level career in an area usually reserved for men, and involvement in an organization for women's rights), or traditional beliefs. The men then had the opportunity to harass the woman by sending her pornographic material on a computer (she did not actually receive it). The men exposed to the feminist sent significantly more pornography than did men in the control group. However, not all men in the feminist-threat condition responded with harassment; those who did so were mainly men who identified strongly with the male role. The findings of this experiment are consistent with the type of harassment known as hostile environment harassment. Sexual harassment at work is more than just an annoyance. Particularly for women, because they are more likely to be harassed by supervisors, it can make a critical difference in career advancement. For the woman who supports her family, being fired for sexual non-compliance is a catastrophe. The power of coercion is enormous.

SEXUAL HARASSMENT IN EDUCATION: AN A FOR A LAY

Sexual harassment on campus is not rare (Pyke, 1996). For example, a 1989 survey at the University of Prince Edward Island found that 29 percent of the female students reported that they had been personally sexually harassed by a faculty member (Mazer & Percival, 1989). Harassment ranged from sexual teasing and jokes to unwanted touching and offers of favours for sex. More than 85 percent of male and female students had experienced sexual harassment in class, most commonly sexual jokes and faculty remarks that put down women, men, gay men, or lesbians. Women report dropping courses, changing majors, or dropping out of university as a result of sexual harassment (Fitzgerald, 1993).

Many Canadian universities have sexual harassment policies and have set up reporting and grievance procedures for dealing with sexual harassment cases.

Sexual harassment is not confined either to universities or to teachers harassing students. One survey of 14- and 15-year-olds in the Netherlands found that 24 percent of the girls and 11 percent of the boys had been the objects of sexual harassment (Timmerman, 2003). Of those cases, 73 percent represented harassment by peers and 27 percent harassment by teachers (or other school-related adults such as a tutor or principal). Of the teachers who were harassers, 90 percent were men. The psychological consequences were more severe when the harassment was done by a teacher than by a peer. An Ontario study of 1213 youth in grades 6 to 8 found that 36 percent of boys and 21 percent of girls reported have perpetrated sexual harassment; 42 percent of boys and 38 percent of girls reported have experienced sexual harassment (McMaster et al., 2002). The two most common sexually harassing behaviours were homophobic name-calling and sexual comments, jokes, gestures, and looks.

SEX BETWEEN PROFESSIONALS AND PATIENTS

There is another category of coercive and potentially damaging sexual encounters—those between a psychotherapist and a client, or between other professionals, such as physicians, and a patient. Professional associations, such as the Canadian Psychological Association (1991), state clearly in their codes of ethics that such behaviours are unethical. Nonetheless, professional sexual misconduct does occur, and can be extremely damaging.

One survey of a sample of licensed Ph.D. psychologists found that 5.5 percent of the male and 0.6 of the female psychologists admitted having engaged in sexual intercourse with a client during the time the patient was in therapy, and an additional 2.6 percent of male and 0.3 percent of female therapists had intercourse with clients within three months of the termination of therapy (Holroyd & Brodsky, 1977). These are probably best regarded as minimum figures because they are based on the self-reports of the therapists and some might not be willing to admit such activity even though the questionnaire was anonymous. The Ontario College of Physicians and Surgeons (1991) estimated that 10 percent of Ontario women had been sexually abused by a physician.

Experts regard this kind of situation as having the potential for serious emotional damage to the client (Pope, 2001). Like the cases of sexual harassment discussed earlier, it is a situation of unequal power, in which the more powerful person, the therapist, imposes sexual activity on the less powerful person, the client. The situation is regarded as particularly serious because people in psychotherapy have opened themselves up emotionally to the therapist and therefore are extremely vulnerable. Some provinces, such as Ontario and New Brunswick, have passed legislation that defines sexual contact between a patient or client and any health professional in a position of trust as sexual abuse or misconduct. What are the responses of professionals accused of sexual misconduct? According to two Quebec therapists, they generally fall into three groups: deniers, rationalizers, and repentants. Deniers refuse to acknowledge that the sexual activities occurred. Rationalizers tend to avoid responsibility for their behaviour by minimizing its impact. Those in the repentant group take full responsibility for their action, are sincerely sorry that it occurred, and take steps to ensure that it will not occur again.

SUMMARY

In the Criminal Code of Canada, sexual assault is any activity to which the victim did not consent, ranging from unwanted touching to forced oral, anal, or vaginal intercourse. There are three levels of sexual assault, depending on the amount of force used, not on the nature of the sexual activity. The law is gender-neutral in that it applies equally to men and women as victims.

The Violence Against Women Survey found that 39 percent of Canadian women reported having been sexually assaulted. Other surveys have found that some men report having experienced sexual coercion, although a smaller percentage of men than women report these experiences. Victims may experience post-traumatic stress disorder (PTSD) as a result of the assault.

Sexual assault by a dating or romantic partner is more common than many people realize. There are four major theoretical views of sexual assault: victim-precipitated, psychopathology of sex offenders, feminist, and social disorganization. The incidence of sexual assault differs markedly between the various ethnocultural communities in Canada.

Approximately 18 percent of women and 8 percent of men report that they had experienced unwanted sexual contact with an adult or older adolescent by age 16. There are currently several statutes related to the sexual abuse of children in the Criminal Code of Canada, including sexual assault, sexual interference, invitation to sexual touching, and sexual exploitation. Most sexual abuse of children is committed by a relative or by a family friend. Sexually abused children are more likely than other children to have symptoms such as anxiety, PTSD, depression, and health complaints. More severe psychological consequences are likely to occur when the perpetrator is a close family member who is an adult (sibling incest seems less likely to be harmful) and when the sexual contact is extensive and involves penetration. Pedophiles are more likely to be attracted to girls than to boys. Some types of child molesters have a low rate of recidivism, but certain types are highly likely to repeat their offence. Drugs such as CPA are effective treatments for sex offenders, as is cognitive–behavioural therapy. There is controversy over whether the public should be notified about the release of all sex offenders.

There is a controversy among professionals over whether adults can recover memories of child sexual abuse that they had forgotten (recovered memory), or whether these are cases of false memory syndrome, in which the supposedly remembered incidents never actually occurred.

Most schools offer child abuse prevention programs. Their goals are to provide children with the knowledge and skills to resist people who attempt to abuse them.

Sexual harassment, whether on the job or in education, involves unwelcome sexual advances when there is some coercion involved, such as making the sexual contact a condition of being hired or receiving an A grade in a course. In another form of sexual harassment, the work or educational environment is made so hostile, on a sexual and gender basis, that the employee cannot work effectively. Surveys show that sexual harassment at work is fairly common. In severe cases it can lead to damaging psychological consequences, such as PTSD for the victim. In education, the data indicate that about one-third of female students have been individually harassed by professors, although many more have experienced sexual harassment in class. This abuse can lead to negative consequences for the student, such as being forced to change majors or drop out of school. Sex between psychotherapist and client also carries the strong potential for psychological damage to the client.

QUESTIONS FOR THOUGHT, DISCUSSION, AND DEBATE

1. On your campus, what services are available for sexual assault victims? Do these services seem adequate, given what you have read in this chapter about victim responses to sexual assault? What could be done to improve the services?

2. Find out what procedures are available on your campus to deal with incidents of sexual harassment of a student by a professor.

3. Apply the four theoretical views of sexual assault to child sexual abuse.

4. Angie was sexually assaulted last night at a party, by a man she had met previously in one of her classes. Should she report it to the police?

5. Under Canadian law, sexual harassment is a form of sex discrimination. Sexual harassment involves repeated unwelcome sexual advances or a requirement of sex in return for something like being hired or getting a raise, or an environment that is so sexually hostile that the person has difficulty working. Discrimination based on sexual orientation is also prohibited. Do you think there is a sexual orientation parallel to sexual harassment? That is, do you think that homosexual harassment exists? If yes, how would you define it?

SUGGESTIONS FOR FURTHER READING

Antilla, Susan (2002). *Tales from the boom-boom room: Women vs. Wall Street.* Princeton, NJ: Bloomberg Press. The author chronicles sexual harassment against women in the financial industry.

Brady, Katherine. (1979). *Father's days.* New York: Dell Paperback. This autobiography of an incest victim is both moving and insightful.

Byers, E. S., and O'Sullivan, L. F. (Eds.). (1996). *Sexual coercion in dating relationships.* New York: Haworth. This monograph presents a series of research articles on various aspects related to sexual coercion in dating relationships.

Cruise, David, and Griffiths, Alison. (1997). *On South Mountain: The dark secrets of the Goler clan.* Toronto: Viking. The horrific tale of child sexual abuse within the Goler family of Nova Scotia. In 1984, 14 members of the Goler family were convicted of 100 counts of sexually abusing children in their family.

Lalumière, Martin L., Harris, Grant T., Quinsey, Vernon L., and Rice, Marnie E. (2005). *The causes of rape: Understanding individual differences in male propensity for sexual aggression.* Washington: American Psychological Association. These well-known Canadian researchers provide a comprehensive review of research on why some men rape.

Raine, Nancy V. (1998). *After silence: Rape and my journey back.* New York: Crown. Raine, a professional writer, provides an intense account of the aftermath of being raped.

Seto, Michael C. (2008). *Pedophilia and sexual offending against children: Theory, assessment, and intervention.* Washington: American Psychological Association. This comprehensive book by a respected Canadian researcher addresses key questions about pedophiles, such as how to detect pedophilia, the causes of sexual offending against children, and what prevention and intervention strategies are effective at reducing the sexual abuse of children.

For review questions, web resources, and other learning and study tools, visit the *Understanding Human Sexuality* Online Learning Centre at www.mcgrawhill.ca/olc/hyde.

SEX FOR SALE

Chapter Highlights

> IF ONE THING BECAME CLEAR DURING THE PUBLIC HEARINGS ACROSS CANADA, IT WAS THAT THERE IS NO CONSENSUS ON THE SUBJECT OF PROSTITUTION IN THIS COUNTRY . . . [OPINIONS RANGE] FROM THOSE WHO WOULD HAVE THE LAW ELIMINATE PROSTITUTION ENTIRELY TO THOSE WHO WOULD LEGALIZE OR DECRIMINALIZE IT.*

The exchange of sexual gratification for money is a prominent feature of many contemporary societies and one that involves large amounts of money. In this chapter, we consider two ways in which sex can be bought and sold: commercial sex work and pornography. Both involve complex legal issues and public controversy, but also attract a steady stream of eager customers.

COMMERCIAL SEX WORK

Sex workers are individuals who work as prostitutes, escorts, erotic dancers, phone sex workers, in non-therapeutic massage parlours, and as pornographic models and actors. According to Ontario sociologist Eleanor Maticka-Tyndale and her colleagues, what is common to all these types of activities is that they involve the sale of a service to "satisfy a sexual fantasy, produce sexual excitement or arousal, and/or provide sexual satisfaction to the customer" (Maticka-Tyndale et al., 2000b, p. 88). Therefore, we will use the term "sex worker" as much as possible throughout this chapter

Commercial sex workers:
A person who engages in sexual acts in return for money or drugs and does so in a fairly non-discriminating fashion; prostitute.

Commercial sex workers ("hookers") engage in partnered sexual activity or interactions in return for money, material gifts, or some other form of payment such as drugs. As social critics have pointed out, some dating and living arrangements and long-term relationships, including certain marriages, also fall in this category.

Although prostitution per se—that is, the buying and selling of sex—has never been illegal in Canada, various activities related to prostitution are criminal offences (Shaver, 1996). These offences are listed in In Focus 2.2 (see page 44). The Criminal Code of Canada prohibits stopping cars, impeding the flow of traffic, or communicating in public for the purposes of engaging in prostitution or obtaining the sexual services of a prostitute. These are often called "communication offences." The statute clearly states that a prostitute can be a person of either gender and that both the sex workers and their customers can be charged. In addition, cities attempt to control sex work through bylaws pertaining to zoning, traffic, and licensing of businesses.

Common bawdy-house: A place kept, occupied, or used by one or more persons to engage in prostitution or indecency.

Enforcement of these statutes has largely been aimed at street sex workers and their customers in order to make sex workers less visible and less of a nuisance. Prostitution is considered a minor offence punishable usually by a fine or by a short jail term for repeat offenders. Keeping or being found in a **common bawdy-house** (the legal term for a place in which prostitution occurs), procuring (pimping), and living on money made from prostitution are also illegal, and the maximum sentences for these offences are significantly higher than for the communication offences. It is also illegal to keep a common bawdy-house for performance of "indecent acts," although what is considered indecent is determined by community standards. One criticism of the current law is that although prostitution is legal, there are no clear guidelines on where it can take place. Further, these laws are difficult to enforce, and the probability of arrest is low. Thus, the laws do little to discourage women from entering prostitution.

*P. Fraser et al. (1985), *Pornography and Prostitution in Canada*, vol. II, Report of the Special Committee on Pornography and Prostitution, Ottawa: Minister of Supply and Services Canada.

How are the prostitution laws enforced? The answer is with great inconsistency (Gemme, 1998; Shaver, 1993, 1994, 1996). Almost all charges are for communication offences involving street prostitution—people working within massage parlours, escort services, brothels, and call operations rarely get charged. More sex workers than customers are charged and their sentences are more severe. In addition, more men who pay for sex with women are charged than men who pay for sex with men, in part because male police officers do not like to pose as prostitutes to entrap clients. Thus charges are disproportionately laid against female sex workers. As Quebec sociologist Frances Shaver concluded:

> The women and men involved are both culpable under the law—as are all persons engaged in any form of prostitution—nevertheless, the enforcement patterns penalize women more often and more severely than men; they penalize prostitutes more than customers, procurers, or pimps; and they penalize on-street prostitution more than off-street prostitution. (Shaver, 1993, p. 165)

How do Canadians view sex work? According to a 2002 Leger Marketing Poll, 69 percent of Canadians believe that prostitution is immoral; however, fewer Canadians believe prostitution is immoral than believe that shoplifting (89 percent) or having an extramarital affair (81 percent) are immoral. Men, individuals who had higher incomes, and those with university educations were less likely to see prostitution as immoral. Further, Canadians have varying views on whether prostitution should be illegal (Fraser Committee, 1985). Some people argue that prostitution is a victimless crime, and that because both parties in prostitution are consenting, prostitution should not be illegal. The argument against the criminalization of prostitution assumes that if prostitution-related activities were legal or at least decriminalized, they could be regulated and the problems of crime, public offence, and the spread of sexually transmitted infections associated with prostitution might be avoided. Under decriminalization, prostitution is viewed as a personal choice and therefore a private matter between adults rather than a crime. The law could still be involved to ensure that people, particularly children, are not forced into prostitution and to penalize pimps and other people who profit from sex work.

Quebec sexologist Robert Gemme argues that in addition to eliminating the legal consequences of prostitution, we also need to remove the negative effects that result from the social stigma attached to prostitution—thus the term "sex worker." From this perspective, prostitution is sex-*work* (emphasis on the word "work") and is a trade to be regulated like any other trade. Thus, sex workers should be entitled to all the benefits and protection given to other workers, such as freedom from harassment, proper pay, humane living and working conditions, the right to be treated with respect, and worker compensation (MacDonald & Jeffrey, 2000; Lewis et al., 2005). In several Canadian cities there are movements to unionize sex workers.

Other Canadians do not favour decriminalizing the activities related to prostitution. They argue that the activities of prostitution have turned some areas of large cities into unpleasant and possibly dangerous places for many citizens, because prostitution brings with it added traffic, loitering, noise, illegal drugs, and exposure of children and residents to discarded condoms and needles. Thus, they want better enforcement of current laws to contain prostitution in non-residential areas in order to reduce visibility and the nuisance aspects of prostitution (Duchesne, 1999). Still other Canadians want stronger laws and stiffer sentences imposed by the courts.

VENUES FOR FEMALE SEX WORKERS

There are a number of settings or venues in which commercial sexual activity occurs. The nature of the venue or of the social or sexual context influences the type of sex worker and client found there (e.g., race, social class), the activity that occurs, and its associated risks. Research in New Brunswick found that 80 percent of sex workers work the streets; the remainder work for an escort agency or strip club (Lee & Coates, 2007). In Vancouver, on the other hand, most sex workers work in a variety of venues, sometimes more than one at a time

(Benoit & Millar, 2001). The discussion that follows focuses on female workers and their male clients, but keep in mind that there are male, female, gay, lesbian, bisexual, and transgender sex workers and clients.

The **call girl** (notice the diminutive "girl") works out of her own residence, making appointments with clients by a landline or cell phone. She is often from a middle-class background and may be a university graduate. She dresses expensively and lives in an upscale neighbourhood. A call girl in a medium-size city may charge a minimum of $100 per hour and more if she engages in atypical activities; call girls in major metropolitan areas charge $200 or more per hour. A call girl can earn a great deal of money. But she also has heavy business expenses: an expensive residence, an extensive wardrobe, bills for makeup and hairdressers, high medical bills for maintaining her health, and tips for porters and landlords.

A call girl may have a number of regular customers and may accept new clients only on referral. Because she makes dates by telephone, she can exercise close control over whom she sees and over her schedule. She usually sees clients in her residence, which also allows her to control the setting in which she works. In addition to sexual gratification, she may provide other services, such as accompanying clients to business and social gatherings. Call girls have considerable autonomy, and their physical and health risks are reduced by the setting in which they work.

Another venue for commercial sex work is the **brothel**. In the 1800s and early 1900s there were many successful brothels in North America. They varied from storefront clipjoints, where the customer's money was stolen while he was sexually occupied, to elegant mansions where the customer was treated like a distinguished dinner guest. Brothels declined in number after World War II. In the past 20 years, they have been replaced by **in-call services**, which employ women working regular shifts in an apartment or condo, servicing clients who come to the apartment. In major cities the charge is $150 or $200 per hour; in exchange, the client can participate in standard sexual activity including fellatio, cunnilingus, and vaginal intercourse. Many in-call services also require initial contact by telephone, although others advertise their location in specialized media or even telephone books. A sex worker in this setting generally has less autonomy than a call girl; there is usually a manager or madam (discussed shortly) who determines the conditions of work, the fees to be charged, and collects a substantial percentage of each fee. In-call workers have less choice of clients and may be expected to service several per shift. Brothels and in-call services are illegal in Canada under the Criminal Code provision that it is illegal to be involved in a "common bawdy-house."

Another contemporary setting for commercial sex is the **massage parlour**. Some massage parlours provide legitimate massage therapy. In others, the employees sell sexual services; these often advertise "sensual massage" or "erotic massage," making it pretty clear which type of parlour they are. Some parlours offer a standard list of services and prices; others allow the masseuse or masseur to decide what she or he will do with a particular client, and possibly how much of a "tip" is required for that activity. Massage parlours vary greatly in decor and price. Some are located in "professional" buildings, expensively decorated, and provide food and drinks in addition to sexual gratification. Charges may range from $100 to $300 or more. Such parlours may accept charge cards, with the business listed on the monthly statement as a restaurant. At the other end of the scale, storefront parlours, often located in "commercial sex districts," offer no amenities and charge rates of $40 to $100.

Another venue for a sex business is the *escort service*. These services have revealing names such as Alternative Lifestyle Services, First Affair, All Yours, Versatile Entertainment, and Hubbies for Hire. Most escort services employ both men and women who will engage in sexual activity; like massage parlours, the service may have a standard menu, or the escort may have the autonomy to decide what activities he or she will do with a client. Prostitution in this setting is referred to as an **out-call service**, since the escorts go to the clients. This is obviously a

Call girl: The most expensive and exclusive category of sex workers.

Brothel (BRAH-thul): A house of prostitution where sex workers and customers meet for sexual activity.

In-call service: A residence in which sex workers work regular shifts, selling sexual services on an hourly basis.

Massage parlour: A place where massages, as well as sexual services, can generally be purchased.

Out-call service: A service that sends a sex worker to a location specified by the client to provide sexual services.

IN FOCUS 17.1

Talking Back: Stories of Sex Work in the Maritimes

One really doesn't expect a sex worker to be articulate, to resist, or to "talk back" to dominant stereotypes of her work but that's what we found when we started asking, and recording the words of sex workers in the Maritimes.

Many of us have stereotypes of people in sex work. Sex workers are often depicted by the media, some police, and certain conservative religious groups as victims, or as deserving of a certain fate. Rarely are sex workers depicted as the people they are—mothers, friends, sisters, brothers, fathers, grandparents, lovers, or workers. Equally problematic is the view that sex workers are passive and lacking agency, the ability to act in the social world, to make choices, or to resist dominant, negative beliefs about their lives. In our study, we asked 62 sex workers (men, women, and transgender) in three Maritime cities about their perceptions and attitudes about the work they do, as well as about others' views of them. In answering our questions, they were articulate, witty, and courageous. They did not hesitate to "talk back" to dominant, erroneous images of them. Their words were the most important part of our study because we saw ourselves as engaged in a politics of solidarity rather than a politics of saving. Here are some of their insights.

We asked about the best and worst aspects of sex work that they encountered. The best parts of the work they claimed were "the money, honey." Colleen from Moncton couldn't understand why anyone would not do her work, given the amount of money she makes compared to other service work:

There's one woman at my work (call centre), she's a psychology major, and she has her Master's. And she's working at a call centre for $8.00 an hour. I think she's making a little bit more now 'cause she's been there for a long time. I think she's making $8.40 an hour. Like, still, you spent $50 000 on university, to make $8.40 an hour?

On the other hand, Eric from Moncton claimed he'd never go back to sex work, and that he'd "rather work for twelve hours a day than go out and stand for an hour in the cold. It's degrading." Money was talked about in terms of refusal to "budget" according to what the state (read social assistance) was demanding. As Jacqueline of Saint John said: "It's cash in my pocket. Welfare doesn't know. It gives my son better clothes, better food . . . I spend all my money on him." Sex workers' refusal to "be poor," to accept "handouts," and to be their own boss was a common theme as well.

Violence was the worst part of sex work; all participants reported an increase in violence. Dana, of Halifax, blamed the increase in violence as squarely connected to people's stereotypes:

The reason I feel that (clients have become more violent) is because the media portrays us as non-people. And yeah, they do, they make us more . . . like the word *prostitute*, this is where I have the big problem, it dehumanizes people . . . they use the word "prostitute" or "hooker" as opposed to "a woman who was working as a prostitute." It's a job—it's not a person.

more risky business in that the escort cannot control the setting in which the services are provided. Escorts are usually required to telephone the service when they arrive and when they leave the client's location. This not only contributes to their safety but also allows the service to monitor how long the escort spent with the clients, and therefore the amount owed the service. Several Canadian cities license escorting, including Calgary, Edmonton, Winnipeg, and Windsor. The bylaw in Windsor differs from that in other Canadian cities because it allows escorts to work out of their own homes instead of requiring them to set up offices in specially zoned areas of the city. This was an attempt to treat escorts the same as other independent businesspeople (Maticka-Tyndale et al., 2005).

In most communities, the most visible sex worker is the **streetwalker**. She sells her wares on the streets of cities. She is generally less attractive and less fashionably dressed than the call girl, and she charges correspondingly less for services, perhaps as little as $20 for a "quickie."

Streetwalker: A lower-status sex worker who walks the streets selling sexual services.

They've made it a person and they've made it a stereotypical low-life person and a disposable person and the more that the media continues to do that, the more the tricks feel that they are allowed to be violent.

Stigma was also cited by Jason in Moncton:

Okay, how can I put this? We're not scum because you're the ones paying. . . . You guys are looking down on us . . . yeah, but who's paying us? It's you guys. How do we make our money? You guys.

Stigma extends beyond behaviour on the street. Many reported the kind of experience that Jill, from Saint John, had when she went to emergency services at the local hospital:

I've gone in for a coffee burn, and you know what I mean, all of a sudden it's turned into my drug use, and the way I was dressed and stuff: "Well, you're just a prostitute, you know and you probably deserved it." And it was a coffee burn, so you know what I mean, so. . . . They make you feel like you're diseased or something.

Others, such as Denise, an ex-worker in Halifax, spoke of how much they grew in the experience of sex work, how much they learned:

I learned a lot. I learned a lot about myself: how strong I really could be. I met a lot of other people, like girls like myself. We were all normal, and then things happened. And I learned a lot about people in general. . . . I can survive, and I have survived. I have become strong. You look into the face of death every day and you're either gonna make it or break it. You're gonna be found dead, or you're gonna survive. . . . But I never forget the times and I'm not embarrassed. I learned a lot about society, and the law.

Felicity from Halifax reported that her clients were one of the best parts of her job, and that she deplored any kind of discrimination they might face:

They [her clients] are missing something, whether they don't have a wife at home that's giving them enough attention, or they have no one in their lives. You know, some of them just need to be close to someone, or they just need somebody to love them even if it's a half-hour or an hour at a time. . . .

In sum, the world of sex workers is far from the usual stereotypes that people create. It isn't always safe, it isn't always pretty, but as they point out, many other jobs have similar types of stories—of exploitation, of addiction, and of liberation and independence.

The last words belong to Alexis, a 17-year-old former sex worker from Moncton:

If I had a chance to tell the media so that they— . . . so the world would hear what I had to say, something I'd tell them is, "Don't speak. You want to know about a whore, you get to know a whore and you'll see that she's just like you." That's what I'd tell them.

Source: Written by Gayle MacDonald, based on the Leslie Ann Jeffrey and Gayle MacDonald interviews (2006) for the UBC Press article *Sex Workers in the Maritimes Talk Back.*

She is more likely to impose strict time constraints on the customer. In one study, female street sex workers in Montreal earned between $1800 and $2000 per week. On the other hand, a study in Vancouver found that the median annual income of the sex workers they interviewed was only $18 000 (Benoit & Millar, 2001). Because her mode of operation is obvious, she is most likely to be arrested; 95 percent of prostitution-related charges in Canada are for street prostitution (Wolff & Geissel, 1994). Because streetwalkers have relatively little control over the conditions in which they work, they are at greater risk of disease and of violence at the hands of their customers, pimps, and even police officers. In one study of 30 female sex workers in Montreal, 14 had been sexually assaulted and 22 had been physically assaulted in the previous 12 months (Shaver, 1996). In Vancouver, more than 50 women, most of them sex workers, were murdered between 1983 and 2001.

Child or juvenile sex workers also work as street prostitutes. About one-half of sex workers enter the trade when they are under 16 years old (Badgley, 1984). There has been an increasing demand in recent years for child prostitutes. In 1988, Parliament passed specific legislation prohibiting purchasing sexual services from someone under 18 years old. The Federal/Provincial/Territorial Working Group on Prostitution has recommended that youths involved in prostitution be treated as persons in need of assistance and not as offenders (Canadian Centre for Justice Statistics, 1999).

Research on commercial sex workers in a large Canadian city has found that the same person may work in several different venues over time (Lewis et al., 2004). For example, in areas with cold winters, people who work on the streets in the summer and fall may work in in-call services or bars during the winter. Women also may move back and forth between an escort service and working as a call girl.

THE ROLE OF THIRD PARTIES

Pimp: A sex worker's companion, protector, and master.

Many people associate sex workers with a **pimp** ("The Man"), portrayed as her companion-master. If she has a pimp, she supports him with her earnings, and in return he may provide her with companionship and sex, bail her out of jail, and provide her with food, shelter, clothing, and drugs. If he keeps an eye on her when she is working, he may provide some protection against theft and violence because a sex worker is scarcely in a position to go to the police if she is robbed by a customer. But the same pimp also may exercise considerable control over her and engage in verbal, physical, and sexual abuse toward her if she fails to do what he tells her. In Canada, a majority of adult sex workers work without a pimp (Shaver, 1994). For example, in New Brunswick 74 percent of sex workers work for themselves (Lee & Coats, 2007). However, many child prostitutes do have a pimp.

Madam: A woman who manages a brothel, in-call, out-call, or escort service.

Another third party in commercial sex work is the **madam**, a woman who manages or owns an in-call service, out-call service, brothel, or escort service. A madam is usually experienced and skilled at managing sex workers and businesses. Sometimes she also is socially skilled with a network of contacts in the community.

In other venues there may be other third parties. Massage parlours employ managers who are on the premises at all times and may exercise close control of their employees. The importance of these third parties is that they reduce the autonomy of the sex workers they supervise, and may coerce them to perform activities or work with clients that they do not want to. There is sharp disagreement among observers over the extent to which a sex worker can exercise choice with regard to his or her activities. Some argue workers choose who they serve and what acts they perform; others argue that they have little choice if they need the money. The reality depends, in part, on the involvement of the third parties in the worker's daily life.

Sex trafficking: The recruitment and control of persons for sexual exploitation.

Although there is disagreement about whether call girls, in-call workers, and streetwalkers have autonomy or are coerced to participate, everyone agrees that girls and women caught up in sex trafficking are forced to engage in it. **Sex trafficking** refers to the recruitment and control of persons, by threat or use of force or deception, for purposes of sexual exploitation (Hynes & Raymond, 2002). Typically, girls and young women are recruited in Third World or developing countries, by ads or by people who promise them a good job (as a dancer, nanny, secretary), education, or a husband in a developed country. Recruiters may even supply forged travel documents, often for a price. When the women arrive in the destination country, they find themselves captives; often their travel documents are taken away, the money earned by their activity goes to those who control them, and their controllers threaten physical harm to the women or their families if they disobey or run away. The women often work in bars, brothels, and massage parlours, and may be moved every few weeks. One woman interviewed in the United States reported having 10 to 30 customers per day. The United Nations estimates that tens of thousands of young women and girls are trafficked each year; half are children, with most of these victims ending up in Germany, the United States, and Italy. Thousands of these women are brought to Canada every year to work in the sex trade; some are kept as virtual prisoners (McClelland, 2001). Clearly, these women are being exploited because third parties control every detail of their lives.

THE CAREER OF A SEX WORKER

The first step in a sex worker's career is entry. Women enter sex work for a variety of reasons (Vanwesenbeeck, 2001). For sex workers in western countries the most important one is economics. Some women, for various reasons, are attracted by a desire for money, material goods, and an exciting lifestyle. These women are attracted by the image of the call girl, a status that some of them are fortunate enough to attain. For some women—for example, a poor but attractive woman—prostitution can be a means of upward economic mobility. Other women enter out of economic necessity, in order to survive. A poorly educated single mother may have no alternative means of earning a living. For example, a sex worker in Vancouver said:

> I worked for a couple of months as a house cleaner, scrubbing floors and toilets to survive and make money to afford an apartment. From that amount, I couldn't survive . . . so I started to work in an escort agency. (Benoit & Millar, 2001, p. 12)

Some women become sex workers in order to support a drug addiction.

Force or coercion is another factor. Some women report being coerced physically or psychologically by a husband or lover into selling sex for money. As noted earlier, coercion is a major factor in sex trafficking. Another category of reasons involves gaining power. For example, a woman who serves as a call girl to famous politicians may think of herself as having access to real political power. Some women become involved in prostitution through a family member or friend who is already a sex worker and can teach them the ropes (Miller, 1986).

On entering prostitution, most women go through an apprenticeship in which they learn the skills of the profession. The apprentice learns sexual techniques, especially fellatio, since many customers want oral sex. She learns how to hustle, to successfully negotiate her services and price with potential customers. She learns how to maintain control over the interaction so that she can protect herself as much as possible from being hurt or robbed by clients (and many sex workers are hurt or robbed). She learns values, like "the customer is always right," and fairness to other "working girls."[1] Women who are recruited into the life by a pimp may be trained by one of his more experienced "wives." Some women are trained by an experienced madam, in exchange for a large percentage of their fees.

There has been relatively little research on the "mid-career" sex worker. We have noted that a sex worker may work in several different venues over time. A woman might move from in-call to out-call as she becomes more experienced at managing clients. She might move from the street into work in bars or at truck stops in response to changes in the weather or her health. Sex workers who are addicted to drugs may be forced to work long hours and service many customers in more than one venue in order to support their habit. Again, some of these changes may result from coercion or exploitation by a pimp or a sex trafficker.

Research in New Brunswick and Nova Scotia found that when asked "What is the best part of sex work?" almost all sex workers replied "the money" (Jeffrey & MacDonald, 2006a, 2006b). This did not mean that they were forced into sex work by economic factors but rather that they chose sex work over their other alternatives such as a minimum-wage job or social assistance. They also identified independence and flexibility of work as a positive part of their work. Thus, these sex workers chose sex work as a way of earning a better income (between $30 and $300 per night for outdoor work and between $50 and $150 per hour for indoor work)

---

[1] A 1986 film entitled *Working Girls* provides a realistic look at an in-call service.

in a relatively short period of time while being able to set their own schedule. Their chief concerns were avoiding police, the desire to remain anonymous, and fear of violence.

"Squaring up" or "leaving the life" refers to giving up sex work. Financially and psychologically it is a difficult thing to do, particularly for the woman with no job skills. As Gwen wrote:

> When you can't understand why a woman can't leave the sex trade or why she goes back or why she can't just get a job, I want you to remember that her life is not like yours. I want you to remember that your experiences are as foreign to her as hers are to you. She can no more become a bureaucrat tomorrow than you can become a sexually exploited youth tonight. (Field & Rabinovitch, 2003)

Recognizing this, some analysts call for comprehensive programs that provide education and job training, shelters, and counselling for women (and men) who want to leave commercial sex work (Hynes & Raymond, 2002). For example PEERS, which stands for Prostitutes, Empowerment, Education, and Resource Society, has branches in several Canadian cities, and provides support, training, and resources to help male and female sex workers leave the trade.

Sex workers who are in long-term relationships may return full-time to their previous lifestyle, often as homemakers. Single sex workers may leave the sex trade upon meeting a partner.

The major hazards associated with being a sex worker are being a victim of a "bad trick" (i.e., physical or sexual assault or even murder), drug addiction, sexually transmitted infections, and arrest by police (Badgley, 1984; Church et al., 2001). However, there are variations across the country in how vigorously laws pertaining to prostitution are enforced as well as in the sentences (fines compared to prison terms) given to women who are convicted of prostitution-related offences (Wolff & Geissel, 1994).

SEX WORKERS' WELL-BEING

There are a variety of images of the contemporary sex worker: young, attractive, autonomous, healthy, "the happy hooker"; young, brazen, aggressive, "the tough chick"; not-so-young, bruised emotionally and physically, a victim. Which one is valid?

According to a landmark study (Vanwesenbeeck, 1994), all these images are accurate. In the first phase, researchers recruited 90 prostitutes and former prostitutes in the Netherlands and conducted extended interviews with them about their daily lives. Two years later, 100 women who had been working for at least one year were recruited for a study of "sex and health"; these women were interviewed and completed several measures of coping style and well-being. The samples included women who worked on the street, in windows, in clubs and brothels, for escort services, and in their own homes. The results indicated that one-fourth of the women were doing well. They had few physical or psychosocial complaints, used problem-focused coping strategies, and were satisfied with their lives. Another quarter were at the opposite end. They complained of headaches, backaches, anxiety, and depression; their coping strategies involved dissociation (seeing problems as unrelated to the self) and denial, and they were dissatisfied with prostitution. The remaining women were in the middle.

The risks to a woman and thus her well-being varied according to the venue in which she worked. In the Netherlands, where sex work has been legalized, women who worked in windows and on the streets were at greater risk. Similarly, research in Canada has found that working the streets is associated with greater risk of arrest and of violence by clients (Lewis et al., 2005; Shaver, 2005). This obviously influences physical and mental health. Women who worked in windows or on the streets worked faster, had more clients, and earned less per customer than those working in in-call and out-call services. In a more recent study of indoor sex workers in the Netherlands, workers reported having an average nine-hour workday; more than one-third worked more than 40 hours per week, and half had taken no holidays in the preceding year (Venicz & Vanwesenbeeck, 2000). Scores of indoor sex workers on measures of burnout—depersonalization and emotional exhaustion—were compared with scores of female health care workers and persons in treatment for work-related problems. Sex workers scored significantly higher on depersonalization, which was mainly explained by contextual factors—working due to coercion, experiences of violence, and lack of control in interaction with clients (Vanwesenbeeck, 2005). An important caveat in interpreting these studies is that they were conducted in the context of legalized prostitution in the Netherlands. Doubtless the health outcomes would be worse in countries in which prostitution was illegal and therefore sex workers have little recourse if, for example, they are assaulted. Risks are especially high for women who are being trafficked because they are at risk of suffering abuse and injury by both clients and masters, experiencing illness and infection, and facing medical neglect (Hynes & Raymond, 2002).

There is also the risk of exposure to sexually transmitted infections, especially HIV/AIDS. Sex workers infected with HIV are often workers who are also injecting drugs; research indicates that it is the injecting that is the greatest risk. In the Western world, studies show that the sex worker's risk of HIV infection is greater in his or her private sex life than in the sex work. The risk varies greatly in other parts of the world, with high rates of HIV/AIDS in some cities and countries but low rates in others (Vanwesenbeeck, 2001).

It has been suggested that the high levels of violence and of psychological distress found among sex workers are not due to the nature of the sex work per se, but instead reflect the stigma associated with sex work (Vanwesenbeeck, 2001). Sex workers are at risk of rape because of attitudes such as the view that you can't rape a prostitute so no harm is done if you do force them to have sex (Miller & Schwartz, 1995). The risk of arrest and mistreatment by law enforcement personnel, and the resulting anxiety and distress, reflect the fact that some aspects of sex work are illegal.

Sex workers use a variety of cognitive and behavioural strategies to cope with the risks of their work. Some use drugs and alcohol to increase their confidence and decrease their guilt. Others use a strategy of shutting down their feelings and focusing narrowly on the task. The consequences of this distancing are often referred to as *depersonalization* (not, of course, an experience unique to sex work). Some emphasize the rewarding aspects of the work; perhaps that it supports their children. Many sex workers use as a coping technique the careful management of time and place, locating their sex work in a specific physical and temporal place separated from their private sexual and familial relationships (also not unique to sex work). Sex workers also may use the network of contacts with other sex workers as a source of support; workers on one "stroll" worked together to protect a pregnant colleague by giving her all the customers who wanted a "blow job" and protecting her from clients known to be rough (Anderson, 2004).

THE ROLE OF EARLY ABUSE

The study of women working in the Netherlands found that, in addition to their work venue, having a history of victimization and trauma as children or adolescents before they entered prostitution was associated with poorer well-being (Vanwesenbeeck, 1994). Much of the research literature prior to 1990 reported that a high percentage of sex workers had been physically or sexually abused as children, which was then often taken as the cause of their entry into sex work (Vanwesenbeeck, 2001). It was often suggested that childhood abuse leads to feelings of stigmatization that in turn results in early sexual activity and/or drug use, running away from home, and a drift into sex work. There is no doubt that some men and women do enter commercial sex work via this path. But the research upon which this is based utilized samples of streetwalkers, women in jail, or former sex workers located through social service agencies. These respondents are not representative of all sex workers, so these results cannot be generalized. Further, according to Quebec sociologist Frances Shaver (2007), much of this research has failed to use an appropriate comparison group—that is, a comparison group that is similar to the group of sex workers in age and socioeconomic status. We don't, in fact, know how important a history of abuse might be in any individual's entry into sex work. Clearly, any adult who has experienced childhood victimization may have poor well-being.

CUSTOMERS

At the time of the Kinsey research, about 69 percent of all white males had had some experience with sex workers (Kinsey et al., 1948). In 1992 the NHSLS asked all respondents whether they had had sex with someone they paid or who paid them (Laumann et al., 1994). Only 17 percent of men and 2 percent of women reported that they had had sex with such a partner since age 18. Thus, the use of prostitutes has declined dramatically in the past 50 years. This likely reflects the increased frequency of non-marital and casual sexual activity during this same period (see Chapters 10 and 11).

Sex workers refer to their customers as "johns." About 50 percent of the clients are occasional johns; they may be businessmen who seek only occasional contacts with sex workers, perhaps while on business trips. Nearly 50 percent are repeat clients who seek a regular relationship with one particular sex worker or a small group of them (Freund et al., 1991). The remainder are compulsive johns, who use sex workers for their major sexual outlet. They are driven to them and cannot stay away (see Chapter 15).[2] About half of these men are married (Lowman, 1995).

A study of men who purchase sexual services in the Vancouver area found that on the average, they were 38 years old; 79 percent had completed high school and 21 percent had a bachelor's degree. Forty-nine percent had a regular sexual partner or spouse; most of these men were happy with this relationship. About a quarter of the men (23 percent) had a history of child sexual abuse as defined by the Criminal Code of Canada. On average, the men had first purchased sex when they were 24 years old. Although some of the respondents had only purchased sex once, 33 percent had purchased sex between 11 and 50 times, and 10 percent had purchased sex between 51 and 100 times (Lowman & Atchison, 2006). The participants were recruited through newspaper ads and by leaving questionnaires in a number of locations in downtown Vancouver, so they are probably not a representative sample. Nonetheless, they give us a glimpse of at least some of the customers.

Research in Quebec indicates that men use the services of sex workers for a variety of reasons (Gemme et al., 1984). Some have long-term partners but want sex more frequently than their partner does or want to engage in practices—such as fellatio—that they feel their partner would not be willing to do. Some use sex workers to satisfy their exotic sexual needs, such as being whipped or having sex with a woman who pretends to be a corpse. Others, particularly adolescents, may have sex with sex workers to prove their manhood or gain sexual experience. Finally, for some men it is a way to engage in discreet same-sex activity. A survey of visitors to a commercial sex event in Australia found that 23 percent of the men had paid for sex at least once. These men reported that their main reasons were to satisfy sexual needs, that it was easy, and that it would be entertaining (Pitss et al., 2004).

MALE SEX WORKERS

Although under the Criminal Code of Canada a prostitute can be either male or female, male sex workers are less likely to be charged than are female sex workers (Shaver 1994, 1996). Overall, 25 percent of sex workers in Canada are male (Fraser, 1985). Most male sex workers serve a male clientele—97 percent of clients of Canadian sex workers are male (Badgley, 1984). However, some sell their services to women or to both women and men.

Male sex workers serving a female clientele work in three settings. These male sex workers virtually never work in the street, in contrast to female streetwalkers and male *hustlers* (discussed shortly). This reflects gender-role socialization; female clients are unlikely to cruise

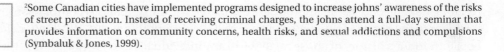

[2]Some Canadian cities have implemented programs designed to increase johns' awareness of the risks of street prostitution. Instead of receiving criminal charges, the johns attend a full-day seminar that provides information on community concerns, health risks, and sexual addictions and compulsions (Symbaluk & Jones, 1999).

Figure 17.1   Sex for sale on Jarvis Street in Toronto.

the streets and pick up a sex worker, because they have been taught to let the male take the initiative and because women are not supposed to be that interested in sex, especially not interested enough to be willing to pay for it. Some male sex workers work for escort services and provide companionship and sexual gratification on an out-call basis. Some men work in massage parlours, under the same conditions as female employees. A third type is the gigolo, a man who provides companionship and sexual gratification on a continuing basis to a woman in exchange for money. A gigolo often, though not always, has only one client at a time. The demand for gigolos reflects the fact that women, like men, desire sexual gratification on a continuing basis and will pay for it when circumstances require or allow them to do so. On the other hand, most women prefer their sexual activity to be part of an ongoing relationship.

Hustlers are male sex workers who cater to men. Interestingly, some of them consider themselves to be straight, not gay. In one study of male sex workers in Canada, 23 percent reported that they were heterosexual (Badgley, 1984). They may have strict rules for their customers to follow, such as only permitting the customer to perform fellatio on them.

Parallel to patterns of heterosexual prostitution, there are male escort services for a more upscale male clientele (Salamon, 1989).

Male hustlers seem to fall into three main categories (Allen, 1980). First are the full-time street and bar hustlers, who operate much as female streetwalkers do except that they rarely have a pimp (Lowman, 1991). They tend to be younger than other sex workers, and there is some market for "chickens" (young boys) as sex workers. They are less likely to experience violence from pimps or customers. Increasingly, male sex workers are working from indoor locations by using telephones, and working as licensed escorts and masseurs rather than as street sex workers, particularly in small Canadian cities (Allman, 1999). Second are full-time call boys or kept boys. They tend to have a more exclusive clientele and to be more attractive

Gigolo (JIG-uh-loh): A male who provides companionship and sexual gratification on a continuing basis to a woman in exchange for money.

Hustler: A male sex worker who sells his services to men.

and more sexually versatile than the streetwalkers. Surprisingly, by far the largest group is the third: part-time hustlers, who are typically students or individuals employed in another occupation. They generally work at prostitution only when they need money. The part-time hustlers are notable because unlike those in the other groups, they are less likely to come from dysfunctional families. They also have the best long-term chance for acquiring an education and a stable job and achieving a good social adjustment.

In one study of male sex workers in Montreal between the ages of 16 and 29, the main reason for engaging in sex work, stated by 88 percent, was money, although some said they engaged in sex work as a way to meet people (Earls & David, 1989). Many of these young men came from troubled home environments, often leaving home at an early age. The majority (78 percent) reported using drugs on a regular basis.

TRANSGENDER SEX WORKERS

Some transgender individuals work as sex workers. These are genetic males who may or may not live full-time as women. They are typically taking estrogen, which feminizes their body including giving them breasts. Transgender sex workers serve a male clientele. A study of 46 women, 46 men, and 48 transgender individuals working as street sex workers found that the transgender sex workers were more similar to the female sex workers than to the male sex workers in keeping regular hours and spending less time with each client (Weinberg et al., 1999). Few of the transgender sex workers reported never enjoying sexual activities with clients; in this way they were more similar to the male than to the female sex workers in the study. The transgender sex workers typically provided oral sex, hand jobs, and receptive anal intercourse. More than half never or rarely told their customers that they were male; they would deceive their customers by restricting services (e.g., to oral sex), taping or tucking their penis back between their legs, and providing an excuse not to remove their skirt or panties (e.g., having their period).

SEX TOURISM

Sex tourism: Leisure travel with the purpose of purchasing sexual services.

An increasingly important type of commercial sex is **sex tourism**, which refers to varieties of leisure travel that have as their purpose the purchase of sexual services (Wonders & Michalowski, 2001). Sex tourism is made possible by three large-scale social forces: the migration of men and women from less developed nations, or from rural to urban areas, in search of jobs; the commodification of sexual intimacy making all types of sex a commodity or service for sale; and increased travel for recreational purposes. All three of these forces are tied to increasing globalization, the movement of information and people freely across national boundaries.

The migration of people in search of economic opportunities provides a large group of young men and women in search of work. In some locales, they are aggressively recruited into sex work by pimps or persons with ties to sex trafficking. In other places, they enter into the life more or less voluntarily, often because there are few other opportunities for persons of their racial or ethnic background. In Amsterdam, where the attitude toward sex work can be described as regulated tolerance, a few individuals control much of the commercial sex work, recruiting foreign migrants to work in windows and brothels. In Havana, Cuba, commercial sex work is decentralized, with many men and women working independently. They contact potential clients in hotels, bars, and on the street, hoping to connect with someone who will employ them for several days. In some countries, sex tourism is the most rapidly growing economic sector and a major source of hard currency; in such places, governments have little incentive to attempt to reduce or eliminate it. One estimate places the value of the global sex industry at $20 billion per year.

The tourists who can purchase sexual services are obviously wealthy enough to travel, which in turn often means they are citizens of developed countries and members of the middle and upper classes in their home societies. The sex workers are often from a different national and ethnic background. One of the attractions for the tourist is sex with this "dark-skinned other," perhaps someone from a group stereotyped as sexually free and uninhibited. The encounter is appealing because it is a sharp contrast to the tourist's usual sexual experience (Frank, 2003). Unfortunately, one such appeal for men is sex with a young girl, and in some Asian cities girls as young as 12 and 13 are available in brothels tightly controlled by their managers.

PORNOGRAPHY

A debate over pornography has been raging for more than five decades. Religious fundamentalists and some feminists (strange bedfellows, indeed!) agree that some kinds of pornography should be made illegal, while civil liberties groups and some other feminists argue that freedom of expression, guaranteed in the Charter of Rights and Freedoms, must be preserved and therefore pornography should not be restricted by law. Meanwhile, Joe Brown stops at his local video store, buys *Wall to Wall Sex, v. 46,* and drives home for a pleasurable evening's entertainment. Here we will examine what the issues are, paying particular attention to social scientists' research on the effects of pornography on people who are exposed to it. First, we need to clarify some terminology.

TERMS

We can distinguish among pornography, obscenity,and erotica. Pornography comes from the Greek words *porneia,* which means, quite simply, "prostitution," and *graphos,* which means "writing." In general usage today, pornography refers to magazines, films, and so on, that are intended to be sexually arousing (Malamuth, 1998).

The Criminal Code of Canada uses the term "obscenity," not pornography. It is a crime to sell or possess for the purposes of distribution any material that is "obscene." It is also illegal to present an "immoral, indecent or obscene" play, film, or other live performance. Obscenity refers to "any publication a dominant characteristic of which is the undue exploitation of sex." Because "undue exploitation" is rather vague, the courts have used the community standards of tolerance test to determine whether material is obscene. Community standards of tolerance do not refer to what Canadians would look at themselves; they refer to what Canadians would accept other Canadians being exposed to. Using the community standards of tolerance test means that standards can change over time as societal attitudes change. For example, some experts estimate that 30 percent of all Canadian periodical sales are of magazines that would have been illegal 30 years ago (Robertson, 1992). In 2005, the Supreme Court of Canada ruled that the test for indecency should not just be whether an activity violates community standards, but whether it actually causes harm.

In the debate over pornography, some make the distinction between pornography (which is unacceptable to them) and erotica (which is acceptable to them). According to this distinction, sexually explicit material that depicts sex coupled with violence, that is degrading or dehumanizing (usually to women), or that includes children is *pornography* (Russell, 1980). In contrast, erotica depicts explicit sex that is not violent and is neither degrading nor dehumanizing. According to this definition, a movie of a woman being sexually assaulted would be pornography, whereas a movie of two mutually consenting adults who are both enjoying having intercourse together would be considered erotica.

Pornography: Sexually arousing art, literature, or films.

Obscenity: Something that is offensive according to accepted standards of decency; the legal term for pornography.

Community standards of tolerance test: The test used by courts to determine whether something is obscene based on what Canadians would accept other Canadians being exposed to.

Erotica: Sexually arousing material that is not degrading or demeaning to women, men, or children.

In keeping with this distinction, the Supreme Court of Canada in the *Butler* case ruled in 1992 that sexually explicit material depicting adults engaging in consensual sexual activity that does not depict violence, and that is not degrading or dehumanizing, is not obscene. This decision divided pornography into three categories: (1) explicit sex with violence, (2) explicit sex without violence but in which people are treated in a way that is degrading or dehumanizing, and (3) explicit sex that is neither degrading nor dehumanizing. The Court ruled that the first category, sex with violence, constitutes "undue exploitation of sex" and thus fits the definition of obscenity in the Criminal Code. The Court indicated that the third category (erotica) is generally accepted in Canadian society (unless it involves children) and thus is not obscene. However, explicit sex that is degrading or dehumanizing may or may not be obscene depending on the risk of harm involved and whether the material has artistic merit. While the Supreme Court decision gave a good deal of guidance to the courts, there is still ambiguity in the law. For example, what exactly constitutes degrading or dehumanizing sex? Are depictions of BDSM (see Chapter 15) degrading and/or violent if the activity is consensual? What criteria should be used to determine whether material has artistic merit? Should material depicting sadomasochistic activity in which partners consensually participate in some types of pain rituals be considered obscene (MacDonald, 2000)?

Another complication is that Canada Customs officials have the power to refuse to allow books, magazines, DVDs, and other materials "deemed to be obscene" to enter Canada without having to lay criminal charges or have the materials reviewed by the courts. In 1994 the Little Sisters Bookstore and Art Emporium in Vancouver challenged the right of Customs officials to do so. They argued that Customs officials specifically target gay and lesbian bookstores and that they deem material that does not include violence or degradation to be obscene just because it depicts gay or lesbian sex. Ultimately, the Supreme Court of Canada upheld the Customs Act but criticized Customs inspectors for unfairly targeting the store.

Beyond these definitions by experts and by the courts, it is interesting to see what typical Canadians find acceptable. Research shows that there is a great diversity in what people consider pornographic. A well-sampled study of 2018 Canadians showed that although 31 percent of Canadians feel that all sexually explicit material is obscene, 42 percent do not, and the beliefs of the remainder are somewhere in between (Peat et al., 1984). Most respondents, 66 percent, agreed that everyone has the right to view sexually explicit material in private. Younger people and men tended to find sexually explicit material more acceptable, as do people living in Quebec. Sex combined with violence is seen as the least acceptable. The same poll showed that the majority of Canadians have been exposed to various kinds of sexually explicit material.

TYPES OF PORNOGRAPHY

Pornography is a multibillion-dollar business in North America. Included in this business are a number of products: magazines directed to various audiences, films, X-rated DVDs, live sex shows, telephone sex, computer porn, and child pornography. Some of this activity is legal (e.g., publishing *Penthouse*); some of it is illegal (e.g., producing films featuring children engaged in sex); and the legality of the rest is hotly debated. It is impossible to obtain precise data on the economics of pornography in Canada. However, it is estimated that Americans spend between US$4 billion and US$10 billion per year on pornography (*Forbes*, 2001; ABC News, 2004).

MAGAZINES

A large chunk of the Canadian pornography market consists of U.S. magazines, ranging from *Playboy* and *Penthouse*—soft-core—to *Hustler* and hundreds of other less well-known hard-core magazines, although now even soft-core magazines may contain some "hard-core" pictures. The soft-core magazines mushroomed in the 1970s. In the 1990s the market was large and included both general magazines and those catering to specialized tastes. In 2006 in Canada, *Playboy* had a circulation of 45 361 copies per issue, and *Penthouse* a circulation of 20 744 copies per issue. Each of the other pornography magazines had a circulation of less than 25 000. Sales of these and other pornographic magazines have dropped by as much as half in recent years, likely as a result of the availability of sexual images on the Internet, including through Digital Playboy.

Much pornography is designed for the heterosexual male reader. *Playgirl,* however, features "beefcake" (i.e., muscular men in minimal clothing) in an attempt to attract heterosexual women. There is also a large variety of printed material designed for gay men, lesbians, people interested in interracial sex, swingers, and other groups.

Figure 17.2 Porn magazines designed for a male audience. They run the gamut from the relatively tame *Playboy* to the raunchier and more sexually explicit *Hustler.*

Hard-core magazines have a no-holds-barred approach to what they present. Photographs may include everything from vaginal intercourse to anal intercourse, sadomasochism, bondage, and sex with animals. A study of the titles of magazines and books found in "adult" bookstores in the United States revealed that 17 percent were about a paraphilia or sexual variation (Lebeque, 1991). Of those, 50 percent featured sadomasochism. An additional 21 percent dealt with incest.

The profit on magazines is great. The markups may be as high as 600 percent, and it is estimated that there are approximately 20 000 outlets in the United States selling hard-core magazines, mostly to repeat customers. Yet more profit comes from customers who have regular subscriptions for pornographic magazines by mail.

FILMS, VIDEOS, AND DVDs

Although sexually explicit movies were made as early as 1915, only in the last four decades have these films been slick and well produced. The *hard-core film* industry began to emerge in a big way around 1970. Two films were especially important in this breakthrough. *I Am Curious, Yellow,* appearing in 1970, showed sexual intercourse explicitly. In part because it was a foreign film with an intellectual tone, it became fashionable for people, including married couples, to see it. The other important early film was *Deep Throat,* appearing in 1973. With its humour and creative plot, it was respectable and popular among the middle class. Linda Lovelace, the female star, gained national recognition and later appeared on the cover of *Esquire.*

After the success of *Deep Throat,* many more full-length, technically well-made hard-core films soon appeared. *Deep Throat* had made it clear that there were big profits to be made. It cost US$24 000 to make, yet by 1982 it had yielded US$25 million in profits.

Loops are short (10-minute) hard-core videos. They are set up in coin-operated computers

IN FOCUS 17.2

Behind the Scene: Making X-Rated Videos

Dave Cummings bounces out of bed. He's working today, so he goes through his routine; he showers, shaves extremely close to get a smooth face, trims his fingernails and his pubic hair, applies lotion to his groin, and finishes with hand lotion. He dresses casually, and drives to a large, expensive home in Beverly Hills rented for the shoot. When he arrives, he greets the other performers, mostly young women and men in their 20s and 30s. In this group, Dave is "odd man out." He is 59 years old, balding, and looks like your doctor, not the typical male performer in an X-rated video. It is that appearance that gets him work. Dave provides the realism in the video; he is believable as a doctor, lawyer, judge, or schoolteacher in roles where a hard-bodied, bronzed guy in his 20s is not credible (Kikuras, 2004).

Dave points to one of the most important qualifications for a male actor in the world of X-rated videos: the ability to perform sexually. Many videos are budgeted to be shot in three days. The script calls for six to nine episodes of sex, each requiring one or more erect penises; the majority are to end with visible ejaculation. In other words, these videos place a premium on male sexual performance, perhaps not surprising in a performance-oriented culture. It costs money and frustrates everyone involved if a male actor has a long refractory period (see Chapter 9). To make it in the industry, a man has to demonstrate that he is up to the demands. Dave is lucky; he has good genes and stamina. In his own words, he can "get it up, keep

it up, not come before [I am] told to, and can climax on cue." In years past, a man without Dave's talents would not last in this line of work. But a pharmaceutical breakthrough—Viagra—changed all that. Many male porn actors routinely use Viagra or similar medications, which enable them to get and keep an erection. As a result, there are hundreds of men competing for the available jobs.

One consequence of this competition is pressure to perform acts and take risks that the actor might prefer to avoid. Even in this era of widespread knowledge of HIV/AIDS, condom use is rare in the porn industry; some viewers don't like to see them, some directors and producers don't allow them, some actors and actresses don't like the resulting hassle or change in sensation. The risk became very real in May 2004 when it was announced that five performers had positive HIV tests.

Another consequence of the competition is low pay. Men may be paid as little as $500 for a video. The industry is built primarily around women. It is the women who achieve a kind of stardom, whose names appear in the publicity and on the video boxes, and whose bodies are featured in the videos. Relatively new performers may be paid $350 to $1000 for a film featuring conventional sex. Engaging in unconventional or rough sex brings a higher fee. Needless to say, there are no royalties paid to the performers. The typical film is budgeted at $5000 to $35 000 (Huffstutter & Frammolino, 2001). A typical release sells 1000 to 2000 copies; it is only the rare hit

in private booths, usually in adult bookstores. The patron can enter and view the film in privacy and perhaps masturbate while doing so. They cater to both the straight and gay communities.

In the early 1980s, X-rated videocassettes for home viewing began to replace porn theatres. For example, *Deep Throat* became available on cassette in 1977, and by 1982, 300 000 copies had been sold (Cohn, 1983). Cable and satellite television have also entered the arena, with porn channels thriving in some areas. The latest advance is the DVD.

There are also increasing numbers of adult videos made for gay men and lesbians. Canadian gay men criticize pornography aimed at gay men for depicting hypermasculine men, being non-egalitarian, and simulating a heterosexual model (Morrison, 2004). Research with lesbian women in Canada identified two types of lesbian pornography: "pseudo-lesbian" pornography, which is actually created to cater to meet the erotic interests and fantasies of male viewers, and lesbian pornography, which is created by and designed for lesbians. In lesbian-created pornography, performers don't necessarily have "ideal" bodies, there is a greater

that brings in $1 million (*Forbes*, 2001). Thus, there is constant pressure to keep costs to a minimum.

We noted that there are a variety of pathways into commercial sex work. Dave Cummings voluntarily entered the industry at age 54. Once he had demonstrated his prowess, he found himself in continuing demand. In fact, he is now producing his own line of videos. Cummings says he does it because he enjoys sex, and for the opportunity to have sex with lots of attractive young women. A 21-year-old starlet, Sienna, drifted into performing in adult videos. She had worked in a fast-food outlet and bagel shop; she saw an ad in the newspaper for "nude modelling" and tried it. For the first year she did still photo shoots, $350 to $400 for a few hours. Then she moved to working for an Internet company, engaging in masturbation while clients watched her via the Net. After a few months she thought, "If I'm gonna do this, I might as well do porn and make more money." Sienna says she may leave the industry soon; "I've just been pounded so much in these movies that I'm starting to get tired" (Petkovich, 2004). Some performers report being coerced into performing for stills or movies, through the use of alcohol, drugs, or physical force by others on camera.

The emphasis on sexual performance reflects the larger North American culture, and it is often chemically enhanced as are many other performances in the contemporary world. The distribution and sale of the DVDs reflects the commercialization of sex, turning access to sexual images and sexual gratification into a commodity to be sold for cash or credit.

Figure 17.3 The greying porngraphy: as baby boomers get older, the demand for older performers is increasing. Here De'Bella, 50, waits for the director's call for her close-ups; her male co-stars are usually in their 20s.

attempt to convey intimacy and emotion, and there is a focus on the body rather than on genitals and penetration (Morrison & Tallack, 2005). However, even in lesbian-created pornography women's bodies are still unrealistic in terms of weight and breast size. Further, too much focus on intimacy and emotion sometimes results in depictions that are not sexually arousing.

Many hard-core films, X-rated videocassettes, and DVDs are made for a heterosexual audience. In the United States, "adult videos" earn US$4 billion per year and account for more than 700 million rentals annually (Rich, 2001). Based on an informal survey, an adult video distributor estimated that in 1998 more than 38 000 adult videos were rented each day in Ontario, resulting in an annual revenue of more than $52 million. There are no national data available. These videos portray couples engaging in both fellatio and cunnilingus, and vaginal and anal intercourse in various settings and bodily positions. Less often, films and videos show sexual activity involving three or more people, or two women (Davis & Bauserman, 1993).

A rapidly expanding part of the porn industry is the "amateur" video. The development of the home-video camera has enabled anybody with a willing partner, friends, or neighbours

Figure 17.4   The sexual content of many music videos played on MuchMusic is unmistakable.

to produce homemade porn. Such videos cost virtually nothing to make, and distributors are eager to purchase them. These films account for at least 20 percent of all adult videos made in the United States ("The Sex Industry," 1998).

In the 1990s, a number of companies began marketing videos designed to educate people about various aspects of human sexuality. With names like the "Better Sex" video series, these include explicit portrayals of a wide variety of consenting heterosexual activities. As such, these are erotica, not pornography. They often include commentary by a psychologist or sex therapist reassuring viewers that the activities portrayed are normal and providing factual information. These series are advertised in national magazines and some daily newspapers.

The continuum noted in magazines from the subtle to the explicit also exists in video. The subtle end is found in *music videos*. The sexual content of many videos shown on MuchMusic is unmistakable. Men are portrayed as dominant and aggressive, with prominent posturing and a clear characterization that they are wanted by and have sex with attractive women (Ward et al., 2005). Women are portrayed in a condescending manner and are valued almost exclusively for their physical appearance and sex appeal.

Live Entertainment

Shows providing live, sexualized entertainment are yet another part of the sex industry. Burlesque, which featured women seductively undressing on a stage in a theatre, has been transformed into strip clubs. These provide semi-nude (i.e., with pasties and a g-string) or nude dancing in a lounge setting; often dancers circulate among the patrons when not on stage. These clubs range in style from converted neighbourhood bars to upscale gentlemen's clubs. Participant observation research, supplemented by interviews, indicates that many of the customers are regulars; they come, not for sexual release, but for the opportunity to interact with attractive young women, and the pleasure of a sexualized interaction without the

Figure 17.5 Canadians are divided in their opinions about lap-dancing. The Supreme Court of Canada banned lap-dancing in public areas because it inflicts "attitudinal harm" to those watching but ruled that lap-dancing in private cubicles where people passing by can't see it is not indecent.

need to perform sexually (Frank, 2005). Male strippers catering to a female audience are less common but perform periodically in many communities. In the commercial sex districts of large cities, there are also live sex shows featuring couples or groups engaging in sexual acts onstage. These shows are second cousins to the elaborately staged reviews in major casinos and hotels, which often feature nudity and simulated sexual activity in a lavish setting.

In 1997, there were 2478 licensed exotic dancers in Toronto alone (Maticka-Tyndale et al., 1999). Dancers perform stage shows, table dances, and lap dances. Dancers earn only a small wage for dancing on stage and are typically expected to offer table dances or lap dances if requested. Lap dances can be performed either in public or in private areas of the club. In the private areas the stripper allows the patron to touch her body, excluding her genitals, as she dances. Most often she will gyrate in his lap and rub herself against him. An Ontario study found that lap-dancers made between $10 and $20 per dance, although customers pay more for dances in private rooms (Lewis & Maticka-Tyndale, 1998). Some strip clubs also offer VIP rooms in which a greater level of sexual activity takes place, although not all strippers provide these services. Typically, this involves fellatio and manual stimulation to ejaculation as well as a lap dance. The price is typically between $100 and $150.

The question of whether lap-dancing is legal or constitutes an "indecent performance," particularly when done in a private room, has not been fully settled by the courts. However, in general, the courts have ruled that the community's level of tolerance can be placed quite high when activities occur in private. This is complicated by the fact that lap-dancing is safest for dancers if it is done in a public area of the club where they are less likely to be assaulted or forced to go beyond "dancing" (Lewis & Maticka-Tyndale, 1998; Maticka-Tyndale et al., 2000b).

There is also more protection for the customer in these public areas from pressure to engage in activities beyond watching the dancer. Some cities, such as Toronto, have enacted bylaws that prohibit physical contact, including touching, between patrons and persons providing services in adult entertainment parlours as a way of restricting table dancing and lap-dancing.

TELEPHONE SEX

Telephone sex provides another example of enlisting technology to sell sexual titillation. A 1991 study of a sample of prerecorded messages identified several patterns (Glascock & LaRose, 1993). The typical recording was of a female voice describing a series of sexual activities in which the caller was a participant such as fantasies involving masturbation, vaginal intercourse, and oral sex. Few of the descriptions included violence or rape. More frequent were descriptions of activities in which the woman dominated and degraded the man.

There are also phone sex services that provide live conversation. In some cases, large numbers of chat-line workers may be in the same location talking to callers. Prices are typically $5 to $10 per minute. In other cases, the phone sex worker takes calls at his or her home. Some phone sex workers are students who need money for tuition and books. One such student set up a 1-900 line in her home after reading an advertisement for phone sex operators in a Winnipeg newspaper (Schroeder, 2000). Callers were charged $1.30 per minute.

Most callers are men; most chat-line workers are women. The men typically masturbate during the conversation. A male described one conversation:

> I say, "When you give a guy a blow job, what's your favorite way to do it?" She says, "Well, I love being on my knees, cause being on my knees with him standing is so submissive." I said, "Do you like looking at his cock in his pants, does that really turn you on?" She says, "I love that." I say, "I would love to be standing in front of you." She says, "Oh, that would really turn me on." "Do you like having your breasts played with when you're giving a blow job?" "Yes, I like it very much. I also like to be fingered." "How many fingers do you like inside you?" "I love two fingers." "And why do you like blowing a guy so much?" "Because I'm getting him excited and I know I can't wait for him to fuck me." "Do you like to fuck for a long time?" "Yes, I get lost in it." So then I said, "Well, I've really been thinking about you on top of me, and while you're riding me, I'll be spanking you." She said, "Oh God, I love that." I was masturbating and I came. It was great. (Maurer, 1994, 349–350)

PORNOGRAPHY ONLINE

In the past 15 years the Internet has made available a wide variety of sex-related services for every computer attached to a modem or DSL line, whether at work, at school, or at home. An analysis of random samples of 50 000 websites from the Google index and 1 million sites from the MSN index found that 1.1 percent of the sites on both were sexually explicit adult entertainment sites (Stark, 2006). The samples were drawn in late 2005 and early 2006. These services include online chats or conversations; exchanging messages with like-minded persons via discussion groups; access to sexually arousing stories, photographs, videos, and films; and access to a broad array of goods and services via specialized websites. Research in Ontario has shown that people who view more sexually explicit material online also tend to view more non-Internet pornography (L. Byers et al., 2004).

CHAT ROOMS

Chat rooms, or Internet relay chat groups, provide a location where individuals can meet and carry on conversations electronically. These rooms are often oriented toward persons with particular sexual interests, often captured by their names. An Internet resource guide had links to 147 sex-oriented chat rooms in February 2007. The conversations often involve graphic descriptions of sexual activities or fantasies typically through instant messaging. The

Figure 17.6 The newest innovation in the porn business is computer porn.

telephone sex conversation reproduced earlier could have taken place electronically, with the words displayed on a computer screen or through audio connections instead of spoken over a phone line. In this context, an interesting feature of these chats can be that the other person cannot see you. This allows you to present yourself in any way you desire, to rehearse or try out a broad range of identities:

> Doug is a midwestern college junior. He plays four characters . . . One is a seductive woman. One is a macho, cowboy type whose self-description stresses that he is a "Marlboros-rolled-in-the-T-shirt sleeve kind of guy." The third is a rabbit of unspecified gender . . . a character he calls Carrot. (Turkle, 1995, p. 13)

Doug would not describe the fourth character, beyond saying it was furry. Remember that the character you are chatting with may not be who she or he seems to be.

On some sites, customers can actually see the performers as well as communicate with them either through text messaging or audio connections, so as to direct the sexual activity they are viewing. They may also be able to control the video camera from their home computer. Sexual activities run the full range from masturbation to couple activity to unusual sexual interests. Some people also make use of webcams or cell phone cams as part of the interaction.

NEWS GROUPS

People can also log on to sex-oriented news or discussion groups, read messages posted by others, and post messages themselves. The messages may include personal information, or they may be a story or a file containing pornographic pictures in digital format. Stories can be printed by the user; picture files can be downloaded and viewed through a "plug-in." Often, the messages are simply advertisements for or links to sex-oriented websites that sell pornographic material. The resource guide mentioned previously had links to 677 sex-oriented news groups.

COMMERCIAL BULLETIN BOARDS

There are numerous commercial bulletin boards that contain sexually explicit photographs in digital form. The aforementioned resource guide listed 35 sex-oriented bulletin boards. Users may log on to these bulletin boards and download images for a fee. Each image is listed in an electronic catalogue with a short description. Table 17.1 displays the results of a large-scale analysis of images of bulletin boards. Hard-core images (sample description: "Girl with big tits gets fucked by guy") made up 38 percent of the downloaded images. Another 33 percent were images of paraphilias ("Girl with big tits gets fucked by horse"). Of particular concern is the popularity of pedophilic images, which accounted for 15.6 percent of the downloaded images. Possessing such images are illegal in Canada (see In Focus 2.2 on page 44) and not readily available elsewhere. The researchers concluded: "The adult BBS market is driven largely by the demand for paraphilic and pedophilic imagery. The availability of, and the demand for, vaginal sex imagery is relatively small" (Rimm, 1995, p. 1890). Canadian and U.S. authorities continue to debate what, if anything, can be done to regulate the flow of these materials on computer networks.

Table 17.1   Total Surveyed "Adult" Usenet Files and Downloads by Classification

Classification	Total Files		Total Downloads	
Hard-core	133 180	(45.6%)	2 102 329	(37.9%)
Soft-core	75 659	(25.9%)	760 009	(13.7%)
Paraphilia	63 232	(21.6%)	1 821 444	(32.8%)
Pedophilia	20 043	(6.9%)	864 333	(15.6%)

Source: Rimm, 1995, p. 1891.

ADULT WEBSITES

Adult websites sell a variety of pornographic services and sexual materials. The resource guide mentioned earlier had links to 768 such sites, with names like Amateur Yearbook, Asian Pleasures, Cheerleader Ezine, Lydia Lashes, Pantyhose Ezine, and Sorority Girls. Each site typically includes thousands of photos organized by content, videos that can be viewed on a computer screen, stories, links to live sex shows, and links to live video cameras in places such as men's and women's locker rooms. Some also sell videos, CD-ROMs, sex aids such as dildos, and other sexual devices and costumes. Some also include "interactive" sex shows, where the viewer can request that the actors perform specific acts. Many of these sites specialize, featuring "teenagers" (if the actors are under 18, the material violates the law), black, Asian, or Latina women, gays, lesbians, pregnant women, and on and on. Each site charges a daily, weekly, or monthly "membership fee" for access; the fee can usually be paid by supplying a valid credit card number.

Computer pornography can be a positive alternative sexual outlet. Further, it allows people access to sexually explicit images in privacy, letting them explore their individual interests without experiencing shyness or shame (Nosko et al., 2007). However, computer pornography may also be a cause for concern, for several reasons. One is that the large and ever-increasing number of chat rooms, news groups, and websites facilitate a person becoming dependent on or addicted to (see Chapter 15) this type of sexual content (Yellowlees & Marks, 2007). None of these involves face-to-face social interaction, which is central to most sexual relationships; the risk is that they become a substitute. However, only a small percentage of people who use the Internet for sexual activities (1 percent in one study) develop a sexual addiction or compulsion (Griffiths, 2001). There is also a great deal of concern that children will access these materials. For example, children may receive unsolicited sexually explicit material through email, junk mail, and pop-ups. They may unwittingly link to a pornographic site by typing in an ambiguous term. Some parents try to counter this by installing software filters. All adult sites include a printed notice that one must be over 18 to access the site, and that one who is offended by sexually explicit material should not enter the site. This "honour system" is not an effective control. It is true that to access a website or download photographs from bulletin boards the user must supply a valid credit card number, but this is not a major deterrent for many adolescents. To date, there has been little guidance from Canadian courts on the issues involved in computer pornography.

Finally, the Internet facilitates the distribution of child pornography, which is illegal in Canada. Existing Canadian laws governing child pornography apply to the Internet, and some law enforcement agencies seek out and arrest offenders. However, this material can be easily transferred across borders, and may be legal in the country where it originated, making enforcement of the child pornography laws difficult (Canadian Centre for Justice Statistics, 1999).

CHILD PORNOGRAPHY

Child pornography, or kiddie porn, features photographs or films of sexual acts involving children. It is viewed as the most reprehensible part of the porn industry because it produces such an obvious victim, the child model. Children, by virtue of their developmental level, cannot give truly informed consent to participation in such activities, and the potential for doing psychological and physical damage to them is great.

In 1993, a specific statute prohibiting people from possessing, making, or distributing child pornography, defined as any depiction of a person under the age of 18 engaging in explicit sexual activity, was added to the Criminal Code of Canada (see In Focus 2.2 on page 44). These statutes use the term "pornography" rather than "obscenity" as with the adult provisions, and they specifically prohibit the making, sale, or possession of child pornography. The purpose of these laws is to protect children from harm by ensuring that they are not involved in the making of pornography and by preventing child sexual abuse by users of child pornography. Indeed, research in Ontario has shown that most men convicted of child pornography offences are pedophiles—that is, show a preference for prepubescent children and thus are at risk to offend against children (Seto et al., 2006). Child pornography is defined as any material that shows a child's genitals for a sexual purpose or depicts a child engaged in sexual activity. A child is defined as anyone under the age of 18. These statutes also outlaw "pseudo-child pornography"—that is, pornography that uses adults but makes them look like children.

There are several ways in which the child pornography offences differ from offences governing adult pornography. Displaying or offering to sell pornography to persons under 16 is an offence, whether or not these materials would be viewed as obscene under the Criminal Code. In addition, the sentences for child pornography offences are greater than for obscenity offences. Finally, it is an offence to be in the possession of child pornography, whereas it is only illegal to sell or distribute obscene material involving adults.

In 2001, the Supreme Court upheld the law criminalizing the possession of child pornography with two narrow exceptions. It ruled that possessing private works of imagination that have artistic merit and photographic depictions of oneself are legal. Thus, it is legal to write or draw sexually explicit depictions of children for one's own personal pleasure. In response to this ruling, Parliament passed amendments to the child pornography legislation in 2002 that

Child pornography: Pictures or films of sexual acts involving children.

In Focus 17.3

Ernie: A Pedophile and Child Pornographer

In a study of child sexual abuse and child pornography, the investigators reported the following description of one offender:

Contact was made with Ernie, a northern Indiana man, and arrangements were made to meet with him to share child pornography collections. Ernie arrived at a motel room carrying a small suitcase containing approximately 75 magazines and a metal file box containing twelve super-8-mm movies. The metal box was also filled with numerous photographs. Ernie then began to discuss his collection. He described himself as a pedophile and showed a series of instant photographs he had taken of his seven-year-old niece while she slept. The pictures revealed Ernie's middle finger inserted into the young girl's uncovered genitals, and he described how he had worked his finger up into her. Other photographs featured the girl being molested in various ways by Ernie while she remained asleep.

Despite the fact that he had engaged in numerous incidents of child molestation, Ernie had not been discovered because his victims remained asleep. He had molested and exploited both males and females, his own children, grandchildren, and neighbourhood children. In order to photograph the uncovered genitals of his sleeping victims, Ernie had devised a string and hook mechanism.

The hook was attached to the crotch of the underpants, and he would uncover his sleeping victims' genitals as he photographed them with an instant-developing camera.

Ernie displayed his collection with the pride of a hobbyist. He exhibited photographs he had reproduced from magazines; he had reproduced these same photographs repeatedly and had engaged in a child pornography business from his residence.

While displaying his magazines and films, Ernie was arrested. A search warrant was obtained for his residence, and material seized from his one-bedroom apartment filled two pickup trucks. Numerous sexually explicit films, photographs, magazines, advertisements, and children's soiled underwear were confiscated. The panties had been encased in plastic, the child's school photograph featured with the panties. Also confiscated were nine cameras and a projector.

Several months passed before investigators found proof that Ernie had processed, through a central Indiana photographic lab, approximately 1500 photographs per week. It is believed that Ernie sold these pictures at $2 each, grossing an estimated $3000 per week.

Source: Burgess, 1984, pp. 26–27.

broadened the definition of child pornography, prohibited advertising child pornography, increased penalties, and ensured that people using the artistic merit defence will have to show that they have a legitimate purpose for possessing the child pornography.

A major study of people who produce child pornography found that all of the 69 offenders studied were male. They ranged in age from 20 to 70, with an average age of 43. Thirty-eight percent had an already established relationship with the child before the illicit activity began—they were family friends or relatives, neighbours, teachers, or counsellors (Burgess, 1984). For a profile of one child pornographer, see In Focus 17.3. Interpol, the International Criminal Police Organization, has an office in Ottawa and tracks Internet child pornography cases in Canada. In 2001, it identified 500 cases.

ADVERTISING

Let's close our discussion of pornography by considering a mating of sex and money that all of us encounter every day—*sex in advertising.* Both subtle and obvious sexual promises are used to sell a wide variety of products. A muscular young man wearing low-slung jeans and no shirt sells Calvin Kleins. Abercrombie & Fitch catalogues feature photos of nude young people in bed or in pools. Perfumes promise that they will make women instantly sexually attractive. One brand of coffee seems to guarantee a warm, romantic, sensuous evening for the couple who drink it.

How much sexual content is there in advertising? One study analyzed the sexual content of magazine advertising in 1983 and 2003 (Reichert & Carpenter, 2004). Sexual clothing as well as portrayals of intimate contact became more frequent. In 2003, for example, 78 percent of women in ads in men's magazines were attired in sexually suggestive clothing. Sexually provocative behaviour is another aspect of sex found in magazine advertising; in ads portraying heterosexual couples, 53 percent engage in sexual contact (passionate kissing, simulated intercourse) (Reichert, 2002).

Television advertising uses not only bodily display or nudity and sexually suggestive interaction but also context (a Caribbean beach, a bed or bedroom) and language including double entendre (a message with two meanings, one being sexual) and talk about sexual activity. Some advertisers, such as Victoria's Secret and Calvin Klein, cultivate a sexually suggestive image. A study of prime-time commercials broadcast on NBC found that 12 percent of the female models and 2 percent of the male models were dressed to be sexually suggestive. Network promotional ads were more likely to include sexual content. Sexual contact increased from 12 percent in 1990 to 21 percent in 1998. A review of the research on the effects of advertising concludes that sexual information attracts attention, and viewers are more likely to remember the sexual image; paradoxically, however, they are less likely to remember the brand name (Reichert, 2002). Beyond the effects of ads on brand images and purchasing, there is concern that continuing exposure to ads that contain gender stereotyped ideas and images, such as thin, attractive females and taut, buff males, may affect attitudes toward one's body. Male and female college students were shown either 20 sexist ads, 15 sexist ads, and 5 neutral ads, or no ads. The results indicated that exposure to the sexist ads was associated with dissatisfaction with one's own body among *both* men and women (Lavine et al., 1999).

Figure 17.7 Sex in advertising. Many advertisers, including Calvin Klein, use sexual images to sell products.

THE CUSTOMERS

What is known about the consumer of pornography? As shown in Table 17.2 on page 553, most people using pornography are men between the ages of 18 and 40. Studies consistently find that the typical customer in an X-rated bookstore is an educated, middle-class male between the ages of 22 and 34 (Mahoney, 1983). That is, the use of the materials sold in such stores is "typical" or "normal" (in the statistical sense) among males. But the range is wide. The manager of one store said,

> We get everyone in here from millionaires to scum of the earth. The blue-collar and white-collar men come for the tapes. Married couples come in for things to help their sex life. The gay crowd cruises the booths in back. Groups of women come in for gag items. ("Porn Shop," 1994)

Figure 17.8 While there are differences between men and women in their response to pornography, some women enjoy watching a stripper as much as some men do.

Women purchase and watch pornographic videos. Research conducted in Australia in 1999 reported that 65 percent of X-rated videos were purchased by a woman or a heterosexual couple. In data from 280 women, 20 percent said they selected the video, 50 percent said both selected it, 18 percent said the partner selected it with both their preferences in mind, and 9 percent said the partner selected it (Contessini, 2003). Female interest in erotica was recognized 20 years ago by Candida Royalle, then a film star; she became a producer and director and has made more than a dozen films directed toward women. A growing number of men and women are attempting to market to women, producing what is called "female empowered" adult entertainment, including films, cable TV programs, sex-toy stores, and websites.

Surveys also suggest that many students use sexually explicit materials. Researchers in Ontario found that 63 percent of women had read erotic novels, 45 percent had read *Playboy*-type magazines, 36 percent had read *Playgirl*-type magazines, and 39 percent had watched an X-rated video in the last year (Lawrance & Herold, 1988). Male students have more positive feelings about online sexual content and are more likely to follow up unsolicited sexually related emails and pop-ups (Nosko et al., 2007).

Repeat customers are a crucial part of the success of the porn business: "There are people who come in here three to five times a day for their fix. Before work. At lunch. After work. Late at night. Their addiction isn't to the perversion of it, just the pornography" ("Porn Shop," 1994). Adult retail stores are potentially important as sources of sexual health information and products (Reece et al., 2004). A survey of employees of 80 stores in the United States found that most sold condoms and lubricants, and up to half provided written health information. Partnerships with sexual health professionals and training for employees could enhance this potential.

Computer porn attracts a more varied clientele. Chat rooms and news groups attract both men and women of diverse ages (assuming that those who describe themselves are doing so accurately). Some of these people are married. Depending on the focus of the room or group, participants may be from diverse racial or ethnic backgrounds. For the most part, bulletin boards and adult websites probably attract the same types of clients as adult bookstores—young, middle-class, white men. However, Nielson/NetRatings found that one-quarter of visitors to adult websites are women (Navano, 2004). Table 17.2 presents results from an online survey that assessed the number of times and hours per month that users view sexually explicit materials.

Table 17.2	Do you use porn? A survey by the Kinsey Institute (N = 10 453)	
Sex		
Male	80%	
Female	17%	
Age		
18 to 20	11%	
21 to 30	31%	
31 to 40	29%	
41 to 50	15%	
51 to 60	7%	
61 to 70	2%	
71 or older	1%	
Viewed sexual images in the past month?		
Never have viewed them	3%	
Not once, but I have in the past	20%	
One or two times	16%	
Once a week	10%	
A few times a week	27%	
Once a day	9%	
Several times a day	10%	
How much time per week in the past month?		
I did not use porn in the past month	11%	
Less than one hour	18%	
1 to 5 hours	37%	
6 to 15 hours	16%	
16 to 25 hours	6%	
26 to 50 hours	3%	
More than 50 hours	3%	
Why do you use porn? (Top 5 answers)		
To masturbate/for physical release	72%	
To sexually arouse myself and/or others	69%	
Out of curiosity	54%	
To fantasize about things I would not necessarily want in real life	43%	
To distract myself	38%	

Source: © Erick Janssen/PBS/Frontline.

FEMINIST OBJECTIONS TO PORNOGRAPHY

Some—though not all—feminists are very critical of pornography (e.g., Griffin, 1981; Jensen, 2007; Lederer, 1980). Why would feminists, who prize sexual liberation, be opposed to pornography?

There are four basic reasons why some feminists object to pornography. First, they argue that pornography debases women. In the milder, soft-core versions it portrays women as sex objects whose breasts, legs, and buttocks can be purchased and then ogled. In the hardcore versions women may be shown being urinated upon or being chained. To what extent does mainstream pornography objectify women? The answer depends in part on how one defines the term, and there is controversy over that. Defining objectification as including treating another person as an object, one partner dominating another, and penis worship,

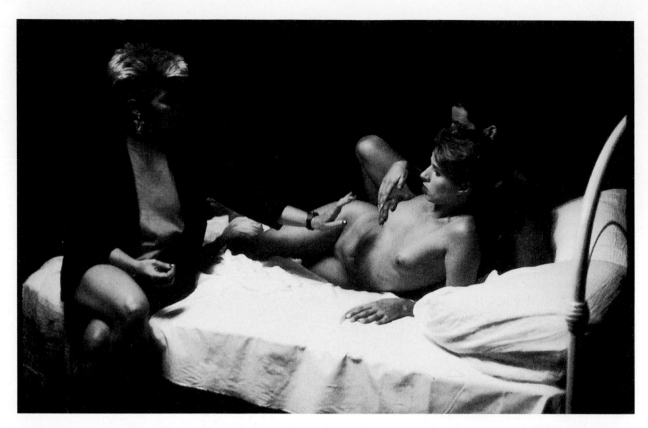

Figure 17.9   Candida Royalle (left), a former porn star, now produces and directs soft-core films geared toward a female audience.

one researcher performed a content analysis of the 50 best-selling pornographic videos in Australia (McKee, 2005). Many of the videos were imports from the United States and Europe. Seven measures allowed direct comparison of portrayals of men and portrayals of women. On one, not having an orgasm, women were significantly higher than men. On three, less time spent looking at the camera, less time spent talking to the camera, and less likely to initiate sex, men were significantly higher than women. On three measures, having a name, being a central character, and time spent talking, there were no significant differences.

Second, pornography associates sex with violence toward women. As such, some feminists believe it contributes to sexual assault and other forms of violence against women and girls. Robin Morgan has put it bluntly: "pornography is the theory and rape is the practice" (Morgan, 1980, p. 139). This is a point that can be tested with scientific data, producing evidence that will be covered shortly.

Third, pornography shows, indeed glamorizes, unequal power relationships between women and men. A common theme in pornography is men forcing women to have sex, so the power of men and subordination of women are emphasized. Consistent with this point, feminists do not object to sexual materials that portray women and men in equal, humanized relationships—what we have termed *erotica*.

Finally, they object to the structure of the pornography industry. Anti-pornography feminists believe that many models and actors in the pornography industry are physically, sexually, and emotionally abused in doing their work.

Feminists also note the intimate relationship between pornography and traditional gender roles. Pornography is enmeshed as both cause and effect. That is, pornography in part results from traditional gender roles that make it socially acceptable for men to use and require hypersexuality and aggressiveness as part of the male role. In turn, pornography may serve to perpetuate traditional gender roles. By seeing or reading about dominant males and submissive, dehumanized females, each new generation of adolescent boys is socialized to accept these roles. On the other hand, the female-oriented videos discussed earlier attempt to equalize the power relationships between the male and female characters and are often filmed from the woman's point of view.

THE EFFECTS OF VIOLENT PORNOGRAPHY[3]

Some of the assertions just summarized—for example, that using violent pornography may predispose men toward committing violent crimes against women—can be tested using the methods of social science. A number of social psychologists have been collecting data for 35 years to test such assertions.

Four questions can be asked about the effects of using pornography. First, does it produce sexual arousal? Second, does it affect users' attitudes, particularly about sexual and non-sexual violence toward women? Third, does it affect the sexual behaviour of users? Fourth, does it affect the aggressive or criminal behaviour of users, particularly aggressive behaviour toward women?

More than 40 studies have examined the effect of sexually explicit material on sexual arousal. This research consistently finds that exposure to *material that the viewer finds acceptable* does produce arousal (Davis & Bauserman, 1993). Exposure to portrayals that the viewer finds objectionable produces a negative reaction. Most people disapprove of paraphilic behaviours (see Chapter 15), sexual assault, and sexual activity involving children, so they react negatively to hard-core and child pornography.

There are gender differences in self-reports of response to sexually explicit materials. Men report higher levels of arousal to such portrayals than do women (Malamuth, 1998). The differences are larger in response to pornography than to erotica, and the difference is much larger among university students than among older persons (Murnen & Stockton, 1997). This difference between men and women is often attributed to the fact that most erotica and pornography is male-oriented. The focus is almost exclusively on sexual behaviour, with little character development or concern for relationships. There is limited foreplay and afterplay; the male typically ejaculates on some part of the woman's body (the "cum shot") rather than inside her. Former porn film star Candida Royalle produces videos made for women. An experiment found that male university students responded positively to and were aroused by videos made for men and for women; females reported negative responses to the videos intended for men and positive responses and sexual arousal to the videos designed for women (Mosher & MacIan, 1994).

What about the effect of pornography on attitudes? The research indicates that a single exposure to stories, photographs, or videos has little or no effect. Massive exposure (such as viewing videos for five hours) does lead to more permissive attitudes. In this situation, viewers become more tolerant of the behaviour observed and less in favour of restrictions on it (Davis & Bauserman, 1993). What about attitudes toward aggression against women? Some studies show that exposure to portrayals of forced intercourse lead men to be more tolerant of sexual assault, but other studies do not find a relationship between exposure and attitudes (Fisher & Grenier, 1994). Men exposed to portrayals of sexual aggression against women do not report a greater willingness to sexually assault a woman (Davis & Bauserman, 1993).

With regard to sexual behaviour, the research shows that, in response to erotic portrayals of consenting heterosexual activity, both men and women may report an increase in sexual thoughts and fantasies and in behaviours such as masturbation and intercourse. Exposure to portrayals of behaviour the person has not personally engaged in does *not* lead to an increase in these behaviours (Davis & Bauserman, 1993).

[3]Note that this discussion refers to violent pornography. There are many other sexually explicit images that are not of concern.

Finally, there has been great interest in whether exposure to portrayals of sexual aggression (which almost always involve men behaving aggressively toward women) increase aggressive behaviour. In laboratory studies, a number of studies have shown that men who are insulted or provoked by a woman and have been exposed to violent pornography are significantly more aggressive toward the woman in the experimental situation compared with men exposed to sexually explicit but non-violent material. If the comparison group is men exposed to non-sexual violent films, many studies find no difference between the two, but some find that exposure to sexual violence increases aggression toward a woman more than exposure just to violence (Davis & Bauserman, 1993). Research in Ontario suggests that men with lower IQs may be more influenced by violent pornography than men with higher IQs (Bogaert et al., 1999). However, few men (5 to 6 percent in one Ontario study) choose to watch violent pornography when given the opportunity (Bogaert, 1993, 2001).

Ontario psychologists William Fisher and Guy Grenier have questioned the extent to which these laboratory studies capture the relationship between pornography and aggression in the "real world" (Fisher & Grenier, 1994). They point out that, in these laboratory studies, the men are told by the experimenter to send some level of shock to the female confederate. Although they can choose the level of shock to administer, they are not given the opportunity to engage in a non-aggressive response. However, in a real-life situation, a man could choose to speak to a woman who angered him or to walk away from the situation, instead of engaging in an aggressive response. The researchers found that when given the choice, 86 percent of the men chose not to make an aggressive response.

In sum, then, we can conclude that exposure to sexually explicit material that the viewer finds acceptable is arousing to both men and women. Exposure to aggressive pornography does increase men's aggression toward women under certain laboratory conditions. The extent to which these results are generalizable to a real-life situation is not known, however. Exposure to aggressive pornography may also affect males' attitudes, making them more accepting of violence against women. However, researchers in Ontario have concluded that men who are already predisposed to sexual aggression are the most likely to be affected by pornography; men who are not predisposed toward violence are unlikely to be affected (Seto et al., 2001).

What about the effects of pornography on women? Researchers in Ontario found that exposure to violent and dehumanizing pornography, but not to erotica, has a negative emotional impact on women (Senn & Radtke, 1990). Of particular interest is that women who reported having had more forceful sexual experiences in the past were particularly negative in their evaluations of pornography but not of erotica. It may be that, for these women, violent sexual images bring back painful memories.

WHAT IS THE SOLUTION?

Some of the conclusions about pornography (not about erotica) are disturbing. What is the solution? Should pornography be censored or made illegal? Or would this only make it forbidden and therefore more attractive, and still available on the black market? Or should all forms of pornography be legal and readily available, and should we rely on other methods—such as education of parents and students through the school system—to abolish its use? Or should we adopt some in-between strategy, making some forms of pornography—such as child pornography and violent porn—illegal, while allowing free access to erotica? Note that the 1992 Supreme Court decision in the *Butler* case adopted this latter approach.

Our own opinion is that legal restrictions of sexually explicit material depicting adults—known less politely as censorship—are probably not the solution. We agree with the view of Donnerstein and his colleagues that a better solution is education (Donnerstein et al., 1987; Linz et al., 1987). In their experiments, they debrief male participants at the conclusion of the procedures. They convey to the participants that media depictions are unreal and that the portrayal of women enjoying forced sex is fictitious. They dispel common myths about sexual assault, especially any that were shown in the film used in the experiment. Participants who have been debriefed in this way show less acceptance of myths about sexual aggression and more sensitivity to victims of sexual assault than participants shown a neutral film (Donnerstein et al., 1987). More recently, researchers in Ontario examined the effects of a similar intervention on men's responses to Internet pornography (Isaacs & Fisher 2008). This intervention reduced the men's attraction to and enjoyment of violent pornography compared to men who did not get the intervention. The experimental group was also more able to recognize and reject violent pornography.

Subsequently, some researchers introduced *pre*-briefing of participants in research involving exposure to sexually explicit materials. The typical briefing (pre or post) consists of a short audiotape or a printed handout pointing out that the material is fictional. It reminds participants that women do not enjoy forced sex and that sexual assault is a serious crime. Researchers identified ten studies that included pre- or post-debriefing, and measures of the effects of exposure to the material. All ten found that there were no negative effects of exposure accompanied by an educational briefing; in six of the studies, participants were less accepting of rape myths at the conclusion of the study than at the beginning (Allen et al., 1996). This research provides solid evidence that education can eliminate at least negative effects on attitudes.

SUMMARY

Commercial sex is a major industry in Canada, and increasingly around the world. Two prominent aspects of it are sex work and pornography. Although sex work is not illegal in Canada, various activities related to it are. It is also a crime to sec or distribute any material that is "obscene." Obscenity is determined using the community standards of tolerance test. Possession of child pornography is also illegal.

Commercial sex workers engage in partnered sexual activity in return for payment, such as money, gifts, or drugs. There are several venues in which they work in Canada, including their own homes, in-call services, out-call services, and massage parlours. The working conditions, risks, and income of a sex worker depend on the setting. Third parties who may be involved include a pimp, madam, or manager; the involvement of these people generally limits a worker's autonomy. Sex trafficking involves exploitation and is a major problem. Research suggests that a female sex worker's well-being depends upon the risk level of the setting in which she works, the reasons she entered sex work, and whether she experienced victimization as a child or adolescent.

Data indicate that the use of sex workers has declined substantially in North America in the past 50 years. About one-half of the clients of female sex workers are occasional johns; the other 50 percent are repeat clients. Some men rely on sex workers for their sexual outlet.

Some male sex workers serve a female clientele. They may work as escorts, employees of massage parlours, or gigolos. More common are hustlers who cater to a male clientele.

Distinctions are made among pornography (sexually arousing art, literature, or film), obscenity (material offensive to Canadians), and erotica

Continued on next page.

SUMMARY *cont.*

(sexual material that shows men and women in equal, humane relationships). Pornographic magazines, films, and DVDs, both soft-core (erotica) and hard-core, are a multi-billion-dollar business. Electronic porn has mushroomed in the past 20 years; people can discuss explicit sexual activity online, read sexually arousing stories, download sexually explicit images, or purchase a variety of goods and services at adult websites. Children—often runaways—are the star-victims in child pornography.

Some feminists object to pornography on the grounds that it debases women, encourages violence against women, and portrays unequal relationships between men and women.

Social-psychological research indicates that exposure to portrayals that the viewer finds acceptable is arousing to both men and women. Men are more likely to report arousal than women. Massive exposure leads to more favourable attitudes toward the behaviour observed. Some studies find that exposure to violent pornography creates more tolerant attitudes toward violence against women but others find no such effect. Exposure of heterosexuals to portrayals of consenting heterosexual activity leads to an increase in sexual thoughts and behaviour. Exposure to portrayals of sexual or non-sexual violence toward women increases men's aggression against women in the laboratory. Education about the effects of pornography is probably the best solution to the problems created by violent and dehumanizing pornography.

QUESTIONS FOR THOUGHT, DISCUSSION, AND DEBATE

1. What is your position on the issue of censoring pornography? Do you think that all pornography should be illegal? Or should all pornography be legal? Or should some kinds—such as child pornography and violent pornography—be illegal, but not other kinds? What reasoning led you to your position?

2. In Canada, sex work is not illegal but many of the activities associated with sex work, such as communicating for the purposes of sex work, are illegal. Some people argue that we should have stricter laws and tougher sentences to deter the exchange of sex for money. Other people argue that sex work should be decriminalized, as it is a private matter between consenting adults. Based on what you know about sex workers and their clients, what approach would you suggest? Should the act of sex work be a criminal offence? If sex work-related activities were legal, in what ways should the sex trade be regulated, if at all?

3. Many of the streetwalkers in major cities are black or Asian women. Adult websites often prominently display photographs, stories, and videos about "interracial sex." Yet most of the customers of both sex workers and adult websites are white males. Why are white men attracted by materials featuring women from other ethnic groups?

SUGGESTIONS FOR FURTHER READING

Albert, Alexa. (2001). *Brothel: Mustang Ranch and its women.* New York: Random House. This book is based on a qualitative study of the Mustang Ranch. It includes the stories of some of the women who work there, their attitudes, their circumstances, and their sense of professionalism.

Bullough, Vern, and Bullough, Bonnie. (1987). *Women and prostitution: A social history.* Buffalo, NY: Prometheus Books. A fascinating history of the oldest profession, from ancient Greece and Rome, through medieval times, India, and China, to the present.

Jeffrey, L. A., and MacDonald, G. (2006). *Sex workers in the Maritimes talk back.* Vancouver: UBC Press. A book based on interviews with sex workers in the Maritimes that calls many assumptions about their lives into question.

Vanwesenbeeck, Ine. (1994). *Prostitutes' well-being and risk.* Amsterdam: VU University Press. An excellent empirical study of the determinants of psychological well-being among prostitutes.

For review questions, web resources, and other learning and study tools, visit the *Understanding Human Sexuality* Online Learning Centre at www.mcgrawhill.ca/olc/hyde.

SEXUAL DISORDERS AND SEX THERAPY

Chapter Highlights

Sexual Disorders
Desire Disorders
Arousal Disorders
Orgasmic Disorders
Sexual Pain Disorders

What Causes Sexual Disorders?
Physical Causes
Drugs
Psychological Causes
Combined Cognitive and Physiological Factors

Therapies for Sexual Disorders
Behaviour Therapy
Cognitive–Behavioural Therapy
Couple Therapy
Specific Treatments for Specific Problems
Biomedical Therapies

Critiques of Sex Therapy

Some Practical Advice
Avoiding Sexual Disorders
Choosing a Sex Therapist

Many people experience sexual problems and concerns from time to time that go away without treatment. When a problem with sexual response causes significant psychological distress or interpersonal difficulty, it is called a sexual disorder. The term *sexual dysfunction* is also used. Examples are a man's difficulty getting an erection and a woman's difficulty having an orgasm.

This definition seems fairly simple. As we will see, however, in practice it can be difficult to determine exactly when something is a sexual disorder. Indeed, whether we define something as a sexual disorder is affected by the social and cultural context in which we live. In addition, there is a tendency to think in terms of only two categories, people with a sexual disorder and "normal" people. In fact, there is a continuum. Most of us have had, at one time or another, a sexual problem that went away in a day or a few months without treatment. In one New Brunswick study, 59 percent of the men and 68 percent of the women reported experiencing a sexual problem in the previous 18 months, but none had sought treatment (MacNeil & Byers, 1997). These cases represent the shades of grey that lie between absolutely great sexual functioning and long-term difficulties that require sex therapy.

Long-term sexual difficulties can cause a great deal of psychological distress to individuals troubled by them, not to mention to their partners, and many of these people seek out treatment. Until the 1960s, the only available treatment was long-term psychoanalysis, which is costly and wasn't particularly effective. A new era in understanding and treatment was ushered in with the publication, in 1970, of *Human Sexual Inadequacy* by Masters and Johnson. This book reported on the team's research on sexual disorders, as well as on their rapid-treatment program of behavioural therapy. Since then, many additional developments have taken place in the field, including cognitive–behavioural therapy and medical (drug) treatments.

Sex disorders and treatments for them are the topics of this chapter. First we will consider the kinds of sexual disorders. Following that, we will review the causes of these disorders, and then the treatments for them.

SEXUAL DISORDERS

In this section we will consider the four categories of sexual disorders listed in the *DSM-IV*: desire disorders (hypoactive sexual desire, sexual aversion), arousal disorders (erectile disorder, female sexual arousal disorder), orgasmic disorders (rapid ejaculation, male orgasmic disorder, female orgasmic disorder), and sexual pain disorders (dyspareunia, vaginismus). They are presented in Table 18.1. Notice that the first three categories correspond to components of the sexual response cycle described by Helen Singer Kaplan and discussed and critiqued in Chapter 9. This response cycle has been criticized, particularly for women, because it assumes that people proceed in a linear fashion from one phase to the other and because the diagnostic categories focus on genital responding and neglect subjective arousal (Basson, 2005). Various groups have proposed alternative categories for understanding sexual disorders, some of which are described in this chapter. Of course, sexual disorders do not always fall so neatly into these distinct categories. For example, a person who has difficulty with orgasm or who experiences sexual pain is likely to develop low desire as a result.

Sexual disorder: A problem with sexual response that causes a person mental distress.

*Margaret Avison (1982), The Agnes Cleves Papers, *In Winter Sun/The Dumbfounding: Poems 1940–66,* Toronto: McClelland & Stewart.

Table 18.1   Sexual Disorders That Correspond to Each Phase of the Sexual Response Cycle. Sexual pain disorders may affect any or all phases of the sexual response cycle.

Type of Disorder	Men	Women
Desire	Hypoactive sexual desire disorder Sexual aversion disorder	Hypoactive sexual desire disorder Sexual aversion disorder
Arousal	Erectile disorder	Female sexual arousal disorder
Orgasmic	Premature ejaculation Male orgasmic disorder	Female orgasmic disorder
Sexual Pain	Dyspareunia	Dyspareunia Vaginismus

Source: American Psychiatric Association (2000).

Lifelong sexual disorder: A sexual disorder that has been present since the person began sexual functioning.

Acquired sexual disorder: A sexual disorder that develops after a period of normal functioning.

Situational sexual disorder: A sexual disorder that a person has in some situations but not in others.

Hypoactive sexual desire (HSD): A sexual disorder in which there is a lack of interest in sexual activity; also termed inhibited sexual desire or low sexual desire.

Each disorder can be seen to vary along two dimensions (Wincze & Carey, 1991). It can be lifelong, sometimes called a primary sexual disorder; or it can be acquired, sometimes called a secondary sexual disorder. A primary sexual disorder occurs when the individual has always had that disorder (e.g., the person has never had an orgasm). A secondary sexual disorder occurs when the individual currently has the problem but did not have the problem in the past (e.g., has had orgasms in the past but is currently unable to orgasm). Sexual disorders can also be either *generalized*, that is, occurring in all situations, or *situational*. A situational sexual disorder is when the disorder occurs in some situations but not in others. That is, many sexual disorders are not absolute. They may occur with one partner (e.g., the spouse) but not another (e.g., the lover) or in one situation (e.g., at home) but not another (e.g., on vacation). Sexual disorders can occur with a partner of the same or other gender.

DESIRE DISORDERS

HYPOACTIVE SEXUAL DESIRE

Sexual desire, or *libido*, refers to an interest in sexual activity, leading the individual to seek out sexual activity or to be pleasurably receptive to it. The term hypoactive sexual desire (HSD; the prefix *hypo* means "low") is used when an individual does not have spontaneous thoughts or fantasies about sexual activity and is not interested in sexual activity (Basson et al., 2001; Rosen & Leiblum, 1995). It is also sometimes termed *inhibited sexual desire* or *low sexual desire*. This disorder is found in both women and men. The defining characteristics are lack of interest in sex or sharply reduced interest, or a lack of responsive desire (Basson, 2007). Many people's desire occurs before sexual activity begins and leads them to initiate sex, whereas in other cases the person begins to feel desire after sexual activity starts. This latter pattern is called responsive desire.

People with HSD typically avoid situations that will evoke sexual feelings. That is, they do not initiate sex, are not receptive when their partner initiates, and do not feel frustrated if they don't engage in sexual activity. When they do engage in sexual activity, it may be because of pressure from their partner or to meet non-sexual needs such as the need for physical comfort or intimacy.

Too little sexual desire is the most common sexual issue reported by women (Basson, 2006); about 39 percent of Canadian women report diminished sexual desire, with no differences in prevalence as women age (Fisher et al., 1999). Further, roughly 10 to 15 percent of women report *no* sexual desire, with the percentage increasing as women age (West et al., 2004). About half as many men as women experience desire problems, but men definitely can experience them (Laumann et al., 1999; Maurice, 2007).

Like other sexual disorders, HSD poses complex problems of definition. There are many circumstances when it is perfectly normal for a person not to experience sexual desire. For example, one cannot be expected to be turned on by every potential partner.

It is also often true that the problem is not the individual's absolute level of sexual desire, but a discrepancy between the partners' levels (Zilbergeld & Ellison, 1980). That is, if one partner wants sex considerably less frequently than the other partner does, there is a conflict, even if neither partner is experiencing a sexual disorder. This problem is termed a **discrepancy of sexual desire**.

Discrepancy of sexual desire: A sexual problem in which the partners have considerably different levels of sexual desire.

SEXUAL AVERSION DISORDER

In sexual aversion disorder, the person has a strong aversion involving anxiety, fear, or disgust to sexual interaction and actively avoids any kind of genital contact with a partner (American Psychiatric Association, 2000). This problem causes great difficulty in the person's relationships. The prevalence of this disorder in the general population has not been documented in well-sampled studies, but experts believe that it is rare (Heiman, 2002a). It is fairly common, though, in persons who have panic disorder (Figueira et al., 2001).

AROUSAL DISORDERS

ERECTILE DISORDER

Erectile disorder is the inability to have an erection or maintain one. Other terms for it are *erectile dysfunction* and *inhibited sexual excitement*. Although erectile disorder used to be called "impotence" (a term many laypeople still use), many professionals prefer not to use this term because of the negative connotations associated with it. One result of erectile disorder is that the man cannot engage in sexual intercourse. Using terminology discussed earlier, cases of erectile disorder can be classified as either *lifelong erectile disorder* (which is quite rare) or *acquired erectile disorder* depending on whether the man has ever been able to have and maintain an erection that is satisfactory for penetration in the past. It may also be *situational* (e.g., occur with a partner but not with masturbation) or *generalized.*

Erectile (eh-REK-tile) disorder: The inability to have or maintain an erection.

According to the NHSLS, about 10 percent of men have experienced an erection problem within the last 12 months (Laumann et al., 1999). This statistic varies a great deal by age: it is only 7 percent for 18- to 29-year-olds, but 18 percent for 50- to 59-year-olds. Another American survey found rates of 19 percent in men aged 50 to 59, and 39 percent in men 60 and older (Carson et al., 2002). Research has shown that the older men are, the more likely they are to experience erectile difficulties, with the incidence of erectile disorder increasing markedly between the ages of 40 and 70 (O'Donnell et al., 2004). Studies in Germany and France have found similar rates (Braun et al., 2000; Giuliano et al., 2002). Erectile disorder is the most common of the disorders among men who seek sex therapy, particularly since the introduction of Viagra.

Psychological reactions to erectile disorder may be severe. For many men, it is one of the most embarrassing things they can imagine. Depression may follow from repeated episodes. It may also cause embarrassment or worry to the man's partner.

FEMALE SEXUAL AROUSAL DISORDER

Female sexual arousal disorder refers to a lack of response to sexual stimulation (American Psychiatric Association, 2000). The disorder involves both a subjective, psychological component and a physiological element (Basson et al., 2000). It is defined partly by the woman's own subjective sense that she does not feel aroused and partly by difficulties with vaginal lubrication. However, researchers in British Columbia have shown that many women who report subjective sexual arousal difficulties did not differ from control women in their physiological arousal to an erotic film. That is, they did get physiologically aroused while viewing the film, just as the control women did (Brotto et al., 2004). In contrast, the women who reported

Female sexual arousal disorder (FSAD): A sexual disorder in which there is a lack of response to sexual stimulation.

physiological arousal difficulties (without subjective arousal difficulties) did get less aroused. This suggests that there may be different subtypes of female sexual arousal disorder.

Difficulties with lubrication are common; they were reported by 19 percent of the women in the NHSLS (Laumann et al., 1994). These problems become particularly frequent among women during and after menopause and this is not a sexual disorder: as estrogen levels decline, vaginal lubrication decreases. The use of sterile lubricants is an easy way to deal with this problem. The absence of subjective feelings of arousal is more complex to treat.

ORGASMIC DISORDERS

PREMATURE (RAPID) EJACULATION

Premature (rapid) ejaculation: A sexual disorder in which the man ejaculates too soon and feels he cannot control when he ejaculates.

Premature ejaculation (or PE) occurs when a man has an orgasm and ejaculates sooner than desired—that is, too soon. In extreme cases, ejaculation may take place so soon after erection that it occurs before penetration can occur. In other cases, the man is able to delay the orgasm to some extent, but not as long as he would like or not long enough to meet his partner's preferences. Some experts prefer the terms *early ejaculation* or *rapid ejaculation* as having fewer negative connotations (Grenier & Byers, 1995, 2001).

While the definition just given—having an orgasm and ejaculating too soon—seems simple enough, in practice it is difficult to specify when a man is a premature or rapid ejaculator (Grenier & Byers, 1995, 2001; Metz et al., 1997). What should the precise criterion for "too soon" be? Should the man be required to last for at least 30 seconds after stimulation begins? For 12 minutes? For two minutes after penetration? The definitions used by authorities in the field vary widely. One source defines "prematurity" as the occurrence of orgasm less than 30 seconds after the penis has been inserted. Another group has extended this to two minutes (Waldinger et al, 2005); for a third, the criterion is ejaculation before there have been ten pelvic thrusts. Psychiatrist and sex therapist Helen Singer Kaplan (1974; see also Grenier & Byers, 2001; McCarthy, 1989) believed that the key to defining rapid ejaculation is the absence of voluntary control of orgasm; that is, the real problem is that the man with premature ejaculation has little or no control over when he orgasms. Another good definition is self-definition: if a man finds that he has become greatly concerned about his lack of ejaculatory control or that it is interfering with his ability to form intimate relationships, or if a couple agree that it is a problem in their relationship, it is entirely legitimate to seek professional assistance for these concerns.

Poor ejaculatory control is a common problem in the general male population. Our research has shown that 24 percent of Canadian men report having a current problem with climaxing too early (Grenier & Byers, 2001). Although the average time to ejaculation after penetration reported by the men in this study was about eight minutes, 7 percent reported ejaculating within one minute and 17 percent reported ejaculating within two minutes. Further, 23 percent of the men felt that they had a sexual difficulty or problem due to early ejaculation. However, not all of these men ejaculated quickly; some were concerned because they had unrealistic expectations about how long intercourse should last. It might be some relief for them to know that their female partners were less likely to see their rapid ejaculation as a problem—only 10 percent of the partners felt the man had a problem related to rapid ejaculation (Byers & Grenier, 2003). Further, PE was associated with lower sexual satisfaction for the men but not for their partners, and it was not associated with relationship satisfaction for either partner. In another study, 53 percent of university men in New Brunswick reported limited ejaculatory control; 59 percent were very concerned about ejaculating sooner than they wanted to (Grenier & Byers, 1997). Very few of these men had ever sought therapy for the problem.

Like erectile disorders, premature ejaculation may create a web of related psychological problems. Because the ability to postpone ejaculation and "satisfy" a partner is so important in our concept of a man who is a competent lover, rapid ejaculation can cause a man to become anxious about his sexual competence. Furthermore, the partner may become frustrated because she or he is not having a satisfying sexual experience either. So the condition may create friction in the relationship.

The negative psychological effects of early ejaculation are illustrated by a young man in one of our sexuality classes who handed in an anonymous question. He described himself as a premature ejaculator and said that after several humiliating experiences during intercourse with dates, he was now convinced that no woman would want him in that condition. He no longer had the courage to ask for dates, so he had stopped dating entirely. He wanted to know how the women in the class would react to a man with such a problem. The question was discussed in class, and most of the women agreed that their reaction to his problem would depend a great deal on the quality of the relationship they had with him. If they cared deeply for him, they would be sympathetic and patient and help him overcome the difficulty. The point is, though, that the early ejaculation had created problems so severe that the young man not only had stopped having sex but also had stopped dating.

Men have developed (mostly ineffective) home remedies for dealing with rapid ejaculation such as doubling up on condoms and using desensitizing creams. Perhaps the most common is to think of something else. We had university men in New Brunswick report the thoughts they used to delay ejaculation (Grenier & Byers, 1997). These thoughts fell into five categories: sex negative (thinking of an unattractive TV personality); sex positive (thinking "we're in no hurry" or visualizing a past episode of prolonged intercourse); non-sexual and negative (thinking of a sad event, unpaid debts); sex neutral (counting backwards from 100); and sexually incongruous (thinking of your grandmother, reciting the Lord's Prayer). Of these options, we recommend the sex-positive alternative because it not only delays ejaculation but also allows both partners to remain in the moment. However, to some extent, any distraction technique may detract from attention to the sensations, and the proximity to the "point of no return." Thus, many clinicians encourage that the focus remain on sensations, and use of the stop/start technique (described later in the chapter) to maintain arousal at manageable levels.

Male Orgasmic Disorder

Male orgasmic disorder (also sometimes called *delayed* or *retarded ejaculation*) is the opposite of rapid ejaculation. The man is unable to orgasm or orgasm is greatly delayed, even though he has a solid erection and has had more than adequate stimulation (Apfelbaum, 2000; Perelman & Rowland, 2006). The severity of the problem may range from only occasional problems with orgasming to a history of never having experienced an orgasm. In the most common version, the man is incapable of orgasm during intercourse but may be able to orgasm as a result of hand or mouth stimulation. Fortunately, these problems are rare.

Male orgasmic disorder is far less common than premature ejaculation. In the NHSLS, 8 percent of the male respondents had had a problem in the last 12 months with being unable to orgasm (Laumann et al., 1999). The incidence varies only slightly as a function of age: it was 7 percent for 18- to 29-year-olds and 9 percent for 50- to 59-year-olds.

Male orgasmic disorder is, to say the least, a frustrating experience for a man. One would think that any partner would be delighted to have intercourse with a man who has a long-lasting erection that is not terminated by orgasm. In fact, though, some people react negatively to this condition, seeing their partner's inability to have an orgasm as a personal rejection. Some men, anticipating these negative reactions, have adopted the practice of faking orgasm. In some cases, the man's orgasmic disorder can create painful intercourse because intercourse goes on too long.

Female Orgasmic Disorder

Female orgasmic disorder is the inability to orgasm. This condition goes by a variety of other terms, including *orgasmic dysfunction, anorgasmia,* and *inhibited female orgasm.*

Male orgasmic disorder: A sexual disorder in which the male cannot have an orgasm, even though he has an erection and has had a great deal of sexual stimulation.

Female orgasmic disorder: A sexual disorder in which the woman is unable to have an orgasm.

Laypersons may call it "frigidity," but sex therapists reject this term because it has derogatory connotations and is imprecise because it may refer to a variety of conditions ranging from total lack of sexual arousal to arousal without orgasm. Therefore, the term female orgasmic disorder is preferred.

Like other sexual disorders, cases of female orgasmic disorder may be classified into *lifelong* and *acquired* depending on whether the woman has ever had orgasms in the past (American Psychiatric Association, 2000). A common pattern is *situational orgasmic disorder*, in which the woman has orgasms in some situations but not others. For example, she may be able to have orgasms while masturbating, but not while being stimulated by a partner.

Orgasmic disorders are common among women (Heiman, 2007). Twenty-one percent of Canadian women report that they do not usually have an orgasm during intercourse (Fisher et al., 1999). Younger women were more likely to report infrequent orgasms than were older women.

Once again, though, these definitions become more complicated in practice than in theory. Consider the case of the heterosexual woman who orgasms as a result of masturbation or hand or mouth stimulation by a partner but who does not orgasm in vaginal intercourse. Is this really a sexual disorder? The notion that it is a disorder can be traced to sexual scripts and beliefs that there is a "right" way to have sex—with the penis inside the vagina—and a corresponding "right" way to have orgasms. Because this pattern of situational orgasmic disorder is so common, some experts consider it to be well within the normal range of female sexual response. Perhaps the woman who orgasms as a result of hand or mouth stimulation, but not penile thrusting, is simply having orgasms when she is adequately stimulated and is not having them when she is inadequately stimulated.

Nonetheless, there should be room for self-definition of sexual concerns and problems as deserving of attention. If a woman has situational orgasmic disorder, is truly distressed that she is not able to orgasm during vaginal intercourse, and wants therapy, then it may be appropriate to do so even if she does not meet the criteria for having a disorder. The therapist, however, should be careful to explain to her the problems of definition just raised, in order to be sure that her request for therapy stems from her own dissatisfaction with her sexual responding rather than from an overly idealistic sexual script. Therapy in such cases probably is best viewed as an effort to enrich the client's experience rather than to fix a problem.

SEXUAL PAIN DISORDERS

PAINFUL INTERCOURSE

Dyspareunia (dis-pah-ROO-nee-uh): Painful intercourse.

Painful intercourse, or **dyspareunia**, refers to genital pain experienced during intercourse (America Psychiatric Association, 2000). It is usually thought of as a female sexual disorder, but males occasionally experience it as well. In the NHSLS, 14 percent of the women reported pain during sex, compared with 3 percent of the men (Laumann et al., 1994). Similarly, 14 percent of Canadian women reported pain during intercourse (Fisher et al., 1999). While complaints of occasional pain during intercourse are fairly common among women, persistent dyspareunia is not as common. In women, the pain may be felt in the vagina, around the vaginal entrance and clitoris, or deep in the pelvis. The pain may also differ in quality and in intensity (Pukall et al., 2003). Some women describe a burning sensation, others a sharp pain or an aching feeling. Most of these women also experience pain in non-sexual situations affecting the vulva, such as sports or inserting a tampon (Binik et al., 2000; Meana et al., 1997). In men, the pain is felt in the penis or testes. To put it mildly, dyspareunia decreases one's enjoyment of the sexual experience, frequently causes problems with arousal and orgasm, and may even lead one to abstain from sexual activity.

Quebec psychologist Yitzchak Binik and his colleagues have criticized the notion of sexual pain disorders (Binik et al., 2007; Meana et al., 1997; Pukall et al., 2000). They point out that just because pain interferes with sexual activity such as intercourse, this does not make it a sexual disorder. They use the analogy of lower back pain that interferes with work. Although lower back pain may prevent a person from working, this pain is classified by its location (i.e., lower back pain) rather than by the activity it interferes with (i.e., work pain). Further, the pain associated with intercourse often also occurs in non-sexual situations, such as inserting a tampon or physical exercise. Thus, they argue that painful intercourse should be reclassified and treated as a pain disorder that interferes with sexual activity rather than as a sexual disorder (Binik, 2005; Payne et al., 2005).

Painful intercourse may be related to a variety of physical factors, to be discussed here.

VAGINISMUS

Vaginismus (the suffix "-ismus" means "spasm") is a spastic contraction of the outer third of the vagina (Figure 18.1); in some cases it is so severe that the entrance to the vagina is closed, and penetration is impossible (Leiblum, 2000). Vaginismus and dyspareunia are often associated (Binik et al., 2000; Reissing et al., 1999). That is, if attempted intercourse is painful, one result may be spasms that close off the entrance to the vagina. Research in Canada has found that women diagnosed with vaginismus had greater muscle tension, lower muscle strength, and greater fear and avoidance of intercourse than did women with other forms of dyspareunia and control women. However, contrary to the diagnostic criteria, not all women diagnosed with vaginismus had muscle spasms (Reissing et al., 2004).

Vaginismus is not a very common sexual disorder in the general population. Women may be particularly likely to seek treatment for it when it makes intercourse impossible and they are interested in conceiving a child (Binik et al., 2000).

Vaginismus (Vaj-in-IS-mus): A sexual disorder in which there is a spastic contraction of the muscles surrounding the entrance to the vagina, in some cases so severe that penetration is impossible.

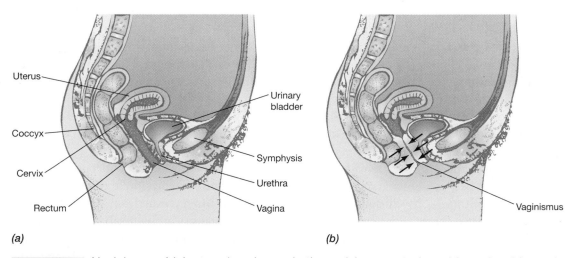

(a)   *(b)*

Figure 18.1   Vaginismus. *(a)* A normal vagina and other pelvic organs, viewed from the side, and *(b)* vaginismus, or involuntary constriction of the outer third of the vagina.

WHAT CAUSES SEXUAL DISORDERS?

There are many causes of sexual disorders, varying from person to person and from one disorder to another. Several categories of factors may be related to sexual disorders: physical factors (organic factors and drugs), individual psychological factors, and interpersonal factors. These factors interact with each other so that the causes of most disorders can best be understood from a biopsychosocial perspective. According to the **biopsychosocial model**, biological, psychological, and social factors all play a role in the development and maintenance of sexual disorders. For example, disorders that are largely due to physical factors affect

Biopsychosocial model: A general model that argues that physical, psychological, and social factors all contribute to sexual disorders.

people's thoughts, feelings, and relationships; in turn, their thoughts and feelings may make the problem worse. Conversely, disorders that are primarily due to psychological or social factors nonetheless affect nerves and blood vessels in a physical way. Each of these categories is discussed separately.

PHYSICAL CAUSES

Physical factors that cause sexual disorders include organic factors (physical factors such as diseases) and drugs. Organic factors that have been implicated in various disorders are discussed first, followed by a discussion of the effects of drugs.

ERECTILE DISORDER

Organic factors are a major contributor to 50 percent or more of cases of erectile disorder (ED) (Buvat et al., 1990; Richardson, 1991).

Diseases associated with the heart and the circulatory system are particularly likely to be associated with the condition, since erection itself depends on the circulatory system (Rosen, 2007). Any kind of vascular pathology (problems in the blood vessels supplying the penis) can produce erection problems. Erection depends on having a great deal of blood flowing into the penis via the arteries, with simultaneous constricting of the veins so that the blood cannot flow out as rapidly as it is coming in. Thus, damage to either these arteries or the veins may produce erectile disorder.

Erectile disorder is associated with diabetes mellitus, although the exact mechanism by which diabetes or a prediabetic condition may cause erectile disorder is not known (Bancroft & Gutierrez, 1996). In fact, erectile disorder may in some cases be the earliest symptom of a developing case of diabetes. Of course, not all diabetic men have erectile disorders; indeed, the majority do not. One estimate is that 35 percent of men with diabetes have an erectile disorder (Weinhardt & Carey, 1996).

Hypogonadism—an underfunctioning of the testes so that testosterone levels are very low— is associated with ED (Morales & Heaton, 2001). ED is also associated with a condition called hyperprolactinemia in which there is excessive production of prolactin (Johri et al., 2001).

Any disease or injury that damages the lower part of the spinal cord may cause erectile disorder, since that is the location of the erection reflex centre (see Chapter 9). Finally, some—though not all—kinds of prostate surgery may cause the condition (Libman & Fichten, 1987; Libman et al., 1989).

With erectile disorders, as with most sexual disorders, it is important to recognize that the distinction between organic causes and psychological causes is too simple (Rosen, 2007). In keeping with the biopsychosocial model, most sexual disorders result from a complex interplay of the two causes. For example, a man who has circulatory problems that initially cause him to have erection problems is likely to develop anxieties about erection, which in turn may create further difficulties. This notion of dual causes has important implications for therapy. A comprehensive approach to treatment should include attention to physical, psychological, and interpersonal factors.

PREMATURE EJACULATION

Rapid ejaculation is more often caused by psychological than physical factors. However, for some men rapid ejaculation may be due to a malfunctioning of the ejaculatory reflexes (Grenier & Byers, 1995). These men have a physiological hypersensitivity that results in faster ejaculation. (See Chapter 9 for a discussion of ejaculation.) Physical factors may also be involved in cases of acquired premature ejaculation in which the man at one time had ejaculatory control but later lost it. A local infection such as prostatitis may be the cause, as may degeneration in the related parts of the nervous system, which may occur in neural disorders such as multiple sclerosis.

An intriguing explanation for early ejaculation comes from the sociobiologists (Hong, 1984). Their idea is that rapid ejaculation has been selected for in the process of evolution—what we might call "survival of the fastest." Monkeys and apes (and humans) who copulated and ejaculated rapidly, the argument goes, would be more likely to survive and reproduce in that the female would be less likely to get away, and the male would be less likely to be attacked by other sexually aroused males while he was copulating. In fact, the average time from intromission (insertion of the penis into the vagina) to ejaculation among chimpanzees is rapid—about seven seconds (Tutin & McGinnis, 1981). However, primates engage in lengthy courtship and foreplay behaviours that would not be predicted by sociobiologists (Bixler, 1986). Nonetheless, according to sociobiologists, the genes for rapid ejaculation are still around.

MALE ORGASMIC DISORDER

Male orgasmic disorder, or retarded ejaculation, may be associated with a variety of medical or surgical conditions, such as multiple sclerosis, spinal cord injury, and prostate surgery (Rosen & Leiblum, 1995). Most commonly, though, it is associated with psychological factors.

FEMALE ORGASMIC DISORDER

Orgasmic disorder in women may be caused by severe illness, general ill health, or extreme fatigue. Injury to the spinal cord can cause orgasm problems (Sipski et al., 2001). However, most cases are primarily caused by psychological factors.

PAINFUL INTERCOURSE

Although dyspareunia in women is often caused by organic factors, the experience of sexual pain is influenced by psychological factors (Bergeron et al., 1997). Organic factors include:

1. *Disorders of the vaginal entrance.* Irritated remnants of the hymen; painful scars, perhaps from an episiotomy or sexual assault; or infection of the Bartholin glands.
2. *Disorders of the vagina.* Vaginal infections; allergic reactions to spermicidal creams or the latex in condoms or diaphragms; a thinning of the vaginal walls, which occurs naturally with age or chemically induced menopause; or scarring of the roof of the vagina, which can occur after hysterectomy.
3. *Pelvic disorders.* Pelvic infection such as pelvic inflammatory disease, endometriosis, tumours, cysts, or a tearing of the ligaments supporting the uterus.

Sexual pain in men can also be caused by a variety of organic factors. For an uncircumcised man, poor hygiene may be a cause; if the penis is not washed thoroughly with the foreskin retracted, material may collect under the foreskin, causing infection. Phimosis, a condition in which the foreskin cannot be pulled back, can also cause sexual pain. An allergic reaction to spermicidal creams or to the latex in condoms may also be involved. Finally, various prostate problems may cause pain during intercourse, after intercourse, or on ejaculation (Smith et al., 2007).

VAGINISMUS

Vaginismus is sometimes caused by painful intercourse, and therefore by organic factors that cause that condition (Binik et al., 2007). More frequently, though, it is caused by individual psychological factors or interpersonal factors (Rosen & Leiblum, 1995).

DRUGS

Some drugs may have side effects that cause sexual disorders (Segraves & Balon, 2003). For example, some drugs used to treat high blood pressure increase problems with erection in men and decrease sexual desire in both men and women. Although it would be impossible to list every drug effect on every aspect of sexual functioning, a list of some of the major drugs that may cause sexual disorders is provided in Table 18.2. Here we will consider the effects of alcohol, illicit drugs, and prescription drugs.

Table 18.2   Drugs That May Impair or Improve Sexual Response

Drug	How It Affects Sexual Functioning	Common Medical Uses
1. Psychoactive Drugs		
Antianxiety drugs/tranquillizers		Anxiety, panic disorders
Buspirone	Enhanced desire, orgasm	
Benzodiazepines (Librium, Valium, Ativan)	Decreases hypoactive desire, improves premature ejaculation	
Antidepressants I: Tricyclics and MAO inhibitors	Desire disorders, erection problems, orgasm problems, ejaculation problems May treat hypersexuality, premature ejaculation	Depression
Antidepressants II: Serotonin Reuptake Inhibitors (Paxil, Prozac, Zoloft)	Desire disorders, erection problems, orgasm problems	Depression, obsessive-compulsive disorder, panic disorders
Lithium	Desire disorders, erection problems	Bipolar disorder
Antipsychotics Thorazine, Haldol	Desire disorders, erection problems orgasm problems, ejaculation problems	Schizophrenia
2. Antihypertensives		
Reserpine, Methyldopa	Desire disorders, erection difficulties, orgasm delayed or blocked	High blood pressure
ACE inhibitors (Vasotec)	Erection difficulties	
3. Substance Use and Abuse		
Alcohol	At low doses, increases desire At high doses, decreases erection, arousal, orgasm Alcoholism creates many disorders and atrophied testicles, infertility	
Nicotine	Decreases blood flow to penis, creates erectile disorder	
Opioids		
Endogenous: Endorphins	Sense of well-being and relaxation	
Heroin	Decrease in desire, orgasm, ejaculation, replaces sex	
Marijuana	Enhances sexual pleasure but not actual "performance"; chronic use decreases desire	

Sources: Ashton, 2007; Meston et al., 2004; Segraves & Balon, 2003.

ALCOHOL

The effects of alcohol on sexual responding vary considerably. We can think of these effects as falling into three categories: (1) short-term pharmacological effects, (2) expectancy effects, and (3) long-term effects of chronic alcohol abuse. In regard to the last category, alcoholics, particularly in the later stages of alcoholism, frequently have sexual disorders, typically including erectile disorder, orgasmic disorder, and loss of desire (Segraves & Balon, 2003). These sex problems may be the result of any of a number of organic effects of long-term alcoholism. For example, chronic alcoholism in men may cause disturbances in sex hormone production because of atrophy of the testes or liver damage. Chronic alcohol abuse, too, generally has negative effects on the person's interpersonal relationships, which may contribute to sexual disorders.

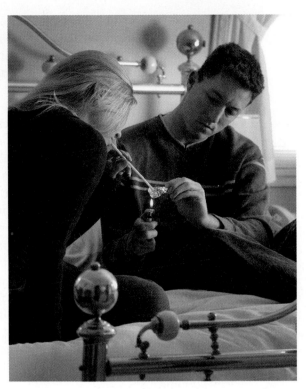

Figure 18.2 Alcohol and cocaine are popular recreational drugs that many people believe enhance sexual experience. Research shows, though, that high levels of alcohol suppress sexual arousal, and repeated use of cocaine is associated with loss of sexual desire, orgasm disorders, and erection problems.

What about the person who is not an alcoholic, but rather has had one or many drinks on a particular evening and then proceeds to a sexual interaction? As noted earlier, there is an interplay of two effects: expectancy effects and actual pharmacological effects (George & Stoner, 2000; George et al., 2006). Many people have the expectation that alcohol will loosen them up, making them more sociable and sexually uninhibited. These expectancy effects in themselves produce increased physiological arousal and subjective feelings of arousal. Expectancy effects, though, interact with the pharmacological effects and work mainly at low doses, that is, when only a little alcohol has been consumed. At high dosage levels, alcohol acts as a depressant and sexual arousal is markedly suppressed, in both men and women.[1]

ILLICIT OR RECREATIONAL DRUGS

There is a widespread belief that *marijuana* has aphrodisiac properties. Little scientific research has been done on its actual effects, and most of what has been done is old and based on small samples. Therefore, we can provide only tentative ideas about the effects of marijuana on sexual functioning. In surveys of users, many respondents report that it increases sexual desire and makes sexual interactions more pleasurable (McKay, 2005). In regard to potential negative effects, there is concern that marijuana use contributes to risky sexual behaviour such as unprotected sex (Collins et al., 2005). Chronic users report decreased sexual desire (Segraves & Balon, 2003). In community studies, marijuana use has been associated with orgasmic disorder (Johnson et al., 2004).

Among drug users, *cocaine* is reported to be one of the drugs of choice for enhancing sexual experiences. It is said to increase sexual desire, enhance sensuality, and delay orgasm. Chronic use of cocaine, however, is associated with loss of sexual desire, orgasmic disor-

---

[1]Some refer to the resulting erection problems as "whisky dick."

ders, and erectile disorders (Segraves & Balon, 2003). The effects also depend on the means of administration—whether the cocaine is inhaled, smoked, or injected. The most negative effects on sexual functioning occur among those who regularly inject the drug. Crack cocaine is highly addictive and the crack epidemic, especially in city downtown areas, often involves the exchange of sex for drugs (Green et al., 2005).

Stimulant drugs, notably *amphetamines*, are associated with increased sexual desire and better control of orgasm in some studies (Segraves & Balon, 2003). Injection of amphetamines itself causes a physical sensation that is described by some as a total-body orgasm. In some cases, though, orgasm becomes difficult or impossible when using amphetamines.

Crystal methamphetamine ("ice") is the popular new recreational drug. This drug is of particular concern because, while high on it, people have a tendency to engage in risky sexual behaviours (Semple et al., 2004; Urbina & Jones, 2004; Wohl et al., 2002). One study of heterosexual, HIV-negative adults using crystal meth indicated that, over a two-month period, they averaged 22 acts of unprotected vaginal sex and nine different sex partners (Semple et al., 2004). Crystal meth can also lead to paranoia, hallucinations, and violent behaviour (Brecht et al., 2004).

The *opiates* or narcotics, such as morphine, heroin, and methadone, have strong suppression effects on sexual desire and response (Segraves & Balon, 2003). Long-term use of heroin, in particular, leads to decreased testosterone levels in males.

PRESCRIPTION DRUGS

Table 18.2 on page 570 provides a partial list of prescription drugs that can affect sexual responding.

Some *psychiatric drugs*—that is, drugs used in the treatment of psychological disorders—may affect sexual functioning (Segraves & Balon, 2003). In general, these drugs have their beneficial psychological effects because they alter the functioning of the central nervous system (CNS). But these CNS alterations in turn affect sexual functioning. For example, the drugs used to treat schizophrenia may cause delayed orgasm or "dry orgasm" in men—that is, orgasm with no ejaculation. Tranquillizers and antidepressants often improve sexual responding as a result of improvement of the person's mental state. However, there may also be negative effects.

Many of the antidepressants, especially selective serotonin reuptake inhibitors (SSRIs), for example, are associated with desire, arousal, and delayed orgasm problems in men as well as women. This is a problem because, according to Health Canada, there were over 15 million prescriptions for SSRI antidepressants filled in Canada in 2003 and these are very common side effects—between 30 and 60 percent of people taking SSRIs experience a sexual disorder (Gregorian et al., 2002; Hemels et al., 2002). On the other hand, they are sometimes used to treat premature ejaculation precisely because they delay orgasm. A few antidepressants—most notably bupropion (Wellbutrin)—have fewer sexual side effects and are becoming popular for that very reason.

The list of other prescription drugs that can affect sexual functioning is long, so we will mention just two examples. Some of the antihypertensive drugs (used to treat high blood pressure) can cause erection problems in men (Segraves & Balon, 2003). Most of the research on antihypertensive drug effects has been done with men, so we have less knowledge of their effects on women, although sexual problems have been reported among women using antihypertensive medication. Some of the medications used to treat epilepsy appear to cause erection problems and decreased sexual desire, although epilepsy by itself also seems to be associated with sexual disorders.

PSYCHOLOGICAL CAUSES

The psychological sources of sexual disorders can be separated into **predisposing factors** and maintaining or ongoing causes (Wincze & Carey, 1991). Predisposing factors are people's

Predisposing factors: Experiences that people have had in the past—for example, in childhood—that now affect their sexual response.

prior life experiences—for example, things that happened in childhood—that now inhibit the sexual response. **Maintaining factors** are ongoing life circumstances, personal characteristics, and characteristics of lovemaking that help explain why the problem continues.

MAINTAINING PSYCHOLOGICAL CAUSES

The following eight factors are frequently maintaining psychological causes of sexual disorder: (1) myths or misinformation; (2) negative attitudes; (3) anxieties such as fear of failure; (4) cognitive interference; (5) individual psychological distress such as depression; (6) behavioural or lifestyle factors; (7) failure to engage in effective, sexually stimulating behaviour, often due to failure of the partners to communicate; and (8) relationship distress.

Myths or misinformation can be a source of sexual dysfunction. Many people have beliefs about lovemaking that are incorrect, or are unaware of sexual information (such as the effects of aging on the sexual response) that is important to sexual functioning. For example, some couples seek sex therapy because of a woman's failure to orgasm; the therapist soon discovers that neither partner is aware of the location of the clitoris, much less its fantastic erotic potential. Misinformation can lead to a sexual script that does not fully enhance sexual arousal and pleasure or to anxiety and worry. These cases can often be cleared up by simple educational techniques.

A second possible source of sexual dysfunction is *negative attitudes* about sexual activity, one's own body, or one's partner's body. For example, the beliefs that "good" people do not enjoy sex or that one is ugly or fat may result in anxiety or other negative feelings during sexual activity that may affect sexual functioning.

Masters and Johnson theorized that *anxiety* during intercourse can be a source of sexual disorders. Anxiety may be caused by negative or traumatic experiences in the past such as child sexual abuse. However, anxiety also may be caused by fear of failure—that is, fear of being unable to perform. But anxiety itself can block sexual response in some people. Often anxiety can create a vicious circle of self-fulfilling prophecy in which fear of failure produces a failure, which produces more fear, which produces another failure, and so on. For example, a man may have one episode of erectile dysfunction, perhaps after drinking too much at a party. The next time he has sex, he anxiously wonders whether he will "fail" again. His anxiety is so great that he cannot get an erection. At this point he is convinced that the condition is permanent, and all future sexual activity is marked by such intense fear of failure that erectile disorder results. The prophecy is fulfilled.

Cognitive interference is a fourth maintaining cause of sexual disorders. Cognitive interference refers to thoughts that distract the person from focusing on the erotic experience. The problem is basically one of attention and of whether the person is focusing his or her attention on erotic thoughts and feelings or on distracting thoughts (Will my technique be good enough to please her? Will my body be beautiful enough to arouse him?). Research in Ontario asked undergraduate students about the non-erotic thoughts they had during their most recent sexual encounter that took away from their sexual experience (Purdon & Holdaway, 2006). More than 90 percent of participants reported having at least one such non-erotic thought. These thoughts most often related to performance concerns, concerns related to external consequences (e.g., STIs) and emotional consequences (e.g., consequences for the relationship), and body image. The men were more likely to have thoughts related to performance and the women were more likely to have thoughts related to body image. Students who reported more non-erotic thoughts, particularly non-erotic thoughts that caused anxiety, had poorer sexual functioning. Similarly, research in New Brunswick has shown that poor body image is associated with poorer sexual functioning in women, beyond the effects of actual body size (Weaver & Byers, 2006). This is likely because poor body image leads to non-erotic thoughts and anxiety about the body in sexual situations.

Spectatoring, a term coined by Masters and Johnson, is one kind of cognitive interference. The person behaves like a spectator or judge of his or her own sexual "performance." People

---

Maintaining factors: Various ongoing life circumstances, personal characteristics, and lovemaking patterns that inhibit sexual response.

Cognitive interference: Negative thoughts that distract a person from focusing on the erotic experience.

Spectatoring: Masters and Johnson's term for acting as an observer or judge of one's own sexual performance; hypothesized to contribute to sexual disorders.

who do this are constantly (mentally) stepping outside the sexual activities in which they are engaged, to evaluate how they are doing, mentally commenting, "Good job," or "Lousy," or "Could stand improvement." These ideas on the importance of cognition in sexual disorder derive from the cognitive theories of sexual responding discussed in Chapters 2 and 9.

Sex researcher David Barlow (1986) ran an elegant series of experiments to test the ways in which anxiety and cognitive interference affect sexual functioning. He studied men with and without sexual disorders, particularly erectile disorder, whom he calls the "functionals" and the "dysfunctionals." He found that functionals and dysfunctionals respond very differently to stimuli in sexual situations. For example, anxiety (induced by the threat of being shocked) *increases* the arousal of functional men, but *decreases* the arousal of dysfunctional men while watching erotic films. Similarly, demands for performance (e.g., the experimenter says the research participant must have an erection or he will be shocked) increase the arousal of functionals but are distracting to (create cognitive interference in) and decrease the arousal of dysfunctionals. When both self-reports of arousal and physiological measures of arousal (the penile strain gauge) are used, dysfunctional men consistently underestimate their physical arousal, whereas functional men are accurate in their reporting.

From these laboratory findings, Barlow constructed a model that describes how anxiety and cognitive interference act together to produce sexual disorders such as erectile disorder. When dysfunctionals are in a sexual situation, there is a performance demand. This causes them to feel negative emotions such as anxiety. They then experience cognitive interference and focus their attention on non-erotic thoughts, such as thinking about how awful it will be when they don't have an erection. This increases arousal of their autonomic nervous system. To them, that feels like anxiety, whereas a functional person would experience it as sexual arousal. For the dysfunctionals, the anxiety creates further cognitive interference, and eventually the sexual performance is dysfunctional—they don't manage to get an erection. This leads them to avoid future sexual encounters or, when they are in one, to experience negative feelings, and the vicious cycle repeats itself.

Research in Quebec suggests there may be a similar process in women who experience sexual pain. That is, anxiety and fear about sexual pain leads women who experience pain to focus their attention on possible pain cues rather than on erotic stimuli (Payne et al., 2005). In turn, this cognitive interference may interfere with the sexual response over and above any pain experienced.

It is important to note that anxiety produces sex problems only in some men. For the majority of men, who function well sexually, anxiety does not impair sexual responding, at least in the lab. The same is true for women (Elliott & O'Donohue, 1997).

A fifth possible cause of sexual disorders is individual *psychological distress*. That is, sexual disorder may be one symptom of a more general psychological disorder. For example, individuals who are depressed often experience low sexual desire or have difficulty becoming aroused (Araujo et al., 1998; Frohlich & Meston, 2002). Emotions such as anger and sadness (as well as anxiety, as we saw earlier) can interfere with sexual responding (Araujo et al., 2000). These are examples of the mind–body connection.

Behavioural and lifestyle factors can also affect sexual functioning. Smoking, alcohol consumption, and obesity are all behaviours that are associated with higher rates of sexual disorders (Derby et al., 2000; Segraves & Balon, 2003). However, these behaviours are quite modifiable. A study of obese men between the ages of 35 and 55 showed that regular physical exercise reduced their body mass index (BMI) and the incidence of erectile disorder (Esposito et al., 2004). A stressful lifestyle, such as a difficult work environment, long work hours, or a lack of privacy in the home, may also affect sexual functioning. Surprisingly, couples often fail to recognize how their lifestyle impacts on their sexual functioning.

The last two maintaining factors relate to the couple's interactions and relationship. Sexual disorders may be caused by *failure to engage in effective sexually stimulating behaviour.*

Sometimes this is a result of simple ignorance—that is, myths and misinformation. More often poor technique is due to the failure of the partners to communicate with each other about their sexual preferences. We often expect our partners to read our minds (which most of us are not particularly good at) to determine what we like and don't like. In fact, a survey of more than 3000 Canadian men and women found that only 28 percent had had even one serious discussion about sex in their relationship in the previous year (Auld et al., 2002). Two New Brunswick researchers examined whether sexual self-disclosure does, in fact, enhance sexual functioning (MacNeil & Byers, 2005). They had 74 heterosexual couples independently complete measures of their sexual likes and dislikes, their partner's sexual likes and dislikes, and their own sexual satisfaction. They found that, for both the men and the women, individuals who self-disclosed more about their sexual preferences had partners who had a better understanding of what pleased and displeased them sexually. In turn, the more the partner understood their sexual likes and dislikes, the more the couple engaged in mutually pleasing (and not in displeasing) sexual activities during lovemaking; the more pleasing and less displeasing the sexual script the more sexually satisfied they were.

In short, you are the leading expert in the field of what feels good to you, and your partner will never know what turns you on or what you desire at a particular moment unless you make this known, either verbally or non-verbally. But many people do not communicate their sexual desires. For example, a woman who needs a great deal of clitoral stimulation to have an orgasm may never tell her partner this; as a result, her partner provides some clitoral stimulation but not the amount of stimulation she needs. Consequently, she does not orgasm.

Relationship distress, that is, disturbances in a couple's relationship, is another leading cause of sexual disorders. Frequent arguments or anger and resentment toward one's partner do not create an optimal environment for sexual enjoyment. Intimacy problems in the relationship can be a factor in sexual disorders. Poor communication, not feeling understood, a lack of common interests, and a lack of trust may interfere with the feelings of closeness and intimacy that are important to quality lovemaking and to being able to respond sexually (Basson, 2001). Sometimes individual psychological factors contribute to a lack of intimacy in the relationship. Some individuals have a fear of intimacy—that is, of deep emotional closeness to another person—often due to insecure attachment relationships with parents (Kaplan, 1979). A lack of quality time together due to an overly hectic lifestyle can also contribute to reduced feelings of intimacy and closeness and thus to relationship distress.

PREDISPOSING FACTORS

The immediate or maintaining causes of sexual dysfunction are often a result of things that were learned or experienced in childhood, adolescence, or even adulthood. These early events result in negative attitudes, misinformation, cognitive interference, difficulty communicating, and so on.

In some cases of sexual disorder, the person's first sexual act was traumatic. An example would be a young man who could not get an erection the first time he attempted penetration and was laughed at by his partner. Such an experience sets the stage for future erectile disorder.

Child sexual abuse by parents or other adults is probably the most serious of the traumatic early experiences that lead to later sexual disorders (Najman et al., 2005). A history of sexual abuse is frequently reported by women seeking therapy for problems with sexual desire, arousal, or aversion (Leonard & Follette, 2002). The findings are similar for men with desire or arousal problems (Loeb et al., 2002).

Growing up in a family that communicates negative messages about sex is often a predisposing factor to sexual disorders because it creates negative attitudes. The person who grew up in a very strict, religious family and was taught that sex is dirty and sinful may believe that sex is not pleasurable, that it should be gotten over with as quickly as possible, and that it is for purposes of procreation only. It is the rigid belief in sexual rights and wrongs (particularly wrongs), not religiosity per se, that likely impacts sexual functioning (Kleinplatz & Krippner, 2000). The child who is punished severely for masturbating and told never to "touch herself" again may develop negative attitudes about her genitals, and genital touching. Parents who teach their children the double standard may contribute to sexual disorders, particularly in daughters who were told that no nice woman is interested in sex or enjoys it. Growing up in a homonegative family or culture may contribute to internalizing homonegativity among gays and lesbians, which in turn may affect their sexual functioning. Such learning inhibits the enjoyment of a full sexual response.

COMBINED COGNITIVE AND PHYSIOLOGICAL FACTORS

According to the cognitive–physiological model of sexual functioning and dysfunction, we function well sexually when we are physiologically aroused and we interpret it as sexual arousal rather than something else, like nervousness (Palace, 1995a, 1995b). As Barlow's research shows, people with sexual disorders tend to interpret their arousal as anxiety. In addition, the physiological processes and cognitive interpretations form a feedback loop (see discussion of cognitive theories in Chapter 2). That is, interpreting arousal as sexual arousal increases one's arousal further.

In a clever experiment, British Columbia women with sexual disorders were exposed, in a laboratory setting, to a frightening movie that increased their general autonomic arousal (Palace, 1995b). The women were then shown a brief erotic video and given feedback (actually false) that their genitals had shown a strong arousal response to it. This feedback created a cognitive interpretation for the way they were feeling. The combination of general autonomic arousal and the belief that they were responding with strong sexual arousal led these women, compared with the controls, to greater vaginal arousal responses and subjective reports of arousal in subsequent sessions. This demonstration of the effectiveness of combined physiological and cognitive factors is particularly striking because the women began with problems in sexual responding.

THERAPIES FOR SEXUAL DISORDERS

A variety of therapies for sexual disorders are available, each relying on a different theoretical understanding of what causes sexual disorders. Here we examine four major categories of therapies: behaviour therapy, cognitive–behavioural therapy, couple therapy, and biomedical therapies. Effective treatments for sexual disorders focus on factors that are currently maintaining the sexual disorder rather than on predisposing factors.

BEHAVIOUR THERAPY

Behaviour therapy: A system of therapy based on learning theory, in which the focus is on the problem behaviour and how it can be modified or changed.

Behaviour therapy has its roots in learning theory. The basic assumption is that sex problems are the result of prior learning and that they are maintained by ongoing reinforcements and punishments (immediate causes). It follows that these problem behaviours can be unlearned by new conditioning. One of the key techniques is in vivo desensitization, in which the client is gradually led through exercises that reduce anxiety.

In 1970, Masters and Johnson reported on their development of a set of techniques for sex therapy with heterosexual couples and ushered in a new era of sex therapy. They operated from a behaviour therapy model because they saw sexual disorders as learned behaviours rather than as symptoms of psychiatric illness. Masters and Johnson used a rapid two-week program of intensive daily therapy that consisted mainly of education and specific behavioural exercises, or "homework assignments."

One of the basic goals of Masters and Johnson's therapy was to eliminate goal-oriented sexual performance. Many clients believe that in sex they must perform and achieve certain things. If sex is an achievement situation, it also can become the scene of failure, and perceived failures lead people to believe that they have a sexual problem. The form of cognitive interference known as *spectatoring* (discussed earlier) contributes to this problem because it generates anxiety and other unpleasant feelings and interferes with the experience of positive sensations. The idea is to use therapy techniques to reduce anxiety.

In one technique used in behaviour therapy to eliminate a goal-oriented attitude toward sex, the couple is forbidden to have sexual intercourse until they are specifically permitted to by the therapists. They are assigned sensate focus exercises that reduce the demands on them. As the couple successfully completes each of these exercises, the sexual component of subsequent exercises is gradually increased. The couple chalk up a series of successes until eventually they are having intercourse and the disorder has disappeared.

Sensate focus exercises are based on the notion that touching and being touched are important forms of sexual expression and that touching is also an important form of communication; for example, a touch can express affection, desire, understanding, or a lack of caring. In the exercises, one member of the couple plays the "giving" role (touches and strokes the other), while the other person plays the "receiving" role (is touched by the other). The giving partner is instructed to massage or caress the other, while the receiving partner is instructed to communicate to the giver what is most pleasurable. Thus the exercise fosters communication. The partners switch roles after a certain period of time. In the first exercises, the giver is not to stroke the genitals or breasts (nor should the receiver ask for this) but may touch any other area. As the couple progress through the exercises, they are instructed to begin touching the genitals and breasts. These exercises also encourage the partners to focus their attention or concentrate on the sensuous pleasures they are receiving. Many people's sexual response is dulled because they are distracted; they are thinking about how to solve a family financial problem, or are spectatoring their own performance. They are victims of cognitive interference. The sensate focus exercises train people to concentrate only on their sexual experience, thereby increasing the pleasure of it.

In addition to these exercises, behaviour therapists provide simple education. The couple is given thorough instruction in the anatomy and physiology of the male and/or female sexual organs (depending on whether the couple are of the same sex or not). Some couples, for example, have no idea what or where the clitoris is. These instructions may also clear up myths and misinformation that either member of the couple may have had since childhood. For example, a man with an erectile disorder may have been told as a child that men can have only a fixed number of orgasms in their lifetime. As he approaches middle age, he starts to worry because his erections may come and go during lovemaking (see Chapter 11) or about whether he may have used up almost all of his orgasms, and this creates the erectile disorder. It is important for such men to learn that nature has imposed no quota on them.

Masters and Johnson collected data on the success and failure rates of their therapy. In their book *Human Sexual Inadequacy*, they reported on the treatment of 790 persons. Of these, 142 still had a disorder at the end of the two-week therapy program. This translates to a failure rate of 18 percent, or a *success rate of 82 percent*. While the failure rate ran around 18 percent for most disorders, there were two exceptions: Therapy for rapid ejaculation had a very low failure rate (2.2 percent), and therapy for lifelong erectile disorder had a high failure rate (40.6 percent). That is, rapid ejaculation was quite easy to cure, lifelong erectile disorder very difficult. Masters and Johnson's success rate is impressive, although their results have been called into question, as we shall see later in this chapter.

In Masters and Johnson's initial development of their therapy techniques, all the couples were heterosexual. They later used the same techniques in treating sexual disorders in gay and lesbian couples, with a comparable success rate (Masters & Johnson, 1979).

Sensate focus exercise: A part of the sex therapy developed by Masters and Johnson in which one partner caresses the other, the other communicates what is pleasurable, and there are no performance demands.

IN FOCUS 18.1

A Case of Low Sexual Desire

Sarah, age 27, was referred to a sex therapist by an endocrinologist, to be considered for testosterone treatment for her complaints of low sexual desire. Sarah had no ovarian tissue. One ovary that had a large cyst had been removed when she was 13, and her other ovary had undergone torsion (twisting that cut off the blood supply) and had to be removed when she was 16. She had been given estrogen and progesterone replacement immediately so that her menstrual periods never stopped.

When Sarah met with the therapist, she explained that sex with her partner Carl was enjoyable. They had been together four years and were sexual approximately once a week. Carl would have preferred to be sexual every day, but Sarah resisted. She said that even though sex was enjoyable and satisfying, if she never had sex again, it would be fine with her. She reported that Carl thought that she was very abnormal and so did her endocrinologist.

Sarah had very few sexual thoughts about arousal or anticipating sexual activity. Her sexual thoughts were instead troubling and focused on her guilt that their sexual interactions were infrequent and that she was abnormal. During sexual interactions with Carl, she was aroused, she enjoyed the experience, and had orgasms. She found arousing Carl to be pleasurable and arousing for her.

Using the *New View of Women's Sexual Problems* described in In Focus 18.2 (see page 587), the therapist explained to Sarah that her experience was within normal limits. In a meeting with Carl, the therapist described the range of women's sexual experiences. The next question was whether some factors were causing Sarah's behaviour to be toward the end of the spectrum.

COGNITIVE–BEHAVIOURAL THERAPY

Paralleling the increased importance of cognitive theories in psychology (see Chapter 2) is the increased importance of cognitive approaches to psychotherapy. Today, many sex therapists use a combination of the behavioural exercises pioneered by Masters and Johnson and cognitive therapy (Bancroft, 1997a; Heiman, 2002; Trudel et al., 1996, 2001). This is termed **cognitive–behavioural therapy**.

Cognitive–behavioural therapy: A form of therapy that combines behaviour therapy and restructuring of negative thought patterns.

Cognitive restructuring is an important technique in a cognitive approach to sex therapy (Wincze & Carey, 1991). In cognitive restructuring, the therapist essentially helps the client restructure his or her thought patterns, helping them to become more positive (for an example, see In Focus 18.1). Cognitive restructuring is particularly useful in addressing two of the maintaining causes of sexual disorders described earlier in this chapter—negative attitudes and cognitive interference. In one form of cognitive restructuring, the therapist challenges the client's negative attitudes. These attitudes may be as general as a woman's distrusting attitudes toward all men, or as specific as a man's negative attitudes toward masturbation. The client is helped to reshape these attitudes into more positive ones.

Cognitive therapists also like to address cognitive interference. The general idea is to reduce the presence of interfering thoughts during sex. First the therapist must help the client identify the presence of such thoughts. The therapist then suggests techniques for reducing these thoughts, generally by replacing them with erotic thoughts—perhaps focusing attention on a particular part of one's body and how it is responding with arousal, or perhaps having an erotic fantasy. Out go the bad thoughts, and in come the good thoughts.

COUPLE THERAPY

As we noted earlier, poor communication and relationship distress are important maintaining causes of sexual disorders. Accordingly, many sex therapists use couple therapy as part of the treatment. This approach rests on the assumption that there is a reciprocal relationship

Both biological and psychological factors seemed to be involved. Because of the removal of her ovaries, she was manufacturing no testosterone, although androgens manufactured by the adrenal gland were present. Sarah's life history also gave clues regarding possible psychological factors. Sarah grew up with an alcoholic father who was prone to shouting, arguing, and engaging in emotional abuse; Sarah coped by retreating to her bedroom. She suppressed her feelings of anger and did not rebel even when she was a teenager. This coping style worked well at the time. However, as an adult, she was still in the habit of suppressing emotions generally. Sarah agreed that her sexual emotions were probably also suppressed.

The therapist decided against testosterone treatment and instead focused on encouraging Sarah to deliberately attempt to feel more non-sexual emotion throughout the day. In addition, she was to deliberately allow more sexual stimuli in her life, such as music, movies, dancing, and erotic conversations.

The therapist met with Carl to explain the situation and assess his own family history. His parents had a bitter divorce when he was just ten. He felt that neither parent had really loved him. For Carl, having sex with his partner was a sign that he was loved. Carl was able to realize that pressuring Sarah did not help the situation and he ceased doing so, which Sarah appreciated. In addition, when Sarah realized the origins and extent of Carl's need to feel loved, she became strongly motivated to find the triggers that were able to make her feel more sexual. Salsa dancing proved to be one of those triggers, combined with encouraging Carl to flirt with her more often. Sarah's sexual self-image increased markedly, as did her sexual desire.

Source: Basson, 2007, pp. 42–43.

between interpersonal conflict and sex problems. Sex problems can cause conflicts, and conflicts can cause sex problems. In couple therapy, the relationship itself is treated, with the goal of reducing antagonisms and tensions between the partners. As the relationship improves, the sex problem should be reduced.

For certain disorders and certain couples, therapists may use a combination of cognitive–behavioural and couple therapy. For example, sex therapists Raymond Rosen, Sandra Leiblum, and Ilana Spector (1994) use a five-part model in treating men with erectile disorder:

1. *Sexual and performance anxiety reduction.* Individuals with sexual disorders, particularly men with erectile disorder, often have a great deal of performance anxiety. This can be treated using such techniques as sensate focus exercises.
2. *Education and cognitive intervention.* As noted earlier, people with sexual disorders often lack sexual information. Many also have unrealistic expectations about sexual functioning and satisfaction. For example, older men may not be aware of the natural effects of aging on male sexual response. Cognitive interventions may help men with erection problems to overcome "all or nothing" thinking—that is, the belief that if any aspect of his sexual performance is not perfect, the whole interaction is a disaster. An example is the belief "I failed sexually because my erection was not 100 percent rigid."
3. *Script assessment and modification.* All couples have a sexual script that they enact together. People with sexual disorders typically have a restricted, repetitive, and inflexible script, using a small number of techniques that they never change. Novelty is one of the greatest turn-ons, so therapy is designed to help the couple break out of their restricted script.
4. *Conflict resolution and relationship enhancement.* As we have discussed, conflicts in a couple's relationship can lead to sexual disorders. In therapy, these conflicts are identified and the couple can work to resolve them.
5. *Relapse prevention training.* Sometimes a relapse—a return of the disorder—occurs following therapy. Therapists have developed techniques to help couples avoid or deal with

such relapses. For example, they are told to engage in sensate focus sessions at least once a month.

Notice that part 1 represents the behaviour therapy techniques pioneered by Masters and Johnson; parts 2 and 3 are cognitive therapy techniques; and part 4 is couple therapy. Most skilled sex therapists today use combined or integrated techniques such as these, tailored to the specific disorder and situation of the couple.

SPECIFIC TREATMENTS FOR SPECIFIC PROBLEMS

Some very specific techniques have been developed for the treatment of certain sexual disorders. Of course, each of these techniques is typically only one part of a comprehensive treatment approach.

THE STOP-START TECHNIQUE

The stop-start technique is used in the treatment of rapid ejaculation (see Figure 18.3). The man first learns to identify sensations prior to the point of ejaculatory inevitability (see Chapter 9). The partner manually stimulates the man to erection and then stops the stimulation prior to this point. Gradually he loses his erection. The partner resumes stimulation, he gets another erection, the partner stops, and so on. After doing this three or four times, the man can allow himself to orgasm. The man learns that he can have an erection and be highly aroused without having an orgasm. Using this technique, the couple may extend their sex play to 15 or 20 minutes, and the man gains control over his orgasm. Another version of this method that is occasionally used is the squeeze technique, in which the partner adds a squeeze around the coronal ridge, which also stops orgasm.

MASTURBATION

The most effective form of therapy for women with primary orgasmic disorder is a program of directed masturbation (LoPiccolo & Stock, 1986; Meston et al., 2004). The data indicate that masturbation is the technique most likely to produce orgasm in women; it is therefore a logical treatment for women who have problems with having orgasms, many of whom have never masturbated. Women can use a vibrator to learn to bring themselves to orgasm. Masturbation is sometimes recommended as therapy for men as well.

KEGEL EXERCISES

Kegel (KAY-gul) exercises: A part of sex therapy for women with orgasmic disorder, in which the woman exercises the muscles surrounding the vagina; also called pubococcygeal or PC muscle exercises.

One technique that is used with women is the **Kegel exercises**, named for the physician who devised them (Kegel, 1952). They are designed to exercise and strengthen the *pubococcygeal muscle*, or PC muscle, which runs along the sides of the entrance of the vagina (refer to Figure 4.1 on page 82). The exercises are particularly helpful for women who have had this muscle stretched in childbirth, who have poor muscle tone, or who have vaginismus. The woman is instructed first to find her PC muscle by sitting on a toilet with her legs spread apart, beginning to urinate, and stopping the flow of urine voluntarily. The muscle that stops the flow is the PC muscle. After that, the woman is told to contract the muscle ten times during each of six sessions per day. Gradually, she can work up to more.[2] These exercises seem to enhance arousal and facilitate orgasm by increasing women's awareness of and comfort with their genitals (Heiman, 2007). They also permit the heterosexual woman to stimulate her partner more because her vagina can grip his penis more tightly, and they are a cure for women who have problems with involuntarily urinating as they orgasm.

Pelvic floor muscle exercises and physiotherapy can also be used on their own or as part of a comprehensive treatment of dyspareunia in women (Bergeron et al., 2001, 2002; Binik et al.,

[2]Students should recognize the exciting possibilities for doing these exercises. For example, they are a good way to amuse yourself in the middle of a lecture, and no one will ever know you are doing them.

Figure 18.3   The stop-start technique for treating rapid ejaculation and the position of the couple while using the stop-start technique.

2000, 2001). Physiotherapists provide physical assurance to make sure that the woman is doing the exercises correctly—about half of women do not do them correctly with just verbal instructions (Rosenbaum, 2005, 2007). Often physiotherapists use biofeedback to help women learn to isolate and contract the correct muscles of the pelvic floor. Kegel exercises are sometimes also used in treating men.

BIBLIOTHERAPY

Bibliotherapy refers simply to the use of a self-help book to treat a disorder. Research shows that bibliotherapy is effective for orgasmic disorders in women (van Lankveld, 1998). Julia Heiman and Joseph LoPiccolo's *Becoming Orgasmic: A Sexual Growth Program for Women* (1998) has been used extensively for this purpose. Bibliotherapy has also been shown to be effective for couples with a mixture of male and female sexual disorders (van Lankveld et al., 2001). In addition, many people describe Bernie Zilbergeld's self-help book, *The New Male Sexuality* (1999), as helpful. Other couples find sex therapy videotapes to be helpful. Interestingly, as early as 1973, Steven Neiger, a Canadian pioneer in sex therapy and sex education, developed a series of 12 audiotapes to help couples overcome sexual problems (Alexander, 1990). It may be that in the future the Internet will replace bibliotherapy as self-help methods for treating sexual disorders. The advice columns at these sites can provide accurate, explicit, and non-judgmental information. Specialized message boards and chat rooms for people who share a common interest (e.g., bisexuals, persons with disabilities) can help to create a sense of community and provide useful information, especially for those who are geographically isolated or in countries where sex therapy is unknown.

Bibliotherapy: The use of a self-help book to treat a disorder.

BIOMEDICAL THERAPIES

In the last decade, there has been increased recognition of the biological bases of some sexual disorders. Consistent with this emphasis, many developments in medical and drug treatments and even surgical treatment have occurred. From the biopsychosocial perspective, biomedical therapies need to be used in conjunction with other interventions that address the psychosocial factors associated with the sexual disorder. The medicalization of sexuality, with its emphasis on performance and medical treatment, is discussed later in this chapter.

DRUG TREATMENTS

Many promising advances have been made in the identification of drugs that cure sexual disorders or work well when used together with cognitive–behavioural therapy or other psychological forms of sex therapy (Ashton, 2007; Rosen, 2007; Rowland & Burnett, 2000). Some are drugs that have direct sexual effects, whereas others are psychotherapeutic drugs (such as antidepressants) that work by improving the person's mood.

Viagra: A drug used in the treatment of erectile disorder; sildenafil.

Certainly the most widely publicized breakthrough among these treatments was the release in the United States, in 1998, of Viagra (sildenafil) for the treatment of erectile disorder. Viagra was approved by Health Canada in 1999. Earlier biomedical treatments such as intracavernosal injections were unsatisfactory for various reasons (these are discussed in the next section). Viagra is taken by mouth approximately one hour before anticipated sexual activity. It does not, by itself, produce an erection. Rather, when the man is stimulated sexually after taking Viagra, the drug facilitates the physiological processes that produce erection. Specifically, it relaxes the smooth muscles in the corpora cavernosa, allowing blood to flow in and create an erection. Averaged over 27 clinical trials, about 57 percent of men respond successfully to Viagra, compared with 21 percent responding to the placebo (Fink et al., 2002). Men have generally been quite satisfied with Viagra. Side effects are not common; if present, they included headache, flushing, and vision disturbances (Ashton, 2007).

On balance, Viagra seems to be quite safe (Morales et al., 1998; Rosen & McKenna, 2002). It does not seem to cause priapism (an erection that just won't go away). Yet the very ease of its use may lead physicians to over-prescribe it and men to demand it in inappropriate circumstances. Today it is easily available on the Internet. If the erection difficulties are due to relationship problems or individual issues, Viagra will provide at most a temporary solution. It is not helpful for sexual disorders other than erectile disorder. And there is no evidence that it enhances sexual performance in men who function sexually within the normal range. In addition, its recreational or high-performance use are causes for concern.

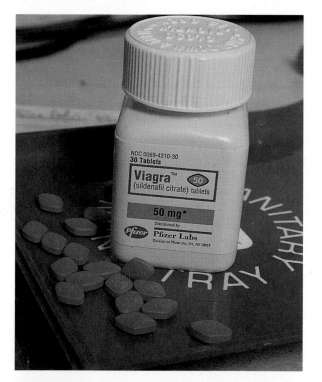

Figure 18.4 Viagra, one of the drugs for treating erectile disorder.

Viagra was such a success, financially and otherwise, that drug companies immediately sought successors—drugs that would be more convenient, or would work in cases that were not effectively treated with Viagra. One of these, Cialis (tadalafil), is very much like

Viagra in that it relaxes the smooth muscle surrounding the arteries to the penis, facilitating engorgement (Brock et al., 2002; Montorsi et al., 2004; Padma-Nathan et al., 2001). Whereas Viagra lasts only a maximum of 8 to 10 hours, Cialis can be effective for as long as 24 to 36 hours. Drugs such as Cialis have been shown to have no negative effects on sperm production or sex hormone production (Hellstrom et al., 2003a).

Levitra (vardenafil) is another new drug that works much like Viagra but has a slightly different formulation (Hatzichristou et al., 2004; Hellstrom et al., 2003b; Rosen & McKenna, 2002). A particularly important success story is that these drugs can be effective in treating erectile dysfunction that results from complete surgical removal of the prostate (Brock et al., 2003).

Viagra, Cialis, and Levitra each act peripherally—that is, they act on sites in the penis. Another alternative is centrally acting drugs, meaning drugs that act on regions of the brain involved in arousal. One of these is Uprima (apomorphine SL[3]; Heaton, 2001). It acts in about 20 minutes and, like other drugs, does not produce a spontaneous erection. Rather, it has to be accompanied by sexual stimulation. Uprima acts by boosting levels of the neurotransmitter dopamine in the brain, particularly in the hypothalamus, and is effective in about 55 percent of cases (Heaton, 2001; Montorsi et al., 2003a, 2003b).

And how about a Viagra for women? The drug company Pfizer, as well as many scientists, hoped that Viagra also would work for women—that is, it would cure their orgasm problems. The problem is that Viagra works by increasing vasocongestion, and insufficient vasocongestion is probably not what causes most women's orgasm difficulties. After many failed clinical trials, Pfizer announced in 2004 that it would give up on testing Viagra for women (Harris, 2004). For example, British Columbia researcher Rosemary Basson and her colleagues found that Viagra does not increase either arousal or orgasm in either premenopausal or postmenopausal women with sexual dysfunction (Basson & Brotto, 2003; Basson et al., 2002).

Women's sexual problems most commonly involve orgasm difficulties and low sexual desire, the latter being a problem particularly as women age and their ovaries decline in production of testosterone. The most promising lead at the moment is administration of testosterone or some other androgen (Baulieu et al., 2000), although use of testosterone in women is still quite controversial. As of this writing, Procter & Gamble is in the midst of clinical trials of Intrinsa, a testosterone patch designed for postmenopausal women experiencing low sexual desire. However, initial results have not been sufficiently positive to receive approval to market the patch in Canada or the United States. A testosterone patch for women is available in Europe.

The other issue concerning women and Viagra involves the partners of men with Viagra-aided erections. Not all partners, some of whom had adjusted to a relationship without intercourse, welcome the man's new capacity, an issue that has been ignored in the medical "fix" approach (Potts et al., 2003; Rosen & McKenna, 2002). For example, for a couple with relationship problems, it may create additional problems if taking Viagra results in pressure to engage in unwanted sexual activity. Often it is important to combine couple therapy with drug therapy. Some women, of course, are absolutely delighted with the results (Montorsi & Althof, 2003).

INTRACAVERNOSAL INJECTION FOR ERECTILE DISORDER

Intracavernosal injection (ICI) is a treatment for erectile disorders (Shabsigh et al., 2000). It involves injecting a drug (such as alprostadil, or Edex) into the corpora cavernosa of the penis. The drugs used are vasodilators—that is, they dilate the blood vessels in the penis so that much more blood can accumulate there, producing an erection.

---

[3]The SL means "sub-lingual"; that is, you take it by putting it under your tongue and letting it dissolve, rather than by swallowing it. It gets to the brain more efficiently that way. Previously, apomorphine had been used to treat Parkinson's disease.

Since the introduction of Viagra, ICI is now used mainly in cases in which the erection problem is organic and the man does not respond to Viagra or its successors (Shabsigh et al., 2000). It can also be used in conjunction with cognitive–behavioural therapy in cases that have combined organic and psychological causes. Like Viagra, ICI can have positive psychological effects because it restores the man's confidence in his ability to get erections. It also reduces his performance anxiety because he is able to engage in intercourse successfully. Some men experience pain from treatment and, according to research in British Columbia, about 50 percent of men who begin using ICI discontinue its use (Basson, 1998). ICI can also result in a prolonged erection that does not go away even in the absence of stimulation, called *priapism*. This condition is painful and requires medical treatment. There are also potential abuses. Men who have normal erections should not use ICI in an attempt to produce a "super erection."

Alprostadil is now also available as a suppository to place inside the urethra or as a cream to rub on, eliminating the need for the needle. This system is often called MUSE which stands for "medicated urethral system for erections." However, MUSE is not as effective as ICI.

Vacuum Devices for Sexual Arousal Disorder

Vacuum devices are another treatment for sexual arousal disorders. Essentially, they pump you up! A tube is placed over the penis (see Figure 18.5). With some devices, the mouth can produce enough suction; with others, a small hand pump is used. Once a reasonably firm erection is present, the tube is removed and a rubber ring is placed around the base of the penis to maintain the penis's engorgement with blood. These devices have been used successfully with, for example, diabetic men. They can also be helpful in combination with cognitive–behavioural couple therapy for cases of erectile dysfunction that are mainly psychological in origin (Wylie et al., 2003).

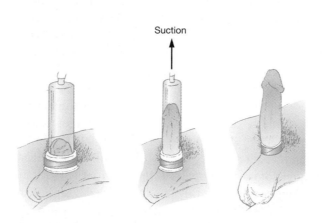

Suction

Figure 18.5   A treatment for erectile disorder. An external tube, with a rubberband around it, is placed over the lubricated penis. Suction applied to the tube produces erection, which is maintained by the constricting action of the rubberband once the plastic tube has been removed.

There is also now a vacuum device to assist women with clitoral engorgement. However, there is little research supporting the effectiveness of this device; for most women the subjective aspects of arousal are at least equally important as is clitoral engorgement per se.

Surgical Therapy

There is promising evidence that surgery can help women with some types of dyspareunia (Bergeron et al., 2001; Landry et al., 2008). Nonetheless, most surgical treatments are currently focused on male sexual problems.

Penile prosthesis (prahs-THEE-sis): A surgical treatment for erectile dysfunction, in which inflatable tubes are inserted into the penis.

For severe cases of erectile disorder, surgical therapy is possible. The surgery involves implanting a **prosthesis** into the penis (Hellstrom, 2003; Kabalin & Kuo, 1997). A sac or bladder of sterile fluid is implanted in the lower abdomen, connected to two inflatable tubes running the length of the corpus spongiosum, with a pump in the scrotum. Thus the man can literally pump up or inflate his penis so that he has a full erection.

The surgery takes approximately one and a half hours and requires only one incision, where the penis and scrotum meet. The cost of the procedure is usually covered by medicare.

It should be emphasized that this is a radical treatment that should be reserved only for those cases that have not been successfully treated by sex therapy or drug therapy. Typically, it should be a case of erectile disorder that is the result of organic factors such as diabetes. The patient must understand that the surgery itself destroys some portions of the penis, so that a natural erection will never again be possible. Research shows that about one-fourth of men who have had this treatment are dissatisfied afterward. Reasons for dissatisfaction include the penis being smaller when erect than it was presurgery, different sensations during arousal, and different sensations during ejaculation (Steege et al., 1986). Although the treatment is radical and should be used conservatively, it is a godsend for some men who have been incapable of erection because of organic difficulties. Indeed, more than a dozen children have been born as a result of this surgery, to women whose partners were previously incapable of intercourse.

In another version of a surgical approach, a semirigid, silicone-like rod is implanted into the penis (Melman & Tiefer, 1992; Shandera & Thompson, 1994). This non-inflatable device is less costly than the inflatable version and has a lower rate of complications (Rosen & Leiblum, 1995b).

CRITIQUES OF SEX THERAPY

One of the most basic questions we must ask about sex therapy is: Is it effective?

Psychologists Bernie Zilbergeld and Michael Evans (1980) did an extensive critique of the research methods used by Masters and Johnson in evaluating the success of their sex therapy. Zilbergeld and Evans concluded that there are a number of substantial problems. In brief, the criticisms suggest that we really do not know what the success rate of Masters and Johnson's therapy was. A discussion of the specific criticisms follows. These points are important to bear in mind when evaluating any type of sex therapy.

First, Masters and Johnson never actually reported a *success* rate for the therapy. Instead, they reported a *failure* rate of about 20 percent. The other 80 percent apparently included a mixture of clear successes and cases that were ambiguous as to whether they were successes or failures—in short, they had 80 percent non-failures, but that does not mean 80 percent successes.

Furthermore, Masters and Johnson never defined what they meant by a "success" in therapy. This is an important issue. How improved does a person have to be to be counted as a success? Suppose a woman seeks help for anorgasmia; she has never had an orgasm. By the end of therapy, she is able to orgasm from a vibrator, but not from hand stimulation or mouth stimulation by her partner, nor by penetration. Is this case a success? How would Masters and Johnson have classified her?

Zilbergeld and Evans initiated their critical appraisal after finding that they and other sex therapists were unable to obtain success rates as dramatic or relapse rates as low as the ones Masters and Johnson reported. One possibility is that other sex therapists have been using definitions of therapy success that are much stricter and more precise than the definition used by Masters and Johnson. Another possibility is that current therapists are seeing clients who are significantly different from the clients seen by Masters and Johnson. For example, today individuals with straightforward problems can often resolve the problem with information they find in books or on the Internet. These options were not available when Masters and Johnson were doing their work.

A broader critique pointed out that a major shortcoming of the field of sex therapy is the lack of carefully controlled studies that (1) investigate the success of various therapies compared with other therapies and with untreated controls; and (2) examine what aspect of a particular therapy or combination of therapies seems to have the beneficial effect (Rosen & Leiblum, 1995b).

Nonetheless, there is sufficient evidence evaluating certain treatments for certain disorders to reach the following conclusions (Heiman, 2002; Heiman & Meston, 1997):

- Primary orgasmic dysfunction is successfully treated with directed masturbation, and the treatment can be enhanced with sensate focus exercises.
- Treatments for secondary orgasmic dysfunction are somewhat less successful. Therapy that combines some or all of the following components seems to be most effective: sex education, sexual skills training, communication skills training, and body image therapy. The problem here, most likely, is that there are many different patterns of secondary anorgasmia, with a need to match treatment to the pattern of the disorder, something that research has not been able to untangle.
- Vaginismus can be successfully treated with progressive vaginal dilators; relaxation and Kegel exercises may also be helpful, but the evidence is not as strong. A recent study compared cognitive–behavioural therapy including these and other components to a control group and found that 14 percent of the treated participants but none of the control participants reported successful intercourse (van Lankveld et al., 2006)—a significant but small effect for treatment.
- The squeeze technique is effective for treating premature ejaculation. Drugs, specifically some antidepressants (serotonin reuptake inhibitors), also may be effective.
- For some disorders—sexual desire disorders, dyspareunia, and delayed orgasm in men—research is insufficient to conclude that there is an effective treatment. Of course, this does not mean that current treatments are not effective; just that the research has not been done to determine one way or the other.

Another critique points out the *medicalization* of sexual disorders (Kleinplatz, 2003; Tiefer, 1994, 2000). Research has increasingly identified organic sources of male erectile disorder, and with these advances have come attempts to identify drugs and surgeries, rather than psychotherapies, to treat problems. In part, political issues are involved, as physicians try to seize the treatment of sexual disorders from psychologists. But there is also a cost to the patient, as the disorder may be given a quick fix with drugs while the patient's anxieties and relationship problems are ignored. That is, we treat the symptoms, not the problem (Kleinplatz, 2003). For biomedical treatments to be successful over the long term, the cognitive, affective, and interpersonal issues must also be addressed (Basson, 1998).

There also has been a move toward the medicalization of women's sexual problems, both in terms of understanding their causes and in terms of seeking drug treatments (Tiefer, 2001). The Working Group on a New View of Women's Sexual Problems (2001), a group of 12 clinicians and social scientists, has criticized the categories used to classify women's sexual problems in the *DSM-IV* listed in Table 18.1 (page 562) as being too medical and mechanical, focusing too much on genital response, and thus not fitting with women's experiences. They argue that any classification scheme for women's sexual problems needs to take sociocultural and relationship factors into account. Further, research suggests that the *DSM-IV* criteria are not good predictors of the extent to which women are distressed about their sexual functioning (Bancroft et al., 2003). The new classification scheme that they propose is summarized in In Focus 18.2.

In contrast to these scientific criticisms, sex therapy has also been criticized on philosophical grounds. Ottawa psychologist and sex therapist Peggy Kleinplatz (1992, 1998) has argued that the current approach to sex therapy is goal-oriented rather than pleasure-oriented. By defining problems in terms of sexual disorders, sex therapists and their clients may focus on physiological and mechanical outcomes (getting an erection, having an orgasm) rather than on clients' subjective experience of sexuality, sexual satisfaction, and eroticism (Kleinplatz, 2003). Sexual satisfaction is not just the absence of a sexual disorder (Byers, 1999).

IN FOCUS 18.2

Do We Need a New View of Women's Sexual Problems?

The Working Group on a New View of Women's Sexual Problems has criticized the current way of classifying women's sexual problems in the *DSM-IV* as being too medical and mechanical. They argue that even if the diagnostic categories fit for men, they do not correspond to women's experience. They have proposed a new classification scheme that is not based on the Masters and Johnson sexual response cycle, as the current classifications scheme is. Rather, it defines a sexual problem as dissatisfaction with any emotional, physical, or relational aspect of sexual experience, and takes social, cultural, and relationship factors into account. They propose the following way of classifying women's sexual problems:

I. **Sexual problems due to sociocultural, political, or economic factors:**

  A. Ignorance and anxiety due to inadequate sex education, lack of access to health services, or other social constraints.

  B. Sexual avoidance or distress due to perceived inability to meet cultural norms regarding correct or ideal sexuality.

  C. Inhibition due to conflict between the sexual norms of one's subculture or culture of origin and those of the dominant culture.

  D. Lack of interest, fatigue, or lack of time due to family and work obligations.

II. **Sexual problems relating to partner and relationship:**

  A. Inhibition, avoidance, or distress arising from betrayal, dislike, or fear of partner, partner's abuse or couple's unequal power, or arising from partner's negative patterns of communication.

  B. Discrepancies in desire for sexual activity or in preferences for various sexual activities.

  C. Ignorance or inhibition about communicating preferences or initiating, pacing, or shaping sexual activities.

  D. Loss of sexual interest and reciprocity as a result of conflicts over commonplace issues such as money, schedules, or relatives, or resulting from traumatic experiences, e.g., infertility or the death of a child.

  E. Inhibitions in arousal or spontaneity due to partner's health status or sexual problems.

III. **Sexual problems due to psychological factors:**

  A. Sexual aversion, mistrust, or inhibition of sexual pleasure due to [experience of abuse, problems with attachment depression or anxiety].

  B. Sexual inhibition due to fear of sexual activities or of their possible consequences, e.g., pain during intercourse, pregnancy, sexually transmitted infections, loss of partner, loss of reputation.

IV. **Sexual problems due to medical factors:**

  A. Pain or lack of response during sexual activity despite a supportive and safe interpersonal situation, adequate sexual knowledge and positive sexual attitudes. Such problems can arise from medical conditions, pregnancy, STIs, and medication.

As you can see, this way of thinking about sexual disorders and their causes in women is considerably different from the dominant ways of thinking and categories used in the *DSM-IV*. The Working Group on a New View of Women's Sexual Problems developed this framework to assist researchers, educators, and clinicians. They also hope that it will help the public better understand women's sexual problems. However, the proposed classification is too new for us to know whether it will change the thinking of any of these groups. Still, it challenges assumptions about the nature and causes of sexual problems. Perhaps we need a new view of men's sexual problems as well.

Source: Kaschak & Tiefer, 2001.

Often individuals get aroused and have orgasms but experience disappointment with the quality of their sexual encounters with their partner. Evaluation of the success of sex therapy should include more attention to whether therapy has resulted in enhanced sexual satisfaction (Handy et al., 1985). Resolving a sexual disorder often results in a decrease in sexual *dissatisfaction*, but it does not necessarily result in increased sexual satisfaction.

Psychiatrist Thomas Szasz (1980) argued that sex therapists have essentially produced a lot of illness by creating the (somewhat arbitrary) diagnostic categories of sexual disorder. This criticism may especially apply to individuals with disabilities. Ontario researcher Gina Di Giulio (2003) has argued that the diagnostic categories for sexual dysfunction do not fit for such persons. In particular, the focus on genital response may imply that persons with disabilities cannot experience a highly pleasurable and satisfying sex life. Yet, a woman with a spinal cord injury who has little genital sensation might get great pleasure from having her breasts or other parts of her body stroked, and reach orgasm from this type of pleasuring. That is, she has adapted her lovemaking to meet her own needs and situation. It is important for sex therapists to communicate to their clients with disabilities that they are fully sexual, and that there is no right way to make love.

In summary, a number of criticisms have been raised about the field of sex therapy. The research methods used by Masters and Johnson to evaluate the success of their therapy had a number of problems and, as a result, their implied success rate of 80 percent is probably unrealistically high. Despite three decades of rapid advances in both psychological and medical treatments of sexual disorders, adequate research has not yet been done on the effectiveness of many of these treatments. There is a trend to medicalize sexual disorders, particularly erectile disorder, which may lead to the neglect of patients' needs for psychological treatment. There has also been a tendency to focus on physiological outcomes such as orgasm and erection rather than on the individual's subjective experience of sexuality and sexual satisfaction. Finally, Szasz questions the whole notion of sexual disorders as such.

Where do these criticisms leave us? In our opinion, they do not invalidate the work of sex therapists. Rather, they urge us to be cautious. Most sexual disorders will not have success rates of 80 percent (but then, most therapies for other disorders don't either) but they may well turn out to have success rates of 60 percent or more, which is still pretty good. Many other clients may feel that their sexual functioning has been enhanced by sex therapy (Kaplan, 1979). A single method of therapy, such as Masters and Johnson's behaviour therapy, will not be effective with every disorder. Finally, we must be sensitive to the values expressed in labelling something as being, or someone as having, a "disorder."

SOME PRACTICAL ADVICE

AVOIDING SEXUAL DISORDERS

People can use some of the principles that emerge from sex therapists' work to avoid having sexual disorders in the first place. As the saying goes, an ounce of prevention is worth a pound of cure. In Chapter 1, we introduced the concept of sexual health. The following are some principles of good sexual mental health:

1. *Communicate with your partner.* Don't expect him or her to be a mind reader concerning what is pleasurable to you. One way to do this is to make it a habit to talk to your partner while you are having sex; verbal communication then does not come as a shock. Some people, though, feel uncomfortable talking at such times; non-verbal communication, such as placing your hand on top of your partner's and moving it where you want it, works well too (see Chapter 12 for more detail about good sexual communication).

2. *Concentrate on giving and receiving sexual pleasure.* Don't be a spectator, feeling as if you are putting on a sexual performance that you constantly need to evaluate. Concentrate as much as possible on the giving and receiving of sensual pleasures, not on how well you are doing.

3. *Relax and enjoy yourself.* Don't set up goals for sexual performance. If you have a goal, you can fail, and failure can produce disorders. Don't set your heart on having simultaneous orgasms or, if you are a woman, on having five orgasms before your partner has one. Just relax and enjoy yourself.

4. *Be choosy about the situations in which you have sex.* Don't have sex when you are in a terrific hurry or are afraid you will be disturbed. Also be choosy about who your partner is. Trusting your partner is essential to good sexual functioning; similarly, a partner who really cares for you will be understanding if things don't go well and will not laugh or be sarcastic.

5. *Accept that disappointments will occur.* They do in any sexual relationship. What is important is how you interpret them. It is important that you don't see yourself as a failure and don't let them ruin the relationship. Instead, try to think, "How can we make this turn out well anyhow?"

CHOOSING A SEX THERAPIST

No provinces have licensing or certification requirements to practise sex therapy. This means that anyone can hang out a shingle saying "Sex Therapist," and some people with no training in the area have done so.

How do you go about finding a good, qualified sex therapist? Although they are not required by law to do so, some Ontario sex therapists choose to become certified by the Board of Examiners in Sexual Therapy and Counselling and some Quebec sex therapists by L'Association des Sexologues du Québec. The other provinces do not have such boards. A very few Canadian sex therapists choose to get certified by a U.S. organization. However, most sex therapists in Canada operate under their discipline licences—such as psychology, clinical social work, or psychiatry—and therefore do not seek additional certification as a sex therapist even if they have training in sex therapy. Your local medical or psychological association can provide a list of therapists in your area and may be able to tell you which ones have special training in sex therapy. In any case, it is important to ask potential sex therapists about their specific training in sex therapy as well as about their approach to sex therapy to make sure that they are qualified to provide sex therapy. Choose a therapist or clinic that offers an individualized *integrated biopsychosocial approach* that recognizes the potential biological, psychological, and relationship influences on any sexual disorder and is prepared to address all of these and work in conjunction with professionals from other disciplines if needed.

What about people who live in an area where there are no sex therapists? Some therapists provide sex therapy online. Proponents of sex therapy online argue that it is more affordable than traditional in-person therapy and that its anonymity is a major advantage. Interactions with a therapist online can break the wall of isolation surrounding a person with a sexual disorder. There are disadvantages, too. Currently, there is no system for licensing online sex therapists, so unqualified and perhaps unethical persons could easily present themselves as therapists. In fact, it is difficult to find legitimate sex therapy websites because searching for terms such as "sex therapy" leads to a deluge of porn sites. Moreover, online sex therapists probably will not be able to give true intensive therapy of the kind one would get in multiple in-person sessions with a therapist. However, qualified online therapists can provide permission and positive encouragement as well as accurate information, and that's enough to solve many people's problems. Unfortunately, many people who would benefit from sex therapy are unlikely to seek help, even over the Internet, for religious or cultural reasons, because they are embarrassed about it, or because they are erotophobic.

SUMMARY

Sexual disorders fall into four categories according to the *DSM-IV*: desire disorders (hypoactive sexual desire, discrepancy of sexual desire, sexual aversion disorder), arousal disorders (female sexual arousal disorder, erectile disorder), orgasmic disorders (rapid ejaculation, male orgasmic disorder, female orgasmic disorder), and sexual pain disorders (dyspareunia, vaginismus).

Sexual disorders may be caused by physical factors, individual psychological factors, and interpersonal factors. Organic causes include some illnesses, infections, and damage to the spinal cord. Certain drugs may also create problems with sexual functioning. Psychological causes are categorized into predisposing factors and maintaining causes including myths and misinformation, negative attitudes, anxiety, cognitive interference, psychological distress, and behavioural or lifestyle factors. Interpersonal factors include failure to engage in effective stimulation often due to poor sexual communication and relationship distress caused by, for example, conflict in the couple's relationship or lack of intimacy.

Therapies for sexual disorders include behaviour therapy (pioneered by Masters and Johnson) based on learning theory, cognitive–behavioural therapy, couple therapy, specific treatments for specific problems (e.g., stop-start for premature ejaculation), and a variety of biomedical treatments, which include drug treatments (e.g., Viagra).

A number of criticisms of sex therapy have been raised, including concerns about the research methods used to evaluate the success of Masters and Johnson's therapy, the medicalization of sexual disorders, focusing on physiological outcomes rather than on sexual pleasure and satisfaction, and the entire enterprise of identifying and labelling sexual disorders.

QUESTIONS FOR THOUGHT, DISCUSSION, AND DEBATE

1. When (or if) you engage in sexual activity with a partner, do you feel that you are under pressure to perform and that you engage in spectatoring? If so, what might you do to change this pattern?
2. Considering the predisposing causes of sexual disorders, what are the implications for parents who want to raise sexually healthy children? Could parents do certain things that would avoid or prevent sexual disorders in their children?
3. Your best friend, Steve, who is 22, discloses to you a long history of rapid ejaculation, which has been very embarrassing and frustrating for him. He has heard about Viagra and, knowing that you are taking a human sexuality course, comes to you for advice about whether he should go to a doctor to get a prescription for it. What advice would you give him?
4. Hypoactive sexual desire is a common sexual disorder in Canada today. Given what you know about this disorder and its causes, do you think it is also common in other cultures? Think about Britain, China, India, and Mexico as examples. (For further information, see Bhurga & de Silva, 1993.)

SUGGESTIONS FOR FURTHER READING

Barbach, Lonnie G. (1975). *For yourself: The fulfillment of female sexuality.* Garden City, NY: Doubleday. Provides good information for women with orgasmic disorders, based on the author's experiences as a sex therapist. Still the classic in the field.

Barbach, Lonnie G. (1983). *For each other: Sharing sexual intimacy.* Garden City, NY: Anchor Books. Barbach's sequel to *For Yourself* (see above); this volume is designed for couples.

Heiman, Julia R., and LoPiccolo, Joseph. (1988). *Becoming orgasmic: A sexual and personal growth program for women* (Revised and expanded edition). New York: Simon & Schuster.

McCarthy, Barry, and McCarthy, Emily. (2002). *Sexual awareness: Couple sexual therapy for the twenty-first century.* New York: Carroll and Graf.

Tiefer, Leonore. (2004). *Sex is not a natural act, and other essays.* 2nd ed. Boulder, CO: Westview. Tiefer is a brilliant and entertaining writer, and her criticisms of sex therapy are insightful.

Zilbergeld, Bernie. (1999). *The new male sexuality* (Revised edition). New York: Bantam.

Online LearningCentre

For review questions, web resources, and other learning and study tools, visit the *Understanding Human Sexuality* Online Learning Centre at www.mcgrawhill.ca/olc/hyde.

SEXUALITY EDUCATION

> FORMAL SEX EDUCATION IN CANADIAN SCHOOLS GOES BACK AT LEAST TO THE EARLY 1900S WHEN ARTHUR W. BEALL GAVE HIS "ADVANCED PURITY LECTURES." . . . THOSE INVOLVED IN PUBLIC AND SCHOOL SEX EDUCATION SAW THEMSELVES AT THE FOREFRONT OF "MODERN THINKING." NEVERTHELESS, THEIR MESSAGE STRONGLY REINFORCED CONVENTIONAL MORALITY. . . . [T]HEY APPEAR TO HAVE BEEN 100% SUCCESSFUL IN ELIMINATING MASTURBATORY INSANITY AS A SOCIAL PROBLEM. YOU HARDLY HEAR ABOUT THAT THESE DAYS.*

As we look to the future, a top priority for society has to be sexuality education. If you have studied this textbook, you should be prepared to be a good sex educator for your own children. You should also be a well-informed citizen who can make thoughtful decisions about sexuality education in schools. However, it is not just children who require sex education. Most people need additional information about sexuality throughout their lives so that they can adapt to changes in their life circumstances (e.g., becoming single again, physical changes due to aging, and illness). This chapter concerns sexuality education. Sexuality education is the lifelong process of acquiring information about sexual behaviour and forming attitudes, beliefs, and values about identity, relationships, and intimacy (SIECUS, 1991). Sex education can occur in many settings: home, school, church or synagogue, youth programs, relationships, and via information found on the Internet.

> **Sexuality education:** The lifelong process of acquiring information about sexual behaviour and forming attitudes, beliefs, and values about identity, relationships, and intimacy.

PURPOSES OF SEXUALITY EDUCATION

The goal of sexuality education is to promote healthy sexuality. What is healthy sexuality? In the words of Health Canada:

> Healthy sexuality is a positive and life affirming part of being human. It includes knowledge of self, opportunities for healthy sexual development and sexual experience, the capacity for intimacy, an ability to share relationships, and comfort with different expressions of sexuality including love, joy, caring, sensuality, or celibacy. Our attitudes about sexuality, our ability to understand and accept our own sexuality, to make healthy choices and respect the choices of others, are essential aspects of who we are and how we interact with the world. (Health Canada, 1999)

The Sex Education and Information Council of Canada (SIECCAN) is active in promoting high-quality sex education in Canada and coordinated the development of the *Canadian Guidelines for Sexual Health Education* (Health Canada, 2003). The *Guidelines* provide a framework for sexual health education for persons of all ages that balances the well-being and desires of the individual with the rights of others and of society. There are five principles stated in the *Guidelines:* (1) Everyone should have access to effective sexual health education; (2) sexual health education should be comprehensive and address a broad range of issues relevant to diverse populations; (3) sexual health education should use methods based on the information–motivation–behavioural skills model (Fisher & Fisher, 1992, 1998; described in Chapter 7), as this model has been shown to be effective; (4) sexual health education teachers should be well trained and supported by their administration or organization; and (5) the impact of sexual health education should be evaluated so that programs can be updated. According to the *Guidelines*, sexuality education should help people both to achieve positive outcomes and to avoid negative ones. Positive outcomes include self-esteem, respect for self

> **SIECCAN:** The Sex Information and Education Council of Canada, a national resource for up-to-date information, research, and publication on human sexuality, including sexual health.

---

*Michael Barrett (1990). Chair, Sex Information and Education Council of Canada (SIECCAN).

and others, non-exploitative sexual satisfaction, rewarding human relationships, and the joy of desired parenthood. Negative outcomes include unwanted pregnancy, sexually transmitted infection, sexual coercion, and sexual dysfunction. Effective sexual health education integrates four key components through a variety of activities. These allow individuals:

1. to acquire knowledge that is relevant to their specific sexual health issues;
2. to develop the motivation and personal insight that they will need to act on that knowledge;
3. to acquire the skills necessary to enhance sexual health and avoid negative sexual health outcomes;
4. to help create an environment that is conducive to sexual health. (Health Canada, 2003, p. 12)

To achieve these goals, youth need to have an opportunity to explore attitudes, feelings, and values that may influence their decisions and behaviour. Sex education should emphasize the self-worth and dignity of the individual as well as encourage respect for diversity in values, background, and sexual orientation. The *Guidelines* recognize that students need to make their own informed and responsible choices rather than have choices imposed on them. For example, some adolescents will choose abstinence over sexual involvement; others will choose to have sexual relationships.

IN THE HOME, IN THE SCHOOL, OR SOMEWHERE ELSE?

When parents of children and teenagers get together to urge their school system to adopt a sex education curriculum, invariably some citizens of the community raise a protest. They might say that sex education promotes sexual intercourse, teenage pregnancy, or AIDS, and they are sure that it should take place only in the home (or possibly the church), but certainly not in the schools.

As shown in Table 19.1, school is the main source of sexual health education for grade 9 students in Canada; 41 percent of the girls and 51 percent of the boys gave this response (Boyce et al., 2003). In contrast, only 6 percent of the boys and 14 percent of the girls identified parents or other family members as their main source of sexuality information. The fact is that many children are given little or no sexuality education at home; of course, parents not talking about sex with their children is also a form of communication and sends a variety of negative messages. Notice that TV, printed materials such as magazines, and the Internet are important sources of information for many youth, as are friends. In many cases the information provided on TV

Table 19.1   Main Sources of Grade 9 Students' Information about Sex

	Boys	Girls
Parents or other family members	6%	14%
Friends	9	17
Internet	12	3
School	51	41
Magazines, newspapers, books	5	12
Television/movies	9	5
Physician or nurse	5	5

Source: Research conducted by the Council of Ministers of Education, Canada, with funding provided by Health Canada.

is sensationalized and unrealistic (refer to In Focus 10.1 on page 304). Relying on friends for information is a classic case of the blind leading the blind. The problem with the Internet as the primary source of sexuality information for youth is that there is no quality control; there are some sites with excellent and accurate information (such as www.sexualityandu.ca) but others that promote misinformation. Thus, it is appropriate that school has become the main and preferred source of information (McKay & Holowaty, 1997).

Sex education in the school is not "instead of" education in the home. Most Canadian parents, teachers, and students feel that both parents and schools have a role to play in providing sex education (Byers et al., 2003a, 2003b; Cohen et al., 2004; McKay & Holowaty, 1997; McKay et al., 1998; Weaver et al., 2002). For example, in a survey of parents in New Brunswick, 95 percent felt that responsibility for sexual health education should be shared by parents and schools (Weaver et al., 2002); somewhat fewer high school students (77 percent) and middle school students (69 percent) shared this view (Byers et al., 2003a, 2003b). In a survey conducted in the United States in 2003, 88 percent of the parents of students in grades 7 and 8 and 80 percent of the parents of students in grades 9 through 12 agreed that the program in the school makes it easier to talk to their children about sexual issues (Kaiser Family Foundation, 2004a). Some sexuality education programs actively involve parents by including homework to be done jointly by parent and child. The evaluation of one program of this type found that students receiving classroom instruction plus homework felt more able to refuse high-risk behaviours, and more often intended to delay initiation of intercourse compared to students receiving only classroom instruction (Blake et al., 2003). The homework assignments appeared to reinforce the school-based program, and resulted in greater parent–child communication about sex.

How well are parents and schools doing in providing sex education? According to parents and students who participated in four New Brunswick studies described in In Focus 19.1, only between 24 percent (according to middle school students) and 38 percent (according to the parents) of children are getting excellent or very good sex education at home. According to the teachers and students, the schools are not doing much better: between 13 percent (according to high school students) and 37 percent (according to middle school students) rated the sexual health education they had received in school as very good or excellent. One research study involved interviews with 40 rural and urban youth in Nova Scotia and British Columbia about their sexual experiences, including their experiences with sexual health education (Shoveller et al., 2004). The youth indicated that neither schools nor parents promoted meaningful discussions about sex. Rather they perceived that both sexual health education and discussion with parents (if they had any) focused on prevention of pregnancy and STIs; what was missing for these respondents was discussion of issues related to sexual relationships, especially the emotional and

DENNIS the MENACE

"THAT'S FUNNY... MY DAD CAN TELL IF IT'S A BOY OR A GIRL JUST BY LOOKIN' AT THE BOTTOM OF ITS FEET."

Dennis the Menace cartoon by T.M. 1983. Dennis the Menace ®: used by permission of Hank Ketcham and © North American Syndicate.

Figure 19.1 Children often have inaccurate ideas about sex.

IN FOCUS 19.1

Attitudes toward Sexual Health Education

A team of New Brunswick researchers collaborated with the New Brunswick Department of Education to conduct parallel surveys of New Brunswick teacher, parent, middle school student, and high school student ideas about sexual health education. They surveyed 4206 parents, 336 teachers, 745 middle school students, and 1666 high school students.

Some of the results are presented in Table 19.2. The four groups were consistent with each other in many of their views. For example, all four groups were strongly in support of sexual health education in the schools—more than 90 percent agreed that sexual health education should be provided in schools. Further, they were in favour of a comprehensive curriculum that covers a broad range of topics. This is important because the teachers reported that the greatest barrier to teaching sexual health is fear of negative reactions from parents. Although the teachers were overwhelmingly in favour of sexual health education in the schools,

they indicated that they felt only somewhat knowledgeable, less comfortable to teach sexual health, and, perhaps as a result, reluctant to teach it. The teachers felt particularly unknowledgeable and uncomfortable teaching about the more controversial topics, such as sexual pleasure, masturbation, and homosexuality. The authors pointed to a need for training for teachers who teach sexual health.

Parents and teachers were somewhat more positive than students were about parents and schools sharing the responsibility for sexual health education. In fact, 40 percent of the students did not wish to talk more with their parents about sexuality. Students' opinions were influenced by the quality of the sex education they had received at home. Students who rated their parents' efforts less highly were less likely to support shared responsibility between parents and schools. This may be because these students did not perceive their parents to be experts in sexual health or because

potentially positive aspects of sexual relationships. For example, one male youth described the sexual health education he had received in school:

> It [sex] was only talked about in Sex Ed . . . it was very *technical* and, of course, you couldn't ask *real* questions about your own experience. I think I understand the physical stuff but it's so emotional. And, it's the emotional stuff that you are always fucked up about when you are young. So, that's the part that was difficult. There's no question-and-answer period for that. You would never do that [emotional stuff] in a science class. (Shoveller et al., 2004, p. 480)

Similarly, youth indicated that they picked up subtle and not-so-subtle messages from their parents that certain kinds of questions and discussions about sex were "off limits."

The goal of this chapter is to describe effective sex education in school and at home. We will also look at the potential of the Internet for providing sexual education. However, we first examine what research can tell us about what children should be taught about sex at different ages.

WHAT TO TEACH AT DIFFERENT AGES

Sexuality education, whether at home or at school, is not something that can be carried out all at once in one week during grade 5 or by having "the talk." Like teaching math or life skills, it is a process that must begin when children are small. They should learn simple concepts first, progressing to more difficult ones as they grow older. Although sex education should always come before experience, what is taught at any particular age depends, in part, on the child's sexual behaviour (see Chapter 10), sexual knowledge, and sexual interests at that age. This section will concentrate on theories and research that provide information on the last two points.

Table 19.2 Responses of Parents, Teachers, and Students

	Percentage Agreeing with Each Statement			
	Parents	Teachers	Middle School Students	High School Students
Sexual health education should be provided in the schools.	94%	93%	93%	92%
The schools and parents should share responsibility for providing children with sexual health education.	95%	95%	69%	77%
Sexual health education should start in grades K–5.	65%	78%	30%	23%

they perceived their parents to be uncomfortable talking about sex. Only about half of the parents indicated that they often encouraged their children to ask questions about sex.

Students were more conservative than parents or teachers about when sexual health education should start. While most parents and teachers felt that it should begin in elementary school, most students felt it should start in middle school. This may be because these students had not received sex education in elementary school and thus did not have a clear idea of how sexual health education would be taught to children younger than themselves. The results of these studies were used to revise the sexual health education curriculum in New Brunswick.

Sources: Byers et al., 2003a; Byers et al., 2003b; Cohen et al., 2004; Weaver et al., 2002.

CHILDREN'S SEXUAL KNOWLEDGE

A few researchers have investigated what children in Western countries know about sex and reproduction at various ages. Children begin to develop an understanding of pregnancy and birth at a very early age. Very young children may believe that a baby has always existed, that it existed somewhere else before it got inside the mother. The following dialogue demonstrates this:

(How did the baby happen to be in your Mommy's tummy?) It just grows inside. (How did it get there?) It's there all the time. Mommy doesn't have to do anything. She waits until she feels it. (You said that the baby wasn't in there when you were there.) Yeah, then he was in the other place . . . in America. (In America?) Yeah, in somebody else's tummy. (Bernstein & Cowan, 1975, p. 86)

As children get older, they develop—we hope—a more accurate understanding!

By age seven or eight, children have a more sophisticated understanding of reproduction. They may know that three things are involved in making a baby: a social relationship between two people, such as love or marriage; sexual activity; and the union of sperm and egg. However, they may not understand that the sexual activity involves intercourse. At age 12, some children can give a good physiological explanation of reproduction that includes the idea that the embryo begins its biological existence at the moment of conception and is the product of genetic material from both parents. As one preteen explained:

The sperm encounters one ovum, and one sperm breaks into the ovum which produces, the sperm makes like a cell, and the cell separates and divides. And so it's dividing, and the ovum goes through a tube and embeds itself in the wall of the, I think it's the fetus of the woman. (Bernstein & Cowan, 1975, p. 89)

Some 10- and 11-year-olds understand that one of the reasons parents want to be alone is to have sex; others are reluctant to recognize the sexual dimension of their parents' relationship (De La Vega Salas & Thériault, 2001).

As we discussed in Chapter 10, research suggests that many children engage in sexual play and exploration. How does sexual behaviour relate to sexual knowledge? One review of the literature concluded that young children often engage in sexual behaviour without having a clear understanding of what it means (Gordon & Schroeder, 1995). These findings have important implications for sex education. Educators need to be aware of the level of the child's understanding and should not inundate him or her with information inappropriate for his or her age. Instead, the educator should attempt to clarify misunderstandings in the child's beliefs. For example, if a child believes a baby has always existed, the educator might say, "To make a baby, you need two grown-ups, a man and a woman."

CHILDREN'S SEXUAL INTERESTS

Children's knowledge of and interest in sex are reflected in the questions they ask. At age five, kids may be asking where babies come from. At age nine, a boy or girl may ask about sexual behaviours: "What's oral sex?" Such questions are often stimulated by hearing the term in conversation or in the media. A ten-year-old may be interested in bodily processes and ask, "What's a period?" By age 11, many kids are asking questions related to puberty, such as "When will I get breasts?" or "When will I grow taller?" Such questions typically reflect an awareness that other youth are experiencing such growth. At age 13 or 14, many youth have specific questions about sexual activity. One young man asked, "Do girls move a lot when they have sex?" A 14-year-old girl asked her mom, "Where do people have sex?" (Blake, 2004). It is important that sex education for a particular age group address the questions of that age group, rather than questions children of that age thought about but answered long ago.

High school students agree that sex education should begin in early elementary school, and should progress from the simple to the complex (Byers et al., 2003a). They believe that it should cover a wide range of topics, including reproduction, pregnancy, abortion, birth control options, disease prevention, sexual violence, relationships and gender roles, sexual pleasure, homosexuality, and sexual decision making. They would like all of these topics presented by grade 8, but then revisited in high school. In particular, they want sexual health education that talks more about sex—feelings, arousal, foreplay, contraception, condoms, weighing alternatives—and is respectful of their choices (Caputo, 2000; Langille, 2000; Maticka-Tyndale, 2001).

We can also tell something about children's sexual knowledge and interest by the dirty jokes they tell. Anthropologist Rosemary Zumwalt collected dirty jokes from girls between the ages of seven and ten as part of her study of children's folklore (1976). The following is typical of the jokes they told her:

> There's this little boy, and he wanted to take a bath with his dad. And his dad said, "If you promise not to look under the curtain." And then he took a shower, and he looked under the curtain. And he said, "Dad, what's that long hairy thing?" And the father says, "That's my banana."
>
> Then he asks his Mom, "Can I take a shower with you, Mom?" She says, "If you promise not to look under the curtain." And they get into the shower, and he looks under the curtain. And he says, "Mom, what's that thing?" And she says, "That's my fruit bowl." And he says, "Mom, can I sleep with you and Dad?" And she says, "Yes, if you promise not to look under the covers." And he looks under the covers and says, "Mom, Dad's banana is in your fruit bowl!" (Zumwalt, 1976, p. 261)

Children's dirty jokes reflect several themes in their attitudes toward sexuality and in their interactions with their parents on the issue. First, children seem to view their parents as always trying to keep sex a secret from them. The parents consistently tell children not to look under the curtain, for example. Second, the jokes reflect children's fascination with sex, particularly with the penis, the vagina, the breasts, and intercourse. The jokes generally revolve around these topics and children's attempts to find out about them. Third, the jokes seem to satirize adults' use of euphemisms for sexual terms. The joke just given hinges on a parent's using the term "banana" instead of "penis." Most frequently, the fanciful names used for the sexual organs involve food (banana, hot dog), power (light bulbs, light sockets), or animals (gorilla). Commenting on the bathtub-shower form of dirty joke, an authority said, "In all forms of the . . . joke, the wonderful humor to the child is the mocking of the parents' evasions, which are somehow so foolishly phrased" (Legman, 1968, p. 53).

Teenagers have outgrown this sort of joke, but they tell a parallel one:

> This little boy walks into the bathroom, and he catches his mother naked. She was a little embarrassed. He said, "Mommy, what's that?" And she says, "Oh, that's where God hit me with an axe." And the little kid says, "Got you right in the cunt, eh?" (Zumwalt, 1976, p. 267)

Once again, this joke has the theme of a parent's embarrassment and use of evasions and euphemisms when dealing with sex. But now the child (teenager) reflects a sophistication about sex, perhaps even a greater sophistication than the parent has.

Sex educators should remember that children are aware of adults' attempts to "cover up" and of their embarrassment and their use of euphemisms, as these jokes indicate.

ATTITUDES TOWARD SCHOOL-BASED SEXUALITY EDUCATION

Surveys have shown repeatedly that the vast majority of parents are in favour of sex education in the schools. Research in Ontario, Nova Scotia, and New Brunswick has found very high levels of support among parents (Langille et al., 1996; McKay, 1996; McKay et al., 1998; Weaver et al., 2002). For example, a survey of 6833 parents in rural southern Ontario found 95 percent in favour of sex education in the schools; 82 percent felt it should begin in the primary grades and continue throughout high school (McKay et al., 1998). Similarly, 94 percent of New Brunswick parents with children in kindergarten through grade 8 support sex education in schools (Weaver et al., 2002). The great majority of parents in both Ontario and New Brunswick favoured teaching a wide range of topics including AIDS and other STIs, sexual decision making, sexual communication, sexual assault, birth control, abortion, and homosexuality. The point is that there is strong support for detailed sex education in schools, beginning in the primary grades.

You may be surprised to learn that most adults favour sex education. The media regularly publicize controversies, cases in which parents are protesting sex education in the schools. There are three things to keep in mind about such episodes. First, they are rare. The vast majority of schools with sex education programs have not experienced such conflict. Second, the protesters are usually in a minority. Third, the controversy is often not over whether there should be a program, but over the use of a particular curriculum, book, or video.

THE CURRICULUM

The term *sexuality education* has been used to refer to a wide variety of programs. All Canadian provinces and territories have, as part of their health programs, province-wide, school-based sexual health curricula (Barrett, 1994; Health Canada, 2003). However, there are major differences in how fully these curricula are implemented in different communities (Barrett, 1990). The comprehensiveness of the curriculum that is taught varies considerably from school to school, from school board to school board, and from province to province. For example, a study in British Columbia concluded that sexual health education in that province does not meet the criteria set out by the *Canadian Guidelines for Sexual Health Education* and that it is "hit or miss" as to whether students get quality sexual health education (Options for Sexual Health, 2004).

There is also considerable controversy over whether the curriculum should address homonegativity. Toronto's Human Sexuality Program was developed following the fatal beating of a gay student in Toronto in 1985 and provides classroom presentations on gay-related issues. However, there was a strong public outcry in 1997 in some parts of British Columbia when the B.C. Teachers Federation announced a decision to develop resources to help teachers address homonegativity in the classroom. For example, the conservative Citizens Research Institute developed a pamphlet to help parents demand that children not "be exposed to and/or involved in any activity or program which: discusses or portrays the lifestyle of gays, lesbians, bisexual and/or transgendered individuals as one which is normal, acceptable or must be tolerated" (*Macleans*, 1997). Most Canadian parents, teachers, and students want sexual orientation included in sex education programs (Byers et al., 2003a, 2003b; Cohen et al., 2004; McKay et al., 1998; Weaver et al., 2002). As most classrooms will have one or two students who are not heterosexual, discussion of sexual orientation helps to meet their needs, as well as to increase acceptance of diversity among their classmates (McKay, 2000).

Margulies/The Record/Rothco

Figure 19.2   Although some parents claim that sex education belongs in the home, it is rarely conducted there effectively.

We will focus in the next section on the more comprehensive programs.

EARLY SEX EDUCATION

The first programs, developed 30 years ago, were concerned with the transmission of knowledge. The goal of these programs was to reduce the number of teen pregnancies. Accordingly, the emphasis was on teaching students about sexual intercourse, pregnancy and birth control, and the consequences of having a baby. Later programs retained the informational content of the first ones, but the emphasis was placed on values clarification and decision-making skills. Proponents of these programs believed that young people engage in sexual risk taking because they are unsure of their values and have difficulty making decisions. These programs also taught skills designed to improve communication with partners. Subsequently, evaluations demonstrated that these programs were not particularly effective at reducing teenage pregnancy or sexual risk-taking behaviour (Kirby, 1992).

In the 1990s, the focus of sex education shifted from pregnancy prevention to AIDS and other STIs. All provinces and territories have school-based programs that include information about HIV and AIDS (Barrett, 1994). Research has shown that more than 99 percent of Canadian parents approve of HIV/AIDS education in the schools (Weaver et al., 2002).

Programs of this type are often sharply focused on disease prevention. They have a variety of goals, including removing myths about HIV/AIDS and other STIs, encouraging delay of sexual intercourse, and supporting condom use or abstinence from unprotected intercourse. Each curriculum relies on lectures and class discussion facilitated by a teacher, a public health nurse or, more recently, a peer educator (Dunn et al., 1998). On occasion, someone with AIDS is brought in to talk with the class. These programs were usually short, often lasting only one or two class periods.

A review of the effectiveness of these programs found that they improved knowledge significantly (Kim et al., 1997). In addition, many studies reported positive changes in respondents' intentions to use condoms.

One example of an HIV/AIDS education program in Canadian schools is the 20-hour *Skills for Healthy Relationships* program developed jointly by the federal and provincial governments. This program was designed for grade 9 students and included components aimed at delaying sexual activity, increasing condom use, creating compassion for persons living with HIV/AIDS, combating homonegativity, and improving communications and negotiating skills. It is based on a theoretical model that includes acquiring knowledge, developing responsible attitudes, increasing motivation, and developing skills. The program uses students as peer group leaders and encourages parental involvement. An evaluation of the effectiveness of the program found that, compared to the regular program, students gained significantly in knowledge, became more positive in their attitudes toward people living with HIV/AIDS, increased their intentions to communicate assertively in sexual situations, and improved their skills in being able to use condoms correctly. However, the program did not affect the likelihood that students would engage in sexual intercourse or use a condom when they did engage in intercourse (Boyce et al., 2000).

The Canada Youth Sexual Health and HIV/AIDS Study found that students in 2002 had less sexual knowledge than students who participated in the 1989 Canada Youth and AIDS Study (Boyce et al., 2003). For example, two thirds of grade 7 students and half of grade 9 students did not know that there is no cure for HIV/AIDS. Fewer than half of the students knew that Vaseline is not a good lubricant to use with condoms. Most students knew that sharing needles and having multiple partners increases the risk of HIV infection.

Figure 19.3 A sexual health education class for middle school students in Toronto. Questions range from "How do you know when you need a bra?" to "Can you have sex at 12?"

ABSTINENCE-ONLY PROGRAMS

Abstinence-only programs developed out of opposition to sex education in the schools. Some people were opposed to any sex education in the schools; others felt that the existing programs were too liberal or permissive. The concerns led to passage by the U.S. Congress of an act that limits the use of U.S. federal funds to abstinence-only programs that "promote sexual abstinence as the sole means of preventing pregnancy and exposure to sexually transmitted diseases" (Wilcox & Wyatt, 1997, p. 4). Millions of dollars have been spent by U.S. state and federal governments to support the development and widespread use of these programs. The two most widely known of these curricula are called *Sex Respect* and *Teen Aid*. *Sex Respect* is designed for

Abstinence-only (sex education) programs: Programs that promote sexual abstinence until marriage as the sole means of preventing pregnancy and exposure to sexually transmitted infections.

middle-school students and includes catchy slogans for children to chant in class, such as "Don't be a louse, wait for your spouse!"; "Do the right thing, wait for the ring!"; and "Pet your dog, not your date!" All students take a "chastity pledge," and there is a chart of physical intimacy in which a prolonged kiss is characterized as the "beginning of danger." The curriculum teaches that condoms can be the road to ruin because many fail, resulting in pregnancy.

Sex Respect throws in a lot of gender-role stereotypes as well, characterizing boys as "sexual aggressors" and girls as "virginity protectors." It presents the two-parent, heterosexual couple as "the sole model of a healthy, 'real' family."

Neither the federal nor provincial governments in Canada have supported the development or implementation of abstinence-only sexuality education in the schools. In general, school-based sexuality education in Canada has taken the approach of not promoting a particular set of values, teaching about abstinence but also about birth control and safer sex (McKay, 1998). Nonetheless, these programs are being offered in some Canadian schools. For example, in 1992 *Teen Aid* was taught to more than 20 000 students in 203 Saskatchewan schools, even though the Department of Education in that province offers a comprehensive sexuality education curriculum (Mitchell, 1997). School boards paid $150 to $250 a day to the *Teen Aid* organization for it to offer the program. More often the programs are offered in the community, by church groups for example.

So, how effective are these curricula? Researchers who assessed the content of *Sex Respect* concluded that it omits a number of important topics, including sexual anatomy, sexual physiology, sexual response, contraception, and abortion (Goodson & Edmundson, 1994). We noted earlier that high school students say that all of these topics should be included in an "ideal" class. As a result of their widespread use, there have been many evaluations of these programs' effects on student attitudes and behaviour. A review of 52 evaluations concluded that for the most part the research showed these programs did not delay the onset of sexual activity or reduce the percentage of students having sex, getting pregnant, or acquiring an STI (Wilcox & Wyatt, 1997). That is, these programs are not effective at delaying intercourse or reducing the rates of teenage pregnancy (Bennett & Assefi, 2005; Technical Working Group, 2002; Trenholm et al., 2007). Further, they may put youth at greater risk when they do start having sex, as they are less likely to use condoms.

COMPREHENSIVE, THEORETICALLY BASED PROGRAMS

The newest programs are comprehensive, and are explicitly based on social science theories of health promotion, including the Health Belief Model, social inoculation theory, social learning theory, and the information–motivation–behavioural skills approach (McKay, 1993). Stress inoculation theory proposes that people are better able to resist social pressure when they recognize the pressure, are motivated to resist it, and have rehearsed resisting it. These programs include discussion of the social pressures to engage in sex, and ways to resist these influences (based on inoculation theory). Social learning theory and the information–motivation–behavioural skill model emphasize the importance of practising new skills that can be easily translated into behaviour, so these curricula include rehearsal and role-playing activities. The Sex Information and Education Council of the United States has developed a curriculum of this kind (SIECUS, 1991).

In light of the continuing high levels of teenage pregnancy (about 33 500 pregnancies per year), the sharp increases in rates of STIs among persons 15 to 24 years of age, and the increasing rate of HIV infection in adolescents, it is imperative that we identify sex education programs that appear to be effective in reducing sexual risk-taking behaviour. Although most programs increase students' knowledge, many programs are not effective at changing behaviour. Unfortunately, there are few published studies evaluating school-based sex education programs in Canada (Barrett, 1990; DiCenso et al., 2002). The effectiveness of school-based programs in the United States has been reviewed, however (Kirby et al., 1994). Researchers identified six characteristics that, according to the scientific evidence, are associated with delaying the initiation of intercourse, reducing the frequency of intercourse, reducing the number of sexual partners, and increasing the use of condoms and other contraceptives:

- *Effective programs focus on reducing risk-taking behaviour.* Such programs have a small number of specific goals. They do not emphasize general issues such as gender equality and dating.

- *Effective programs are based on theories of social learning.* Programs that utilize theory in designing the curriculum are more effective than non-theoretical programs. The theories suggest that, to be effective, the program must increase knowledge, elicit or increase motivation to protect oneself, demonstrate that specific behaviours will protect the person, and teach the person how to use those behaviours effectively.

Figure 19.4 Research indicates that sex education programs are most effective when they include experiential and skill-building activities that personalize the message. Here students learn how to use a condom.

- *Effective programs teach through experiential activities that personalize the messages.* Such programs avoid lectures and videos; instead they utilize small-group discussions, simulation and games, role-playing, rehearsal, and similar educational techniques. Some of these programs rely on peer educators.

- *Effective programs address media and other social influences that encourage sexual risk-taking behaviours.* Some programs look at how the media use sex to sell products. All the effective programs analyze the "lines" that young people use to try to get someone else to engage in sex, and teach ways of responding to these approaches.

- *Effective programs reinforce clear and appropriate values.* These programs are not value-free. They emphasize the values of postponing sex and avoiding unprotected sex and high risk partners. The values and norms must be tailored to the target population. Different programs are needed for middle school students, for white middle-class high school students, and for ethnic minority high school students.

- *Effective programs enhance communication skills.* Such programs provide models of good communication and opportunities for practice and skill rehearsal.

The length of the program and teacher training are also important. Effective programs are long enough to complete all these components and activities and are delivered by teachers or peers who believed in the program and had received training in how to deliver it (Kirby, 2002).

The United Nations Program on HIV/AIDS commissioned a review of the effectiveness of sexuality education programs, with data from countries as diverse as Mexico, France, Thailand, and the United States (UNAIDS, 1997). The review focused on studies that measured the impact of educational programs on behaviour. Three studies found an increase in sexual behaviour following a program. Twenty-two of 53 studies reported that the program delayed the initiation of sexual activity, led to a reduction in the number of partners, or reduced rates of unwanted pregnancy and STIs. The characteristics of the most effective programs were similar to those just identified.

Sex education programs that reduce sexual risk-taking behaviour by adolescents do exist, and the inclusion of such programs in the schools is supported by a large majority of the parents in every survey. In addition, effective sexuality education is cost-effective. A school-based program that prevents HIV infection, STIs, and unintended pregnancy among high school students can actually save money. Data from 345 sexually active high school students in California and Texas found that the program *Safer Choices* resulted in a 15 percent increase in condom use and an 11 percent increase in use of other contraceptives. Using a statistical model, researchers estimated the program prevented 0.12 cases of HIV infection, 24 cases of chlamydia, 2.8 cases of gonorrhea, 5.9 cases of pelvic inflammatory disease, and 18 pregnancies. The researchers conclude that the program saved $2.65 in medical and social costs for every dollar spent on the program (Davis et al., 2000).

We need to convince school administrators to implement such programs, to provide adequate training and support to the teachers, and to stand firm in the face of opposition from vocal opponents of these programs. We also need to make sure that our programs not only reduce negative outcomes such as unwanted teenage pregnancies, STIs, and HIV/AIDS, but also achieve positive outcomes such as self-esteem, sexual comfort, and fulfilling interpersonal relationships.

CONDOM DISTRIBUTION

One visible conflict has been over whether schools should distribute condoms to students. Different schools and school districts in Canada have widely differing policies on making condoms available in the schools. In some schools, condoms are available through the sex education program. In other schools, clinics providing health care services to adolescents dispense condoms. In still other schools, condoms are sold in vending machines—one high school in Ottawa and two on Vancouver Island were the first to install condom machines, in 1989. Again, data indicate widespread support for the distribution of condoms in schools. A survey of Canadian adults found that 60 percent were in favour of making condoms available in schools (Ornstein, 1989). It is likely that the percentage is higher today. For example, a survey of all the students in one Denver, Colorado, high school in 1995 found that 85 percent of parents supported distribution of condoms in their school (Fanburg et al., 1995).

The most visible opposition to condom distribution programs is by the Roman Catholic Church and other religious groups. These groups oppose such programs on the grounds that they will encourage sexual intercourse outside of marriage. However, research does not support their fears. For example, in a study comparing students in Massachusetts high schools that did and did not have such programs, students in schools with condoms available were less likely to report having ever had intercourse and *less* likely to report recent intercourse (Blake et al., 2003). In addition, sexually active students in schools that made condoms available were twice as likely to use condoms.

Research indicates that condom distribution programs are associated with reductions in teenage pregnancies and abortions. For example, making condoms available through specialized health units in high schools in one county in rural Ontario resulted in a 21 percent drop in the pregnancy rate and an 11 percent drop in the number of abortions among teenagers aged 18 years and younger.

SEXUAL ORIENTATION

It is likely that in every classroom there are at least one or two gay, lesbian, or bisexual students. It is important that sex education programs do not assume that all students are heterosexual, but also addresses the needs of LGBT students. Because harassment of LGBT youth is so common (see Chapter 14), it is important that sex education address heterosexism, homonegativity, transphobia, and discrimination on the basis of sexual orientation and gender identity (Grace & Wells, 2001; McKay, 2005). In fact, in 2005 the B.C. Court of Appeal ruled that schools have a duty to take strong action to address homonegativity in order to ensure that no students experience discrimination and harassment at school. This ruling was the result of a complaint by Azmi Jubran, a student in North Vancouver's Handsworth Secondary School, who was the victim of homophobic bullying, including being called names like "faggot" and "queer" and being pushed, punched, and spat on because the other students thought he was gay. The court ruled that it was not enough that the school punished the offending students. Instead, they had a duty to provide "anti-homophobia" education to all students. This is important because although more and more high school students are coming out and there are more and more gay–straight alliance clubs in schools, LGBT students nonetheless frequently experience psychological and physical harassment from other students, as well as a lack of support from homophobic school teachers and principals (Grace & Wells, 2001). A lesbian high school student in Alberta living in a safe house described her experience:

> The high school I went to in grades 10 and 11 was awful. It was very, very homophobic. It's funny. When I got involved in going to gay bars, I even saw some of my teachers that are gay. But why aren't they out in school? I don't know, but I wish they were. Then at least I could have gone to them. But I can understand why they're not because it is a really homophobic high school. If I ever did hear a queer-related topic, it was always something negative. So I always had to shut up because I was too scared. (Grace & Wells, 2001, pp. 138–139)

What changes are needed? First, sex education needs to include discussion of sexual orientation, including being gay, bisexual, and transgender. In this way, straight and questioning students would learn about being gay, lesbian, or bisexual. Second, LGBT students need to see themselves represented throughout the curriculum. For example, elementary school children could read books that feature same-sex parents. Math problems might feature a same-sex couple (e.g., Jim wanted to give David an engagement ring that cost . . ."). Third, schools need to be supportive of LGBT teachers so that these teachers can serve as respected role models for LGBT and questioning students. Finally, all schools need to be pro-active in establishing a gay-positive environment. This would mean hanging gay-positive posters where all students can see them. Schools could hand out student bookmarks that list contact information for a number of support groups including gay youth groups. All schools would establish **gay–straight alliance clubs**. These are school-based clubs run by students and, importantly, supported by teachers that work to create a safe,

Figure 19.5 While a grade 12 student in Coquitlam, British Columbia, Brent Power formed a gay–straight alliance club to combat homophobia, some B.C. parents strongly objected to discussion of homosexuality in the classroom.

Gay–straight alliance clubs: school-based clubs run by students and, importantly, supported by teachers that work to create a safe, caring and inclusive environment for LGBT students.

caring, and inclusive environment for LGBT students. They are open to all students, regardless of sexual orientation. Schools would also have clear policies that protect students from discrimination on the basis of sexual orientation (Grace & Wells, 2001, 2006, 2007).

THE TEACHER

Suppose you have decided to start a program of sexuality education. You have found a curriculum that is consistent with your objectives. Wherever the program is to be carried out—in the home, the school, the place of worship, or someplace else—the next resource you need is the teacher. There are two essential qualifications: the person must be educated about sexuality, and he or she must be comfortable and skillful in interacting with learners about sexual topics (Health Canada, 2003). Interviews with female high school students in Amherst, Nova Scotia, identified teacher discomfort and lack of knowledge as important barriers in sexual health education (Langille et al., 1999). Students also see as important the ability of teachers to personalize the information; that is, to relate the material to the students' lives (Eisenberg et al., 1997).

Sex education teachers need to be educated about sex. Reading a comprehensive text such as this one or taking a college or university course in sexuality are good ways to acquire the information that is needed. The teacher does not have to have a graduate degree in sexology; the important qualifications are a good basic knowledge, a willingness to admit when he or she does not know the answer, and the patience to look things up. A survey of Canadian B.Ed. programs found that only 16 percent of them included sexuality as part of a required course (10 to 13 hours on average); about a quarter had an optional sexuality course (McKay & Barrett, 1999). In contrast, undergraduate students in the Department of Sexology at the University of Quebec in Montreal take 28 courses related to sexuality and the department offers a master's degree in sexual health education (Dupras, 2001; Gemme, 1990). A national survey found that only about half of school districts regularly offer in-service training in sexuality education, and teachers do not feel comfortable or competent in teaching about sex (McCall et al., 1999). Perhaps as a result, most teachers do not cover the more sensitive issues associated with sexuality and do not use active learning strategies such as role-playing and small group discussions (Cohen et al., 2004). Clearly, there is a need for more training in sexuality to prepare teachers to teach sexual health education (Barrett, 1990).

Equally important is the teacher's comfort with sexual topics. Even when parents or other adults willingly give factual information about sex to a child or adolescent, they may convey negative attitudes because they become anxious or blush or because they use euphemisms rather than explicit sexual language. According to one 16-year-old girl, "The personal development classes are a joke. Even the teacher looks uncomfortable. There is no way anybody is going to ask a serious question" (Stodghill, 1998).

Some people are relaxed and comfortable in discussing sex. Others must work to learn this attitude. There are a number of ways to do this. For example, the teacher can role-play, with another adult, having sexual discussions with children. Some communities periodically offer programs designed to increase the comfort of the sexuality teacher or enhance awareness of his or her own sexual values and attitudes.

A good teacher is also a good listener who can assess what the learner knows from the questions asked and who can understand what a child really wants to know when she or he asks a question. As one joke had it, little Billy ran into the kitchen one day after kindergarten and asked his mother where he had come from; she gritted her teeth, realized the time had come, and proceeded with a 15-minute discussion of intercourse, conception, and birth, blushing the whole time. Billy listened, but at the end he appeared somewhat confused and walked away shaking his head, saying, "That's funny. Jimmy says he came from Winnipeg."

Finally, it is important that teachers receive training and professional development to address their own homonegativity and learn how to help make schools safe for and inclusive of LGBT students (Grace & Wells, 2006).

HOME-BASED SEXUALITY EDUCATION

Most children are given little or poor sex education at home. A New Brunswick study asked parents of elementary and middle school students about the extent to which they had discussed a number of sexual topics with their child (Weaver et al., 2002). The topics they had discussed in the most detail were child sexual abuse and the correct names for genitals, but even these topics most parents had discussed only in some detail but not in a lot of detail. On average, the parents said that they had discussed the other topics, including puberty, STIs, birth control, and sexual decision making, in general terms or not at all. Few parents of even the middle school students had discussed these topics in a lot of detail. The results of this study also point to three major reasons why parents do not provide much explicit education to their children.

First, many people (and parents *are* people!) are embarrassed about discussing sexuality. We see few models of how to have an explicit, matter-of-fact discussion; we are much more likely to see people discussing sex indirectly, with euphemisms and innuendo, or telling dirty jokes. (As a partial corrective, we have tried to write this book in an explicit, straightforward way.)

Second, there are many things about sexuality that many adults do not know. They did not have good sexuality education themselves, and they may be painfully aware of their ignorance. Even those who received a good sex education, if they took a human sexuality course before 1980, didn't learn of the then-unheard-of disease called AIDS.

Third, parents do not know how to provide sex education to their children. They do not know at what ages they should discuss various topics. They are also not sure how to discuss various topics. They do not feel that they have the resources they need to provide quality sex education to their children. Of course, whether or not sexuality is openly discussed in the home (and many of our students say that it was never talked about in their home), parents communicate to their children about sex. Thus, just as parents convey a positive attitude toward sexuality by, for example, providing children with the correct names for their genitals and comfortably answering their sexual questions, parents convey their negative attitudes toward sex by not doing these things and by not talking about sex. As such, sexual education starts at birth through the non-verbal messages we give that either lead to children feeling good about their bodies or uncomfortable with their bodies and genitals.

Many Canadian parents want to talk to their children about sex. However, they feel that they need to be more knowledgeable about sexuality and more comfortable talking about sex before they can do so. They also feel that they need guidance on how to communicate with their children about sexuality. In Focus 19.2 provides some suggestions to parents who want to communicate with their children about sexuality.

SEXUALITY EDUCATION IN THE COMMUNITY

The need for accurate sexual information does not end when people graduate from high school. For example, 15 000 students in colleges and universities take a human sexuality course, perhaps like the one you are taking, each year—this number likely could be higher but some schools do not offer courses in human sexuality. In addition, people need additional information about sexuality throughout their lives, as they reach different life stages. The pregnant woman may need to learn about pregnancy and childbirth. New parents may want to increase their understanding of sexuality in childhood or of child sexual abuse. LGBT individuals may want information about other people's coming-out process. The middle-

IN FOCUS 19.2

Talking to Your Children about Sex

Many parents want to be able to communicate with their children about sexuality but feel nervous about doing so. Here are a few guidelines for parents taken in part from the materials prepared by SIECCAN for the Canadian Health Network:

Be prepared. This means that parents should educate themselves about sexuality. If they are fortunate and had a good sex education course in high school or university, they may already feel knowledgeable enough to answer their children's questions. These parents tend to talk more to their children about sexuality than do parents who did not take a human sexuality course (King et al., 1994). However, many parents do not feel that they know as much as they should and are afraid that their children will ask them questions that they can't answer. It's okay not to know everything about sex; after all, most children can get the facts from the sexual health education they receive at school. Besides, sharing their feelings and values, not teaching facts, is the most important contribution that parents can make to their children's sexuality education. Nonetheless, many parents will want to take steps to fill in some of the gaps they have in their knowledge about sexuality. To do this they can read books such as this textbook on human sexuality or books on talking to children about sexuality, or they can attend a workshop for parents on that subject. They can also find out what is in the sex education curriculum that their children are learning at school. Remember, parents need to talk to their children about both the positive (e.g., pleasure, sexual self-esteem) as well as about negative aspects of sex (e.g., sexual abuse, sexual coercion, and STIs).

Work to increase your comfort level. One of the most important contributions parents can make to their children's sex education is increasing their children's comfort in talking about and asking questions about sex. Children's comfort will largely reflect the parents'

comfort. Parents need to acknowledge to themselves the areas and topics that make them uncomfortable and take steps to increase their comfort level. Books and workshops about talking to your children about sexuality are good ways to increase comfort level. Planning what to say and practising saying it (preferably in front of the mirror or with a partner) may also help to increase comfort.

Plan ahead. Most of us did not have parents who talked to us about sex, so we can't base our own approach to educating our children about sexuality on our own experiences. As a result, it is important for parents to decide how they want to approach sexuality education with their children. For example, they need to decide what they want to tell their children at various ages, how they plan to share their values with them, how they want to respond to questions about things their child hears at school, and so on. Remember that positive messages are more likely to have an influence than are lectures and threats. Also, parents need to plan for what they might say if their teenager tells them something that they find upsetting. It is important for parents to discuss these matters with teenagers calmly, without yelling, or they will close the doors to further discussions. (For examples of typical questions children and adolescents have at different ages and suggestions about how to respond to these questions, you can check out www.sexualityandu.ca/eng/parents/ts.)

Be proactive. Too many parents wait for their children to ask them questions. Children are naturally curious about sex, but they are unlikely to ask questions if they have been getting non-verbal messages that their parents are uncomfortable talking about sex, or if sex is never mentioned in the home. If you take the first steps, it will be easier for children to raise questions and concerns at a later date. Opening the lines of communication is as important as the information you provide.

---

aged woman may want to learn more about menopause. Older adults may need to learn about the effects of aging on the sexual response. Even for children and youth, sex education can and does occur outside the home and the classroom. For example, HIV/STI prevention interventions occur in public health clinics, in community settings, or through the media. These efforts can be directed at the population at large, or at specific subgroups with specific needs—for example, men who have sex with men, street youth, or members of specific

Figure 19.6 It is important to be prepared, proactive, and honest when talking with your child about sex.

A good way to start talking to children about sex is to use what we often call "teachable moments." For example, bath time is a good opportunity to provide children with the correct term for their genitals just as we provide them with the correct name for their other body parts—nose, knee, toes. Other teachable moments occur when someone the child knows becomes pregnant or gives birth, when something sexual is mentioned on televi-sion, or when a sexually related story is on the news. Parents can use these teachable moments to raise the topic of where babies come from, under what circum-stances it is O.K. for teenagers to have sex, whether a couple in a movie are engaging in safer sex, and so on.

Another way to be proactive is to provide children and youth with books and videotapes about sexuality. Parents will need to read the books or watch the video-tapes with young and preadolescent children. This can lead to interesting discussions on the topics raised in the book or video. Teenagers may prefer to read books on their own, but parents should nonetheless initiate a discussion about the material in order to answer ques-tions or concerns that the teenager has. Parents also need to initiate discussions with their teenage children on sexual decision making, and to try to ensure that their teenagers have the skills to apply their decisions in real-life situations. For example, parents can help teenagers become more comfortable talking to partners about their sexual decisions or, if they do decide to have sex, about safer sex and birth control.

Answer all questions truthfully, honestly, and accu-rately. For young children, this will involve providing short answers containing direct explanations. As chil-dren grow older, they will want and need more detail and will be more likely to ask questions if you've created an open environment. Parents do not need to worry about providing children with too much information too early. Children take the information they need and tend to ignore the rest. Unless you are a sex educator yourself, it is likely that your children will ask you a question and you will not know the answer. It's okay not to know everything about sex. By admitting that they don't know the answer, parents give their children permission not to have to know everything about sex, and that having to seek out answers is normal and healthy at any time in life. Of course, it's important for parents to then try to find the answer with their child.

ethnocultural minority groups. The media can also be used to increase awareness of specific sexual issues, such as prenatal nutrition, homosexuality, or sexual violence.

Physicians and other health professionals have an important role to play in educating youth about sexual health (McCall & McKay, 2004). For example, by routinely asking about sexual involvement in a non-judgmental way, physicians make it more likely that teenagers will approach them for advice on contraception when they do begin having sexual intercourse.

However, many physicians are not comfortable talking about sex with their patients, particularly their adolescent patients, and thus do not routinely ask these questions. Others do not feel knowledgeable about sexuality. A survey of medical schools in the United States and Canada found that in two-thirds of the programs medical students had less than ten hours of instruction related to sexual issues (Solursh et al., 2003). Perhaps as a result, a Nova Scotia study found that few high school students had ever discussed whether they were sexually active with their family doctor. Even among students who were engaging in intercourse, only 56 percent of the girls and 16 percent of the boys had discussed this with their family physician (Langille et al., 2001). A notable exception to the dearth of sexuality instruction in medical schools is l'Université de Québec à Sherbrooke, where medical students attend a four-day retreat related to sexuality. At the retreat, they examine their attitudes and biases related to sexuality with the goal of making students more comfortable in discussing sexual concerns with their clients (Solursh et al., 2003).

The Internet may also be useful in providing information about sexuality. This can be as an addition to formal school-based sex education, or as a way of providing sexual information to people throughout their lives. Certainly, many Canadians already seek out sexuality information on the Internet, and Health Canada maintains a sex information website (see www.canadian-health-network.ca). For example, in an online survey of 760 university students in British Columbia, about half (52.5 percent) had looked for sexuality information on the Internet within the past year (Boies, 2002). Further, 21 percent of the students reported that their first sexuality education material had come from the Internet. The Internet is particularly attractive because it is an affordable, available, anonymous, acceptable way to access sexuality information and people can do so without being observed (Barak & Fisher, 2001; Cooper, 1998; King, 1999). There are several other advantages to sex education on the Internet (Barak & Fisher, 2001):

1. Materials are easily revised so all users can have access to the most up-to-date information.
2. Websites can use multimedia communications, including text, sound, pictures, animation, and videos.
3. The material can be accessed from any computer, at any time.
4. Users can exchange information with other users.
5. The location can provide access to information and services outside the instructional site by providing links to other sites.
6. Potentially, information and programs provided can be individualized to the needs of each user based on responses to prescreening questions administered on the site.

There are also potential problems with sex education on the Internet. Anybody can establish an Internet site and nobody monitors these sites for the accuracy of their content, so the unsuspecting user may be getting incorrect information. Further, right now there are not many sex education websites; in contrast there are a large number of pornographic websites and online sex shops (Fisher & Barak, 2000).

Finally, not everybody has access to the Internet; people who are socioeconomically disadvantaged and who belong to ethnocultural minorities tend to have less access. Nonetheless, the Internet certainly has the potential to enhance traditional approaches to sex education.

Effective Multicultural Sexuality Education

Much of the discussion in this chapter has assumed that the participants in a sexuality education program are homogeneous, that they are all from the same ethnocultural community. In some situations that assumption is valid; but in other settings, the learners may be from diverse ethnocultural backgrounds.

Cultures vary in a number of ways that are directly related to the success or failure of a sexuality education program (Irvine, 1995). There are cultural differences in sexual practices; some of these were discussed in Chapter 1. The acceptability of explicit sexual language or of particular types of language, such as street slang, varies from one cultural community to another. Cultures vary in the meaning they attach to sexuality. The majority cultures in Europe and North America have emphasized sex for the purpose of reproduction and thus tend to regard vaginal intercourse as the norm (see Chapter 20 on the Online Learning Centre). Other cultures place greater emphasis on the pleasure that can be derived from sexual stimulation. Finally, cultures vary in the definition of and the roles expected within the family.

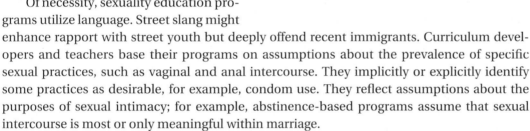

Figure 19.7 Sex education around the world. At this family-planning clinic in India, an educator explains the female reproductive system to these mothers.

Of necessity, sexuality education programs utilize language. Street slang might enhance rapport with street youth but deeply offend recent immigrants. Curriculum developers and teachers base their programs on assumptions about the prevalence of specific sexual practices, such as vaginal and anal intercourse. They implicitly or explicitly identify some practices as desirable, for example, condom use. They reflect assumptions about the purposes of sexual intimacy; for example, abstinence-based programs assume that sexual intercourse is most or only meaningful within marriage.

If sexuality education is to be successful, it must reflect, or at least accept, the cultures of the participants. The educator must assess the audience, the intended messages, and the context, and target the program accordingly (Irvine, 1995). Educators must recognize their own sexual culture, learn about the sexual cultures of the participants, and be aware of the power differences between groups in our society. In the classroom, they should use this knowledge to enhance the effectiveness of the presentation. The use of communication styles and media common to the cultures of the participants—for example, music—can be a valuable tool. Finally, it is important that the program not advocate beliefs and practices that are incompatible with participants' cultures. Such programs are doomed to failure. This is true for school-based sexuality education as well as for workshops and outreach programs. For example, researchers in Toronto documented a need for educational outreach and services specifically for East Asian and Southeast Asian men who have sex with men. They used the results of a needs assessment to make specific recommendations about how to best provide culturally appropriate services (Poon et al., 2001).

The *First Nations HIV/TB Training Kit* is designed to train community health educators to deliver culturally based training sessions on HIV and TB (tuberculosis) (Association of Iroquois and Allied Indians, 1997). Training emphasizes cultural sensitivity to distinct rituals, cultural practices, and methods within each First Nations community, such as storytelling, the talking circle, traditional medicines, and the medicine wheel. Resources like this one, and the programs that result from this type of training, respond to the call for sexuality education that incorporates the family and community context in which our sexuality is grounded (Health Canada, 1994; Maddock, 1997; Young, 1996).

IN FOCUS 19.3

Sexual Health Education for Persons with Developmental Disabilities

Persons with IQs below 70 are generally classified as having an intellectual or developmental disability (officially called "mental retardation"). There is a great range of capacities of individuals with developmental disabilities, from some who require constant care to those who function quite well in the community, who can read and write and hold simple jobs. It is important to recognize that the great majority of persons with intellectual disabilities in the moderate range (IQs between 50 and 70) are in the category of near-normal functioning.

In the past, society has regarded persons with intellectual disabilities as asexual. Although many of these attitudes remain, society, parents, and caregivers are increasingly recognizing that persons with intellectual disabilities have normal sexual desires. However, because these children are often slower to learn the norms of society, they may express themselves sexually in ways that are not acceptable to others, such as masturbating in public. Further, persons with intellectual disabilities may be particularly vulnerable to sexual exploitation and abuse.

Unfortunately, not all youth with intellectual disabilities have access to adequate sexual health education; in fact, many receive little or no such education. For stu-

Figure 19.8 There is a need to provide sex education to children with disabilities.

dents enrolled in regular classes, the sexual health education curriculum may not fit their learning style or level of understanding. For these reasons and others, careful sexuality education for persons with intellectual disabilities is essential. Fortunately, there are now a number of compre-

Another group that needs to have sexuality education tailored to its needs is those with developmental disabilities (see In Focus 19.3). We cannot assume that curricula designed for students in grade 6 can be presented to 12-year-olds with these disabilities (DiGiulio, 2003). Instead, programs need to assess the cognitive and emotional abilities of each child and adolescent, and then present developmentally appropriate materials. Information about forms of romantic and sexual expression may have to emphasize social norms about what is appropriate, and discourage inappropriate behaviours in public. Also, programs for persons with disabilities must recognize their vulnerability to exploitation and make special efforts to teach them self-protection skills.

An institute in Mexico had been involved in a long-term project to develop sex education programs appropriate for that culture (Pick et al., 2003). In that cultural context, programs must take into account strong, traditional gender roles. Men who have many sex partners are widely admired; women are to be modest and not display pleasure in sexuality. Decisions regarding sexuality and reproduction are made by the man, with the woman playing a passive role. Ninety-five percent of the population is Roman Catholic, and the traditions of that

hensive guides and curricula that have been developed precisely to teach youth with intellectual disabilities about their sexuality. For example, the *Knowing Where You Stand* resource developed by Planned Parenthood Fredericton (2004) teaches intellectually disabled youth

- about their own bodies;
- to feel comfortable with their bodies;
- to make healthy informed choices for themselves;
- how to set boundaries for themselves and respect the boundaries of others;
- how to be safe whether or not they choose to engage in sexual activity; and
- about healthy and abusive relationships.

It is important that persons with intellectual disabilities be educated about contraception and that contraceptives be made available to them. Because persons with intellectual disabilities have normal sexual desires, they may engage in sexual activity including intercourse. In one study, 24 percent of boys and 8 percent of girls with developmental delays had engaged in intercourse by age 16 (Cheng & Udry, 2003). If these youth lack sexuality education, they may not realize that pregnancy and STIs can result. An unwanted pregnancy for a woman or couple with intellectual disabilities may be a difficult situation; they may be able to function well when taking care of themselves but not with the added burden of a baby. On the other hand, some persons with intellectual disabilities do function sufficiently well to care for a child. The important thing is that they make as educated a decision as possible and that they have access to contraceptives. Many experts recommend an IUD or other methods that do not require memory or forethought for effective use for women with intellectual disabilities.

In the 1920s, both Alberta and British Columbia passed laws allowing sterilization without consent of people deemed to have mental retardation. While we now view this as a violation of human rights, the law was not repealed in Alberta until 1972, after 2900 such operations had been performed. In 1996, an Alberta woman successfully sued the government for damages related to her involuntary sterilization. She had been sterilized at the age of 14 without her knowledge or consent.

In summary, persons with intellectual disabilities have sexual needs and desires. Because of their special needs, it is especially important that they receive appropriate sexual health education.

Sources: Ames, 1991; Baladerian, 1991; DiGuilio, 2003; Kempton & Kahn, 1991; Nemeth, 1995; Planned Parenthood Fredericton, 2004.

religion must be taken into account. Taking all of these factors into account, the educational programs that the institute developed emphasize a participatory learning style, concrete knowledge about not only sexuality but also gender roles and expectations, and communication skills, especially those for communicating with parents.

As we increasingly recognize diversity both within Canada and around the world, creating developmentally and culturally effective sexuality educational programs should be an important priority. Another important priority is helping parents from diverse cultures talk to their children about sexuality in ways that promote the children's sexual health. For example, research in Pakistan has found that youth do not consider their parents to be reliable sources of information about sex (Khan, 2003). Similarly, few parents in a study conducted in rural Nigeria had discussed sexual issues with their children; the ones that had done so typically had provided incorrect, frightening information in an attempt to prevent them from engaging in sexual activity (Izugbara, 2008).

SUMMARY

Many children receive their sex education from their peers or other sources, not from their parents. As a result, those who argue for sex education being taught only in the home rather than in the school are being unrealistic. Most Canadians do favour sex education in the school. Cases of opposition to sex education are rare and involve a small number of people.

The purposes of sexuality education include providing children with adequate knowledge of the physical and emotional aspects of sex, with an opportunity to develop their own values and interpersonal skills, and with the maturity to take responsibility for their sexuality.

What is taught at each age should depend on what children are thinking about at that age. Children pass through various stages in their understanding of sexuality. For example, at first they believe that a baby has always existed. Later, they realize that the parents caused the baby's creation, but they don't know exactly how. Older children acquire a more scientific understanding of reproduction. Children's sexual play seems to precede rather than follow the development of sexual knowledge. Children's dirty jokes reflect their parents' attempts to hide sex from them, their parents' use of euphemisms rather than actual terms, and their great fascination with sexual organs and intercourse.

Sexuality education curricula have evolved a great deal over the past three decades. The early programs focused on preventing adolescent pregnancy and HIV/AIDS through knowledge, values clarification, and decision-making skills. They resulted in increased knowledge and intentions to use condoms. Conservative programs such as *Sex Respect* emphasize abstinence and are limited in content. The evidence indicates they are not effective and may lead to increased risk. Contemporary comprehensive programs are based on social science theory and emphasize the importance of not only providing information but also allowing students to practise new behaviours such as communication skills. Research suggests that sexuality education programs that are effective at delaying the onset of intercourse, reducing the frequency of intercourse and the number of partners, and increasing condom use share several characteristics. They focus on specific risk-taking behaviours, are based on theory, utilize experiential activities, address social influences on sexual behaviour, reinforce values, and provide opportunities to practise new skills.

There is a good deal of conflict over the distribution of condoms in high schools. There is widespread support among both high school students and their parents for such programs, but the Catholic Church, among others, is a vocal opponent.

It is important that sex education programs address the needs of LGBT students as well as heterosexism, homonegativity, and discrimination on the basis of sexual orientation.

A good sexuality education instructor must have accurate knowledge about sexuality, be comfortable discussing it, and be good at listening to the questions learners ask. Students say that the instructor's ability to relate the material to their lives is also important.

It also is important that parents talk to their children about sexuality. Some guidelines for parents are (1) be prepared, (2) work to increase your comfort level, (3) plan ahead, (4) be proactive, and (5) answer all questions truthfully, honestly, and accurately.

People have a need for continuing sex education throughout their lives. Physicians, other health professionals, and the Internet are all important sources of ongoing sex education.

To be effective, multicultural sexuality education must reflect or be consistent with the culture(s) of participants. It should present messages that are compatible with their beliefs and practices. Such programs should utilize language and styles of communication that are appropriate.

QUESTIONS FOR THOUGHT, DISCUSSION, AND DEBATE

1. Design a sample sexuality education curriculum for the schools, indicating what topics you think would be important to teach at various age levels and what your reasoning is behind your choices.

2. Debate the following topic. Resolved: A sexuality education unit, at least a week long, should be included in all grades in all schools.

3. Data from surveys indicate that the mass media are a major source of information about sexuality for children and adolescents. We saw, in Chapter 1 and In Focus 10.1 (page 304), that media portrayals in North America are generally unrealistic. How would you deal with access to media portrayals of sexuality for your child at ages 5, 10, and 15? What would you do, and what would you tell your child at each age?

SUGGESTIONS FOR FURTHER READING

Gordon, Sol. (1986, Oct.). What kids need to know. *Psychology Today*. Reprinted in O. Pocs (Ed.), *Human Sexuality 88/89*. Guilford, CT: Dushkin. Sol Gordon, a leading sex educator, provides a humorous view of what sexuality education ought to be accomplishing.

Harris, Robie H. (1994). *It's perfectly normal*. Cambridge, MA: Candlewick Press. An entertaining and thorough sexuality education book for children aged ten and over.

Health Canada. (2003). *Canadian guidelines for sexual health education*. Ottawa: Health Canada. The guidelines outline five principles of sexual health education as well as specific guidelines to achieve each principle. They are useful for developing sexual health education programs or in evaluating existing programs.

Mayle, P., Robins, A., and Walter, P. (1973). *Where did I come from?* Secaucus, NJ: Lyle Stuart. A delightful sexuality education book for young children. A companion volume—*What's happening to me?*—is for children approaching or experiencing puberty.

McKay, Alexander. (1998). *Sexual ideology and schooling: Towards democratic sexuality education*. Alex McKay, research coordinator at SIECCAN, describes the controversies around sexuality education. He also proposes a philosophy of sexuality education.

Planned Parenthood Federation of Canada. (2001). *Beyond the basics: A sourcebook on sexual and reproductive health education*. Ottawa: Author. This outstanding Canadian tool for educators who deliver sex education to 9- to 18-year-olds contains a wide range of participatory activities.

Shrader, A. M., and Wells, K., (2007). *Challenging silence, challenging censorship*. Ottawa: Canadian Teachers Federation. This book is designed to help teachers, principals, counsellors and school librarians learn how they can take action to positively change the school climate for LGBT youth and children from same-sex parented families.

SIECUS. (1991). *Guidelines for comprehensive sexuality education: Kindergarten–12th grade*. New York: Sexuality Information and Education Council of the United States. The guidelines outline a comprehensive program, divided into 36 topics, and contain developmentally appropriate messages according to school level.

For review questions, web resources, and other learning and study tools, visit the *Understanding Human Sexuality* Online Learning Centre at www.mcgrawhill.ca/olc/hyde.

REFERENCES

Abbey, A. (1991). Misperception as an antecedent of acquaintance rape: A consequence of ambiguity in communication between men and women. In A. Parrott & L. Bechhofer (Eds.), *Acquaintance rape: The hidden crime.* New York: Wiley.

Abbey, A. & McAuslan, P. (2004). A longitudinal examination of male college students' perpetration of sexual assault. *Journal of Consulting and Clinical Psychology, 72,* 747–756.

ABC News. (2004, May 27). American Porn: Corporate America is profiting from porn—quietly. Retrieved from Abcnews.go.com/sections/Primetime/Entertainment/porn_business.

Abel, G. G., Becker, J. V., Mittelman, M., Cunningham-Rathner, J., Rouleau, J. L., & Murphy, W. D. (1987). Self-reported sex crimes of nonincarcerated paraphiliacs. *Journal of Interpersonal Violence, 2,* 3–25.

Abel, G. G., Osborn, C., Anthony, D., & Gardos, P. (1992). Current treatments of paraphiliacs. *Annual Review of Sex Research, 3,* 255–290.

Abel, G., & Rouleau, J.-L. (1990). The nature and extent of sexual assault. In W. L. Marshall, D. R. Laws, & H. E. Bartarce (Eds.), *Handbook of sexual assault* (pp. 9–21). New York: Plenum.

Abram, D., Viki, G., Masser, B., & Bohner, G. (2003). Perceptions of stranger and acquaintance rape: The role of benevolent and hostile sexism in victim blame and rape proclivity. *Journal of Personality and Social Psychology, 84,* 111–125.

Abramowitz, S. I. (1986). Psychosocial outcomes of sex reassignment surgery. *Journal of Consulting and Clinical Psychology, 54,* 183–189.

Acker, M., & Davis, M. (1992). Intimacy, passion and commitment in adult romantic relationships: A test of the triangular theory of love. *Journal of Social and Personal Relationships, 9,* 21–50.

ACSF Investigators. (1992). AIDS and sexual behaviour in France. *Nature, 360,* 407–409.

Adam, B. D. (2005). Constructing the neoliberal sexual actor: Responsibility and care of the self in the discourse of barebackers. *Culture, Health, and Sexuality, 7,* 333–346.

Adam, B. D. (2007). Why be queer? In G. Pavlich & M. Hird (Eds.), *Questioning sociology* (pp. 71–79). Don Mills, ON: Oxford University Press.

Adam, B. D., Sears, A., & Schellenberg, E. G. (2000). Accounting for unsafe sex: Interviews with men who have sex with men. *The Journal of Sex Research, 37,* 24–36.

Adam & Eve. (2004). *Sex Stat: Sexy Internet sites gain in popularity.* Atlanta, GA: Adam & Eve.

Adams, M. A., et al. (1997). Vascular control mechanisms in penile erection: Phylogeny and the inevitability of multiple and overlapping systems. *International Journal of Impotence Research, 9,* 85–91.

Addiego, F., Belzer, E. G., Comolli, J., Moger, W., Perry, J. D., & Whipple, B. (1981). Female ejaculation: A case study. *Journal of Sex Research, 17,* 13–21.

Adkins-Regan, E. (2002). Development of sexual partner preference in the zebra finch: A socially monogamous, pair-bonding animal. *Archives of Sexual Behavior, 31,* 27–34.

Adoya-Osiguwa. S. A., Markoulaki, S., Pocock, V., Milligan, S. R., & Fraser, L. R. (2003). 17B-estradiol and environmental estrogens significantly affect mammalian sperm function. *Human Reproduction, 18,* 101–107.

Afriat, C. (1995). Antepartum care. In D. R. Coustan, R. V. Hunning, Jr., & D. Singer (Eds.), *Human reproduction: Growth and development* (pp. 213–234). Boston: Little, Brown.

Aggarwal, A. P. (1992). *Sexual harassment: A guide for understanding and prevention.* Toronto: Butterworths.

Agnew, T. (1997). *A multicultural perspective of breastfeeding in Canada.* Ottawa: Minister of Public Works and Government Services Canada.

Ahluwalia, I. B., Merritt, R., Beck, L. E., & Rogers, M. (2001). Multiple lifestyle and psychosocial risks and delivery of small for gestational age infants. *Obstetrics and Gynecology, 97,* 649–656.

Ahmadi, N. (2003). Rocking sexualities: Iranian migrants' views on sexuality. *Archives of Sexual Behavior, 32,* 317–326.

Ainsworth, C. (2005). The secret life of sperm. *Nature, 436,* 770–771.

Albin, R. S. (1977). Psychological studies of rape. *Signs, 3,* 423–435.

Alderson, K. G. (2003). The ecological model of gay male identity. *Canadian Journal of Human Sexuality, 12,* 75–85.

Alderson, K. G. (2004). A phenomenological investigation of same-sex marriage. *Canadian Journal of Human Sexuality, 13,* 107–122.

Alexander, E. (1990). Sexual therapy in English-speaking Canada. *SIECCAN Journal, 5*(1), 37–43.

Alexander, M. G., & Fisher, T. D. (2003). Truth and consequences: Using the bogus pipeline to examine sex differences in self-reported sexuality. *Journal of Sex Research, 40,* 27–35.

Allen, M., & Burrell, N. A. (2002). Sexual orientation of the parent: The impact on the child. In M. Allen & R. W. Preiss et al. (Eds.), *Interpersonal communication research: Advances through meta-analysis* (pp. 125–143). Mahwah, NJ: Erlbaum.

Allen, M., D'Alessio, D., Emmers, T., & Gebhardt, L. (1996). The role of educational briefings in mitigating effects of experimental exposure to violent sexually explicit material. *Journal of Sex Research, 33,* 135–141.

Allen, D. M. (1980). Young male prostitutes: A psychological study. *Archives of Sexual Behavior, 9,* 399–426.

Allgeier, E. R., & Wiederman, M. W. (1994). How useful is evolutionary psychology for understanding contemporary human sexual behavior? *Annual Review of Sex Research, 5,* 218–256.

Almroth, L., Almroth-Berggren, V., & Hassanein, O. M. (2001). Male complications of female genital mutilation. *Social Science & Medicine, 53,* 1455–1460.

Amara, R. R., Villinger, F., Altman, J. D., Lydy, S. L., O'Neil, S. P., Staprans, S. I., et al. (2001). Control of a mucosal challenge and prevention of AIDS by a multiprotein DNA/MVA vaccine. *Science, 292,* 69–74.

Ambert, A. (2005). Divorce: Facts, causes, and consequences. *Contemporary Family Trends.* Vanier Institute of the Family. Retrieved October 16, 2007, from www.vifamily.ca.

American Academy of Pediatrics Committee on Genetics. (2000). Evaluation of the newborn with developmental anomalies of the external genitalia. *Pediatrics, 106,* 138–142.

American Cancer Society (2007). *Cancer facts & figures 2007.* Atlanta, GA: American Cancer Society, www.cancer.org.

American Psychiatric Association. (1994). *Diagnostic and statistical manual of mental disorders* (4th ed.). Washington, DC: Author.

American Psychiatric Association. (2000). *Diagnostic and statistical manual of mental disorders* (4th ed.). Washington, DC: American Psychiatric Association.

American Psychiatric Association. (2000). *Diagnostic and statistical manual of mental disorders* (4th ed., Text Revision). Washington, DC: Author.

American Psychiatric Association. (2000). Position statement on therapies focused on attempts to change sexual orientation (reparative or conversion therapies). *American Journal of Psychiatry, 157,* 1719–1721.

American Psychological Association, Task Force on the Sexualization of Girls. (2007). *Report of the APA Task Force on the Sexualization of Girls.* Washington, DC: American Psychological Association. Retrieved from www.apa.org/pi/wpo/sexualization.html.

American Urological Association Practice Guidelines Committee (2003). AUA guideline on management of benign prostatic hyperplasia (2003). Chapter 1: Diagnosis and treatment recommendations. *Journal of Urology, 170,* 530–547.

Ames, T.-R. (1991). Guidelines for providing sexuality-related services to severely and profoundly retarded individuals: The challenge for the 1990s. *Sexuality and Disability, 9,* 113–122.

Anderson, K., Kaplan, H., & Lancaster, J. (2001). *Men's financial expenditures on genetic children and stepchildren from current and former relationships* (Report No. 01-484). Ann Arbor, MI: Population Studies Center.

Anderson, M. C., et al. (2004). Neural systems underlying the suppression of unwanted memories. *Science, 303,* 232–235.

Anderson, M. C., Ochsner, K. N., Kuhl, B., Cooper, J., Robertson, E., Gabrieli, S. W., et al. (2004). Neural systems underlying the suppression of unwanted memories. *Science, 303,* 232–235.

Antle, K. (1978). Active involvement of expectant fathers in pregnancy: Some further considerations. *Journal of Obstetric, Gynecologic and Neonatal Nursing, 7*(2), 7–12.

Antoni, M. H., & Carver, C. S. (2001). Cognitive–behavioral stress management intervention decreases the prevalence of depression and enhances benefit finding among women under treatment for early-stage breast cancer. *Health Psychology, 20,* 20–32.

Apfelbaum, B. (2000). Retarded ejaculation: A much misunderstood syndrome. In S. Leiblum & R. Rosen (Eds.), *Principles and practice of sex therapy,* (3rd ed., pp. 205–241). New York: Guilford.

Appleby, B. M. (1999). *Responsible parenthood: Decriminalizing contraception in Canada.* Toronto: University of Toronto Press.

Aquinas, St. Thomas. (1968). *Summa theologica* (Vol. 43). (Thomas Gilly, Trans.). New York: McGraw-Hill.

Araujo, A. B., Durante, R., Feldman, H. A., Goldstein, I., & McKinlay, J. B. (1998). The relationship between depressive symptoms and male erectile dysfunction: Cross-sectional results from the Massachusetts Male Aging Study. *Psychosomatic Medicine, 60,* 458–465.

Araujo, A. B., Johannes, C. B., Feldman, H. A., Derby, C. A., & McKinlay, J. B. (2000). Relation between psychosocial risk factors and incident erectile dysfunction: Prospective results from the Massachusetts Male Aging Study. *American Journal of Epidemiology, 152,* 533–541.

Archibald, S. A., Lemieux, S., Byers, E. S., Tamlyn, K. & Worth, J. (2006). Chemically-induced menopause and the sexual functioning of breast cancer survivors. *Women and Therapy.*

Aries, E. (1996). *Men and women in interaction: Reconsidering the differences.* New York: Oxford University Press.

Arnold, A. P. (2003). The gender of the voice within: The neural origin of sex differences in the brain. *Current Opinion in Neurobiology, 13,* 759–764.

Arnow, B. A., Desmond, J. E., Banner, L. L., Glover, G. H., Solomon, A., Polan, M. L., et al. (2002). Brain activation and sexual arousal in healthy, heterosexual males. *Brain, 125,* 1014–1023.

Arthur, L., & Driscoll, A. (2002, May 16). Castration or life term? Judge to rule. *Miami Herald.*

Ascensio, M. (2002). *Sex and sexuality among New York's Puerto Rican youth.* Boulder, CO: Lynne Rienner.

Ashton, A. K. (2007). The new sexual pharmacology: A guide for the clinician. In S. Leiblum (Ed.), *Principles and practice of sex therapy* (4th ed., pp. 509–542).

Assalian, P., & Ravart, M. (2003). Management of professional sexual misconduct: Evaluation and recommendations. *Journal of Sexual & Reproductive Medicine, 3,* 89–92.

Associated Press. (1984, March 25). Baby girl is born from transferred embryo. *New York Times.*

Atkins, D., Yi, J., Baucom, D., & Christensen, A. (2005). Infidelity in couples seeking marital therapy. *Journal of Family Psychology, 19,* 470–473.

Aubrey, J. S. (2004). Sex and punishment: An examination of sexual consequences and the sexual double standard in teen programming. *Sex Roles, 50,* 505–514.

Aucoin, M. W., & Wasserug, R. J. (2006). The sexuality and social performance of androgen-deprived (castrated) men throughout history: Implications for modern day cancer patients. *Social Science & Medicine, 63,* 3162–3173.

Audet, M. C., et al. (2001). Evaluation of contraceptive efficacy and cycle control of a transdermal contraceptive patch vs. an oral contraceptive: A randomized controlled trial. *Journal of the American Medical Association, 285,* 2347–2354.

Augustinova, H., Hoeller, D., & Yao, F. (2004). The dominant-negative herpes simplex virus type 1 (HSV-1) recombinant CJ83193 can serve as an effective vaccine against wild-type HSV-1 infection in mice. *Journal of Virology, 78,* 5756–5765.

Auld, B. R., & Brock, G. (2002). Sexuality and erectile dysfunction: Results of a national survey. *Journal of Sexual & Reproductive Medicine, 2,* 50–54.

Autry, A. M., Hayes, E. C., Jacobson, G. F., & Kirby, R. S. (2002). A comparison of medical induction and dilation and evacuation for second-trimester abortion. *American Journal of Obstetrics and Gynecology, 187,* 393–397.

Avis, N. E., & McKinlay, S. M. (1995, March–April). The Massachusetts Women's Health Study: An epidemiological investigation of the menopause. *Journal of the American Medical Women's Association, 50,* 45–63.

Aylwin, A. S., Reddon, J. R., & Burke, A. R. (2005). Sexual fantasies of adolescent male sex offenders in residential treatment: A descriptive study. *Archives of Sexual Behavior, 34,* 231–239.

Bach, G., & Wyden, P. (1969). *The intimate enemy: How to fight fair in love and marriage.* New York: Morrow.

Bachmann, G. A., & Leiblum, S. R. (1991). Sexuality in sexagenarian women. *Maturitas, 13,* 43–50.

Badgley, R. (1984). *Sexual offences against children: Report of the Committee on Sexual Offences Against Children and Youths.* Ottawa: Canadian Government Publishing.

Bagemihl, B. (1999). *Biological exuberance: Animal homosexuality and natural diversity.* New York: St. Martin's Press.

Bagley, C. (1989). Prevalence and correlates of unwanted sexual acts in childhood in a national Canadian sample. *Canadian Journal of Public Health, 80,* 295–296.

Bailey, J. M., Bobrow, D., Wolfe, M., & Mikach, S. (1995). Sexual orientation of adult sons of gay fathers. *Developmental Psychology, 31,* 124–129.

Bailey, J. M., & Pillard, R. C. (1991). A genetic study of male sexual orientation. *Archives of General Psychiatry, 48,* 1089–1096.

Bailey, J. M., & Pillard, R. C. (1995). Genetics of human sexual orientation. *Annual Review of Sex Research, 6,* 126–150.

Bailey, J. M., Pillard, R. C., Neale, M. C., & Agyei, Y. (1993). Heritable factors influence sexual orientation in women. *Archives of General Psychiatry, 50,* 217–223.

Bailey, J. M., Willerman, L., & Parks, C. (1991). A test of the maternal stress theory of human male homosexuality. *Archives of Sexual Behavior, 20,* 277–294.

Bailey, J. M., & Zucker, K. J. (1995). Childhood sex-typed behavior and sexual orientation. *Developmental Psychology, 31,* 43–55.

Baker, F. C., Driver, H. S., Paiker, J., Rogers, G. G., & Mitchell, D. (2002). Acetaminophen does not affect 24-h body temperature or sleep in the luteal phase of the menstrual cycle. *Journal of Applied Physiology, 92,* 1684–1691.

Baladerian, N. J. (1991). Sexual abuse of people with developmental disabilities. *Sexuality and Disability, 9,* 323–335.

Baldwin, J. D., & Baldwin, J. I. (1989). The socialization of homosexuality and heterosexuality in a non-Western society. *Archives of Sexual Behavior, 18,* 13–30.

Baldwin, J. D., & Baldwin, J. I. (1997). Gender differences in sexual interest. *Archives of Sexual Behavior, 26,* 181–210.

Baldwin, S. B., et al. (2004). Condom use and other factors affecting penile human papillomavirus detection in men attending a sexually transmitted disease clinic. *Sexually Transmitted Diseases, 31,* 601–607.

Balsam, K. F. (2004, August). Identity, community, and outness: Comparing bisexual and lesbian/gay adults. Paper presented at the 111th Annual Convention of the American Psychological Association, Toronto, ON.

Balter, M. (1995). Elusive HIV-suppressor factors found. *Science, 270,* 1560–1561.

Bancroft, J. (1978). The prevention of sexual offenses. In C. B. Qualls et al. (Eds.), *The prevention of sexual disorders* (pp. 95–116). New York: Plenum.

Bancroft, J. (2004). Alfred C. Kinsey and the politics of sex research. *Annual Review of Sex Research, 15,* 1–39.

Bancroft, J., Herbenick, D., & Reynolds, M. (2003). Masturbation as a marker of sexual development. In John Bancroft (Ed.), *Sexual development.* Bloomington, IN: Indiana University Press.

Bancroft, J., & Gutierrez, P. (1996). Erectile dysfunction in men with and without diabetes mellitus. *Diabetic Medicine, 13,* 84–89.

Bancroft, J., Herbenick, D., & Reynolds, M. (2002). Masturbation as a marker of sexual development. In J. Bancroft (Ed.), *Sexual development.* Bloomington, IN: Indiana University Press.

Bancroft, J., Loftus, J., & Long, J. S. (2003). Distress about sex: A national survey of women in heterosexual relationships. *Archives of Sexual Behavior, 32,* 193–208.

Bancroft, J. & Vikadinovic, Z. (2004). Sexual addiction, sexual compulsivity, sexual impulsivity, or what? Toward a theoretical model. *Journal of Sex Research, 41,* 225–234.

Bandura, A. J. (1977). *Social learning theory.* Englewood Cliffs, NJ: Prentice-Hall.

Bandura, A. (1982). Self-efficacy mechanism in human agency. *American Psychologist, 37,* 122–147.

Bandura, A., & Walters, R. H. (1963). *Social learning and personality development.* New York: Holt.

Bang, A. K., et al. (2005). A study of finger lengths, semen quality and sex hormones in 360 young men from the general Danish population. *Human Reproduction, 20,* 3109–3113.

Banks, A., & Gartrell, N. K. (1995). Hormones and sexual orientation: A questionable link. *Journal of Homosexuality, 28,* 247–268.

Barak, A., & Fisher, W. A. (2001). Toward an Internet-driven, theoretically based, innovative approach to sex education. *The Journal of Sex Research, 38,* 324–332.

Barash, D. P. (1982). *Sociobiology and behavior* (2nd ed.). New York: Elsevier.

Barbaree, H. E., & Marshall, W. L. (1991). The role of male sexual arousal in rape: Six models. *Journal of Consulting and Clinical Psychology, 59,* 621–630.

Barlow, D. H. (1986). Causes of sexual dysfunction: The role of cognitive interference. *Journal of Consulting and Clinical Psychology, 54,* 140–148.

Barlow, D. H., Leitenberg, H., & Agras, W. S. (1969). Experimental control of sexual deviation through manipulation of noxious scenes in covert sensitization. *Journal of Abnormal Psychology, 74,* 596–601.

Baron, L., & Straus, M. A. (1989). *Four theories of rape in American society.* New Haven, CT: Yale University Press.

Barouch, D. H., Santra, S., Schmitz, J. E., Kuroda, M. J., Fu, T. M., Wagner, W., et al. (2000). Control of viremia and prevention of clinical AIDS in rhesus monkeys by cytokine-augmented DNA vaccination. *Science, 290,* 486–492.

Barr, A., Bryan, A., & Kenrick, D. (2002). Sexual peak: Socially shared cognitions about desire, frequency, and satisfaction in men and women. *Personal Relationships, 9,* 287–299.

Barr, H. M., Streissguth, A. P., Darby, B. L., & Sampson, P. D. (1990). Prenatal exposure to alcohol, caffeine, tobacco and aspirin: Effects on fine and gross motor performance in 4-year-old children. *Developmental Psychology, 26,* 339–348.

Barrett, F. M., King, A., Levy, J., Maticka-Tyndale, E., McKay, A., & Fraser, J. (2003). Sexuality and Canada. In *Complete Encyclopedia of Human Sexuality* (pp. 126–181). London & New York: Continuum Publishing.

Barrett, J. R. (2006). Fertile grounds of inquiry: Environmental effects on human reproduction *Environmental Health Perspectives, 114,* A644–A649.

Barrett, M. (1990). Selected observations of sex education in Canada. *SIECCAN Journal, 5*(1), 21–30.

Barrett, M. (1994). Sexuality education in Canadian schools: An overview in 1994. *The Canadian Journal of Human Sexuality, 3,* 199–225.

Barrett, M., King, A., Levy, J., Maticka-Tyndale, E., & McKay, A. (1997). *The international encyclopedia of sexuality,* vol. 1, 221–343. New York: Continuum Publishing.

Bartell, G. D. (1970). Group sex among the mid-Americans. *Journal of Sex Research, 6,* 113–130.

Bartels, A., & Zeki, S. (2004). The neural correlates of maternal and romantic love. *Neuroimage, 21,* 1155–1166.

Bartholomew, K., & Horowitz, L. M. (1991). Attachment styles among young adults: A test of a 4-category model. *Journal of Personality and Social Psychology, 61,* 226–244.

Bartlett, N. H., & Vasey, P. L. (2006). A retrospective study of childhood gender-atypical behavior in Samoan Fa'afafine. *Archives of Sexual Behavior, 35,* 659–666.

Bartlett, N. H., Vasey, P. L., & Bukowski, W. M. (2000). Is gender identity disorder in children a mental disorder? *Sex Roles, 43,* 753–785.

Basson, R. (2000). The female sexual response: A different model. *Journal of Sex & Marital Therapy, 26,* 51–65.

Basson, R. (2001). Human sex-response cycles. *Journal of Sex & Marital Therapy, 27,* 33–43.

Basson, R. (2001). Using a different model for female sexual response to address women's problematic low sexual desire. *Journal of Sex & Marital Therapy, 27,* 395–403.

Basson, R. (2005). Women's sexual dysfunction: Revised and expanded definitions. *Canadian Medical Association Journal, 172,* 1327–1333.

Basson, R. (2006). Sexual desire and arousal disorders in women. *New England Journal of Medicine, 354,* 1497–1506.

Basson, R. (2007). Hormones and sexuality: Current complexities and future directions. *Maturitas, 57,* 66–70.

Basson, R., & Brotto, L. A. (2003). Sexual psychophysiology and effects of sildenafil citrate in oestrogenised women with acquired genital arousal disorder and impaired orgasm: A randomised controlled trial. *BJOG: International Journal of Obstetrics and Gynaecology, 110,* 1014–1024.

Basson, R., Berman, J., Burnett, A., Derogatis, L., Ferguson, D., Fourcroy, J., et al. (2001). Report of the International Consensus Development Conference on female sexual dysfunction: Definitions and classifications. *Journal of Sex & Marital Therapy, 27,* 83–94.

Basson, R., McInnes, R., Smith, M., Hodgson, G., & Koppiker, N. (2002). Efficacy and safety of sildenafil citrate in women with sexual dysfunction associated with female sexual arousal disorder. *Journal of Women's Health & Gender-Based Medicine, 11,* 367–377.

Basson, R., & VHHSC Centre for Sexuality, Gender Identity, & Reproductive Health. (1998). Integrating new biomedical treatments into the assessment and management of erectile dysfunction. *The Canadian Journal of Human Sexuality, 7,* 213–229.

Baulieu, E. E., et al. (2000). Dehydroepiandrosterone (DHEA), DHEA sulfate, and aging: Contributions of the DHEAge Study to a sociobiomedical issue. *Proceedings of the National Academy of Sciences, 97,* 4279–4284.

Baumeister, R. F. (1988a). Masochism as escape from the self. *Journal of Sex Research, 25,* 28–59.

Baumeister, R. F. (1988b). Gender differences in masochistic scripts. *Journal of Sex Research, 25,* 478–499.

Baumeister, R. F. (2000). Gender differences in erotic plasticity: The female sex drive as socially flexible and responsive. *Psychological Bulletin, 126,* 347–374.

Baumeister, R. F., Catanese, K., & Vohs, K. (2001). Is there a gender difference in strength of sex drive? Theoretical views, conceptual distinctions, and a review of relevant evidence. *Personality and Social Psychology Review, 5,* 242–273.

Baumeister, R. F., Catanese, K., & Wallace, H. (2002). Conquest by force: A narcissistic reactance theory of rape and sexual coercion. *Review of General Psychology, 6,* 92–135.

Bazelon, E. (2007, Jan. 21). Is there a post-abortion syndrome? *New York Times Magazine.*

Beach, F. A. (Ed.). (1976). *Human sexuality in four perspectives.* Baltimore: Johns Hopkins University Press.

Beall, A., & Sternberg, R. (1995). The social construction of love. *Journal of Social and Personal Relationships, 12,* 417–438.

Beaulieu, M. (1994). Screening for D (Rh) sensitization in pregnancy. *The Canadian Guide to Clinical Preventive Health Care.* Cat. No. H21-117/1994E. Ottawa: Public Health Agency of Canada.

Beier, E. G., & Sternberg, D. P. (1977). Marital communication. *Journal of Communication, 27,* 92–103.

Bell, A. P. (1974a, Summer). *Childhood and adolescent sexuality.* Address delivered at the Institute for Sex Research, Indiana University.

Bell, A. P. (1974b). Homosexualities: Their range and character. In *Nebraska symposium on motivation 1973.* Lincoln, NE: University of Nebraska Press.

Bell, A. P., & Weinberg, M. S. (1978). *Homosexualities.* New York: Simon & Schuster.

Bell, A. P., Weinberg, M. S., & Hammersmith, S. K. (1981). *Sexual preference.* Bloomington, IN: Indiana University Press.

Belzer, E. G. (1981). Orgasmic expulsions of women: A review and heuristic inquiry. *Journal of Sex Research, 17,* 1–12.

Bem, D. J. (1996). Exotic becomes erotic: A developmental theory of sexual orientation. *Psychological Review, 103,* 320–335.

Bem, D. J. (1998). Is EBE theory supported by the evidence? Is it androcentric? A reply to Peplau et al. (1998). *Psychological Review, 105,* 395–398.

Bem, S. L. (1981). Gender schema theory: A cognitive account of sex typing. *Psychological Review, 88,* 354–364.

Bem, S. L. (1993). *The lenses of gender: Transforming the debate on sexual inequality.* New Haven: Yale University Press.

Bennett, S., & Assefi, N. (2005). School-based teenage pregnancy prevention programs: A systematic review of randomized controlled trials. *Journal of Adolescent Health, 36,* 72–81.

Benoit, C., Jannson, M., Millar, A., & Phillips, R. (2005). Community-academic research on hard-to-reach populations: Benefits and challenges. *Qualitative Health Research, 15,* 263–282.

Benoit, C., & Millar, A. (2001). *Dispelling myths/understanding realities: Working conditions, health status and exiting experiences of sex workers* [Report prepared for the Prostitutes Empowerment and Resource Society]. Vancouver: British Columbia Health Research Foundation.

Ben-Ze'ev, A. (2004). *Love online: Emotions on the Internet.* Cambridge, UK: Cambridge University Press.

Bérard, E. J. J. (1989). The sexuality of spinal cord injured women: Physiology and pathophysiology: A Review. *Paraplegia, 27,* 99–112.

Beres, M. A., Herold, E., & Maitland, S. B. (2004). Sexual consent behaviours in same-sex relationships. *Archives of Sexual Behavior, 33,* 475–486.

Beretta, G., Chelo, E., & Zanollo, A. (1989). Reproductive aspects in spinal cord injured males. *Paraplegia, 27,* 113–118.

Berg, J. H., & Derlega, V. J. (1987). Themes in the study of self-disclosure. In V. J. Derlega & J. H. Berg (Eds.), *Self-disclosure: Theory, research and therapy* (pp. 1–8). New York: Plenum.

Bergen, D. J., & Williams, J. E. (1991). Sex stereotypes in the United States revisited: 1972–1988. *Sex Roles, 24,* 413–423.

Bergeron, S., Binik, Y. M., Khalife, S., & Pagidas, K. (1997). Vulvar vestibulitis syndrome: A critical review. *The Clinical Journal of Pain, 13*(1), 27–42.

Bergeron, S., Binik, Y. M., Khalifé, S., Pagidas, K., Glazer, H. I., Meana, M., & Amsel, R. (2001). A randomized comparison of group cognitive-behavioral therapy, surface electromyographic biofeedback, and vestibulectomy in the treatment of dyspareunia resulting from vulvar vestibulitis. *Pain, 91,* 297–306.

Bergeron, S., Brown, C., Lord, M-J., Oala, M., Binik, Y. M., & Khalifé, S. (2002). Physical therapy for vulvar vestibulitis syndrome: A retrospective study. *Journal of Sex & Marital Therapy, 28,* 183–192.

Berglund, H., et al. (2006). Brain response to putative pheromones in lesbian women. *Proceedings of the National Academy of Sciences, 103,* 8269–8274.

Berkman, C., & Zinberg, G. (1997). Homophobia and heterosexism in social workers. *Journal of the National Association of Social Workers, 42,* 319–332.

Berman, J. R., Adhikari, S. P., & Goldstein, I. (2000). Anatomy and physiology of female sexual function and dysfunction. *European Urology, 38,* 20–29.

Berman, L., Berman, J., Miles, M., Pollets, D., & Powell, J. A. (2003). Genital self-image as a component of sexual health: Relationship between genital self-image, female sexual function, and quality of life measures. *Journal of Sex & Marital Therapy, 29,* 11–21.

Bermant, G., & Davidson, J. M. (1974). *Biological bases of sexual behavior.* New York: Harper & Row.

Berne, E. (1970). *Sex in human loving.* New York: Simon & Schuster.

Bernstein, A. C., & Cowan, P. A. (1975). Children's concepts of how people get babies. *Child Development, 46,* 77–92.

Berry, L. J., Hickey, D. K., Skelding, K. A., Bao, S., Rendina, A. M., Hansbro, P. M., et al. (2004). Transcutaneous immunization with combined cholera toxin and CpG adjuvant protects against clamydia muridarum genital tract infection. *Infection and Immunity, 72,* 1019–1028.

Berscheid, E., & Walster, E. (1974a). A little bit about love. In T. L. Huston (Ed.), *Foundations of interpersonal attraction.* New York: Academic.

Berscheid, E., & Walster, E. (1974b). Physical attractiveness. *Advances in Experimental Social Psychology, 7,* 157–215.

Berscheid, E., & Hatfield, E. (1978). *Interpersonal attraction* (2nd ed.). Reading, MA: Addison-Wesley.

Berscheid, E., et al. (1971). Physical attractiveness and dating choice: A test of the matching hypothesis. *Journal of Experimental Social Psychology, 7,* 173–189.

Best, D. L. (2001). Gender concepts: Convergence in cross-cultural research and methodologies. *Cross-Cultural Research, 35,* 23–43.

Bibby, R. (1987). *Fragmented gods: The poverty and potential of religion in Canada.* Toronto: Irwin.

Bibby, R. (1993). *Unknown gods: The ongoing story of religion in Canada.* Toronto: Stoddart.

Bibby, R. W. (2001). *Canada's teens: Today, yesterday, and tomorrow.* Toronto: Stoddart.

Bibby, R. W. (2004). *The future families project.* Vanier Institute of the Family. Retrieved October 16, 2007, from www.vifamily.ca.

Bibby, R. W. (2006). *The Boomer Factor: What Canada's most famous generation is leaving behind.* Toronto: Bastian Books.

Bibby, R. W., & Posterski, D. (1992). *Teen trends: A nation in motion.* Toronto: Stoddart.

Bibby, R. W., & Posterski, D. (1995). *The Bibby report: Social trends Canadian style.* Toronto: Stoddart.

Biller, H., & Meredith, D. (1975). *Father power.* New York: Anchor Books.

Billings, A. (1979). Conflict resolution in distressed and non-distressed married couples. *Journal of Consulting and Clinical Psychology, 47,* 368–376.

Binik, Y. M. (2005). Should dyspareunia be retained as a sexual dysfunction in DSM-V? A painful classification decision. *Archives of Sexual Behavior, 34,* 11–21.

Binik, Y. M., et al. (2007). Dyspareunia and vaginismus: So-called sexual pain. In S. Leiblum (Ed.), *Principles and practice of sex therapy* (4th ed., pp. 124–156). New York: Guilford.

Binik, Y. M., Meana, M., Berkley, K., & Khalife, S. (2000). The sexual pain disorders: Is the pain sexual or is the sex painful? *Annual Review of Sex Research.*

Binik, Y. M., Pukall, C. F., Reissing, E. D., & Khalifé, S. (2001). The sexual pain disorders: A desexualized approach. *Journal of Sex & Marital Therapy, 27,* 113–116.

Bird, S. E. (1999). Gendered construction of the American Indian in popular media. *Journal of Communication,* 61–83.

Bissell, M. (2000). Socio-economic outcomes of teen pregnancy and parenthood: A review of the literature. *The Canadian Journal of Human Sexuality, 9,* 191–204.

Bixler, R. H. (1986). Of apes and men (including females). *Journal of Sex Research, 22,* 255–267.

Black, D., et al. (2000). Demographics of the gay and lesbian population in the United States: Evidence from available systematic data sources. *Demography, 37,* 139–154.

Blackless, M., et al. (2000). How sexually dimorphic are we? Review and synthesis. *American Journal of Human Biology, 12,* 151–166.

Blair, C. D., & Lanyon, R. I. (1981). Exhibitionism: Etiology and treatment. *Psychological Bulletin, 89,* 439–463.

Blake, J. (2004). *Words can work: When talking with kids about sexual health.* Gloucester, MA: Blake Works, Inc.

Blake, S., Ledsky, R., Goodenow, C., Sawyer, R., Lohrmann, D., & Windsor, R. (2003). Condom availability programs in Massachusetts high schools: Relationships with condom use and sexual behavior. *American Journal of Public Health, 93,* 955–962.

Blanchard, R. (1997). Birth order and sibling sex ratio in homosexual versus heterosexual males and females. *Annual Review of Sex Research, 8,* 27–67.

Blanchard, R. (2004). Quantitative and theoretical analyses of the relation between older brothers and homosexuality in men. *Journal of Theoretical Biology, 230,* 173–187.

Blanchard, R. (2007). Sex ratio of older siblings in heterosexual and homosexual, right-handed and non-right-handed men. *Archives of Sexual Behavior.*

Blanchard, R., & Bogaert, A. F. (2004). Proportion of homosexual men who owe their sexual orientation to fraternal birth order: An estimate based on two national probability samples. *American Journal of Human Biology, 16,* 151–157.

Blanchard, R., Christensen, B. K., Strong, S. M., Cantor, J. M., Kuban, M. E., Klassen, P., et al. (2002). Retrospective self-reports of childhood accidents causing unconsciousness in phallometrically diagnosed pedophiles. *Archives of Sexual Behavior, 31,* 511–526.

Blanchard, R., Clemmensen, L. H., & Steiner, B. W. (1983). Gender reorientation and psychosocial adjustment in male-to-female transsexuals. *Archives of Sexual Behavior, 12,* 503–510.

Blanchard, R., & Lippa, R. A. (2007). The sex ratio of older siblings in non-right-handed homosexual men. *Archives of Sexual Behavior.*

Blanchard, R., Steiner, B. W., & Clemmenson, L. H. (1985). Gender dysphoria, gender reorientation and the clinical management of transsexualism. *Journal of Consulting & Clinical Psychology, 53*(3), 295–304.

Blanchard, R., Watson, M. S., Choy, A., Dickey, R., Klassen, P., Kuban, M., et al. (1999). Pedophiles: Mental retardation, maternal age, and sexual orientation. *Archives of Sexual Behavior, 28,* 111–127.

Blumberg, E. (2003). The lives and voices of highly sexual women. *Journal of Sex Research, 40,* 146–157.

Blumstein, P. W., & Schwartz, P. (1983). *American couples.* New York: Morrow.

Boardman, J., Hummer, R., Padilla, Y., & Powers, D. (Nd). *Low birth weight, social factors, and developmental outcomes among children in the United States* (No. 01-02-05). Austin, TX: Population Research Center.

Bockting, W. O. (1999, Oct./Nov.). From construction to context: Gender through the eyes of the transgendered. *SIECUS Report,* 3–7.

Bockting, W. O. (2004). Plastic and reconstructive surgery for transgender and transsexual patients. In D. B. Sarwer et al. (Eds.), *Psychological aspects of plastic surgery.* Philadelphia: Lippincott Williams & Wilkins.

Bodlund, O., & Kullgren, G. (1996). Transsexualism-General outcome and prognostic factors: A five-year follow-up study of 19 transsexuals in the process of changing sex. *Archives of Sexual Behavior, 25,* 303–316.

Bodner, L. M., Markovic, N., Harger, G., & Roberts, J. M. (2004). Prepregnancy body mass index and the risk of preeclampsia. *Federation of American Societies for Experimental Biology Journal, 18*(5), A928.

Bogaert, A. F. (1993). *The sexual media: The role of individual differences.* Unpublished doctoral dissertation. University of Western Ontario, London, Ontario, Canada.

Bogaert, A. F. (1996). Volunteer bias in human sexuality research: Evidence for both sexuality and personality differences in males. *Archives of Sexual Behavior, 25*(2), 125–140.

Bogaert, A. F. (2001). Personality, individual differences, and preferences for the sexual media. *Archives of Sexual Behavior, 30,* 29–53.

Bogaert, A. F. (2003). Number of older brothers and sexual orientation: New tests and the attraction/behaviour distinction in two national probability samples. *Journal of Personality and Social Psychology, 84,* 644–652.

Bogaert, A. F. (2004). Asexuality: Prevalence and associated factors in a national probability sample. *Journal of Sex Research, 41,* 279–287.

Bogaert, A. F. (2005). Age at puberty and father absence in a national probability sample. *Journal of Adolescence, 28,* 541–546.

Bogaert, A. F., & Sadava, S. (2002). Adult attachment and sexual behavior. *Personal Relationships, 9,* 191–204.

Bogaert, A. F., Woodard, U., & Hafer, C. L. (1999). Intellectual ability and reactions to pornography. *Journal of Sex Research, 26*(3), 283–291.

Bogren, L. Y. (1991). Changes in sexuality in women and men during pregnancy. *Archives of Sexual Behavior, 20,* 35–45.

Boies, S. C. (2002). University students uses of and reactions to online sexual information and entertainment: Links to online and offline sexual behaviour. *Canadian Journal of Human Sexuality, 11,* 77–89.

Boonstra, H. (2001). Islam, women and family planning: A primer. *The Guttmacher Report on Public Policy, 4,* 4–7.

Booth, C. L., & Meltzoff, A. N. (1984). Expected and actual experience in labour and delivery and their relationship to maternal attachment. *Journal of Reproductive and Infant Psychology, 2,* 79–91.

Bootzin, R. R., & Natsoulas, T. (1965). Evidence for perceptual defense uncontaminated by response bias. *Journal of Personality and Social Psychology, 1,* 461–468.

Bornstein, R. F. (1989). Exposure and affect: Overview and meta-analysis of research, 1968–1987. *Psychological Bulletin, 106,* 265–289.

Boroditsky, R., Fisher, W., & Sand, M. (1996, December). The 1996 Canadian contraceptive study. *Journal of the Society of Obstetricians and Gynaecologists of Canada.*

Boston Women's Health Book Collective. (2005). *Our bodies, ourselves for the new century.* New York: Simon and Schuster.

Boswell, J. (1980). *Christianity, social tolerance, and homosexuality.* Chicago: University of Chicago Press.

Boswell, J. (1994). *Same-sex unions in premodern Europe.* New York: Villard Books.

Bouyer, J., Coste, J., Shojaei, T., Pouly, J. L., Fernandez, H., Gerbaud, L., et al. (2003). Risk factors for ectopic pregnancy: a comprehensive analysis based on a large case-control, population-based study in France. *American Journal of Epidemiology, 157,* 185–194.

Bowe, J. (2006, November 19). Gay donor or gay dad? *New York Times Magazine,* 66–73.

Bowen, A. (2005). Internet sexuality research with rural men who have sex with men: Can we recruit and retain them? *Journal of Sex Research, 42,* 317–323.

Bower, J. Gurevich, M., & Mathieson, C. (2002). (Con)tested identities: Bisexual women reorient sexuality. *Journal of Bisexuality, 2,* 23–52.

Boyce, W., Doherty-Poirier, M., MacKinnon, D., Fortin, C., Saab, H., King, M., & Gallupe, O. (2006). Sexual health of Canadian youth: Findings from the Canadian youth, sexual health and HIV/AIDS Study. *The Canadian Journal of Human Sexuality, 15,* 59–68.

Boyce, W. F., King, A. J. C., & Warren, W. K. (2000). The effectiveness of a school-based HIV education program: A longitudinal comparative evaluation. *Canadian Journal of Program Evaluation, 15,* 93–116.

Boyd, K., Callaghan, B., & Shotter, E. (1986). *Life before birth.* London: SPCK.

Bradford, J. M. W. (2000). The treatment of sexual deviation using a pharmacological approach. *Journal of Sex Research, 37,* 248–257.

Bradford, J. M. W., & Greenberg, D. M. (1996). Pharmacological treatment of deviant sexual behaviour. *Annual Review of Sex Research, 7,* 283–306.

Brant, C. C. (1990). Native ethics and rules of behaviour. *The Canadian Journal of Psychiatry, 35,* 534–539.

Braun, M., Wassmer, G., Klotz, T., Reifenrath, B., Mathers, M., & Engelmann, U. (2000). Epidemiology of erectile dysfunction: Results of the "Cologne Male Survey." *International Journal of Impotence Research, 12,* 305–311.

Braun, V., & Kitzinger, C. (2001). "Snatch," "hole," or "honey-pot"? Semantic categories and the problem of nonspecificity in female genital slang. *Journal of Sex Research, 38,* 146–158.

Brecher, E. M. (1984). *Love, sex, and aging.* Mount Vernon, NY: Consumers Union.

Brecht M. L., O'Brien, A., von Mayrhauser, C., & Anglin, M. D. (2004). Methamphetamine use behaviors and gender differences. *Addictive Behaviors, 29,* 89–106.

Brecklin, L. R. & Ullman, S. E. (2005). Self-defense or assertiveness training and women's responses to sexual attacks. *Journal of Interpersonal Violence, 20,* 738–762.

Breitenbecher, K. H. (2000). Sexual assault on college campuses: Is an ounce of prevention enough? *Applied and Preventive Psychology, 9,* 23–52.

Brennan, P. A. & Zufall, F. (2006). Pheromonal communication in vertebrates. *Nature, 444,* 308–315.

Brenton, M. (1972). *Sex talk.* New York: Stein and Day.

Breslow, N., Evans, L., & Langley, J. (1985). On the prevalence and roles of females in the sadomasochistic subculture: Report of an empirical study. *Archives of Sexual Behavior, 14,* 303–318.

Breton, S., Smith, P. J. S., Lut, B., & Brown, D. (1996). Acidification of the male reproductive tract by a proton pumping (H1)-ATPase. *Nature Medicine, 2,* 470–472.

Bretschneider, J. G., & McCoy, N. L. (1988). Sexual interest and behavior in healthy 80- and 102-year-olds. *Archives of Sexual Behavior, 17,* 109–130.

Brewer, C. (1997, Feb 7). My first priority is just to live. Retrieved March 27, 2008, from www.acor.org/TCRC/lance.html.

Brock, G., McMahon, C. G., Chen K K., Costigan, T., Shen, W., Watkins, V., et al. (2002). Efficacy and safety of tadalafil in men with erectile dysfunction: An integrated analysis of registration trials. *Journal of Urology, 167,* 178.

Brock, G., Nehra, A., Lipshultz, L. I., Karlin, G. S., Gleave, M. P., Seger, M., et al. (2003). Safety and efficacy of vardenafil for the treatment of men with erectile dysfunction after radical retropubic prostatectomy. *Journal of Urology, 170,* 1278–1283.

Broderick, C. B. (1966a). Sexual behavior among preadolescents. *Journal of Social Issues, 22*(2), 6–21.

Broderick, C. B. (1966b). Socio-sexual development in a suburban community. *Journal of Sex Research, 2,* 1–24.

Broers, T., King, W. D., Arbuckle, T. E., & Liu, S. (2004). The occurrence of abruptio placentae in Canada: 1990 to 1997. *Chronic Diseases in Canada, 25,* 16–20.

Brotman, H. (1984, Jan. 8). Human embryo transplants. *New York Times Magazine,* 42ff.

Brotto, L. A., & Gorzalka, B. B. (2002). Genital and subjective sexual arousal in postmenopausal women: Influence of laboratory-induced hyperventilation. *Journal of Sex & Marital Therapy, 28,* 39–53.

Brotto, L. A., Basson, R., & Gorzalka, B. B. (2004). Psychophysiological assessment in premenopausal sexual arousal disorder. *Journal of Sexual Medicine, 1,* 266–277.

Brotto, L. A., Chik, H. M., Ryder, A. G., Gorzalka, B. B., & Seal, B. N. (2005). Acculturation and sexual function in Asian women. *Archives of Sexual Behaviour, 34,* 613–626.

Brotto, L. A., Heiman, J. R., Goff, B., Greer, B., Lentz, G., Swisher, E., Tamimi, H., & Van Blaricom, A. (2008). A psychoeducational intervention for sexual dysfunction in women with gynecologic cancer. Archives of Sexual Behavior, 37, 317–329.

Brotto, L. A., Woo, J. S. T., & Ryder, A. G. (2007). Acculturation and sexual function in Canadian East Asian men. *Journal of Sexual Medicine, 4,* 72–82.

Brown, G., Maycock, B., & Burns, S. (2005). Your picture is your bait: Use and meaning of cyberspace among gay men. *Journal of Sex Research, 42,* 63–73.

Brown, J. D. (2002). Mass media influences on sexuality. *Journal of Sex Research, 39,* 42–45.

Brown, J., & Steele, J. R. (1995). Sexuality and the mass media: An overview. *SIECUS Report, 24*(4), 3–9.

Brown, Z. A., et al. (2005). Genital herpes complicating pregnancy. *Obstetrics & Gynecology, 106,* 845–856.

Brownmiller, S. (1975). *Against our will: Men, women, and rape.* New York: Simon & Schuster.

Bryant, J., & Rockwell, S. C. (1994). Effects of massive exposure to sexually oriented prime-time television programming on adolescents' moral judgment. In D. Zillman, J. Bryant, and A. C. Houston (Eds.), *Media, children, and the family: Social, scientific, psychodynamic, and clinical perspectives* (pp. 183–195). Hillsdale, NJ: Lawrence Erlbaum.

Brym, R. J., & Lenton, R. L. (2001). Love online: A report on digital dating in Canada. Retrieved December 5, 2007, from www.nelson.com.

Brym, R. J., & Lenton, R. L. (2003). Love at first byte: Internet Dating in Canada. Retrieved June 13, 2005, from www.societyinquestion4e.nelson.com/article2.html.

Brzozowski, J. A. (Ed.). (2004). *Family Violence in Canada: A Statistical Profile, 2004.* (Catalogue no. 85-224-XIE). Ottawa: Canadian Centre for Justice Statistics.

Brzozowski, J. A (2007). Family violence against children and youth. In L. Ogrodnik (Ed.) *Family Violence in Canada: A Statistical Profile, 2007.* (Catalogue no. 85-224-XIE). Ottawa: Canadian Centre for Justice Statistics.

Buchanan, K. M. (1986). *Apache women warriors.* El Paso, TX: Texas Western Press.

Bufkin, J., & Eschholz, S. (2000). Images of sex and rape. *Violence Against Women, 6,* 1317–1344.

Bulik, C., Prescott, C., & Kendler, K. (2001). Features of childhood sexual abuse and the development of psychiatric and substance use disorders. *British Journal of Psychiatry, 179,* 444–449.

Bullivant, S. B., Sellergren, S. A., & Stern, K. (2004). Women's sexual experience during the menstrual cycle: Identification of the sexual phase by noninvasive measurement of luteinizing hormone. *Journal of Sex Research, 41,* 82–93.

Bullough, B., & Bullough, V. (1997). Are transvestites necessarily heterosexual? *Archives of Sexual Behavior, 26,* 1–12.

Bullough, V. L. (1976). *Sexual variance in society and history.* New York: Wiley.

Bullough, V. L. (1994). *Science in the bedroom: A history of sex research.* New York: Basic Books.

Burack, J. H., et al. (1993). Depressive symptoms and CD4 lymphocyte decline among HIV-infected men. *Journal of the American Medical Association, 270,* 2568–2573.

Burger, H. G. (1993). Evidence for a negative feedback role of inhibin in follicle stimulating hormone regulation in women. *Human Reproduction, 8,* Suppl. 2, 129–132.

Burgess, A. W. (1984). *Child pornography and sex rings.* Lexington, MA: Lexington Books.

Burgess, A. W., & Holmstrom, L. L. (1974). Rape trauma syndrome. *American Journal of Psychiatry, 131,* 981–986.

Burleson, B., & Denton, W. (1997). The relationship between communication skill and marital satisfaction: Some moderating effects. *Journal of Marriage and the Family, 59,* 884–902.

Burt, M. R., & Estep, R. E. (1981). Apprehension and fear: Learning a sense of sexual vulnerability. *Sex Roles, 7,* 511–522.

Burton, D. L. (2000). Were adolescent sexual offenders children with sexual behavior problems? *Sex Abuse, 12,* 37–48.

Burton, F. D. (1970). Sexual climax in Macaca Mulatta. *Proceedings of the Third International Congress on Primatology, 3,* 180–191.

Busby, K. (1999). Not a victim until the conviction is entered: Sexual violence, prosecutions and legal "truth." In *Locating law: Race/class/gender connections.* Halifax: Fernwood Publishing.

Buss, A. (1966). *Psychopathology.* New York: Wiley.

Buss, D. M. (1988). The evolution of human intra-sexual competition: Tactics of mate attraction. *Journal of Personality and Social Psychology, 54,* 616–628.

Buss, D. M. (1989). Sex differences in human mate preferences: Evolutionary hypotheses tested in 37 cultures. *Behavioral and Brain Sciences, 12,* 1–49.

Buss, D. M. (1994). *The evolution of desire: Strategies of human mating.* New York: Basic Books.

Buss, D. M. (2000). *The dangerous passion: Why jealousy is as necessary as love and sex.* New York: The Free Press.

Buss, D. M., & Schmitt, D. P. (1993). Sexual strategies theory: An evolutionary perspective on human mating. *Psychological Review, 100,* 204–232.

Buss, D., & Shackelford, T. (1997a). From vigilance to violence: Mate retention tactics in married couples. *Journal of Personality and Social Psychology, 72,* 346–361.

Buss, D., & Shackelford, T. (1997b). Susceptibility to infidelity in the first year of marriage. *Journal of Research in Personality, 31,* 193–221.

Buss, D. M., Shackelford, T. K., Kirkpatrick, L. A., & Larsen, R. J. (2001). A half century of mate preferences: The cultural evolution of values. *Journal of Marriage & Family, 63,* 491–504.

Buvat, J, et al. (1990). Recent developments in the clinical assessment and diagnosis of erectile dysfunction. *Annual Review of Sex Research, 1,* 265–308.

Byard, R., Hucker, S., & Hazelwood, R. (1993). Fatal and near-fatal autoerotic asphyxial episodes in women. *The American Journal of Forensic Medicine and Pathology, 14,* 70–73.

Byers, E. S. (1988). Effects of sexual arousal on men and women's behaviour on sexual disagreement situations. *The Journal of Sex Research, 25,* 233–254.

Byers, E. S. (1989). Prevention and treatment of relationship distress. *Canadian Family Physician, 35,* 1883–1886.

Byers, E. S. (1996). How well does the traditional sexual script explain sexual coercion? Review of a program of research. *Journal of Psychology and Human Sexuality, 8,* 7–25.

Byers, E. S. (1999). The interpersonal exchange model of sexual satisfaction: Implications for sex therapy with couples. *Canadian Journal of Counselling, 33*(2), 95–111.

Byers, E. S., Crooks, R., Griffiths, B., Mackin, B., MacDonald, G., MacDonald, G., Marcoux-Galarneau, R., Renaud, C., Thomas, B., Thompson, B., & Yates, P. (1997). *The extent of sex offences and the nature of sex offenders in New Brunswick: A research project.* Submitted to the New Brunswick Department of the Solicitor General and Correctional Services Canada.

Byers, E. S., & Demmons, S. (1999). Sexual satisfaction and sexual self disclosure within dating relationships. *The Journal of Sex Research, 36,* 180–189.

Byers, E. S., Demmons, S., & Lawrance, K.-A. (1998). Sexual satisfaction within dating relationships: A test of the interpersonal exchange model of sexual satisfaction. *Journal of Social and Personal Relationships, 15*(2), 257–267.

Byers, E. S., Giles, B. L., & Price, D. L. (1987). Definiteness and effectiveness of women's responses to unwanted sexual advances: A laboratory investigation. *Basic and Applied Social Psychology, 8,* 321–338.

Byers, E. S. & Grenier, G. (2003). Premature or rapid ejaculation: Heterosexual couples' perceptions of men's ejaculatory behavior. *Archives of Sexual Behavior, 32,* 261–270.

Byers, E. S., & Heinlein, L. (1989). Predicting initiation and refusals of sexual activities in married and cohabiting heterosexual couples. *The Journal of Sex Research, 26,* 210–231.

Byers, E. S., Henderson, J., & Hobson, K. (in press). University students' definitions of sexual abstinence and having sex. *Archives of Sexual Behavior.*

Byers, E. S., & Lewis, K. (1988). Dating couples' disagreements over desired level of sexual activity. *The Journal of Sex Research, 24,* 15–29.

Byers, E. S., & MacNeil, S. (2006). Further validation of the interpersonal exchange model of sexual satisfaction. *Journal of Sex & Marital Therapy, 32,* 53–69.

Byers, E. S., & O'Sullivan, L. F. (1998). Similar but different: Men's and women's experiences of sexual coercion. In P. B. Anderson & C. Strickman-Johnson (Eds.), *Sexually aggressive women.* New York: Guilford Press.

Byers, E. S., & O'Sullivan, L. F. (1996). How well does the traditional sexual script explain sexual coercion? Review of a program of research. In E. S. Byers (Ed.), *Sexual coercion in dating relationships.* Binghamton, NY: Hawthorn Press.

Byers, E. S., Purdon, C., & Clark, D. (1998). Sexual intrusive thoughts of college students. *The Journal of Sex Research, 35,* 359–369.

Byers, E. S., Sears, H. A., Voyer, S. D., Thurlow, J. L., Cohen, J. N., & Weaver, A. D. (2001). *New Brunswick students' ideas about sexual health education.* Report prepared for the New Brunswick Department of Education, Fredericton, NB. Retrieved November 11, 2002, from www.gnb.ca/0000/publications/studentsexeducation.pdf.

Byers, E. S., Sears, H. A., Voyer, S. D., Thurlow, J. L., Cohen, J. N., & Weaver, A. D. (2003a). An adolescent perspective on sexual health education at school and at home: I. High school students. *Canadian Journal of Human Sexuality, 12,* 1–17.

Byers, E. S., Sears, H. A., Voyer, S. D., Thurlow, J. L., Cohen, J. N., & Weaver, A. D. (2003b). An adolescent perspective on sexual health education at school and at home: II. Middle school students. *Canadian Journal of Human Sexuality, 12,* 19–32.

Byers, E. S., & Slattery, G. (1997). Sexology in Russia and Estonia: Reflections on an exchange. *Canadian Journal of Human Sexuality, 6,* 53–64.

Byers, E. S., & Wang, A. (2004). Understanding sexuality in close relationships from the social exchange perspective. In J. H. Harvey, A. Wenzel, & S. Sprecher (Eds.), *The handbook of sexuality in close relationships* (pp. 203–234). Mahwah, NJ: Lawrence Erlbaum.

Byers, E. S., & Wilson, P. (1985). Accuracy of women's expectations regarding men's responses to refusals of sexual advances in dating situations. *International Journal of Women's Studies, 4,* 376–387.

Byers, L. J., Menzies, K. S., & W. L. O'Grady (2004). The impact of computer variables on the viewing and sending of sexually explicit material on the Internet: Testing Cooper's "triple-A engine." *Canadian Journal of Human Sexuality, 13,* 157–169.

Byers, M. E. (2005). *Growing up Degrassi.* Toronto: Sumach Press.

Byne, W., Lasco, M. S., Kemether, E., Shinwari, A., Edgar, M. A., & Morgello, S. (2000). The interstitial nuclei of the human anterior hypothalamus: Assessment for sexual variation in volume and neuronal size, density, and number. *Brain Research, 856,* 254–258.

Byrne, D. (1971). *The attraction paradigm.* New York: Academic.

Byrne, D. (1983). Sex without contraception. In D. Byrne & W. A. Fisher (Eds.), *Adolescents, sex, and contraception.* Hillsdale, NJ: Lawrence Erlbaum.

Byrne, D. (1997). An overview (and underview) and research and theory within the attraction paradigm. *Journal of Social and Personal Relationships, 14,* 417–431.

Byrne, D., Ervin, C. E., & Lamberth, J. (1970). Continuity between the experimental study of attraction and real-life computer dating. *Journal of Personality and Social Psychology, 16,* 157–165.

Cado, S., & Leitenberg, H. (1990). Guilt reactions to sexual fantasies during intercourse. *Archives of Sexual Behavior, 19,* 49–64.

Cahill, L. S. (1985). The "seamless garment": Life in its beginnings. *Theological Studies, 46,* 64–80.

Cahill, L. (2005). His brain, her brain. *Scientific American, 292,* 40–47.

Cairns, K. V. (1993). Sexual entitlement and sexual accommodations: implications for female and male experience of sexual coercion. *The Canadian Journal of Human Sexuality, 2,* 203–213.

Calderwood, D. (1987, May). The male rape victim. *Medical Aspects of Human Sexuality,* 53–55.

Call, V., Sprecher, S., & Schwartz, P. (1995). The incidence and frequency of marital sex in a national sample. *Journal of Marriage and the Family, 57,* 639–652.

Callahan, D. (1986, February). How technology is reframing the abortion debate. *Hastings Center Report,* 33–42.

Calzavara, L. M., Burchell, A. N., Myers, T., Bullock, S. L., Escobar, M., & Cockerill, R. (1998). Condom use among Aboriginal people in Ontario, Canada. *International Journal of STD & AIDS, 9,* 272–279.

Cameron, J. J., & Ross, M. (2007). In times of uncertainty: Predicting the survival of long-distance relationships. *The Journal of Social Psychology, 147,* 581–606.

Campbell, A., Shirley, L., & Caygill, L. (2002). Sex-typed preferences in three domains: Do two-year-olds need cognitive variables? *British Journal of Psychology, 93,* 201–217.

Canadian AIDS Society. (2004). *HIV and HCV Transmission: Guidelines for assessing risk.* Ottawa: Author.

Canadian AIDS Society. (2007). *Rapid HIV Testing in Canada.* Retrieved September 5, 2007, from www.cdnaids.ca.

Canadian Cancer Society/ National Cancer Institute of Canada. (2007). *Canadian Cancer Statistics 2007.* Toronto, Canada.

Canadian Centre for Justice Statistics. (1999). *Integration and analysis program: Sex offenders.*

Canadian Federation for Sexual Health (2007). *Sexual Health in Canada: Baseline 2007.* Ottawa: Author.

Canadian HIV/AIDS Legal Network. (2002). *HIV vaccines in Canada: Legal and ethical issues: An Overview.* Retrieved November 11, 2002, from www.aidslaw.ca/Maincontent/issues/vaccines/overviewpaper/toc.htm.

Canadian Midwifery Regulators Consortium (2007). What is a Canadian registered midwife? Retrieved August 30, 2007 from http://cmrc-ccosf.ca/node/18.

Canadian Psychological Association. (1995). *Companion manual to the Canadian Code of Ethics for Psychologists, 1991.* Ottawa: Author.

Canadian Psychological Association. (2003, August 6). Gays and lesbians make bad parents: There is no basis in the scientific literature for this perception. Press Release *2003.* Ottawa: Author.

Canary, D. J., & Dindia, K. (Eds.). (1998). *Sex differences and similarities in communication.* Mahwah, NJ: Erlbaum.

Canary, D. J., & Hause, K. S. (1993). Is there any reason to research sex differences in communication? *Communication Quarterly, 41,* 129–144.

Cantor, J. M., Blanchard, P., Christensen, B. K., Dickey, R., Klassen, P. E., Beckstead, A. L., et al. (2004). Intelligence, memory, and handedness in pedophilia. *Neuropsychology, 18,* 3–14.

Cantor, J. M., Blanchard, R., Paterson, A. D., & Bogaert, A. F. (2002). How many gay men owe their sexual orientation to fraternal birth order? *Archives of Sexual Behavior, 31,* 63–71.

Cantor, J. M., Blanchard, R., Robichaud, L., & Christensen, B. (2005). Quantitative reanalysis of aggregate data on IQ in sexual offenders. *Psychological Bulletin, 131,* 555–568.

Cantor, J. M., Klassen, P. E., Dickey, R., Christensen, B. K., Kuban, M. E., Blak, T., Williams, N. S., & Blanchard, R. (2005). Handedness in pedophilia and hebephilia. *Archives of Sexual Behavior, 34,* 447–459.

Caplan, P. (1995). *How do they decide who is normal?* Reading, MA: Addison-Wesley.

Cappon, P., Adrien, A., Godin, G., Mason Singer, S., Maticka-Tyndale, E., Willms, D., & Daus, T. (1996). HIV/AIDS in the context of culture: Selection of ethnocultural communities for study in Canada. *Canadian Journal of Public Health, 87*(1), S11–S25.

Caputo, T. (2000). *Hearing the voices of youth: Youth participation in selected Canadian municipalities.* Ottawa: ON: Health Canada.

CARAL (n.d.). *Historical biography of Henry Morgentaler,* Ottawa: CARAL.

Carani, C., et al. (1990). Effects of androgen treatment in impotent men with normal and low levels of free testosterone. *Archives of Sexual Behavior, 19,* 223–234.

Carnes, P. (1983). *The sexual addiction*. Minneapolis, MN: Compcare Publications.

Carpenter, L. M. (2001). The ambiguity of "having sex": The subjective experience of virginity loss in the United States. *Journal of Sex Research, 38,* 127–139.

Carroll, L., Gilroy, P. J., & Ryan, J. (2002). Counseling transgendered, transsexual, and gender-variant clients. *Journal of Counseling & Development, 80,* 131–139.

Carson, C. C., West, S. L., Glasser, D. B., Laumann, E. O., Flack, J. M., Rimm, E., et al. (2002). Prevalence and correlates of erectile dysfunction in a United States Nationwide population-based sample: Phase I results. *Journal of Urology, 167,* S29–30.

Carter, C. S. (1992). Hormonal influences on human sexual behavior. In J. B. Becker et al. (Eds.), *Behavioral endocrinology* (pp. 131–142). Cambridge, MA: MIT Press.

Carver. P., Egan, S., & Perry, D. (2004). Children who question their heterosexuality. *Developmental Psychology, 40,* 43–53.

Casimiro, D. R., Tang, A., Chen, L., Fu, T. M., Evans, R. K., Davies, M. E., et al. (2003). Vaccine-induced immunity in baboons by using DNA and replication-incompetent adenovirus type 5 vectors expressing a human immunodeficiency virus type 1 gag gene. *Journal of Virology, 77,* 7663–7668.

Cass, V. C. (1979). Homosexual identity formation: A theoretical model. *Journal of Homosexuality, 4,* 219–235.

Catania, J. A., Binson, D., Van Der Straten, A., & Stone, V. (1995). Methodological research on sexual behavior in the AIDS era. *Annual Review of Sex Research, 6,* 77–125.

Catania, J. A., Gibson, D., Marin, B., Coates, T., & Greenblatt, R. (1990). Response bias in assessing sexual behaviors relevant to HIV transmission. *Evaluation and Program Planning, 13,* 19–29.

Catania, J. A., et al. (2001). National trends in condom use among at-risk heterosexuals in the United States. *Journal of Acquired Immune Deficiency Syndrome, 27,* 176–182.

Catellsagué, X., Bosch, F. X., Muñoz, N., Meijer, C. J. L. M., Shah, K. V., de Sanjosé, S., et al. (2002). Male circumcision, penile human papillomavirus infection, and cervical cancer in female partners. *New England Journal of Medicine, 346,* 1105–1112.

Cates, W. (2001). The NIH condom report: The glass is 90% full. *Family Planning Perspectives, 33,* 231–233.

CDC. (2004). *Intimate partner violence: Fact sheet*. Retrieved June 1, 2004, from www.cdc.gov/ncipc/factsheets/ipvfacts.htm.

Chalker, R. (1995, November/December) Sexual pleasure unscripted. *Ms, 49–52.*

Chalmers, B., & Hashi, K. O. (2000). 432 Somali women's birth experiences in Canada after earlier female genital mutilation. *Birth, 27,* 227–234.

Chan, Connie S. (1995). Issues of sexual identity in an ethnic minority: The case of Chinese American lesbians, gay men, and bisexual people. In A. R. D'Augelli & C. J. Patterson (Eds.), *Lesbian, gay, and bisexual identities over the lifespan* (pp. 87–101). New York: Oxford University Press.

Chapman, H., Hobfoll, S., & Ritter, C. (1997). Partners' stress underestimations lead to women's distress: A study of pregnant inner-city women. *Journal of Personality and Social Psychology, 73,* 418–425.

Charon, J. (1995). *Symbolic interactionism: An introduction, interpretation, and integration* (5th ed). Englewood Cliffs, NJ: Prentice Hall.

Cheng, J., Elam-Evans, L. D., Berg, C. J., Herndon, J., Flowers, L., Seed, K. A., et al. (2003, February 21). Pregnancy-related mortality surveillance: United States, 1991–1999. *Morbidity & Mortality Weekly Report, 52,* 1–8.

Cheng, Mariah M., & Udry, J. Richard. (2003). How much do mentally disabled adolescents know about sex and birth control? *Adolescent & Family Health, 3,* 28–38.

Chesler, E. (1992). *Woman of valor: Margaret Sanger and the birth control movement*. New York: Simon & Schuster.

Chivers, M. L. (2005). A brief review and discussion of sex differences in the specificity of sexual arousal. *Sexual and Relationship Therapy, 20,* 377–390.

Chivers, M. L., & Bailey, J. M. (2000). Sexual orientation of female-to-male transsexuals: A comparison of homosexual and nonhomosexual types. *Archives of Sexual Behavior, 29,* 259–278.

Chivers, M., & Blanchard, R. (1996). Prostitution advertisements suggest association of transvestism and masochism. *Journal of Sex & Marital Therapy, 22*(2), 97–102.

Chivers, M. L., Rieger, G., Latty, E., & Bailey, J. M. (2004). A sex difference in the specificity of sexual arousal. *Psychological Science, 15,* 736–744.

Choi, E. J, Ha, C. M, Choi, J., Kang, S. S., Choi, W. S., Park, S. K., et al. (2001). Low-density DNA array-coupled to PCR differential display identifies new estrogen-responsive genes during the postnatal differentiation of the rat hypothalamus. *Molecular Brain Research, 97,* 115–128.

Chrisler, J. C., et al. (2006). The PMS illusion: Social cognition maintains social construction. *Sex Roles, 54,* 371–376.

Christensen, C. V. (1971). *Kinsey: A biography*. Bloomington, IN: Indiana University Press.

Christopher, F. S., & Sprecher, S. (2000). Sexuality in marriage, dating, and other relationships: A decade review. *Journal of Marriage and the Family, 62,* 999–1017.

Chu, J. A., Frey, L. M., Ganzel, B., & Mattews, J. (1999). Memories of childhood abuse: Dissociation amnesia, and corroboration. *American Journal of Psychiatry, 156,* 749–755.

Chumlea, W. C., et al. (2003). Age at menarche and racial comparison in US girls. *Pediatrics, 111,* 110–113.

Church, S., Henderson, M., Barnard, M., & Hart, G. (2001). Violence by clients towards female prostitutes in different work settings: Questionnaire survey. *British Medical Journal, 322,* 524–525.

Cimbalo, R. S., Faling, B., & Mousaw, P. (1976). The course of love: A cross-sectional design. *Psychological Reports, 38,* 1292–1294.

Clark, L., & Lewis, D. (1977). *Rape: The price of coercive sexuality*. Toronto: Women's Educational Press.

Clark, W., & Crompton, S. (2006). Till death do us part? The risk of first and second marriage dissolution. *Canadian Social Trends*. Statistics Canada, Catalogue no. 11-008E.

Clarke, J. N. (2006). Homophobia out of the closet in the media portrayal of HIV/AIDS 1991, 1996 and 2001: Celebrity, heterosexism and the silent victims. *Critical Public Health, 16,* 317–330.

Clements-Schreiber, M. E., Rempel, J. K., & Desmarais, S. (1998). Women's sexual pressure tactics and adherence to related attitudes: A step towards prediction. *The Journal of Sex Research, 35*(2), 197–205.

Cocchi, F., et al. (1995). Identification of RANTES, MIP-1a, and MIP-1b as the major HIV-suppressive factors produced by CD81 T cells. *Science, 270,* 1811–1815.

Cochran, S., Sullivan, J. G., & Mays, V. (2003). Prevalence of mental disorders, psychological distress, and mental health services use among lesbian, gay, and bisexual adults in the United States. *Journal of Consulting and Clinical Psychology, 71,* 53–61.

Cochran, W. G., Mosteller, F., & Tukey, J. W. (1953). Statistical problems of the Kinsey report. *Journal of the American Statistical Association, 48,* 673–716.

Cohen, D. J., & Bruce, K. E. (1997). Sex and mortality: Real risk and perceived vulnerability. *Journal of Sex Research, 34,* 279–291.

Cohen, J. (1997). Exploiting the HIV-chemokine nexus. *Science, 275,* 1261–1264.

Cohen, J. (1998). Exploring how to get at-and eradicate-hidden HIV. *Science, 279,* 1854–1855.

Cohen, J. (2002). Confronting the limits of success. *Science, 296,* 2320–2326.

Cohen, J. (2003). Thailand and Cambodia: Two hard-hit countries offer rare success stories. *Science, 301,* 1658–1663.

Cohen, J. N., Byers, E. S., Sears, H. A., & Weaver, A. D. (2004). Sexual health education: Attitudes, knowledge, and comfort of teachers in New Brunswick schools. *Canadian Journal of Human Sexuality, 13,* 1–15.

Cohen, K. M. (2002). Relationships among childhood sex-atypical behavior, spatial ability, handedness, and sexual orientation in men. *Archives of Sexual Behavior, 31,* 129–144.

Cohen, J. N., Byers, E. S., Sears, H. A., & Weaver, A. D. (2001). *New Brunswick teachers' ideas about sexual health education*. Report prepared for the New Brunswick Department of Education, Fredericton, NB. Retrieved November 11, 2002, from www.gnb.ca/0000/publications/oo/nbteachersidea/pdf.

Cohn, L. (1983, November 16). Pix less able but porn is stable. *Variety, 313*(3), 1–2.

Cole, L., Khantian, S., Sutton, J., Davies, S., & Rayburn, W. (2004). Accuracy of home pregnancy tests at the time of missed menses. *American Journal of Obstetrics and Gynecology, 190*, 100–105.

Cole, S. W., Kemeny, M. E., Taylor, S. E., & Visscher, B. R. (1996). Elevated physical health risk among gay men who conceal their homosexual identity. *Health Psychology, 15*, 243–251.

Cole, T. M., & Cole, S. (1978). The handicapped and sexual health. In A. Comfort (Ed.), *Sexual consequences of disability*. Philadelphia, PA: G. F. Stickley.

Coleman, E. (1982). Developmental stages of the coming-out process. In W. Paul et al. (Eds.), *Homosexuality: Social, psychological, and biological issues*. Beverly Hills, CA: Sage.

Coleman, E. (1991). Compulsive sexual behavior: New concepts and treatments. *Journal of Psychology and Human Sexuality, 4*(2), 37–51.

Coleman, E., Miner, M., Ohlerking, F., & Raymond, N. (2001). Compulsive Sexual Behavior inventory: A preliminary study of reliability and validity. *Journal of Sex and Marital Therapy, 27*, 325–332.

Coleman, E., Raymond, N., & McBean, A. (2003, July 2003). Assessment and treatment of compulsive sexual behaviour. *Minnesota Medicine, 86*, 42–47.

Collaborative Group on Hormonal Factors in Breast Cancer. (2002). Breast cancer and breast-feeding. *Lancet, 360*, 187–195.

Collins, N. L., & Miller, L. C. (1994). Self-disclosure and liking: A meta-analytic review. *Psychological Bulletin, 116*, 457–475.

Collins, R. L., Elliott, M. N., Berry, S. H., Kanouse, D. E., Kunkel, D., & Hunter, S. B. (2004). Watching sex on television predicts adolescent initiation of sexual behavior. *Pediatrics, 114*, 280–289.

Collins, R. L., et al. (2005). Isolating the nexus of substance use, violence and sexual risk for HIV infection among young adults in the United States. *AIDS and Behavior, 9*, 73–87.

Collin-Vézina, D., & Hébert, M. (2005). Comparing dissociation and PTSD in sexually abused school-aged girls. *Journal of Mental & Nervous Disease, 193*, 47–52.

Comet (Comparative Obstetric Mobile Epidural Trial) Study Group. (2001). Effect of low-dose mobile versus traditional epidural techniques on mode of delivery: A randomised controlled trial. *Lancet, 358*, 19–23.

Committee on Lesbian and Gay Concerns, American Psychological Association. (1991). Avoiding heterosexual bias in language. *American Psychologist, 46*, 973–974.

Compas Inc. (2001). Valentine's Day Poll. Toronto, ON: Author.

Compas Inc. (2005, February 14). Valentine's Day Poll for the National Post. Toronto: Author.

Compas, B. E., & Luecken, L. (2002). Psychological adjustment to breast cancer. *Current Directions in Psychological Science, 11*, 111–114.

Congregation for the Doctrine of the Faith. (1986). The pastoral care of homosexual persons. *Origins, 26*, 378–382.

Congregation for the Doctrine of the Faith. (1987). Instruction on respect for human life in its origin and on the dignity of procreation. *Origins, 16*, 198–211.

Connell, E., & Hunt, A. (2006). Sexual ideology and sexual physiology in the discourses of sex advice literature. *The Canadian Journal of Human Sexuality, 15*, 23–45.

Connolly, J., Craig, W., Goldberg, A., & Pepler, D. (2004). Mixed-gender groups, dating, and romantic relationships in early adolescence. *Journal of Research on Adolescence, 14*, 185–207.

Contessini, C. (2003). Personal communication.

Cook, K., & Rice, E. (2004). Social exchange theory. In J. DeLamater (Ed.), *The handbook of social psychology*. New York: Kluwer-Plenum.

Cook, R. J., & Kelly, L. M. (2006). *Polygyny and Canada's obligations under International human rights law*. Ottawa: Canada: Family, Children and Youth Section, Department of Justice Canada.

Cooper, A. (1998). Sexuality and the Internet: Surfing into the new millennium. *CyberPsychology & Behavior, 1*, 187–193.

Cooper, A., Delmonico, D., & Burg, R. (2000). Cybersex users, abusers, and compulsives: New findings and implications. In A. Cooper (Ed.), *Cybersex: The dark side of the force* (pp. 5–29). Philadelphia: Brunner Routledge.

Cooper, A., Putnam, D., Planchon, L., & Boies, S. (1999). Sexuality on the Internet: from sexual exploration to pathological expression. *Professional Psychology Research and Practice, 30*, 154–164.

Cooper, A., Putnam, D. E., Planchon, L. A., & Boies, S. C. (1999a). Online sexual compulsivity: Getting tangled in the Net. *Sexual Addiction & Compulsivity: The Journal of Treatment and Prevention, 6*, 79–104.

Cooper, A., Scherer, C. R., Gordon, B. L., & Boies, S. C. (1999b). Sexuality on the Internet: From sexual exploration to pathological expression. *Professional Psychology: Research & Practice, 30*(2), 154–164.

Cordova, M. J., Cunningham, L., Carlson, C., & Andrykowski, M. (2001). Posttraumatic growth following breast cancer: A controlled comparison study. *Health Psychology, 20*, 176–185.

Corey, L., Wald, A., Patel, R., Sacks, S. L., Tyring, S. K., Warren, T., et al. (2004). Once-daily valacyclovir to reduce the risk of transmission of genital herpes. *New England Journal of Medicine, 350*, 11–20.

Council on Scientific Affairs. (1995). Female genital mutilation. *Journal of the American Medical Association, 274*, 1714–1716.

Countryman, L. W. (1994). New Testament sexual ethics and today's world. In J. B. Nelson & S. P. Longfellow (Eds.), *Sexuality and the sacred* (pp. 28–53). Louisville, KY: Westminster/ John Knox Press.

Coustan, D. (1995). Obstetric analgesia and anesthesia. In D. R. Coustan, R. V. Hunning, Jr., & D. Singer (Eds.), *Human reproduction: Growth and development* (pp. 327–340). Boston: Little, Brown.

Coustan, Donald, & Angelini, Diane. (1995). The puerperium. In Donald R. Coustan, Ray V. Hunning, Jr., & Don Singer (Eds.), *Human reproduction: Growth and development* (pp. 341–358). Boston: Little, Brown & Co.

Couzinet, B., et al. (1986). Termination of early pregnancy by the progesterone antagonist RU486 (mifepristone). *New England Journal of Medicine, 315*, 1565–1569.

Cowley, J. J., & Brooksbank, B. W. L. (1991). Human exposure to putative pheromones and changes in aspects of social behavior. *Journal of Steroid Biochemistry and Molecular Biology, 39*, 647–659.

Cox, D. J. (1988). Incidence and nature of male genital exposure behavior as reported by college women. *Journal of Sex Research, 24*, 227–234.

Cramer, E. H., Jones, P., Keenan, N. L., & Thompson, B. L. (2003). Is naturopathy as effective as conventional therapy for treatment of menopausal symptoms? *The Journal of Alternative and Complementary Medicine, 8*, 529–538.

Crawford, J., Kippax, S., & Waldby, C. (1994). Women's sex talk and men's sex talk: Different worlds. *Feminism and Psychology*, 571–587.

Crawford, M., & Popp, D. (2003). Sexual double standards: A review and methodological critique of two decades of research. *Journal of Sex Research, 40*, 13–26.

Craze, R. (2003). *Teach yourself tantric sex*. McGraw-Hill, Whitby, ON.

Creighton, J. (1992). *Don't go away mad*. New York: Doubleday.

Creighton, S. M., & Minto, C. (2001). Managing intersex: Most vaginal surgery in childhood should be deferred. *British Medical Journal, 323*, 1264–1265.

Creighton, S. M., Minto, C., & Steele, S. (2001). Objective cosmetic and anatomical outcomes at adolescence of feminising surgery for ambiguous genitalia done in childhood. *Lancet, 358*, 124–125.

Creti, L., & Libman, E. (1989). Cognitions and sexual expression in the aging. *Journal of Sex & Marital Therapy, 15*(2), 83–101.

Crocker, D., & Kalemba, V. (1999). The incidence and impact of women's experiences of sexual harassment in Canadian workplaces. *Canadian Review of Sociology and Anthropology, 36*, 541–558.

Crompton, L. (2003). *Homosexuality and civilization*. Cambridge, MA: Harvard University Press.

Crompton, S. (2005). Always the bridesmaid: People who don't expect to marry. *Canadian Social Trends*. Statistics Canada, Catalogue no. 11-008E.

Cruess, S., Antoni, M. H., Hayes, A., Penedo, F. J., Ironson, G. H, Fletcher, M. A., et al. (2002). Changes in mood and depressive symptoms and related change processes during cognitive-behavioral stress management in HIV-infected men. *Cognitive Therapy & Research, 26*, 373–392.

Cunningham, F. G., MacDonald, P. C., Gant, N. F., Leveno, K. J., & Gilstrap, L. C., III. (1993). *Williams obstetrics* (19th ed.). Norwalk, CT: Appleton and Lange.

Cunningham, M., Roberts, A., Wu, C.-H., Burbee, A., & Druen, P. (1995). "Their ideas of beauty are, on the whole, the same as ours": Consistency and variability in the cross-cultural perception of female physical attractiveness. *Journal of Personality and Social Psychology, 68*, 261–279.

Curran, C. E. (1988). Roman Catholic sexual ethics: A dissenting view. *Christian Century, 105,* 1139–1142.

Curtis, J. T., & Wang, Z. X. (2003). The neurochemistry of pair bonding. *Current Directions in Psychological Science, 12,* 49–53.

Cutler, W. B. (1999). Human sex-attractant hormones. *Psychiatric Annals, 29,* 54–59.

Daignault, I. V., & Hébert, M. (In press). L'adaptation scolaire des enfants ayant dévoilé une aggression sexuelle. *Psychologie Canadienne.*

Dailard, C. (2006). The public health promise and potential pitfalls of the world's first cervical cancer vaccine. *Guttmacher Policy Review, 9,* 6–9.

Daneback, K., Cooper, A., & Månsson, S. (2005). An internet study of cybersex participants. *Archives of Sexual Behavior, 34,* 321–329.

Daniluk, J. C. (1999). When biology isn't destiny: Implications for the sexuality of women without children. *Canadian Journal of Counselling, 33,* 79–94.

Daniluk, J. C. (2001a). "If we had it to do over again…": Couples' reflections on their experiences of infertility treatments. *The Family Journal: Counseling and Therapy for Couples and Families, 9,* 122–133.

Daniluk, J. C. (2001b). Reconstructing their lives: A longitudinal, qualitative analysis of the transition to biological childlessness for infertile couples. *Journal of Counseling & Development, 79,* 439–449.

Darling, C. A., Davidson, J. K., & Conway-Welch, C. (1990). Female ejaculation: Perceived origins, the Gräfenberg spot/ area, and sexual responsiveness. *Archives of Sexual Behavior, 19,* 29–48.

Darroch, J. E., Frost, J. J., Singh, S., and the Study Team. (2001). *Teenage sexual and reproductive behavior in developed countries: Can more progress be made?* New York: Alan Guttmacher Institute.

Darroch, J. E., Singh, S., Frost, J. J., & the Study Team. (2001). Differences in teenage pregnancy rates among five developed countries: The roles of sexual activity and contraceptive use. *Family Planning Perspectives, 33,* 244–250.

D'Augelli, A. R. (2006). Developmental and contextual factors and mental health among lesbian, gay, and bisexual youths. In A. E. Omoto & H. M. Kurtzman (Eds.), *Recent research on sexual orientation.* Washington, DC: APA Books.

D'Augelli, A. (2002). Mental health problems among lesbian, gay, and bisexual youths ages 14 to 21. *Clinical Child Psychology and Psychiatry, 7,* 433–456.

Davey, M. (2003, August 4). Episcopalians give first nod for gay bishop. *New York Times.*

David, H. P., Dytrych, Z., & Matejcek, Z. (2003). Born unwanted: Observations from the Prague study. *American Psychologist, 58,* 224–229.

Davidson, J. K., & Darling, C. A. (1988). The stereotype of single women revisited: Sexual practices and sexual satisfaction among professional women. *Health Care for Women International, 9,* 317–336.

Davis, C. M., & Bauserman, R. (1993). Exposure to sexually explicit materials: An attitude change perspective. *Annual Review of Sex Research, 4,* 121–210.

Davis, K. R., & Weller, S. C. (1999). The effectiveness of condoms in reducing heterosexual transmission of HIV. *Family Planning Perspectives, 31,* 272–279.

Day, R. (1992). The transition to first intercourse among racially and culturally diverse youth. *Journal of Marriage and the Family, 54,* 749–762.

De Cuypere, G., et al. (2005). Sexual and physical health after sex reassignment surgery. *Archives of Sexual Behavior, 34,* 679–690.

DeKeseredy, W. S., & Kelly, K. (1993). Woman abuse in university and college dating relationships: The contribution of the ideology of familial patriarchy. *The Journal of Human Justice, 4*(2), 25–52.

DeKeseredy, W. S., & Schwartz, M. D. (1998). *Women abuse on campus: Results from the Canadian national survey.* Thousand Oaks: Sage Publications.

Dekker, A., & Schmidt, G. (2002). Patterns of masturbatory behaviour: Changes between the sixties and the nineties. *Journal of Psychology & Human Sexuality, 14,* 35–48.

DeLamater, J. (1981). The social control of sexuality. *Annual Review of Sociology, 7,* 263–290.

DeLamater, J. (1982). Response effects of question content. In W. Dijkstra & J. Van derZouwen (Eds.), *Response behavior in the survey-interview.* London, England: Academic.

DeLamater, J. (1987). A sociological perspective. In J. H. Geer & W. T. O'Donohue (Eds.), *Theories of human sexuality* (pp. 237–256). New York: Plenum.

DeLamater, J. (2003). Discussion paper. In John Bancroft (Ed.), *Sexual development* (pp. 186–191). Bloomington, IN: Indiana University Press.

DeLamater, J., & MacCorquodale, P. (1979). *Premarital sexuality: Attitudes, relationships, behavior.* Madison: University of Wisconsin Press.

DeLamater, J., & Moorman, S. (2007). Sexuality and aging. In K. Markides (Ed.), *Encyclopedia of Health and Aging.* Thousand Oaks: Sage Publications.

DeLamater, J., Wagstaff, D., & Havens, K. K. (1994). *The impact of a health-promotion intervention on condom use by Black male adolescents.* Madison, WI: Center for Demography and Ecology, Working Paper 94–26.

DeLamater, J., Wagstaff, D. A., & Havens, K. K. (2000). The impact of a culturally appropriate STD/AIDS education intervention on Black male adolescents' sexual and condom use behavior. *Health Education and Behavior, 27,* 454–470.

De La Vega Salas, M. L., & Thériault, J. (2001). Sexualité parental et relation intime du couple parental: Conceptualisations des enfants âgés de dix et 11 ans. *Gynécologie, obstétrique, & fertilité, 29,* 226–233.

Delemarre-van de Waal, H. & Cohen-Kettenis, P. (2006). Clinical management of gender identity disorder in adolescents: A protocol on psychological and paediatric endocrinology aspects. *European Journal of Endocrinology, 155,* S131–S137.

Deligeor-Oglov, E. (2000). Dysmenorrhea. *Annals of the New York Academy of Sciences, 900,* 237–244.

Delmas, P. D., et al. (1997). Effects of raloxifene on bone mineral density, serum cholesterol concentrations, and uterine endometrium in postmenopausal women. *New England Journal of Medicine, 337,* 1641–1647.

Denizet-Lewis, B. (2004, May 30). Friends, friends with benefits, and the benefits of the local mall. *The New York Times Magazine,* 30–35ff.

Dennis, C. (2005). Psychosocial and psychological interventions for prevention of post-natal depression: Systematic review. *British Medical Journal, 331,* 15.

Denov, M. S. (2003). The myth of innocence: Sexual scripts and the recognition of child sexual abuse by female perpetrators. *Journal of Sex Research, 40,* 303–314.

Denzin, N. K., & Lincoln, Y. S. (1994). Introduction: Entering the field of qualitative research. In N. K. Denzin, & Y. S. Lincoln (Eds.), *Handbook of qualitative research* (pp. 1–17). Thousand Oaks, CA: Sage.

Derby, C. A., Mohr, B. A., Goldstein, I., Feldman, H. A., Johannes, C. B., & McKinlay, J. B. (2000). Modifiable risk factors and erectile dysfunction: Can lifestyle changes modify risk? *Urology, 56,* 302–306.

Derlega, V. J. (Ed.). (1984). *Communication, intimacy, and close relationships.* New York: Academic.

Derlega, V. J., Metts, S., & Margulis, S. T. (1993). *Self-disclosure.* Newbury Park, CA: Sage.

Devor, A. H. (1989). *Gender blending: Confronting the limits of duality.* Bloomington, IN: Indiana University Press.

Devor, A. H. (2004). Witnessing and mirroring. A fourteen stage model of transsexual identity formation. *Journal of Gay and Lesbian Psychotherapy, 8,* 41–67.

Devor, H. (1996). Female gender dysphoria in context: Social problem or personal problem? *Annual Review of Sex Research: An Integrative & Interdisciplinary Review, 7,* 44–89.

Devor, H. (1997). *FTM: Female-to-male transsexuals in society.* Bloomington, IN: Indiana University Press.

Devor, H. (1997). More than manly women: How female to male transsexuals reject lesbian identities. In B. Bullough, V. Bullough, & J. Elias (Eds.), *Gender blending.* Amherst, NJ: Prometheus.

De Waal, F. B. M. (1995). The behavior of a close relative challenges assumptions about male supremacy in human evolution. *Scientific American,* 82–88.

De Waal, F. (2002). Evolutionary psychology: The wheat and the chaff. *Current Directions in Psychological Science, 11,* 187–191.

Diamond, L. M. (1998). Development of sexual orientation among adolescents and young women. *Developmental Psychology, 34,* 1085–1095.

Diamond, L. M. (2000). Sexual identities, attractions, and behavior among young sexual-minority women over a two-year period. *Developmental Psychology, 36*, 241–250.

Diamond, L. M. (2003). Was it a phase? Young women's relinquishment of lesbian/bisexual identities over a 5-year period. *Journal of Personality and Social Psychology, 84*, 352–364.

Diamond, L. M. (2004). Emerging perspectives on distinctions between romantic love and sexual desire. *Current Directions in Psychological Science, 13*, 116–119.

Diamond, L. M. (2007). A dynamic systems approach to the development and expression of female same-sex sexuality. *Perspectives on Psychological Science, 2*, 142–161.

Diamond, M. (1996). Prenatal predisposition and the clinical management of some pediatric conditions. *Journal of Sex and Marital Therapy, 22*, 139–147.

Diamond, M. (1999). Pediatric management of ambiguous and traumatized genitalia. *Journal of Urology, 162*, 1021–1028.

Diamond, M., & Sigmundson, H. K. (1997). Sex reassignment at birth: Long-term review and clinical implications. *Archives of Pediatric and Adolescent Medicine, 151*, 298–304.

DiCenso, A., Gyatt, G., Willan, A., & Griffith, L. (2002). Interventions to reduce unintended pregnancies among adolescents: Systematic review of randomized controlled trials. *British Medical Journal, 324*, 1426.

Dickey, R. P. (2000). *Managing contraceptive pill patients* (10th ed.). Dallas, TX: EMIS.

Dickinson, R. L. (1949). *Atlas of human sex anatomy*. Baltimore: Williams & Wilkins.

Di Giulio, G. (2003). Sexuality and people living with physical or developmental disabilities: A review of key issues. *Canadian Journal of Human Sexuality, 12*, 53–68.

Di Giulio, G., & Reissing, E. D. (2006). Premenstrual dysphoric disorder: Prevalence, diagnostic considerations, and controversies. *Journal of Psychosomatic Obstetrics & Gynecology, 27*, 201–210.

Dieben, T., Roumen, F., & Apter, D. (2002). Efficacy, cycle control, and user acceptability of a novel combined contraceptive vaginal ring. *Obstetrics and Gynecology, 100*, 585–593.

Dill, K. E., et al. (2005). Violence, sex, race, and age in popular video games: A content analysis. In E. Cole & J. H. Daniel (Eds.), *Featuring females: Feminist analyses of media* (pp. 1115–130). Washington, DC: American Psychological Association.

Dindia, K., & Allen, M. (1992). Sex differences in self-disclosure: A meta-analysis. *Psychological Bulletin, 112*, 106–124.

Dindia, K., & Canary, D. (2006). *Sex differences and similarities in communication* (2nd ed.). Mahwah, NJ, US: Lawrence Erlbaum Associates Publishers.

Dion, K. K., & Dion, K. L. (1993b). Individualistic and collectivistic perspectives on gender and the cultural content of love and intimacy. *Journal of Social Issues, 49*, 53–69.

Dion, K. L. (1977). The incentive value of physical attractiveness for young children. *Personality and Social Psychology Bulletin, 3*, 67–70.

Dion, K. L., & Dion, K. K. (1993a). Gender and ethnocultural comparisons in styles of love. *Psychology of Women Quarterly, 17*, 463–474.

DND/CF Human Resources (1999). Harassment in the Canadian Forces: Results of the 1998 survey sponsor research report 99-11. Retrieved June 27, 2005, from www.forces.gc.ca.

Docter, R. F., & Prince, V. (1997). Transvestism: A survey of 1032 cross-dressers. *Archives of Sexual Behavior, 26*, 589–606.

Donahue, J. E., Stopa, E. G, & Chorsky, R. L. (2000). Cells containing immunoreactive estrogen receptor-a in the human basal forebrain. *Brain Research, 856*, 142–151.

Donnelly, D. A. (1993). Sexually inactive marriages. *Journal of Sex Research, 30*, 171–179.

Donnelly, D., Burgess, E., Anderson, S., Davis, R., & Dillard, J. (2001). Involuntary celibacy: A life course analysis. *Journal of Sex Research, 38*, 159–169.

Donnerstein, E., Linz, D., & Penrod, S. (1987). *The question of pornography: Research findings and policy implications*. New York: Free Press.

Doran, T. A. (1990). Chorionic villus sampling as the primary diagnostic tool in prenatal diagnosis. *Journal of Reproductive Medicine, 35*, 935–940.

Douglas, M. (1970). *Purity and danger: An analysis of concepts of pollution and taboo*. Baltimore: Penguin.

Downs, B. (2003). *Fertility of American women: June 2002. Current Population Reports* (P20-548). Washington, DC: U.S. Census Bureau.

Dreznick, M. T. (2003). Heterosocial competence of rapists and child molesters: A meta-analysis. *Journal of Sex Research, 40*, 170–178.

Driscoll, R., Davis, K. E., & Lipetz, M. E. (1972). Parental interference and romantic love: The Romeo and Juliet effect. *Journal of Personality and Social Psychology, 24*, 1–10.

Dryer, P. C., & Horowitz, L. (1997). When do opposites attract? Interpersonal complementarity vs. similarity. *Journal of Personality and Social Psychology, 72*, 592–603.

Duchesne, D. (1999). Street prostitution in Canada. In *The Juristat reader: A statistical overview of the Canadian justice system*. Toronto: Thomson Educational Publishing.

Duff, S. J., & Hampson, E. (2000). A beneficial effect of estrogen on working memory in postmenopausal women taking hormone replacement therapy. *Hormones and Behavior, 38*, 262–276.

Dunmore, E., Clark, D. M., & Ehlers, A. (2001). A prospective investigation of the role of cognitive factors in persistent Posttraumatic Stress Disorder (PTSD) after physical or sexual assault. *Behaviour Research and Therapy, 39*, 1063–1084.

Dunn, L., Ross, B., Caines, T., & Howorth, P. (1998). A school-based HIV/AIDS prevention education program: Outcomes of peer-led versus community health nurse-led interventions. *Canadian Journal of Human Sexuality, 7*, 339–345.

Dunn, M. E., & Trost, J. E. (1989). Male multiple orgasms: A descriptive study. *Archives of Sexual Behavior, 18*, 377–388.

Dunn, S., & Guilbert, E. (2003). Emergency contraception. *SOGC Clinical Practice Guidelines, 131*, 1–7.

Dupras, A. (2001). Sexology as innovation. *Scandinavian Journal of Sexology, 4*, 139–148.

Dutton, D. G., & Aron, A. P. (1974). Some evidence for heightened sexual attraction under conditions of high anxiety. *Journal of Personality and Social Psychology, 30*, 470–517.

Earls, C. M., & David, H. (1989). A psychosocial study of male prostitution. *Archives of Sexual Behavior, 18*, 401–420.

Earls, C. M., & Lalumière, M. L. (2002). A case study of preferential bestiality (zoophilia). *Sexual Abuse: A Journal of Research and Treatment, 14*, 83–88.

Ebel, C. (1994). *Managing herpes: How to live and love with a chronic STD*. Research Triangle Park, NC: American Social Health Association.

Edwards, W. M., & Coleman, E. (2004). Defining sexual health: A descriptive overview. *Archives of Sexual Behavior, 33*, 189–196.

Egan, J. (2000, December 10). Lonely gay teen seeking same. *The New York Times Magazine*, p. 110.

Ehrhardt, A. A., Yingling, S., & Warne, P. A. (1991). Sexual behavior in the era of AIDS: What has changed in the United States? *Annual Review of Sex Research, 2*, 25–48.

Eisenberg, M. E., Wagenaar, A., Neumark-Sztainer, D. (1997). Viewpoints of Minnesota students on school-based sexuality education. *Journal of School Health, 67*, 322–326.

EKOS Research Associates Inc. (2003). HIV/AIDS—An attitudinal survey: Final Report. Ottawa: Health Canada.

Elder, G. (1969). Appearance and education in marriage mobility. *American Sociological Review, 34*, 519–533.

Elias, J., & Gebhard, P. (1969). Sexuality and sexual learning in childhood. *Phi Delta Kappan, 50*, 401–405.

Elias, M. (1997, August 14). Modern matchmaking. *USA Today*, D1–D2.

Elliott, A. N., & O'Donohue, W. T. (1997). The effects of anxiety and distraction on sexual arousal in a nonclinical sample of heterosexual women. *Archives of Sexual Behavior, 26*, 607–624.

Ellis, H. H. (1939). *My life*. Boston: Houghton Mifflin.

Ellis, L. (1996). The role of perinatal factors in determining sexual orientation. In R. C. Savin-Williams & K. M. Cohen (Eds.), *The lives of lesbians, gays, and bisexuals* (pp. 35–70). Fort Worth, TX: Harcourt Brace.

Ellis, L., & Cole-Harding, S. (2001). The effects of prenatal stress, and of prenatal alcohol and nicotine exposure, on human sexual orientation. *Physiology & Behavior, 74*, 213–226.

Emmers-Sommer, T., Allen, M., Bourhis, J., Sahlstein, E., Laskowski, K., Falato, W., et al. (2004). A meta-analysis of the relationship between social skills and sexual offenders. *Communication Reports, 17,* 1–10.

Engler, K., Otis, J., Alary, M., et al. (2005). An exploration of sexual behaviour and self-definition in a cohort of men who have sex with men. *The Canadian Journal of Human Sexuality, 14,* 87–104.

Epting, L. K. & Overman, W. H. (1998). Sex-sensitive tasks in men and women: A search for performance fluctuations across the menstrual cycle. *Behavioral Neuroscience, 112,* 1304–1317.

Erikson, E. H. (1950). *Childhood and society.* New York: Norton.

Ernulf, K. E., & Innala, S. M. (1995). Sexual bondage: A review and ubobtrusive investigation. *Archives of Sexual Behavior, 24,* 631–654.

Eskenazi, B., Wyrobek, A. J., Sloter, E., Kidd, S. A., Moore, L., Young, S., Moore, D. (2003). The association of age and semen quality in healthy men. *Human Reproduction, 18,* 447–454.

Espin, O. (1987). Issues of identity in the psychology of Latina lesbians. In Boston Lesbian Psychologies Collective, *Lesbian psychologies.* Urbana, IL: University of Illinois Press.

Esposito, K., et al. (2004). Effect of lifestyle changes on erectile dysfunction in obese men: A randomized controlled trial. *Journal of the American Medical Association, 291,* 2978–2984.

Esterberg, K. G. (1996). Gay cultures, gay communities: The social organization of lesbians, gay men, and bisexuals. In R. C. Savin-Williams & K. M. Cohen (Eds.), *The lives of lesbians, gays, and bisexuals* (pp. 377–392). Fort Worth, TX: Harcourt Brace.

Everett, G. M. (1975). Amyl nitrate ("poppers") as an aphrodisiac. In M. Sandler and G. L. Gessa (Eds.), *Sexual behavior: Pharmacology and biochemistry.* New York: Raven.

Everitt, B. J., & Bancroft, J. (1991). Of rats and men: The comparative approach to male sexuality. *Annual Review of Sex Research, 2,* 77–118.

Exton, M. S., Bindert, A., Kruger, T., Scheller, F., Hartmann, U., & Schedlowski, M. (1999). Cardiovascular and endocrine alterations after masturbation-induced orgasm in women. *Psychosomatic Medicine, 61,* 280–289.

Eyler, A. E., & Wright, K. (1997, July–September). Gender identification and sexual orientation among genetic females with gender-blended self-perception in childhood and adolescence [Electronic version]. *The International Journal of Transgenderism, 1.* Retrieved May 20, 2001, from www.symposium.com.

Ezzell, C. (1996, May). Gene-therapy trial using BRCA1 to begin with ovarian cancer. *Journal of NIH Research, 8,* 24–25.

Fanburg, J. T., Kaplan, D., & Naylor, K. (1995). Student opinion of condom distribution at a Denver, Colorado high school. *Journal of School Health, 65,* 181–185.

Farkas, G. M., Sine, L. G., & Evans, I. M. (1978). Personality, sexuality, and demographic differences between volunteers and nonvolunteers for a laboratory study of male sexual behavior. *Archives of Sexual Behavior, 7,* 513–520.

Farley, M. A. (1994). Sexual ethics. In J. B. Nelson & S. P. Longfellow (Eds.), *Sexuality and the sacred* (pp. 54–67). Louisville, KY: Westminster/John Knox Press.

Farvid, P. & Braun, V. (2006). "Most of us guys are raring to go anytime, anyplace, anywhere": Male and female sexuality in Cleo and Cosmo. *Sex Roles, 55,* 295–310.

Fasteau, M. F. (1974). *The male machine.* New York: McGraw-Hill.

Fazekas, A., Senn, C. Y., & Ledgerwood, D. M. (2001). Predictors of intention to use condoms among university women: An application and extension of the theory of planned behaviour. *Canadian Journal of Behavioural Science, 33,* 103–117.

Feder, H. H. (1984). Hormones and sexual behavior. *Annual Review of Psychology, 35,* 165–200.

Federman, D. D. (2006). The biology of human sex differences. *New England Journal of Medicine, 354,* 1507–1514.

Federoff, J. P. (1995). Antiandrogens vs. serotonergic medications in the treatment of sex offenders: A preliminary compliance study. *Canadian Journal of Human Sexuality, 4,* 111–122.

Federoff, P. (2007, October). *The long and winding road: How the concept of "lovemap" has changed.* Paper presented at the meeting of the Canadian Sex Research Forum, Banff, AB.

Federoff, J. P., & Moran, B. (1997). Myths and misconceptions about sex offenders. *Canadian Journal of Human Sexuality, 6,* 263–276.

Feingold, A. (1988). Matching for attractiveness in romantic partners and same-sex friends: A meta-analysis and theoretical critique. *Psychological Bulletin, 104,* 226–235.

Feingold, A. (1990). Gender differences in effects of physical attractiveness on romantic attraction. *Journal of Personality and Social Psychology, 59,* 981–993.

Feldman-Summers, S., & Pope, K. S. (1994). The experience of "forgetting" childhood abuse: A national survey of psychologists. *Journal of Consulting and Clinical Psychology, 62,* 636–639.

Felton, G., & Segelman, F. (1978). Lamaze childbirth training and changes in belief about person control. *Birth and the Family Journal, 5,* 141–150.

Fenaughty, J., & Harré, N. (2003). Life on the seesaw: A qualitative study of suicide resiliency factors for young gay men. *Journal of Homosexuality, 45,* 1–22.

Field, D., & Rabinovitch, J. (Eds.) (2003). *Stories from the margins: Writing by sex trade workers past and present.* Retrieved from www.peers.bc.ca/images/StoriesBookletWeb.pdf.

Fields, R. D. (2007). Sex and the secret nerve. *Scientific American Mind, 18,* 20–27.

Figueira, I., Possidente, E., Marques, C., & Hayes, K. (2001). Sexual dysfunction: A neglected complication of panic disorder and social phobia. *Archives of Sexual Behavior, 30,* 369–377.

Filipp, D., et al. (2001). Soluble CD14 enriched in colostrums and milk induces B cell growth and differentiation. *Proceedings of the National Academy of Sciences, 98,* 603–608.

Finkelhor, D., & Daro, D. (1997). Prevention of child sexual abuse. In M. E. Helfer & R. S. Kempe (Eds.), *The battered child* (5th ed., pp. 615–626). Chicago: University of Chicago Press.

Finkelhor, D., & Russell, D. (1984). Women as perpetrators: Review of the evidence. In D. Finkelhor (Ed.), *Child sexual abuse: New theory and research.* New York: The Free Press.

Finkelhor, D., Mitchell, K., & Wolak, J. (2000). *Online victimization: A report on the nation's youth.* Washington, DC: National Center for Missing & Exploited Children.

Finzi, Diana, et al. (1997). Identification of a reservoir for HIV-1 in patients on highly active antiretroviral therapy. *Science, 278,* 1295–1300.

Firestone, P., Bradford, J. M., McCoy, M., Greenberg, D. M., Curry, S., & Larose, M. R. (2000). Prediction of recidivism in extrafamilial child molesters based on court-related assessments. *Sexual Abuse: A Journal of Research and Treatment, 12,* 203–221.

Firestone, P., Bradford, J. M., McCoy, M., Greenberg, D. M, Larose, M. R., & Curry, S. (1999). Prediction of recidivism in incest offenders. *Journal of Interpersonal Violence, 14,* 511–532.

Firestone, P., Nunes, K. L., Moulden, H., Broom, I., & Bradford, J. M. (2005). Hostility and recidivism in sexual offenders. *Archives of Sexual Behavior, 34,* 277–283.

Fischtein, D. S., Herold, E. S., & Desmarais, S. (2005). Canadian attitudes toward female topless behaviour: A national survey. *The Canadian Journal of Human Sexuality, 14,* 63–75.

Fischtein, D. S., Herold, E. S., & Desmarais, S. (2007). How much does gender explain in sexual attitudes and behaviors? A survey of Canadian adults. *Archives of Sexual Behaviors, 36,* 451–461.

Fisher, D., Hill, D., Grube, J., & Grube, E. (2004). *Youth and television: Examining sexual content across program genres.* Presented at Society for Research on Adolescence, Baltimore, MD, March 2004.

Fisher, H. (1992). *Anatomy of love: The mysteries of mating, marriage and why we stray.* New York: Ballantine Books.

Fisher, H., Aron, A. & Brown, L.. (2006). Romantic love: A mammalian brain system for mate choice. *Philosophical Transactions of the Royal Society, B, 361,* 2173–2186.

Fisher, W. A., & Barak, A. (2000). Online sex shops: Phenomenological, psychological, and ideological perspectives on Internet sexuality. *Cyberpsychology & Behavior, 3,* 575–589.

Fisher, W. A., & Boroditsky, R. (2000). Sexual activity, contraceptive choice, and sexual and reproductive health indicators among single Canadian women aged 15–29: Additional findings from the Canadian contraception study. *The Canadian Journal of Human Sexuality, 9,* 79–93.

Fisher, W. A., Boroditsky, R., & Bridges, M. L. (1999). Familiarity with opinions about and use of contraceptive methods among Canadian women. *Canadian Journal of Human Sexuality, 18,* 167–174.

Fisher, W. A., Boroditsky, R., & Bridges, M. L. (1999). The 1998 contraception study. *Canadian Journal of Human Sexuality, 8,* 161–216.

Fisher, W. A., Byrne, D., & White, L. A. (1983). Emotional barriers to contraception. In D. Byrne and W. A. Fisher (Eds.), *Adolescents, sex, and contraception.* Hillsdale, NJ: Lawrence Erlbaum.

Fisher, W. A., Byrne, D., White, L. A., & Kelley, K. (1988). Erotophobia-erotophilia as a dimension of personality. *Journal of Sex Research, 25,* 123–151.

Fisher, W. A., Sukhbir, S. S., Shuper, P. A., Carey, M., Otchet, F., MacLean-Brine, D., Dal Bello, D., & Gunter, J. (2005). Characteristics of women undergoing repeat induced abortion. *Canadian Medical Association Journal, 172,* 637–641.

Fisher, W., Boroditsky, R., & Morris, B. (2004a). The 2002 Canadian contraception study: Part 1. *Journal of Obstetrics and Gynaecology Canada, 26,* 580–590.

Fisher, W., Boroditsky, R., & Morris, B. (2004b). The 2002 Canadian contraception study: Part 2. *Journal of Obstetrics and Gynaecology Canada, 26,* 646–656.

Fisher, W. A., & Fisher, J. D. (1992). Understanding and promoting AIDS preventive behaviour: A conceptual model of educational tools. *Canadian Journal of Human Sexuality, 1,* 99–106.

Fisher, W. A., & Fisher, J. D. (1998). Understanding and promoting sexual and reproductive health behaviour: Theory and method. *Annual Review of Sex Research, 9,* 39–76.

Fisher, W. A., & Grenier, G. (1994). Violent pornography, antiwoman thoughts, and antiwoman acts: In search of reliable effects. *Journal of Sex Research, 31,* 23–38.

Fiske, S. T., & Glick, P. (1995). Ambivalence and stereotypes cause sexual harassment: A theory with implications for organizational change. *Journal of Social Issues, 51*(1), 97–115.

Fitch, R. H., & Bimonte, H. A. (2002). Hormones, brain, and behavior: Putative biological contributions to cognitive sex differences. In A. McGillicuddy-DeLisi & R. DeLisi (Eds.), *Biology, society, and behavior: The development of sex differences in cognition* (pp. 55–92). Westport, CT: Ablex.

Fitzgerald, L. F. (1993). Sexual harassment. *American Psychologist, 48,* 1070–1076.

Flaxman, S. M., & Sherman, P. W. (2000). Morning sickness: A mechanism for protecting mother and embryo. *Quarterly Review of Biology, 75,* 113–148.

Fleming, A., Ruble, D., Krieger, H., & Wong, P. Y. (1997). Hormonal and experiential correlates of internal responsiveness during pregnancy and the puerperium in human mothers. *Hormones and Behavior, 31,* 145–158.

Fleming, J., Mullen, P., Sibthorpe, B., & Bammer, G. (1999). The long-term impact of childhood sexual abuse in Australian women. *Child Abuse & Neglect, 23,* 145–159.

Fleming, M., Steinman, C., & Boeknok, G. (1980). Methodological problems in assessing sex reassignment surgery: A reply to Meyer and Reter. *Archives of Sexual Behavior, 9,* 451–456.

Foa, E. B., Steketee, G., & Olasov, B. (1989). Behavioral/cognitive conceptualization of post-traumatic stress disorder. *Behavior Therapy, 20,* 155–176.

Forbes. (2001, May 25). How big is porn?

Ford, J. G. (2001). Healing homosexuals: A psychologist's journey through the ex-gay movement and the pseudo-science of reparative therapy. In A. Shidlo, M. Schroeder, & J. Drescher (Eds.), *Sexual conversion therapy: Ethical, clinical, and research perspectives* (pp. 69–86). New York: Haworth.

Ford, K., & Norris, A. (1991). Methodological considerations for survey research on sexual behavior: Urban African American and Hispanic youth. *Journal of Sex Research, 28,* 539–555.

Ford, N., & Koetsawang, S. (1991). The socio-cultural context of the transmission of HIV in Thailand. *Social Science and Medicine, 33,* 405–414.

Fortenberry, J. D. (2002). Clinic-based service programs for increasing responsible sexual behavior. *Journal of Sex Research, 39,* 63–66.

Foster, C. A., Witcher, B. S., Campbell, W. K., & Green, J. D. (1998). Arousal and attraction: Evidence for automatic and controlled processes. *Journal of Personality and Social Psychology, 74,* 86–101.

Fox, D. (2002). Gentle persuasion. *New Scientist, 173,* 32.

Fox, R. C. (1995). Bisexual identities. In A. R. D'Augelli & C. J. Patterson (Eds.), *Lesbian, gay, and bisexual identities over the lifespan.* New York: Oxford University Press.

Frank, K. (2003). "Just trying to relax": Masculinity, masculinizing practices, and strip club regulars. *Journal of Sex Research, 40,* 61–75.

Frank, K. (2005). Exploring the motivations and fantasies of strip club customers in relation to legal regulations. *Archives of Sexual Behavior, 34,* 487–504.

Frank, L. K. (1961). *The conduct of sex.* New York: Morrow.

Fraser, P., et al. (1985). *Pornography and prostitution in Canada: Report of the Special Committee on Pornography and Prostitution.* Ottawa: Minister of Supply and Services Canada.

Frayser, S. (2004). Personal communication.

Frayser, S. G. (1985). *Varieties of sexual experience: An anthropological perspective on human sexuality.* New Haven, CT: Human Relations Area Files Press.

Frayser, S. G. (1994). Defining normal childhood sexuality: An anthropological approach. *Annual Review of Sex Research, 5,* 173–217.

Frazier, P., Tashiro, T., Berman, M., Steger, M., & Long, J. (2004). Correlates of levels and patterns of positive life changes following sexual assault. *Journal of Consulting and Clinical Psychology, 72,* 19–30.

Freese, J., & Meland, S. (2002). Seven tenths incorrect: Heterogeneity and change in the waist-to-hip ratios of Playboy centerfold models and Miss America pageant winners. *Journal of Sex Research, 39,* 133–138.

Fried, P. A. (2002). Conceptual issues in behavioral teratology and their application in determining long-term sequelae of prenatal marihuana exposure. *Journal of Child Psychology and Psychiatry, 43,* 81–102.

Fried, P. A., & Smith, A. M. (2001). A literature review of the consequences of prenatal marihuana exposure: An emerging theme of a deficiency in aspects of executive function. *Neurotoxicology and Teratology, 23,* 1–11.

Friedrich, W. N., Fisher, J., Broughton, D., Houston, M., & Shafran, M. (1998). Normative sexual behavior in children: A contemporary sample. *Pediatrics, 101,* 9.

Freud, S. (1924). A general introduction to psychoanalysis. New York: Permabooks, 1953. (Boni & Liveright edition, 1924).

Freud, S. (1948). The psychogenesis of a case of homosexuality in a woman (1920). In *The collected papers* (Vol. II, pp. 202–231). London: Hogarth.

Freund, M., Lee, N., & Leonard, T. (1991). Sexual behavior of clients with street prostitutes in Camden, NJ. *Journal of Sex Research, 28,* 579–591.

Freyd, J. J. (1996). *Betrayal trauma theory.* Cambridge, MA: Harvard University Press.

Freyd, J. J., et al. (2005). The science of child sexual abuse. *Science, 308,* 501.

Friedrich, W. N., Beilke, R. L., & Urquiza, A. J. (1988). Behavior problems in young sexually abused boys. *Journal of Interpersonal Violence, 3,* 1–12.

Frisch, R. E., & McArthur, J. W. (1974). Menstrual cycles: Fatness as a determinant of minimum weight for height necessary for their maintenance or onset. *Science, 185,* 949–951.

Friscolanti, M. (2008, Jan. 14). A national embarrassment. *Maclean's.*

Frohlich, P., & Meston, C. (2002). Sexual functioning and self-reported depressive symptoms among college women. *Journal of Sex Research, 39,* 321–325.

Fromm, E. (1956). *The art of loving.* New York: Harper & Row.

Fuleihan, G. (1997). Tissue-specific estrogens–The promise for the future. *New England Journal of Medicine, 337,* 1686–1687.

Furmanan, W. (2002). The emerging field of adolescent romantic relationships. *Current Directions in Psychological Science, 11,* 177–180.

Furnish, V. P. (1994). The Bible and homosexuality: Reading the texts in context. In J. S. Siker (Ed.), *Homosexuality in the church* (pp. 18–35). Louisville, KY: Westminster/John Knox Press.

Furstenberg, F. F., Brooks-Gunn, J., & Morgan, S. P. (1987). *Adolescent mothers in later life.* New York: Cambridge University Press.

Gabelnick, H. L. (1998). Future methods. In R. Hatcher et al. (Eds.), *Contraceptive technology* (17th ed. pp. 615–622). New York: Ardent Media.

Gagnon, J. H. (1977). *Human sexualities.* Glenview, IL: Scott, Foresman.

Gagnon, J. H. (1990). The explicit and implicit use of the scripting perspective in sex research. *Annual Review of Sex Research, 1,* 1–44.

Gagnon, J. H., & Simon, W. (1973). *Sexual conduct: The social origins of human sexuality.* Chicago: Aldine.

Gagnon, M. D., Husen, M., Kabacoff, R. I., & Van Hasselt, V. B. (1999). Interpersonal and psychological correlates of marital dissatisfaction in late life: A review. *Clinical Psychology Review, 19*(3), 359–378.

Galbreath, N., Berlin, F., & Sawyer, D. (2002). Paraphilias and the Internet. In A. Cooper (Ed.), *Sex and the Internet: A guidebook for clinicians* (pp. 187–205). New York: Brunner-Routledge.

Gallant, S. J, Popiel, D. A., Hoffman, D. M., Chakraborty, P. K., & Hamilton, J. A. (1992). Using daily ratings to confirm premenstrual syndrome/late luteal phase dysphoric disorder: What makes a real difference? *Psychosomatic Medicine, 54,* 167–181.

Galvani, A. & Slatkin, M. (2003). Evaluating plague and smallpox as historical selective pressures for the CCR5-Delta 32 HIV-resistance allele. *Proceedings of the National Academy of Sciences, 100,* 15276–15279.

Gangestad, S. W., & Buss, D. M. (1993). Pathogen prevalence and human mate preferences. *Ethology and Sociobiology, 14,* 89–96.

Gangestad, S. W., & Thornhill, R. (1997). Human sexual selection and developmental stability. In J. A. Simpson & D. T. Kenrick (Eds.), *Evolutionary social psychology* (pp. 169–195). Mahwah, NJ: Lawrence Erlbaum Associates.

Gannon, M., & Mihorean, K. (2005). Criminal victimization in Canada, 2004. *Juristat: Canadian Centre for Justice Statistics, 25.* Statistics Canada catalogue no. 85-002-XPE.

Ganz, T. (2002). Versatile defensins. *Science, 298,* 977–979.

Garcia-Velasco, J., & Mondragon, M. (1991). The incidence of the vomeronasal organ in 1000 human subjects and its possible clinical significance. *Journal of Steroid Biochemistry and Molecular Biology, 39,* 561–563.

Garnets, L. D. & Peplau, L. A. (2001). A new paradigm for women's sexual orientation: Implications for therapy. In Ellyn Kaschak & Leonore Tiefer (Eds.), *A new view of women's sexual problems.* New York: Haworth.

Garriguet, D. (2005). Early sexual intercourse. *Health Reports* (Statistics Canada, Catalogue 82-003), *16,* 9–18.

Garver-Apgar, C., Gangestad, S., Thornhill, R., Miller, R., & Olp, J. (2006). Major histocompatibility complex alleles, sexual responsivity, and unfaithfulness in romantic couples. *Psychological Science, 17,* 830–835.

Gay, P. (1984). *The bourgeois experience: Victoria to Freud.* New York: Oxford University Press.

Gebhard, P. H. (1976). The Institute. In M. S. Weinberg (Ed.), *Sex research: Studies from the Kinsey Institute.* New York: Oxford University Press.

Gebhard, P. H., Gagnon, J. H., Pomeroy, W. B., & Christenson, C. V. (1965). *Sex offenders: An analysis of types.* New York: Harper & Row.

Gemme, R. (1990). Sexology in Quebec. *SIECCAN Journal, 5*(1), 3–10.

Gemme, R. (1998). Legal and sexological aspects of adult street prostitution: A case for sexual pluralism. In James Elias, Vern J. Bullough, Veronica Elias, & Gwen Brewer (Eds.), *Prostitution: On whores, hustlers & johns.* Amherst, NY: Prometheus Books.

Gemme, R., & Payment, N. (1993). Evaluation de la repression de la prostitution de rue à Montréal de 1970 à 1991. *Revue Sexologique, 1*(2), 161–192.

Gender Identity Research and Education Society (GIRES). (2006). Atypical gender development: A review. *International Journal of Transgenderism, 9,* 29–43.

Genel, M. (2000). Gender verification no more? *Medscape Women's Health, 5*(3).

Genovesi, V. J. (1987). *In pursuit of love: Catholic morality and human sexuality.* Wilmington, DE: Michael Glazier.

Gentile, D. A., et al. (2004). The effects of violent video game habits on adolescent attitudes and behaviors. *Journal of Adolescence, 27,* 5–22.

George, W. H., & Stoner, S. A. (2000). Understanding acute alcohol effects on sexual behavior. *Annual Review of Sex Research, 11,* 92–124.

George, W. H., et al. (2006). Postdrinking sexual perceptions and behaviors toward another person: Alcohol expectancy set and gender differences. *Journal of Sex Research, 43,* 282–291.

Georges, E. (1996). Abortion policy and practice in Greece. *Social Science & Medicine, 42,* 509–519.

Gerbner, G., Gross, L., & Morgan, M. (2002). Growing up with television: Cultivation processes. In J. Bryant & D. Zillman (Eds.), *Media effects: Advances in theory and research.* (2nd ed., pp. 43–67). Mahwah, NJ: Erlbaum.

Gilbert, L. (2000, August). Cosmo's hugest sex survey ever. *Cosmopolitan, 186*–189.

Gilligan, C. (1982). *In a different voice: Psychological theory and women's development.* Cambridge, MA: Harvard University Press.

Gilmartin, B. G. (1975). The swinging couple down the block. *Psychology Today, 8*(9), 54.

Girard, A. L., & Senn, C. Y. (2008). The role of the new "date rape drugs" in attributions about date rape. *Journal of Interpersonal Violence, 23,* 3–20.

Giuliano, F., Chevret-Measson, M., Tsatsaris, A., Reitz, C., Murino, M., & Thonneau, P. (2002). Prevalence of erectile dysfunction in France: Results of an epidemiological survey of a representative sample of 1004 men. *European Urology, 42,* 382–389.

Giuliano, F. & Clement, P. (2005). Neuroanatomy and physiology of ejaculation. *Annual Review of Sex Research, 15,* 190–216.

Gjerdingen, D. (2003). The effectiveness of various postpartum depression treatments and the impact of antidepressant drugs on nursing infants. *Journal of the American Board of Family Practice 16,* 372–382.

Glascock, J., & LaRose, R. (1993). Dial-a-porn recordings: The role of the female participant in male sexual fantasies. *Journal of Broadcasting & Electronic Media,* 313–324.

Glass, S. J., & Johnson, R. W. (1944). Limitations and complications of organotherapy in male homosexuality. *Journal of Clinical Endocrinology, 4,* 540–544.

Gold, E. R. (1986). Long-term effects of sexual victimization in childhood: An attributional approach. *Journal of Consulting and Clinical Psychology, 54*(4), 471–475.

Gold, S. D., Marx, B. P., & Lexington, J. M. (2007). Gay male sexual assault survivors: The relations among internalized homophobia, experiential avoidance, and psychological symptom severity. *Behaviour Research and Therapy, 45,* 549–562.

Gold, S. N., Hughes, D., & Hohnecker, L. (1994). Degrees of repression of sexual abuse memories. *American Psychologist, 49,* 441–442.

Goldberg, M. (1987). Understanding hypersexuality in men and women. In G. R. Weeks & L. Hof (Eds.), *Integrating sex and marital therapy.* New York: Brunner-Mazel.

Goldberg, S. (1983). Parent-infant bonding: Another look. *Child Development, 54,* 1355–1382.

Goldfoot, D. A., Westerberg-van Loon, W., Groeneveld, W., & Koos Slob, A. (1980). Behavioral and physiological evidence of sexual climax in the female stump-tailed macaque (Macaca arctoides). *Science, 208,* 1477–1478.

Goldstein, J. M, Seidman, L. J., Horton, N. J., Makris, N., Kennedy, D. N., Caviness, V., et al. (2001). Normal sexual dimorphism of the adult human brain assessed by in vivo magnetic resonance imaging. *Cerebral Cortex, 11,* 490–497.

Golombok, S., Perry, B., Burston, A., Murray, C., Mooney-Somers, J., Stevens, M., et al. (2003). Children with lesbian parents: A community study. *Developmental Psychology, 39,* 20–33.

Golub, S. (1992). *Periods: From menarche to menopause.* Newbury Park, CA: Sage.

Gonsiorek, J. C. (1996). Mental health and sexual orientation. In R. C. Savin-Williams & K. M. Cohen (Eds.), *The lives of lesbians, gays, and bisexuals* (pp. 462–478). Fort Worth, TX: Harcourt Brace.

Gonzaga, G., Turner, R., Keltner, D., Campos, B., & Altemus, M. (2006). Romantic love and sexual desire in close relationships. *Emotion, 6,* 163–179.

Gonzalez, F., & Espin, O. (1996). Latino men, Latina women, and homosexuality. In R. Cabaj & T. Stein (Eds.), *Textbook of homosexuality and mental health* (pp. 583–601). Washington, DC: American Psychiatric Association.

Gooren, L., Fliers, E., & Courtney, K. (1990). Biological determinants of sexual behavior. *Annual Review of Sex Research, 1,* 175–196.

Gordon, B., & Schroeder, C. (1995). *Sexuality: A developmental approach to problems.* New York: Plenum Press.

Gorzalka, B. B., & Hill, M. N. (2006). Cannabinoids, reproduction, and sexual behavior. *Annual Review of Sex Research, 17,* 132–161.

Gosling, S. D., Vazire, S., Srivastava, S., & John, O. P. (2004). Should we trust web-based studies? A comparative analysis of six preconceptions about internet questionnaires. *American Psychologist, 59,* 93–104.

Gosselin, C., & Wilson, G. (1980). *Sexual variations: Fetishism, sadomasochism, transvestism.* New York: Simon & Schuster.

Gottlieb, L. (2006, March). How do I love thee? *The Atlantic Monthly,* 58–70.

Gottman, J., Conn, J., Carrere, S., & Swanson, C. (1998). Predicting marital happiness and stability from newlywed interactions. *Journal of Marriage and the Family, 60,* 5–22.

Gottman, J., Markman, H., & Notarius, C. (1977). The topography of marital conflict: A sequential analysis of verbal and nonverbal behavior. *Journal of Marriage and the Family, 39,* 461–478.

Gottman, J., Notarius, C., Gonso, J., & Markman, H. (1976). *A couple's guide to communication.* Champaign, IL: Research Press.

Gottman, J. M. (1994). *Why marriages succeed or fail.* New York: Simon & Schuster.

Gottman, J. M., & Notarius, C. I. (2002). Marital research in the 20th century and a research agenda for the 21st century. *Family Process, 41,* 159–197.

Gottman, J. M., & Porterfield, A. L. (1981). Communicative competence in the nonverbal behavior of married couples. *Journal of Marriage and the Family, 43,* 817–824.

Gould, S. J. (1987). *An urchin in the storm.* New York: Norton.

Gouliquer, L. (2000). Negotiation sexuality: Lesbians in the Canadian military. In B. Miedema, Janet Stoppard, & V. Anderson (Eds.). Toronto: Second Story Press.

Gower, D. B., & Ruparelia, B. A. (1993). Olfaction in humans with special reference to odorous 16-androstenes: Their occurrence, perception and possible social, psychological and sexual impact. *Journal of Endocrinology, 137,* 167–187.

Grace, A. P., & Wells, K. (2001). Getting an education in Edmonton, Alberta: The case of queer youth. *Journal of the Canadian Lesbian and Gay Studies Association, 3,* 137–151.

Grace, A. P., & Wells, K. (2005). The Marc Hall prom predicament: Queer individual rights v. institutional church rights in Canadian public education. *Canadian Journal of Education, 28,* 237–270.

Grace, A. P., & Wells, K. (2006). The quest for a queer inclusive cultural ethics: Setting directions for teachers' preservice and continuing professional development. *New Directions for Adult and Continuing Education, 112,* 51–61.

Grace, A. P., & Wells, K. (2007). Gay and bisexual male youth as educator activists and cultural workers: The queer critical praxis of three Canadian high-school students. *International Journal of Inclusive Education,* 1–22.

Graham, C. A., et al. (1995). The effects of steroidal contraceptives on the well-being and sexuality of women. *Contraception, 52,* 363–369.

Graham, C. A., Sanders, S. A., Milhausen, R. R., & McBride, K. R. (2004). Turning on and turning off: A focus group study of the factors that affect women's sexual arousal. *Archives of Sexual Behavior, 33,* 527–538.

Grammick, J. (1986). The Vatican's battered wives. *Christian Century, 103,* 17–20.

Grau, I., & Kimpf, M. (1993). Love, sexuality, and satisfaction: Interventions of men and women. *Zeitschrift fur Sozial Psychologie, 24,* 83–93.

Gray, N. S., et al. (2005). An implicit test of the associations between children and sex in pedophiles. *Journal of Abnormal Psychology, 114,* 304–308.

Greeley, A. (1994). Review of the Janus Report on Sexual Behavior. *Contemporary Sociology, 23,* 221–223.

Green, L. L., Fullilove, M. T., & Fullilove, R. E. (2005). Remembering the lizard: Reconstructing sexuality in the rooms of Narcotics Anonymous. *Journal of Sex Research, 42,* 28–34.

Green, R. (1975). Adults who want to change sex; adolescents who cross-dress; and children called "sissy" and "tomboy." In R. Green (Ed.), *Human sexuality: A health practitioner's text.* Baltimore, MD: Williams & Wilkins.

Green, R. (1987). *The Sissy Boy Syndrome and the development of homosexuality.* New Haven: Yale University Press.

Green, R., & Fleming, D. T. (1990). Transsexual surgery follow-up: Status in the 1990s. *Annual Review of Sex Research, 1,* 163–174.

Green, R. M. (1984). Genetic medicine in Jewish legal perspective. *The Annual of the Society of Christian Ethics,* 249–272.

Greenberg, B. S., & Busselle, R. (1996). What's old, what's new: Sexuality on the soaps. *SIECUS Report, 24*(5), 14–16.

Greenberg, D. M., Bradford, J., Firestone, P., & Curry, S. (2000). Relationships of child molesters: A study of victim relationship with the perpetrator. *Child Abuse and Neglect, 24,* 1485–1494.

Greenberg, S., Rabinowitz, R., Firestone, P., Bradford, J. M., & Greenberg, D. M. (2002). Prediction of recidivism in exhibitionists: Psychological, phallometric, and offence factors. *Sexual Abuse: A Journal of Research and Treatment* (pp. 329–347).

Greenspan, E. L., & Rosenberg, M. (2005). *Martin's annual criminal code 2005.* Aurora, ON: Canada Law Book Inc.

Gregersen, E. (1996). *The world of human sexuality: Behaviors, customs, and beliefs.* New York: Irvington.

Gregor, T. (1985). *Anxious pleasures: The sexual lives of an Amazonian people.* Chicago: University of Chicago Press.

Gregorian, R. S., Golden, K. A., Bahce, A., Goodman, C., Kwong, W. J., & Khan, Z. M. (2002). Antidepressant-induced sexual dysfunction. *The Annals of Pharmacotherapy, 36,* 1577–1589.

Grello, C. M., Welsh, D., & Harper, M. (2006). No strings attached: The nature of casual sex in college students. *Journal of Sex Research, 43,* 255–267.

Grenier, G., & Byers, E. S. (1995). Rapid ejaculation: A review of conceptual, etiological, and treatment issues. *Archives of Sexual Behavior, 24,* 447–474.

Grenier, G., & Byers, E. S. (1997). The relationships among ejaculatory control, ejaculatory latency, and attempts to prolong heterosexual intercourse. *Archives of Sexual Behavior, 26,* 27–48.

Grenier, G., & Byers, E. S. (2001). Operationalizing premature or rapid ejaculation. *The Journal of Sex Research, 38,* 369–378.

Griffin, K. (1995, Aug. 1). One-third of homosexuals face threats of violence, study finds. *Vancouver Sun:* Final Edition.

Griffin, S. (1981). *Pornography and silence.* New York: Harper & Row.

Griffith, M. (2000). Excessive Internet use: Implications for sexual behavior. *CyberPsychology and Behavior, 3,* 537–552.

Griffith, M. (2001). Sex on the Internet: Observations and implications for Internet sex addiction. *The Journal of Sex Research, 38,* 333–342.

Grindstaff, C. (1988). Adolescent marriage and childbearing: The long-term economic outcome, Canada in the 1980s. *Adolescence, 23,* 45–58.

Grodstein, F., et al. (1997). Postmenopausal hormone therapy and mortality. *New England Journal of Medicine, 336,* 1769–1775.

Gruenbaum, E. (2000). *The female circumcision controversy: An anthropological perspective.* Philadelphia: University of Pennsylvania Press.

Grumbach, M. M., & Styne, D. M. (1998). Puberty: Ontogeny, neuroendocrinology, physiology, and disorders. In J. D. Wilson et al. (Eds.), *Williams Textbook of Endocrinology* (9th ed., pp. 1509–1625). Philadelphia: Saunders.

Guay, J.-P., Proulx, J., Cusson, M., & Ouimet, M. (2001). Victim-choice polymorphia among serious sex offenders. *Archives of Sexual Behavior, 30,* 521–534.

Guay, S., Boisvert, J., & Freeston, M. H. (2003). Validity of three measures of communication for predicting relationship adjustment and stability among a sample of young couples. *Psychological Assessment, 15,* 392–398.

Guerrero, L., Spitzberg, B., & Yoshimura, S. (2004). Sexual and emotional jealousy. In J. H. Harvey, A. Wenzel, & S. Sprecher (Eds.), *The handbook of sexuality in close relationships* (pp. 311–345). Mahwah, NJ: Lawrence Erlbaum.

Guindon, A. (1977). *The sexual language: An essay in moral theology.* Ottawa: University of Ottawa Press.

Guindon, A. (1986). *The sexual creators: An ethical proposal for concerned Christians*. Lanham, MD: University Press of America.

Guise, J.-M., Palda, V., Westhoff, C., Chan, B. K. S., Helfand, K., & Lieu, T. A. (2003). The effectiveness of primary care-based interventions to promote breastfeeding: Systematic evidence review and meta-analysis for the US Preventive Services Task Force. *Annals of Family Medicine, 1*, 70–78.

Gunderson, B. H., et al. (1981). Sexual behavior of preschool children. In L. L. Constantine & F. M. Martinson (Eds.), *Children and sex* (pp. 45–62). Boston: Little, Brown.

Gunter, B. (2008). Internet dating: A British survey. *Aslib Proceedings: New Information Perspectives, 60*, 88–98.

Gursoy, A. (1996). Abortion in Turkey: A matter of state, family, or individual decision. *Social Science & Medicine, 42*, 531–542.

Gutek, B. A. (1985). *Sex and the workplace*. San Francisco: Jossey-Bass.

Haddock, Geoffrey, Zanna, Mark P., & Esses, Victoria M. (1993). Assessing the structure of prejudicial attitudes: The case of attitudes toward homosexuals. *Journal of Personality and Social Psychology, 65*, 1105–1118.

Hahn, S. R., & Paige, K. E. (1980). American birth practices: A critical review. In J. E. Parsons (Ed.), *The psychobiology of sex differences and sex roles*. New York: McGraw-Hill, Hemisphere.

Haig, D. (1996). Altercation of generations: Genetic conflicts of pregnancy. *American Journal of Reproductive Immunology, 35*, 226–232.

Halbreich, U. (1996). Reflections on the cause of premenstrual syndrome. *Psychiatric Annals, 26*, 581–585.

Haldeman, D. C. (1994). The practice and ethics of sexual orientation conversion therapy. *Journal of Consulting and Clinical Psychology, 62*, 221–227.

Haldeman, D. C. (2001). Therapeutic antidotes: Helping gay and bisexual men recover from conversion therapies. In A. Shidlo, M. Schroeder, & J. Drescher (Eds.), *Sexual conversion therapy: Ethical, clinical, and research perspectives* (pp. 117–130). New York: Haworth.

Hall, G. C. N., (1995). Sexual offender recidivism revisited: A meta-analysis of recent treatment studies. *Journal of Consulting and Clinical Psychology, 63*, 802–809.

Hall, G. C. N., & Barongan, C. (1997). Prevention of sexual aggression. *American Psychologist, 52*, 5–14.

Hall, G. C. N., et al. (2005). Ethnicity, culture, and sexual aggression: Risk and protective factors. *Journal of Consulting and Clinical Psychology, 73*, 830–840.

Hall, G. C. N., et al. (2006). Initiation, desistance, and persistence of men's sexual coercion. *Journal of Consulting and Clinical Psychology, 74*, 732–742.

Hall, J. A. (1998). How big are nonverbal sex differences? The case of smiling and sensitivity to nonverbal cues. In D. Canary & K. Dindia (Eds.), *Sex differences and similarities in communication* (pp. 155–178). Mahwah, NJ: Erlbaum.

Hamann, S., Herman, R. A., & Nolan, C. L. (2004). Men and women differ in amygdala response to visual sexual stimuli. *Nature Neuroscience, 7*, 411–416.

Hamer, D., Hu, S., Magnuson, V. L., Hu, N., & Pattatucci, A. M. L. (1993). A linkage between DNA markers on the X chromosome and male sexual orientation. *Science, 261*, 321–327.

Hamilton, M. C., et al. (2006). Gender stereotypes and under-representation of female characters in 200 popular children's picture books: A twenty-first century update. *Sex Roles, 55*, 757–766.

Hampson, E., & Moffat, S. D. (2004). The psychobiology of gender: Cognitive effects of reproductive hormones in the adult nervous system. In A. H. Eagly, A. E. Beall, & R. J. Sternberg (Eds.). *The psychology of gender* (2nd ed.), New York: Guilford Press.

Hampton, M. R., Jeffery, B., McWatters, B., & Smith, P. (2005). Influence of teens' perceptions of parental disapproval and peer behaviour on their initiation of sexual intercourse. *The Canadian Journal of Human Sexuality, 14*, 105–121.

Hampton, M. R., McWatters, B., & Jeffery, B. (2000). Method-related experiences of Canadian women using Depo-Provera for contraception. *The Canadian Journal of Human Sexuality, 9*, 247–257.

Handy, L. C., Valentich, M., Cammaert, L. P., & Gripton, J. (1985). Feminist issues in sex therapy. In M. Valentich & J. Gripton (Eds.), *Feminist perspectives on social work and human sexuality*. Hawthorne Press.

Hanson, R. K. (2000). Will they do it again? Predicting sex-offense recidivism. *Current Directions in Psychological Science, 9*, 106–109.

Hanson, R. K., & Bussière, M. T. (1998). Predicting relapse: A meta-analysis of sexual offender recidivism studies. *Journal of Consulting and Clinical Psychology, 66*, 348–362.

Hanson, R. K., Gordon, A., Harris, A. J. R., Marques, J. K., Murphy, W., Quinsey, V. L., & Seto, M. C. (2002). First report of the collaborative outcome data project on the effectiveness of psychological treatment for sex offenders. *Sexual Abuse: A Journal of Research and Treatment, 14*, 169–194.

Hardwick, D., & Patychuk, D. (1999). Geographic mapping demonstrates the association between social inequality, teen births and STDs among youth. *The Canadian Journal of Human Sexuality, 8*, 77–90.

Harlow, H. F., Harlow, M. K., & Hause, F. W. (1963). The maternal affectional system of rhesus monkeys. In H. L. Rheingold (Ed.), *Maternal behavior in mammals*. New York: Wiley.

Harper, C. C. et al.(2005). The effect of increased access to emergency contraception among young adolescents. *Obstetrics & Gynecology, 106*, 483–491.

Harris, C. (2002). Sexual and romantic jealousy in heterosexual and homosexual adults. *Psychological Science, 13*, 7–12.

Harris, G. (2004, February 28). Pfizer gives up testing Viagra on women. *New York Times*, pp. C1.

Harris, G. E., & Alderson, K. G. (2006). Gay men living with HIV/AIDS: The potential for empowerment. *Journal of HIV/AIDS & Social Services, 5*, 9–24.

Harris, G. W., & Levine, S. (1965). Sexual differentiation of the brain and its experimental control. *Journal of Physiology, 181*, 379–400.

Harris, N. S., Thompson, S. J., Ball, R., Hussey, J., & Sy, F. (2002). Zidovudine and perinatal Human Immunodeficiency Virus type 1 transmission: A population-based approach. *Pediatrics, 109*, e60.

Harrison, D. (2000). Violence in the military community. In L. Beaman (Ed.), *New perspectives on deviance: The construction of deviance in everyday life*. Scarborough: Prentice Hall.

Hartmann, K., Viswanathan, M., Palmieri, R., Gartlehner, G., Thorp, J., & Lohr, K. (2005). Outcomes of routine episiotomy: A systematic review. *Journal of the American Medical Association, 293*, 2141–2148.

Hartman, W., & Fithian, M. (1984). *Any man can: The multiple orgasmic technique for every loving man*. New York: St. Martin's Press.

Harvey, J., Poulin, C., & Gouliquer, L. (2001). *Developing a positive sexual identity as a gay woman in the Canadian military: An oxymoron?* Paper presented at the Canadian Lesbian and Gay Studies Association Meeting, Social Sciences and Humanities Congress, Laval, Quebec.

Hatcher, R. A., et al. (1994). *Contraceptive technology* (16th ed.). New York: Irvington.

Hatcher, R. A., et al. (1998). *Contraceptive technology* (17th ed.). New York: Ardent Media.

Hatcher, R. A., Trussell, J., Stewart, F., Nelson, A., Cates, W., Guest, F., & Kowal, D. (2004). *Contraceptive technology* (18th ed.). New York: Ardent Media.

Hatfield, E. (1978). Equity and extramarital sexuality. *Archives of Sexual Behavior, 7*, 127–141.

Hatfield, E., & Rapson, R. (1993a). Historical and cross-cultural perspectives on passionate love and sexual desire. *Annual Review of Sex Research, 4*, 67–97.

Hatfield, E., & Rapson, R. (1993b). *Love, sex, and intimacy*. New York: HarperCollins.

Hatfield, E., & Sprecher, S. (1986a). Measuring passionate love in intimate relations. *Journal of Adolescence, 9*, 383–410.

Hatfield, E., & Sprecher, S. (1986b). *Mirror, mirror . . . : The importance of looks in everyday life*. Albany: State University of New York Press.

Hatfield, E., & Walster, G. W. (1978). *A new look at love*. Reading, MA: Addison-Wesley.

Hatfield, E., Walster, G. W., & Berscheid, E. (1978). *Equity theory and research*. Boston: Allyn & Bacon.

Hatzichristou, D., Montorsi, F., Buvat, J., Laferriere, N., Bandel, T. J., & Porst, H. (2004). The efficacy and safety of flexible-dose vardenafil (Levitra) in a broad population of European men. *European Urology, 45*, 634–641.

Hausknecht, R. U. (1995). Methotrexate and misoprostol to terminate early pregnancy. *New England Journal of Medicine, 333*, 537–540.

Hayes, T. B., et al. (2002). Hermaphroditic, demasculinized frogs after exposure to the herbicide atrazine at low ecologically relevant doses. *Processdings of the National Academy of Sciences, 99*, 5476–5480.

Haynes, B. F., Pantaleo, G., & Fauci, A. S. (1996). Toward an understanding of the correlates of protective immunity to HIV infection. *Science, 271*, 324–328.

Hazan, C., & Shaver, P. (1987). Love conceptualized as an attachment process. *Journal of Personality and Social Psychology, 52*, 511–524.

Health Canada. (1996). *Breastfeeding*. Canadian Perinatal Surveillance System—Fact Sheets, 1–6.

Health Canada. (1998, March). Cervical cancer in Canada—cancer updates. Laboratory Centre for Disease Control, 1–8.

Health Canada. (1998). *Cancer in Canada—Estimated number of deaths*. Health Protection Branch—Laboratory Centre for Disease Control—Cancer Bureau. www.hc-sc.gc.ca/hpb/lcdc/bc/canadadeaths/index.html.

Health Canada. (1999, April). Breast cancer in Canada—cancer updates. Laboratory Centre for Disease Control, 1–10.

Health Canada. (1999). *Report from consultations on a framework for sexual and reproductive health.*

Health Canada. (1999). Sequelae of STD: Pelvic inflammatory disease and ectopic pregnancy. Ectopic pregnancies in Canada, 1986–1994. Canada Communicable Disease Report, 25S1.

Health Canada. (1999). Sexually transmitted diseases in Canada: 1996 surveillance report. *Canada Communicable Disease Report*. Ottawa: Author.

Health Canada. (1999). Teen pregnancy and underweight birth. *Statistical Report on the Health of Canadians, 64*, 255–257.

Health Canada. (2000). What everyone should know about human papillomavirus (HPV): Questions and Answers. *Bureau of HIV/AIDS, STD and TB Update Series: Population and Public Health Branch, STD Epi Update*. Ottawa: Health Canada.

Health Canada (2002). Perinatal Transmission of HIV. *Bureau of HIV/ AIDS, STD and TB Update Series: Population and Public Health Branch, STD Epi Update*. Ottawa: Health Canada.

Health Canada. (2003). *Canadian guidelines for sexual health education*. Ottawa: Health Canada.

Health Canada. (2003). *Canadian Perinatal Health Report, 2003*. Ottawa: Minister of Public Works and Government Services Canada.

Health Canada. (2003). *Introduction to assisted human reproduction*. Retrieved December 8, 2004, from www.hc-sc.gc.ca.

Health Canada. (2004). *Health Canada advises of potential adverse effects of SSRIs and other anti-depressants on newborns*. [Advisory 2004-44]. Retrieved October 12, 2004 from www.hcsc.gc.ca.

Health Canada. (2005). *Canadian Tobacco Use Monitoring Survey (CTUMS)*. Retrieved May 25, 2005, from www.gosmokefree.ca.

Hearn, K. D., O'Sullivan, L. F., & Dudley, C. D. (2003). Assessing reliability of early adolescent girls' reports of romantic and sexual behavior. *Archives of Sexual Behavior, 32*, 513–522.

Heaton, J. P. W. (2000). Central neuropharmacological agents and mechanisms in erectile dysfunction: The role of dopamine. *Neuroscience and Biobehavioral Reviews, 24*, 561–569.

Heaton, J. P. W. (2001). Key issues from the clinical trials of apomorphine SL. *World Journal of Urology, 19*, 25–31.

Hébert, M., Lavoie, F., & Parent, N. (2002). An assessment of outcomes following parents' participation in a child abuse prevention program. *Victims and Violence, 17*, 355–372.

Hébert, M., Lavoie, F., Piché, C., & Poitras, M. (2001). Proximate effects of a child sexual abuse prevention program in elementary school children. *Child Abuse & Neglect, 25*, 505–522.

Hébert, M., & Tourigny, M. (2004). Child sexual abuse prevention: A review of evaluative studies and recommendations for program development. *Advances in Psychology Research, 32*, 109–142.

Hébert, M., & Tremblay, C. (2000). La prévention de l'agression sexuelle à l'égard des enfants. In F. Vitaro & C. Gagnon (Eds.), *Prévention des problèmes d'adaptation chez les enfants et les adolescents-Tome 1 Les problèmes internalisès* (pp. 429–503). Ste-Foy: Presses de l'Université du Québec.

Hébert, M., Tremblay, C., Parent, N., Daignault, I. V., & Piché, C. (2006). Correlates of behavioral outcomes in sexually abused children. *Journal of Family Violence, 21*, 287–299.

Heiman, J. R. (2002a). Sexual dysfunction: Overview of prevalence, etiological factors, and treatment. *Journal of Sex Research, 39*, 73–78.

Heiman, J. R. (2002b). Psychologic treatments for female sexual dysfunction: Are they effective and do we need them? *Archives of Sexual Behavior, 31*, 445–450.

Heiman, J. R. (2007). Orgasmic disorders in women. In S. Leiblum (Ed.), *Principles and practice of sex therapy* (4th ed., pp. 84–123). New York: Guilford.

Heiman, J. R., & Meston, C. M. (1997). Empirically validated treatment for sexual dysfunction. *Annual Review of Sex Research, 8*, 148–194.

Heine, S. J. & Norenzayan, A. (2006). Toward a psychological science for a cultural species. *Perspectives in Psychological Science, 1*, 251–269.

Heise, Lori. (1993). Violence against women: The hidden health burden. *World Health Statistics Quarterly, 46*, 78–85.

Helgeson, V., Cohen, S., Schulz, R., & Yasko, J. (2001). Long-term effects of educational and peer discussion group interventions on adjustment to breast cancer. *Health Psychology, 20*, 387–392.

Hellerstein, H. K., & Friedman, E. H. (1969, March). Sexual activity and the post-coronary patient. *Medical Aspects of Human Sexuality, 3*, 70–74.

Hellstrom, W. (2003). Three-piece inflatable penile prosthesis components (surgical pearls on reservoirs, pumps, and rear-tip extenders). *International Journal of Impotence Research, 15*, S136–S138.

Hellstrom, W. J., Gittelman, M., Karlin, G., Segerson, T., Thibonnier, M., & Taylor, T., (2003b). Sustained efficacy and tolerability of vardenafil, a highly potent selective phosphodiesterase type 5 inhibitor, in men with erectile dysfunction: results of a randomized, double-blind, 26-week placebo-controlled pivotal trial. *Urology, 61*, 8–14.

Hellstrom, W., Overstreet, J. W., Yu, A. S., Saikali, K., Shen, W., Beasley, C. M., et al. (2003a). Tadalafil has no detrimental effect on human spermatogenesis or reproductive hormones. *Journal of Urology, 170*, 887–891.

Helminiak, D. A. (2000). *What the Bible really says about homosexuality*. Sacramento, CA: Alamo Square Press.

Helminiak, D. A. (2001a). Sexual ethics in college textbooks: A survey. *Journal of Sex Education and Therapy, 26*, 106–114.

Helminiak, D. A. (2001b). Sexual ethics in college textbooks: A suggestion. *Journal of Sex Education and Therapy, 26*, 320–327.

Helminiak, D. A. (2004). The ethics of sex: A call to the gay community. *Pastoral Psychology, 52*, 259–267.

Hemels, M. E., Koren, G., & Einarson, T. R. (2002). Increased use of antidepressants in Canada: 1981–2000. *The Annals of Pharmacotherapy, 36*, 1375–1379.

Hendrick, C., & Hendrick, S. (2004). Sex and romantic love: Connects and disconnects. In J. H. Harvey, A. Wenzel, & S. Sprecher (Eds.), *The handbook of sexuality in close relationships* (pp. 159–182). Mahwah, NJ: Lawrence Erlbaum.

Hendrick, S. (1981). Self-disclosure and marital satisfaction. *Journal of Personality and Social Psychology, 40*, 1150–1159.

Hendrick, S., & Hendrick, C. (1992). *Liking, loving, and relating* (2nd ed.). Pacific Grove, CA: Brooks/Cole.

Henningsson, S., et al. (2005). Sex steroid-related genes and male-to-female transsexualism. *Psychoneuroendocrinology, 30*, 657–664.

Herdt, G. H. (1984). *Ritualized homosexuality in Melanesia*. Berkeley, CA: University of California Press.

Herdt, G. (1990). Mistaken gender: 5-alpha reductase hermaphroditism and biological reductionism in sexual identity reconsidered. *American Anthropologist, 92*, 433–446.

Herek, G. M. (2000). The psychology of sexual prejudice. *Current Directions In Psychological Science, 9*, 19–22.

Herek, G. M. (2002). Heterosexuals' attitudes toward bisexual men and women in the United States. *Journal of Sex Research, 39*, 264–274.

Hergenhahn, B. R. (2001). *An introduction to the history of psychology* (4th ed.). Toronto: Wadsworth/Thomas Learning.

Herman, J. L. (1981). *Father-daughter incest*. Cambridge, MA: Harvard University Press.

Herold, E. (1981). Contraceptive embarrassment and contraceptive behaviour among young single women. *Journal of Youth & Adolescence, 10*(3), 233–242.

Herold, E. S., & Way, L. (1988). Sexual self disclosure among university women. *Journal of Sex Research, 24*, 1–14.

Herrero, R., Castellsague, X., Pawlita, M., Lissowska, J., Kee, F., Balaram, P., et al. (2003). Human papillomavirus and oral cancer: The International Agency for Research on Cancer multicenter study. *Journal of the National Cancer Institute, 95,* 1772–1783.

Higgins, M. (2002, May 13). The church must change. *Maclean's.*

Hill, D. B. (2000). Categories of sex and gender: Either/or, both/and, and neither/nor. *History and Philosophy of Psychology Bulletin, 12,* 25–33.

Hill, D. B., et al. (2007). Gender identity disorders in childhood and adolescence: A critical inquiry. *International Journal of Sexual Health, 1,* 95–122.

Hill, M. (2002). Skin color and the perception of attractiveness among African Americans: Does gender make a difference? *Social Psychology Quarterly, 65,* 77–91.

Hite, S. (1976). *The Hite report.* New York: Macmillan.

Hite, S. (1981). *The Hite report on male sexuality.* New York: Alfred Knopf.

Ho, G. Y. F., et al. (1998). Natural history of cervicovaginal papillomavirus infection in young women. *New England Journal of Medicine, 338,* 423–428.

Hobfoll, S., Ritter, C., Lavin, J., Hulsizer, M., et al. (1995). Depression prevalence and incidence among inner-city pregnant and postpartum women. *Journal of Consulting and Clinical Psychology, 63,* 445–453.

Hoff, G. A., & Schneiderman, L. J. (1985, December). Having babies at home: Is it safe? Is it ethical? *Hastings Center Report,* 19–27.

Hofferth, S. L. (1990). Trends in adolescent sexual activity, contraception, and pregnancy in the United States. In J. Bancroft & J. Reinisch (Eds.), *Adolescence and puberty* (pp. 217–233). New York: Oxford University Press.

Hoffmann, H., Janssen, E., & Turner, S. L. (2004). Classical conditioning of sexual arousal in women and men: Effects of varying awareness and biological relevance of the conditioned stimulus. *Archives of Sexual Behavior, 33,* 43–54.

Hogben, M., & Byrne, D. (1998). Using social learning theory to explain individual differences in human sexuality. *Journal of Sex Research, 35,* 58–71.

Hollander, D. (1996). Programs to bring down cesarean section rate prove to be successful. *Family Planning Perspectives, 28,* 182–185.

Holmes, M. (2002). Rethinking the meaning and management of intersexuality. *Sexualities, 5,* 159–180.

Holmstrom, L. L., & Burgess, A. W. (1980). Sexual behavior of assailants during reported rapes. *Archives of Sexual Behavior, 9,* 427–440.

Holroyd, J. C., & Brodsky, A. M. (1977). Psychologists' attitudes and practices regarding erotic and nonerotic physical contact with patients. *American Psychologist, 34,* 843–849.

Holstege, G., Georgiadis, J. R., Paans, A. M., Meiners, L. C., van der Graaf, F. H., & Reinders, A. A. (2003). Brain activation during human male ejaculation. *Journal of Neuroscience, 23,* 9185–9193.

Hong, L. K. (1984). Survival of the fastest: On the origin of premature ejaculation. *Journal of Sex Research, 20,* 109–122.

Hopwood, N. J., et al. (1990). The onset of human puberty: Biological and environmental factors. In J. Bancroft & J. M. Reinisch (Eds.), *Adolescence and puberty.* New York: Oxford University Press.

Horney, K. (1973). The flight from womanhood (1926). In K. Horney, *Feminine psychology.* New York: Norton.

Horowitz, C. R., & Jackson, T. C. (1997). Female "circumcision": African women confront American medicine. *Journal of General Internal Medicine, 12,* 491–499.

Horrocks, R. (1997). *An introduction to the study of sexuality.* New York: St. Martin's Press.

Hou, F., & Myles, J. (2007). The changing role of education in the marriage market: Assortative marriage in Canada and the United States since the 1970s. *Analytical Studies Branch Research Paper Series* (Statistics Canada, Catalogue #11F0019MIE).

House, C. (1997). Navajo warrior women: An ancient tradition in a modern world. In S. Jacobs, et al. (Eds.), *Two-spirit people* (pp. 223–227). Urbana, IL: University of Illinois Press.

Hubacher, D. (2002). The checkered history and bright future of intrauterine contraception in the United States. *Perspectives on Sexual and Reproductive Health, 34,* 98–103.

Huber, J. D., & Kleinplatz, P. J. (2002). Sexual orientation identification of men who have sex with men in public settings in Canada. *Journal of Homosexuality, 42,* 1–16.

Hucker, S., & Blanchard, R. (1992). Death scene characteristics in 118 fatal cases of autoerotic asphyxia compared with suicidal asphyxia. *Behavioural Sciences and the Law, 10,* 509–523.

Huffstutter, P. J., & Frammolino, R. (2001). Lights, camera, Viagra: When the show must go on, sometimes a little chemistry helps. *Los Angeles Times,* July 6, A1.

Hughes, J. O., & Sandler, B. R. (1987). *"Friends" raping friends: Could it happen to you?* Washington, DC: Association of American Colleges.

Hulshoff, H. E., et al. (2006). Changing your sex changes your brain: Influences of testosterone and estrogen on adult human brain structure. *European Journal of Endocrinology, 155,* S107–S114.

Humphreys, L. (1970). *Tearoom trade: Impersonal sex in public places.* Chicago: Aldine.

Humphreys, T.P (in press). Perceptions of sexual consent: The impact of relationship history and gender. *The Journal of Sex Research.*

Humphreys, T. P., & Herold, E. (2007). Sexual consent in heterosexual relationships: Development of a new measure. *Sex Roles, 57,* 305–315.

Hunt, M. (1974). *Sexual behavior in the 1970s.* Chicago: Playboy Press.

Hunt, A., & Curtis, B. (2006). A genealogy of the genital kiss: Oral sex in the twentieth century. *Canadian Journal of Human Sexuality, 15,* 69–84.

Hurd Clark, L. (2006). Older women and sexuality: Experiences in marital relationships across the life course. *Canadian Journal on Aging, 25,* 129–140.

Huston, T. L., & Levinger, G. (1978). Interpersonal attraction and relationships. In M. R. Rosenzweig & L. W. Porter (Eds.), *Annual Review of Psychology* (Vol. 29). Palo Alto, CA: Annual Reviews.

Hutchins, L., & Kaahumanu, L. (Eds.). (1991). *Bi any other name: Bisexual people speak out.* Boston: Alyson.

Hutchinson, K. A. (1995). Androgens and sexuality. *American Journal of Medicine, 98* (Suppl. 1A), 1A111S–1A115S.

Hyde, J. S. (1984). How large are gender differences in aggression? A developmental meta-analysis. *Developmental Psychology, 20,* 722–736.

Hyde, J. S. (2007). *Half the human experience: The psychology of women* (7th ed.). Boston: Houghton-Mifflin.

Hyde, J. S., & Jaffee, S. R. (2000). Becoming a heterosexual adult: The experiences of young women. *Journal of Social Issues, 56,* 283–296.

Hyde, J. S., DeLamater, J., & Hewitt, E. (1998). Sexuality and the dual-earner couple: Multiple rules and sexual functioning. *Journal of Family Psychology, 12,* 354–368.

Hyde, J. S., DeLamater, J., Plant, E. A., & Byrd, J. M. (1996). Sexuality during pregnancy and the year postpartum. *Journal of Sex Research, 33,* 143–151.

Hynes, H. P., & Raymond, J. G. (2002). Put in harm's way: The neglected health consequences of sex trafficking in the United States. In J. Silliman, & A. Bhattacharjee (Eds.), *Policing the national body: Sex, race, and criminalization* (pp. 197–229). Cambridge, MA: South End Press.

Hynie, M., & Lydon, J. E. (1996). Sexual attitudes and contraceptive behavior revisited: Can there be too much of a good thing? *The Journal of Sex Research, 33,* 127–134.

Hynie, M., Lydon, J. E., Cote, S., & Weiner, S. (1998). Relational sexual scripts and women's condom use: The importance of internalized norms. *Journal of Sex Research, 35*(4), 370–380.

Hynie, M., Lydon, J. E., & Taradash, A. (1997). Commitment, intimacy, and women's perceptions of premarital sex and contraceptive readiness. *Psychology of Women Quarterly, 21,* 447–464.

Ilies, R., et al. (2003). Reported incidence rates of work-related sexual harassment in the United States: Using meta-analysis to explain reported rate disparities. *Personnel Psychology, 56,* 607 631.

Ilkkaracan, P. (2001). Islam and women's sexuality. In P. B. Jung, M. E. Hunt, & R. Balakrishnan (Eds.) (2001). *Good sex: Feminist perspectives from the world's religions* (pp. 61–76). New Brunswick, NJ: Rutgers University Press.

Imperato-McGinley, J., et al. (1974). Steroid 5 reductase deficiency in man: An inherited form of male pseudohermaphroditism. *Science, 186,* 1213–1215.

Institute of Medicine. (2004). *New frontiers in contraceptive research.* Washington, DC: National Academies Press.

Iqbal, M. M., Gundlapalli, S. P., Ryan, W. G., Ryals, T., & Passman, T. E. (2001). Effects of antimanic mood-stabilizing drugs on fetuses, neonates, and nursing infants. *Southern Medical Journal, 94,* 305–322.

Irvine, J. M. (1995). *Sexuality education across cultures: Working with differences.* San Francisco: Jossey-Bass.

Isaacs, C. R., & Fisher, W. A. (2008). A computer-based educational intervention to address potential negative effects of Internet pornography, *Communication Studies, 59,* 1–18.

Iwaniuk, A. N., et al. (2006). The effects of environmental exposure to DDT on the brain of a songbird: Changes in structures associated with mating and song. *Behavioural Brain Research, 173,* 1–10.

Izugbara, C. O. (2008). Home-based sexuality education: Nigerian parents discussing sex with their children. *Youth & Society, 39,* 575–600.

Jaakkola, J., & Gissler, M. (2004). Maternal smoking in pregnancy, fetal development and childhood asthma. *American Journal of Public Health, 94,* 136–141.

Jacobson, S. W., Jacobson, J. L., & Sokol, R. J. (1994). Effects of fetal alcohol exposure on infant reaction time. *Alcoholism: Clinical and Experimental Research, 18,* 1125–1132.

Jacobson, S. W., Jacobson, J. L., Sokol, R. J., Martier, S. S., & Ager, J. W. (1993). Prenatal alcohol exposure and infant information processing ability. *Child Development, 64,* 1706–1721.

Jamieson, D. J., Kaufman, S. C., Costello, C., Hillis, S. D., Marchbanks, P. A., & Peterson, H. B. (2002). A comparison of women's regret after vasectomy versus tubal sterilization. *Obstetrics and Gynecology, 99,* 1073–1079.

Janicek, M. F., & Averette, H. E. (2001). Cervical cancer: Prevention, diagnosis, and therapeutics. *CA: Cancer Journal for Clinicians, 51,* 92–114.

Janowsky, J. S., Chavez, B. Zamboni, B., & Orwoll, E. (1998). The cognitive neuropsychology of sex hormones in men and women. *Developmental Neuropsychology, 14,* 421–440.

Janssen, P. A., Thiessen, P., Klein, M. C., Whitfield, M. F., MacNab, Y. C., & Cullis-Kuhl, S. C. (2007). Standards for the measurement of birth weight, length and head circumference at term in neonates of European, Chinese and South Asian ancestry. *Open Medicine, 1,* e74–88.

Jantzen, G. (1994). AIDS, shame, and suffering. In J. B. Nelson & S. P. Longfellow (Eds.), *Sexuality and the sacred* (pp. 305–313). Louisville, KY: Westminster/John Knox Press.

Janus, S. S., & Janus, C. L. (1993). *The Janus report on sexual behavior.* New York: Wiley.

Jay, K., & Young, A. (1979). *The gay report.* New York: Summit Books.

Jefferson, E. A. (2005). Grown up parties are turning up the heat. *Denver Post,* November 15.

Jeffrey, L. A., & MacDonald, G. (2006). "It's the money, Honey": The economy of sex work in the Maritimes. *The Canadian Review of Sociology and Anthropology, 43,* 313–327.

Jeffrey, L. A., & MacDonald, G. (2006). *Sex workers in the Maritimes talk back.* Vancouver: UBC Press.

Jemail, J. A., & Geer, J. (1977). Sexual scripts. In R. Gemme & C. C. Wheeler (Eds.), *Progress in sexology.* New York: Plenum.

Jenkins, J. S., & Nussey, S. S. (1991). The role of oxytocin: Present concepts. *Clinical Endocrinology, 34,* 515–525.

Jenks, R. J. (1985). Swinging: A replication and test of a theory. *Journal of Sex Research, 21,* 199–210.

Jenks, R. (1998). Swinging: A review of the literature. *Archives of Sexual Behavior, 27,* 507–521.

Jenny, C., Roesler, T. A., & Poyer, K. A. (1994). Are children at risk for sexual abuse by homosexuals? *Pediatrics, 94,* 41–44.

Jensen, G. D. (1976). Adolescent sexuality. In B. J. Sadock et al. (Eds.), *The sexual experience.* Baltimore: Williams & Wilkins.

Jensen, R. (2007). *Getting off: Pornography and the end of masculinity.* Cambridge: South End Press.

Jha, P., Kumar, R., Vasa, P., Dhingra, N., Thiruchelvam, D., & Maineddin, R. (2006). Low male-to-female sex ratio of children born in India: National survey of 1.1 million households. *The Lancet, 367,* 211–218.

John, E. M., Savitz, D. A., & Sandler, D. P. (1991). Prenatal exposure to parents' smoking and childhood cancer. *American Journal of Epidemiology, 133,* 123–132.

Johnson, A. M., Mercer, C. H., Erens, B., Copas, A. J., McManus, S., Wellings, K., et al. (2001). Sexual behaviour in Britain: Partnerships, practices, and HIV risk behaviours. *Lancet, 358,* 1835–1842.

Johnson, A. M., Wadsworth, J., Wellings, K., Bradshaw, S., & Field, J. (1992). Sexual lifestyles and HIV risk. *Nature, 360,* 410–412.

Johnson, B. R., Horga, M., & Andronache, L. (1996). Women's perspectives on abortion in Romania. *Social Science & Medicine, 42,* 521–530.

Johnson, S. D., Phelps, D., & Cottier, L. (2004). The association of sexual dysfunction and substance use among a community epidemiological sample. *Archives of Sexual Behavior, 33,* 55–64.

Johri, A., Heaton, J., & Morales, A. (2001). Severe erectile dysfunction is a marker for hyperprolactinemia. *International Journal of Impotence Research, 13,* 176–182.

Jones, J. H. (1997). *Alfred C. Kinsey: A public/private life.* New York: Norton.

Jones, J., Pelham, B., Carvallo, M., & Mirenberg, M. (2004). How do I love thee? Let me count the Js: Implicit egotism and interpersonal attraction. *Journal of Personality and Social Psychology, 87,* 665–683.

Jones, R. K., Darroch, J. & Henshaw, S. (2002). Contraceptive use among U.S. women having abortions in 2000–2001. *Perspectives on Sexual and Reproductive Health, 34,* 294–303.

Jorgensen, S. R. (1980). Contraceptive attitude-behavior consistency in adolescence. *Population and Environment, 3,* 174–194.

Jürgens, R. (1998). *HIV testing and confidentiality.* Final Report HIV/AIDS Legal Network & Canadian AIDS Society.

Julien, D., Chartrand, E., Simard, M. C., Bouthillier, D., & Begin, J. (2003). Conflict, social support, and relationship quality: An observational study of heterosexual, gay male, and lesbian couples' communication. *Journal of Family Psychology, 17,* 419–428.

Kabalin, J. N., & Kuo, J. C. (1997). Long-term follow-up of and patient satisfaction with the Dynaflex self-contained inflatable penile prosthesis. *Journal of Urology, 158,* 456–469.

Kabir, A., Pridjian, G., Steinmann, W., Herrera, E., & Khan, M. (2005). Racial differences in cesareans: An analysis of U.S. 2001 national inpatient sample data. *Obstetrics and Gynecology, 195,* 710–718.

Kafka, M. P. (1997). Hypersexual desire in males: An operational definition and clinical implications for males with paraphilias and paraphilia-related disorders. *Archives of Sexual Behavior, 26,* 505–526.

Kai, L., & Pourier, D. J. (2001). Using the National Longitudinal Study of Youth in the U.S. to study the birth process: A Bayesian approach. *Research in Official Statistics, 4,* 127–150.

Kaiser Family Foundation. (1998). *Sex in the 90s: 1998 national survey of Americans on sex and sexual health* (Publication No. 1430). Menlo Park, CA: Author.

Kaiser Family Foundation. (2001). *Biennial report on sex in the media: Executive summary.* Menlo Park, CA: Kaiser Family Foundation.

Kaiser Family Foundation. (2003). *A biennial report of the Kaiser Family Foundation on Sex on TV3: Executive summary.* Menlo Park, CA: Author.

Kaiser Family Foundation. (2004). *Sex education in America: General public/parents survey.* Menlo Park, CA: Kaiser Family Foundation.

Kalick, S. M., Zebowitz, L., Langlois, J., & Johnson, R. (1998). Does human facial attractiveness honestly advertise health? Longitudinal data on an evolutionary question. *Psychological Science, 9,* 8–13.

Kalil, K., Gruber, J., Conley, J., & Sytniac, M. (1993). Social and family pressures on anxiety and stress during pregnancy. *Pre- and Perinatal Psychology Journal, 8,* 113–118.

Kallstrom-Fuqua, A. C., Weston, R., & Marshall, L. (2004). Childhood and adolescent sexual abuse of community women: Mediated effects on psychological distress and social relationships. *Journal of Consulting and Clinical Psychology, 72,* 980–992.

Kambic, R. T. (1999). The effectiveness of natural family planning methods for birth spacing: A comprehensive review. Hopkins Population Center Papers on Population, WP 99-07. Retrieved November 30, 2002, from http://popctr.jhsph.edu/publications/wp/papers/wp9907/fulltext.html.

Kaplan, H. S. (1974). *The new sex therapy.* New York: Brunner/Mazel.

Kaplan, H. S. (1979). *Disorders of sexual desire.* New York: Simon & Schuster.

Kaplan, H. S., & Sager, C. J. (1971, June). Sexual patterns at different ages. *Medical Aspects of Human Sexuality, 10*–23.

Karama, S., Lecours, A. R., Leroux, J. M., Bourgouin, P., Beaudoin, G., Joubert, S., et al. (2002). Areas of brain activation in males and females during viewing of erotic film excerpts. *Human Brain Mapping, 16,* 1–13.

Kaschak, E., & Tiefer, L. (2001). *A new view of women's sexual problems.* New York: Haworth.

Kaufman, M., Silverberg, C., & Odette, F. (2003). *The ultimate guide to sex and disability.* San Francisco: Cleis Press.

Kearns, B. (2007). *How Lance does it. Put the success formula of a champion into everything you do.* Toronto: McGraw Hill.

Keefe, D. L. (2002). Sex hormones and neural mechanisms. *Archives of Sexual Behavior, 31,* 401–404.

Keelan, P. R., Dion, K. L., & Dion, K. K. (1994). Attachment style and heterosexual relationships among young adults: A short-term panel study. *Journal of Social and Personal Relationships, 11,* 201–214.

Keenan, T., & Ward, T. (2000). A theory of mind perspective on cognitive, affective, and intimacy deficits in child sex offenders. *Sex Abuse, 12,* 49–60.

Kegel, A. H. (1952). Sexual functions of the pubococcygeus muscle. *Western Journal of Surgery, 60,* 521–524.

Kempf, D. J., et al. (1995). ABT-538 is a potent inhibitor of human immunodeficiency virus protease. *Proceedings of the National Academy of Sciences, 92,* 2484.

Kempton, W., & Kahn, E. (1991). Sexuality and people with intellectual disabilities: A historical perspective. *Sexuality and Disability, 9,* 93–111.

Kendall-Tackett, K., Williams, L., & Finkelhor, D. (1993). Impact of sexual abuse on children: A review and synthesis of recent empirical studies. *Psychological Bulletin, 113,* 164–180.

Kendler, K. S., Bulik, C. M., Silberg, J., Hettema, J. M., Myers, J., Prescott, C. A., et al. (2000). Childhood sexual abuse and adult psychiatric and substance use disorders in women: An epidemiological and cotwin control analysis. *Archives of General Psychiatry, 57,* 953–959.

Kendler, K. S., Thornton, L., Gilman, S., & Kessler, R. (2000). Sexual orientation in a US national sample of twin and nontwin sibling pairs. *American Journal of Psychiatry, 157,* 1843–1846.

Kennedy, R., & Suttenfield, K. (2001). Postpartum depression. *Medscape Mental Health 6,* No. 4.

Kero, A., Lalos, A., Högberg, U., & Jacobssen, L. (1999). The male partner involved in legal abortion. *Human Reproduction, 14,* 2669–2675.

Keverne, E. B. (1999). The vomeronasal organ. *Science, 286,* 716–720.

Khan A., & Pine, P. (2003). *Adolescent reproductive health in Pakistan: Status, policies, programs, and issues.* Washington, D.C., Futures Group International, POLICY Project (USAID Contract No. HRN-C-00-00-00006-00)

Kiefer, A. K., & Sanchez, D. T. (2007). Scripting sexual passivity: A gender role perspective. *Personal Relationships, 14,* 269–290.

Kikuras, A. (2004). An interview with Dave Cummings, Unchain the underground, www.unchain.com.

Kim, N., Stanton, B., Li, X., Dickersin, K., & Galbraith, J. (1997). Effectiveness of the 40 adolescent AIDS-risk reduction interventions: A quantitative review. *Journal of Adolescent Health, 20,* 204–215.

Kimball, M. M. (1986). Television and sex-role attitudes. In T. M. Williams (Ed.), *The impact of television: A naturalistic experiment in three communities* (pp. 265–301). Orlando: Academic Press.

King, M., & Woollett, E. (1997). Sexually assaulted males: 115 men consulting a counseling service. *Archives of Social Behavior, 26,* 579–588.

King, M., Marks, J., & Mandell, J. (2003). Breast and ovarian cancer risks due to inherited mutations in BRCA1 and BRCA2. *Science, 302,* 643–646.

King, S. A. (1999). Internet gambling and pornography: Illustrative examples of the psychological consequences of communication anarchy. *CyberPsychology & Behavior, 2,* 175–193.

Kinnish, K. K., Strassberg, D., & Turner, C. (2005). Sex differences in the flexibility of sexual orientation: A multidimensional retrospective assessment. *Archives of Sexual Behavior, 34,* 173–184.

Kinsey, A. C., Pomeroy, W. B., Martin, C. E., & Gebhard, P. H. (1953). *Sexual behavior in the human female.* Philadelphia: Saunders.

Kinsman, G. (1996). *The regulation of desire: Sexuality in Canada.* Montreal: Black Rose Books.

Kippin, T. E., Talianakis, S., Schattmann, L., Bartholomew, S., & Pfaus, J. G. (1998). Olfactory conditioning of sexual behavior in the male rat *(Rattus norvegicus). Journal of Comparative Psychology, 112,* 389–399.

Kiragu, K. (1995, October). Female genital mutilation: A reproductive health concern. *Population Reports* (Supplement), Series J, No. 41, Vol. 23.

Kiragu, K., et al. (2001). Can we avoid catastrophe? Youth and HIV/AIDS. *Population Reports, Series L, No. 12.* Johns Hopkins University School of Public Health.

Kirby, D. (2002). Effective approaches to reducing adolescent unprotected sex, pregnancy, and childbearing. *The Journal of Sex Research, 39,* 51–57.

Kirby, D., Short, L., Collins, J., Rugg, D., Kolbe, L., Howard, et al. (1994). School-based programs to reduce sexual risk behaviors: A review of effectiveness. *Public Health Reports, 109,* 339–360.

Kirk, K., Bailey, J., Dunne, M., & Martin, N. (2000). Measurement models for sexual orientation in a community twin sample. *Behavior Genetics, 30,* 345–356.

Kiselica, M., & Scheckel, S. (1995). The couvade syndrome (sympathetic pregnancy) and teenage fathers: A brief primer for counselors. *School Counselor, 43,* 42–51.

Klaus, M., & Kennell, J.. (1976). Human maternal and paternal behavior. In M. Klaus & J. Kennell (Eds.), *Maternal infant bonding.* St. Louis, MO: Mosby.

Klebanov, P. K., & Jemmott, J. B. (1992). Effects of expectations and bodily sensations on self-reports of premenstrual symptoms. *Psychology of Women Quarterly, 16,* 289–310.

Klein, R., & Knäuper, B. (2003). The role of cognitive avoidance of STIs for discussing safer sex practices and for condom use consistency. *Canadian Journal of Human Sexuality, 12,* 137–149.

Kleinhaus, K., Perrin, M., Friedlander, Y., Paltiel, O., Malaspina, D., & Harlap, S. (2006). Paternal age and spontaneous abortion. *Obstetrics and Gynecology, 108,* 369–377.

Kleinplatz, P. J. (2003a). Beyond sexual mechanics and hydraulics: Humanizing the discourse surrounding erectile dysfunction. *Journal of Humanistic Psychology, 43,* 1–29.

Kleinplatz, P. J. (2003b). What's new in sex therapy? From stagnation to fragmentation. *Sexual & Relationship Therapy, 18,* 95–106.

Kleinplatz, P.J., & Krippner, S. (2005). Spirituality and sexuality: Celebrating erotic transcendence and spiritual embodiment. In S. G. Mijares, & G. S. Khalsa (Eds.), *The psychospiritual clinician's handbook: Alternative methods for understanding and treating mental disorders.* Binghamton, NY: Haworth Press, Inc.

Kleinplatz, P. J., & Ménard, A. D. (2007). Building blocks toward optimal sexuality: Constructing a conceptual model. *The Family Journal: Counseling and Therapy for Couples and Families, 15,* 72–78.

Klemetti, R., Sevon, T., Gissler, M., & Hemminki, F. (2006, November). Health of children born as a result of in vitro fertilization. *Pediatrics, 118,* 1819–1827.

Kline, Galena, Stanley, S., Markman, H., Olmos-Gallo, P. A., St. Peters, M., Whitton, S., & Prado, L. (2004). Timing is everything: Pre-engagement cohabitation and increased risk for poor marital outcomes. *Journal of Family Psychology, 18,* 311–318.

Knauper, B., & Kornik, R. (2004). Perceived transmissibility of STIs: Lack of differentiation between HIV and chlamydia. *Sexually Transmitted Infections, 80,* 74–78.

Knauper, B., Kornik, R., Atkinson, K., Guberman, C., & Aydin, C. (2005). Motivation influences the underestimation of cumulative risk. *Personality and Social Psychology Bulletin, 31,* 1511–1523.

Kniffin, K. M., & Wilson, D. S. (2004). The effect of nonphysical traits on perception of physical attractiveness: Three naturalistic studies. *Evolution and Human Behavior, 25,* 88–101.

Koelman, C. A., Coumans, A. B., Nijman, H. W., Doxiadis, I. I., Dekker, G. A., & Claas, F. H. (2000). Correlation between oral sex and a low incidence of preeclampsia: A role for soluble HLA in seminal fluid? *Journal of Reproductive Immunology, 46,* 155–166.

Kolata, G. (2001, March 25). Researchers find grave defect risk in cloning animals. *New York Times,* p. 1ff.

Kolbenschlag, M. (1985). Abortion and moral consensus: Beyond Solomon's choice. *Christian Century, 102,* 179–183.

Kolker, A. (1989). Advances in prenatal diagnosis. *International Journal of Technology Assessment in Health Care, 5,* 601–617.

Komisaruk, B. R., Gerdes, C. A., & Whipple, B. (1997). "Complete" spinal cord injury does not block perceptual responses to genital self-stimulation in women. *Archives of Neurology, 54,* 1513–1520.

Komisaruk, B. R., & Whipple, B. (2005). Function MRI of the brain during orgasm in women. *Annual Review of Sex Research, 15,* 62–86.

Kong, R. Johnson, H., Beattie, S., & Cardillo, A. (2003). Sexual offences in Canada. *Juristat, 23,* 6. Catalogue no. 85-002-XPE. Ottawa: Statistics Canada.

Korff, J., & Geer, J. H. (1983). The relationship between sexual arousal experience and genital response. *Psychophysiology, 20,* 121–127.

Kosfeld, M., Heinrichs, M., Zak, P., Fischbacher, U., & Fehr, E. (2005). Oxytocin increases trust in humans. *Nature, 435* (June 2), 673–676.

Kosnick, A., et al. (1977). *Human sexuality: New directions in American Catholic thought.* New York: Paulist Press.

Koss, M. P. (1993). Rape: Scope, impact, interventions, and public policy response. *American Psychologist, 48,* 1062–1063.

Koss, M., & Figueredo, A. (2004). Change in cognitive mediators of rape's impact on psychosocial health across 2 years of recovery. *Journal of Consulting and Clinical Psychology, 72,* 1063–1072.

Koss, M. P., Goodman, L. A., Browne, A., Fitzgerald, L. F., Russo, N. F., & Keita, G. P. (1994). *No safe haven: Male violence against women at home, at work, and in the community.* Washington, DC: American Psychological Association.

Koss, M P., & Heslet, L. (1992). Somatic consequences of violence against women. *Archives of Family Medicine, 1,* 53–59.

Koss, M. P., Koss, P. G., & Woodruff, W. J. (1991). Deleterious effects of criminal victimization on women's health and medical utilization. *Archives of Internal Medicine, 151,* 342–347.

Kothari, P. (1984). For discussion: Ejaculatory disorders—a new dimension. *British Journal of Sexual Medicine, 11,* 205–209.

Kovacs, P. (2002a). Congenital anomalies and low birth weight associated with assisted reproductive technologies (Article 435963). *Medscape Women's Health 7,* No. 3.

Kovacs, P. (2002b). Preconception sex selection. *Medscape Ob/Gyn & Women's Health, 7,* No 2. Retrieved from www.medscape.com/viewarticle/441313.

Kramer, M. S., Platt, R. W., Wen, S. W., Joseph, K. S., Allen, A., Abrahamowicz, Blondel, B., & Breart, G. (2001). A new and improved population-based Canadian reference for birth weight for gestational age. *Pediatrics, 108,* e35.

Kraut, R., Olson, J., Banaji, M., Bruckman, A., Cohen, J., & Couper, M. (2004). Psychological research online: Report of the Board of Scientific Affairs' Advisory Group on the Conduct of Research on the Internet. *American Psychologist, 59,* 105–117.

Kreimer, A. R., Alberg, A. J., Daniel, R., Gravitt, P. E., Viscidi, R., Garrett, E. S., et al. (2004). Oral human papillomavirus infection in adults is associated with sexual behavior and HIV serostatus. *Journal of Infectious Diseases, 189,* 686–698.

Kowser, O. H., & Entwistle, M. (1995). Female genital mutilation: Cultural and health issues and their implications for sexuality counselling in Canada. *Canadian Journal of Human Sexuality, 4,* 137–148.

Krimmel, H. T. (1983, Oct.). The case against surrogate parenting. *Hastings Center Report,* 35–39.

Kroeber, A. L., & Kluckhohn, C. (1963). *Culture: A critical review of concepts and definitions.* New York: Vintage Books.

Krueger, R. B., & Kaplan, M. S. (2001). Depo-leuprolide acetate for treatment of paraphilias: A report of twelve cases. *Archives of Sexual Behavior, 30,* 409–422.

Kruger, B. S. (2006). The post-orgasmic prolactin increase following intercourse is greater than following masturbation and suggests greater satiety. *Biological Psychology, 71,* 312–315.

Kruger, T. H., Haake, P., Hartmann, U., Schedlowski, M., & Exton, M. S. (2002). Orgasm-induced prolactin secretion: Feedback control of sexual drive? *Neuroscience and Biobehavioral Reviews, 26,* 31–44.

Kruijver, F., et al. (2000). Male-to-female transsexuals have female neuron numbers in a limbic nucleus. *Journal of Clinical Endocrinology and Metabolism, 85,* 2034–2041.

Kukkonen, T. M., Binik, Y. M., Amsel, R., & Carrier, S. (2007). Thermography as a physiological measure of sexual arousal in both men and women. *Journal of Sexual Medicine, 4,* 93–105.

Kunkel, D., et al. (2005). *Sex on TV 4.* Menlo Park, CA: Kaiser Family Foundation.

Kunkel, D., Cope, K. M., & Colvin, C. (1996). *Sexual messages on family hour television: Content and context.* Menlo Park, CA: Kaiser Family Foundation.

Kurdek, L. A. (2005). What do we know about gay and lesbian couples? *Current Directions in Psychological Science, 14,* 251–254.

Laan, E., & Everaerd, W. (1995). Determinants of female sexual arousal: Psychophysiological theory and data. *Annual Review of Sex Research, 6,* 32–76.

Laan, E., Everaerd, W., van Bellen, G., & Hanewald, G. (1994). Women's sexual and emotional responses to male- and female-produced erotica. *Archives of Sexual Behavior, 23,* 153–170.

Lacroix, N. (2003). *Kama Sutra: A modern guide to the ancient art of sex.* Hylas Publishing: New York.

LaFromboise, T. D., Heyle, A. M., & Ozer, E. J. (1990). Changing and diverse roles of women in American Indian cultures. *Sex Roles,* 455–476.

Lahey, K. A. (1999). *Are we "persons" yet? Law and sexuality in Canada.* Toronto: University of Toronto Press.

Laliberté, L. (2006). New vaginas for old. *National Review of Medicine, 3,* 2p.

Lalumière, M., Blanchard, R., & Zucker, K. (2000). Sexual orientation and handedness in men and women: A meta-analysis. *Psychological Bulletin, 126,* 575–592.

Lalumière, M. L., Blanchard, R., & Zucker, K. J. (2000). Sexual orientation and handedness in men and women: A meta-analysis. *Psychological Bulletin, 126,* 575–592.

Lalumière, M. L., Chalmers, L. J., Quinsey, V. L., & Seto, M. C. (1996). A test of mate deprivation hypothesis of sexual coercion. *Ethology & Sociobiology, 17,* 299–318.

Lalumière, M. L., Quinsey, V. L., Harris, G. T., Rice, M. E., & Trautrimas, C. (2003). Are rapists differentially aroused by coercive sex in phallometric assessments? *Annals of the New York Academy of Sciences, 989,* 211–224.

Lalumière, M. L., & Quinsey, V. L. (1996). Sexual deviance, antisociality, mating effort, and the use of sexually coercive behaviors. *Personality and Individual Differences, 21,* 33–48.

Lalumière, M. L., & Quinsey, V. L. (1998). Pavlovian conditioning of sexual interests in human males. *Archives of Sexual Behavior, 27,* 241–252.

Lamb, M. (1982, April). Second thoughts on first touch. *Psychology Today,* 9–10.

Lamb, M. E., & Hwang, C. (1982). Maternal attachment and mother-neonate bonding: A critical review. In M. E. Lamb & A. L. Brown (Eds.), *Advances in developmental psychology* (Vol. 2). Hillsdale, NJ: Lawrence Erlbaum.

Lamberts, S. W. J., et al. (1997). The endocrinology of aging. *Science, 278,* 419–424.

Lande, R. E. (1995). New era for injectables. *Population Reports,* Series K, No. 5.

Landry, T., Bergeron, S., Dupuis, M-J., & Desrochers, G. (2008). The treatment of provoked vestibulodynia: A critical review. *Clinical Journal of Pain, 24,* 155–171.

Langer, E. J., & Dweck, C. S. (1973). *Personal politics: The psychology of making it.* Englewood Cliffs, NJ: Prentice-Hall.

Langille, D. (2000). *Adolescent sexual health services and education: Options for Nova Scotia.* Maritime Centre of Excellence for Women's Health. Policy discussion Series Paper #8. Halifax, NS: Maritime Centre of Excellence for Women's Health.

Langille, D., Beazley, R., & Doncaster, H. (1996). *Amherst parents' attitudes towards school-based sexual health education.* Amherst, NS: Amherst Initiative for Healthy Adolescent Sexuality.

Langille, D. B., Beazley, R., Shoveller, J., & Johnston, G. (1994). Prevalence of high risk sexual behaviour in adolescents attending school in a county in Nova Scotia. *Canadian Journal of Public Health, 85*(4), 227–230.

Langille, D., Graham, J., Marshall, E., Blake, M., Chittey, C., & Doncaster-Scott, H. (1999). *Developing understanding from young women's experiences in obtaining sexual health services and education in a Nova Scotia community.* Maritime Centre of Excellence for Women's Health.

Langille, D. B., Murphy, G. T., Hughes, J., & Rigby, J. A. (2001). Nova Scotia high school students' interactions with physicians for sexual health information and services. *Canadian Journal of Public Health, 92,* 219–222.

Langfeldt, T. (1981). Childhood masturbation. In L. L. Constantine & F. M. Martinson (Eds.), *Children and sex* (pp. 63–74). Boston: Little Brown.

Långström, N. & Zucker, K. J. (2005). Tranvestic fetishism in the general population: Prevalence and correlates. *Journal of Sex & Marital Therapy, 31,* 87–95.

LaMarre, A. K., Paterson, L. Q., & Gorzalka B. B. (2003). Breastfeeding and postpartum maternal sexual functioning: A review. *Canadian Journal of Human Sexuality, 12,* 151–168.

Lambert, T. A., Kahn, A., & Apple, K. (2003). Pluralistic ignorance and hooking up. *Journal of Sex Research, 40,* 129–133.

Landott, M. A., Bartholomew, K., Saffrey, C., Oram, D., & Perlman, D. (2004). Gender nonconformity, childhood rejection, and adult attachment: A study of Gay men. *Archives of Sexual Behavior, 33,* 117–128.

Larson, I., & Svedin, C. G. (2002a). Teachers' and parents' reports on 3- to 6-year-old children's sexual behaviour: A comparison. *Child Abuse & Neglect, 26,* 247–266.

Larsson, I., & Svedin, C. G. (2002b). Sexual experiences in childhood: Young adults' recollections. *Archives of Sexual Behavior, 31,* 263–274.

Latty-Mann, H., & Davis, K. (1996). Attachment theory and partner choice: Preference and actuality. *Journal of Social and Personal Relationships, 13,* 5–23.

Laumann, E. O., Gagnon, J. H., Michael, R. T., & Michaels, S. (1994). *The social organization of sexuality: Sexual practices in the United States.* Chicago: University of Chicago Press.

Laumann, E. O., & Parish, W. (in press). Chinese Family Health Survey (CFHS). In E. Laumann (Ed.).

Laumann, E. O., Paik, A., & Rosen, R. (1999). Sexual dysfunction in the United States: Prevalence and predictors. *Journal of the American Medical Association, 281,* 537–544.

Laurenceau, J.-P., Feldman, B., & Pietromonaco, P. R. (1998). Intimacy as an interpersonal process: The importance of self-disclosure, partner disclosure, and perceived partner responsiveness in interpersonal exchanges. *Journal of Personality and Social Psychology, 74,* 1238–1251.

Lavine, H., Sweeney, D., & Wagner, S. (1999). Depicting women as sex objects in television advertising: Effects on body dissatisfaction. *Personality and Social Psychology Bulletin, 25,* 1049–1058.

Lawrance, K.-A., & Byers, E. S. (1995). Sexual satisfaction in long-term heterosexual relationships: The interpersonal exchange model of sexual satisfaction. *Personal Relationships, 2,* 267–285.

Lawrance, K.-A., & Herold, E. S. (1988). Women's attitudes toward and experience with sexually explicit materials. *Journal of Sex Research, 24,* 161–169.

Lawrance, K.-A., Taylor, D., & Byers, E. S. (1996). Differences in men's and women's global, sexual and ideal-sexual expressiveness and instrumentality. *Sex Roles, 34*(5 & 6), 337–357.

Lawrence, A. A. (2003). Factors associated with satisfaction or regret following male-to-female sex reassignment surgery. *Archives of Sexual Behavior, 32,* 299–316.

Law Reform Commission of Canada. (1992). *Medically assisted procreation working paper 65.* Ottawa: Canada Communication Group-Publishing, cat. #J32-1/65-1992.

Leader, A. (1999). New reproductive technologies: Why are we limiting choices for infertile couples? *Canadian Medical Association Journal, 161,* 1411–1412.

Leaper, C., & Friedman, C. (2007). The Socialization of Gender. *Handbook of socialization: Theory and research* (pp. 561–587). New York, NY, US: Guilford Press.

Leavitt, F. (1974). *Drugs and behavior.* Philadelphia: Saunders.

Lebacqz, K. (1987). Appropriate vulnerability: A sexual ethic for singles. *Christian Century, 104,* 435–438.

Lebeque, B. (1991). Paraphilias in U.S. pornography titles: "Pornography made me do it" (Ted Bundy). *Bulletin of the American Academy of Psychiatry and Law, 19,* 43–48.

Lechner, S. C., Antoni, M. H., Lydston, D., LaPerriere, A., Ishii, M., Devieux, J., et al. (2003). Cognitive-behavioral interventions improve quality of life in women with AIDS. *Journal of Psychosomatic Research, 54,* 253–261.

Lederer, L. (Ed.). (1980). *Take back the night: Women on pornography.* New York: Morrow.

Lee, J. A. (1979). The social organization of sexual risk. *Alternative Lifestyles, 2,* 69–100.

Lee, S. & Coates, J. (2007). *Sex trade research initiative, New Brunswick.* Report prepared for Provincial Government's Executive Council Office, Women's Issues Branch.

Leger Marketing. (2004, May 25). *Canadians and their tolerance towards homosexuality.* Retrieved November 25, 2004, from www.legermarketing.com.

Leger Marketing. (2006, June 11). *Morality barometer.* Retrieved from www.legermarketing.com.

Legman, G. (1968). *Rationale of the dirty joke.* New York: Grove.

Leiblum, S. R. (2000). Vaginismus: A most perplexing problem. In S. R. Leiblum & R. C. Rosen (Eds.), *Principles and practice of sex therapy* (3rd ed.), New York: Guilford.

Leifer, M. (1980). *Psychological effects of motherhood: A study of first pregnancy.* New York: Praeger.

Leitenberg, H., Detzer, M. J., & Srebnik, D. (1993). Gender differences in masturbation and the relation of masturbation experience in pre-adolescence and/or early adolescence to sexual behavior and sexual adjustment in young adulthood. *Archives of Sexual Behavior, 22,* 87–98.

Leitenberg, H., & Henning, K. (1995). Sexual fantasy. *Psychological Bulletin, 117,* 469–496.

Lemieux, S., & Byers, E. S. (1996). *The relationship between child sexual abuse, adult attachment & adult adjustment.* Paper presented at the meeting of the Canadian Sex Research Forum, Montreal.

Lemieux, S. R., & Byers, E. S. (in press). The sexual well-being of women who have experienced child sexual abuse. *Psychology of Women Quarterly.*

L'Engle, K., Jackson, C., & Brown, J. (2006). Early adolescents' cognitive susceptibility to initiating sexual intercourse. *Perspectives on Sexual and Reproductive Health, 38,* 97–105.

Leonard, L. (2000). Interpreting female genital cutting: Moving beyond the impasse. *Annual Review of Sex Research, 11,* 158–190.

Leonard, L. M., & Follette, V. M. (2002). Sex functioning in women reporting a history of child sexual abuse: Clinical and empirical considerations. *Annual Review of Sex Research, 13,* 346–388.

Lerman, H. (1986). From Freud to feminist personality theory. *Psychology of Women Quarterly, 10,* 1–18.

LeVay, S. (1991). A difference in hypothalamic structure between heterosexual and homosexual men. *Science, 253,* 1034–1037.

LeVay, S. (1996). *Queer science: The use and abuse of research into homosexuality.* Cambridge, MA: MIT Press.

Lever, J. (1994, August). Sexual revelations. The 1994 Advocate Survey of Sexuality and Relationships: The Men. *The Advocate,* 17–24.

Lever, J. (1995, August). Lesbian sex survey. The 1995 Advocate Survey of Sexuality and Relationships: The Women. *The Advocate,* 22–30.

Levin, R. J. (2003). Is prolactin the biological "off switch" for human sexual arousal? *Sexual and Relationship Therapy, 18,* 237–243.

Levin, R. J. (2005). Sexual arousal—its physiological roles in human reproduction. *Annual Review of Sex Research, 15,* 154–189.

Levine, C., & Bermel, J. (Eds.). (1985, Aug.). *AIDS: The emerging ethical dilemmas.* Hastings Center Report Special Supplement, 1–31.

Levine, C., & Bermel, J. (Eds.). (1986, Dec.). *AIDS: Public health and civil liberties.* Hastings Center Report Special Supplement, 1–36.

Levine, R., Sato, S., Hashimoto, T., & Verma, J. (1995). Love and marriage in eleven cultures. *Journal of Cross-Cultural Psychology, 26,* 554–571.

Levitas, E., Lunenfeld, E., Weiss, N., Friger, M., Har-Vardi, I., Koifman, A., & Potashnik, G. (2005). Relationship between the duration of sexual abstinence and semen quality: Analysis of 9,489 semen samples. *Fertility and Sterility, 83*, 1680–1686.

Levitt, E., Moser, C., & Jamison, K. (1994). The prevalence and some attributes of females in the sadomasochistic subculture: A second report. *Archives of Sexual Behavior, 23*, 465–473.

Levy, J. J., Maticka-Tyndale, E., & Lew, V. A. (1992). Pratique contraceptives et preventive face au sida parmi un groupe de cegepiens de Montreal: Variations interethniques. *Novelles Pratique Sociale, 5*(2), 25–36.

Lewis, J., & Maticka-Tyndale, E. (1998). *Final report: Erotic/exotic dancing: HIV-related risk factors.* Ottawa: Health Canada.

Lewis, J., Maticka-Tyndale, E., Shaver, F., & Schramm, H. (2005). Managing risk and safety on the job: The experiences of Canadian sex workers. *Journal of Psychology and Human Sexuality, 17*, 147–167.

Lewis, W. J. (1997). Factors associated with post-abortion adjustment problems: Implications for triage. *Canadian Journal of Human Sexuality, 6*, 9–16.

Libman, E. (1989). Sociocultural and cognitive factors in aging and sexual expression: Conceptual and research issues. *Canadian Psychology, 3*(3), 560–567.

Libman, E., & Fichten, C. S. (1987). Prostatectomy and sexual function. *Urology, 24*(5), 467–478.

Libman, E., Fichten, C. S., Creti, L., Weinstein, N., Amsel, R., & Brender, W. (1989). Transurethral prostatectomy: Differential effects of age category and presurgery sexual functioning on postprostatectomy sexual adjustment. *Journal of Behavioural Medicine, 12*(5), 469–485.

Library and Archives Canada (2007). *Henry Morgentaler* (archive reference no: R9264-0-7-E). Retrieved from http://mikan3.archives.ca/.

Liebmann-Smith, J. (1987). *In pursuit of pregnancy: How couples discover, cope with, and resolve their fertility problems.* New York: Newmarket Press.

Lief, H. I., & Hubschman, L. (1993). Orgasm in the postoperative transsexual. *Archives of Sexual Behavior, 22*, 145–156.

Lievore, D. (2003). *Non-reporting and hidden recording of sexual assault: An International literature review.* Canberra: Commonwealth Government of Australia.

Lightfoot-Klein, H. (1993). *Prisoners of ritual: An odyssey into female genital circumcision in Africa.* New York: Haworth.

Liljeros, F., Edling, C. R., Amaral, L. A., Stanley, H. E., & Aberg, Y. (2001). The web of human sexual contacts. *Nature, 411*, 907–908.

Linz, D., Donnerstein, E., & Penrod, S. (1987). The findings and recommendations of the Attorney General's Commission on pornography: Do the psychological "facts" fit the political fury? *American Psychologist, 42*, 946–953.

Lisak, D., & Miller, P. M. (2002). Repeat rape and multiple offending among undetected rapists. *Violence & Victims, 17*, 73–84.

Liskin,. (1985, November–December). Youth in the 1980s: Social and health concerns. *Population Reports, XIII*, No. 5, M350–M388.

Liu, C. (2003). Does quality of marital sex decline with duration? *Archives of Sexual Behavior, 32*, 55–60.

Liu, S., Liston, R. M., Joseph, K. S., Heaman, M., Sauve, R., & Kramer, M. S. (2007). Maternal mortality and severe morbidity associated with low-risk planned cesarean delivery versus planned vaginal delivery at term. *Canadian Medical Association Journal, 176*, 455–460.

Ljunger, E., Cnattingius, S., Lundin, C., & Anneren, G. (2005). Chromosomal anomalies in first-trimester miscarriages. *Acta Obstetrica et Gynecologica Scandinavica, 84*, 1103–1107.

Loeb, T. B., Williams, J. K., Carmona, J. V., Rivkin, I., Wyatt, G. E., Chin, D., et al. (2002). Child sexual abuse: Associations with the sexual functioning of adolescents and adults. *Annual Review of Sex Research, 13*, 307–345.

Loeb, T. B., et al. (2002). Child sexual abuse: Associations with the sexual functioning of adolescents and adults. *Annual Review of Sex Research, 13*, 307–345.

Loffreda, B. (2000). *Losing Matt Shepard: Life and politics in the aftermath of anti-gay murder.* New York: Columbia University Press.

Loftus, E. F. (1993). The reality of repressed memories. *American Psychologist, 48*, 518–537.

Loftus, E. F., Polonsky, S., & Fullilove, M. T. (1994). Memories of childhood sexual abuse: Remembering and repressing. *Psychology of Women Quarterly, 18*, 67–84.

Lombardi, E. L., Wilchins, R., Priesing, D., & Malouf, D. (2001). Gender violence: Transgender experiences with violence and discrimination. *Journal of Homosexuality, 42*, 89–101.

Longo, D. J., Clum, G. A., & Yaeger, N. J. (1988). Psychosocial treatment for recurrent genital herpes. *Journal of Consulting and Clinical Psychology, 56*, 61–66.

Lonsway, K. A. & Kothari, C. (2000). First-year campus acquaintance rape education: Evaluating the impact of a mandatory intervention. *Psychology of Women Quarterly, 24*, 220–232.

LoPiccolo, J., & Stock, W. E. (1986). Treatment of sexual dysfunction. *Journal of Consulting and Clinical Psychology, 54*, 158–167.

Lorius, C.(1999). *Tantric sex: Making love last.* London: Thorsons/HarperCollins.

Los, M. (1994). The struggle to redefine rape in the early 1980s. In J. V. Roberts & R. M. Mohr (Eds.), *Confronting sexual assault: A decade of legal change.* Toronto: University of Toronto Press.

Louv, W. C., et al. (1989). Oral contraceptive use and risk of chlamydial and gonococcal infections. *American Journal of Obstetrics and Gynecology, 160*, 396.

Lowman, J. (1995). Prostitution in Canada. In M. A. Jackson & C. T. Griffiths (Eds.), *Canadian criminology: Perspectives on crime and criminality.* Toronto: Harcourt Brace.

Lowman, J., & Atchison, C. (2006). Men who buy sex: A survey in the Greater Vancouver regional district. *The Canadian Review of Sociology and Anthropology, 43*, 281–296.

Luke, B. (1994). Nutritional influences on fetal growth. *Clinical Obstetrics and Gynecology, 37*, 538–549.

Luker, K. (1975). *Taking chances: Abortion and the decision not to contracept.* Berkeley: University of California Press.

Luker, K. (1984). *Abortion and the politics of motherhood.* Berkeley: University of California Press.

Luo, M., Fee, M., & Katz, L. (2003). Encoding pheromonal signals in the accessory olfactory bulb in behaving mice. *Science, 299*, 1196–1201.

Luo, S., & Klohnen, E. (2005). Assortative mating and marital quality in newly weds: A couple-centered approach. *Journal of Personality and Social Psychology, 88*, 304–326.

Luzuriaga, K., et al. (2006). Vaccines to prevent transmission of HIV-1 via breastmilk: Scientific and logistical priorities. *The Lancet, 368*, 511–521.

Lydon-Rochelle, M., Holt, V., Easterling, T., & Martin, D. (2001). Risk of uterine rupture during labor among women with a prior cesarean delivery. *New England Journal of Medicine, 345*, 3–8.

Lytton, H., & Romney, D. M. (1991). Parents' differential socialization of boys and girls: A meta-analysis. *Psychological Bulletin, 109*, 267–296.

Maass, A., Cadinu, M., Guarnieri, G., & Grasselli, A. (2003). Sexual harassment under social identity threat: The computer harassment paradigm. *Journal of Personality and Social Psychology, 85*, 853–870.

Maccoby, E. (1998). *The two sexes: Growing up apart, coming together.* Cambridge, MA: Harvard University Press.

MacDonald, G., & Jeffrey, L. (2000). The ethics of social control in researching the sex trade: Prostitutes and professors. Prepared for Gendering Ethics/Ethics of Gender Conference at the Centre for Interdisciplinary Gender Studies on June 21, 2000, at the University of Leeds, UK.

MacDonald, T. K., Fong, G. T., Zanna, M. P., & Martineau, A. M. (2000a). Alcohol myopia and condom use: Can alcohol intoxication be associated with more prudent behavior? *Journal of Personality and Social Psychology, 78*, 605–619.

MacDonald, T. K., MacDonald, G., Zanna, M. P., & Fong, G. T. (2000b). Alcohol, sexual arousal, and intentions to use condoms in young men: Applying alcohol myopia theory to risky sexual behavior. *Health Psychology, 19*, 290–298.

MacDonald, N., & Wong, T. (2007). Canadian guidelines on sexually transmitted infections, 2006. *Canadian Medical Association Journal, 176*, 175–176.

MacDonald, T. K., & Ross, M. (1999). Assessing the accuracy of predictions about dating relationships: How and why do lovers' predictions differ from those made by observers? *Personality and Social Psychology Bulletin, 25*, 1417–1429.

Mackie, M. (1991). *Gender relations in Canada: Further explorations.* Toronto: Harcourt Brace Canada.

Maclean's. (2003, Oct. 6). Internet sex unzipped.

Maclean's/CTV Poll. (1994, Jan. 3). Canada under the covers." *Maclean's, 107*(1).

Maclean's/CTV Poll. (1995, Jan. 2). Looking inward. *Maclean's.*

Maclean's/Global Poll. (2000, Dec. 25). Sexual attitudes. *Maclean's.*

MacMillan, H. L., Fleming, J. E., Trocmé, N., Boyle, M. H., Wong, M., Racine, et al. (1997). Prevalence of child physical and sexual abuse in the community: Results from the Ontario Health Supplement. *Journal of the American Medical Association, 278,* 131–135.

MacNeil, S., & Byers, E. S. (1997). The relationship between sexual problems, communication and sexual satisfaction. *Canadian Journal of Human Sexuality, 6,* 277–283.

MacNeil, S., & Byers, E. S. (2005). Dyadic assessment of sexual self-disclosure and sexual satisfaction in heterosexual dating couples. *Journal of Social and Personal Relationships, 22,* 169–181.

Maddock, J. W. (1997). Sexuality education: A history lesson. In J. W. Maddock (Ed.), *Sexuality education in post-secondary and professional training settings* (pp. 1–22). Binghamton, NY: The Haworth Press.

Magana, J. R., & Carrier, J. M. (1991). Mexican and Mexican American male sexual behavior and spread of AIDS in California. *Journal of Sex Research, 28,* 425–441.

Maguire, D. C. (2001). *Sacred choices: The right to contraception and abortion in ten world religions.* Minneapolis: Augsburg Fortress.

Mah, K., & Binik, Y. M. (2001). The nature of human orgasm: A critical review of major trends. *Clinical Psychology Review, 21,* 823–856.

Mah, K., & Binik, Y. M. (2002). Do all orgasms feel alike? Evaluating a two-dimensional model of the orgasm experience across gender and sexual context. *Journal of Sex Research, 39,* 104–113.

Mah, K., & Binik, Y. M. (2005). Are orgasms in the mind or the body? Psychosocial versus physiological correlates of orgasmic pleasure and satisfaction. *Journal of Sex and Marital Therapy, 31,* 187–200.

Mahoney, E. R. (1983). *Human sexuality.* New York: McGraw-Hill.

Maines, R. P. (1999). *The technology of orgasm: "Hysteria," the vibrator, and women's sexual satisfaction.* Baltimore: Johns Hopkins University Press.

Major, B., Cozzarelli, C., Cooper, M. L., Zubek, J., Richards, C., Wilhite, M., et al. (2000). Psychological responses of women after first-trimester abortion. *Archives of General Psychiatry, 57,* 777–784.

Malamuth, N. M. (1998). The confluence model as an organizing framework for research on sexually aggressive men: Risk moderators, imagined aggression and pornography consumption. In R. Geen & E. Donnerstein (Eds.), *Aggression: Theoretical and empirical reviews.* New York: Academic Press.

Malamuth, N. M., & Brown, L. M. (1994). Sexually aggressive men's perceptions of women's communications. *Journal of Personality and Social Psychology, 67,* 699–712.

Malamuth, N. M., Sockloskie, R. J., Koss, M. P., & Tanaka, J. S. (1991). Characteristics of aggressors against women: Testing a model using a national sample of college students. *Journal of Consulting and Clinical Psychology, 59,* 670–781.

Maletzky, B. M. (1997). Exhibitionism: Assessment and treatment. In D. R. Laws & W. O'Donohue (Eds.) *Sexual deviance: Theory, assessment, and treatment.* New York: Guilford.

Maltz, W., & Boss, S. (1997). *In the garden of desire. The intimate world of women's sexual fantasies.* New York: Broadway Books.

Manson Singer, S., Willms, D. G., Adrien, A., Baxter, J., Brabazon, C., Leaune, V., Godin, G., Maticka-Tyndale, E., & Cappon, P. (1996). Many voices—Sociocultural results of the ethnocultural communities facing AIDS study in Canada. *Canadian Journal of Public Health, 8* (Supp. 1), S26–S32.

Markman, H. J. (1979). Application of a behavioral model of marriage in predicting relationship satisfaction of couples planning marriage. *Journal of Consulting and Clinical Psychology, 47,* 743–749.

Markman, H. J. (1981). Prediction of marital distress: A 5-year follow-up. *Journal of Consulting and Clinical Psychology, 49,* 760–762.

Markman, H., & Kadushin, F. (1986). Preventive effects of human training for first-time parents: A short-term longitudinal study. *Journal of Consulting and Clinical Psychology, 54,* 872–874.

Marquis, J. N. (1970). Orgasmic reconditioning: Changing sexual object choice through controlling masturbation fantasies. *Journal of Behavior Therapy and Experimental Psychiatry, 1,* 263–272.

Marshall, D. C. (1971). Sexual behavior on Mangaia. In D. S. Marshall & R. C. Suggs (Eds.), *Human sexual behavior.* New York: Basic Books.

Marshall, E. (1995). NIH's "Gay Gene" study questioned. *Science, 268,* 1841.

Marshall, W. L. (1992). The social values of treatment for sexual offenders. *Canadian Journal of Human Sexuality, 1,* 109–114.

Marshall, W. L. (1993). A revised approach to the treatment of men who sexually assault adult females. In G. N. Hall et al. (Eds.), *Sexual aggression* (pp. 143–165). Washington, DC: Taylor & Francis.

Marshall, W. L., & Eccles, A. (2000). Issues in clinical practice with sex offenders. *Journal of Interpersonal Violence, 16,* 68–93.

Marshall, W. L., Eccles, A., & Barbaree, H. E. (1991). The treatment of exhibitionists: A focus on sexual deviance versus cognitive and relationship features. *Behavioural Research and Therapy, 20,* 120–135.

Marshall, W. L., Jones, R., Ward, T., Johnson, P., & Barbaree, H. E. (1991). Treatment outcome with sex offenders. *Clinical Psychology Review, 11,* 465–485.

Marshall, W. L., Marshall, L. E., & Serran, G. A. (2006). Strategies in the treatment of paraphilias: A critical review. *Annual Review of Sex Research, 17,* 162–182.

Marshall, W. L., Payne, K., Barbaree, H. E., & Eccles, A. (1991). Exhibitionists: Sexual preferences for exposing. *Behavioural Research Therapy, 20*(1), 37–40.

Marshall, W. L., & Pithers, W. D. (1994). A reconsideration of treatment outcome with sex offenders. *Criminal Justice and Behavior, 21,* 10–27.

Martin, C. L., & Halverson, C. F. (1983). The effects of sex typing schemas on young children's memory. *Child Development, 54,* 563–574.

Martin, C. L., Ruble, D., & Szkrybalo, J. (2002). Cognitive theories of early gender development. *Psychological Bulletin, 128,* 903–933.

Martin, C., & Ruble, D. (2004). Children's search for gender cues: Cognitive perspectives on gender development. *Current Directions in Psychological Science, 13,* 67–70.

Martin, J. C. (2007). *Martin's annual criminal code 2007.* Aurora, Ontario: Canada Law Book, Inc.

Martin, S. L., Ray, N., Sotres-Alvarez, D., Kupper, L. L., Moracco, K. E., Dickens, P. A., Scandlin, D., & Gizlice, Z. (2006). Physical and sexual assault of women with disabilities. *Violence Against Women, 12,* 823–837.

Martins, Y., Preti, G. et al., (2005). Preference for human body odors is influenced by gender and sexual orientation. *Psychological Science, 16,* 694–701.

Martinson, F. M. (1994). *The sexual life of children.* Westport, CT: Bergin & Garvey.

Marx, J. (1995). Sharing the genes that divide the sexes for mammals. *Science, 269,* 1824–1827.

Masters, W. H., & Johnson, V. (1966). *Human sexual response.* Boston: Little, Brown.

Masters, W. H., & Johnson, V. (1970). *Human sexual inadequacy.* Boston: Little, Brown.

Masters, W. H., & Johnson, V. (1979). *Homosexuality in perspective.* Boston: Little, Brown.

Masters, W. H., Johnson, V. E., & Kolodny, R. C. (1982). *Human sexuality.* Boston: Little, Brown.

Masterton, G. (1993). *Drive him wild: A hands-on guide to pleasuring your man in bed.* New York: Signet Books.

Mathy, R., & Cooper, A. (2003). The duration and frequency of Internet use in a nonclinical sample: Suicidality, behavioral problems, and treatment history. *Psychotherapy: Theory, Research, Practice, Training, 40,* 125–135.

Maticka-Tyndale, E. (1992). Social construction of HIV transmission and prevention among heterosexual young adults. *Social Problems, 39*(93), 238–252.

Maticka-Tyndale, E. (1997). Reducing the incidence of sexually transmitted disease through behavioural and social change. *Canadian Journal of Human Sexuality, 6,* 89–104.

Maticka-Tyndale, E. (2001). Sexual health and Canadian youth: How do we measure up? *The Canadian Journal of Human Sexuality, 10,* 1–17.

Maticka-Tyndale, E., Barrett, M., & McKay, A. (2000a). Adolescent sexual and reproductive health in Canada: A review of national data sources and their limitations. *The Canadian Journal of Human Sexuality, 9,* 41–65.

Maticka-Tyndale, E., & Bicher, M. (1996). The impact of medicalization on women. In Bernard Schissel & Linda Mahood (Eds.), *Social control in Canada: A reader on the social construction of deviance.* Toronto: Oxford University Press.

Maticka-Tyndale, E., Adams, B. D., & Cohen, J. (2002). Sexual desire and practice among people living with HIV and using combination anti-retroviral therapies. *Canadian Journal of Human Sexuality, 11,* 33–40.

Maticka-Tyndale, E., Godin, G., LeMay, G., Adrien, A., Manson-Singer, S., Willms, D., et al. (1996). Canadian ethnocultural communities facing AIDS: Overview and summary of survey results from phase III. *Canadian Journal of Public Health, 87* (supp. 1), S38–S43.

Maticka-Tyndale, E., & Herold, E. S. (1997). The scripting of sexual behaviour: Canadian university students on spring break in Florida. *Canadian Journal of Human Sexuality, 6,* 317–328.

Maticka-Tyndale, E., & Herold, E. S. (1999). Condom use on spring break vacation: The influence of intention, prior use and context. *Journal of Applied Psychology, 29,* 1010–1027.

Maticka-Tyndale, E., Herold, E. S., & Mewhinney, D. (1998). Casual sex on spring break: Intentions and behaviours of Canadian students. *Journal of Sex Research, 35,* 254–264.

Maticka-Tyndale, E., Herold, E., & Oppermann, M. (2003). Casual sex among Australian schoolies. *Journal of Sex Research, 40,* 158–169.

Maticka-Tyndale, E., Lewis, J., & Street, M. (2005). Making a place for escort work: A case study. *Journal of Sex Research, 42,* 46–53.

Maticka-Tyndale, E., Lewis, J., Clark, J. P., Zubick, J., & Young, S. (1999). Social and cultural vulnerability to sexually transmitted infection: The work of exotic dancers. *Canadian Journal of Public Health, 90,* 19–22.

Maticka-Tyndale, E., Lewis, J., Clark, J. P., Zubrick, J., & Young, S. (2000). Exotic dancing and health. *Women & Health, 31,* 87–108.

Mattson, S., & Riley, E. (1998). A review of the neurobehavioral deficits in children with fetal alcohol syndrome or prenatal exposure to alcohol. *Alcoholism: Clinical and Experimental Research, 22,* 279–294.

Maurice, W. L. (2007). Sexual desire disorders in men. In S. Leiblum (Ed.), *Principles and practice of sex therapy* (4th ed., pp. 181–211). New York: Guilford.

May, R. (1974). *Love and will.* New York: Dell Books.

Mazer, D. B., & Percival, E. F. (1989). Students' experiences of sexual harassment at a small university. *Sex Roles, 20*(1&2), 1–22.

Mazur, A. (1986). U.S. trends in feminine beauty and overadaptation. *Journal of Sex Research, 22,* 281–303.

Mazzuca, J. (2004, November 2). Origin of homosexuality? Britons, Canadians say "nature." *Gallup News Service.* Washington DC: The Gallup Organization.

McCabe, M. P. (2002). Relationship functioning and sexuality among people with multiple sclerosis. *Journal of Sex Research, 39,* 302–309.

McCabe, M. P., & Taleporos, G. (2003). Sexual esteem, sexual satisfaction, and sexual behavior among people with physical disability. *Archives of Sexual Behavior, 32,* 359–370.

McCall, D., & McKay, A. (2004). SOGC policy statement: School-based and school-linked sexual health education and promotion in Canada. *Journal of Obstetrics and Gynaecology Canada, 146,* 596–600.

McBride, A. F., & Hebb, D. O. (1948). Behavior of the captive bottlenose dolphin, Tursiops truncatus. *Journal of Comparative and Physiological Psychology, 41,* 111–123.

McCall, D., Beazley, R., Doherty-Poirier, M., Lovato, C., MacKinnon, D., Otis, J., & Shannon, M. (1999). *Schools, public health, sexuality and HIV: A status report.* Toronto: Council of Ministers of Education.

McCarthy, B. W. (1989). Cognitive-behavioral strategies and techniques in the treatment of early ejaculation. In S. R. Leiblum & R. C. Rosen (Eds.), *Principles and practice of sex therapy* (2nd ed.). New York: Guilford.

McClelland, S. (1999, July 26). The bedroom and the new era of swing. *Maclean's.*

McClelland, S. (2001, December 3). Inside the sex trade. *Maclean's.*

McClintock, M. K. (1971). Menstrual synchrony and suppression. *Nature, 229,* 244–245.

McClintock, M. K. (1998). Whither menstrual synchrony? *Annual Review of Sex Research, 9,* 77–95.

McClintock, M. K. (2000). Human pheromones: Primers, releasers, signalers, or modulators? In K. Wallen & J. Schneider (Eds.), *Reproduction in context* (pp. 355–420). Cambridge, MA: MIT Press.

McClintock, M., & Herdt, G. (1996). Rethinking puberty: The development of sexual attraction. *Current Directions in Psychological Science, 5,* 178–183.

McClure, R., & Brewer, R. T. (1980). Attitudes of new parents towards child and spouse with Lamaze or non-Lamaze methods of childbirth. *Journal of Human Behavior, 17,* 45–48.

McCormick, N. B. (1993). Cultural diversity and women's sexuality. *Canadian Journal of Human Sexuality, 2,* 193–201.

McCoy, N. L., & Matyas, J. R. (1996). Oral contraceptives and sexuality in university women. *Archives of Sexual Behavior, 25,* 73–90.

McCoy, N. L., & Pitino, L. (2002). Pheromonal influences on sociosexual behavior in young women. *Physiology & Behavior, 75,* 367–375.

McCreary Centre Society (2007). *Not yet equal: The health of lesbian, gay, and bisexual youth in BC.* Vancouver, BC: Author.

McDermid, S. A., Zucker, K. J., Bradley, S. J., & Maing, D. M. (1998). Effects of physical appearance on masculine trait ratings of boys and girls with gender identity disorder. *Archives of Sexual Behavior, 27*(3), 253–267.

McDonagh, A., et al. (2005). Randomized trial of cognitive-behavioral therapy for chronic posttraumatic stress disorder in adult female survivors of childhood sexual abuse. *Journal of Consulting and Clinical Psychology, 73,* 515–524.

McDonald, J., & Bradford, W. (2000). The treatment of sexual deviation using a pharmacological approach. *The Journal of Sex Research, 37,* 248–257.

McDowell, J. D. (1983). Ethical implications of in vitro fertilization. *The Christian Century, 100,* 936–938.

McEwen, B. S. (1997). Meeting report–Is there a neurobiology of love? *Molecular Psychiatry, 2,* 15–16.

McEwen, B. S. (2001). Estrogen effects on the brain: Multiple sites and molecular mechanisms. *Journal of Applied Physiology, 91,* 2785–2801.

McFadden, D., Loehlin, J. C., Breedlove, S. M., Lippa, R. A., Manning, J. T., & Rahman, Q. (2005). A reanalysis of five studies on sexual orientation and the relative length of the 2nd and 4th fingers (the 2D:4D ratio). *Archives of Sexual Behavior, 34,* 341–356.

McFarland, W. P. (2001). The legal duty to protect gay and lesbian students from violence in school. *Professional School Counseling, 4,* 171–180.

McFarlane, J. M., & Williams, T. M. (1994). Placing premenstrual syndrome in perspective. *Psychology of Women Quarterly, 18,* 339–374.

McGuire, R. J., Carlisle, J. M., & Young, B. G. (1965). Sexual deviations as conditioned behavior: A hypothesis. *Behavioral Research and Therapy, 2,* 185–190.

McKay, A. (1993). Research supports broadly-based sex education. *Canadian Journal of Human Sexuality, 2,* 89–98.

McKay, A. (1996). Rural parents' attitudes toward school-based sexual health education. *Canadian Journal of Human Sexuality, 5,* 15–29.

McKay, A. (2000). Common questions about sexual health education. *SIECCAN Newsletter, 35,* 129–137.

McKay, A. (2004). Oral sex among teenagers: Research, discourse and education. *The Canadian Journal of Human Sexuality, 13,* 201–203.

McKay, A. (2005). Sexuality and substance use: The impact of tobacco, alcohol, and selected recreational drugs on sexual function. *The Canadian Journal of Human Sexuality, 14,* 47–56.

McKay, A. (2005). *Sexual health education in the schools: Questions and answers.* Toronto: SIECCAN.

McKay, A. (2006). Chlamydia screening programs: A review of the literature. Part 1. Issues in the promotion of chlamydia testing of youth by primary care physicians. *The Canadian Journal of Human Sexuality, 15,* 1–11.

McKay, A., & Barrett, M. (1999). Pre-service sexual health education training of elementary, secondary, and physical health education teachers in Canadian faculties of education. *Canadian Journal of Human Sexuality, 8,* 91–101.

McKay, A., & Holowaty, P. (1997). Sexual health education: A study of adolescents' opinions, self-perceived needs, and current and preferred sources of information. *Canadian Journal of Human Sexuality, 6,* 29–38.

McKay, A., Pietrusiak, M.-A., & Holowaty, P. (1998). Parents' opinions and attitudes towards sexuality education in schools. *Canadian Journal of Human Sexuality, 7,* 139–145.

McKee, A.(2005). The objectification of women in mainstream pornographic videos in Australia. *Journal of Sex Research, 42,* 277–290.

McKeganey, N. (1994). Why do men buy sex and what are their assessments of the HIV-related risks when they do? *AIDS Care, 6,* 289–301.

McKenna, K. E. (2000). Some proposals regarding the organization of the central nervous system control of penile erection. *Neuroscience and Biobehavioral Reviews, 24,* 535–540.

McKenna, K. E. (2005). The central control and pharmacological modulation of sexual function. In J. S. Hyde (Ed.), *Biological substrates of human sexuality* (pp. 75–108). Washington, DC: American Psychological Association.

McKenna, K. Y. A., Green, A. S., & Smith, P. K. (2001). Demarginalizing the sexual self. *Journal of Sex Research, 38,* 302–311.

McKenna, K., & Bargh, J. (1998). Coming out in the age of the Internet: Identity "demarginalization" through virtual group participation. *Journal of Personality and Social Psychology, 75,* 681–694.

McKenzie-Mohr, D., & Zanna, M. P. (1990). Treating women as sexual objects: Look to the (gender schematic) male who has viewed pornography. *Personality and Social Psychology Bulletin, 16*(2), 296–308.

McKinlay, S. M., Brambilla, D. J., & Posner, J. G. (1992). The normal menopause transition. *American Journal of Human Biology, 4,* 37–46.

McMahon, S., Hansen, L., Mann, J., Sevigny, C., Wong, T., & Roache, M. (2004). Contraception. *BMC Women's Health, 4* (Suppl 1), S25.

McMaster, L. E., Connolly, J., Pepler, D., & Craig, W. M. (2002). Peer to peer sexual harassment in early adolescence: A developmental perspective. *Development and Psychopathology, 14,* 91–105.

McMillen, C., Zuravin, S., & Rideout, G. (1995). Perceived benefit from child sexual abuse. *Journal of Consulting and Clinical Psychology, 63,* 1037–1043.

McNair, R., Dempsey, D., Wise, S., & Perlesz, A. (2002). Lesbian parenting: Issues, strengths and challenges. *Family Matters, 63,* 40–49.

McNeill, J. J. (1987). Homosexuality: Challenging the Church to grow. *Christian Century, 104,* 242–246.

Meana, M., Binik, Y. M., Khalife, S., & Cohen, D. R. (1997). Biopsychosocial profile of women with dyspareunia. *Obstetrics & Gynecology, 90,* 583–589.

Medical Research Council of Canada. (1998). *Tri-council policy statement: Ethical conduct for research involving humans.* Ottawa: Public Works and Government Services Canada.

Mehta, A., & Sheth, S. (2006). Postpartum depression: How to recognize and treat this common condition. *Medscape Psychiatry and Mental Health, 11,* article 529930.

Meischke, H. (1995). Implicit sexual portrayals in the movies: Interpretations of young women. *Journal of Sex Research, 32,* 29–36.

Melman, A., & Tiefer, L. (1992). Surgery for erectile disorders: Operative procedures and psychological issues. In R. C. Rosen & S. R. Leiblum (Eds.), *Erectile disorders* (pp. 255– 282). New York: Guilford.

Meseda, C. A., Schmeisser, F., Pedersen, R., Woerner, A., & Weir, J. P. (2004). DNA immunization with a herpes simplex virus 2 bacterial artificial chromosome. *Virology, 318,* 420–428.

Messenger, J. C. (1993). Sex and repression in an Irish folk community. In D. N. Suggs & A. W. Miracle (Eds.), *Culture and human sexuality.* Pacific Grove, CA: Brooks/Cole.

Meston, C. M., & Buss, D. M. (2007). Why humans have sex. *Archives of Sexual Behavior, 36,* 477–507.

Meston, C. M., Trapnell, P. D., & Gorzalka, B. B. (1996). Ethnic and gender differences in sexuality: Variations in sexual behavior between Asian and non-Asian university students. *Archives of Sexual Behavior, 25,* 33–72.

Meston, C., Trapnell, P., & Gorzlaka, B. (1998). Ethnic, gender, and length of residency influences on sexual knowledge and attitudes. *The Journal of Sex Research, 35,* 176–188.

Meston, C. M., et al. (2004). Women's orgasm. *Annual Review of Sex Research, 15,* 173–257.

Metcalf, M. G., Skidmore, D. S. Lowry, G. F., & Mackenzie, J. A. (1983). Incidence of ovulation in the years after the menarche. *Journal of Endocrinology, 97,* 213–219.

Metz, M. E., et al. (1997). Premature ejaculation: A psychophysiological review. *Journal of Sex & Marital Therapy, 23,* 3–23.

Mewhinney, D., Maticka-Tyndale, E., & Herold, E. (1995). Sexual scripts and risk taking of Canadian university students on spring break in Daytona Beach, Florida. *Canadian Journal of Human Sexuality, 4,* 273–288.

Meyer, I. H. (2003). Prejudice, social stress, and mental health in lesbian, gay, and bisexual populations: Conceptual issues and research evidence. *Psychological Bulletin, 129,* 674–697.

Meyer, J. K. (1979). Sex reassignment. *Archives of General Psychiatry, 36,* 1010–1015.

Meyer-Bahlburg, H. F. L. (1997). The role of prenatal estrogens in sexual orientation. In L. Ellis & L. Ebertz (Eds.), *Sexual orientation: Toward biological understanding.* Westport, CT: Praeger.

Meyer-Bahlburg, H. F. L., et al. (1995). Prenatal estrogens and the development of homosexual orientation. *Developmental Psychology, 31,* 12–21.

Meyer-Bahlburg, H., et al. (2004). Prenatal androgenization affects gender-related behavior but not gender identity in 5–12-year-old girls with Congenital Adrenal Hyperplasia. *Archives of Sexual Behavior, 33,* 97–104.

Meyer-Bahlburg, H., et al. (2006). Gender development in women with congenital adrenal hyperplasia as a function of disorder severity. *Archives of Sexual Behavior, 35,* 667–684.

Meyerowitz, B. E. (1980). Psychosocial correlates of breast cancer and its treatments. *Psychological Bulletin, 87,* 108–131.

Mezzacappa, E., & Katkin, E. (2002). Breast-feeding is associated with reduced perceived stress and negative mood in mothers. *Health Psychology, 21,* 187–193.

Michael, R. T., Gagnon, J. H., Laumann, E. O., & Kolata, G. (1994). *Sex in America: A definitive survey.* Boston: Little, Brown.

Milam, J. (2006). Posttraumatic growth and HIV disease progression. *Journal of Consulting and Clinical Psychology, 74,* 817–827.

Milan, R. J., & Kilmann, P. R. (1987). Interpersonal factors in premarital contraception. *Journal of Sex Research, 23,* 289–321.

Miller, E. M. (1986). *Street woman.* Philadelphia: Temple University Press.

Miller, J., & Schwartz, M. (1995). Rape myths and violence against street prostitutes. *Deviant Behavior, 76,* 1–23.

Miller, L. C., & Fishkin, S. A. (1997). On the dynamics of human bonding and reproductive success: Seeking windows on the adapted-for-human-environmental interface. In J. A. Simpson & D. T. Kenrick (Eds.), *Evolutionary social psychology* (pp. 197–235). Mahwah, NJ: Lawrence Erlbaum.

Miller, N. (1992). *Out in the world: Gay and lesbian life from Buenos Aires to Bangkok.* New York: Random House.

Miller, S. A. & Byers, E. S. (2004). Actual and desired duration of foreplay and intercourse: Discordance and misperceptions within heterosexual couples. *Journal of Sex Research, 41,* 301–309.

Miller, S. A., & Byers, E. S. (2004). Actual and desired duration of foreplay and intercourse: Discordance and misperceptions within heterosexual couples. *The Journal of Sex Research, 41,* 301–309.

Miller, S., Corrales, R., & Wachman, D. B. (1975). Recent progress in understanding and facilitating marital communication. *The Family Coordinator, 24,* 143–152.

Milligan, G. N., Dudley-McClain, K. L., Chu, C. F., & Young, C. G. (2004). Efficacy of genital T cell responses to herpes simplex virus type 2 resulting from immunization of the nasal mucosa. *Virology, 318,* 507–515.

Miner, M., & Coleman, E. (2001). Advances in sex offender treatment and challenges for the future. *Journal of Psychology and Human Sexuality, 13,* 5–24.

Minto, C. L., Liao, L. M., Woodhouse, C. R. J., Ransley, P. G., & Creighton, S. M. (2003). The effect of clitoral surgery on sexual outcome in individuals who have intersex conditions with ambiguous genitalia: A cross-sectional study. *Lancet, 361,* 1252–1257.

Misovich, S. J., Fisher, J. D., & Fisher, W. A. (1997). Close relationships and elevated HIV risk behavior: Evidence and possible underlying psychological processes. *Review of General Psychology, 1,* 72–107.

Monro, S. (2000). Theorizing transgender diversity: Towards a social model of health. *Sexual and Relationship Therapy, 15,* 33–45.

Moffatt, M. (1989). *Coming of age in New Jersey.* New Brunswick, NJ: Rutgers University Press.

Mohr, R. M., & Roberts, J. V. (1994). Sexual assault in Canada: Recent developments. In J. V. Roberts & R. M. Mohr (Eds.), *Confronting sexual assault: A decade of legal social change.* Toronto: University of Toronto Press.

Molitch, M. E. (1995). Neuroendocrinology. In P. Felig et al. (Eds.), *Endocrinology and metabolism.* New York: McGraw-Hill.

Money, J. (1987). Sin, sickness, or status: Homosexual gender identity and psychoneuroendocrinology. *American Psychologist, 42,* 384–399.

Money, J., & Ehrhardt, A. (1972). *Man and woman, boy and girl.* Baltimore: Johns Hopkins. Reissued in a facsimile edition by Jason Aronson, Northvale, NJ, 1996.

Montorsi, F., & Althof, S. (2004). Partner responses to sildenafil citrate (Viagra) treatment of erectile dysfunction. *Urology, 63,* 762–767.

Montorsi, F., Perani, D., Anchisi, D., Salonia, A., Scifo, P., Rigiroli, P., et al. (2003a). Apomorphine-induced brain modulation during sexual stimulation: A new look at central phenomena related to erectile dysfunction. *International Journal of Impotence Research, 15,* 203–209.

Montorsi, F., Perani, D., Anchisi, D., Salonia, A., Scifo, P., Rigiroli, P., et al. (2003b). Brain activation patterns during video sexual stimulation following the administration of apomorphine. *European Urology, 43,* 405–411.

Montorsi, F., Verheyden, B., Meuleman, E., Junemann, K. P., Moncada, I., Valiquette, L., et al. (2004). Long-term safety and tolerability of tadalafil in the treatment of erectile dysfunction. *European Urology, 45,* 339–345.

Moore, A. J. (1987). Teenage sexuality and public morality. *Christian Century, 104,* 747–750.

Morales, A., et al. (1998). Clinical safety of oral sildenafil (Viagra) in the treatment of erectile dysfunction. *International Journal of Impotence Research, 10,* 69–74.

Morales, A. & Heaton, J. (2001). Hormonal erectile dysfunction: Evaluation and management. *Urologic Clinics of North America, 28,* 279.

Morell, V. (1998). A new look at monogamy. *Science, 281,* 1982–1983.

Morgan, R. (1980). Theory and practice: Pornography and rape. In L. Lederer (Ed.), *Take back the night: Women on pornography.* New York: Morrow.

Morison, L., Scherf, C., Ekpo, G., Paine, K., West, B., Coleman, R., & Walraven, G. (2001). The long-term reproductive health consequences of female genital cutting in rural Gambia: A community-based survey. *Tropical Medicine & International Health, 6,* 643–653.

Morokoff, P. J. (1986). Volunteer bias in the psychophysiological study of female sexuality. *Journal of Sex Research, 22,* 35–51.

Morris-Rush, J., & Bernstein, P. (2002). Postpartum depression. *Medscape Women's Health, 7.*

Morrison, D. M. (1985). Adolescent contraceptive behavior: A review. *Psychological Bulletin, 98,* 538–568.

Morrison, M. A., & Morrison, T. G. (1999). *Development and validation of a scale measuring modern prejudice toward gay men and lesbians.* Presented at the 26th Annual Convention of the Canadian Sex Research Forum, September.

Morrison, T. G. (2004). "He was treating me like trash, and I was loving it..." Perspectives on gay male pornography. *Journal of Homosexuality, 47,* 167–183.

Morrison, T. G., Ellis, S. R., Morrison, M. A., Bearden, A., & Harriman, R. L. (2006). Exposure to sexually explicit material and variations in body esteem, genital attitudes, and sexual esteem among a sample of Canadian men. *The Journal of Men's Studies, 14,* 209–222.

Morrison, T. G., & Tallack, D. (2005). Lesbian and bisexual women's interpretations of lesbian and ersatz lesbian pornography. *Sexuality & Culture, 9,* 3–30.

Morry, M. M. (2007). The attraction-similarity hypothesis among cross-sex friends: Relationship satisfaction, perceived similarities, and self-serving perceptions. *Journal of Social and Personal Relationships, 24,* 117–138.

Mortola, J. F. (1998). Premenstrual syndrome-pathophysiologic considerations. *New England Journal of Medicine, 338,* 256–257.

Moser, C. (1998). S/M (Sadomasochistic) interactions in semi-public settings. *Journal of Homosexuality, 36,* 19–29.

Moser, C. (2001). Paraphilia: Another confused sexological concept. In P. J. Kleinpatz (Ed.), *New directions in sex therapy: Innovations and alternatives* (pp. 91–108.), Philadelphia, PA: W. B. Saunders Company.

Moser, C., & Kleinpatz, P. J. (2002). Transvestic fetishism: Psychopathology or iatrogenic artifact? *New Jersey Psychologist, 52,* 16–17.

Moser, C., & Kleinpatz, P. J. (2005). DSM-IV-TR and the paraphilias: An argument for removal. *Journal of Psychology and Human Sexuality, 17,* 91–109.

Moser, C., Kleinplatz, P. J., & Zuccarini, D. (2004). Situating unusual child and adolescent sexual behavior in context. *Child & Adolescent Psychiatric Clinics of North America, 13,* 569–589.

Moser, C., & Levitt, E. E. (1987). An exploratory-descriptive study of a sadomasochistically oriented sample. *Journal of Sex Research, 23,* 322–337.

Moses, S., et al. (1990). Geographical patterns of male circumcision practices in Africa: Association with HIV seroprevalence. *International Journal of Epidemiology, 19,* 693–697.

Mosher, D., & MacIan, P. (1994). College men and women respond to X-rated videos intended for male or female audiences: Gender and sexual scripts. *Journal of Sex Research, 31,* 99–113.

Mosher, W. D., Chandra, A., & Jones, J. (2005). Sexual behavior and selected health measures: Men and women 15–44 years of age, United States, 2002. Advance Data, 362. Atlanta: Center for Disease Control and Prevention.

Moss, B. F., & Schwebel, A. I. (1993). Marriage and romantic relationships: Defining intimacy in romantic relationships. *Family Relations, 42,* 31–37.

Mulders, T., & Dieben, T. (2001). Use of the novel combined contraceptive vaginal ring NuvaRing for ovulation inhibition. *Fertility and Sterility, 75,* 865–870.

Muller, J., Mittleman, M., Maclure, M., Sherwood, J., & Tofler, G. (1996). Triggering myocardial infarction by sexual activity. *Journal of the American Medical Association, 275,* 1405–1409.

Murnen, S. K., & Stockton, M. (1997). Gender and self-reported sexual arousal in response to sexual stimuli: A meta-analytic review. *Sex Roles, 37,* 135–154.

Murnen, S. K., Wright, C., & Kaluzny, G. (2002). If "boys will be boys," then girls will be victims? A meta-analytic review of the research that relates masculine ideology to sexual aggression. *Sex Roles, 46,* 359–376.

Murray, S. L. & Holmes, J. G. (1997). A leap of faith? Positive illusions in romantic relationships. *Personality and Social Psychology Bulletin, 23,* 586–604.

Murray, S. L., Holmes, J. G., & Griffin, D. W. (1996). The benefits of positive illusions: Idealization and the construction of satisfaction in close relationships. *Journal of Personality and Social Psychology, 70*(1), 79–98.

Murray, S. O. (2000). *Homosexualities.* Chicago: University of Chicago Press.

Mustanski, B. S. (2001). Getting wired: Exploiting the Internet for the collection of valid sexuality data. *Journal of Sex Research, 38,* 292–301.

Mustanski, B. S., et al. (2005). A genomewide scan of male sexual orientation. *Human Genetics, 116,* 272–278.

Myers, B. J. (1984). Mother-infant bonding: The status of this critical-period hypothesis. *Developmental Review, 4,* 240–274.

Myers, P. N., & Biocca, F. A. (1992). The elastic body image: The effect of television advertising and programming on body image distortions in young women. *Journal of Communication, 42,* 108–133.

Myers, T., Bullock, S. L., Calzavara, L. M., Cockerill, R., Marshall, V. W., & George-Mandoka, C. (1999). Culture and sexual practices in response to HIV among Aboriginal people living on reserve in Ontario. *Culture, Health & Sexuality, 1*(1).

Myers, T., Calzavara, L. M., Bullock, S., Cockerill, R., & Marshall, V. (1994). The Ontario First Nations aids and healthy lifestyle survey: A model for community-based research in diverse reserve communities. *Arctic Medical Research, 53* (suppl. 2), 726–731.

Najman, J. M., et al. (2005). Sexual abuse in childhood and sexual dysfunction in adulthood: An Australian population-based study. *Archives of Sexual Behavior, 34*, 517–526.

Narod, S. A., et al. (1988). Human mutagens: Evidence from paternal exposure? *Environmental and Molecular Mutagenesis, 11*, 401–415.

Nelson, J. B. (1978). *Embodiment: An approach to sexuality and Christian theology.* Minneapolis, MN: Augsburg.

Nemeth, M. (1995, June 26). Nobody has the right to play God. *Maclean's.*

Neville, V. A., & Heppner, M. S. (1999). Contextualizing rape: Reviewing sequelae and proposing a culturally inclusive ecological model of sexual assault recovery. *Applied and Preventive Psychology, 8*, 41–62.

Newhouse, D. (1998). Magic & joy: Traditional aboriginal views of human sexuality. *Canadian Journal of Sexuality, 7*, 183–187.

Newton, N. A. (1972). Childbearing in broad perspective. In Boston Children's Medical Center, *Pregnancy, birth and the newborn baby.* New York: Delacorte Press.

Noll, J., Trickett, P., & Putnam, F. (2003). A prospective investigation of the impact of childhood sexual abuse on the development of sexuality. *Journal of Consulting and Clinical Psychology, 71*, 575–586.

Nosko, A., Wood, E., & Desmarais, S. (2007). Unsolicited online sexual material: What affects our attitudes and likelihood to search for more? *The Canadian Journal of Human Sexuality, 16*, 1–10.

Noss, J. B. (1963). *Man's religions* (3rd ed.). New York: Macmillan.

Notzon, F. C. (1990). International differences in the use of obstetric interventions. *Journal of the American Medical Association, 263*, 3286–3291.

Novak, E., & Novak, E. R. (1952). *Textbook of gynecology.* Baltimore: Williams & Wilkins.

Nova Scotia Department of Community Services. (1991). *Mothers and children: One decade later.* Halifax, NS: Author.

Novembre, J., et al. (2005). The geographic spread of the CCR5 Delta 32 HIV-resistance allele. *PloS Biology, 3*, e339.

Ochs, E. P., Mah, K., & Binik, Y. (2002). Obtaining data about human sexual functioning from the Internet. In A. Cooper (Ed.), *Sex and the Internet: A guidebook for clinicians* (pp. 245–262). New York: Routledge.

O'Connell, H. E., & DeLancey, J. (2005a). Clitoral anatomy in nulliparous, healthy, premenopausal volunteers using unenhanced magnetic resonance imaging. *Journal of Urology, 173*, 2060–2063.

O'Connor, A. (1987). Female sex offenders. *British Journal of Psychiatry, 150*, 615–620.

O'Donnell, A. B., Araujo, A. B., & McKinlay, J. B. (2004). The health of normally aging men: The Massachusetts male aging study (1987–2004). *Experimental Gerontology, 39*, 975–984.

Offman, A., & Kleinplatz, P. J. (2004). Does PMDD belong in the DSM? Challenging the medicalization of women's bodies. *Canadian Journal of Human Sexuality, 13*, 17–27.

Offman, A., & Matheson, K. (2004). The sexual self-perceptions of young women experiencing abuse in dating relationships. *Sex Roles, 51*, 551–560.

Offman, A., & Matheson, K. (2005). Sexual compatibility and sexual functioning in intimate relationships. *Canadian Journal of Human Sexuality, 14*, 21–29.

Ogletree, S. M., & Ginsburg, H. J. (2000). Kept under the hood: Neglect of the clitoris in common vernacular. *Sex Roles, 43*, 917–926.

O'Hara, M. W., & Swain, A. M. (1996). Rates and risk of postpartum depression: A meta-analysis. *International Review of Psychiatry, 8*, 37–54.

Okami, P. (1995). Childhood exposure to parental nudity, parent-child co-sleeping, and "primal scenes": A review of clinical opinion and empirical evidence. *Journal of Sex Research, 32*, 51–64.

Oliver, M. B., & Hyde, J. S. (1993). Gender differences in sexuality: A meta-analysis. *Psychological Bulletin, 114*, 29–51.

Olson, B., & Douglas, W. (1997). The family on television: Evaluation of gender roles in situation comedy. *Sex Roles, 36*, 409–427.

Ontario College of Physicians & Surgeons. (1991). *The Final Report of the Task Force on Sexual Abuse.*

Options for Sexual Health (2004). *An assessment of the effectiveness of sexual health education in BC schools.* Retrieved February 25, 2008, from www.optionsforsexualhealth.org.

Ornstein, M. (1989). *AIDS in Canada: Knowledge, behaviour, and attitudes of adults.* Toronto: Institute for Social Research, York University.

Oosterhuis, H. (2000). *Step children of nature: Krafft-Ebing, psychiatry, and the making of sexual identity.* Chicago: University of Chicago Press.

O'Shea, P. A. (1995). Congenital defects and their causes. In D. R. Constan, R. V. Haning, Jr., & D. B. Singer (Eds.), *Human reproduction: Growth and development.* Boston: Little, Brown.

Osman, S. L. (2003). Predicting men's rape perceptions based on the belief that "no" really means "yes." *Journal of Applied Social Psychology, 33*, 683–692.

Østensten, M. (1994). Optimisation of antirheumatic drug treatment in pregnancy. *Clinical Pharmacokinetics, 27*, 486–503.

O'Sullivan, L., & Brooks-Gunn J. (2005). The timing of changes in girls' sexual cognitions and behaviors in early adolescence: A prospective cohort study. *Journal of Adolescent Health, 37*, 211–219.

O'Sullivan, L., & Byers, E. S. (1992). College students' incorporation of initiator and restrictor role in sexual dating interactions. *Journal of Sex Research, 29*, 435–446.

O'Sullivan, L. F., & Byers, E. S. (1993). Eroding stereotypes: College women's attempts to influence reluctant sexual partners. *Journal of Sex Research, 30*, 270–282.

O'Sullivan, L. F., & Byers, E. S. (1996). Gender differences in responses to discrepancies in desired level of sexual intimacy. *Journal of Psychology & Human Sexuality, 8*(1&2), 49–67.

O'Sullivan, L. F., Byers, E. S., & Finkelman, L. (1998). A comparison of male and female college students' experiences of sexual coercion. *Psychology of Women Quarterly, 22*, 177–195.

O'Sullivan, L., & Meyer-Bahlburg, H. (2003). African-American and Latina inner-city girls' reports of romantic and sexual development. *Journal of Social and Personal Relationships, 20*, 221–238.

Pachankis, J. E. (2007). The psychological implications of concealing a stigma: A cognitive-affective-behavioral model. *Psychological Bulletin, 133*, 328–345.

Padma-Nathan, H., McMurray, J. G., Pullman, W. E., Whitaker, J. S., Saoud, J. B., Ferguson, K. M., et al. (2001). On-demand IC351 (Cialis-trade mark) enhances erectile function in patients with erectile dysfunction. *International Journal of Impotence Research, 13*, 2–9.

Page, D. C., et al. (1987). The sex-determining region of the human Y chromosome encodes a finger protein. *Cell, 51*, 1091–1104.

Page, S. T., et al. (2006). Testosterone gel combined with depomedroxyprogesterone acetate is an effective male hormonal contraceptive regimen and is not enhanced by the addition of a GnRH antagonist. *Journal of Clinical Endocrinology and Metabolism, 91*, 4374–4380.

Pakenham, K. I., Dadds, M. R., & Terry, D. J. (1994). Relationships between adjustment to HIV and both social support and coping. *Journal of Consulting and Clinical Psychology, 62*, 1194–1203.

Palace, E. M. (1995a). A cognitive-physiological process model of sexual arousal and response. *Clinical Psychology: Science and Practice, 2*, 370–384.

Palace, E. M. (1995b). Modification of dysfunctional patterns of sexual response through autonomic arousal and false physiological feedback. *Journal of Consulting and Clinical Psychology, 63*, 604–615.

Park, K., et al. (2001). A new potential of blood oxygenation level dependent (BOLD) functional MRI for evaluating cerebral centers of penile erection. *International Journal of Impotence Research, 13*, 73–81.

Parker, G. (1983). The legal regulation of sexual activity and the protection of females. *Osgoode Hall Law Journal, 21*, 187–244.

Parker, R., et al. (2004). Global transformations and intimate relations in the 21st century: Social science research on sexuality and the emergence of Sexual Health and Sexual Rights frameworks. *Annual Review of Sex Research, 15*, 362–398.

Parrinder, G. (1980). *Sex in the world's religions.* New York: Oxford University Press.

Parrinder, G. (1996). *Sexual morality in the world's religions.* Oxford: Oneworld.

Pasacreta, J. V., & McCorkle, R. (1998). Providing accurate information to women about tamoxifen therapy for breast cancer: Current indications, effects, and controversies. *Oncology Nursing Forum, 0*, 1577–1583

Patterson, C. (1992). Children of lesbian and gay parents. *Child Development, 63,* 1025–1042.

Patterson, C. J. (2006). Children of lesbian and gay parents. *Current Directions in Psychological Science, 15,* 241–244.

Paul, E., McManus, B., & Hayes, A. (2000). "Hookups": Characteristics and correlates of college students' spontaneous and anonymous sexual experiences. *Journal of Sex Research, 37,* 76–88.

Payne, K. A., & Binik, Y. M (2006). Reviving the labial thermistor clip. *Archives of Sexual Behavior, 35,* 111–113.

Payne, K. A., Binik, Y. M., Amsel, R., & Khalifé, S. (2005). When sex hurts, anxiety and fear orient attention towards pain. *European Journal of Pain, 9,* 427–436.

Payne, K. A., Reissing, E. D., Lahaie, M., Binik, Y. M., Amsel, R., & Khalifé, S. (2005). What is sexual pain? A critique of DSM's classification of dyspareunia and vaginismus. *Journal of Psychology & Human Sexuality, 17,* 141–154.

Payne, K., Thaler, L., Kukkonen, T., Carrier S., & Binik, Y. (2007). Sensation and sexual arousal in circumcised and uncircumcised men. *Journal of Sexual Medicine, 4,* 667–674.

Peat, Marwick & Partners. (1984). Canadians' attitudes toward and perceptions of pornography and prostitution. *Working Papers on Pornography and Prostitution, Report #6.* Ottawa: Department of Justice.

Pedersen, W., Miller, L. C., Putcha-Bhagavatula, A., & Yang, Y. (2002). Evolved sex differences in the number of partners desired? The long and short of it. *Psychological Science, 13,* 157–159.

Pennisi, E. (1996). Homing in on a prostate cancer gene. *Science, 274,* 1301.

Peplau, L. A. (2003). Human sexuality: How do men and women differ? *Current Directions in Psychological Science, 12,* 37–40.

Peplau, L. A., Garnets, L. D., Spalding, L. R., Conley, T. D., & Veniegas, R. C. (1998). A critique of Bem's "Exotic becomes erotic" theory of sexual orientation. *Psychological Review, 105,* 387–394.

Peplau, L. A., Veniegas, R. C., & Campbell, S. M. (1996). Gay and lesbian relationships. In R. C. Savin-Williams & K. M. Cohen (Eds.), *The lives of lesbians, gays, and bisexuals* (pp. 250–273). Fort Worth, TX: Harcourt Brace.

Perelman, M. A., & Rowland, D. L. (2006). Retarded ejaculation. *World Journal of Urology.*

Perez, M. A., Skinner, E. C., & Meyerowitz, B. E. (2002). Sexuality and intimacy following radical prostatectomy: Patient and partner perspectives. *Health Psychology, 21,* 288–293.

Perlman, D., & Fehr, B. (1987). The development of intimate relationships. In D. Perlman & S. Duck (Eds.), *Intimate relationships: Development, dynamics, and deterioration.* Newbury Park, CA: Sage.

Perovic, S. V., & Djordjevic, M. L. (2003). Metoidioplasty: A variant of phalloplasty in female transsexuals. *BJU International, 92,* 981–985.

Perry, J. D., & Whipple, B. (1981). Pelvic muscle strength of female ejaculators: Evidence in support of a new theory of orgasm. *Journal of Sex Research, 17,* 22–39.

Petersen, M. E., & Dickey, R. (1995). Surgical sex reassignment: *A comparative survey of international centers. Archives of Sexual Behavior, 24,* 135–156.

Petkovich, A. (2004). From gonzo porn to mainstream? Porn starlet Sienna. *Spectator,* www.spectator.net.

Pfaus, J. G., Kippin, T. E., & Coria-Avila, G. (2003). What can animal models tell us about human sexual response? *Annual Review of Sex Research, 14,* 1–63.

Pfeiffer, E., Verwoerdt, A., & Wang, H. S. (1968). Sexual behavior in aged men and women. *Archives of General Psychiatry, 19,* 753–758.

Phelps, J., Albo, M., Dunn, K., & Joseph, A. (2001). Spinal cord injury and sexuality in married or partnered men: Activities, function, needs, and predictors of sexual adjustment. *Archives of Sexual Behavior, 30,* 591–602.

Phoenix, C. H., Goy, R. W., Gerall, A. A., & Young, W. C. (1959). Organizing action of prenatally administered testosterone propionate on the tissues mediating mating behavior in the female guinea pig. *Endocrinology, 65,* 369–382.

Phoolcharoen, W. (1998). HIV/AIDS prevention in Thailand: Success and challenges. *Science, 280,* 1873–1874.

Pick, S. Givaudan, M., & Poortinga, Y. (2003). Sexuality and life skills education: A multistrategy intervention in Mexico. *American Psychologist, 58,* 230–234.

Pilkington, N. W., & Lydon, J. E. (1997). The relative effect of attitude similarity and attitude dissimilarity and interpersonal attraction: Investigating the moderating roles of prejudice and group membership. *Journal of Personality and Social Psychology Bulletin, 23*(2), 107–122.

Pillard, R. C., & Weinrich, J. D. (1987). Periodic table model of transpositions. *Journal of Sex Research, 23,* 425–454.

Pinheiro, R. C., Lambert, J., Benard, F., Mauffette, F., & Miron, P. (1999). Effectiveness of in vitro fertilization with intracytoplasmic sperm injection for severe male infertility. *Canadian Medical Association Journal, 161,* 1397–1442.

Pithers, W. D. (1993). Treatment of rapists. In G. N. Hall et al. (Eds.), *Sexual aggression* (pp. 167–196). Washington, D.C.: Taylor & Francis.

Pittenger, W. Norman. (1970). *Making sexuality human.* Philadelphia: Pilgrim Press.

Pittman, F., III. (1993, May–June). Beyond betrayal: Life after infidelity. *Psychology Today,* 32–38, ff.

Pitts, M. K., Smith, A., Grierson, J., O'Brien, M., & Mission, S. (2004). Who pays for sex and why? An analysis of social and motivational factors associated with male clients of sex workers. *Archives of Sexual Behavior, 33,* 353–368.

Planned Parenthood Federation of America (2002). *White Paper: Masturbation-from stigma to sexual health.* Washington, DC: Katharine Dexter McCormick Library.

Planned Parenthood Federation of Canada (n.d.). *A history of birth control in Canada.*

Planned Parenthood Fredericton. (2004). *Knowing where you stand: A resource for providing sexuality education to individuals with intellectual disabilities.* Fredericton, NB: Planned Parenthood Fredericton.

Plant, T. M., Winters, S. J., Attardi, B. J., & Majumdar, S. S. (1993). The follicle stimulating hormone-inhibin feedback loop in male primates. *Human Reproduction, 8,* Suppl. 2, 41–44.

Ploem, C., & Byers, E. S. (1997). The effects of two AIDS risk-reduction interventions on heterosexual college women's AIDS-related knowledge and condom use. *Journal of Psychology & Human Sexuality, 9*(1), 1–24.

Plummer, K. (1975). *Sexual stigma: An interactionist account.* London: Routledge & Kegan Paul.

Poasa, K. H., Blanchard, R., & Zucker, K. J. (2004). Birth order in transgendered males from Polynesia: A quantitative study of Samoan *Fa'afāfine. Journal of Sex & Marital Therapy, 30,* 13–23.

Pollack, A., Dean, C., & Dreifus, C. (2004, February 13). Medical and ethical issues cloud plans to clone for therapy. *New York Times.*

Pomeroy, W. B. (1972). *Dr. Kinsey and the Institute for Sex Research.* New York: Harper & Row.

Poon, M. K-L., Ho, Peter T-T, & Wong, J. P-H. (2001). Developing a comprehensive AIDS prevention outreach program: A needs assessment survey of MSM of East and Southeast Asian descent who visit bars and/or bath houses in Toronto. *The Canadian Journal of Human Sexuality, 10,* 25–37.

Pope, K. (2001). Sex between therapists and clients. In J. Worell (Ed.), *Encyclopedia of women and gender* (pp. 955–862). New York: Academic Press.

Pope Paul VI. (1968, July 30). Humanae vitae. (English text in the *New York Times,* p. 20.)

Population Information Program. (1983). Vasectomy–Safe and simple. *Population Reports,* Series D, No. 4, D61–D100.

Posner, R. (1992). *Sex and reason.* Cambridge, MA: Harvard University Press.

Posner, R. B. (2006). Early menarche: A review of research on trends in timing, racial differences, etiology, and psychosocial consequences. *Sex Roles, 54,* 315–322.

Potts, A., Gavey, N., Grace, V. M., & Vares, T. (2003). The downside of Viagra: Women's experiences and concerns. *Sociology of Health & Illness, 25,* 697–719.

Poulin, C., & Gouliquer, L. (2003). Part-time disabled lesbian passing on roller blades, or PMS, Prozac, and essentializing women's ailments. *Women & Therapy: A Feminist Quarterly, 26,* 95–108.

Powdermaker, H. (1933). *Life in Lesu*. New York: Norton.

Prather, R. S. (2000). Pigs is pigs. *Science, 289*, 1886–1887

Prause, N., & Graham, C. A. (2007). Asexuality: Classification and characterization. *Archives of Sexual Behavior, 36*.

Price, E. L., Byers, E. S., Sears, H., Whelan, J., & Saint-Pierre, M. (2000, January). Dating violence amongst New Brunswick adolescents: A summary of two studies. *Research Paper Series, #2*. Muriel McQueen Fergusson Centre for Family Violence Research.

Price, J., Allensworth, D., & Hillman, K. (1985). Comparison of sexual fantasies of homosexuals and heterosexuals. *Psychological Reports, 57*, 871–877.

Price, J. H. (1981). Toxic shock syndrome—An update. *Journal of School Health, 51*, 143–145.

Propper, C. R. (2005). The study of endocrine-disrupting compounds: Past approaches and new directions. *Integrative and Comparative Biology, 45*, 194–200.

Proulx, J., Pellerin, B., Paradis, Y., McKibben, A., Aubut, J., & Ouimet, M. (1997). Static and dynamic predictors of recidivism in sexual aggressors. *Sexual Abuse: A Journal of Research and Treatment, 9*, 7–27.

Puar, J. K. (2001). Global circuits: Transnational sexualities and Trinidad. *Signs: Journal of Women in Culture and Society, 26*, 1039–1065.

Public Health Agency of Canada (2004). *HIV/AIDSEpi Notes: Understanding the HIV/AIDS epidemic among Aboriginal Peoples in Canada*. Surveillance and Risk Assessment Division, Centre for Infectious Disease Prevention and Control, Public Health Agency of Canada.

Public Health Agency of Canada (2005). *Fetal alcohol spectrum disorder (FASD)*. Cat. No H124-4/2004. Available at www.phac-aspc.gc.ca/fasd-etcaf/pdf/faq_fasd_e.pdf.

Public Health Agency of Canada (2006). *HIV and AIDS in Canada. Surveillance report to June 30, 2006*. Surveillance and Risk Assessment Division, Centre for Infectious Disease Prevention and Control, Public Health Agency of Canada.

Public Health Agency of Canada (2007). *Frequently asked questions on emergency contraception*. Available at www.phac-aspc.gc.ca/std-mts/ec_cu_e.html.

Pukall, C. F., Payne, K. A., Binik, Y. M., & Khalifé, S. (2003). Pain measurement in vulvodynia. *Journal of Sex & Marital Therapy, 29(s)*, 111–120.

Pukall, C. F., Reissing, E. D., Binik, Y. M., Khalifé, S., & Abbott, F. V. (2000). New clinical and research perspectives on the sexual pain disorders. *Journal of Sex Education and Therapy, 25*, 36–44.

Purdon, C., & Holdaway, L. (2006). Non-erotic thoughts: Content and relation to sexual functioning and sexual satisfaction. *The Journal of Sex Research, 43*, 154–162.

Purnine, D., & Carey, M. (1997). Interpersonal communication and sexual adjustment: The roles of understanding and agreement. *Journal of Consulting & Clinical Psychology, 65*, 1017–1025.

Pyke, S. (1996). Sexual harassment and sexual intimacy in learning environments. *Canadian Psychology, 37(1)*, 13–22.

Quadagno, D., et al. (1991). The menstrual cycle: Does it affect athletic performance? *Physician & Sports Medicine, 19*, 121–124.

Qualls, C. B., Wincze, J. P., & Barlow, D. H. (1978). *The prevention of sexual disorders*. New York: Plenum.

Quas, J. A., et al. (2005). Childhood sexual assault victims: Long-term outcomes after testifying in criminal court. *Monographs of the Society for Research in Child Development, 70*, 1–127.

Quinn, T. C., et al. (2000). Viral load and heterosexual transmission of human immunodeficiency virus type 1. *The New England Journal of Medicine, 342*, 921–929.

Quittner, J. (1997, April 14). Divorce, Internet style. *Time*, 72.

Rachman, S. (1966). Sexual fetishism: An experimental analogue. *Psychological Record, 16*, 293–296.

Rako, S., & Friebely, J. (2004). Pheromonal influences on sociosexual behavior in postmenopausal women. *Journal of Sex Research, 41*, 372–380.

Ramchandani, P., Stein, A., Evans, J., O'Connor, T., & the ALSPAC Study Team. (2005). Paternal depression in the postnatal period and child development: A prospective population study. *Lancet, 365*, 2201–2205.

Randall, H. E. & Byers, E. S. (2003). What is sex?: Students' definitions of having sex, sexual partner, and unfaithful sexual behaviour. *Canadian Journal of Human Sexuality, 12*, 87–96.

Ratnam, S., Franco, E., & Ferenczy, A. (2000). Human papillomavirus testing for primary screening of cervical cancer precursors. *Cancer Epidemiology Biomarkers & Prevention, 9*, 945–951.

Rawicki, H. B., & Hill, S. (1991). Semen retrieval in spinal cord injured men. *Paraplegia, 29*, 443–446.

Raymond, E., Chen, P., & Luoto, J. (2004). Contraceptive effectiveness and safety of five nonoxynol-9 spermicides: A randomized trial. *Obstetrics and Gynecology, 103*, 430–439.

Raymond, N. C., Grant, J. E., Kim, S. W., & Coleman, E. (2002). Treatment of compulsive sexual behaviour with naltrexone and serotonin reuptake inhibitors: Two case studies. *International Clinical Psychopharmacology 127*, 201–205.

Ream, G., & Savin-Williams, R. (2005). Reciprocal associations between adolescent sexual activity and quality of youth-parent interactions. *Journal of Family Psychology, 19*, 171–179.

Reamy, K. J., & White, S. E. (1987). Sexuality in the puerperium: A review. *Archives of Sexual Behavior, 16*, 165–186.

Rederstorff, J. C., et al. (2007). The moderating roles of race and gender-role attitudes in the relationship between sexual harassment and psychological well-being. *Psychology of Women Quarterly, 31*, 50–61.

Reece, M., Herbenick, D., & Sherwood-Puzzello, C. (2004). Sexual health promotion and adult retail stores. *Journal of Sex Research, 41*, 173–180.

Regan, P. (2004). Sex and the attraction process: Lessons from science (and Shakespeare) on lust, love, chastity, and fidelity. In J. H. Harvey, A. Wenzel, & S. Sprecher (Eds.), *The handbook of sexuality in close relationships* (pp. 159–182). Mahwah, NJ: Lawrence Erlbaum.

Reichert, T. (2002). Sex in advertising research: A review of content, effects, and functions of sexual information in consumer advertising. *Annual Review of Sex Research, 13*, 241–273.

Reichert, T. & Carpenter, C. (2004). An update on sex in magazine advertising: 1983 to 2003. *Journalism and Mass Communication Quarterly, 81*, 823–837.

Reinharz, S. (1992). *Feminist methods in social research*. New York: Oxford University Press.

Reisenzein, R. (1983). The Schachter theory of emotion: Two decades later. *Psychological Bulletin, 94*, 239–264.

Reiss, I. L. (1960). *Premarital sexual standards in America*. New York: Free Press.

Reiss, I. L. (1967). *The social context of premarital sex permissiveness*. New York: Holt.

Reiss, I. L. (1986). *Journey into sexuality: An exploratory voyage*. Englewood Cliffs, NJ: Prentice-Hall.

Reissing, E. D., Binik, Y. M., & Khalife, S. (1999). Does vaginismus exist? A critical review of the literature. *Journal of Nervous and Mental Disease, 187*, 261–274.

Reissing, E. D., Binik, Y., Khalife, S., Cohen, D., & Arose, R. (2004). Vaginal spasm, pain, and behavior: An empirical investigation of the diagnosis of vaginismus. *Archives of Sexual Behavior, 33*, 5–18.

Reissing, E. D., Brown, C., Lord, M. J., Binik, Y. M., & Khalifé, S. (2005). Pelvic floor muscle functioning in women with vulvar vestibulitis syndrome. *Journal of Psychosomatic Obstetrics & Gynecology, 26*, 107–113.

Rempel, J. K., & Baumgartner, B. (2003). The relationship between attitudes towards menstruation and sexual attitudes, desires, and behavior in women. *Archives of Sexual Behavior, 32*, 155–163.

Rempel, L. A., & Rempel, J. K. (2004). Partner influence on health behavior decision-making: Increasing breastfeeding duration. *Journal of Social and Personal Relationships, 21*, 92–111.

Renaud, C. A. & Byers, E. S. (2001). Positive and negative sexual cognitions: Subjective experience and relationships to sexual adjustment. *The Journal of Sex Research, 38*, 252–262.

Renaud, C. A., & Byers, E. S. (1999). Exploring the frequency, diversity, and content of university students' positive and negative sexual cognitions. *Canadian Journal of Human Sexuality, 8*, 17–30.

Renaud, C., & Byers, E. S. (2001). Positive and negative sexual cognitions: Subjective experience and relationships to sexual adjustment. *The Journal of Sex Research, 38*, 252–262.

Renaud, C., Byers, E. S., & Pan, S. (1997). Sexual and relationship satisfaction in mainland China. *Journal of Sex Research, 34*, 399–410.

Renne, E. P. (1996). The pregnancy that doesn't stay: The practice and perception of abortion by Ekiti Yoruba women. *Social Science & Medicine, 42,* 483–494.

Renner, K. E., & Wackett, C. (1987). Sexual assault: Social and stranger rape. *Canadian Journal of Community Mental Health, 6*(1), 49–57.

Repke, J. T. (1994). Calcium and vitamin D. *Clinical Obstetrics and Gynecology, 37,* 550–557.

Reppucci, N. D., Land, D., & Haugaard, J. J. (1999). Child sexual abuse prevention programs that target young children. In P. K. Trickett, and C. J. Schellenbach (Eds.), *Violence against children in the family and the community.* Washington, DC: American Psychological Association.

Reuther, R. R. (1985). Catholics and abortion: Authority vs. dissent. *Christian Century, 102,* 859–862.

Reynolds, M. A., Herbenick, D., & Bancroft, J. (2003). The nature of childhood sexual experiences: Two studies 50 years apart. In J. Bancroft (Ed.), *Sexual development in childhood* (pp. 134–155). Bloomington, IN: Indiana University Press.

Rhoades, Galena K., Stanley, S., & Markman, H. (2006). Pre-engagement cohabitation and gender asymmetry in marital commitment. *Journal of Family Psychology, 20,* 553–560.

Ribner, D. S., & Kleinplatz, P. J. (2007). The hole in the sheet and other myths about sexuality and Judaism. *Sex and Relationship Therapy, 22,* 445–456.

Rice, G., Anderson, C., Risch, N., & Ebers, G. (1999). Male homosexuality: Absence of linkage to microsatellite markers at Xq28. *Science, 284,* 665–667.

Rice, M. E., Quinsey, V. L., & Harris, G. T. (1991). Sexual recidivism among child molesters released from a maximum security psychiatric institution. *Journal of Consulting and Clinical Psychology, 59,* 381–386.

Richardson, H. R. L., & Beazley, R. P. (1997). Factors influencing condom use among students attending high school in Nova Scotia. *Canadian Journal of Human Sexuality, 6,* 185–196.

Richardson, J. D. (1991). I. Medical causes of male sexual dysfunction. *Medical Journal of Australia, 155,* 29–33.

Richters, J., de Visser, R., Rissel, C., & Smith, A. (2006). Sexual practices at last heterosexual encounter and occurrence of orgasm in a national survey. *Journal of Sex Research, 43,* 217–226.

Ridley, C. A., et al. (2006). The ebb and flow of marital lust: A relational approach. *Journal of Sex Research, 43,* 144–153.

Rigdon, S. M. (1996). Abortion law and practice in China: An overview with comparisons to the United States. *Social Science & Medicine, 42,* 543–560.

Rimm, M. (1995). Marketing pornography on the information superhighway: A survey of 917,410 images. *Georgetown Law Journal, 83,* 1849–1925.

Rind, B., Tromovitch, P., & Bauserman, R. (1998). A meta-analytic examination of assumed properties of child sexual abuse using college samples. *Psychological Bulletin, 124,* 22–53.

Rini, C., Dunkel Schetter, C., Hobel, C., Glynn, L., & Sandman, C. (2006). Effective social support: Antecedents and consequences of partner support during pregnancy. *Personal Relationships, 13,* 207–229.

Riportella-Muller, R. (1989). Sexuality in the elderly: A review. In K. McKinney & S. Sprecher (Eds.), *Human sexuality: The societal and interpersonal context* (pp. 210–236). New York: Ablex.

Ritchie, A., & Barker, M. (2006). There aren't words for what we do or how we feel so we have to make them up: Constructing polyamorous languages in a culture of compulsory monogamy. *Sexualities, 9,* 584–601.

Roach, K. (2000). *Criminal law* (2nd ed.). Toronto: Irwin.

Robertson, S., & Sharkey, D. (2001). The role of semen in induction of maternal immune tolerance to pregnancy. *Seminars in Immunology, 13,* 243.

Robinson, D., & Rock, J. (1967). Intrascrotal hyperthermia induced by scrotal insulation: Effect on spermatogenesis. *Obstetrics and Gynecology, 29,* 217.

Rodriguez, I., Greer, C. A., Mok, M. Y., & Mombaerts, P. (2000). A putative pheromone receptor gene expressed in human olfactory mucosa. *Nature Genetics, 26,* 18–19.

Roehr, B. (2007). Dramatic drop in HIV infections halts circumcision trials. *British Medical Journal, 334,* 11.

Roisman, G., Masten, A., Coatsworth, J. D., & Tellegen, A. (2004). Salient and emerging developmental tasks in the transition to adulthood. *Child Development, 75,* 123–133.

Romer, D., et al. (1997). "Talking computers": A reliable and private method to conduct interviews on sensitive topics with children. *Journal of Sex Research, 34,* 3–9.

Rosaldo, M. A. (1974). Woman, culture, and society: A theoretical overview. In M. S. Rosaldo & L. Lamphere (Eds.), *Woman, culture, and society.* Stanford, CA: Stanford University Press.

Rosario, M., Meyer-Bahlburg, H., Hunter, J., Exner, T., Swadz, M., & Keller, A. (1996). The psychosexual development of urban lesbian, gay and bisexual youths. *Journal of Sex Research, 33,* 113–126.

Roscoe, B., Cavanaugh, L., & Kennedy, D. (1988). Dating infidelity: Behaviors, reasons, and consequences. *Adolescence, 89,* 36–43.

Roscoe, B., Kennedy, D., & Pope, T. (1987). Adolescents' views of intimacy: Distinguishing intimate from nonintimate relationships. *Adolescence, 22,* 511–516.

Rose, S., & Frieze, I. H. (1993). Young singles' contemporary dating scripts. *Sex Roles, 28,* 499–509.

Roselli, C. E., Resko, J. A., & Stormshak, F. (2002). Hormonal influences on sexual partner preference in rams. *Archives of Sexual Behavior, 31,* 43–49.

Rosen, D. H. (1974). *Lesbianism: A study of female homosexuality.* Springfield, IL: Charles C. Thomas.

Rosen, N. O., Knauper, B., Mozessohn, L., & Ho, M. R. (2005). Factors affecting knowledge of sexually transmitted infection transmissibility in healthcare providers: Results from a national survey. *Sexually Transmitted Diseases, 32,* 619–624.

Rosen, R. C. (1991). Alcohol and drug effects on sexual response: Human experimental and clinical studies. Annual *Review of Sex Research, 2,* 119–180.

Rosen, R. C. (2007). Erectile dysfunction: Integration of medical and psychological approaches. In S. Leiblum (Ed.), *Principles and practice of sex therapy* (4th ed., pp. 277–312). New York: Guilford.

Rosen, R. C. & McKenna, K. E. (2002). PDE-5 inhibition and sexual response: Pharmacological mechanisms and clinical outcomes. *Annual Review of Sex Research, 13,* 36–88.

Rosen, R. C., & Leiblum, S. R. (1995). Hypoactive sexual desire. *Psychiatric Clinics of North America, 18,* 107–121.

Rosen, R. C., Leiblum, S. R., & Spector, I. P. (1994). Psychologically-based treatment for male erectile disorder: A cognitive-interpersonal model. *Journal of Sex & Marital Therapy, 20,* 67–85.

Rosenbaum, T. Y. (2005). Physiotherapy treatment of sexual pain disorders. *Journal of Sex & Marital Therapy, 31,* 329–340.

Rosenbaum, T. Y. (2007). Pelvic floor involvement in male and female sexual dysfunction and the role of pelvic floor rehabilitation in treatment: A literature review. *Journal of Sexual Medicine, 4,* 4–13.

Rosenberg, E. S., Altfeld, M., Poon, S. H., Phillips, M. N., Wilkes, B. M., Eldridge, R. L., et al. (2000). Immune control of HIV-1 after early treatment of acute infection. *Nature, 407,* 523–526.

Rosenblatt, K. A., Wicklund, K., & Stanford, J. (2001). Sexual factors and the risk of prostate cancer. *American Journal of Epidemiology, 153,* 1152–1158.

Rosler, A., & Witztum, E. (1998). Treatment of men with paraphilia with a long-lasting analogue of gonadotropin-releasing hormone. *New England Journal of Medicine, 338,* 416–422.

Rosner, F. (1983). In vitro fertilization and surrogate motherhood: The Jewish view. *Journal of Religion and Health, 22,* 139–160.

Ross, L. R., & Spinner, B. (2001). General and specific attachment representations in adulthood: Is there a relationship? *Journal of Social and Personal Relationships, 18,* 747–766.

Ross, M. W. (2005). Typing, being, and doing: Sexuality and the internet. *Journal of Sex Research, 42,* 342–354.

Ross, M., & Williams, M. (2002). Effective targeted and community HIV/STD prevention programs. *Journal of Sex Research, 39,* 58–62.

Ross, M. N., Paulsen, J. A., & Stalstrom, O. W. (1988). Homosexuality and mental health: A cross-cultural review. *Journal of Homosexuality, 15,* 131–152.

Rotello, G. (1997). *Sexual ecology: AIDS and the destiny of gay men.* New York: Dutton.

Rotermann, M. (2005). Sex, condoms, and STDS among young people. *Health Reports* (Statistics Canada, Catalogue 82-003), *16,* 39–45.

Rotermann, M. (2007). Second or subsequent births to teenagers. *Health Reports* (Statistics Canada, Catalogue 82-003), *18,* 39–42.

Rothbaum, B. O., Foa, E. B., Riggs, D. S., Murdock, T., & Walsh, W. (1992). A prospective examination of post-traumatic stress disorder in rape victims. *Journal of Traumatic Stress, 5,* 455–475.

Rothblum, E. D. (1994). "I only read about myself on bathroom walls": The need for research on the mental health of lesbians and gay men. *Journal of Consulting and Clinical Psychology, 62,* 213–220.

Rothblum, E. D. (2007). Personal communication.

Rothblum, E. D., & Bond, L. A. (Eds.). (1996). *Preventing heterosexism and homophobia.* Thousand Oaks, CA: Sage.

Rousseau, S., et al. (1983). The expectancy of pregnancy for "normal" infertile couples. *Fertility & Sterility, 40,* 768–772.

Rowland, D. A., & Slob, A. K. (1997). Premature ejaculation: Psychophysiological considerations in theory, research, and treatment. *Annual Review of Sex Research, 8,* 224–253.

Rowland, D. L., & Burnett, A. L. (2000). Pharmacotherapy in treatment of male sexual dysfunction. *Journal of Sex Research, 37,* 226–243.

Royal Commission on New Reproductive Technologies. (1993). *Proceed with care: Final report of the Royal Commission on New Reproductive Technologies.* Ottawa: Minister of Government Services Canada.

Rozée, P. D., & Koss, M. P. (2001). Rape: A century of resistance. *Psychology of Women Quarterly, 25,* 295–311.

Ruan, F. F., & Lau, M. P. (1998). China. In R. Francoeur (Ed.), *The international encyclopedia of sexuality* (Vol. 1, pp. 344–399). New York: Continuum.

Rubin, I. (1966). Sex after forty—and after seventy. In R. Brecher & E. Brecher (Eds.), *An analysis of human sexual response.* New York: Signet Books, New American Library.

Rubin, R. T., Reinisch, J. M., & Haskett, R. F. (1981). Postnatal gonadal steroid effects on human behavior. *Science, 211,* 1318–1324.

Rubin, Z. (1973). *Liking and loving: An invitation to social psychology.* New York: Holt.

Rubin, Z., et al. (1980). Self-disclosure in dating couples: Sex roles and the ethic of openness. *Journal of Marriage and the Family, 42,* 305–317.

Ruble, D. N. (1977). Premenstrual symptoms: A reinterpretation. *Science, 197,* 291–292.

Ruble, D. N., & Stangor, C. (1986). Stalking the elusive schema: Insights from developmental and social-psychological analyses of gender schemas. *Social Cognition, 4,* 227–261.

Runtz, M. G., & Roche, D. N. (1999). Validation of the trauma symptom inventory in a Canadian sample of university women. *Child Maltreatment, 4*(1), 69–80.

Runtz, M. G., & Schallow, J. R. (1997). Social support and coping strategies as mediators of adult adjustment following childhood maltreatment. *Child Abuse & Neglect, 21,* 211–226.

Rusbult, C. (1983). A longitudinal test of the investment model: The development (and deterioration) of satisfaction and commitment in heterosexual involvements. *Journal of Personality and Social Psychology, 45,* 101–117.

Rusbult, C., Johnson, D. J., & Morrow, G. D. (1986). Predicting satisfaction and commitment in adult romantic involvements: An assessment of the generalizability of the investment model. *Social Psychology Quarterly, 49,* 81–89.

Russell, D. E. H. (1980). Pornography and violence: What does the new research say? In L. Lederer (Ed.), *Take back the night: Women on pornography.* New York: Morrow.

Russell, D. E. H. (1990). *Rape in marriage.* (Rev. ed.). Bloomington, IN: Indiana University Press.

Russell, G. M., & Richards, J. A. (2003). Stressor and resilence factors for Lesbians, Gay men, and Bisexuals confronting antigay politics. *American Journal of Community Psychology, 31,* 313–328.

Rust, P. C. (2000a). Bisexuality: A contemporary paradox for women. *Journal of Social Issues, 56,* 205–221.

Rust, P. C. (2000b). *Bisexuality in the United States: A social science reader.* New York: Columbia University Press.

Rust, P. C. (2001). Two many and not enough: The meaning of bisexual identities. *Journal of Bisexuality, 1,* 31–68.

Rust, P. C. (2002). Bisexuality: The state of the union. *Annual Review of Sex Research, 13,* 180–240.

Rye, B. J., Greatrix, S. A., & Enright, C. S. (2006). The case of the guilty victim: The effects of gender of victim and gender of perpetrator on attributions of blame and responsibility. *Sex Roles, 54,* 639–649.

Rye, B. J., & Meaney, G. J. (2007). The pursuit of sexual pleasure. *Sexuality & Culture, 11,* 28–51.

Rye, B. J., & Meaney, G. J. (2007). Voyeurism: It is good as long as we do not get caught. *International Journal of Sexual Health, 19,* 47–56.

Rye, B. J., & Meaney, G. J. (in press). Impact of a homonegativity awareness workshop on attitudes toward homosexuality. *Journal of Homosexuality.*

Rylko-Bauer, B. (1996). Abortion from a cross-cultural perspective. *Social Science & Medicine, 42,* 479–482.

Sachs-Ericsson, N., et al. (2005). Childhood sexual and physical abuse and the 1-year prevalence of medical problems in the National Comorbidity Survey. *Health Psychology, 24,* 32–40.

Sacred Congregation for the Doctrine of the Faith (1976, January 16). Declaration on certain questions concerning sexual ethics. (English text in the *New York Times,* p. 2).

Sadock, B. J., & Sadock, V. A. (1976). Techniques of coitus. In B. J. Sadock et al. (Eds.), *The sexual experience.* Baltimore, MD: Williams & Wilkins.

Saegert, S., Swap, W., & Zajonc, R. B. (1973). Exposure, context, and interpersonal attraction. *Journal of Personality and Social Psychology, 25,* 234–242.

Sagarin, E. (1973). Power to the peephole. *Sexual Behavior, 3,* 2–7.

St. Augustine. (1950). *The city of God.* (Marcus Dods, Trans.). New York: Modern Library.

Salamon, E. (1989). The homosexual escort agency: Deviance disavowal. *British Journal of Sociology, 40,* 1–21.

Saleh, F. M., & Berlin, F. S. (2003). Sex hormones, neurotransmitters, and psychopharmacological treatments in men with paraphilic disorders. *Journal of Child Sexual Abuse, 12,* 233–253.

Saleh, F. M., Niel, T., & Fishman, M. J. (2004). Treatment of paraphilia in young adults with leuprolide acetate: A preliminary case report series. *Journal of Forensic Science, 49,* 1343–1348.

Salem, R. N. (2005). World Health Organization updates guidance on how to use contraceptives. *INFO Reports, 4,* Baltimore: Johns Hopkins University.

Samson, J.-M., Levy, J. J., Dupras, A., & Tessier, D. (1991). Coitus frequency among married or cohabiting heterosexual adults: A survey in French Canada. *Australian Journal of Marriage & Family, 12,* 103–109.

Samson, J.-M., Levy, J. J., Dupras, A., & Tessier, D. (1993). Active oral-genital sex among married and cohabiting heterosexual adults. *Sexological Review, 1,* 143–156.

Sanchez, D. T., Kiefer, A. K., & Ybarra, O. (2006). Sexual submissiveness in women: Costs for sexual autonomy and arousal. *Personality and Social Psychology Bulletin, 32,* 512–524.

Sand, M., & Fisher, W. A. (2007). Women's endorsement of models of female sexual response: The nurses' sexuality study. *Journal of Sexual Medicine, 4,* 708–719.

Sanday, P. R. (1981). The socio-cultural context of rape: A cross-cultural study. *Journal of Social Issues, 37*(4), 5–27.

Sandfort, T., & Ehrhardt, A. (2004). Sexual health: A useful public health paradigm or a moral imperative? *Archives of Sexual Behavior, 33,* 181–187.

Sanghavi, D. M. (2006, Oct. 17). Preschool puberty, and a search for the causes. *New York Times.*

Santen, R. J. (1995). The testis. In P. Felig, J. D. Baxter, & L. A. Frohman (Eds.), *Endocrinology and metabolism* (3rd ed.). New York: McGraw-Hill.

Santilla, P., Sandnabba, N., K., Laurence, A., & Nordling, N. (2002). Investigating the underlying structure in sadomasochistically oriented behavior. *Archives of Sexual Behavior, 31,* 185–196.

Sauvageau, A., & Racette, S. (2006). Autoerotic deaths in the literature from 1954 to 2004: A review. *Journal of Forensic Science, 51,* 140–146.

Savin-Williams, R. (1995). An exploratory study of pubertal maturation timing and self-esteem among gay and bisexual male youths. *Developmental Psychology, 31*, 56–64.

Savin-Williams, R. (2001). Suicide attempts among sexual-minority youths: Population and measurement issues. *Journal of Consulting and Clinical Psychology, 69*, 983–991.

Savin-Williams, R. C. (2006). Who's gay? Does it matter? *Current Directions in Psychological Science, 15*, 40–44.

Savin-Williams, R., & Diamond, L. (2000). Sexual identity trajectories among sexual-minority youths: Gender comparisons. *Archives of Sexual Behavior, 29*, 607–627.

Savin-Williams, R. C., & Ream, G. L. (2003). Suicide attempts among sexual-minority male youth. *Journal of Clinical Child and Adolescent Psychology, 32*, 509–522.

Sayle, A. E., Savitz, D. A., Thorpe, J. M., Jr., Hertz-Picciotto, L., & Wilcox, A. J. (2001). Sexual activity during late pregnancy and risk of preterm delivery. *Obstetrics and Gynecology, 97*, 283–289.

Sbraga, T. P., & O'Donohue, W. (2000). Sexual harassment. *Annual Review of Sex Research, 11*, 258–285.

Schachter, S. (1964). The interaction of cognitive and physiological determinants of emotional state. In L. Berkowitz (Ed.), *Advances in experimental social psychology* (Vol. I). New York: Academic.

Schaefer, M. T., & Olson, D. H. (1981). Assessing intimacy: The PAIR Inventory. *Journal of Marital and Family Therapy*, 47–60.

Schaffer, H. R., & Emerson, Peggy E. (1964). Patterns of response to physical contact in early human development. *Journal of Child Psychology and Psychiatry, 5*, 1–13.

Schaffir, J. (2006). Sexual intercourse at term and onset of labor. *Obstetrics and Gynecology, 107*, 1310–1314.

Scharfe, E., & Bartholomew, K. (1995). Accommodation and attachment representations in young couples. *Journal of Social and Personal Relationships, 12*, 389–401.

Schenker, J. G., & Evron, S. (1983). New concepts in the surgical management of tubal pregnancy and the consequent postoperative results. *Fertility and Sterility, 40*, 709–723.

Schiavi, R. C., Mandeli, J., & Schreiner-Engel. (1994). Sexual satisfaction in healthy aging men. *Journal of Sex and Marital Therapy, 20*, 3–13.

Schieffelin, E. L. (1976). *The sorrow of the lonely and the burning of the dancers.* New York: St. Martin's Press.

Schmiege, S., & Russo, N. F. (2005). Depression and unwanted first pregnancy: Longitudinal cohort study. *British Medical Journal, 331*, 1303.

Schmitt, D., & Buss, D. (1996). Strategic self-promotion and competitor derogation: Sex and content effects on the perceived effectiveness of mate attraction tactics. *Journal of Personality and Social Psychology, 70*, 1185–1204.

Schmitt, D. P. (2003). Universal sex differences in the desire for sexual variety: Tests from 52 nations, 6 continents, and 13 islands. *Journal of Personality and Social Psychology, 85*, 85–104.

Schneider, E. D. (Ed.). (1985). *Questions about the beginning of life.* Minneapolis, MN: Augsburg.

Schneider, M. (1991). Developing service for lesbian and gay adolescents. *Canadian Journal of Community Mental Health, 10*, 133–151.

Schofield, A. T., & Vaughan-Jackson, P. (1913). *What a boy should know.* New York: Cassell.

Schooley, R. T., Spino, C., Kuritzkes, D., Walker, B. D., Valentine, F. A., Hirsch, M. S., et al. (2000). Two double-blinded, randomized, comparative trials of 4 human immunodeficiency virus type 1 (HIV-1) envelope vaccines in HIV-1-infected individuals across a spectrum of disease severity. *Journal of Infectious Diseases, 182*, 1357–1364.

Schroeder, A. (2000, Jan. 28). The money was great, risks were real. Student reflects on her year as a phone sex operator. *The Brunswickan.*

Schroeder, P. (1994). Female genital mutilation—a form of child abuse. *New England Journal of Medicine, 331*, 739–740.

Schubach, G. (2002). The G-spot is the female prostate. *American Journal of Obstetrics and Gynecology, 186*, 850.

Schultz, W. C. M., et al. (1989). Vaginal sensitivity to electric stimuli: Theoretical and practical implications. *Archives of Sexual Behavior, 18*, 87–96.

Schultz, W. W., van Andel, P., Sabelis, I., & Mooyaart, E. (1999). Magnetic resonance imaging of male and female genitals during coitus and female sexual arousal. *British Medical Journal, 319*, 1596–1600.

Schwartz, L. B. (1997, December 20/27). Understanding human parturition. *The Lancet, 350*, 1792–1793.

Scott, J. P. (1964). The effects of early experience on social behavior and organization. In W. Etkin (Ed.), *Social behavior and organization among vertebrates.* Chicago: University of Chicago Press.

Scott, V. M., Mottarella, K. E., & Lavooy, M. J. (2006). Does virtual intimacy exist? A brief exploration into reported levels of intimacy in online relationships. *Cyberpsychology & Behavior, 9*, 759–761.

Seal, B. N., Brotto, L. A., & Gorzalka, B. B. (2005). Oral contraceptive use and female genital arousal: Methodological considerations. *The Journal of Sex Research, 42*, 249–258.

Sears, H. A., Byers, E. S., & Price, E. L. (2007). The co-occurrence of adolescent boys' and girls' use of psychologically, physically, and sexually abusive behaviours in their dating relationships. *Journal of Adolescence, 30*, 487–504.

Segraves, R. T. & Balon, R. (2003). *Sexual pharmacology: Fast facts.* New York: Norton.

Sell, R. L. (1997). Defining and measuring sexual orientation: A review. *Archives of Sexual Behavior, 26*, 643–658.

Sell, R. L., Wells, J. A., & Wypij, D. (1995). The prevalence of homosexual behavior and attraction in the United States, the United Kingdom and France. *Archives of Sexual Behavior, 24*, 235–248.

Sellors, J. W., Mahoney, J. B., Kczorowski, J., Lytwyn, A., Bangura, H., Chong, S., et al. (2000). Prevalence and predictors of human papillomavirus infection in women in Ontario, Canada. *Canadian Medical Association Journal, 163*, 503–509.

Semple, S. J., Patterson, T. L., & Grant, I. (2004). The context of sexual risk behavior among heterosexual methamphetamine users. *Addictive Behaviors, 29*, 807–810.

Senn, C. Y., & Desmarais, S. (2001). Are our recruitment practices for sex studies working across gender? The effect of topic and gender of recruiter on participation rates of university men and women. *The Journal of Sex Research, 38*, 111–117.

Senn, C. Y., Desmarais, S., Verberg, N., & Wood, E. (2000). Predicting coercive sexual behaviour across the lifespan in a random sample of Canadian men. *Journal of Social and Personal Relationships, 17*, 95–113.

Senn, C. Y., & Dzinas, K. (1996). Measuring fear of rape: A new scale. *Canadian Journal of Behavioural Science, 28*, 141–144.

Senn, C. Y., & Radtke, H. L. (1990). Women's evaluations of and affective reactions to mainstream violent pornography, nonviolent pornography and erotica. *Violence and Victims, 5*, 143–155.

Seto, M. C. (2004). Pedophilia and sexual offenses against children. *Annual Review of Sex Research, 15*, 321–361.

Seto, M. C., Cantor, J. M., & Blanchard, R. (2006). Child pornography offenses are a valid diagnostic indicator of pedophilia. *Journal of Abnormal Psychology, 115*, 610–615.

Seto, M. C., Lalumière, M. L., & Blanchard, R. (2000). The discriminative validity of a phallometric test for pedophilic interests among adolescent sex offenders against children. *Psychological Assessment, 12*, 319–327.

Seto, M. C., Maric, A., & Barbaree, H. E. (2001). The role of pornography in the etiology of sexual aggression. *Aggression and Violent Behavior, 6*, 35–53.

Seto, M. C., Murphy, W. D., Page, J., & Ennis, L. (2003). Detecting anomalous sexual interests in juvenile sex offenders. *Annals of the New York Academy of Sciences, 898*, 118–130.

Setty-Venugopal, V., & Upadhyay, U. D. (2002). Three to five saves lives. Population Reports, Series L, Number 13. Baltimore: Johns Hopkins University School of Public Health.

Sex Industry, The. (1998, February 14). *The Economist*, 21–23.

Shackelford, T., & Buss, D. (1997). Cues to infidelity. *Personality and Social Psychology Bulletin, 23*, 1034–1045.

Shabsigh, R., et al. (2000). Intracavernous alprostadil alfadex (Edex/viridal) is effective and safe in patients with erectile dysfunction after failing sildenafil (Viagra). *Urology, 55*, 477–480.

Shandera, K. C., & Thompson, I. M. (1994). Urologic prostheses. *Emergency Medicine Clinics of North America, 12*, 729–748.

Sharpstein, D. J., & Kirkpatrick, L. (1997). Romantic jealousy and adult romantic attachment. *Journal of Personality and Social Psychology, 72,* 627–640.

Shaver, F. (1996). Prostitution: On the dark side of the service industry. In Tom Fleming (Ed.), *Post critical criminology.* Scarborough: Prentice Hall.

Shaver, F. (1996). Regulation of prostitution: Setting the morality trap. In B. Schissel & L. Mahood (Eds.), *Social control in Canada.* Toronto: Oxford University Press.

Shaver, F. M. (1994). The regulation of prostitution: Avoiding morality traps. *CHS/RCDS, 9*(1), 123–145.

Shaver, F. M. (2005). Sex work research: Methodological and ethical challenges. *Journal of Interpersonal Violence, 20,* 296–319.

Shaw, J. (2006). *Reality check: A close look at accessing abortion services in Canadian hospitals.* Ottawa: Canadians for Choice.

Shidlo, A., Schroeder, M., & Drescher, J. (Eds.) (2002). *Sexual conversion therapy: Ethical, clinical, and research perspectives.* New York: Haworth.

Shifren, J. L., Braunstein, G. D., Simon, J. A., Casson, P. R., Buster, J. E., & Redmond, G. P. (2000). Transdermal testosterone treatment in women with impaired sexual function after oophorectomy. *New England Journal of Medicine, 343,* 682–688.

Shifren, J. L., Nahum, R., & Mazer, N. A. (1998). Incidence of sexual dysfunction in surgically menopausal women. *Menopause, 5,* 189–190.

Shoveller, J. A., Johnson, J. L., Langille, D. B., & Mitchell, T. (2004). Sociocultural influences on young people's sexual development. *Social Sciences & Medicine, 59,* 473–487.

SIECCAN. (2004). Adolescent sexual and reproductive health in Canada: A report card in 2004. *The Canadian Journal of Human Sexuality, 13,* 67–81.

SIECUS. (1991). *Guidelines for comprehensive sexuality education.* New York: Sexuality Information and Education Council of the United States.

Siegel, K., & Scrimshaw, E. (2003). Reasons for the adoption of celibacy among older men and women living with HIV/AIDS. *Journal of Sex Research, 40,* 189–200.

Siegel, K., Krauss, B. J., & Karus, D. (1994). Reporting recent sexual practices: Gay men's disclosure of HIV risk by questionnaire and interview. *Archives of Sexual Behavior, 23,* 217–230.

Siegel, L. J., & McCormick, C. (1999). *Criminology in Canada: Theories, patterns and typologies.* Scarborough: ITP Nelson.

Signorielli, N. (1990). Children, television, and gender roles. *Journal of Adolescent Health Care, 11,* 50–58.

Signorile, M. (1997). *Life on the outside: The Signorile report on gay men.* New York: HarperCollins.

Sik Ying Ho, P. (2006). The (charmed) circle game: Reflections on sexual hierarchy through multiple sexual relationships. *Sexualities, 9,* 547–564.

Siker, J. S. (Ed.). (1994). *Homosexuality in the church: Both sides of the debate.* Louisville, KY: Westminster/John Knox Press.

Silver, W. (2007). *Crime statistics in Canada, 2006.* Statistics Canada, Canadian Centre for Justice Statistics. Catalogue no. 85-002, Vol 27, no 5.

Silvera, M. (1990). Man royal and sodomites: Some thought on the invisibility of Afro-Caribbean lesbians. In Sharon Dale Stone (Ed.), *Lesbians in Canada.* Toronto: Between the Lines.

Silvestre, L., et al. (1990). Voluntary interruption of pregnancy with mifepristone (RU-486) and a prostaglandin analogue: A large-scale French experience. *New England Journal of Medicine, 322,* 645.

Simon, V., Ho, D., & Karim, Q. (2006). HIV/AIDS epidemiology, pathogenesis, prevention, and treatment. *The Lancet, 368,* 489–504.

Simpson, J. A. (1990). Influence of attachment styles on romantic relationships. *Journal of Personality and Social Psychology, 59,* 971–980.

Singh, D. (1993). Adaptive significance of female physical attractiveness: Role of waist-to-hip ratio. *Journal of Personality and Social Psychology, 65,* 293–307.

Singh, D., & Bronstad, P. (2001). Female body odour is a potential cue to ovulation. *Proceedings of the Royal Society London B Biology, 268,* 797–801.

Singh, S., & Darroch, J. E. (2000). Adolescent pregnancy and childbearing: Levels and trends in developed countries. *Family Planning Perspectives, 32,* 14–23.

Singh, S., Darroch, J. E., Frost, J. J., & the Study Team. (2001). Socioeconomic disadvantage and adolescent women's sexual and reproductive behavior: The case of five developed countries. *Family Planning Perspectives, 33,* 251–258, 289.

Siosteen, A., et al. (1990). Sexual ability, activity, attitudes and satisfaction as part of adjustment in spinal cord–injured subjects. *Paraplegia, 28,* 285–295.

Sipe, A. W. R. (1995). *Sex priests, and power: Anatomy of a crisis.* New York: Brunner/Mazel.

Sipski, M. L. (2002). Central nervous system based neurogenic female sexual dysfunction: Current status and future trends. *Archives of Sexual Behavior, 31,* 421–424.

Sipski, M. L., Alexander, C., & Rosen, R. (2001). Sexual arousal and orgasm in women: Effects of spinal cord injury. *Annals of Neurology, 49,* 35–44.

Sipski, M. L., & Alexander, C. J. (1995). Spinal cord injury and female sexuality. *Annual Review of Sex Research, 6,* 224–244.

Sipski, M. L., & Alexander, C. J. (Eds.). (1997). *Sexual function in people with disability and chronic illness.* Gaithersburg, MD: Aspen.

Sipski, M. L., Rosen, R., Alexander, C., & Gómez-Marín, O. (2004). Sexual responsiveness in women with spinal cord injuries: Differential effects of anxiety-eliciting stimulation. *Archives of Sexual Behavior, 33,* 295–302.

Skaletsky, H., Kuroda-Kawaguchi, T., Minx, P. J., Cordum, H. S., Hillier, L., Brown, L. G., et al. (2003). The male-specific region of the human Y chromosome is a mosaic of discrete sequence classes. *Nature, 423,* 825–837.

Slob, A. K., et al. (1991). Menstrual cycle phase and sexual arousability in women. *Archives of Sexual Behavior, 20,* 567–578.

Small, M. F. (1993). *Female choices: Sexual behavior of female primates.* Ithaca, NY: Cornell University Press.

Smallwood, G. H., Meador, M. L., Lenihan, J. P., Shangold, G. A., Fisher, A. C., & Creasy, G. W. (2001). Efficacy and safety of a transdermal contraceptive system. *Obstetrics and Gynecology, 98,* 799–805.

Smith, D. (2002, October). Canceled trial is yielding useful data. *Monitor on Psychology, 33,* 52.

Smith, G., Frankel, S., & Yarnell, J. (1997). Sex and death: Are they related? Findings from the Caerphilly cohort study. *British Medical Journal, 315,* 1641–1645.

Smith, K. B., Pukall, C. F., Tripp, D. A., & Nickel, J. C. (2007). Sexual and relationship functioning in men with chronic prostatitis/chronic pelvic pain syndrome and their partners. *Archives of Sexual Behavior, 36,* 301–311.

Smith, J. R., et al. (1996). Major susceptibility locus for prostate cancer on chromosome 1 suggested by a genome-wide search. *Science, 274,* 1371–1373.

Smith, M. (1999). *Lesbian and gay rights in Canada: Social movements and equality seeking, 1971–1995.* Toronto: University of Toronto Press.

Snowdon, C. T., et al. (2006). Social odours, sexual arousal and pairbonding in primates. *Philosophical Transactions of the Royal Society B, 361,* 2079–2089.

Society of Obstetricians and Gynaecologists of Canada. (2000). *Sex sense: Canadian contraception guide.* Ottawa: Author.

Society of Obstetricians and Gynaecologists of Canada (2006). Canadian consensus conference on menopause, 2006 update. *Journal of Obstetrics and Gynaecology of Canada, 171,* S7-S10.

Solms, M. (1997). *The neuropsychology of dreams: A clinico-anatomical study.* Mahwah, NJ: Erlbaum.

Solomon, S. E., Rothblum, E., & Balsam, K. (2005). Money, housework, sex, and conflict: Same-sex couples in civil unions, those not in civil unions, and heterosexual married siblings. *Sex Roles, 52,* 561–576.

Solursh, D. S., Ernst, I. L., Lewis, R. W., Prisant, L. M., Mills, T. M., Solursh, L. P., Jarvis, R. G., Salazar, W. H. & The Human Sexuality Multispecialty Group (2003). The human sexuality education of physicians in North American medical schools. *International Journal of Impotence Research, 15,* S41–S45.

Song, Y. I. (1991). Single Asian women as a result of divorce: Depressive affect and changes in social support. *Journal of Divorce and Remarriage, 14,* 219–230.

Soon, J. A., Levine, M., Osmond, B. L., Ensom, M. H. H., & Fielding, D. W. (2005). Effects of making emergency contraception available without a physician's prescription: A population-based study. *Canadian Medical Association Journal, 172,* 878–883.

Spalding, L. R., & Peplau, L. A. (1997). The unfaithful lover: Heterosexuals' perceptions of bisexuals and their relationships. *Psychology of Women Quarterly, 21,* 611–625.

Spehr, M., Gisselmann, G., Poplawski, A., Riffell, J. A., Wetzel, C. H., Zimmer, R. K., & Hatt, H. (2003). Identification of a testicular odorant receptor mediating human sperm chemotaxis. *Science, 299,* 2054–2058.

Spitz, I. M., et al. (1998). Early pregnancy termination with mifepristone and misoprostol in the United States. *New England Journal of Medicine, 338,* 1241–1247.

Spitz, R. A. (1949). Autoeroticism: Some empirical findings and hypotheses on three of its manifestations in the first year of life. *The Psychoanalytic Study of the Child* (Vols. III–IV, pp. 85–120). New York: International Universities Press.

Spourk, R. F. (2002). Dehydroepiandrosterone: A springboard hormone for female sexuality. *Fertility and Sterility, 77,* S19–S25.

Sprecher, S. (1987). The effects of self-disclosure given and received on affection for an intimate partner and stability of the relationship. *Journal of Social and Personal Relationships, 4,* 115–127.

Sprecher, S., Barbee, A., & Schwartz, P. (1995). "Was it good for you, too?": Gender differences in first sexual intercourse experiences. *Journal of Sex Research, 32,* 3–15.

Sprecher, S., & McKinney, K. (1993). *Sexuality.* Newbury Park, CA: Sage.

Sprecher, S., Sullivan, Q., & Hatfield, E. (1994). Mate selection preferences: Gender differences examined in a national sample. *Journal of Personality and Social Psychology, 66,* 1074–1080.

Springen, K., & Noonan, D. (2002). Sperm banks go online. MSNBC News 899016.

Stack, S., & Gundlach, J. H. (1992). Divorce and sex. *Archives of Sexual Behavior, 21,* 359–368.

Stafford, L., & Merolla, A. J., Idealization, reunions, and stability in long-distance dating relationships. *Journal of Social and Personal Relationships, 24,* 37–54.

Stanton, A. L., Lobel, M., Sears, S., & DeLuca, R. (2002). Psychosocial aspects of selected issues in women's reproductive health: Current status and future directions. *Journal of Consulting and Clinical Psychology, 70,* 751–770.

Stark, P. (2006). Expert Report of Philip B. Stark, PH.D. ACLU v Gonzales. Civ. Action No. 98-5591 (E.D. Pa.).

Starks, K. J., & Morrison, E. S. (1996). *Growing up sexual* (2nd ed.). New York: HarperCollins.

Statistics Canada. (1993). The violence against women survey. *The Daily.* Catalogue no. 11-001E.

Statistics Canada. (1995). Therapeutic abortions. *Statistical report on the health of Canadians: Conditions and diseases.* Statistics Canada. Catalogue no. 82-219-XPB.

Statistics Canada. (1997). Population in private households by age group (17a) and sex showing living arrangements for Canada, provinces, territories and census metropolitan areas, 1996 census (93F0022XDB96010). In *Census of Population 1996: Nation Series* [computer file].

Statistics Canada. (1998). *National population health survey, 1996–1997* [computer file]. Ottawa: Author.

Statistics Canada. (2000, March 16). Canadian social trends: The changing face of conjugal relationships. *The Daily.*

Statistics Canada. (2000, July 25). Family violence. *The Daily.*

Statistics Canada. (2002, January 18). Therapeutic abortions. *The Daily.*

Statistics Canada. (2002). *Canadian community health survey* (Cycle 1) [data file]. Ottawa: Statistics Canada.

Statistics Canada. (2003, January 21). Census of Population: Immigration, birthplace and birthplace of parents, citizenship, ethnic origin, visible minorities and Aboriginal peoples. *The Daily.*

Statistics Canada. (2006, August 15). Canadian Internet use survey. *The Daily.*

Statistics Canada. (2006, November 27). Maternity experiences survey. *The Daily.*

Statistics Canada. (2006). Report on the demographic situatuation in Canada 2003 and 2004. Alain Bélanger (ed.). Statistics Canada Catalogue no. 91-209-XIE. Ottawa: Industry Canada. Available: www.statcan.ca/english/freepub/91-209-XIE/91-209-XIE2003000.pdf.

Statistics Canada. (2007, June 13). General Social Survey: Navigating family transitions. *The Daily.*

Statistics Canada. (2007, July 13). Induced Abortions. *The Daily.*

Statistics Canada. (2007). *Persons in same-sex unions by broad age groups and sex for both sexes, 2006 counts, for Canada, provinces and territories-20% sample data (table). Families and Household Highlight Tables.* 2006 Census. Statistics Canada Catalogue no. 97-553-XWE2006002. Ottawa. Released September 12, 2007. Accessed October 10, 2007.

Steben, M., & Sacks, Sn. (1997). Genital herpes: The epidemiology and control of a common sexually transmitted disease. *Canadian Journal of Human Sexuality, 6,* 127–134.

Steege, J. F., Stout, A. L., & Carson, Culley C. (1986). Patient satisfaction in Scott and Small-Carrion penile implant recipients. *Archives of Sexual Behavior, 15,* 393–400.

Steinberg, L. (2005). *Adolescence* (7th ed). New York: McGraw-Hill.

Steiner, M. J. & Cates, W. (2006). Condoms and sexually-transmitted infections. *New England Journal of Medicine, 354,* 2642–2643.

Steinman, D. L., et al. (1981). A comparison of male and female patterns of sexual arousal. *Archives of Sexual Behavior, 10,* 529–548.

Stern, K., & McClintock, M. K. (1998). Regulation of ovulation by human pheromones. *Nature, 392,* 177–179.

Sternberg, R. J. (1986). A triangular theory of love. *Psychological Review, 93,* 119–135.

Sternberg, R. J. (1987). Liking versus loving: A comparative evaluation of theories. *Psychological Bulletin, 102,* 331–345.

Sternberg, R. (1996). Love stories. *Personal Relationships, 3,* 59–79.

Sternberg, R. (1997). Construct validation of a triangular love scale. *European Journal of Social Psychology, 27,* 313–335.

Sternberg, R. (1998). *Love is a story: A new theory of relationships.* New York: Oxford University Press.

Sternberg, R. J., Hojjat, M., & Barnes, M. L. (2001). Empirical tests of aspects of a theory of love as a story. *European Journal of Personality, 15,* 199–218.

Stevenson, M. R. (1995). Searching for a gay identity in Indonesia. *Journal of Men's Studies, 4,* 93–108.

Stewart, S., Stinnett, H., & Rosenfeld, L. B. (2000). Sex differences in desired characteristics of short-term and long-term relationship partners. *Journal of Social and Personal Relationships, 17,* 843–853.

Stobert, S. & Kemeny, A. (2003, Summer). *Childfree by choice* (Catalogue No. 11-008). Ottawa: Statistics Canada.

Stodghill, R., II. (1998, June 15). Where'd you learn that? *Time 151,* 52–59.

Stone, K. M. (1994). HIV, other STDs, and barriers. In C. Mauck et al. (Eds.), *Barrier contraceptives: Current status and future prospects* pp. 203–212, New York: Wiley.

Stoneburner, R. L., & Low-Beer, D. (2004). Population-level HIV declines and behavioral risk avoidance in Uganda. *Science, 304,* 714–718.

Stoneburner, R. L., Sato, P., Burton, A., & Mertens, T. (1994). The global HIV pandemic. *Acta Paediatrica,* Suppl. 400, 1–4.

Storey, A. E., Walsh, C. J., Quinton, R. L., & Wynne-Edwards, K. E. (2000). Hormonal correlates of paternal responsiveness in new and expectant fathers. *Evolution and Human Behavior, 21,* 79–95.

Storms, M. D. (1980). Theories of sexual orientation. *Journal of Personality and Social Psychology, 38,* 783–792.

Strachan, T. & Read, A. P. (2004). *Human molecular genetics* (3rd ed.). New York: Garland Science.

Strassberg, D. S., & Lowe, K. (1995). Volunteer bias in sex research. *Archives of Sexual Behavior, 24,* 369–382.

Streissguth, A. P., Barr, H. M., Bookstein, F. L., Sampson, P. D., & Olson, H. C. (1999). The long-term neurocognitive consequences of prenatal alcohol exposure: A 14-year study. *Psychological Science, 10,* 186–190.

Strickland, B. R. (1995). Research on sexual orientation and human development. *Developmental Psychology, 31,* 137–140.

Striegel-Moore, R., Goldman, S., Garvin, V., & Rodin, J. (1996). A prospective study of somatic and emotional symptoms of pregnancy. *Psychology of Women Quarterly, 20,* 393–408.

Striepe, M. I., & Tolman, D. I. (2003). Mom, Dad, I'm straight: The coming out of gender ideologies in adolescent sexual-identity development. *Journal of Clinical Child and Adolescent Psychology, 32*, 523–530.

Strong, C. (1997). *Ethics in reproductive and perinatal medicine*. New Haven: Yale University Press.

Struckman-Johnson, C. (1988). Forced sex on dates: It happens to men, too. *Journal of Sex Research, 24*, 234–241.

Struckman-Johnson, C., et al. (1996). Sexual coercion reported by men and women in prison. *Journal of Sex Research, 33*, 67–76.

Struckman-Johnson, C., Struckman-Johnson, D., & Anderson, P. B. (2003). Tactics of sexual coercion: When men and women won't take no for an answer. *Journal of Sex Research, 40*, 76–86.

Stryker, S. (1987). The vitalization of symbolic interactionism. Social Psychology *Quarterly, 50*, 83–94.

Sun, S. S., et al. (2002). National estimates of the timing of sexual maturation and racial differences among US children. *Pediatrics, 110*, 911–919.

Swaab, D. F. (2005). The role of the hypothalamus and endocrine system in sexuality. In J. Hyde (Ed.), *Biological substrates of human sexuality*. Washington, DC: American Psychological Association.

Swygard, H., Sena, A. C., Hobbs, M. M., & Cohen, M. S. (2004). Trichomoniasis: Clinical manifestations, diagnosis, and management. *Sexually Transmitted Infections, 80*, 91–95.

Symbalauk, D. G., & Jones, K. M. (1999). Prostitution offender programs: An educational alternative to sentencing. *Law Now, 23*, 38.

Szabo, R. (2000). How does male circumcision protect against HIV infection? *British Medical Journal, 320*, 1592.

Szasz, T. S. (1980). *Sex by prescription*. Garden City, NY: Anchor Press/Doubleday.

Taberner, P. V. (1985). *Aphrodisiacs: The science and the myth*. Philadelphia: University of Pennsylvania Press.

Tafoya, T., & Wirth, D. A. (1996). Native American two-spirit men. In J. F. Longres (Ed.), *Men of color* (pp. 51–67). New York: Haworth.

Talamini, J. T. (1982). *Boys will be girls: The hidden world of the heterosexual male transvestite*. Washington, DC: University Press of America.

Tamir, L. M. (1982). *Men in their forties: The transition to middle age*. New York: Springer.

Tannahill, Reay (1980). *Sex in history*. New York: Stein & Day.

Tannen, D. (1991). *You just don't understand: Women and men in conversation*. New York: William Morrow.

Tanner, J. M. (1967). Puberty. In A. McLaren (Ed.), *Advances in reproductive physiology* (Vol. II). New York: Academic.

Taylor, D. (2006). From "It's all in your head" to "Taking back the month": Premenstrual syndrome (PMS) research and the contributions of the society for Menstrual Cycle Research. *Sex Roles, 54*, 377–392.

Taylor, L. D. (2005). All for him: Articles about sex in American lad magazines. *Sex Roles, 52*, 153–164.

Technical Working Group. (2002). Evaluation of abstinence education programs funded under Title V, Section 510: Interim Report. U.S. Department of Health and Human Services: Office of the Assistant Secretary for Planning and Evaluation.

Templeman, T. L., & Stinnett, R. D. (1991). Patterns of sexual arousal and history in a "normal" sample of young men. *Archives of Sexual Behavior, 20*, 137–150.

Terman, L., et al. (1938). *Psychological factors in marital happiness*. New York: McGraw-Hill.

Terman, L. M. (1948). Kinsey's *Sexual Behavior in the Human Male*: Some comments and criticisms. *Psychological Bulletin, 45*, 443–459.

Tessler Lindau, S., Schumm, L. P., Laumann, E. O., Levinson, W., O'Muircheartaigh, C. A., & Waite, L. J. (2007). A study of sexuality and health among older adults in the United States. *The New England Journal of Medicine, 357*, 762–774.

Testa, M., VanZile-Tamsen, C., & Livingston, J. A. (2005). Childhood sexual abuse, relationship satisfaction, and sexual risk taking in a community sample of women. *Journal of Consulting and Clinical Psychology, 73*, 1116–1124.

Thompson, Anthony P. (1983). Extramarital sex: A review of the research literature. *Journal of Sex Research, 19*, 1–22.

Thompson, S. K. (1975). Gender labels and early sex role development. *Child Development, 46*, 339–347.

Thorne, B. (1993). *Gender play: Girls and boys in school*. New Brunswick, NJ: Rutgers University Press.

Thorne, N., & Amrein, H. (2003). Vomeronasal organ: Pheromone recognition with a twist. *Current Biology, 13*, R220–R222.

Thorpe, L. P., Katz, B., & Lewis, R. T. (1961). *The psychology of abnormal behavior*. New York: Ronald Press.

Tiefer, L. (1991a). Historical, scientific, clinical, and feminist criticisms of "The Human Sexual Response Cycle" model. *Annual Review of Sex Research, 2*, 1–24.

Tiefer, L. (1991b). New perspectives in sexology: From rigor (mortis) to richness. *Journal of Sex Research, 28*, 593–602.

Tiefer, L. (1994). Three crises facing sexology. *Archives of Sexual Behavior, 23*, 361–374.

Tiefer, L. (1995). *Sex is not a natural act, and other essays*. Boulder, CO: Westview.

Tiefer, L. (2000). Sexology and the pharmaceutical industry: The threat of co-optation. *Journal of Sex Research, 37*, 273–283.

Tiefer, L. (2001). Arriving at a "new view" of women's sexual problems: Background, theory, and activism. In E. Kachak & L. Tiefer (Eds.), *A new view of women's sexual problems* (pp. 63–98). New York: Haworth Press.

Tiefer, L. (2004). *Sex is not a natural act and other essays* (2nd ed.). Boulder, CO: Westview Press.

Timmerman, G. (2003). Sexual harassment of adolescents perpetrated by teachers and by peers; An exploration of the dynamics of power, culture, and gender in secondary schools. *Sex Roles, 48*, 231–244.

Toubia, N. (1994). Female circumcision as a public health issue. *New England Journal of Medicine, 331*, 712–716.

Toubia, N. (1995). *Female genital mutilation: A call for global action*. New York: Women Ink.

Townsend, J. W. (2003). Reproductive behavior in the context of global population. *American Psychologist, 58*, 197–2004.

Traish, A. M., Kim, N. N., Munarriz, R., Moreland, R., & Goldstein, I. (2002). Biochemical and physiological mechanisms of female genital sexual arousal. *Archives of Sexual Behavior, 31*, 393–400.

Traven, S., Cuyllen, K., & Protter, B. (1990). Female sexual offenders: Severe victims and victimizers. *Journal of Forensic Sciences, 35*, 140–150.

Treiman, K., et al. (1995). IUDs—An update. *Population Reports*, Series B, No. 6. Baltimore, MD: Johns Hopkins School of Public Health.

Tremblay, C., Hébert, M., & Piché, C. (1999). Coping strategies and social support as mediators of consequences in child sexual abuse victims. *Child Abuse & Neglect, 23*, 929–945.

Tremblay, C., Hébert, M., & Piché, C. (2000). Type I and type II posttraumatic stress disorder in sexually abused children. *Journal of Child Sexual Abuse, 9*, 65–90.

Tremblay, L., & Frignon J. (2004). Biobehavioural and cognitive determinants of adolescent girls' involvement in sexual risk behaviours: A test of three theoretical models. *Canadian Journal of Human Sexuality, 13*, 29–43.

Trenholm, C., Devaney, B., Fortson, K., Quay, L., Wheeler, J., & Clark, M. (2007). *Impacts of four Title V section 510 abstinence education programs: Final report* (MPR Ref. No. 8549-110). Princeton, NJ: Mathematica Policy Research Inc.

Triandis, H. C., McCusker, C., & Hui, C. H. (1990). Multimethod probes of individualism and collectivism. *Journal of Personality and Social Psychology, 59*, 1006–1020.

Trocmé, N., MacLaurin, B., Fallon, B., Daciuk, J., Billingsley, D., Tourigny, M., et al. (2001). *Canadian Incidence Study of Reported Child Abuse and Neglect: Final Report*. Ottawa, Ontario: Minister of Public Works and Government Services Canada.

Trudel, G. (2002). Sexuality and marital life: Results of a survey. *Journal of Sex & Marital Therapy, 28*, 241–261.

Trudel, G., Marchand, A., Ravart, M., Aubin, S., Turgeon, L., & Fortier, P. (2001). The effect of a cognitive-behavioral group treatment program on hypoactive sexual desire in women. *Sexual and Relationship Therapy, 16*, 145–164.

Trudel, G., Ravart, M., & Aubin, S.. (1996). Hypoactive sexual desire in couples: A cognitive-behavioral perspective. In J. Lonsdale, S. Powell, & L. Solomon (Eds.), *The Hatherleigh guide to marriage and family therapy*. New York: Hatherleigh Press.

Trussell, J., et al. (2000). Emergency contraception: A cost-effective approach to preventing unintended pregnancy. *Women's Health, 5*.

Trynka, S., & Tucker, N. (1995). Overview. In Tucker, N. (Ed.), *Bisexual politics: Theories, queries, and visions.* New York: Harrington Park Press.

Tsui, L., & Nicoladis, E. (2004). Losing it: Similarities and differences in first intercourse experiences of men and women. *The Canadian Journal of Human Sexuality, 13,* 95–106.

Turkle, S. (1995). *Life on the screen: Identity in the age of the Internet.* New York: Simon & Schuster.

Turner, P. K., Runtz, M. G., & Galambos, N. L. (1999). Sexual abuse, pubertal timing, and subjective age in adolescent girls: A research note. *Journal of Reproductive and Infant Psychology, 17*(2), 111–118.

Tutin, C. E. G., & McGinnis, P. R. (1981). Chimpanzee reproduction in the wild. In C. E. Graham (Ed.), *Reproductive biology of the great apes* (pp. 239–264). New York: Academic Press.

Tutty, L. M. (1997). Child sexual abuse prevention programs: Evaluating who do you tell. *Child Abuse & Neglect, 21,* 869–881.

Udry, J. R. (1988). Biological predispositions and social control in adolescent sexual behavior. *American Sociological Review, 53,* 709–722.

Udry, J. R., et al. (1985). Serum androgenic hormones motivate sexual behavior in adolescent boys. *Fertility and Sterility, 43,* 90–94.

Udry, J. R., & Eckland, B. K. (1984). Benefits of being attractive: Differential payoffs for men and women. *Psychological Reports, 54,* 47–56.

Ulmann, A., Teutsch, G., & Philibert, D. (1990, June). RU-486. *Scientific American, 262,* 42–48.

Ullman, S. E. (2004). Sexual assault victimization and suicidal behavior in women: A review of the literature. *Aggression & Violent Behavior, 9,* 331–351.

Ullman, S. E., et al. (2007). Structural models of the relations of assault severity, social support, avoidance coping, self-blame, and PTSD among sexual assault survivors. *Psychology of Women Quarterly, 31,* 23–27.

UNAIDS–United Nations Program on HIV/AIDS. (1997). *Impact of HIV and sexual health education on the sexual behavior of young people.* Geneva, SU.

Union for Reform Judaism. (2004). What is the Reform perspective on abortion? Retrieved from http://uahc.org.

United Synagogue of Conservative Judaism. (1989). Retrieved from www.ncrc.org.

UPI (1981, November 5). Toxicologist warns against butyl nitrite. *Delaware Gazette,* p. 3.

Upadhyay, U. D., & Robey, B. (1999). Why family planning matters. *Population Reports,* Series J, No. 49. Baltimore, Johns Hopkins University School of Public Health, Population Information Program.

Upadhyay, U., et al. (2005). New contraceptive choices. *Population Reports, Series M, 19.* Baltimore: Johns Hopkins Bloomberg School of Public Health, www.populationreports.org/m19.

Upadhyay, U., et al. (2005). Microbicides: new potential for protection. *Inforeports, 3.* Baltimore: Johns Hopkins School of Public Health. Www.infoforhealth.org.

Urban, J. R. (1992). Neuroendocrinology of aging in the male and female. *Endocrinology and Metabolism Clinics of North America, 21,* 921–931.

Urbina, A., & Jones, K. (2004). Crystal methamphetamine, its analogues, and HIV infection; Medical and psychiatric aspects of a new epidemic. *Clinical Infectious Diseases, 38,* 890–894.

Valentich, M. (1994). Rape revisited: Sexual violence against women in the former Yugoslavia. *Canadian Journal of Human Sexuality, 3,* 53–64.

Van Anders, S. M., Hamilton, L. D., & Watson, N. V. (2007). Multiple partners are associated with higher testosterone in North American men and women. *Hormones and Behavior, 51,* 454–459.

Van Anders, S. M., & Watson, N. V. (2006). Menstrual cycle irregularities are associated with testosterone levels in healthy premenopausal women. *American Journal of Human Biology, 18,* 841–844.

Vance, E. B., & Wagner, N. N. (1976). Written descriptions of orgasm: A study of sex differences. *Archives of Sexual Behavior, 5,* 87–98.

Van Damme, L., Ramjee, G., Alary, M., Vuylsteke, B., Chandeying, V., Rees, H., et al. (2002a). Effectiveness of COL-1492, a nonxynol-9 vaginal gel, on HIV-1 transmission in female sex workers: A randomised controlled trial. *Lancet, 360,* 971–977.

Van Goozen, S. H. M., et al. (1997). Psychoendocrinological assessment of the menstrual cycle: The relationship between hormones, sexuality, and mood. *Archives of Sexual Behavior, 26,* 359–382.

Van Horn, K. R., Arnone, A., Nesbitt, K., Desilets, L., Sears, T., Giffin, M., & Brudi, R. (1997). Physical distance and interpersonal characteristics in college students' romantic relationships. *Personal Relationships, 4,* 25–34.

Van Lankveld, J. (1998). Bibliotherapy in the treatment of sexual dysfunctions: A meta-analysis. *Journal of Consulting and Clinical Psychology, 66,* 702–708.

Van Lankveld, J. J. D. M., ter Kuile, M. M., de Groot, H. E., Melles, R., Nefs, J. & Zandbergen, M. (2006). Cognitive-behavioral therapy for women with lifelong vaginismus: A randomized waiting-list controlled trial of efficacy. *Journal of Consulting and Clinical Psychology, 74,* 168–178.

Van Lent, P. (1996). Her beautiful savage: The current sexual image of the Native American male. In S. E. Bird (Ed.), *Dressing in feathers: The construction of the Indian in American popular culture* (pp. 211–228). Boulder, CO: Westview.

Vanwesenbeeck, I. (1994). *Prostitutes' well-being and risk.* Amsterdam: VU University Press.

Vanwesenbeeck, I. (2004). Another decade of social scientific work on sex work: A review of research 1990–2000. *Annual Review of Sex Research, 12,* 242–289.

Vanwesenbeeck, I. (2005). Burnout among female indoor sex workers. *Archives of Sexual Behavior, 34,* 627–640.

Varghese, B., Maher, J. E., Peterman, T. A., Branson, B. M., & Steketee, R. W. (2002). Reducing the risk of sexual HIV transmission: quantifying the per-act risk for HIV on the basis of choice of partner, sex act, and condom use. *Sexually Transmitted Diseases, 29,* 38–43.

Vasey, P. L., & Bartlett, N. H. (2007). What can the Samoan "fa'afafine" teach us about the Western concept of gender identity disorder in childhood? *Perspectives in Biology and Medicine, 50,* 481–490.

Vasey, P. L., & Duckworth, N. (2006). Sexual reward via vulvar, perineal, and anal stimulation: A proximate mechanism for female homosexual mounting in Japanese Macaques. *Archives of Sexual Behavior, 35,* 523–532.

Vasey, P. L., Foroud, A., Duckworth, N., & Kovacovsky, S. D. (2006). Male-female and female-female mounting in Japanese Macaques: A comparative study of posture and movement. *Archives of Sexual Behavior, 35,* 117–129.

Ve Ard, C., & Veaux, F. (2003). Polyamory 101. Retrieved from www.xeromag.com/poly101.pdf.

Venicz, L., & Vanwesenbeeck, I. (2000). *Something is going to change in prostitution: Social position and the psychological well being of indoor prostitutes before the law reform.* Utrecht/The Hague, The Netherlands: NISSO/Ministry of Justice.

Vasey, P. L. (2002). Sexual partner preference in female Japanese macaques. *Archives of Sexual Behavior, 31,* 51–62.

Vilain, E. (2000). The genetics of sexual development. *Annual Review of Sex Research, 11,* 1–25.

Villa, L. L., et al. (2006). High sustained efficacy of a prophylactic quadrivalent human papillomavirus types 6/11/16/18 L1 virus-like particle vaccine through 5 years of follow-up. *British Journal of Cancer, 95,* 1459–1466.

Vincent, J. P., Friedman, L. C., Nugent, J., & Messerly, L. (1979). Demand characteristics in observations of marital interaction. *Journal of Consulting and Clinical Psychology, 47,* 557–566.

Von Hertzen, H., Piaggio, G., Ding, J., Chen, J., Song, S., & Bartfai, G. (2002). Low dose mifepristone and two regimens of levonorgestrel for emergency contraception: A WHO multicentre randomised trial. *Lancet, 360,* 1803–1810.

Von Hertzen, H., & Van Look, P. (1996). Research on new methods of emergency contraception. *Family Planning Perspectives, 28,* 52–57.

Von Krafft-Ebing, R. (1886). *Psychopathia sexualis.* (Reprinted by Putnam, New York, 1965).

Von Kries, R., Koletzko, B., Sauerwald, T., von Mutius, E., Barnert, D., Grunert, V., von Voss, H. (1999). Breast feeding and obesity: Cross sectional study. *British Medical Journal, 319,* 147–150.

Wade, L., & DeLamater, J. (2002). Relationship dissolution as a life stage transition: Effects on sexual attitudes and behaviors. *Journal of Marriage and the Family, 64,* 898–914.

Wald, A., et al. (2005). The relationship between condom use and herpes simplex virus acquisition. *Annals of Internal Medicine, 143,* 707–713.

Wald, A., et al. (2006). Comparative efficacy of famciclovir and valacy-clovir for suppression of recurrent genital herpes and viral shedding. *Sexually Transmitted Diseases, 33*, 529–533.

Waldinger, M. D., Quinn, P., Dilleen, M., Mundayat, R., Schweitzer, D. H., & Boolell, M. (2005). A multinational population survey of intravaginal ejaculation latency time. *Journal of Sexual Medicine, 2*, 492–497.

Walen, S. R., & Roth, D. (1987). A cognitive approach in J. H. Geer & W. T. O'Donohue (Eds.), *Theories of human sexuality.* New York: Plenum.

Walker, J., Archer, J., & Davies, M. (2005). Effects of rape on men: A descriptive analysis. *Archives of Sexual Behavior, 34*, 69–80.

Wallen, K. (2001). Sex and context: Hormones and primate sexual motivation. *Hormones and Behavior, 40*, 339–357.

Wallen, K., & Parsons, W. A. (1997). Sexual behavior in same-sexed nonhuman primates: Is it relevant to understanding human homosexuality? *Annual Review of Sex Research, 8*, 195–223.

Wallen, K., & Zehr, J. L. (2004). Hormones and history: The evolution and development of primate female sexuality. *Journal of Sex Research, 41*, 101–112.

Wallerstein, E. (1980). *Circumcision: An American health fallacy.* New York: Springer.

Wallin, P. (1949). An appraisal of some methodological aspects of the Kinsey report. *American Sociological Review, 14*, 197–210.

Walsh, T. L., Frezieres, R. G., Peacock, K., Nelson, A. L., Clark, V. A., & Bernstein, L. (2003). Evaluation of the efficacy of a nonlatex condom: Results from a randomized, controlled clinical trial. *Perspectives on Sexual and Reproductive Health, 35*, 79–86.

Walster, E., Walster, W., & Berscheid, E. (1978). *Equity: Theory and research.* Boston, MA: Allyn and Bacon.

Wang, P. J., McCarrey, J., Yang, F., & Page, D. (2001). An abundance of X-linked genes expressed in spermatogonia. *Nature Genetics, 27*, 422–426.

Ward, L. M. (2002). Does television exposure affect emerging adults' attitudes and assumptions about sexual relationships? Correlational and experimental confirmation. *Journal of Youth and Adolescence, 31*, 1–15.

Ward, L. M., Hansbrough, E., & Walker, E. (2005). Contributions of music video exposure to Black adolescents' gender and sexual schemas. *Journal of Adolescent Research, 20*, 143–166.

Ward, O. B., Ward, I. L., Denning, J. H., Hendricks, S. E., & French, J. A. (2002). Hormonal mechanisms underlying aberrant sexual differentiation in male rats prenatally exposed to alcohol, stress, or both. *Archives of Sexual Behavior, 31*, 9–16.

Wassersug, R. J., Zelenietz, S. A., & Squire, G. F. (2004). New age eunuchs: Motivation and rationale for voluntary castration. *Archives of Sexual Behavior, 33*, 433–442.

Weaver, A. D., & Byers, E. S. (2006). The relationships among body image, body mass index, exercise, and sexual functioning in heterosexual women. *Psychology of Women Quarterly, 30*, 333–339.

Weaver, A. D., Byers, E. S., Sears, H. A., Cohen, J. N., & Randall, H. E. S. (2001). *New Brunswick parents' ideas about sexual health education.* Report prepared for the New Brunswick Department of Education, Fredericton, NB. Retrieved November 11, 2002, from www.gnb.ca/0000/publications/ss/nbparentidea.pdf.

Weaver, A. D., Byers, E. S., Sears, H. A, Cohen, J. N., & Randall, H. E. S. (2002). New Brunswick parents' attitudes towards sexual health education at school and at home. *Canadian Journal of Human Sexuality, 11*, 19–31.

Weber, R. P. (1990). *Basic content analysis* (2nd ed.). Newbury Park, CA: Sage.

Weideger, P. (1976). *Menstruation and menopause.* New York: Knopf.

Weight gain during pregnancy. (2003). *The Journal of Midwifery and Women's Health, 48*, 229–230.

Weinberg, M., Williams, C., & Calhan, C. (1995). "If the shoe fits . . .": Exploring male homosexual foot fetishism. *Journal of Sex Research, 32*, 17–27.

Weinberg, M. S., Shaver, F. S., & Williams, C. J. (1999). Gendered sex work in the San Francisco tenderloin. *Archives of Sexual Behavior, 28*, 503–521.

Weinberg, M. S., Williams, C. J., & Pryor, D. W. (1994). *Dual attraction: Understanding bisexuality.* New York: Oxford University Press.

Weinberg, M. S., Williams, C., & Pryor, D. (2001). Bisexuals at midlife: Commitment, salience, and identity. *Journal of Contemporary Ethnography, 30*, 180–208.

Weinberg, T. S. (1994). Research in sadomasochism: A review of sociological and social psychological literature. *Annual Review of Sex Research, 5*, 257–279.

Weinberg, T. S. (1987). Sadomasochism in the United States: A review of recent sociological literature. *Journal of Sex Research, 23*, 50–69.

Weinhardt, L. S., & Carey, M. P. (1996). Prevalence of erectile disorder among men with diabetes mellitus. *Journal of Sex Research, 33*, 205–214.

Wellings, K., Collumbien, M., Slaymaker, E., Singh, S., Hodges, Z., Patel, D., & Bajos, N. (2006). Sexual and reproductive health 2: Sexual behaviour in context: A global perspective. *The Lancet, 368*, 1706–1728.

Wellings, K., Nanchahal, K., Macdowall, W., McManus, S., Erens, B., Mercer, C. H., et al. (2001). Sexual behaviour in Britain: Early heterosexual experience. *The Lancet, 358*, 1843–1850.

Welsh, S. (1999). Gender and sexual harassment. *Annual Review of Sociology, 25*, 169–190.

Wenk, M. & Nieschlag, E. (2006). Male contraception; A realistic option? *The European Journal of Contraception and Reproductive Health Care, 11*, 69–80.

Wessells, H., Lue, T. F., & McAninch, J. W. (1996). Penile length in the flaccid and erect states: Guidelines for penile augmentation. *The Journal of Urology, 156*, 995–997.

West, S. L., Vinikoor, L. C., & Zolnoum, D. (2004). A systematic review of the literature on female sexual dysfunction prevalence and predictors. *Annual Review of Sex Research, 15*, 40–172.

Wheeler, G. D., et al. (1984). Reduced serum testosterone and prolactin levels in male distance runners. *Journal of the American Medical Association, 252*, 514–516.

Whipple, B., Ogden, G., & Komisanak, B. (1992). Physiological correlates of imagery-induced orgasm in women. *Archives of Sexual Behavior, 21*, 121–133.

Whitam, F. L. (1983). Culturally invariable properties of male homosexuality: Tentative conclusions from cross-cultural research. *Archives of Sexual Behavior, 12*, 207–226.

Whitam, F. L., & Mathy, R. M. (1991). Childhood cross-gender behavior of homosexual females in Brazil, Peru, the Philippines, and the United States. *Archives of Sexual Behavior, 20*, 151–170.

White, G. L., Fishbein, S., & Rutstein, J. (1981). Passionate love and the misattribution of arousal. *Journal of Personality and Social Psychology, 41*, 56–62.

White, G. L., & Mullen, P. E. (1989). *Jealousy: Theory, research, and clinical strategies.* New York: Guilford.

White, L. J. (2001). Romans 1:26–27: The claim that homosexuality is unnatural. In P. Jung & J. Coray (Eds.), *Sexual diversity and Catholicism* (pp. 133–149). Collegeville, MN: The Liturgical Press.

Whitley, B., Jr. (1993). Reliability and aspects of the construct validity of Sternberg's Triangular Love Scale. *Journal of Social and Personal Relationships, 10*, 475–480.

Wickham, D. (2001, September 3). Castration often fails to halt offenders. *USA Today.*

Wickler, W. (1973). *The sexual code.* New York: Anchor Books. (Original in German, 1969).

Widmer M, Villar J, Benigni A, Conde-Agudelo A, Karumanchi SA, & Lindheimer M. (2007). Mapping the theories of preeclampsia and the role of angiogenic factors: A systematic review. *Obstetrics & Gynecology, 109*:168–180.

Wiederman, M. W., & Hurd, C. (1999). Extradyadic involvement during dating. *Journal of Social and Personal Relationships, 16*, 265–274.

Wiederman, M. W., Weis, D. L., & Allgeier, E. R. (1994). The effect of question preface on response rates to a telephone survey of sexual experience. *Archives of Sexual Behavior, 23*, 203–216.

Wiesenfeld, H. C., Lowry, D. L., Heine, R. P., Krohn, M. A., Bittner, H., Kellinger, K., et al. (2001). Self-collection of vaginal swabs for the detection of chlamydia, gonorrhea, and trichomoniasis: Opportunity to encourage sexually transmitted disease testing among adolescents. *Sexually Transmitted Diseases, 28*, 321–325.

Wilcox, A. J., Weinberg, C. R., & Baird, D. D. (1995). Timing of sexual intercourse in relation to ovulation. *New England Journal of Medicine, 333,* 1517–1521.

Wilcox, B. L., & Wyatt, J. (1997). *Adolescent abstinence education programs: A meta-analysis.* Presented at the annual meeting, Society for the Scientific Study of Sexuality, Arlington, VA.

Wilkinson, Ross. (1995). Changes in psychological health and the marital relationship through child bearing: Transition or process as stressor. *Australian Journal of Psychology, 47,* 86–92.

Willetts, M., Sprecher, S., & Beck, F. (2004). Overview of sexual practices and attitudes within relational contexts. In J. H. Harvey, A. Wenzel, & S. Sprecher (Eds.), *The handbook of sexuality in close relationships* (pp. 57–85). Mahwah, NJ: Lawrence Erlbaum.

Williams, C., & Weinberg, M. (2003). Zoophilia in men: A study of sexual interest in animals. *Archives of Sexual Behavior, 32,* 523–535.

Williams, L. M. (1994). Recall of childhood trauma: A prospective study of women's memories of child sexual abuse. *Journal of Consulting and Clinical Psychology, 62,* 1167–1176.

Williams, T. M. (Ed.) (1986). *The impact of television: A naturalistic experiment in three communities.* Orlando: Academic Press.

Williams, T., Taradash, A., & Connolly, J. (2004). *Sexual behavior and dating activities among young Canadian adolescents: Normative patterns and biosocial links.* Presented at Society for Research on Adolescence, Baltimore, MD.

Wilson, G. (1997). Gender differences in sexual fantasy: An evolutionary analysis. *Personality and Individual Differences, 22,* 27–31.

Wilt, T. J., Fink, H. A., MacDonald, R., & Rutks, I. R. (2002). Sildenafil for male erectile dysfunction: A systematic review and meta-analysis. *Archives of Internal Medicine, 162,* 1349–1360.

Wincze, J. P., & Carey, M. P. (1991). *Sexual dysfunction: A guide for assessment and treatment.* New York: Guilford.

Wincze, J. P., & Carey, M. P. (2001). *Sexual dysfunction: A guide for assessment and treatment* (2nd ed.). New York: The Guilford Press.

Winer, R. L., et al. (2006). Condom use and the risk of genital human papillomavirus infection in young women. *New England Journal of Medicine, 354,* 2645–2654.

Winn, R. L., & Newton, N. (1982). Sexuality in aging: A study of 106 cultures. *Archives of Sexual Behavior, 11,* 283–298.

Winter, J. S. D., & Couch, R. M. (1995). Sexual differentiation. In P. Felig, J. D. Baxter, & L. A. Frohman (Eds.), *Endocrinology and metabolism* (3rd ed., pp. 1053–1104). New York: McGraw-Hill.

Wise, P. M., Krajnak, K. M., & Kashon, M. L. (1996). Menopause: The aging of multiple pacemakers. *Science, 273,* 67–70.

Wisniewski, A. B., et al. (2000). Complete androgen insensitivity syndrome: Long-term medical, surgical, and psychosexual outcome. *Journal of Clinical Endocrinology & Metabolism, 85,* 2664–2669.

Wisniewski, A. B., Migeon, C. J., Gearhart, J. P., Rock, J. A., Berkovitz, G. D., Plotnick, L. P., et al. (2001). Congenital micropenis: Long-term medical, surgical, and psychosexual follow-up of individuals raised male or female. *Hormone Research, 56,* 3–11.

Wiswell, T. E., Enzenauer, R. W., Cornish, J. D., & Hawkins, C. T. (1987). Declining frequency of circumcision: Implications for changes in the absolute incidence and male to female sex ratio of urinary tract infections in early infancy. *Pediatrics, 79,* 338–342.

Wohl, A. R., Johnson, D. F., Lu, S., Jordan, W., Beall, G., Currier, J., et al. (2002). HIV risk behaviors among African American men in Los Angeles County who self-identify as heterosexual. *Journal of Acquired Immune Deficiency Syndromes, 31,* 354–360.

Wolchik, S. A., Spencer, S. L., & Lisi, I. S. (1983). Volunteer bias in research employing vaginal measures of sexual arousal. *Archives of Sexual Behavior, 12,* 399–408.

Wolff, L., & Geissel, D. (1994). Street prostitution in Canada. *Canadian Social Trends.* Statistics Canada, Catalogue no. 11-008E.

Wonders, N. A., & Michalowski, R. (2001). Bodies, borders, and sex tourism in a globalized world: A tale of two cities—Amsterdam and Havana. *Social Problems, 48,* 645–571.

Wong, J. K., et al. (1997). Recovery of replication-competent HIV despite prolonged suppression of plasma viremia. *Science, 278,* 1291–1295.

Wong, T., & Jordan, R. A. (2000). Commentary: Syphilis elimination in Canada: If not now, when? *The Canadian Journal of Human Sexuality, 9,* 205–209.

Wood, N. S., et al. (2000). Neurologic and developmental disability after extreme preterm birth. *New England Journal of Medicine, 343,* 378–384.

Woods, S., & Raju, U. (2001). Maternal smoking and the risk of congenital birth defects: *A cohort study. Journal of the American Board of Family Practice, 14,* 330–334.

Woodzicka, J. A., & LaFrance, M. (2005). The effects of subtle sexual harassment on women's performance in a job interview. *Sex Roles, 53,* 67–78.

Working Group for a New View of Women's Sexual Problems. (2001). Part I: A new view of women's sexual problems. In E. Kachak & L. Tiefer (Eds.), *A new view of women's sexual problems* (pp. 1–8). New York: Haworth Press.

World Health Organization. (2004). Gender and reproductive rights. Retrieved November 16, 2004, from www.who.int.

World Health Organization. (2004). Unsafe abortion: Global and regional estimates of incidence of unsafe abortion and associated mortality in 2000 (4th ed.). Retrieved from www.who.int.

Worthington, E., Martin, G., Shumate, M., & Carpenter, J. (1983). The effect of brief Lamaze training and social encouragement on pain endurance in a cold pressor task. *Journal of Applied Social Psychology, 13,* 223–233.

Wright, V., Schieve, L., Reynolds, M., & Jeng, G. (2005). Assisted reproductive technology surveillance - United States, 2002. *Morbidity and Mortality Weekly Report,54* (SS02), 1–24.

Writing Group for the Women's Health Initiative Investigators. (2002). Risks and benefits of estrogen plus progestin in healthy postmenopausal women. *Journal of the American Medical Association, 288,* 321–333.

Wyatt, G. E. (1991). Child sexual abuse and its effects on sexual functioning. *Annual Review of Sex Research, 2,* 249–266.

Wyatt, G. E., Peters, S. D., & Guthrie, D. (1988). Kinsey revisited, Part I: Comparisons of the sexual socialization and sexual behavior of white women over 33 years. *Archives of Sexual Behavior, 17,* 201–240.

Wyatt, G. E. (1997). *Stolen women: Reclaiming our sexuality, taking back our lives.* New York: Wiley.

Wyatt, T. D. (2003). *Pheromones and animal behaviour.* New York: Cambridge University Press.

Wylie, K. R., Jones, R., & Walters, S. (2003). The potential benefit of vacuum devices augmenting psychosexual therapy for erectile dysfunction: A randomized controlled trial. *Journal of Sex & Marital Therapy, 29,* 227–236.

Wyrobek, A., Eskenazi, B., Young, WS., Arnheim, N., Tiemann-Boegr, I., Jabs, E., Glaser, R. Pearson, F., & Evenson, D. (2006). Advancing age has different effects on DNA damage, chromatin integrity, gene mutations, and aneuploidies in sperm. *Proceedings of the National Academy of Sciences, 103,* 9601–9606.

Xu, F., et al. (2006). Trends in herpes simplex virus type 1 and type 2 seroprevalence in the United States. *Journal of the American Medical Association, 296,* 964–973.

Yalom, I. D. (1960). Aggression and forbiddenness in voyeurism. *Archives of General Psychiatry, 3,* 317.

Yeh, Hsiu-Chen, Lorenz, F., Wickrama, K. A. S., Conger, R., and Elder, G. H. Jr. (2006). Relationships among sexual satisfaction, marital quality and marital instability at midlife. *Journal of Family Psychology, 20,* 336–343.

Yellowlees, P., & Marks, S. (2007). Problematic Internet use or Internet addiction? *Computers in Human Behavior, 23,* 1447–1453.

Yoder, P. Stanley et al. (2004). *Female genital cutting in the demographic and health surveys: A critical and comparative analysis.* DHS Comparative Reports No. 7. Calverton, MD: ORC Macro.

Yost, L. (1991). Bisexual tendencies. In L. Hutchins & L. Kaahumanu (Eds.), *Bi any other name: Bisexual people speak out.* Boston: Alyson.

Yost, M. R. & Zurbriggen, E. L. (2006). Gender differences in the enactment of sociosexuality: An examination of implicit social motives, sexual fantasies, coercive sexual attitudes, and aggressive sexual behavior. *Journal of Sex Research, 43,* 163–173.

Young, I. (1996). Education for sexuality—the role of the school. *Journal of Biological Education, 30,* 250–255.

Young, K., Griffin-Shelley, E., Cooper, A., O'mam, J., & Buchananan, J. (2000). Online infidelity: A new dimension in couple relationships with implications for evaluation and treatment. *Sexual Addiction and Compulsivity, 7,* 59–74.

Zabin, L. S., Hirsch, M. B., Smith, E. A., & Hardy, J. B. (1984). Adolescent sexual attitudes and behaviors: Are they consistent? *Family Planning Perspectives, 4,* 181–185.

Zak, P. J., Kursban, R. O., & Matzner, W. L. (2004). The neurobiology of trust. *Annals of the New York Academy of Science, 1032,* 224–227.

Zala, S. M. & Penn, D. J. (2004). Abnormal behaviours induced by chemical pollution: A review of the evidence and new challenges. *Animal Behaviour, 68,* 649–664 .

Zaslow, M. J., et al. (1985). Depressed mood in new fathers: Association with parent-infant interaction. *Genetic, Social, and General Psychology Monographs, 111*(2), 133–150.

Zaviačič, M. (1994). Sexual asphyxiophilia (Koczwarism) in women and the biological phenomenon of female ejaculation. *Medical Hypotheses, 42,* 318–322.

Zaviačič, M., et al. (2000). Immunohistochemical study of prostate-specific antigen in normal and pathological human tissues: Special reference to the male and female prostate and breast. *Journal of Histotechnology, 23,* 105–111.

Zaviačič, M., Ablin, R. J., Zaviacic, T., Kopani, M., Stvrtina, S., Holoman, K., et al. (2000). Weight, size, macroanatomy, and histology of the normal prostate in the adult human female: A minireview. *Journal of Histotechnology, 23,* 61–69.

Zax, M., Sameroff, A., & Farnum, J. (1975). Childbirth education, maternal attitude and delivery. *American Journal of Obstetrics and Gynecology, 123,* 185–190.

Zhang, J., Zou, S., & Giulivi, A. (2001). *Hepatitis B in Canada: Viral hepatitis and emerging bloodborne pathogens in Canada.* Canada Communicable Disease Report, 27S3.

Zhou, J., Hogman, M., Gooren, L., & Swaab, D. (1995). A sex difference in the human brain and its relation to transsexuality. *Nature, 378,* 68–70.

Zilbergeld, B. (1978). *Male sexuality.* Boston: Little, Brown.

Zilbergeld, B. (1992). *The new male sexuality.* New York: Bantam Books.

Zilbergeld, B. (1999). The truth about men, sex, and pleasure. In *The new male sexuality* (Rev. ed.). New York: Bantam.

Zilbergeld, B., & Ellison, C. R. (1980). Desire discrepancies and arousal problems in sex therapy. In S. R. Leiblum & L. A. Pervin (Eds.), *Principles and practice of sex therapy* (pp. 65–104). New York: Guilford.

Zilbergeld, B., & Evans, M. (1980, August). The inadequacy of Masters and Johnson. *Psychology Today, 14,* 28–43.

Zillmann, D., Schweitzer, K. J., & Mundorf, N. (1994). Menstrual cycle variations of women's interest in erotica. *Archives of Sexual Behavior, 23,* 579–598.

Zimmer, D. (1983). Interaction patterns and communication skills in sexually distressed and normal couples: Two experimental studies. *Journal of Sex and Marital Therapy, 9,* 251–265.

Zimmerman-Tansella, C., Bertagni, P., Siani, R., & Micciolo, R. (1994). Marital relationships and somatic and psychological symptoms in pregnancy. *Social Science and Medicine, 38,* 559–564.

Zoldbrod, A. P. (1993). *Men, women, and infertility: Intervention and treatment strategies.* New York: Lexington Books.

Zoucha-Jensen, J. M., & Coyne, A. (1993). The effects of resistance strategies on rape. *American Journal of Public Health, 83,* 1633–1634.

Zucker, K. J. (2000). Gender identity disorder. In A. J. Sameroff et al. (Eds.), *Handbook of developmental psychopathology,* (2nd ed., pp. 671–686).

Zucker, K. J., & Green, R. (1993). Psychological and familial aspects of gender identity disorder. *Sexual and Gender Identity Disorders, 2,* 513–542.

Zucker, K. J., Wilson-Smith, D. N., Kurita, J. A., & Stern, A. (1995). Children's appraisals of sex-typed behaviour in their peers. *Sex Roles, 33,* 703–725.

Zuger, A. (1987, June). AIDS on the wards: A residency in medical ethics. *Hastings Center Report,* 16–20.

Zuk, M. (2002). *Sexual selections: What we can and can't learn about sex from animals.* Berkeley: University of California Press.

Zumpe, D., & Michael, R. P. (1968). The clutching reaction and orgasm in the female rhesus monkey (Macaca mulatta). *Journal of Endocrinology, 40,* 117–123.

Zumwalt, R. (1976). Plain and fancy: A content analysis of children's jokes dealing with adult sexuality. *Western Folklore, 35,* 258–267.

Zurbriggen, E. & Morgan, E. (2006). Who wants to marry a millionaire? Reality dating television programs, attitudes toward sex, and sexual behaviors. *Sex Roles, 54,* 1–17.

Zussman, L., Zussman, S., Sunley, R., & Bjornson, E. (1981). Sexual response after hysterectomy-oophorectomy. *American Journal of Obstetrics and Gynecology, 140,* 725–729.

ACKNOWLEDGEMENTS

PHOTOGRAPHS

CHAPTER 1

p. 7 (left): © AP/Wide World Photos; (right) Culver; p. 8: © Science Museum/SSPL; p. 9: ©Stephen Lovekin/Getty Images; p. 10: © AP/Wide World Photos; p.14 (left): © Art Wolfe/Getty; (right): ©Reuters/Ho New; p. 19 (left): © Courtesy Prof. Robert Gemme, Département de Sexologie, Université du Québec à Montréal; (right): © Lawrence Migdale/Stock, Boston; p. 20 (left): © Meredith F. Small; (right): © Thomas Michael Corcoran/PhotoEdit.

CHAPTER 2

p. 28 (left): © J.H. Robinson/Photo Researchers; (right): © Super-Stock, Inc.; p. 33: © Lester Lefkowitz/Taxi/Getty; p. 37: © Joel Gordon; p. 40: © Queerstock/Davis Freeman; p. 42: © CP Picture Archive/Chuck Mitchell; p. 47: © EyeWire Collection/Getty Images.

CHAPTER 3

p. 54: © S. Young-Wolff/PhotoEdit; p. 62: Reprinted by permission of The Kinsey Institute for Research in Sex, Gender and Reproduction, Inc., photo by Bill Dellenback; p. 63: © Matthew Peyton/Getty Images; p. 66: © Thinkstock/Getty; p. 71: © Western News; p. 73: © Bob Daemmrich; p. 77: © David Young-Wolff/PhotoEdit.

CHAPTER 4

p. 82: © Wikimedia Commons, http://en.wikipedia.org; p. 84: ©Ulrike Kotermann/epa/Corbis; p. 84: © Hazel Hankin Photography; p. 92 (left): ©Jessica Abad de Gail/AGE Fotostock; (middle): © Joel Gordon; (right): © Joel Gordon; p. 94 (left and right): © Joel Gordon; p. 100: © Susan Lerner/Joel Gordon Photography; p. 103: ©Stefano Rellandini/Corbis.

CHAPTER 5

p. 112 (top): Dr. Landrum B. Shettles; (bottom): © www.thekeeper-inc.com; p. 123: © CP PictureArchive/Winnipeg Free Press; p. 124 (left): © Joe Sohm/The Image Works; (right): © Elizabeth Crews/The Image Works; p. 126 (left): © Jason Laure/Woodfin Camp; (right): © Blair Seitz/Photo Researchers, Inc.; p. 131: © Amy Etra/PhotoEdit.

CHAPTER 6

p. 137: Dr. Landrum B. Shettles; p. 141 (top left): © Petit Format/Nestle/Science Source/Photo Researchers; (top right): Lennart Nilsson, from *A Child is Born*, Dell Publishing Company; (bottom left): Lennart Nilsson, from *A Child is Born*, Dell Publishing Company; (bottom right): Lennart Nilsson, from *A Child is Born*, Dell Publishing Company; p. 144: © George Pimentel/Getty Images; p. 144: © Spencer Grant/Monkmeyer; p. 149 (left): Streissguth, A. P.; Landesman-Dwyer, S.; Martin, J.C., & Smith, D.W. (1980). "Teratogenic effects of alcohol in humans and laboratory animals," *Science, 209*, pp. 353–361; (right): © John Chiasson/Gamma Liaison; p. 152 (left): © D. Van Rossum/Petit Format/Photo Researchers, Inc.; (right): © O.V.N./Petit Format/Photo Researchers, Inc.; p. 155: © SuperStock/Alamy; p. 157: © Monkmeyer/Byron; p. 163: © Digital Vision/Getty; p. 173 (left): © ISM/Phototake; (right): © Paltera Stefano/Gamma.

CHAPTER 7

p. 183: Courtesy Special Collections Department, Hamilton Public Library; p. 184: © Tony Freeman/PhotoEdit; p. 185: © Joel Gordon p. 187: © Mauritius, GMBH/Phototake; p. 192: © Joel Gordon;

p. 193: © Joel Gordon; p. 194: © Tony Freeman/PhotoEdit; p. 195: Used with permission of The Children's Defense Fund; p. 197: Used with permission of The Children's Defense Fund; p. 210: © CP Picture Archive/Paul Chiasson.

CHAPTER 8

p. 224 (top): © Science VU/Visuals Unlimited; (bottom): © Bart's Medical Library/Phototake; p. 226 (top and bottom): © Biophoto Associates/Photo Researchers, Inc.; p. 229: © "The Get Tested! Campaign," produced by Planned Parenthood Toronto; Creative by Due North Communications, Inc. p. 235 (left): © Thomas Bow-mnan/PhotoEdit; (right): © Spencer Platt/Getty Images; p. 239: Courtesy U.S. Centers for Disease Control; p. 241 (left and right): Courtesy U.S. Centers for Disease Control; p. 244: © E. Gray/Science Photo Library/Photo Researchers, Inc.

CHAPTER 9

p. 261: © Owen Franken/Corbis; p. 263: Courtesy Ellen Stohl; p. 264 (top): Courtesy Ellen Stohl; p. 266: © Dr. Scott T. Grafton/Visuals Unlimited; p. 270 (left): © Betts Loman/PhotoEdit; (right): © Luis Fernandez/SuperStock; p. 272 (top): © Joel Gordon; (bottom): © Peter Klashorst; p. 275: © Gero Breloer/dpa/Corbis; p. 276: © Wikimedia Commons, http://en.wikipedia.org; p. 282: © Luiz C. Marico/Peter Arnold, Inc.

CHAPTER 10

p. 296: © Amy C. Etra/PhotoEdit; p. 297: © Maya Barnes/The Image Works; p. 299: © Cassy Cohen/PhotoEdit; p. 303: © Getty Images/Image Source; p. 309: © CP Picture Archive/Aaron Harris; p. 310: © SW Productions/PhotoDisc/Getty Images; p. 314: © Francesco Venturi/Corbis.

CHAPTER 11

p. 331: © Doug Menuez/PhotoDisc/Getty Images; p. 337 (left): © CP Picture Archive/Edmonton SunóDale MacMillan; (right): ©Jerome Tisne/Getty Images; p. 341 (left): © Ryan McVay/Getty Images; (right): © Paul Vozdic/The Image Bank; p. 347: © CP Picture Archive/Ryan Remiorz; p. 348 (left): © Ryan McVay/Getty Images; p. 358: © Mike Siluk/The Image Works; p. 359: © Photo-disc/Getty Images.

CHAPTER 12

p. 371: © Wayne Levin/Getty Images; p. 373: © Barbara Penoyar/PhotoDisc/Getty Images; p. 379: © Michael Krasowitz/Taxi/Getty Images; p. 385: © David Young-Wolff/PhotoEdit; p. 386: © Jerry Cooke/Photo Researchers; p. 393: Reprinted with special permission of King Features Syndicate; p. 397 (top): © Digital Vision/Getty Images; (bottom): © Bruce Ayres/Tony Stone/Getty Images; p. 398: © Jack Star/PhotoLink/Getty Images.

CHAPTER 13

p. 404 (left): © George Simian/Corbis; (right): © Getty Images/Laurence Monneret; p. 407: © CP Picture Archive/John Kenney; p. 408: © age fotostock; p. 409: © F.A. Rinehart for B.A.E./Smithsonian Institute; p. 413: Photo courtesy of Julia R. Heiman; p. 421: © China Photos/Stringer/Getty Images; p. 424 (left and right): © AP Wide World Photos; p. 425: All photos courtesy of Dr. Daniel Greenwald; p. 426 (left): © Hulton Archive/Getty Images; (right): © AP/Wide World Photos; p. 427: © Philip Blenksop/Agence VU.

CHAPTER 14

p. 437: © CP Picture Archive/Fred Chartrand; p. 439: © CP Picture Archive/Frank Gunn; p. 442: © CP Photo/Kevin Frayer; p. 446: © Serendipity Point Films and Barna-Aslper Productions; p. 447: © Plush Studios/Brand X Pictures/Getty Images; p. 449 (left): © Geoff Manasse/IPN/Aurora; (right): © Colin McPherson/Corbis Sygma; p. 459: © Jeff Greenberg/PhotoEdit.

CHAPTER 15

p. 466: © CP Picture Archive/Mike Conley; p. 470: © Joel Gordon; p. 473 (left): © Photofest; (right): © Kevin Winter/Getty Images; p. 478: © Jacques Prayer/Gamma; p. 480: © Jutta Klee/Corbis; p. 481: © Christie's Images/SuperStock; p. 491: © David Harry Stewart/Tony Stone/Getty Images.

CHAPTER 16

p. 497: © M. Rutz/Satchen/Niven/Corbis; p. 508: © CP Picture Archive/J. T. Lewis; p. 509: © McPherson Colin/Corbis Sygma; p. 511: © Yvonne Hemsey/Gamma Liaison; p. 514 (left): © CP Picture Archive/Darren Makowichuk; (right): © CP Picture Archive/Jonathan Hayward; p. 518: © Bob Daemmrich/Stock Boston; p. 521: © Richard Townshen/Corbis.

CHAPTER 17

p. 537: © Mats Bakken; p. 541: © Joel Gordon; p. 543: Axel Koester for *The New York Times*; p. 544: © 8425/Gamma; p. 545: © Gary Houlder/Corbis; p. 547: © Joel Gordon; p. 551: © Francis Dean/The Image Works; p. 552: © Jack Hollingsworth/Corbis; p. 554: © Candida Royalle, creator of female-centric movies and author of *How to Tell a Naked Man What to Do.*

CHAPTER 18

p. 571 (left): © Jeff Greenberg/PhotoEdit; (right): © David Young-Wolff/PhotoEdit; p. 582: © Larry Mulvehill/The Image Works.

CHAPTER 19

p. 601: © CP Photo Archive/John Mahler; p. 603: © Keith Dannemiller/Corbis; p. 605: © CP Photo Archive/Chuck Stoody; p. 609: ©Odilon Dimier/Getty Images; p. 611: © Jeff Greenberg/PhotoEdit; p. 612: © Robert Nickelsberg/Gamma Liaison/Getty.

CHAPTER 20

p. 5: The Metropolitan Museum of Art, Rogers Fund, 1941 (41.162.101) Neg. #177754; p. 7: Courtesy Hermitage Museum, St. Petersburg, Russia/SuperStock; p. 8: Courtesy Ognissanti Church, Florence, Italy/Bridgeman Art Library, London/SuperStock; p. 10: © Frances M. Roberts; p. 12: © Lauren Goodsmith/The Image Works; p. 13: © Sujoy Das/Stock, Boston; p. 17: © CP Picture Archive/Tom Hanson; p. 21: National Gallery of Art, Washington, D.C./SuperStock; p. 23: © CP Picture Archive/John Mahoney; p. 27: © Najlah Feanny/Stock, Boston.

LINE ART AND TEXT

CHAPTER 1

p. 8:	© David Young-Wolff/PhotoEdit.
Table 1.1:	"Social-Class Variations in Sexual Behaviour in Canada," adapted from Statistics Canada *National Population Health Survey*, 1996–1997.
Table 1.2:	Bibby, R.W. (2006). *The Boomer Factor: What Canada's most famous generation is leaving behind* (pp.28, 176). Toronto: Bastian Books.
Table 1.3:	Data is adapted in part from Statistics Canada, *National Longitudinal Survey of Children and Youth (NLSCY)*, 2000–20001.

CHAPTER 3

Table 3.1:	From "The Janus Report," Andrew M. Greeley, *Contemporary Sociology*, vol. 23, pp. 221–23. Reprinted by permission of the American Sociological Society and Andrew M. Greeley.
In Focus 3.3:	© Dr. William Fisher.

CHAPTER 5

Table 5.2:	Bernard Goldstein (1976). *Introduction to Human Sexuality*. New York: McGraw-Hill, pp. 80–81. Reprinted with permission of Bernard Goldstein.

CHAPTER 6

Table 6.1:	Adapted from E. Hetherington and R. Parke, *Child Psychology*, Table 4.2. © McGraw-Hill Companies, Inc. (2003).
Table 6.2:	From "Sexuality during Pregnancy and the Year Postpartum," by J. S. Hyde, J. D. DeLamater, E. A. Plant, and J. M. Byrd. *The Journal of Sex Research, 33.* © 1996 by The Society for the Scientific Study of Sexuality, via Copyright Clearance Centre. Reprinted with permission.

CHAPTER 7

Table 7.1:	From Fisher, Borolitsky, & Morris (2003) U.S.; Bureau of the Census, International Data Base (2004), www.census.gov/ipc/www/idbprint.html; Zlidar et al., 2003.
Table 7.2:	Shaw (2006); Childbirth by Choice Trust, 2003.
Table 7.3:	Reproduced with the permission of The Alan Guttmacher Institute, from Henshaw, S. K., "Induced abortion: a world review," *Family Planning Perspectives*, 1990, 22(2): 59–65, 76.; "Abortion Rates around the World." Canadian data only, is adapted in part from the Statistics Canada publication *The Daily*, Catalogue 11-001, "Induced Abortions," 2001; Wednesday, March 31, 2004.
Table 7.4:	R. A. Hatcher et al, 2004.

CHAPTER 8

Table 8.1:	From *Barrier Contraceptives: Current Status and Future Prospects* by Christine K. Mauck, 1994, John Wiley & Sons, Inc., pp. 203–12. © 1994 Wiley-Liss. This material is used by permission of Wiley-Liss, Inc., a subsidiary of John Wiley & Sons, Inc.

CHAPTER 9

p. 259:	"Human Sex-Response Cycles," by Rosemary Basson. *Journal of Sex and Marital Therapy*. Reprinted with permission of Taylor and Francis Ltd. http://www.tandf.co.uk/journals.
p. 278:	From *Sex: An Oral History* by Harry Maurer. Used by permission of Viking Penguin, a division of Penguin Group (USA) Inc.

CHAPTER 10

Table 10.1:	From Boyce et al (2006). "Sexual health of Canadian youth: Findings from the Canadian youth, sexual health and HIV/AIDS Study." *The Canadian Journal of Human Sexuality, 15*, 59-68.
Table 10.2:	Canadian data is adapted from Statistics Canada, Canadian Community Health Survey (CCHS), 2000–01.
Table 10.3:	Reginald W. Bibby (2001). *Canada's teens: Yesterday, today, and tomorrow*. Toronto: Stoddart.

Table 10.4:   Reginald W. Bibby (1995). *Social trends Canadian style.* Toronto: Stoddart, pp. 69, 76.

p. 296–297, 299: Floyd M. Martinson, *The Sexual Life of Children,* 1994, Greenwood Publishing Group, Inc. pp. 37, 59, 62. © 1994 by Floyd M. Martinson. Reproduced with the permission of Greenwood Publishing Group, Inc., Westport, CT.

p. 300:   From Starts, Kay J. and Morrison, Eleanor S., *Growing Up Sexual,* Second Edition, Harper-Collins, 1996. (c) 1996 HarperCollins Publishers. Reprinted with permission.

p. 301, 315:   From *Sexual Behavior in the 1970s* by Morton Hunt. © 1974, 2005. Reproduced with permission from Playboy Enterprises, Inc.

p. 324–325:   From *Sex in America* by Robert T. Michael et al. © 1994 by CSG Enterprises, Inc., Edward O. Laumann, Robert T. Michael, and Gina Kolatta. By permission of Little, Brown and Company, Inc.

CHAPTER 11

p. 338:   From the Janus Report on Sexual Behaviour by Samuel S. Janus and Cynthia L. Janus, 1993, John Wiley & Sons, Inc., p. 383. © 1993 by Samuel S. Janus and Cynthia L. Janus. This material is used by permission of John Wiley & Sons, Inc.

Table 11.2:   This information was reprinted with permission of the Henry J. Kaiser Family Foundation. The Kaiser Family Foundation, based in Menlo Park, California, is a nonprofit, independent national health care philanthropy and is not associated with Kaiser Permanente or Kaiser Industries.

CHAPTER 12

Table 12.1:   Edward O. Laumann et al. (1994). *The Social Organization of Sexuality: Sexual Practices in the United States.* Reprinted by permission of the University of Chicago Press and Edward O. Laumann.

p. 378:   "Bartholomew and Horowitz's (1991) four-category, two-dimensional model of adult attachment." *Journal of Personality and Social Psychology, 61,* Figure 1, p. 227. © American Psychological Association. Reprinted by permission of Dr. Kim Bartholomew.

CHAPTER 13

p. 418:   From *Sexual Behaviour in the 1970s* by Morton Hunt. © 1974, 2005 by Morton Hunt. Reproduced with permission from Playboy Enterprises, Inc.

CHAPTER 14

Table 14.1:   Mosher, W. D., Chandra, A., & Jones, J. (2005). "Sexual behavior and selected health measures: Men and women 15–44 years of age, United States." 2002. *Advance Data,* 362. Atlanta: Center for Disease Control and Prevention. Adapted from Statistics Canada, "Canadian Community Health Survey, 2003", *The Daily,* Catalogue no. 11-001, June 15, 2005. (http://www.statcan.ca/Daily/English/040615/d040615b.htm).

Table 14.2:   Leger Marketing. (2004, May 25). "Canadians and their tolerance towards homosexuality." Retrieved November 25, 2004 from http://www.legermarketing.com.

CHAPTER 15

p. 466:   Reprinted with permission from the Diagnostic and Statistical Manual of Mental Disorders, Fourth Edition, Text Revision. © 2000 American Psychiatric Association.

CHAPTER 16

p. 498:   From Jean O. Hughes and Bernice R. Sandler, *"Friends" Raping Friends: Could It Happen to You?* 1987, Washington, D.C.: Association of American Colleges.

In Focus 16.2:   From Jean O. Hughes and Bernice R. Sandler, *"Friends" Raping Friends: Could It Happen to You?* 1987, Washington, D.C.: Association of American Colleges.

CHAPTER 17

p. 546:   From *Sex: An Oral History* by Harry Maurer. © 1994 by Harry Maurer. Used by permission of Viking Penguin, a division of Penguin Group (USA) Inc.

Table 17.1:   Martin Rimm, "Marketing Pornography on the Information Superhighway," *Georgetown Law Journal,* Vol. 83, 1995, p. 1891. Reprinted with the permission of the publisher, *Georgetown Law Journal.* © 1995.

In Focus 17.3:   "Ernie: A Pedophile and Child Pornographer," from *Child Pornography and Sex Rings,* by Ann W. Burgess, 1984, Lexington Books, pp. 26–27. Reprinted by permission of author.

CHAPTER 18

John P. Wincze & Michael P. Cary, "Sexual Dysfunction: The Role of Cognitive Interference," *Journal of Consulting and Clinical Psychology,* 1986, 54, pp. 140–148. © 1986 by the American Psychological Association.

In Focus 18.2:   "A New View of Women's Sexual Problems" by the Working Group for a New View of Women's Sexual Problems. From *A New View of Women's Sexual Problems.* (Eds. Ellyn Kaschak & Leonore Tiefer). pp. 1–8. © 2001 The Haworth Press, Inc., Binghamton, NY.

CHAPTER 19

Table 19.1:   Research conducted by Council of Ministers of Education, Canada, with funding provided by Health Canada.

p. 597:   Anne C. Bernstein and Philip A. Cowan, "Children's Concepts of How People Get Babies," *Child Development, 46,* 1975, pp. 77–92. Reprinted with permission of the Society for Research in Child Development.

p. 598:   Rosemary Zumwalt, "Plain and Fancy: A Content Analysis of Children's Jokes Dealing with Adult Sexuality," *Western Folklore, 35,* 1976, pp. 261, 267. Reprinted with permission of the California Folklore Society.

In Focus 19.2:   From *Sex Education.* Reproduced with permission of the Sexuality Information and Education Council of the United States, Inc. (SIECUS). © SIECUS, 130 West 42nd Street, Suite 350, New York, NY, 10036.

CHAPTER 20

Table 20.1:   Adapted from Statistics Canada, Census of the Population, 2001, available on the Statistics Canada Web site: www40.statcan.ca/101/cst01/demo30a.htm.

INDEX